COMPLETE BOOK OF AUSTRALIAN BIRDS

SECOND EDITION

first revise

Published by Reader's Digest (Australia) Pty Ltd (Inc. in NSW)
26-32 Waterloo Street, Surry Hills, NSW 2010
© 1976, 1977, 1979, 1982, 1983, 1986, 1988, 1990 Reader's Digest (Australia) Pty Ltd
© 1990 Reader's Digest (New Zealand) Limited
© 1976, 1977, 1979, 1982, 1983, 1986, 1988, 1990 Reader's Digest Association
Far East Limited
Philippines copyright 1976, 1977, 1979, 1982, 1983, 1986, 1988, 1990
Reader's Digest Association Far East Limited

National Library of Australia cataloguing-in-publication data

Reader's Digest Complete Book of Australian Birds

    Index
    Bibliography
    ISBN 0 949819 99 9
    1. Birds — Australia

598.2994

READER'S DIGEST

COMPLETE BOOK OF AUSTRALIAN BIRDS

READER'S DIGEST SYDNEY

The Reader's Digest Complete Book of Australian Birds
was edited and designed by Reader's Digest Services Pty Ltd, Sydney

SECOND EDITION CONSULTANT EDITORS

Dr Richard Schodde, BSc (Hons), PhD, CFAOU
Principal Research Scientist
Division of Wildlife and Rangelands
Research, CSIRO, Canberra

Dr Sonia C. Tidemann, DipT, MSc, PhD
Research Scientist
Conservation Commission of the Northern
Territory, Darwin

CONTRIBUTORS

Harry L. Bell, MSc, PhD
Department of Zoology, University of New
England, Armidale

Richard and Molly Brown

Graeme Chapman
Division of Wildlife and Rangelands Research,
CSIRO, Canberra

Leslie Christidis, BSc (Hons), PhD
Post-doctoral Fellow
Division of Wildlife and Rangelands Research,
CSIRO, Canberra

Simon Ferrier
Department of Zoology, University of New
England, Armidale

Jon Fjeldsa, DPhil
Head, Ornithology Section
Zoological Museum, Copenhagen

Richard Jordan, DipEd, BSc
Royal Australasian Ornithologists Union,
Barren Grounds, Jamberoo

Greg Jones, BSc (Hons)

Richard T. Kingsford, BSc
Department of Zoology, University of Sydney

John Liddy

Ian James Mason
Division of Wildlife and Rangelands Research,
CSIRO, Canberra

Richard Noske, MSc
Department of Zoology, University of New
England, Armidale

Brian O'Gorman

Gerry C. O'Neill, BAppSc
Northern Territory Conservation Commission,
Alice Springs

David C. Paton, BSc (Hons), PhD
Department of Zoology, University of Adelaide

Lester L. Short, PhD
American Museum of Natural History,
New York

Graeme T. Smith, BSc (Hons), PhD
Division of Wildlife and Rangelands Research,
CSIRO, Perth

Sonia C. Tidemann, DipT, MSc, PhD
Conservation Commission of the Northern
Territory, Darwin

Richard Weatherly

Edward Wyndham, PhD
Department of Zoology, University of New
England, Armidale

FIRST EDITION CONSULTANT EDITOR

H.J. Frith, DSc (Agr), FAA, FTS
formerly Chief, Division of Wildlife Research,
CSIRO, Canberra

CONTRIBUTORS

Ian Abbott, PhD
University of Western Australia, Perth

Allan J. Baker, PhD
Royal Ontario Museum, Toronto, Canada and
University of Toronto

Robert Beeton
University of New England, Armidale

Erhard Boehm

L.W. Braithwaite, MSc, PhD
CSIRO, Canberra

Michael Brooker, MSc (Agr)
CSIRO, Perth

Murray Bruce

John Calaby, DSc
CSIRO, Canberra

Graeme Chapman
CSIRO, Canberra

Alex H. Chisholm, OBE, FRZS, FRAOU

Mark Clayton
CSIRO, Canberra

J.J. Counsilman, MA
University of Queensland, Brisbane

Frank Crome, BSc (Hons) ARMIT
CSIRO, Atherton

Stephen Davies, BA, PhD, FRAOU
Royal Australasian Ornithologists Union, Perth

H.J. de S. Disney, MA

Douglas D. Dow, PhD
University of Queensland, Brisbane

Julian Ford, BSc, PhD, CFAOU
Western Australian Institute of Technology, Perth

Joseph M. Forshaw
Australian National Parks and Wildlife Service,
Canberra

Peter Fullagar, BSc, PhD
CSIRO, Canberra

H.B. Gill
CSIRO, Canberra

Warren Hitchcock

S.G. Lane, ED, Colonel (RL)

Hugh Lavery, MSc, PhD, MEc
National Parks and Wildlife Service, Brisbane

Arnold McGill, OA, FRAOU

John McKean
Northern Territory Conservation Commission,
Darwin

G. Maclean, PhD, DSc
University of Natal, Pietermaritzburg,
South Africa

Ian James Mason
CSIRO, Canberra

Alex Middleton, PhD
University of Guelph, Guelph, Ontario, Canada

David Milledge

K.A. Muller, BSc
San Diego Zoo, California

M.D. Murray, BSc, FRCVS, MACVSc
CSIRO, Sydney

Ronald I. Orenstein, MSc, PhD
University of Michigan, Ann Arbor, Michigan,
USA

Shane Parker, BSc
South Australian Museum, Adelaide

Veronica Parry, BA, MSc

Judy Turley Recher
National Trust of Australia, Sydney

Pauline Reilly, FRAOU

Michael Ridpath, PhD
CSIRO, Darwin

Norman Robinson, BA

Ian Rowley, CFAOU
CSIRO, Perth

David Rushton
CSIRO, Canberra

Denis A. Saunders, BSc (Hons), PhD
CSIRO, Perth

Richard Schodde, BSc (Hons), PhD, CFAOU
CSIRO, Canberra

Kenneth Simpson, MSc
Burwood State College, Melbourne

Fred Smith

G.T. Smith, PhD
CSIRO, Perth

Frank Stewart

Professor Robert Storer
University of Michigan, Ann Arbor, Michigan,
USA

G.F. van Tets, MA, PhD
CSIRO, Canberra

W.J.M. Vestjens
CSIRO, Canberra

Stephen J. Wilson

Richard Zann, BSc, PhD, DipEd
La Trobe University, Melbourne

The National Photographic Index of Australian Birds was the source of nearly all the photographs reproduced in this book and the existence of this huge reference collection greatly simplified the process of finding illustrations. The publishers are grateful to the trustees, the then executive officer (Mr A.D. Trounson) and staff of the index for their co-operation. They also thank many others who assisted in the production of the first edition of this book including the trustees of the Australian Museum, Sydney; Mr Stephen Marchant, then editor of Emu; Mr Ronald Orenstein, Museum of Zoology, University of Michigan; Mr John Warham, of the Department of Zoology, University of Canterbury; Mr John McKean of the CSIRO, Canberra. For this second edition, further thanks go to Ms Sue Briggs, Dr Peter Fullagar, Dr Phil Ladd, Ms Penny Olsen, Mr Ian Rowley, Dr A. A. Saunders, Mr Kurt Thaler and Dr Gerard van Tets.

Foreword

Australia's birds command worldwide attention for their variety, colour and individuality; they are justifiably a source of national pride, popularity—and concern. More than 700 different species occur naturally in Australia, filling its ecological niches like no other vertebrates. There are glittering fairy-wrens and robins, predatory owls and hawks, mound-building megapodes, giant kingfishers, cuckoos and cassowaries, spectacular lyrebirds, and a host of waterfowl and waders.

Australia's dominant birds—its cockatoos and parrots, honeyeaters, bowerbirds, nocturnal frogmouths, kingfishers and robin-whistlers—are found on no other continent or barely so. Just how singular they are is only now being realised, after 200 years of study. Because so many of them resemble Eurasian 'counterparts' in appearance, Australian birds had been thought to have immigrated in successive waves from that great continent.

But molecular research—still preliminary and in need of further testing—suggests that their similarities are accidental, simply reflecting convergent adaptations in bill and plumage to the same life styles. More than that, it suggests that Australia's 300 or more different songbirds are more closely related to one another than to any presumed ancestors overseas.

The next few decades will be of major importance. Scientists have the task of unravelling the mystery of the origins of our birds—and thus fitting an important piece into the jigsaw that traces the evolution of life on earth. And this research will bring a wider appreciation of the environment in which we live. Such knowledge helps us to understand the uniqueness of Australia's birds, and to identify those of special concern. Knowing how they have coped and been shaped by environment in the past, we can plan development of the land in better harmony with nature in the future. That is, if we want quality as well as quantity in life—and a landscape not bereft of its native trees and animals.

The future of our birds is limited by their habitat. For nearly all of them—the birds of undisturbed forests, woodlands, plains and swamps—the situation can only stay the same or get worse, never better. The crucial question is: how much worse does it have to get, how much more change can there be, before species are lost? Two habitats are particularly vulnerable. One is the rainforest along the east coast which, although barely half gone, is very small in area and very rich in wildlife. The other is the unsung mallee on the rolling plains of the southern inland. Over three-quarters of it has now been cleared for marginal wheat farming. Its many unique birds—the Malleefowl, Regent Parrot and Mallee Emu-wren, among others—have been cut to tiny, isolated fractions of their past numbers and range. Whether they still have enough habitat left to survive, only time will tell—but extinction must be perilously close in most regions. Already the Black-eared Miner has been virtually hybridised out of existence by the opening-up of the Murray Mallee.

One of the many purposes of this book is to provide the information that will allow general appreciation of the life style and habitat needs of Australia's birds. From the moment it appeared, the Reader's Digest Complete Book of Australian Birds became the pacemaker as the most comprehensive and authoritative of popular references to the birds of our continent. Its authority stemmed—as now—from its association with the CSIRO's Division of Wildlife and Rangelands Research. Most of the first edition, published in 1976, was compiled by staff of the Division; its then Chief, Dr H. J. Frith, was consultant editor.

The second edition seeks to maintain that standing, its input increased by members of the Division and augmented by additions from other new contributors whose help we gratefully acknowledge.

Because few field guides were then available, the first edition featured identification notes and the biology of our birds. Many gaps have since been filled, allowing us to stress their habits more: where they live, what they feed on and how they breed, aspects not emphasised in any other publication on Australian birds.

The comprehensiveness of the new text springs from a careful updating of information from research on all species. Readers who skim its surface will notice at once the expanded text, the corrections in classification—though these are few—and the many changes to maps of distribution, based on the Atlas of Australian Birds just published by the Royal Australasian Ornithologists Union. Others who dig deeper will find that the accounts of most species have been revised extensively and many completely rewritten, including all additional species; not one species has been left unadjusted.

Richard Schodde, Sonia C. Tidemann
Canberra, 1986

CONTENTS

Part 1

Zebra Finches, birds of the dry interior.

Where birds live/ 1

Power of flight, particular physiological adaptations and a protective coat of feathers have enabled birds to reach and exploit a myriad of land and water habitats—the environments in which they live. Each species has its own preferences, honed by adaptation to particular foods, perhaps competition, and by changes in the Earth's climate over many thousands of years. As a result, different species use their habitat in different ways.

There are four basic strategies. First there are those birds that range through a variety of habitats without ever moving far. The Willie Wagtail is one, occurring wherever it has some open ground for perching and fly-catching. Most sedentary birds utilising a variety of habitats are nonetheless usually centred in one. Thus, although the Eastern Yellow Robin is found from coastal rainforest to cypress woodland inland, it is most widespread and abundant in the intervening wet eucalypt forest that has shrubby understorey.

Then there are those birds that wander widely, some even migrating. Such are the aerial feeders—the swifts and swallows—whose essential habitat is the sky itself. The Mistletoebird is another, following the fruiting of its food plants wherever they occur. Many desert nomads—the rat-eating Letter-winged Kite, seed-eating Cockatiel and Budgerigar, and nectarivorous Black and Pied Honeyeaters—also follow the erratic flushes of their foods, from steppe and mulga woodlands to mallee and spinifex.

There are also those birds that use the same habitat in different places at different times. Foremost among them are migrants, birds that shift seasonally, both within and out of Australia, making the best use of their food resources. Some are waders—curlews, sandpipers and plovers—that summer on Australian shores and return to the boreal tundras each year to breed. Others include water fowl, such as the Rufous Night Heron, Glossy Ibis and Hardhead which refuge in the swamp lands of northern Australia until the Murray–Darling basin floods and revives breeding grounds. Then there are insectivores like the Rainbow Bee-eater, Noisy Friarbird, Yellow-faced Honeyeater, and Masked and White-browed Woodswallows that migrate from southern to mid-northern Australian woodlands each winter. Fruit pigeons—Flock and White-headed Pigeons, and the Rose-crowned Fruit-Dove—follow the seasonal fruiting up and down the east coast rainforests.

Then come the sedentary birds, species which live all year round in one habitat where they often hold territories that exclude others of their kind. Rock Warblers live only on the Hawkesbury sandstone escarpments; Brown Gerygones live only in subtropical rainforest; Mangrove Robins live only in mangroves; Eyrean Grasswrens live only in cane-grass–spinifex tussocks on sand dunes; and Comb-crested Jacanas live only on lagoons growing water lilies on which they can walk.

As a rule, the more reliably watered the habitat, the higher its proportion of resident species. In Australia, rainforest is highest with almost 90 per cent of species sedentary. Lowest in resident species are the habitats of the arid inland: around 50 per cent.

Because it extends from the tropics to the cool temperate region, the Australian continent offers birds a wide range of environments. This accounts for much of the rich diversity in Australia's bird life. However, the latitudes in which Australia sits, and the landforms of the continent, limit the variety and distribution of its environments; and some important habitats are poorly represented.

Australia is mainly flat. There are few ranges and no really high mountains—the highest, Mt Kosciusko, is only 2208 metres. Consequently the land is poor in alpine and montane habitats.

The continent is also arid. Sixty per cent of it receives less than 250 millimetres of rain a year, so vegetation is sparse over vast areas. The annual run-off of water corresponds to a depth of 33 millimetres—compared with an average of 249 millimetres for all the land surfaces of the world. Not surprisingly, wetlands in Australia are rather limited.

The most arid part of the continent is a great central zone which is surrounded by more or less concentric bands of increasing rainfall towards the coast. In general the habitats for birds become increasingly luxuriant as the rainfall increases with the result that there is a greater diversity of birds towards the wetter coastal districts. From the centre of the continent the sequence of habitats begins with sand, spinifex and arid mulga woodland and ranges through Mitchell grassland, mallee, semi-arid woodland and temperate and tropical woodland to sclerophyll forests.

What man has done
All the habitats in Australia have been altered since European settlement began. None has been completely destroyed but some, such as subtropical rainforest and mallee, have been gravely depleted. Natural grasslands have been grazed by stock and rabbits, and their specific composition has been altered; woodlands have been removed or replaced by crops or thinned out for pasture; forests have been logged or replaced by plantations of exotic conifers; heathlands have been churned up by mining; mangroves and mudflats have been polluted with industrial effluents; and swamps have been drained to provide extra grazing, or to control water for irrigation or hydro-electric power.

If there is much alteration to a habitat the birds specialised to live there are dispossessed and perish. Few rainforest birds can survive the clearing of their cover. The Malleefowl cannot withstand sheep grazing the mallee in which it lives. And spinifex-inhabiting birds such as several grasswrens and emu-wrens are burnt out by fires lit to provide green pick for stock.

However, some birds find suitable living space in the altered districts and expand in both range and number. The Galah, Crested Pigeon and Australian Magpie, for instance, have greatly increased in numbers because of the shortening of the grass on the plains and the provision of stock water in the arid zone, because of the abundance of grain to eat in the wheat belt, and because of the clearing or opening of woodlands and forests around the more humid coast.

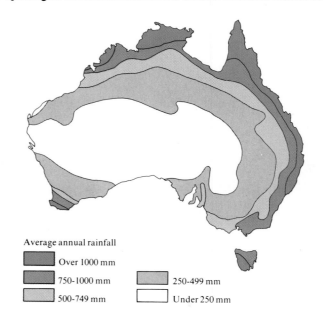

Average annual rainfall

Over 1000 mm

750-1000 mm   250-499 mm

500-749 mm   Under 250 mm

Land over 500 m

There are few ranges and no really high mountains in Australia. Consequently it is poor in truly alpine and montane habitats.

Much of Australia receives less than 250 mm of rain a year, and the annual run-off is only 33 mm, compared to a world average of 249 mm. As a result wetlands are not extensive.

Vegetation habitats

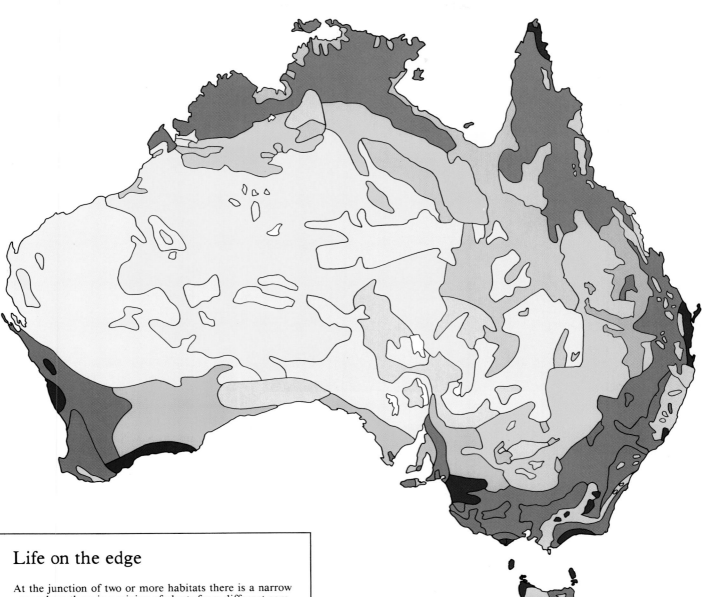

Life on the edge

At the junction of two or more habitats there is a narrow zone where there is a mixing of plants from different communities. Birds can be very numerous and of diverse species at these edges. Here wet sclerophyll forest, rainforest, cleared land and stream banks all meet, together with the many and varied birds found in them.

RAINFOREST
  Rainforest

FOREST
  Wet sclerophyll forest
  Dry sclerophyll forest
  Brigalow forest

WOODLAND
  Woodland
  Shrub steppe

SCRUBLAND
  Mallee scrub
  Mulga scrub
  Saltbush

GRASSLAND
  Spinifex grassland
  Mitchell and other grassland
  Heath

Where birds live/ 2

Tropical rainforest at Cape Tribulation, Qld. The trees are often more than 30 metres tall.

Temperate rainforest in Lamington National Park, in Queensland, on the border of New South Wales, is dominated by negro-head beech *Nothofagus moorei.*

Rainforest

Dense, dark and evergreen, rainforest is composed of a variety of trees growing tall and close to form a continuous canopy that keeps out sunlight. It grows only in areas of high, year-round rainfall, and as a result is restricted to patches along the east coast. Outlying pockets of the tropical rainforest found on Cape York Peninsula also persist as depauperate vine scrub in the wetter parts of Arnhem Land and northwestern Kimberleys. Altogether, rainforest in Australia supports about 140 species of birds, over 60 of which are virtually confined to it. Fruit-eaters are prominent among them: cassowaries, fruit pigeons, fig-parrots and bowerbirds.

There are three main forms of rainforest in Australia, each with its own suite of birds. One is tropical or megaphyllous rainforest which is strung out in strands along eastern Cape York Peninsula at Bamaga, Iron Range and the McIlwraith Range, and filters south among subtropical rainforest to about Sarina. Packed with lianas and reaching 30–40 metres high in two or three layers of trees, it is an outlier of the rich lowland rainforests of New Guinea. Nearly all rainforest birds on Cape York Peninsula are New Guinean in origin and found nowhere else in Australia—Eclectus Parrot, Red-cheeked Parrot, Yellow-billed Kingfisher, Blue-breasted Pitta, Red-bellied Pitta, White-faced Robin, Tawny-breasted and Green-backed Honeyeaters, Trumpet Manucode and Magnificent Riflebird.

Subtropical or mesophyllous rainforest is still the most widespread rainforest in Australia, occurring north in large stands to the tablelands of the Cairns–Cooktown area and south to the Illawarra area in New South Wales. From there isolated pockets occur just beyond the Victorian border. Only two layers of trees are the rule, with a canopy at 20–35 metres; lianas, though present, are often less abundant than ferns and epiphytes. Laurels, myrtles, cunoriads and sassafrasses are dominant trees and they harbour a distinctive bird fauna: Australian Brush Turkey, Topknot Pigeon, sooty owls, Pale-yellow Robin, logrunners, Yellow-throated Scrub-wren, Brown Gerygone, bridled honeyeater group, and unplumed riflebirds.

The third type of rainforest—temperate or microphyllous rainforest—is limited to Tasmania and wet montane southeastern Australia; a few isolated pockets extend north on mountain tops to the Queensland border. It is simple forest, usually with only one canopy layer and often only one or two dominant trees, such as Antarctic beech *Nothofagus* and Southern sassafras *Atherosperma;* however, its floor and trunks are covered with ferns and moss. Only a handful of bird species are centred in it: Pink Robins, Scrubtits and Tasmanian Thornbills in Tasmania, and Rufous Scrub-birds and Olive Whistlers in northern New South Wales.

Patches of rainforest are found down the east coast of Australia.

Subtropical rainforest on basaltic soils, such as this near Lismore, NSW, has bangalow palms *Archontophoenix cunninghamiana* intermixed with trees.

This wet sclerophyll forest on the southeast coast has *Eucalyptus nitens* as the dominant species.

Dry sclerophyll forest, in the Blue Mountains, NSW.

Sclerophyll Forest

Tall to medium-high eucalypts are almost invariably the dominant trees, forming a fairly open canopy. Beneath is a ground storey of sclerophyllous (hard-leaved) shrubs, or grasses. Brigalow *Acacia harpophylla* also grows dense and tall enough in parts of Queensland to form a forest, as do scattered pockets of eucalypts in the northern Kimberleys, Arnhem Land and Cape York Peninsula.

In the coastal and tableland districts of the southeast and southwest there are wet sclerophyll forests. These are communities of eucalypts, usually over 30 metres tall and sometimes—as in mountain ash *Eucalyptus regnans*—as high as 70 metres. There is a dense understorey of tall shrubs and small trees and, in moist places, tree ferns.

Dry sclerophyll forests are common on the less fertile soils of the coast and tablelands. Again they are dominated by eucalypts, usually less than 30 metres tall. The canopy is more open, with a well-developed shrub or grass layer.

Of the approximately 140 bird species that use eucalypt forest, about 130 range into rainforest on one side or open woodlands on the other. Obligate wet sclerophyll species, nonetheless, are Wonga Pigeons, Long-billed Black and Gang-gang Cockatoos, Powerful Owls, Pilotbirds, Red-browed Treecreepers and Bell Miners. Drier sclerophyll forests support Scarlet Robins, Spotted Quail-thrushes, Speckled Warblers and Buff-rumped Thornbills.

Wet sclerophyll is found in the wetter ranges of southeastern and southwestern Australia.

Dry sclerophyll forest grades into wet sclerophyll forest at one extreme and into woodland at the other.

Brigalow forest is restricted to central eastern Queensland. No species of birds are limited to it.

Woodland

This formation is mostly dominated by eucalypts and extends right around Australia, intergrading with forest towards the coast and with grasslands and shrub steppes inland. It resembles parkland in appearance, its small to medium-high trees usually well scattered and branching into big, round crowns that are taller than the trunks. The ground sward is grassy, and when the grass is extensive and the trees sparse, it is known as savanna.

There are three main types of woodland in Australia: tropical eucalypt woodland across all northern Australia, temperate eucalypt woodland in the southeast and southwest, and arid–semi-arid woodland ringing arid central Australia and scattered patchily through it. The grassy sward in tropical woodlands, commonly dominated by *Sorghum,* is annual. It sprouts one–three metres high in the summer wet season, then dies, falls and shrivels away through the dry. Ground cover in temperate woodlands, though shorter, may still be over a metre high, is more persistent and includes many perennial grasses and herbs.

The main elements of arid and semi-arid woodlands are mallee–eucalypt and mulga–acacia communities (see p16). Others, usually with a shrub layer mixed in with annuals, are the poplar box *Eucalyptus populnea* community in central New South Wales–Queensland, belah–bull oak *Casuarina* and cypress pine *Callitris* belts around the fringes of mallee, and desert oak *Casuarina* woodlands in central Australia.

One hundred and seventy or so species of birds occur in tropical eucalypt woodlands alone, and another 170 in temperate woodlands. Together these habitats support over half of Australia's land birds, testifying to how well the birds have adapted to life in open eucalypt communities. Characteristic species are the Sulphur-

In this tropical woodland eucalypts and cycads rise from a ground cover of grass.

crested Cockatoo, White-cheeked Rosella, Grey-crowned Babbler, Jacky Winter, Brown Treecreeper, Noisy Miner and White-plumed Honeyeater. None, however, is restricted to temperate woodland and only about 20 are limited to tropical woodland, including Chestnut-backed and Buff-breasted Button-quail, Squatter and Partridge Pigeons, Golden-shouldered and Hooded Parrots, Black-tailed Treecreeper, White-throated Honeyeater, Masked Finch and Black-backed Butcherbird.

Woodland grades into forest at one extreme and into more open plant communities at the other.

In temperate woodland in southeastern Australia short grasses and herbs cover the ground.

Where birds live/ 4

Mallee and Mulga

A dense growth of low trees, usually less than eight metres high with an almost continuous canopy, form mallee and mulga. There is usually a lower layer of shrubs and some ground cover.

Mallee, dominated by low, three–six metre high eucalypts, is widespread in the low winter rainfall belt around the southern fringes of the inland deserts. In wetter, coastwards regions receiving 300–500 millimetres of rain each year, it has a close understorey of sclerophyllous shrubs, particularly of tea-tree *Melaleuca;* in drier areas inland these are replaced by sparser chenopods, such as *Atriplex, Maireana* and *Sclerolaena.* Wherever there is deep sand or broken rock, hummocks of spring spinifex grass *Triodia* cover much of the ground.

About 160 species of birds are found naturally in mallee, and many are characteristic of it: Mallee Ringneck, Gilbert's Whistler, the black-backed race of the Splendid Fairy-wren, yellow-rumped race of the Spotted Pardalote, black-eared race of the Yellow-throated Miner, and many others. Only seven are restricted to it, however: Regent Parrot, Southern Scrub-robin, Chestnut Quail-thrush, Shy Hylacola, Mallee Emu-wren, Purple-gaped Honeyeater and Yellow-plumed Honeyeater.

Mulga occurs patchily across the alluvial flat lands and tablelands of inland Australia, where rainfall is usually less than 300 millimetres a year. Southwards it reaches the fringes of the mallee, often forming an abrupt mulga-eucalypt line. Northwards it cuts out at the Great Sandy, Tanami and Sandover Deserts and grassed Barkly Tableland.

The two–nine metre high trees of mulga woodland are all acacias of various species: myall, gidgee, lancewood, and mulga itself, *A. aneura.* Undergrowth, usually sparse, is of shrubs of *Cassia* and *Eremophila,* and there is a patchy

Typical mallee eucalypts develop a number of trunks from a swollen base. Mallee occurs in arid and semi-arid zones around the southern fringes of inland deserts.

ground layer of spinifex on sandy soils and annual grasses on red and grey loams.

Although 80–90 species of birds occur regularly in mulga, only five are restricted to it: Bourke's Parrot, Chestnut-breasted Quail-thrush, Slaty-backed thornbill, Grey Honeyeater and, if belah–bull oak woodland is included, White-browed Treecreeper.

Mallee *Eucalypt* woodland merges into temperate woodland and heath.

Low shrubs with hairy succulent leaves, as well as saltbush *Atriplex,* near Tibooburra, far western NSW.

Mulga *Acacia* woodland.

Shrub steppe

Low shrubs with hairy succulent leaves, bluebush *Maireana* and saltbush *Atriplex* are the dominant plants in treeless shrub steppe. This grows on the red and grey loam and gibber plains of the southern inland, including the Nullarbor, where the annual rainfall is less than 500

millimetres and most falls in winter months. About 50 species of birds occur in shrub steppe, and a few are specialised to live in it alone. Such are the Inland Dotterel, Cinnamon and Nullarbor Quail-thrushes, Gibber-bird, and Thick-billed Grasswren.

Shrub steppe.

Grassland

Areas covered by grasses, which are for the most part treeless, are known as grasslands. The most extensive and important grasslands for birds in Australia are arid hummock and arid tussock grasslands. Arid hummock, or spinifex, grasslands cover about 23 per cent of the continent and occupy much of the arid zone, both in sand-ridged deserts and on stony, well-drained ranges. The dominant grasses, *Triodia* and *Plectrachne,* grow in spiny hummocks 900–1500 millimetres in diameter and 300–600 millimetres high. The ground between them is usually bare but ephemeral grasses and herbs spring up after rain has fallen. Low trees and shrubs, spaced far apart, are common in spinifex areas.

There are usually no trees in the arid tussock, or Mitchell grass *Astrebla,* grasslands. These grasslands are widespread on the plains and tablelands of western Queensland and eastern Northern Territory, and from there they run south around the eastern fringe of the Simpson Desert to Sturts Stony Desert. The tussocks are 150–230 millimetres in diameter at the base, up to 900 millimetres high, and spaced about 600 millimetres apart on ground that is usually bare.

Other grasslands include small areas of natural alpine grassland in the southeastern highlands, large areas of swampy grasslands on the flood plains of major tropical coastal rivers, and a considerable area of tropical grassland inland from the Gulf of Carpentaria.

Grasslands as a whole support almost 100 species of birds and at least 18 of them live almost nowhere else. Endemics of the spiny hummock grasslands are the Spinifex Pigeon, Spinifexbird, Rufous-crowned Emu-wren, and six of the eight species of grasswrens. Those dependent on other grasslands include several grass-parrots *Neophema,* Singing Bushlark, Tawny Grassbird, Golden-headed Cisticola, and several mannikin finches.

Hummocks of spinifex *Triodia* near Wittenoom Gorge, WA. The ground between is usually bare.

Dry grasslands with few trees are common in much of arid Australia.

Arid hummock or spinifex grassland.

Arid tussock grassland.

Where birds live/ 5

Coastal heathland is full of birds, which are protected by the dense cover.

The arching roots of these mangroves *Rhizophora* help anchor the trees firmly in the mud.

Heathland

There are many kinds of heath but all are dense, treeless communities of shrubs, usually less than two metres tall, with hard or prickly leaves. Herbs and grasses are not conspicuous.

Coastal heaths are the most widespread. In tropical and temperate regions they are confined to nutrient-poor acid soils and the common shrubs include *Banksia*, tea-tree *Leptospermum, Calytrix, Hakea, Acacia* and *Grevillea.* Often they merge into dry sclerophyll forest.

Heaths also occur in other places. In the southeastern highlands there is an alpine heath; and on the low-nutrient sand plains of southwestern Australia and Ninety-Mile and Big Deserts straddling the South Australian–Victorian border, stunted mallee and *Casuarina* combine with proteaceous and other myrtaceous shrubs to form a sand heath.

Coastal heathlands are full of birds because of the dense cover and many flowering shrubs, which provide nectar and pollen and attract insects. In spite of this the number of species of birds is not great; Ground Parrots, honeyeaters, bristlebirds, thornbills and Southern Emu-wrens are the most characteristic.

The inland heaths support many of the same birds as the coastal ones, although a few others, including the Western Whipbird, are found in them as well. Alpine heaths are poor in birds. Altogether heathland is used by about 80 species, but only six or seven of them are virtually confined to it.

Heathlands are most extensive in coastal districts.

Mangroves

Their crowns forming a closed canopy like a depauperate rainforest, mangroves line the sheltered muddy bays and estuaries of northern Australia. In the west they come south to Carnarvon and in the east reach Westernport, Victoria. *Avicennia marina* is the only species to reach the southern limit, where it is often less than three metres high. In the tropical north they are most diverse, reaching over 20 metres high and comprising a dozen or more species. There they are an important habitat for mud- and foliage-feeding birds.

Up to 60–70 different species of birds use mangroves. Some 20 or so species are characteristic of them and 12–13 live nowhere else in Australia. These include the Striated Heron, Collared Kingfisher, Mangrove Gerygone, Red-headed Honeyeater and Yellow White-eye.

Curiously, mangroves are richest in birds not in northeastern Queensland where they are most luxuriant, but along the northwest coast between the Kimberleys and Gulf of Carpentaria. There, it seems, they are the remnants of a mangrove biota that once ranged widely and diversely around the Arafura Plain north of Australia when it was exposed by lower sea-level through much of the past million or so years.

The wet season in Arnhem Land. Rivers flood, forming many lagoons and swamps where waterlilies grow. Waterfowl are attracted to these areas.

Wetlands

Once covering almost a third of Australia and inhabited by an unmatched variety of flamingos, wetlands have dried up as rainfall declined over the past several million years. Today they persist mainly around the coast and support about 110 species of birds, over 50 of which are restricted to them.

In the north, water in the river channels, lagoons and flood plains evaporates away through the dry season, from April to November. These quickly refill and spill out again with the arrival of heavy monsoonal rains each summer. Because the monsoons come at a time when surface waters are drying up in southern Australia, many waterfowl from the south—Rufous Night Herons, Glossy and Straw-necked Ibis, Hardheads and Grey Teal—may fly north regularly to the refuges in the northern wetlands.

Along the northeast coast, swamplands are more permanent because rain is more evenly spread. At the same time they are much less extensive because there is little low-lying land between the Great Dividing Range and the sea. Just as permanent and as limited are the swamps around the south coast which are mainly replenished every year by winter rain.

The only inland swamp system filled with any consistency is that in the Murray-Darling basin. Covering a vast series of billabongs and braided channels from the Paroo River and Macquarie Marshes to the river red gum swamps of the Murray–Murrumbidgee, it is filled by summer and winter rain and snow melt. In good years it harbours huge heronries and major breeding colonies of ibis, spoonbills and ducks through spring and early summer. Depressions and flood-outs in the Lake Eyre basin, once the heartland of Australia's wetlands, now flood only erratically and briefly. The only waterfowl relying on them for their breeding to any great extent are Freckled and Pink-eared Ducks, Banded Stilts and Black-tailed Native-hens.

Shores and mud flats

Many water birds—plovers, sandpipers and curlews—are in fact waders and feed not in water but on the muds, sands and reefs left exposed at low tides. They are found right around the shores of Australia as well as along the estuaries of rivers and the edges of lakes inland. Some are breeding residents, such as the Beach Stone-curlew, Hooded Plover, Red-kneed Dotterel, Sooty Oystercatcher and nocturnal Painted Snipe. Most, however, are migrants that spend the summer in Australia: all sandpipers, curlews and true snipe, *Gallinago,* and most of the small plovers, *Charadrius.* They have favoured feeding grounds where they congregate in hundreds of thousands: the Eighty Mile Beach in northwestern Australia, the head of the Gulf of Carpentaria and the Coorong–Murray mouth in South Australia. Their habitat is protected under international treaty.

Islands

The habitat of sea birds—the seas and oceans of the world—is hardly unique to Australia. There are, however, islands off the coast—usually bare and windswept—that provide breeding grounds for 26 of them.

Some of the more important are the coral cays of the Great Barrier Reef where Wedge-tailed Shearwaters, Black-winged Petrels, several boobys, Red-tailed Tropicbirds and a number of tropical terns nest. Others such as Bedout Island and the Abrolhos group off the Western Australian coast also carry colonies of terns, Least Tropicbirds, White-faced Storm-Petrels and Little Shearwaters. Cabbage Tree Island off Port Stephens is the only known breeding ground for the Australian race of Gould's Petrel. Phillip Island at Westernport is a popular refuge for Little Penguins. And islands in Bass Strait are famous not so much as the only Australian gannefries as for their vast colonies of Short-tailed Shearwaters or muttonbirds.

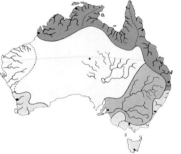

Northern drainage region
Murray-Darling river system
Southern drainage region
Central drainage region

Part 2

Australian Pelican feeding its chick.

The functions of feathers

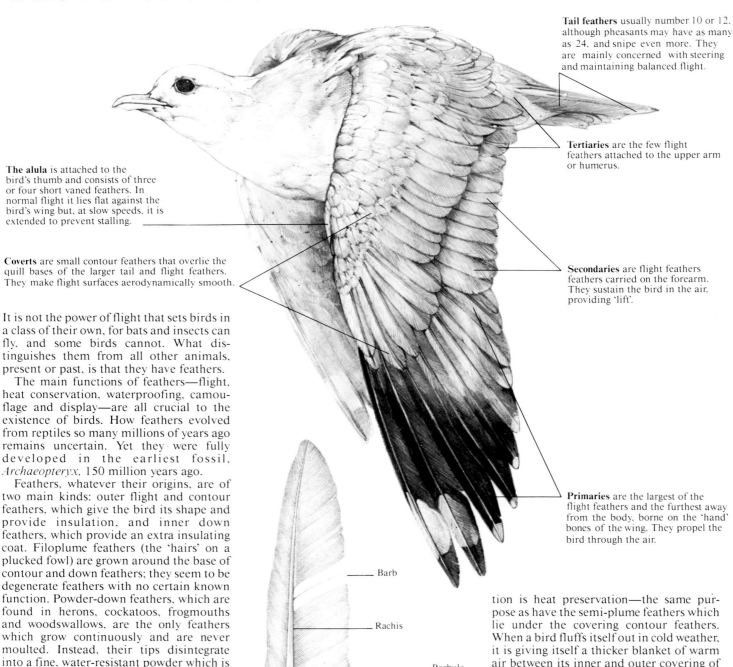

Tail feathers usually number 10 or 12, although pheasants may have as many as 24, and snipe even more. They are mainly concerned with steering and maintaining balanced flight.

Tertiaries are the few flight feathers attached to the upper arm or humerus.

The alula is attached to the bird's thumb and consists of three or four short vaned feathers. In normal flight it lies flat against the bird's wing but, at slow speeds, it is extended to prevent stalling.

Coverts are small contour feathers that overlie the quill bases of the larger tail and flight feathers. They make flight surfaces aerodynamically smooth.

Secondaries are flight feathers feathers carried on the forearm. They sustain the bird in the air, providing 'lift'.

Primaries are the largest of the flight feathers and the furthest away from the body, borne on the 'hand' bones of the wing. They propel the bird through the air.

Barb

Rachis

Vane

Barbule

Barbicels

Shaft

It is not the power of flight that sets birds in a class of their own, for bats and insects can fly, and some birds cannot. What distinguishes them from all other animals, present or past, is that they have feathers.

The main functions of feathers—flight, heat conservation, waterproofing, camouflage and display—are all crucial to the existence of birds. How feathers evolved from reptiles so many millions of years ago remains uncertain. Yet they were fully developed in the earliest fossil, *Archaeopteryx*, 150 million years ago.

Feathers, whatever their origins, are of two main kinds: outer flight and contour feathers, which give the bird its shape and provide insulation, and inner down feathers, which provide an extra insulating coat. Filoplume feathers (the 'hairs' on a plucked fowl) are grown around the base of contour and down feathers; they seem to be degenerate feathers with no certain known function. Powder-down feathers, which are found in herons, cockatoos, frogmouths and woodswallows, are the only feathers which grow continuously and are never moulted. Instead, their tips disintegrate into a fine, water-resistant powder which is used in preening to waterproof and preserve the other feathers.

The structure of a flight feather

The typical flight contour feather is made up of a central shaft, hollow at its base for conveying nourishment, and becoming solid for strength further up, in a part called the rachis, where it supports the two webs of the vane. These webs reveal a fascinating interlocking system whereby hundreds of parallel barbs in turn carry barbules equipped with tiny hooks (or barbicels). To interlock separated barbs in ruffled feathers, a bird simply draws the feather through its beak a few times during preening. It restores the entire web.

Often, the vaned feather grows a secondary after-feather or -shaft from a tiny opening at the point where the base and rachis meet. This after-feather is usually small and downy, and was probably developed as an extra layer of insulation against heat loss; only in Emus and cassowaries is it fully developed like the vane proper.

Down feathers are fluffy because their barbules have no hooks. Their main func-

Shown microscopically, each barb of a vaned feather is revealed as a miniature feather. Every barb carries several hundred barbules, equipped with minute hooks— the barbicels. Each hooked barbule is able to interlock with its unhooked neighbour on the next barb.

tion is heat preservation—the same purpose as have the semi-plume feathers which lie under the covering contour feathers. When a bird fluffs itself out in cold weather, it is giving itself a thicker blanket of warm air between its inner and outer covering of feathers. Conversely, in warm weather the bird often disarranges its outer feathers to speed up the process of heat loss.

Birds need effective insulation, especially against cold, because they live at what for a human would be fever heat: they must maintain a body temperature of approximately 41°C (106°F).

Body size is the main factor affecting the number of feathers. A large bird, such as a swan, can carry more than 25 000, while most small songbirds have 1500 to 3000.

Feather growth

Apart from powder-down feathers, which never stop growing, all fully formed feathers are dead structures, receiving nothing from the body but physical support. But at first each feather grows from a tiny papilla, or 'goose pimple', and is built up largely of the horny, lightweight protein, keratin. During its growth, the feather is nourished through its open-ended base.

Despite the 'fully clothed' appearance of most birds, feathers do not grow all over the body—except in rare cases such as the penguins—but in clearly defined feather tracts. Areas in between are naked and called apteria; among birds with dense plumage, such as ducks, such areas are reduced and often covered with down.

Apart from these featherless regions, many birds develop brood patches—an area on the breast and belly from which feathers moult when the bird is incubating eggs. The exposed naked skin becomes warmer than normal, as swollen vessels carry more blood to them.

The moulting process

Feathers are continually subject to wear and need to be replaced at regular intervals. Old feathers are pushed out by the growth of new ones in the same follicles.

In almost all birds, the feathers are replaced in sequence, a few at a time so that the body is never left exposed and unprotected, and usually in pairs from either side of the body. Often the large wing and tail feathers begin to moult first, and this is followed by a progressive shedding of body feathers. The sequence of wing and tail moult is often a distinguishing characteristic of different families of birds.

The loss of vital feathers renders some birds, for a time, particularly vulnerable. To ensure that penguins, most of which inhabit cold waters, have a uniformly warm coat, old feathers are not lost until the new have grown completely. Then the bird combs off the old feathers with its feet and beak to complete the process of renewal. All this happens briefly on land once a year.

Birds which depend greatly on flight for their livelihood are also susceptible when they replace their flight feathers. Most do so one at a time, not shedding the next in line until the last has been replaced fully. Some water birds moult all at once, taking sanctuary in water-protected marshes and lakes; some species even migrate to moult in traditionally safe areas.

It is difficult to establish firm rules as to why and when birds moult. Research suggests that a combination of factors may trigger the process: the length of daylight, action of the pituitary and thyroid glands, and changes in the reproductive organs.

Usually birds do not moult while breeding, during migration, or in times of food shortage. These are critical periods when extra energy is required, leaving little in reserve to grow new feathers. Yet some seabirds—which cannot risk moulting at sea on the wing—moult during their breeding season. For many species the period immediately after the breeding season—when they recuperate physiologically—is the optimum time for moulting.

In its lifetime a bird may progress through a number of plumages, from a natal down, through to juvenile, immature, partial 'pre-nuptial' and full adult display plumages. Some birds, especially migrants, have an interrupted moult which is completed in the winter quarters.

The colour of plumage

Birds as a class are the most vividly coloured of all backboned animals, though bright colouring is far from universal. A general rule is that the warmer and more tropical the climate, the brighter the bird; the drier it is, the paler the bird. Australian birds tend to be more brightly coloured than those which live in New Zealand.

Two of the main functions of plumage colour are self-advertisement and self-concealment. In many species a balance is struck between these two needs; the male is brightly coloured, especially in the breeding season, and the female is camouflaged by drab colouring. This is particularly marked among the fairy-wrens, whistlers, birds-of-paradise and bowerbirds.

Brilliant plumage does more than simply attract the opposite sex; it serves also as a kind of flag or battle standard to warn off rivals when the bird is defending territory.

A third function of colour is to reduce wear and tear on feathers. Black feathers, for instance, contain wear-resistant pigments; the white wings of many seabirds are tipped with black, because the wing-tip feathers are those most likely to be scuffed.

The different hues in the feathers of a bird are built up in two ways: by pigments and by the surface structure of the feathers themselves. Pigments known as melanins, produced in the body of the bird, give rise to colours ranging from blacks and browns to light tans. They are laid down in the barbules as the feathers grow. Those known as carotenoids, taken in with food and usually deposited directly in the feathers, produce bright yellows, oranges and reds.

Blue is not a pigment in feathers; it is produced by the structure of the barbs, which reflect blue light and filter through the rest of the spectrum to be absorbed by the dark melanin layer beneath. Green— except in a few cases—is produced in the same way, though the reflective part of the barb may be pigmented with melanin for olive-greens, or with carotenoids for brighter greens. White is produced by barbs which reflect almost all light.

Care of the feathers

The feathers of a bird require frequent and careful attention if they are to function efficiently. All feathers require oiling to preserve their water-repellence, and during the day many feathers become ruffled and disarrayed so that the small barbs that make up the vanes on each side of the stalk need to be reconnected.

Grooming is done mainly by shuffling the feathers, by anointing them with oil from the preen gland—situated above the base of the tail feathers—and by passing ruffled feathers through the bill so that the little barbs reconnect, rather like a zip fastener.

Most birds maintain their own plumage but some preen one another in addition to themselves. This habit, known as allopreening, takes care of the hard-to-reach facial and head regions. Unless it has an allopreening partner the bird scratches its head with its foot. This can be done in either of two ways—over the lowered wing or directly, without shifting the wing. Some families habitually scratch in one way and others in the other way.

Many birds bathe in water to keep themselves clean and probably to cool off as well. Water birds, land birds and aerial feeders tend to bathe in different ways. Ducks, for example, either swoosh water over themselves by submerging the head quickly as they swim forward or else they flap their wings rapidly to splash themselves thoroughly.

Most land birds walk into water from the edge or dive in from a low perch. They tend to bathe in two stages—front end and then back end. Aerial feeders generally dip into the water and out again on the wing.

The Pacific Heron bathes by flapping its wings and splashing itself with water.

Besides bathing in water, birds sunbathe, dust-bathe and 'ant' themselves. Sunbathing is common early in the morning and in spring, autumn and winter. The bird ruffles its feathers, spreads out the wing nearest to the sun and fans its tail to that side, opening back feathers to the air.

Dusting and anting may benefit birds by displacing or discouraging skin parasites, or the feathers themselves may benefit. Either action can be active or passive. The bird can pick up dust or an ant and insert it among its feathers or it can simply find a suitable dust-bowl or ant heap, shuffle into it and remain still while the dust or the ants penetrate the plumage.

The feathers are not the only parts that require attention. The legs and feet are covered with scales and they, and the bill, may become encrusted during feeding or walking and need regular cleaning.

The bill and the surrounding skin and bristles usually get oiled and cleaned as a result of preening the rest of the body. Leg scales may require careful oiling after the dirt and loose scales have been removed by the bill.

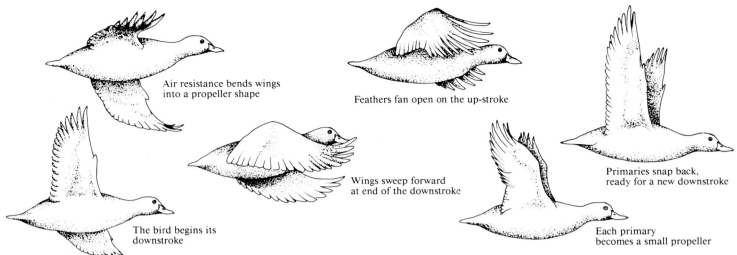

Air resistance bends wings into a propeller shape

Feathers fan open on the up-stroke

Wings sweep forward at end of the downstroke

The bird begins its downstroke

Primaries snap back, ready for a new downstroke

Each primary becomes a small propeller

Powered flight: what happens when a bird flaps its wings

Most people rely on the visible external characteristics—size, shape and colour—to tell them the difference between species of animals. To the animals themselves behaviour can be just as important.

Within any one species behaviour tends to be stereotyped—members of the same species tend to do the same things in the same way when confronted with the same situation. Comparison of the behaviour patterns of different species can be helpful in deciding whether they belong to the same genus or family.

The behaviour of birds can be studied from many angles, but it is conveniently divided into locomotion, foraging, grooming, communication, territorial defence, courtship, and breeding.

Modes of locomotion
On land, birds usually move across relatively flat ground on their feet but they also occupy rocks or cliffs and trees. Some birds travel by walking—moving one foot after

Defying gravity

Though humans have unlocked many of the secrets of flight, a bird on the wing nevertheless remains a source of wonder and envy. To make flight possible, the body of a bird—the most efficient of flying machines—has evolved several noteworthy features.

The most important are lightness and strength. Lightness is essential— so the bones of the skeleton are extremely thin and, in many cases, hollow and crisscrossed with struts. In those parts of the skeleton where strength is paramount—such as the skull, chest region, pelvis and wing—the bones may fuse together.

A powerful musculature has evolved to facilitate powered flight. The most important muscles are those attached to the breast which transmit their power through long tendons and provide the powerful downstroke. Muscles also extend and fold the wing while a series of tendons holds the flight feathers in their correct position.

The shape of a bird is another adaptation for flight. Whatever variations there may be to the shape, the body of a bird is always streamlined. As air passes over it in flight, friction must be reduced to a minimum, so feathers provide a smooth outer surface.

The aerodynamic design of a bird's body enables it to resist impediments to flight. For a start, the wing is designed to obtain lift. As air passes over the wing, the air travels faster over the upper rounded surface than it does over the lower surface. This is because it has further to go. The faster the air travels across the surface, the lower the pressure it exerts. Pressure is therefore lower on the upper surface, and lift is produced, counteracting the force of gravity.

If the air does not continue to flow at sufficient speed over the upper surface, lift is lost and the bird stalls. To maintain a continous flow of air and control turbulence, the bird projects its alula to smooth and control the air flow. (The alula is a tuft of feathers from the thumb which can form a slot on the wing's leading edge.)

The passage of air over the wing, though it helps to create lift, also produces drag: a tendency to blow the wing backwards. The stream-lined shape of the wing reduces drag—the leading edge, reinforced by bones, is blunt, rounded and stiff —and feathers ensure that the trailing edge tapers neatly to a point. The flatter the wing surface the less drag there is.

Taking off
Because a bird cannot become airborne unless it is moving against an airstream, it must either take off into the wind or make an airstream of its own. Most birds gain the initial impetus by jumping into the air, flapping their wings backwards and forwards rather than up and down, to create an airstream; or they make a short run, and push off strongly from the ground.

The swift, airborne for much of its life, has poorly developed legs—to take off, it falls forward from a high ledge.

Steering
Once in flight, a bird is able to adjust its course by bringing into play a number of factors. By tilting its body against the direction of motion, the bird will be moved to one side— and so produce a turn. Its tail, and sometimes its feet, also fan and twist to contribute to the steering process. Alternatively, by folding one wing, even slightly, the bird can reduce the drag on that side and begin to bank. The faster the flight, the more precise and effective these operations become.

Approaching and landing
Landing places great demands upon a bird's body. Wings play a major part in this process and the bird's undercarriage—feet, legs and tail, braced to withstand the transfer of weight—brings a complex range of factors into play.

A simple form of landing is, in many ways, an extension of gliding. Judging the landing position, the bird glides down onto it just to the point of stalling and then gently alights. If the bird finds it is approaching too quickly, it may dip down on the approach and then reduce momentum by gliding upwards.

A more demanding method requires that, as the bird nears its landing position, it brakes by spreading its wings and tail and moving its body into a near-vertical position. It further reduces momentum by flapping its wings against the direction of flight. To prevent stalling, the alula are brought into play. At the moment of landing, the legs absorb the final shock.

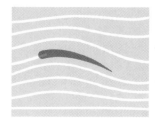

Staying in the air When wings cut through an airstream, air travels faster over the rounded upper surface. This creates pressure beneath the wings, which are hollowed, and a partial vacuum above them, resulting in the upward force known as 'lift'.

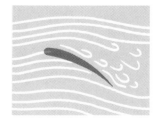

Gaining height To climb higher, a bird tilts up the leading edge of its wings. The greater the angle between the wings and the airstream, the greater the turbulence. Too steep an angle, and the turbulence would break up the flow of air, and the bird would stall.

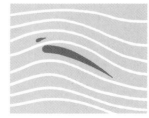

Preventing stalling To prevent stalling the bird spreads the alula (normally folded against the wing) forward, to form a slot on the leading edge of the wing. Air rushes through, keeping the airstream over the whole wing fast and turbulence-free.

the other. This merges into running, and some flightless birds, such as the Emu and native hens, can run at speeds as fast as 45 km/h. Many water birds, with their feet adapted to swimming, move less freely.

Other birds move by hopping—moving both feet together. This is a common mode of progress on the ground and along branches for most perching birds, or passerines. Wrens, whistlers and pittas are particularly adept hoppers.

The power of flight
Not all birds can fly but most can and they use flight for many purposes in their daily life—to travel, to search for food and water, to capture prey, find a mate or to escape from danger. All flight does not take the same form and it is convenient to separate it into flapping, hovering, gliding, soaring and diving.

The most common form of flying is that in which the bird flaps its wings. Considerable energy is required, and the downstroke, flexed by the pectoral muscles to drive the wing, is the power stroke.

It is made with the feathers closed flat against one another, creating an unbroken airtight surface, so that the maximum amount of air resistance is encountered. The wing moves downwards and forwards and, as it does so, the primaries are bent back at their ends, shaping the wing into a propeller which pulls the bird forward.

During the up-stroke, which is mainly a passive recovery stroke, the primary feathers twist open (with an action similar to that of venetian blinds). This allows the air to pass easily through the gaps between them. On this stroke, the bird rotates its wing at the shoulder, increasing its angle of attack to maintain lift. The primary feathers are again bent back on this stroke and each individual feather becomes a small separate propeller.

In the complete cycle of a flap, the wing-tips, which move faster and further than the rest of the wings, go through a figure-of-eight pattern, with a wide loop at the top. They complete the up-stroke with a rapid snap, which helps drive the bird forward.

Hovering is another strenuous form of flight; in a bird it is equivalent to a stationary air-borne helicopter and is energetically demanding because the bird derives no lift from movement. The flapping flight is reduced so that it only just compensates for the head wind and the hovering bird remains above the same spot on the ground. This is achieved by flapping the wings backwards and forwards. To maintain a fixed position in relation to the ground, falcons fly into the wind at the same speed as it is blowing them back.

Gliding, the most effortless form of flight, is forward movement without flapping, dependent on lift from the body and outspread wings. To glide a bird may simply launch itself from its perch, open its wings, and 'parachute' down. By losing height it travels forwards. On long flights birds often flap and glide alternately.

Soaring is like gliding, but it involves no loss of altitude. The pull of gravity is compensated for by rising air, due either to a thermal column of hot air or an updraught from a landform such as a cliff. In a method sometimes referred to as dynamic soaring, seabirds are able to take advantage of the friction caused by wind passing over the surface of the waves.

Diving is extreme gliding, with minimal forward movement and reduced drag from part-folded wings. Birds usually dive to catch prey or to avoid being caught.

An interesting variant in flocks is formation flying whereby birds such as ibis, ducks and gulls fly in 'V' formations on long journeys. The eddies of air caused by a bird in flight represent much wasted energy. To conserve some of this energy, each bird flies just off behind the bird in front to get extra lift from the slipstream.

Moving on land and water: special adaptations of legs and feet

Though hopping is a most efficient way of moving from branch to branch, it is energy-consuming. Species such as starlings, which spend a good deal of time on the ground, have therefore evolved a way of moving on land which is more economical—walking. A bird walks on its toes, not on the entire area of its foot, because what looks like a knee joint is in fact really a heel. Most birds have four toes, three pointing forwards and one, which is known as the hallux, pointing to the rear. In running birds this is often little more than a stub, creating a minimum area of contact with the ground.

There are many variations to the legs and feet; these are in accordance with the bird's habitat and sometimes its food. Most waders, for example, have long toes that are spread wide apart. This increases the area of foot that comes in contact with the ground so that the bird will not sink too readily in the soft mud of riverbeds, swamps and marshes. The conditions underfoot along stretches of water are extremely varied and the range of adaptations of the feet of wading birds reflects this.

Long legs are an obvious advantage for birds which wade in shallows to hunt prey, but webbed feet and paddle-shaped toes are necessary for water birds to swim on the water or in it.

The amount of water that can be pushed back by the spread foot is a rough gauge of the importance of swimming in the life of each species. The rear positioning of the legs is marked in many swimming birds such as grebes and diving ducks. Just as a ship's propeller is located at the back of a ship, so the legs of these birds are at the ends of their bodies, providing power unimpeded by obstacles. This results in a rather ungainly inefficient waddling movement on land, however, as the legs are positioned too far back from the bird's centre of gravity. In grazing waterfowl that spend much time on land—such as geese—the legs are further forward, allowing more efficient walking than in most purely aquatic birds.

WALKING
The hind claw of a pipit is elongated, to brace the bird and prevent it from falling backwards.

RUNNING
The Plains-wanderer runs. Its lack of a hind toe reduces the area of foot touching the ground.

HUNTING
The boobook's powerful talons are used for perching, and for seizing and killing its prey.

CLIMBING
Strong claws and two backward-pointing toes enable rosellas to grip bark and branchlets.

PERCHING
The backward-pointing toe of a honeyeater curls around to meet the other toes, clamping it to its perch.

WADING
Stilts have long, widely spaced toes adapted for walking on soft mud without sinking into it.

HALF-WEBBED TOES
The phalarope is a wader which feeds in water. It has evolved semi-webbed feet for swimming at sea.

THREE-WEBBED TOES
Webs between three toes increase the area of the surface-feeding Pacific Black Duck's foot.

FOUR-WEBBED TOES
Webs between all four toes create powerful propulsion for the shags and cormorants.

PADDLE-SHAPED TOES
The Great Crested Grebe spreads the paddle-shaped lobes on its feet to maximise the power stroke. They are folded back on the return stroke.

Feeding habits

The life of a bird is an almost constant search for food. As birds fly they expend immense amounts of energy; this can be replaced only by consuming large amounts of food. Birds have no teeth and, in the case of insect-eating or flesh-eating birds, food is often ingested whole, broken down by an acid gizzard, and indigestible parts regurgitated as pellets. Seed-eating birds have a more complicated digestive system that allows for storage of undigested food in the crop (an extension of the lower throat). The muscular walls of the gizzard—with the assistance of grit, which all seed-eating birds must consume regularly—grind down the food.

To replace supplies of energy and to maintain body heat, some birds spend up to 95 per cent of daylight hours searching for food. Birds respond to seasonal changes and will gorge in times of plenty. Incubating birds may fast for several days at a time.

The bill is a feeding tool. Its great variety of shape and form attests to the enormous range of foods upon which birds are able to feed. Of the seed-eating birds, only a few species eat seeds all year round. At certain times of the year, such as breeding times, they may eat insects. Similarly, few insect-eating birds rely upon insects as their only source of food. In order to accommodate other types of food, the bills of these birds are not highly specialised and are sometimes referred to as all-purpose bills. That, of course, is their own specialisation.

Searching for food

Birds have many ways of finding food. Among water birds there are species that are surface feeders, dabbling with their bills, and others that, while remaining on the surface, upend themselves and reach for food well below. Penguins pursue their prey under water. Grebes forage on the muddy bottom after diving several metres. Around the edge of the water, waders feed by walking and probing in different depths according to the lengths of their legs and bills.

Budgerigars drinking. Unlike most birds, they ladle water down the throat with the tongue; other birds usually scoop it up with the bill and let it run down.

On land, a few birds probe the soil for insects, bulbs and seeds, but the search seldom goes very deep. Birds of the forest sometimes rake over the litter of leaves and other debris on the floor, using their bills and feet to expose food items.

Other birds hunt for insects on the trunks and larger limbs of trees, clinging with sharp claws and probing fissures in the bark. Some of them can forage upside down just as well as they can when they are the right way up.

In the canopy, diminutive birds such as pardalotes hunt over leaf surfaces in search of scale and other insects. Besides insect-eaters there are feeders on nectar, pollen, fruit and seeds. In times of food shortages, species may avoid competing with each other by using different foraging techniques and taking different types of food.

Trees and shrubs not only provide a lot of the food needed by birds but they serve as vantage points from which insect-eaters and predators can launch their sorties.

Adaptations to feeding

Above the trees, the aerial feeders swoop and trawl for insects of many different

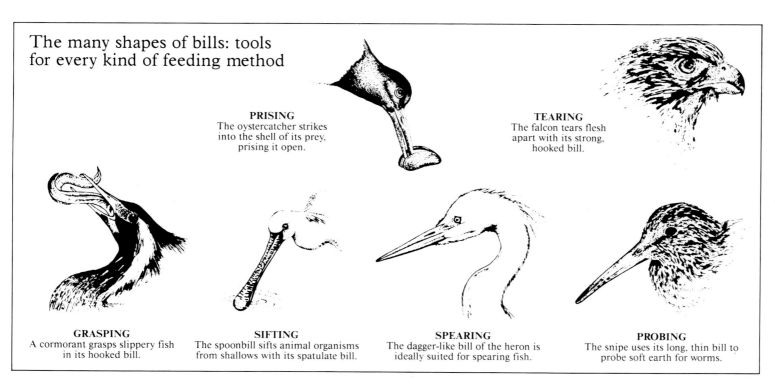

The many shapes of bills: tools for every kind of feeding method

PRISING
The oystercatcher strikes into the shell of its prey, prising it open.

TEARING
The falcon tears flesh apart with its strong, hooked bill.

GRASPING
A cormorant grasps slippery fish in its hooked bill.

SIFTING
The spoonbill sifts animal organisms from shallows with its spatulate bill.

SPEARING
The dagger-like bill of the heron is ideally suited for spearing fish.

PROBING
The snipe uses its long, thin bill to probe soft earth for worms.

kinds on the wing. These birds include the swallows, martins, swifts and woodswallows. Many birds of prey also search in flight and when they see a victim swoop down on it.

Several species are able to exploit the food and other resources of trees and cliff-faces efficiently, displaying physical and behavioural adaptations to these situations. Treecreepers for example, have stiff tail-feathers and partly joined forward toes which support them as they forage on vertical tree trunks.

Honeyeaters are able to cling to branches, twigs and leaves in almost any position necessary to gain nectar with their brush-tipped tongues. Some parrots use a well-developed and strong bill as a third leg when climbing about in the forest canopy. They are also helped by having two toes pointing forwards and two backwards.

Other specialised adaptations for feeding can be found among birds. Ground-feeding walkers, such as the Emu, have long legs. Swifts dash through the air after insects on long, narrow wings. Some birds crack shells and nuts with heavy bills, and others probe long fine bills into flowers or mud. Fish-eating birds are equipped with special adaptations, such as a sharply hooked or serrated bill or spines on the soles of their feet, to fix the slippery prey more securely. Nearly all these adaptations go hand-in-hand with special foraging behaviour and may be characteristic of anything from a single species to a family of birds.

Drinking is as important as feeding and methods vary; penguins even eat snow. To cope with salt water, seabirds extract most of the salt through the blood supply and carry it to the nose where large nasal glands excrete it in highly concentrated droplets.

But not all birds need to drink. Many small insect-eaters, for example, gain all the liquid they need from the fluids in their prey. Some grain-eaters make do with metabolic water, a by-product of the digestion of seeds. Even dew can supply the requirements of some small birds, so that although much of Australia is very dry the aridity does not preclude the existence of birds.

Birds tend to be very regular in both the manner and the timing of their drinking. Some drink only in the early morning, some only at dusk and others more frequently.

Most birds drink by repeatedly dipping the bill in water, scooping up a billful and letting it run down the throat. This is quite a slow process and although birds drink usually at exposed places, only a few species—pigeons, doves and a few finches—have evolved the quicker method of drinking by sucking.

The world of the senses

Birds have the same five senses as humans, but smell and taste are poorly developed compared to the stage they have reached in many mammals. Touch, sight and hearing vary in importance between different species, and the last two are the most generally used and best developed.

Sight, the sense that provides the greatest possible amount of information most quickly, has reached in birds a degree of perfection found in no other animals; like humans, birds see colour. In almost every facet of its existence, a bird depends most on sharp, wide-ranging vision. Predators need keen sight for spotting their prey; victims need it for recognising and evading their enemies. Birds that live in the open need to be able to change focus rapidly; birds living in dense cover need rapid and reliable warning of obstacles as they dart through bushes.

Hearing, too, is acute, within its limits. A range of calls may keep birds together in flocks, alert them to predators and play an important part in mating and defending territory. As in other mammals, including man, a bird's ears also control its equilibrium.

The colour, shape and arrangement of the plumage are not chance effects but have evolved by natural selection over the years to perform certain visual functions, including use in displays. Plumage patterns convey important messages to other birds, such as sex, age and position of dominance. Birds are born with the capacity to display, and many performances are often characteristic of particular groups.

A bird may display by erecting plumage that was previously hidden, by fluffing up certain tracts of feathers, by spreading a wing or fanning the tail. It may walk or keep still, be silent or call or sing.

It is tempting to interpret these actions in birds in emotional terms: joy, desire, anger, fear. But these are premeditated human emotions, and we do not know whether birds experience them. Rather, birds seem to react spontaneously or involuntarily to their display signals, and so these are best described objectively not subjectively or 'anthropomorphically'.

The calls of birds, for example, are used for communication and so may be thought to approximate human language. Yet few species of birds have more than 40 different utterances and many have far fewer. For them calls simply signal intention or response; they do not carry on a conversation. The nature of the call or song uttered depends largely upon its purpose. The early morning chorus that advertises territory needs to be clearly identified and to carry beyond the borders of the territory. An alarm call, to be effective, must be loud. Contact calls can be quite soft and yet keep a family or a flock together as its members forage.

Birds can vary their vocalisation by using different notes, or by altering the volume, the pitch or the tempo. The frequencies used by birds range from about 30 Hz to well beyond the range of human hearing—above 15 000 Hz. Birds and humans seem to have similar peaks of sensitivity in hearing—with pitches ranging from 1500 Hz to 4000 Hz—and similar powers of discrimination between pitches. However, birds can perceive time intervals ten times better than humans. A bird will hear individual clicks where we would hear only a continuous buzz.

What the birds' taste buds actually taste is not established; chickens can distinguish several sugars and the bitter taste of quinine, while pigeons have shown preferences for salty foods.

Touch, which includes the sensation of heat, cold and pain, is perceived in essentially the same way as by man, through nerve endings concentrated in easily exposed areas of skin. Birds, though, do have the specialised touch receptors which occur in other parts of the body and are probably more sensitive instead to vibrations and pressure changes.

The field of vision

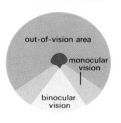

In birds of prey, such as the owl, eyes are more to the front than in most other birds—ideal for keeping a likely victim in view. The visual fields of both eyes overlap, allowing accurate judgment of distance and giving an area of binocular, three-dimensional vision.

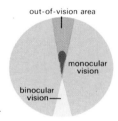

Birds which are preyed upon, such as pigeons, have to be aware of danger that can come from any direction. Their eyes are therefore positioned at the sides of their heads. This gives a greater total field of vision, but limits the angle of binocular sight.

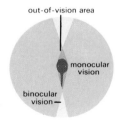

The snipe can literally see out of the back of its head. As the bird has evolved, its eyes have moved to a position high in its head, as well as to the sides. This allows a full 360° visual field but lessens the overlap between the fields of the two eyes.

Pinpointing sound

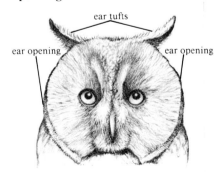

The Long-eared Owl's ears, like those of many other owls, are placed asymmetrically on its head, increasing the time-lag between the arrival at each ear of the same sound wave, so allowing the bird to pinpoint the source of the sound. The facial disc but not the 'ear' tufts may assist in conducting sound to the ears.

Discerning detail

BIRD'S EYE VIEW

MAN'S EYE VIEW

The ability to discern detail sharply may be as much as eight times keener in the large birds of prey than in man. The difference may be illustrated by imagining the retinas of both as television screens, on which the sharpness of detail in the picture depends on the number of lines. The greater the number, the better the definition produced.

Behaviour that distinguishes species/ 3

Living together

The social behaviour of birds has great bearing on the success of many of their essential activities: feeding and sleeping, breeding and nesting, migration, safety from predators—and even learning. Instinct guides the passage of a bird through these major tasks, but many of its skills may be improved or perfected.

Through trial and error, and continued practice, inappropriate responses may be modified and corrected. This capacity for learning is limited, however, for birds possess no extraneous skills. Their intelligent behaviour is confined to those skills essential to surviving in their natural habitat.

To perform instinctive activities, many birds gather together in groups—or flocks. Their lives are not so much 'sociable' as 'social'. A flock may be composed of birds of a single species or of mixed species, or consist solely of family groups, established pairs, or birds of one sex. Within small flocks especially, there is often a 'peck order' in which each bird gives way in turn to a more dominant bird.

Flocks are most frequently observed gathering at roosting areas or sources of abundant food. There is safety in numbers and flocking heightens awareness of the approach of predators. A solitary bird is less likely to notice a predator.

'Following reactions', which involve the immediate copying of one individual by another, are thought to assist in maintaining the cohesion of the flock, as do the recognisable markings (such as wing flashes) in many species. On the ground, flocks often synchronise such activities as feeding and drinking, preening, sleeping and hopping about. It is not entirely certain whether this is a result of following reactions or a direct reaction to a stimulus, such as an alarm call, and responses may vary.

Safety in colonies

Although most birds are solitary nesters, approximately 13 per cent of the world's birds live in colonies. More than any other species, seabirds are the most colonial and each year, at breeding time, are likely to return in their thousands to favoured, secure sites on cliffs, beaches and islands. Land birds and waterfowl often breed in relatively small colonies of tens rather than thousands of birds.

The young of most colonial birds are particularly vulnerable and may not be immediately able to leave the nest. Living in large groups gives them greater protection. On the approach of predators, alarm-calls immediately alert other birds and a joint attack may repel the intruder. As egg-laying is usually a well synchronised activity in colonies, the young also have a greater chance of survival than they would if eggs or nestlings were available to predators over a more prolonged period.

Choice of a resting and sleeping site—or roost—is as important as the selection of a nest-site. It is a matter of survival. The roost may be in a sheltered position where wind, rain and extreme cold are unable to penetrate. It must also be one that is relatively safe from predators. Birds must maintain a constant body temperature, so conserving body heat is vital. Some small birds, such as woodswallows and fairy-wrens, roost in clusters to obtain warmth from each other.

In a typical sleeping position a bird may hunch up and insert its bill under its feathers on its breast or back, with head turned; some birds even sit down on their legs, covering them with their fluffed-up feathers to conserve warmth; and hanging parrots *Loriculus* hang upside down like little balls of green fruit. The most unusual sleeping behaviour is that exhibited by some swifts and petrels, which seem to be able to sleep on the wing. Swifts are also among those species that are able to conserve body heat in extreme conditions by going into a state of torpidity, which allows the body's metabolic processes to slow down dramatically.

Territorial competition

The drive to establish territory is another powerful and immensely important characteristic of bird behaviour and there is a general code of conduct to which most birds adhere: the owner of territory shows aggression only within its own defended area, and retreats when it is discovered trespassing in another bird's territory. Though there is inevitably competition for nest-sites, food and mates, it rarely develops into full-scale fighting. Natural selection ensures that birds whose aggressive drive leads them to the risk of being killed or maimed rarely live long enough to breed. Instead, when conflict looms, most birds advertise their ownership by an elaborate system of bluff—frightening calls and threatening physical displays—which usually stops short of violence. It is in this central cause that songbirds sing.

Such displays are often conspicuous. Like other aspects of behaviour, aggressive display can be helpful in classification by showing relationships between species.

Direct competition for resources—giving birds space in which to feed and nest—causes most aggression. Indeed, some birds, which are said to have a specific 'individual distance', either aggressively repulse trespassers within that range or move away. In contrast, members of some social species actively seek bodily contact with others of the same species by perching, nesting or roosting close together. These are called 'contact species', the contact helping to maintain social bonds.

Apart from conflicts arising from competition for food and territory, many birds

The male Pied Cormorant in courtship display. This serves to attract the female.

will boldly defend themselves if attacked. If spectacular displays and noisy song fail to frighten off a rival or predator, birds have a vast array of tactics to fall back on. Some species assume menacing postures—they increase their size by puffing out feathers or raising crests; or they may display striking plumage markings. Frogmouths are masters at this, fluffing out bristling plumage and snapping open their great bills to flash their startling pale yellow mouths.

A bird's initial response to a rival or competitor is a mixture of appeasement and aggression. If unsure of whether to fight or flee the bird may adopt a sleeping position or suddenly begin to preen itself. Fights rarely involve more than two birds fully and are relatively bloodless. Perching birds flutter breast to breast, grappling with their bills; plovers use their feet as well. Grebes grapple in the water, bills interlocked, and try to force the rival's head under water.

A contest—whether bluff or physical combat—ends when one bird concedes defeat. It may simply fly away or, if unable to do so, may enact a fresh set of stylised actions indicating submission. Alternatively, it may remain motionless, head withdrawn, and attempt to minimise or conceal its more threatening markings.

The rituals of courtship
Territory is generally established by the male. Once a female has entered a territory, pair-formation, and later mating, can proceed with minimum interference from rivals. To attract and court a mate, some male birds have evolved special plumages and ornaments (crests, plumes and wattles) to emphasise the stereotyped displays distinctive of each species. For most perching birds (passerines), song is also a special element in this form of communication.

In many species in which there is little variation between male and female plumages, both sexes may be aggressive towards one another in the early stages of courtship. Displays or ceremonies help establish a pair-bond. Another bird's response to the display of the male will indicate its sex; if the response continues to be aggressive rather than passive this indicates the other bird is also a male.

Among birds of similar plumage, courtship displays are often mutual. The Great Crested Grebe has an intricate courtship dance in which both sexes take part. But not all birds with similar plumages display together—in rosellas, chlamyderine bowerbirds and various pigeons, display is left to the male alone.

Most courtship begins in late winter and spring, before nesting gets under way. It is usually the male which takes the initiative. In the exceptions—such as the button-quail, Emus and cassowaries—the female is the larger, brighter sex, and the male takes over the duties of incubation and tending the young.

The reproductive cycles of birds which breed outside the tropics are mainly set in motion by changes in the length of the day. The readiness of the female for mating also depends on her mate; in many species it is courtship that is largely responsible for synchronising interactions and inducing the necessary hormonal changes in the body and make it ready both to ovulate and to accept the male for copulation.

Once birds have become paired, the bond between them—so important for most species if they are to raise young successfully—is strengthened by special displays such as mutual preening, courtship feeding and showing a nest-site.

Mutual preening is characteristic of penguins, petrels, gannets, cormorants, shags and herons; all pigeons and doves; many parrots and cockatoos; owls; swifts; and fairy-wrens. This preening is largely confined to the head and neck of the other bird, for these are areas of the plumage the bird cannot preen with its own bill. Birds sometimes assume a preening invitation posture.

Courtship feeding is a widespread practice, particularly among species in which

A Bush Thick-knee protecting its nest by spreading its wings in aggressive display.

the female is responsible for incubation. In general, the female behaves like a begging chick and the male behaves as a parent would. Kingfishers and robins, for example, pass food from bill to bill; pigeons and parrots partially digest the food first, then pass the regurgitated food from bill to bill. The male Azure Kingfisher carries a fish to the female bird before mating. Courtship feeding, once regarded primarily as a bond-forming display, also has a practical dimension—it contributes to the nourishment of the female up to the period when she has finished brooding young.

Song and dance are also important elements of many courtship displays and some birds, such as bowerbirds, incorporate the construction of the nest into their courtship ritual.

Conspicuous displays
Mating displays, a prelude to mating, are not the sole preserve of the male bird. A female cormorant solicits by sitting in the nest with tail cocked while bending down and moving nest material. Mating then follows, during which the male grips the female's neck in his bill and shakes it gently.

In promiscuous species, in which no monogamous pair-bond is formed and males meet females only for mating, there is intense competition between males for females. This has resulted in the evolution of marked differences in size and appearance between the sexes, most notably in the birds-of-paradise and lyrebirds. Usually larger and more brightly coloured, the males have elaborate plumage features to accompany their highly ritualised displays.

Gannets demonstrate a wide range of seasonal displays. At the beginning of the nesting season there is often much competition among males for nesting sites. To proclaim his ownership of a site, the male performs a 'bowing display'. Dipping his bill from side to side, with wings held out, he gives a loud repeated threat call—*urrah-urrah*. His 'advertising display' to prospective females, which fly over the territory repeatedly before landing, resembles a low-intensity form of bowing. After their mutual courtship rituals and mating, the male eventually surrenders the nest-site to the female. Gannets also perform special displays to indicate they are about to leave their mate on the nest. Similarly, throughout the breeding cycle, they perform a special 'greeting ceremony' whenever a bird rejoins its mate at the site. The returning bird flies into the nest calling loudly, and its sitting mate shakes its head rapidly, before vigorously greeting the returning bird and finishing with quieter mutual preening.

THE COURTSHIP RITUALS OF THE GANNET

Male advertises for a female

Either sex may use 'pelican posture'

Male and female in mutual fencing

Male bites female's neck; female faces away

Both sexes adopt sky-pointing posture

Reproduction: birth and survival

Successful breeding demands a temporary change in a bird's behaviour pattern. Most species have a restricted breeding period—at roughly the same time, once a year; or, in some species, such as the larger albatrosses, only once every two years. When conditions are most suitable for raising young efficiently, the male expresses his readiness for mating, often in elaborate courtship displays or song; a pair is formed and a nest-site chosen (though not necessarily in that order); and, singly or together, the partners construct a nest that is safe from predators. Once the female lays the eggs they are incubated until they hatch. The young must then be fed, sheltered and protected from enemies until or after fledging.

Mating is a relatively simple affair. Except for ducks and some flightless species, most birds have no external reproductive organs during mating. Mating involves a bringing together of the respective cloaca openings as the male bird (which has an evertible cloaca) mounts the female who has her tail to one side.

Mammals, whose evolution is further developed than that of birds, reproduce their young alive from inside their bodies. Birds develop their young outside their bodies in eggs shelled with calcium—a distinct advantage for a creature so intricately designed for flight.

The eggs laid for incubation at one sitting are referred to as a clutch. The size of the clutch varies but it is generally limited to how many young the parent bird is able to care for successfully.

Only two basic pigments determine the colouring and marking of the eggs—a blue and a buff-brown. The blue, when it is present, pervades the whole shell and without it the shell is white. Brown colouring may be present on or just below the surface. On white shells this produces the yellow-buff-brown range of colours, and on blue shells it produces the green-olive range. Markings on shells are made by a single chemical substance which may appear as black, brown or red-brown. Spots of it are incorporated at various levels as the layers of shell build up during laying. The spots, which may appear as pale grey, mauve or blue patches on the shell, do not dry until some time after the egg is laid; they may be smeared into streaks as the egg is laid.

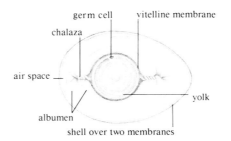

Inside the egg The egg is finely adapted for its purpose protecting and nourishing the developing embryo. The yolk supplies food for its growth, albumen cushions the yolk against shock, and the two membranes keep out harmful bacteria. The shell, which consists mostly of calcium carbonate, 'breathes' to let in essential oxygen.

Three-day old Blackbird Unlike precocial young, which are born at a more advanced stage of development, altricial young are born blind, naked and totally dependent on their parents for food. While they are in the nest, these helpless young are also referred to as nestlings.

Three-day-old lapwing Alert and covered with down, the precocial lapwing chick runs and feeds itself three days after hatching. These types of young are known as 'nidifugous' (nest-leaving) though many may stay with the parents near the nest-site for some time afterwards.

The process of incubation

The egg nurtures the developing embryo. The germ cell from which it will grow lies on the upper surface of the yolk, which supplies fats and proteins. So that the germ cell remains uppermost, the yolk is encased in the tough vitelline membrane, which extends on both sides and attaches to the shell membranes as a twisted strand, the chalaza. Suspended in this fashion, the yolk is able to compensate for any chance movement. Albumen, which cushions the yolk against shock, is 90 per cent water and provides a further store of protein. The remarkably strong egg shell encloses the two sturdy membranes which surround the contents of the egg.

The embryo must be kept warm until the egg hatches. During this incubation period the male or female—sometimes both, in shifts—warms the eggs with its feet or with specially developed brood patches on its breast or abdomen. The King Penguin keeps its egg warm by supporting it on its feet and enveloping it in a fold of skin.

The new young

When the egg is hatched the young chick breaks through the shell with an egg-tooth on the tip of its bill (which disappears shortly after hatching) and the use of a strong 'hatching muscle' at the back of its neck. There are two types of young—precocial, which, well-downed, can run around within a few hours of hatching, and altricial, which are totally dependent, nest-bound and often naked for some days.

Parental duties continue to be demanding once the chicks have hatched. In many birds, both sexes share these duties; among some birds, living in small clans in permanent territories, all members join in.

The nest must be cleaned, the chicks protected from predators, kept warm and provided with a continual supply of food. Though chicks instinctively seek food, their skills are sharpened by practice. First they are fed in response to their begging. A common method of attracting attention is gaping, where the young open wide their bills displaying the bright pink interior (or gape). Gaping is often accompanied by high-pitched calls. Later, young learn to find food themselves, from that dropped in the nest and then after they leave. Here parents lead by example.

Nests: shelters for the young

A nest is a cradle in which eggs and the helpless young can be relatively safe from predators. Accordingly, birds often conceal their nests in unlikely or inaccessible places such as tall trees or remote islands, or cover them with camouflaging material. A nest can be the most rudimentary scrape in the ground or a remarkably intricate covered or hanging structure. Materials used in nest-building—which may be the sole responsibility of one sex or a joint effort—are mainly vegetable, and include sticks, seaweed, grass, leaves and bark. Animal materials such as feathers, wool, hair, cobwebs and droppings may be also used, and some birds surface or reinforce their nests with mud or bind them with saliva.

ROBIN'S CUP NEST
A strong nest of grass, roots, moss and twigs, lined with fibre.

GREBE'S FLOATING NEST
The Great Crested Grebe's floating platform of reeds and rushes.

TREECREEPER'S HOLE NEST
The floor of a ready-made cavity, in a hollow limb or tree-trunk with added nest material.

SWALLOW'S BRACKET NEST
A nail supports a nest of small straws, grass stems and mud.

SHEARWATER'S BURROW
A tunnel, one or two metres long, is excavated in well-drained soil.

Migrants and nomads *by H. J. Frith*

Some birds spend their whole lives in one area. One such sedentary bird is the Malleefowl, which seldom moves more than two kilometres from the mound in which it was hatched. Most Malleefowl remain within a couple of hundred metres of their birthplace throughout their lives. Many small songbirds, including fairy-wrens and scrubwrens, are also sedentary and during banding studies are repeatedly retrapped near their banding place.

Even in the most sedentary species, however, some movement of individuals is to be expected as local conditions change and birds are forced to move. Also, in most species there is a dispersal after the breeding season, when young birds leave their parents' territories to seek their own.

Other species are more mobile and long journeys are an essential part of their lives. Many waders, for example, leave southern Australia and travel to northern Siberia to breed each winter. Others do not leave the continent but are likely to travel to every corner of it. In many species the movements are regular and these birds are said to be migratory. In others the movements are irregular in direction or timing, and these birds are called nomadic.

Little was known of bird migration in Australia when the Australian Bird Banding Scheme was set up by the CSIRO in 1953. Now data are accumulating rapidly, although there are still considerable gaps in our knowledge of migratory birds. It is not possible to say exactly how many species undertake the various types of movement. However, it is clear that migration is an important phenomenon. At least 44 per cent of the 260 species of birds found near Canberra undertake some kind of movement, if only small-scale between high and low altitudes. Of the 60 or so wading birds in Australia at least 38 are migrants from Asia. And there are at least 80 species of migratory seabirds off the coast.

Types of migration
The word migration refers to the regular, annual movements of a whole population, or a large part of it, between two areas, each of which is occupied for part of the year. Usually one area is occupied for breeding whereas the other is more suitable for the support of the population at the opposite season of the year. If the whole population moves the migration is said to be total.

Migration is most commonly between north and south, but it may involve only a change of altitude, and it can be in any direction. It can be long or short.

Across the Equator
Many birds leave Australia each year and move across the Equator to the Northern Hemisphere, some as far as Siberia, to breed. These birds are mainly waders but they also include two swifts, four terns, a cuckoo, a wagtail and a reed-warbler. Other birds breed in Australia and travel northwards across the Equator in autumn. These include the Flesh-footed Sooty, and Short-tailed Shearwater, and probably the White-faced Storm-petrel.

Among the best-known trans-equatorial migrants are Latham's Snipe and the Short-tailed Shearwater. The snipe breeds in grassland on the Japanese islands of

Honshu and Hokkaido and on southern Sakhalin (USSR) and in August and September the populations move to southeastern Australia to avoid the northern winter. They leave Australia on the return journey in March and April. Latham's Snipe have been seen in New Guinea and banded in the Philippines, but their exact route between Australia and Japan is still unknown.

The Short-tailed Shearwater, or muttonbird, breeds on islands off the coast of New South Wales and in Bass Strait as well as further south, and moves each autumn to waters of the northern Pacific including the Bering Sea. Some also pass through the Bering Straits into the Arctic Ocean. Individual birds return to the same nesting burrows they had occupied the previous year and they lay their eggs within a few days of the same date each year.

Trans-equatorial migration is less important in Australia than in the other southern continents. Africa and South America are visited each year by many species and individuals of all kinds, including small perching birds from the north. The main migration stream of these birds terminates among the islands to the north of the continent, though stragglers sometimes continue on to Australia.

Within the continent
Banding records and observations are so scanty that the true extent of migration within Australia is not known, but up to 50 species may be involved. These include some pigeons, parrots, cuckoos, nightjars, kingfishers, pittas, bee-eaters, the Dollarbird, cuckoo-shrikes, honeyeaters, flycatchers, whistlers and gerygones.

Migration is less pronounced in the west than in the east, doubtless because in the west the arid zone reaches the coast, where it stretches a great distance, forming a barrier. Nor is winter climate so extreme there.

The scale of movement varies greatly among the species. The Rainbow Bee-eater, for example, completely vacates the south. Some birds reach the islands north of Australia. On the return journey most of the population leaves the far north.

Silvereyes belong to two populations in central eastern Australia. One is sedentary and one is migratory, so that while birds are always present in many districts there is a stream of migrants moving through at the same time. Some Silvereyes travel from Tasmania to Queensland for the winter.

There seem to be similar situations with the Yellow-faced Honeyeater and the White-naped Honeyeater. These travel through eastern New South Wales in noisy flocks each autumn, along the same routes and even along the same rows of trees.

Across the Tasman Sea
Many vagrants reach New Zealand from Australia but there is very little regular migration. Only a few species are known to be involved—the Double-banded Plover, the Fluttering Shearwater, and the White-fronted Tern. It is possible that the Cattle Egret can now be classed as a regular migrant—although large numbers visit New Zealand each winter, it is not known whether these are simply young birds as is the case with the Australasian Gannets that

visit Australia from New Zealand. Most birds that migrate to and from New Zealand probably travel through Polynesia.

Changes of altitude
Altitudinal movements are particularly marked in the highlands of the southeast. For instance, of 63 species found in summer in the ranges above Canberra only 19 are residents. The rest move to lower altitudes in winter. Only one, the Pink Robin, winters at high altitudes. The most obvious altitudinal migrants in this region are the Pied Currawong, Gang-gang Cockatoo, Australian King Parrot, Crimson Rosella, Golden Whistler, Crescent Honeyeater and Red Wattlebird.

The exodus from the high altitudes is associated with low temperatures, which vary in timing and intensity. This affects the dates on which the birds reach the lower altitudes and the numbers involved.

Nomadic wanderings
Many Australian birds are nomadic, and the phenomenon may be more widespread here than on the other continents. It has been estimated that 26 per cent of the land birds that breed in Australia undertake nomadic movements. This widespread development of nomadism reflects the variability of the climate.

The most spectacular nomadic movements are among the birds of the arid zone. The rainfall there is erratic and the suitability of habitat, particularly in food supply, fluctuates. To find suitable living conditions, the birds must move widely.

Many seed-eating and nectarivorous birds, including the Budgerigar, Pied Honeyeater and the insect-eating Crimson Chat, are spectacular nomads in the arid zone. When rain falls and parts of the desert bloom, they arrive in great numbers, breed and depart as the food is exhausted.

Nomadism is not restricted to the arid zone. There are also many nomadic species in the eucalypt forests of coastal districts with fairly regular climate. The lorikeets and some honeyeaters wander widely there as different species of trees flower.

In the rainforests the Wompoo Fruit-Dove, the Rose-crowned Fruit-Dove and many other fruit-eaters are also nomadic, following the fruiting of different trees.

Nomadism also occurs in pelicans, cormorants, teal and ducks in the inland. Water is seldom permanent there, so some species must depend on temporary water brought by floods. In general these aquatic habitats are most extensive in winter and spring, but in summer the waters recede and the birds must move out. They disperse in all directions. In times of drought, there is an explosive random dispersal of ducks, and some travel very long distances.

All the inland waterfowl are nomadic to various degrees. The Musk Duck is usually sedentary and wanders only locally, and the Blue-billed Duck migrates only on a small scale. The Grey Teal and the Pink-eared Duck are more extreme nomads but in different ways. When the Pink-eared Duck leaves a district the whole population moves out and it may be years before any are seen there again. Conversely, some Grey Teal may remain behind, ready to take advantage of any improvement in conditions.

How birds' numbers are regulated — *by H. J. Frith*

Birds have an enormous potential for multiplying their numbers. It has been calculated that if a pair of birds—say Zebra Finches—reared two broods, each of five young, every year, and if all the young and their descendants survived and bred at the same rate, in ten years that pair would have increased the population by ten million.

Increases of this magnitude rarely happen in nature and then only in unusual circumstances, such as the introduction of a bird to a country where the things that usually control its population are lacking. Examples of this in Australia are the Common Starling and the House Sparrow, which have increased in a little more than 100 years from a few pairs to millions of birds—but even this falls short of the real potential for those species.

Although birds have the reproductive capacity to increase very rapidly, natural populations in the wild are relatively stable. Numbers will increase over a run of good seasons and decrease over a run of bad.

As the numbers increase, environmental factors and traits in the birds' own behaviour come into play to slow down and finally halt the increase. The numbers then remain fairly stable while the environment is unchanged. There is still much discussion on the nature of the controls that operate on the populations of different species, but it is clear that availability of food and nesting sites, the ravages of predators and disease, and aversion to crowding are all involved and often work in combination to control populations.

The food supply is one of the most important controls. There is not enough food in the environment to support the number of birds that enter the population after each breeding. A population is at its largest then, when the young have left the nest. It brings more intense competition for available food. Birds that are less efficient at securing food starve, or—because they are weak—are taken by predators.

For a stable population to be maintained, the number of young produced each year must be balanced by the death of an equal number of birds. Such regular mortality may occur during a run of equable seasons, while during a run of good years there may be unusually high survival so that the population increases rapidly for a time. But following extremes of temperature or low rainfall over a season or longer, numbers fall rapidly. Wide fluctuations are usual among the nomadic birds of the arid zone but less common in the more stable environment of coastal regions.

Changes of habitat

Many major changes in the numbers and distribution of species of birds are occurring in Australia because of alterations to their habitats. Some birds are becoming more numerous, others are declining.

On the inland plains the introduction of grazing stock and rabbits has had dramatic effects on the numbers of some birds, including the Partridge Pigeon, several parrots of the genus *Neophema* and the Bustard. These birds depended on native grasses, which grew to maturity, set seed on which they fed, and left tall straw as cover. The grazing animals have reduced these grasslands to short swards of mainly annual plants and introduced weeds. These provide neither food nor cover for many birds.

Elsewhere large tracts of woodland have

Not leaves but Budgerigars clothe this tree. These little parrots often form enormous flocks in the arid interior of Australia. Their populations, like those of other birds, are largest after the breeding season. Budgerigars breed at any time after good rain brings the promise of more abundant food.

been cleared and the land has been devoted to wheat-growing. This has provided abundant food for several birds, including the Galah, the Crested Pigeon and the Cockatiel, which have expanded their ranges and numbers. On the debit side, many mallee-living species have disappeared from vast areas of former habitat: the Southern Scrub-robin, Mallee Emu-wren, and Regent Parrot.

Wheatfields also provide abundant food and cover for Stubble Quail and in some districts their numbers have grown enormously, but it is not known whether the total population of Stubble Quail has grown or shrunk because much suitable habitat in the grasslands on the plains has been destroyed by grazing.

The size of the clutch
Birds vary widely in the number of eggs they lay in a single clutch. Some always lay the same number. The Wandering Albatross lays only one egg every two years. The Australian fruit-doves lay each year, but only one egg, never more; the ground-living pigeons lay two eggs. The Spotted Nightjar lays one egg and the Large-tailed Nightjar lays two. The Red-kneed Dotterel lays four.

On the other hand the clutch size of many birds covers a range. The Black Swan, for example, lays between four and ten eggs, though 70 per cent of its clutches are five or six eggs. True quails lay as many as 12 eggs, but button-quails lay only three or four. The Malleefowl can lay as many as 33 eggs in a season, but clutch size varies greatly from one female to another and from year to year in the same female. One Malleefowl that laid 33 eggs one year laid only 17 the next, when there was a drought.

Some young are helpless, blind and naked when they hatch from the egg, and must remain in the nest for up to several weeks while they grow. In these species the size of the clutch may be related to the maximum number of young the parents can rear in an average year—which is ultimately determined by the quantity of food that can be brought to the nest to feed the growing young. This is not a perfect adaptation to circumstances because in a bad season the normal number of young has to share an abnormally scanty supply of food and many die in the nest.

It is not known what determines the clutch size in birds whose precocial young leave the nest soon after hatching.

Increasing the clutch
Many birds normally lay only one clutch a season. If it is destroyed they may lay a new clutch after a suitable interval, but if the eggs are then removed during the laying often the bird cannot produce extra eggs to compensate. Other birds will continue to lay more eggs if eggs are successively removed during laying. There are many examples, particularly among game birds. The Feral Chicken is the extreme case.

The size of the clutch may be limited genetically or may be related to the bird's physiological capacity to continue to produce eggs. This is the case with the Malleefowl and the other mound-builders, which do not sit on their eggs or rear their young. In those species the number of eggs laid in a season is determined by the length

of the laying period and the interval between eggs. The length of the laying period is determined each year by the weather, and the period between eggs by the abundance of food. Some female Malleefowl can produce one egg every five days in some years but in a drought they take up to nine days.

The eggs of many birds of prey hatch at intervals of a few days and this results in young of different ages and sizes in the nest. When food is scarce and the parents are struggling to feed the brood, the larger young are able to gain a disproportionate share of what is brought to the nest. They increase in weight but the smaller nestlings fall behind and die. Had they all been the same size and strength all would have been undernourished and the whole clutch may have perished—a less effective result for survival of the species.

There are other ways in which clutch size is related to environmental opportunites for breeding. Widely distributed birds lay smaller clutches in tropical Australia than they do in the south, where the breeding season with abundant food is shorter. Changes in the clutch size are also related to the abundance of food in successive years. Some birds of prey tend to lay larger clutches in times of rabbit or rodent plagues than they do in less bountiful years.

Some birds lay more than one clutch in a season and in many of them the first clutch is the largest. In other birds, older females lay larger clutches. In all birds the breeding season is timed to occur at the time of year most favourable for feeding the young.

Conditions for breeding
Most species of birds have restricted breeding periods and nest at roughly the same time each year. The breeding season varies greatly between different climatic regions and between different types of birds. In temperate southeastern Australia, for example, food is most abundant in spring and that is when most small birds breed.

Near Darwin, in the tropics, there are two seasons—a wet season from October to March and a long dry season, from April to September. In any month some birds can be found breeding, but the breeding seasons of the different species correspond to times when their needs are best met. Water birds, for example, breed mainly in the late wet season when swamps are full and aquatic animals and plants—which provide food and cover—have had time to flourish.

The forest birds breed throughout the wet season, though there are differences among them, probably related to the food cycle of each group. The insect-eaters tend to breed first, followed by the fruit-eaters and finally the seed-eaters. The birds of prey breed almost entirely in the dry season, when the grass is short and, presumably, it is easiest to see and catch prey.

The ultimate factors
In the arid zone the climate varies erratically and suitable conditions may arrive at different times each year. Some birds, such as the Emu, have regular breeding seasons—though in poor years the young may not survive—but many species breed at any time when conditions are suitable.

For most species the food supply is the

most important of the ultimate factors that have, through natural selection, adjusted the breeding season of particular species to particular times. It is during the breeding season and immediately afterwards, when all the young are fledged and the population is at its largest, that the maximum demand is made on the food supply.

Predicting abundant food
Other ultimate factors include the availability of nest material and cover, competition from similar species, air temperature and rainfall and its effects on the environment. Generally, however, ultimate factors alert the species to the availability of suitable breeding conditions but operate too late to enable the birds to go through the necessary physiological and behavioural processes to form pairs and to come into a suitable sexual state to breed. Birds need to predict a potential abundance of food to be fully capable of breeding when the appropriate season comes. These predictions are made possible by factors in the environment called proximate factors.

The most reliable events in the environment are the shortening of daylight hours before the winter solstice and the lengthening of days after it. This increase in day-length is the overwhelmingly important proximate factor in temperate regions such as southeastern Australia. It stimulates the birds' sexual cycle so that when the warm days of spring come and the food supply increases, the birds are paired and sexually ready to breed.

In the arid and semi-arid regions of inland Australia a regular event like this is not so dependable for many birds. Conditions there are so erratic that longer days may come in the middle of a drought, when there is no food and conditions are quite unsuitable for breeding. For these birds rain is a further proximate factor. At any season it stimulates plant growth and the production of seed and encourages insects.

Rapid response to rain
Many birds of the inland respond remarkably swiftly to rain. Zebra Finches, for instance, can begin building nests within a day or two of a storm. Some of the many other birds that respond to rain are the Bustards, Banded Lapwing, Diamond Dove, plumed pigeons, Budgerigar, Crested Bellbird and Crimson Chat.

For many water birds of the inland, even rain is not a suitable proximate factor. The rain that falls in a bird's locality does not necessarily fill the local swamps, whereas rain on the highlands hundreds of kilometres away can flood rivers and ultimately fill swamps in the inland.

The higher water in the billabongs stimulates the growth of the swamp plants and the breeding of the insects on which the birds feed. The rising water level itself is the sexual stimulus for the birds, and they can respond very rapidly. Grey Teal, for example, can pair, become sexually mature and lay eggs within 14 days of a rise in water level at any season. Other birds with this capacity to respond to a rise in water level include the Pink-eared Duck, Pacific Black Duck, the Shoveler, Black-tailed Native-hen, White-headed Stilt, the Whiskered Tern and many others.

Birds of prehistoric Australia
by G. F. van Tets

Studying the fossil remains of birds in Australia is like taking part in the assembly of a gigantic jigsaw puzzle, and the picture that emerges is still very fragmentary. This is not because of a lack of fossil material, but because there are few students and there is little adequate reference material on the modern species of birds for the comparison.

Nevertheless the fossil material contains a rich source of information on the environments that prevailed in prehistoric times. It consists of large quantities of bones and a few feathers, eggs and tracks. The bones are usually broken and incomplete, though if at least one end of a long bone is reasonably intact it is usually possible for the species to be determined.

From the species of birds represented in a deposit, and a knowledge of the habitat requirements of those species, the environment they lived in can be deduced. In addition, from the parts of birds found in ancient refuse heaps, or middens, it can be seen how Aborigines used them for food, clothing, tools and ornaments.

Australia's giant penguins
The earliest fossil remains of an identifiable bird in Australia are of a giant penguin *Anthropornis nordenskjoldi*. It was about 1.4 metres tall. The height of the tallest living penguin, the Emperor Penguin, is about one metre.

The fragmentary remains of *Anthropornis nordenskjoldi* were found in a deposit from the Upper Eocene epoch, 45

million years ago, at the Blanche Point Marls, 37 kilometres south-southwest of Adelaide. Elsewhere in South Australia and in Victoria, remains have been found of at least two more genera of extinct penguins. These remains are from deposits older than the late Miocene epoch, which ended seven million years ago.

Similar remains of fossil penguins have been found in New Zealand and at Seymour Island, near the tip of the Antarctic Peninsula. The fossil penguins are more diverse than the modern species, while odd anatomic details provide further evidence that penguins had petrel-like flying ancestors, some time during the Cretaceous period, 136–65 million years ago.

During the late Eocene, about 45 million years ago, Australia was farther south and closer to Antarctica than it is now, and the temperature of its seas is estimated to have varied from 12°C to 16°C. It is not known why the giant penguins died out, though it

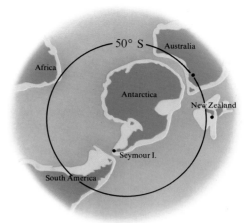

The southern continents 45 million years ago, and places where penguin fossils have been found.

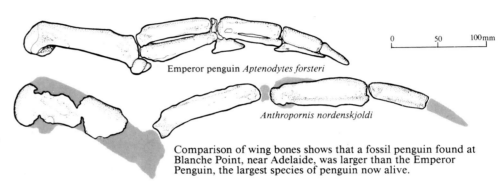

Emperor penguin *Aptenodytes forsteri*

Anthropornis nordenskjoldi

Comparison of wing bones shows that a fossil penguin found at Blanche Point, near Adelaide, was larger than the Emperor Penguin, the largest species of penguin now alive.

One of the oldest feathers ever found is this fossil from Koonwarra, Vic. The inset shows the actual size.

The second oldest feathers

At a roadcut four kilometres east of Koonwarra, 132 kilometres southeast of Melbourne, deposits from an ancient freshwater lake, 125–110 million years old, were found. They contained an abundance of fossil remains of plants, fish,

insects and other invertebrates with jointed limbs—and also at least four body feathers. It has not been possible to determine what kind of bird the Koonwarra feathers came from.

Almost as old are bones and feathers of

Ambiortus found recently in Russia.

The oldest feathers yet found are those of *Archaeopteryx,* a reptile-like winged and feathered creature that lived in Germany about 150 million years ago and is regarded as the first bird.

has been suggested that they were eliminated by competition from marine mammals, such as the seals and porpoises.

Extinct birds of the inland sea
During the Cretaceous period, Australia was cut in two by an inland sea, of which the remnants are Lake Eyre and the other lakes of northeastern South Australia. During the Tertiary period, 65–3 million years ago, the inland sea lost its connection, first to the Gulf of Carpentaria in the north and later to the Great Australian Bight, by way of Lake Torrens and Spencer Gulf, in the south. It has been suggested alternatively that the inland sea was drained by the Murray–Darling river systems.

Some time during the Pleistocene, three million to 10 000 years ago, the Lake Eyre basin dried up and a unique community of plants and animals was eliminated. Along the shores of Cooper Creek and the Warburton River, which drain into Lake Eyre, and in nearby lakes, fossilised remains from the Miocene to Pleistocene—30 million to 10 000 years ago—have been found. They include the remains of crocodiles, giant monotremes, giant marsupials and dolphins.

The associated bird life was equally remarkable. During the Miocene there were at least two and during the Pleistocene at least four species of flamingos. Flamingos are extinct in Australia but live in tropical and subtropical parts of America, Africa and Asia, breeding on large shallow lagoons and inland lakes.

At Lake Palankarinna near Lake Eyre, Miocene fossils of the Palaelodidae, an extinct family of flamingo-like wading birds, have also been found. Similar fossils are also known from the Miocene in Europe and North America.

The fossil birds of the Lake Eyre basin are still being studied. Preliminary results show that they included extinct species of pelican, darter, cormorant, stork and eagle as well as many existing kinds of water birds. Most numerous are the remains of Black and Pied Cormorants and the Black-faced Shag. The Black-faced Shag now lives only on marine waters, the Pied Cormorant

Giant birds the Aborigines knew

In western Victoria the Tjapwurong tribe had legends about giant emus they called *mihirung parimal* which lived in their area when the local volcanoes were still active. The last lava flowed as recently as 8000 years ago. At Pimba, near Woomera, SA, there are Aboriginal rock carvings of giant bird tracks beside recognisable tracks of Emus.

Throughout Australia, including Tasmania, findings include bones, a few tracks and a couple of eggs of birds that were substantially bigger than Emus and cassowaries. Some of these have been calculated to belong to birds bigger by weight than any known kind of bird, even the elephant birds of Madagascar and the four-metre-tall moas of New Zealand. The Australian birds were probably not taller than these giant birds, however.

The giant birds of Australia belong to the family Dromornithidae, which included one or two species in each of five genera. They were flightless with huge legs and thick powerful bills for browsing. They are known to have been in Australia since at least the Miocene, 30–7 million years ago, and there may have been some still in existence when man first arrived in Australia about 40 000 years ago.

The giant birds of Australia are related to some of those of other continents and large islands. Presumably they all descended from a stock in Gondwanaland, the great southern supercontinent that began to split at least 100 million years ago into Australia, New Zealand, Antarctica, New Guinea, India, South America and Africa.

Genyornis newtoni, two metres tall

mainly on marine waters, and the Black Cormorant mainly on inland waters.

Clues from Aboriginal middens
Around the Australian coast are the refuse tips, or middens, of the Aborigines. These mounds contain mainly mollusc shells but also stone implements and the bones of fish, reptiles, seals, marsupials and birds.

The birds represented in the middens are those that may be found washed up on nearby beaches after a storm. There is a wide variety of penguins, albatrosses, petrels, gannets and cormorants, and a sprinkling of inland water and land birds. Where bones of the Short-tailed Shearwater, or Tasmanian muttonbird, or of several species of cormorants predominate, a nearby breeding colony is suggested.

Several middens are being systematically excavated and some go back 14 000 years to the time of the last ice age, when sea levels were lower and Bass Strait was mostly land. These middens are yielding assemblages of animal material of known dates. One midden on the north coast of Tasmania goes back 8000 years and contains many bones of the Pied Cormorant, a bird that has been extinct in Tasmania in historic times. The Pied Cormorant prefers sheltered marine waters. Presumably the north coast of Tasmania became too exposed for it to survive. In an 800-year-old midden, bones of an extinct penguin, *Tasidyptes hunteri,* have also been found.

Excavations around buildings occupied by the last Tasmanian Aborigines on Flinders Island have revealed early remains of introduced European birds, including starlings and sparrows.

Bones in limestone caves

The limestone caves in various parts of southern Australia contain large quantities of bones that have accumulated there during the past 100 000 years. They are the bones of animals that either dwelt in the caves or stumbled down shafts, or were the prey of cave-dwelling predators.

Owls and hawks that lived in the caves have deposited mounds of pellets which now form rock composed of fragments of bones of small reptiles, mammals and birds. The bird remains are mainly bones of quails and perching birds, but there are also bones of waders, ducks, rails and parrots.

Identification of the perching bird material by species is difficult because there are many species in Australia and there is a lack of adequate reference material in museum study collections. When the perching bird bones are identified they should yield a wealth of information about the habitats in the country around the caves during recent millennia. This is because, as a rule, small birds are more exacting in habitat requirements than large birds—hence the greater number of species of small birds.

Prominent in some caves are the bones of *Progura gallinacea*, a species of the giant mound-builders which died out soon after the arrival of man in Australia.

The giant mound-builder *Progura gallinacea* died out about 35 000 years ago. It was a relative of the Malleefowl.

Malleefowl *Leipoa ocellata*

Progura gallinacea

The origins of Australian birds *by Richard Schodde*

Where did the Australian birds come from? How and when did they radiate and diversify in the land and adapt to the habitats in which they are found today? The only potentially complete answers lie in the fossil record. This, however, is so scattered, so imperfect and so little studied that biologists have had to seek clues to the past from evolutionary relationships and patterns of distribution among living birds.

But here problems have arisen again. The different kinds of birds living in Australia are well known, and so are the places where they are found, but little is understood about the birds themselves.

Gaps in knowledge are most obvious in the science of classifying birds according to their relationships, because all the attributes of each species—plumage patterns, genetics, structure, behavioural traits, distribution, nest and eggs—need to be known before its relationship with other species becomes clear. The origins of Australia's birds and their nearest relatives elsewhere remain very much in the dark.

Birds unique to Australia

The answers to these questions are important to ornithologists because the bird life of Australia is, area for area, among the richest and most colourful in the world. Some 700 native species and naturally occurring migrants have been recorded, compared with 750 in North America, and 950 in Europe and northern Asia. The diversity of Australian birds is exemplified by honeyeaters. With 65 species, they are the largest Australian family of birds and have colonised every corner of the continent.

Colour and uniqueness are blended in the parrots, the lyrebirds, the fairy-wrens and the birds-of-paradise and bowerbirds. Birds-of-paradise, bowerbirds and lyrebirds are found only in Australia and New Guinea, and the fairy-wrens are equally restricted.

Parrots are found on all southern continents and across the tropics, but nowhere else do they display such variation of form as in Australasia and only here are the cockatoos, the nectar-feeding lorikeets and the ground-feeding rosellas to be found.

Other less colourful yet familiar and typical Australasian birds are the butcherbirds and currawongs, the treecreepers, the pardalotes, the whistlers, the Australian warblers, the owlet-nightjars, the mound-builders, the bronzewings, the Emus and cassowaries. To this day their relationship with birds outside the region is uncertain.

Dominance of these groups and species that are endemic—found nowhere else—compounds the distinctive nature of the Australian bird life. Few of the prominent bird families of Asia and Africa are represented in Australia, and then only by one or two members of each. Examples are Richard's Pipit, the Singing Bushlark, the Metallic Starling and the Yellow-bellied Sunbird. Others are conspicuously absent, notably the bulbuls (except as an introduced bird), the woodpeckers, the hornbills, the titmice, the Old World vultures, the true wrens, the nuthatches, the shrikes and the buntings.

In their absence the endemic families have radiated to fill the habitats in all corners of the continent. For instance, the honeyeaters which barely range beyond Australia and New Guinea to New Zealand and other Pacific islands, have spread abundantly and evolved diversely within Australia, between them occupying much the same ecological niches as sunbirds and bulbuls do separately in southeastern Asia. It can be dangerous to carry ecological parallels too far, but there are nevertheless similarities in the feeding methods of Australian fantails, treecreepers and sittellas, and the American redstarts and the creepers and nuthatches of the rest of the world.

Part and parcel of the radiation of many Australian groups, moreover, has been adaptation to diverse feeding habitats. The Australian butcherbird family shows this well. Butcherbirds themselves are sedentary and tree-living birds of woodland and employ shrike-like feeding methods. Their nearest relatives, Australian Magpies, are terrestrial insect-eaters which feed in open fields. Currawongs, perhaps the most advanced members of the family, are adept scavengers and tree-living gleaners which spend much of their time roaming when they are not breeding.

Even the most versatile family of the Australian tree-feeders, the honeyeaters, appear to have members adapted to feeding and living on the ground. These are the red, yellow and pied chats, whose relationship with the honeyeaters has become clear only in the 1970s.

Search for clues

The very fact that the Australian land birds include many apparently old endemic groups of uncertain origin makes it difficult to reconstruct their sources and their diverse lines of evolution. The clues that are needed are the intermediate and linking forms that would connect these birds with groups living on other continents.

The seabirds, shore birds and freshwater birds of Australia shed little light on these questions for just the opposite reason. Here not only the families but also the principal genera and sometimes even species are distributed throughout Africa and Asia, or even all over the world. The ranges of seabirds are as continuous as the oceans themselves. The species of petrels, gulls and terns that occur about Australian shores are found throughout much of the world or they have counterparts there.

Freshwater birds are in similar circumstances. The Australian Pelican, Brolga, Black-necked Stork, White Ibis, Royal Spoonbill, Great Egret, Brown Bittern, Purple Swamphen, Eurasian Coot, Pacific Black Duck and the Hardhead are all represented by the same or immediately related species throughout the Eastern Hemisphere and sometimes in the Western Hemisphere as well.

Dispersal in such birds is so active and constant and is prompted by such peculiar circumstances—for example, the need for new surface water—that movements and colonisation by land birds cannot usually be linked with it. Old endemic Australian waterfowl are few, but they appear to include the Yellow-billed Spoonbill, the Straw-necked Ibis, the Magpie Goose and an aberrant swan, the Freckled Duck.

The traditional and most widely accepted view of the origins of Australian bird life sees Asia as the source. It sees the early bird colonists moving in waves down through the Indonesian archipelago and New Guinea to northern Australia. It is presumed that the first arrivals were the ancestors of the main group of endemic birds such as the mound-builders, the parrots, the lyrebirds, the honeyeaters, the mudnesters, the butcherbirds, and the birds-of-paradise and bowerbirds. For them to have evolved into the distinctive forms living today they must have reached Australia at least 20 million or more years ago.

Late immigrants

Later arrivals are thought to have included some of the flycatchers, Australian wrens, White-backed Swallow, ground pigeons, some cuckoos, frogmouths and such birds of prey as the Black-breasted Buzzard, Square-tailed Kite and Red Goshawk.

The last to come were the representatives of species that are widespread elsewhere today—the pittas, Richard's Pipit, Singing Bushlark, Metallic Starling, some fruit pigeons, Peregrine Falcon, Nankeen Kestrel, Barn Owl, Welcome Swallow, orioles and the crows.

There is some certainty about the immigration of only the last, most recent group of species. This is because the theory of colonisation by waves of birds rests on two shaky foundations. One is that the dominant elements of the Australian bird fauna are most closely related to, and presumably derived from, equivalent groups in Asia.

It has been traditionally thought, for example, that the Asian tree and leaf warblers, flycatchers and scimitar babblers are the relatives of, respectively, the Australian wrens, robin flycatchers and babblers. Likewise, the ancestors of the Australian treecreepers and sittellas, pardalotes and birds-of-paradise and bowerbirds are usually believed to have come from among the creepers and nuthatches, flowerpeckers and starlings or crows of the Old World.

Doubtful affinities

Over the past decade, however, research on DNA hybridisation—the genetic material in birds' cells—and on structural morphology has suggested that affinity between these Australian groups and their apparent Asian counterparts is doubtful. Even more significantly, the Australian groups may be more closely related to one another than to any groups outside the continent. It seems likely, for example, that the butcherbirds, the wood swallows and the Australian mudnesters are very closely related, and that the Australian flycatchers, far from being closely allied to flycatchers overseas, are really diminutive crows.

Should such close relationships within groups of Australian birds be confirmed, it would mean that all species of typical Australian songbirds have evolved from a few obscure ancestors, and that similarities in appearance and way of life to Asian birds result from similar adaptation to similar circumstances, not from common ancestry. These are the characteristics of a bird fauna that has evolved in long isolation.

The second foundation of the colonisation theory is a presumption that the continents have always been fixed in their present positions. It used to be believed that land and island bridges helped land birds to invade Australia from Asia. Now it is known that the continents are, and probably always have been, drifting about.

Some 30–20 million years ago, at a time when the first Australian land birds might have begun to trickle in, Australia itself was some 1000–1500 kilometres south of its present position. Where the intervening archipelagos off the Asian continent lay then and what forms they took is still uncertain. It is obvious, however, that the water barriers to invasion from Asia were much wider, more difficult, and for many groups, even impossible to cross.

A search for alternative theories to explain the origin of Australia's present-day bird life has been prompted by the drifting of the continents. About 100 million years ago, Australia was still part of a huge southern supercontinent called Gondwanaland, which also included Africa, India, Madagascar, Antarctica, New Zealand and South America.

The question is, did Australia, along with other southern continents, inherit its land birds from Gondwanaland? It seems almost certain that some Australasian groups are Gondwanan in origin—the cassowaries and Emus, the mound-builders, the Plains-wanderers, the parrots, and perhaps the pigeons, the cuckoos and the rails. They are all among the more primitive, or less highly evolved, living birds, and most of them have relatives on other southern continents, either exclusively or in greater abun-

dance than in North America or Eurasia. The giant flightless running birds—the ostrich in Africa, the rheas in South America, the extinct moas in New Zealand and the cassowaries and Emus in Australia—are an often-quoted example.

The primitive families of perching birds are today centred in the southern continents and may have arisen there. These are the pittas and the broadbills in Africa and southeastern Asia; the oven birds, the ant thrushes, the contingas and tyrant flycatchers in South America; the New Zealand wrens; and the Madagascan asities. The possibility that these birds had a com-

mon Gondwanan origin is, nevertheless, rather doubtful on the present evidence. Gondwanaland began to break up at least 100 million years ago, probably long before the evolution of their ancestors.

Africa and Antarctica broke apart first, soon followed by India, Madagascar, New Zealand and then South America from western Antarctica. Australia finally severed from eastern Antarctica some 55–50 million years ago. If the Australian perching birds and songbirds originated in the south, they might be expected to have nearer relatives in South America than in Africa, but it seems that the converse is likely.

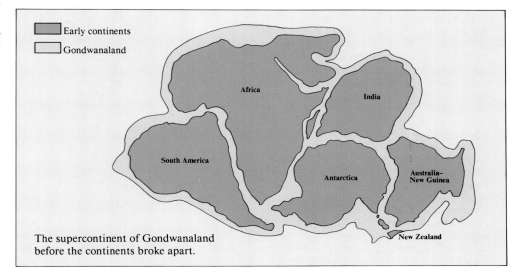

Early continents
Gondwanaland

The supercontinent of Gondwanaland before the continents broke apart.

Radiation, extinction and the New Guinea connection

The history of the land and freshwater bird fauna of Australasia is rather clearer after its establishment than before. The Australasian region includes Australia, New Zealand and New Guinea and is bound in the north and east by the Pacific Ocean, in the south by the Southern Ocean, in the west by the Indian Ocean and in the northwest by Wallace's and Weber's lines.

Wallace's line, which runs between the Indonesian islands of Lombok and Bali, has long been regarded as separating the Oriental and Australasian bird faunas. Cockatoos and honeyeaters have penetrated as far westwards as Lombok, but hardly farther. Many Asian birds have filtered through to the east of Wallace's line, however—woodpeckers have reached Celebes and the Asian muscicapine flycatchers have reached Timor. The eastern Indonesian archipelagos—the Lesser Sundas, Celebes and the Moluccas—in fact form a ground where limited elements of the Asian and Australian bird faunas intermingle.

Weber's line, which closely follows the continental shelf of Australia–New Guinea, is regarded nowadays as a more realistic boundary for the Australasian fauna.

Of the three main lands of the Australasian region, New Zealand has by far the poorest bird fauna. The naturally occurring land birds that breed there total a mere 37 species. Some of these belong to old groups whose relationships are uncertain, such as the kiwis, the New Zealand wattlebirds, the New Zealand wrens, and the kakapo, kaka and kea parrots. Others are distinctive members of typically Aus-

tralian families— honeyeaters, thickheads and Australian warblers. Still others, such as the White-faced Heron, Sacred Kingfisher, Purple Swamphen, Shining Bronze-Cuckoo, Richard's Pipit, Grey Fantail and the Silvereye, appear to be recent immigrants from Australia. There can be little doubt that New Zealand has received much of its present-day land and freshwater birds by dispersal across the sea from Australia.

The islands of New Guinea and Australia itself are about equally rich in land birds. Differences between their bird faunas are differences between birds adapted to life in tropical rainforests on one hand and to life in drier eucalypt forest and woodland on the other. New Guinea has, for example, a great diversity of tree-living, fruit-eating

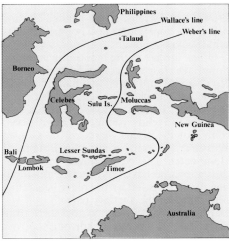

Australasian–Asian fauna boundaries.

and nectar-eating fruit doves and lories. These are paralleled in Australia by an array of ground-feeding, seed-eating bronzewings and broad-tailed parrots.

Likewise, the many thornbills, whitefaces and weebills of dry open woodlands are the Australian counterparts of the various scrubwrens and fernwrens and gerygones of the dense rainforests of New Guinea. Even the feeding movements of New Guinean and Australian birds show contrasts. Most species of the New Guinean honeyeaters are usually sedentary, in communes, but many Australian honeyeaters, responding to uncertainties of weather and flowering, have become highly nomadic.

Because of such differences and their isolation by sea, New Guinean birds have not usually been thought to have been involved in the diversification and adaptation of Australian birds to their present environment. The traditional view has been that at best New Guinea contributed a good number of rainforest species which trickled down the eastern coast of Australia across land bridges exposed between Australia and New Guinea during ice ages of up to a million or more years ago.

By that time three basic Australian bird groups, or avifaunulas, may already have been well established. These were the Bassian group, in the temperate southeast and southwest of the continent; the Torresian group, across the monsoonal north; and the Eyrean group, in the arid centre. These groups were proposed by the Melbourne zoologist Sir Walter Baldwin Spencer in 1896 and they remain in use today to explain the distribution patterns.

Some of the best examples of Baldwin Spencer's divisions are to be found among the fairy-wrens. The Superb Fairy-wren is southeastern Bassian, the Splendid, Red-winged and Blue-breasted Fairy-wrens are southwestern Bassian, the White-winged is Eyrean and the Purple-crowned and Red-backed are Torresian.

But the ranges of some of these and others overlap boundaries of the regions. The Variegated Fairy-wren in its various forms enters all the regions. So do the Australian Magpie, Australian Magpie-lark, Grey Fantail, Rufous Whistler, Black-faced Cuckoo-shrike and Australian Raven.

This does not mean that Bassian, Torresian and Eyrean regions and groups are artefacts, but rather that they are not enough to account for the origin and radiation of older groups of species of Australian birds. For example, are fairy-wrens Torresian or Eyrean in origin and which one is the most primitive?

The formation of New Guinea

The key appears to rest in New Guinea. Lying along the northern edge of the Australian continental plate, New Guinea has had a turbulent geological history. Until about five–three million years ago, the central mountain chains that dominate its landscape had not risen from the sea. What is now northern New Guinea was then a chain of disconnected islands. Southern New Guinea was part of Australia itself.

The island reached its present form and size with the raising of the central mountain spine, no more than one or two million years ago. Later, encroachments by the sea began to isolate southern New Guinea from Australia periodically. The last break came about 10–12 000 years ago with the sinking of the Gulf of Carpentaria and the flooding of Torres Strait. Under such circumstances, it is unlikely that New Guinea's present bird fauna—which is diverse and rich in old genera, represented by cassowaries, crowned pigeons, kingfishers, chowchillas, thickheads and birds-of-paradise—would have had the time and opportunity to evolve and radiate there.

Before Australia became dry

Australia itself is the likely source of the New Guinea bird fauna. In the more recent past, according to the meagre and still incompletely researched fossil record, Australia was nowhere near as dry or as devoid of rainforest as it is today. Some 40–30 million years ago, Australia seems to have been extensively rainforested. There is evidence that the kinds of Antarctic beech and flesh-fruited conifers that today are confined to the distant ranges of New Guinea and New Caledonia then spread as far westwards as Western Australia.

From then on, as Australia drifted into the earth's desert latitudes, its climate appears to have become gradually drier. This trend culminated in sequences of extreme cold and dry periods and warm and semi-humid periods during the ice ages of the past million or more years. The effect on Australia's already rich and distinctive bird fauna was catastrophic. Towards the end of the last ice age the last of the giant runners and a cassowary resembling the

The continent of Australia and New Guinea, at times of greatest exposure of land during much of the Pliocene and Pleistocene periods, two million to 10 000 years ago. The present land masses are outlined in black.

Sea present from time to time

Land above sea level

muruk of the New Guinea mountains, the Australian flamingos, giant flightless mound-builders and a host of other birds became extinct. Australia's bird fauna may well be little more than two-thirds of the size it was 100 000 years ago.

Under the arid conditions, the rainforests and their birds contracted to the moister northern and eastern periphery of the Australia–New Guinea continent. The Great Dividing Range as far north as Cooktown and the rising mountain ranges of New Guinea provided a haven for species adapted to temperate conditions.

Evidence for this remains today. The birds of these ranges, although separated by more than 1000 kilometres, have more in common with each other than with adjacent tropical birds in lowland southern New Guinea and Cape York Peninsula. The two highland regions share a number of species or groups of species not generally found in tropical rainforest—brush turkeys, king parrots, chowchillas, fernwrens, treecreepers, mountain thornbills, the uniformly brown scrubwrens, Grey-headed Robin, caligavine honeyeaters and bowerbirds that build maypole bowers.

Other species in the New Guinea mountains have close relatives in Australia which have spread into drier woodland habitats. These are the whipbirds and scrub-robins, the Grey Fantail, Varied Sittella, the firetails, the yellow robins, the red-breasted robins of the genus *Petroica*, the Golden Whistler, the miners and the Blue-faced Honeyeater. The New Guinea mountains thus appear to have served as the main refuge for what is left of the older Australian bird fauna of the Tertiary period.

The birds in the isolated pockets of tropical rainforest towards the top of Cape York Peninsula are rather different and represent an immigrant outlier of the New

Guinea bird fauna. They include the Palm Cockatoo, the Red-cheeked and Eclectus Parrots, the Glossy Swiftlet, Red-bellied Pitta, Tropical Scrubwren, Green-backed Honeyeater, the Tawny-breasted Honeyeater and a manucode.

None of them is found anywhere else in Australia but they are all found in the lowland forests of New Guinea. Even the Cape York members of groups common to all Australian rainforests have as close or closer ties with New Guinea representatives than with those birds of the Atherton Tableland, just 100 or more kilometres farther south. This is the case with the Wompoo Fruit-Dove and Brown Cuckoo-Dove, the fig-parrots, White-faced Robin, Magnificent Riflebird and several others.

Some of the Cape York rainforest birds—the cassowary, the Helmeted Friarbird and other honeyeaters, the Yellow-bellied Sunbird, the Spangled Drongo, the Black Butcherbird and others—have trickled farther south along the east coast of Australia, and have tended to mask the importance of the more southerly rainforests as a haven for the remnants of Australia's old rainforest-adapted birds.

To place the components of the Australian bird fauna in truer perspective, the three divisions of Baldwin Spencer have recently been extended to five. The Tumbunan division has been added to encompass the 'old' birds of the highland rainforest of eastern Australia; and the avifaunula of the rainforests of Cape York Peninsula, together with the very small pockets of outliers in Arnhem Land and the Kimberleys, now form the Irian division.

Baldwin Spencer's divisions are now restricted to the birds of the eucalypt forest, woodland and desert, all of which grade into one another to some extent. In the absence of any concrete evidence, it is assumed that the members of these divisions have evolved from rainforest forms.

How birds have coped, through evolution, with changing habitats is reflected in the distribution of the Australian treecreepers. One group of two isolated but closely allied species has remained in the Tumbunan rainforest and occurs in an arc from the New Guinea mountains down the eastern seaboard of Australia. These are the Papuan and White-throated Treecreepers. Only one of them, the White-throated, has been able to expand its range into the fringing eucalypt forests.

Another group adapted to life in eucalypt woodlands forms an integral part of the Bassian and Torresian faunas. This is the brown treecreeper group and its members—Black-tailed, Brown and Rufous—form a ring of isolated forms, one replacing another around the moister periphery of Australia. The last group, comprising the Red-browed and White-browed Treecreepers, is curiously split between the Bassian eucalypt forests of the southeast and the Eyrean woodlands of the inland.

Thus in the treecreepers, evolution and adaptation is manifest on at least two levels, each related to different radiations. One represents the more ancient break-up into groups of species adapted to fundamentally different habitats and seems to be linked with the development of the Tumbunan, Bassian-Torresian and Eyrean faunas. The other, reflecting a recent splitting of species within each group, has been brought about

by recent periods of aridity in Australia.

These periods of aridity, tied to the ice ages and alternating with periods of higher rainfall over the past several hundred thousand years, seem to have been the main force that shaped the present distribution of Australian birds. They have repeatedly joined populations in rings around the drier centre and then broken, isolated and fragmented them in refuges at the periphery. Many of the populations began to evolve into the species and subspecies of today, and many of them formed hybrid zones whenever and wherever they met again. A striking example of a fragmented and intergrading ring is to be found in the White-cheeked Rosellas. They are represented by the 'northern' rosella in the northwest and north, the 'pale-headed' rosella in the northeast, the 'eastern' rosella in the southeast and the 'western' rosella in the southwest.

Mountain refuges
Some of the principal refuges, apart from eastern coastal Australia and Tasmania, have been the Mt Lofty and Flinders Ranges in South Australia, and the Musgrave, MacDonnell and Everard Ranges in central Australia. These shelter small enclaves of Bassian or Torresian species in the Eyrean heartland.

Other refuges are the Bassian southwest of Western Australia, and the rainforest pockets in the Kimberleys and Arnhem Land, where members of the Irian fauna—

the Scrubfowl, Rose-crowned Fruit-Dove, Rainbow Pitta, Dusky and White-lined Honeyeaters and others—have survived.

During the course of these events, some physical barriers to the distribution of birds have been more important than others. One is the Eyrean barrier which, following the site of a former inland sea and edged by the Flinders Ranges, stretches north from the head of Spencer Gulf to the Simpson Desert, and marks the separation of many inland birds. Examples are the Chiming and Chirruping Wedgebills, the distinctive subspecies of Grey Shrike-thrush, the Thick-billed Grasswren, White-browed Treecreeper, Splendid Fairy-wren, and the Ringnecks.

Hot, flat treeless plains wedging south from the Gulf of Carpentaria form the Carpentaria barrier. This separates even more forms—the Brown Treecreeper from the Black-tailed Treecreeper, and subspecies of the Grey-crowned Babbler, White-browed Robin, Varied Sittella, Forest Kingfisher, Rose-crowned Fruit-Dove, Rainbow Lorikeet, and others.

There are also other barriers, such as the combined Torresian and Burdekin barriers across the foot of Cape York Peninsula, the first running inland from Cooktown and the second in from Townsville. They separate many subspecies of species; between them there are broad zones of intergradation in eucalypt woodlands. Their role and those of others in promoting evolution in Australian birds still needs much study.

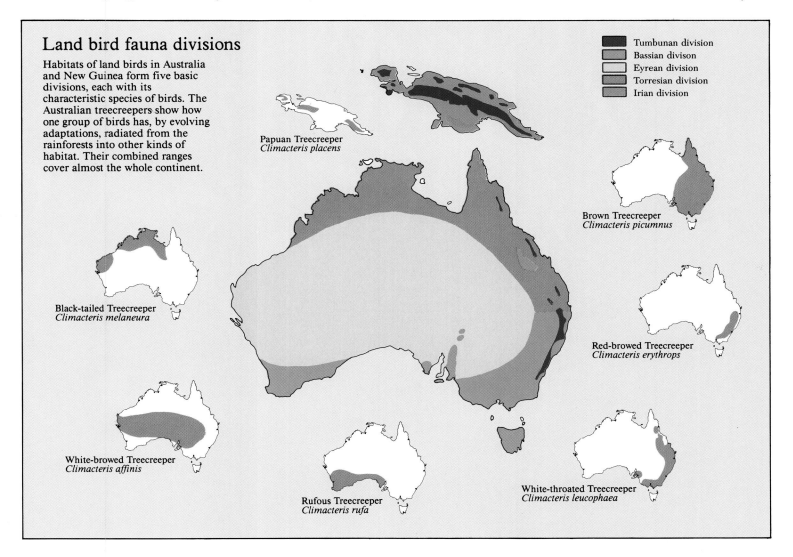

Land bird fauna divisions

Habitats of land birds in Australia and New Guinea form five basic divisions, each with its characteristic species of birds. The Australian treecreepers show how one group of birds has, by evolving adaptations, radiated from the rainforests into other kinds of habitat. Their combined ranges cover almost the whole continent.

Tumbunan division
Bassian divison
Eyrean division
Torresian division
Irian division

Papuan Treecreeper
Climacteris placens

Brown Treecreeper
Climacteris picumnus

Black-tailed Treecreeper
Climacteris melaneura

Red-browed Treecreeper
Climacteris erythrops

White-browed Treecreeper
Climacteris affinis

Rufous Treecreeper
Climacteris rufa

White-throated Treecreeper
Climacteris leucophaea

Part 3

Pied Cormorants.

Naming and identifying birds

This part of the book presents descriptions of the habits, behaviour, appearance and distribution of every species of bird that breeds in or regularly visits Australia.

Species names
Every species of animal and plant is given a formal and unique scientific name by which it can be known; no two species can have the same name under the International Code of Zoological Nomenclature. In birds, a species is a group or population of similar-looking and similar-behaving individuals that interbreed in the wild and produce fertile offspring.

The scientific name of a species—derived from Greek or Latin—has two parts, a second part or specific epithet that identifies the species itself and a first part or generic name which identifies the genus—that is, the group of species to which it belongs. Closely related species are grouped in genera so that their relationships may be understood at a glance. Thus the Long-Tailed Finch, identified by its epithet *acuticauda,* is closely allied to other species of grass finches in the genus *Poephila:* hence its full scientific name, *Poephila acuticauda.*

The generic name always begins with a capital letter and the species epithet always with a small one. The scientific name is, by convention, always printed in italics except where it occurs in italic context.

In some cases a triple name is used. The third name indicates the subspecies, or race, a level of classification for birds of the same species that look different and live in different regions. For example, there are at least five races of the Australian Magpie, *Gymnorhina tibicen,* in Australia: the black-backed, steep-billed *Gymnorhina tibicen tibicen* of eastern Australia; the large white-backed *Gymnorhina tibicen leuconota* in southeastern Australia; the small white-backed *Gymnorhina tibicen hypoleuca* in Tasmania; the western *Gymnorhina tibicen dorsalis;* and the variably black-backed, slender-billed *Gymnorhina tibicen longirostris* of northwestern and central Australia.

Unlike other zoological and botanical fields, in ornithology every bird also has a recognised English or common name. Birds may be known by many common names and at times popular names are superseded by others more widely used internationally. The most frequent of these alternative names are listed under 'Other Names'.

Birds and animals are also grouped into many other hierarchies of classification above the levels of species and genus. The Australian Magpie, for instance, is grouped with currawongs and butcherbirds in the family Cracticidae. This family is, in turn, grouped with approximately 33 other families occurring naturally in Australia in the order Passeriformes, the perching birds, or songbirds. This and 26 other orders are grouped in the class Aves, which comprises all birds. In this book the family to which each species belongs is shown at the bottom of each page. A description of the orders and families of birds found in Australia is given on pp. 622–29.

Ornithologists are constantly reclassifying birds in the light of new studies, necessitating frequent changes in scientific names and their order. Most changes flow from generic readjustments to the position of species, and from the discovery that distinctive populations previously regarded as separate species hybridise and intergrade and so are one.

After each bird's name, the describer is credited, together with the year of first description. This shows that most Australian birds were named over 100 years ago. Brackets around a describer's name indicate that the genus in which the species is now placed is different from the one in which it was first described.

Source of classification
The classification of species and genera follows the forthcoming edition of the Royal Australasian Ornithologists Union's (RAOU) checklist of the Birds of Australia and Territories, published in the Zoological Catalogue of Australia series by the Bureau of Flora and Fauna (BFF), Canberra. There are some minor departures from the catalogue in the sequence of species, genera and families, but the taxonomic adjustments already reached by the compilers are incorporated here.

Authority for names
Scientific and English names used here also follow those of the RAOU-BFF catalogue. By convention, and concensus, that list sets the standard for Australian nomenclature and has done so for the past 50 years. The recommendations of the RAOU's committee of experts—B. Glover, F. Kinsky, S. Marchant, A.R. McGill, S.A. Parker and R. Schodde—have been adopted in the forthcoming catalogue, and here, except in a few cases affected by classificatory change. To perpetuate popular but parochial names where they conflict serves little purpose other than to destabilise nomenclature, stir controversy and certainly bewilder the amateur bird-watcher.

Size
The length or height of each bird is given. Measured from the tip of the bill to the tip of the tail, it is rounded off to the nearest five millimetres. Where the bill or the tail is unusually long, its form is stressed.

Identification
The bird's colour pattern is described working usually down the back and then down the front to the belly and undertail region, ending with the colours of the iris of the eye, the bill and feet. The technical terms for parts of a bird's body are explained on the facing page.

Different authorities sometimes use different names for the same colour, especially subtle greys and browns, but the accompanying photographs provide guidance.

Some birds, especially males, have two or more different plumages during the year. Dull plumage is often replaced by bright at the beginning of the breeding season, and both plumages are described.

Young birds are called chicks or nestlings until they can fly. When young leave the nest they are said to fledge. Free-ranging chicks that are likely to be seen, such as ducklings, are described as downy young. Those of Northern Hemisphere breeding waders, however, are excluded because they are never seen in Australia. So are the chicks of most songbirds, because they are so naked.

The next stage a young bird passes through is its first plumages of true feathers. It is then called immature. This stage may last for several years in some species, such as the Satin Bowerbird, and the birds may pass through several plumage phases. Where there is a distinct immature plumage it is described briefly.

Voice
The sounds birds make can be important guides to identification. They call to warn of danger, to keep in contact with one another, to keep a flock together while feeding. These calls can sometimes be described—as *zit-zit-zit,* for instance—but others are so elusive that they can only be described in general terms such as 'harsh chattering sounds'.

During the breeding season, and even throughout the year, birds utter phrases to proclaim their territory and attract a mate. Those phrases are often pleasant to hear and, in the case of songbirds or passerines, are called songs. Wherever possible, each bird's different calls and song are described separately in the passerines.

Nesting
Many birds have distinct breeding seasons, in the spring in the south, for example. In the north other birds—seed-eating parrots and finches—have their breeding geared to the end of the wet season, when food is plentiful. Still others, in arid regions, may breed at any time after good rains have fallen. Most birds build a nest, fairly typical for that species, in a fairly consistent place and height. The form and structure of each nest are described. Eggs are also described by number, size, approximate shape, and colour. Eggs laid in concealed places are often white, whereas those laid in the open are often coloured and marked in a way that blends with their substrate. The large end, which emerges first, is often more heavily marked.

The size of eggs varies; the average is usually given for each species, to the nearest millimetre. The common clutch size is also given. This is usually the same within a range for each species, but where food is unusually abundant the clutch may be exceptionally large; and in times of scarcity eggs may not be laid at all.

Incubation and fledging periods are given wherever possible, the latter recording the period to flight, not the day of quitting the nest by precocial chicks. If they are lacking, they have not been found.

Distribution
Each species has its own range, determined by the availability of suitable habitat and food. This is described in detail just for Australia. Within their ranges some birds are sedentary—they stay in one locality throughout the year—while others migrate between two places and yet others wander nomadically. Because Australia is so vast and sparsely populated, knowledge of bird distribution has been sketchy. To rectify this, the Royal Australasian Ornithologists Union has just finished a five-year project studying the distribution of birds throughout Aus-

tralia, and has produced an atlas of their ranges. Those interested in more information should write to the RAOU at the address given on p637.

The maps in this book show the ranges of most of the species and are based on the RAOU Atlas. These maps are necessarily simplifications of complex patterns and few if any birds will be seen at all places throughout their ranges.

Places where species occur as rare vagrants are not shown on the map, but are mentioned in the accompanying text. Maps have not been included for some birds that visit Australia only occasionally. These are mostly seabirds, which can be blown ashore anywhere along the coast.

For seabirds only the coastal distribution is mapped. Many of them, of course, range far beyond the coast. The overseas range of these birds, and of others occurring beyond

Australia, is summarised in the text.

The maps include the Tropic of Capricorn, state boundaries and, as reference points, the sites of Adelaide, Perth, Broome, Darwin, Alice Springs, Cairns, Brisbane, Sydney, Melbourne and Hobart.

At the end of the distribution notes, the approximate number of races is given, stressing those found in Australia.

What to look for
For most people, an interest in birds begins with identification—with the pleasure to be had from putting the right name to a bird. But success in identifying birds depends on knowing how to look at them. This is not simply a matter of being alert, but is a technique that can easily be learnt.

The most important clues to a bird's identity—the points to which special attention should be paid—are: size; shape,

including the shape and length of the bill; general colouring of the plumage and noticeable markings; behaviour; call and song; when and where the bird was seen.

Because some birds visit Australia at only a certain time of the year, when a bird is seen may be a clue to its identity. Flight pattern is another. Is it direct or meandering? Powerful or fluttering? Does the bird fly in short bursts or is flight sustained?

Then there is the method of flight. A bird may use its wings almost all the time in flapping flight or it may glide on outstretched wings; it may hover in one place or it may soar. Or its flight may be undulating—a fairly regular pattern of alternate flapping and gliding.

Further points to watch for are the way a bird walks, runs or hops, and where and how it feeds—by diving or hawking, or by probing bark or gleaning foliage.

Shapes of eggs

Birds' eggs vary greatly in their shapes. Some basic shapes are shown here, but there are many intergradations. Birds of the same species usually lay eggs of the same shape.

ellipsoidal or oblong-oval

round or spherical

pyriform or conical

long-oval or ellipsoid-oval

The parts of a bird's body

The principal regions or parts encountered in descriptions of birds are indicated here. Some grade into others and some are clear-cut.

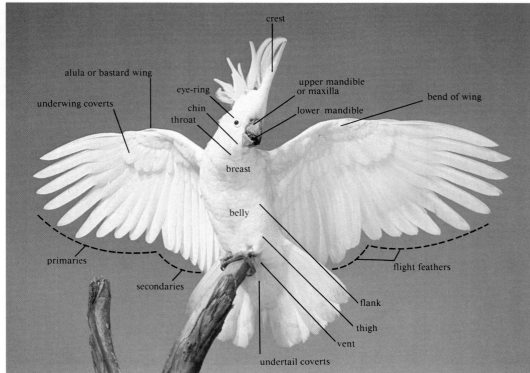

Emus going to drink. The name emu comes from the Portuguese word *ema* meaning 'crane', which was applied to large ostrich-like birds.

Emu _Dromaius novaehollandiae_ (LATHAM, 1790)

THIS LARGE, FLIGHTLESS bird is a nomadic wanderer in most parts of Australia. Intensive studies in Western Australia have shown that groups make regular seasonal movements or migrations — to the southwest in spring and to the northeast in autumn — in certain regions. Individuals may move several hundred kilometres in a year.

Emus are omnivorous, eating a variety of leaves, grasses, fruits and flowers of native plants, as well as insects. In spring and summer in the mulga zone of Western Australia, their diet consists mainly of flowers and seeds of shrubs. In autumn, as these foods become scarce, they graze on young grass that sprouts after the summer rains. In winter, herbs form the Emus' main food. They eat insects when these are available — during grasshopper plagues, for example.

Emus usually pair during summer or autumn, and couples remain together for about five months, keeping within a certain area but often walking long distances, and sometimes driving other Emus away. When necessary Emus can run at speeds up to 48 km/h.

Birds sometimes bathe in puddles by squatting on their haunches and splashing about with the beak while fluffing the feathers and shaking vigorously. The feathers are primitive with two long plumes growing from each feather-base.

Immediately after laying the clutch the female leaves the nest area and pays no more attention to the eggs. She wanders off or joins a group of migrating non-breeding birds. Meanwhile, the male incubates the eggs, starting before the female has completed the clutch. He sits continuously during the eight weeks required for incubation, leaving the eggs only rarely and eating little. He may lose 4–8 kg in weight during this time, and conserves energy by lowering his metabolic rate to become almost torpid.

After the eggs have hatched, the male leads the striped, downy chicks around and broods them beneath his feathers at night. To sleep, they settle on their 'haunches' with heads resting on their backs. This period of parental care may last up to 18 months in semi-arid areas. Emus do not breed until they are more than two years old, and males looking after chicks cannot start another breeding cycle until the second December after the chicks have hatched.

Chicks hatch when their main food, young green growth, is most likely to be abundant. In dry seasons the birds leave the affected regions, but appear to move back later in the year. In a bad year many may die; the survivors — living around waterholes, eating the available seeds — breed and soon build up the population again.

In the past, Emus were avidly hunted by Aborigines, and a hunter had many ways of securing his prey, including spearing it at waterholes, driving it into a net, poisoning waterholes with shrubs containing narcotic chemicals, or attracting the birds by imitating their booming calls.

Today, predation by Aborigines has been largely replaced by persecution from farmers, particularly in wheat-growing areas in Western Australia where an influx of Emus may cause considerable damage. This led to the famous 'Emu War' of 1932, when an army detachment with two Lewis guns attempted to exterminate the Emus. The offensive was a failure. Even so, many thousands of Emus have been killed in Western Australia. In the eastern states, however, farmers often regard the Emu as an attraction rather than a pest.

An Emu with its large clutch. The female may lay as many as 20 eggs, though seven to eleven are more usual. After laying, she wanders off, leaving nesting duties to her mate.

OTHER NAMES
None.

IDENTIFICATION
LENGTH: _Stands up to 2 m high._
ADULTS: _Sexes similar; female slightly larger. General plumage dusky-brown to grey-brown with shafts and tips of feathers black. Feathers of upper neck short and sparse, revealing blue neck skin, which is darker in females. Vestigial wings about 20 cm long. Eye yellow-brown to dak brown. Bill brown to black. Legs dark brown to black; large foot with three toes. Female develops nuptial plumage in breeding season. Body colour darkens and thick black feathering covers neck and head, except around the ears — appears much darker than male._

IMMATURES: _Greyer or paler than adults, somewhat streaked in appearance; body feathers have pale ends; heads and necks blackish haired._
DOWNY YOUNG: _Dark brown with cream stripes for several months._

VOICE
Deep guttural grunts made by both sexes; female emits dull, resonant booming sound.

NESTING
Breeds usually in winter. Egg-laying starts in April or May and breeding season continues until September or October. Nest a trampled bed of grasses, bark or leaves, in a scrape in the ground often near a tree or bush. Eggs: five to 20, but usually seven to 11; dark green with granular surface; a blue bloom when freshly laid; ellipsoidal, about 130–140 x 90 mm; weight 700–900 g. Incubation about 60 days, by male.

DISTRIBUTION
Avoids thickly forested regions. Has been eliminated from many closely settled areas and central Victoria. Habitat varies from arid plains of interior to tropical woodland on Cape York and eucalypt woodlands of Snowy Mountains. Recently introduced to Maria Island, Tasmania, and Kangaroo Island, SA. No races but Emus from wetter habits are generally darker than those from drier areas. Other recently extinct species and races on Kangaroo Island and Tasmania–King Island respectively.

The large and flightless cassowary lives in northeast Queensland. It feeds on fruit and sometimes leaves the rainforest to rob gardens. This is a male.

Southern Cassowary *Casuarius casuarius* (LINNÉ, 1758)

IN THE TROPICAL RAINFORESTS of northeastern Queensland, where it is difficult to see in the dim light, the first indication that a cassowary is nearby is usually a low rumble, like the sound of an approaching truck — the noise the bird makes when it meets a strange object. If the bird is approached it will usually keep quite still. If an intruder comes too close the bird will stretch itself as high as it can, raise all its feathers and give a loud hiss. This is usually sufficient to scare off a casual observer. If the observer does not depart, however, the cassowary will slowly walk away — sometimes with a stamp of the feet — or, if chased, run crashing through the forest undergrowth, body horizontal and head and neck stretched forward, slipping easily through dense tangles of plants that would stop most other large animals.

For most of the year cassowaries live alone. They appear to have some sort of territory: individual birds — recognisable by facial characteristics and particular colours on the head and neck — can usually be found time and again in the same areas. If two male cassowaries accidently meet, they stretch their bodies, fluff their feathers and rumble at each other until one retires. But if a male meets a female, she can usually make him flee merely by stretching a little and staring quietly, or rumbling slightly at him, because females are dominant.

With the approach of the breeding season, females become more tolerant and eventually form pairs with males of their choice. The pair remains together for a few weeks until the female is ready to lay, when they go to the chosen nest site. Before copulating, the male displays to the female by 'dancing' around her in a circle, his throat trembling and swelling and emitting a series of low 'boos'. The male then leads the female a short distance where she squats and allows him to mount. After egg-laying the female takes no more interest and leaves the male to incubate the eggs and rear the chicks. Once fin-

ished with a mate, the female may take another, and lay another set of eggs. One female has been known to take three mates in succession in a season. The incubation period is about two months, during which the male is not seen in his usual haunts.

Once the chicks have hatched the male reappears, taking his string of small striped youngsters to his regular feeding places. The chicks grow rapidly and begin to lose their stripes after about three months. By the time they are six months old, their brown sub-adult plumage is developed and the neck and head are beginning to colour. The male looks after the young for about nine months and then he chases them away to fend for themselves. It takes about three years for the glossy black adult plumage to develop fully, but cassowaries probably mature sexually before this, as brown birds sometimes attempt to mate with adult females.

Cassowaries can be aggressive, particularly when guarding their chicks, and it seems that some individuals are naturally bad-tempered. They are armed with formidable, though seldom used, weapons — the claw of the inside toe of each foot is a large straight spike, 120 mm long and 30 mm wide at the base. When cassowaries fight they raise their feathers and bend their necks right under the body, roaring loudly. They then charge each other, kicking with both feet at once. The bout is usually brief and not much damage is done.

Cassowaries feed on fallen fruit, particularly of the family Lauraceae, from rainforest trees and vines. Usually only one bird comes at a time to an area of fallen fruit although different birds come at different times. At times of food shortage they may enter gardens and orchards to eat cultivated fruits such as bananas and mulberries. Besides fruit, cassowaries will eat almost any edible object — fungi, snails, dead birds and even large dead rats, but they do, strangely enough, often refuse citrus fruit.

OTHER NAMES
Double-wattled Cassowary, Australian Cassowary.

IDENTIFICATION
LENGTH: *Adults stand 1.5–2.0 m high to top of head. More thickset than Emu.*
ADULTS: *Sexes alike; female larger, more brightly coloured, with taller casque or helmet. Entire plumage of both sexes of glossy black hair-like feathers which consist of two shafts. Wings rudimentary, reduced to a few long, bare quills. Head and neck naked except for scattered bristles. Face dark becoming blue towards back; sides and front of neck blue, darker on lower neck; a pair of red wattles hang from front of neck; back of upper neck light blue grading below to bright red. On top of head a large, blade-shaped horny casque or helmet. Eye and bill very dark brown. Legs green-grey to horn; three toes, inner toe has nail elongated to spike 120 mm long and 30 mm at base.*
IMMATURES: *Brown with heads and necks in adult colouring but duller.*
DOWNY YOUNG: *Striped yellow and black.*

VOICE
A variety of rumbles, booms, roars and hisses.

NESTING
Breeds June–October, coinciding with the maximum availability of fruit. Nest a scrape in the ground lined with grasses, fern fronds and leaves; situated deep in forest. Eggs: usually four; lustrous mid-green; ellipsoidal, about

The female cassowary usually lays four eggs, which are incubated by the male. He also rears the young, looking after them for about nine months.

140 x 90 mm. Incubation about two months, by male.

DISTRIBUTION
Restricted to tropical rainforests in northeastern Queensland where it is fairly common. Solitary throughout most of year; sedentary, probably maintaining a feeding territory. Member of a wide-ranging species that also occurs naturally in western and southern lowland New Guinea; one small race in Australia.

Common Diving-Petrel *Pelecanoides urinator* (GMELIN, 1789)

THIS TUBBY, SHORT-TAILED little petrel uses its short wings not only in the air but also under water, for propulsion in the dives that it makes in search of food: small crustaceans and fish but not, unlike most petrels, squid. It bursts from the water like a flying fish and, bouncing off through wave crests, whirrs along on its fast-beating little wings low over the water, looking like a big bumble-bee; then it sets its wings in a straight, brief glide before plunging back into the sea after prey.

For waterproofing it has compact oily plumage and short, upward-facing nostril-tubes protected by flaps. It bears a great resemblance to the auklets of the Northern Hemisphere, their common shape and appearance evidently having arisen in adaptation to the same diving habits. Taking off from land or after swimming on calm seas is difficult, the birds rising only after the pattering run. They moult at sea after breeding, shedding their flight feathers together and often becoming temporarily flightless.

Common Diving-Petrels are rather sedentary birds of rough subantarctic and cool temperate seas. Although some disperse north in non-breeding winter months, others remain close to their breeding grounds, resting ashore as far south as Heard Island.

Spring nesting can begin as early as July in northern Australia but is evidently delayed by cold until September–November further south. In Australia, Common Diving-Petrels begin to gather off their breeding grounds in April. For several months they fly ashore at night to dig or clean out nesting burrows, hurtling straight in without circling. Overhead they court in high-speed display flights, uttering wild cries; and courtship continues on the ground outside the burrow, where the birds mate. The birds can breed when only two years old, earlier than most petrels.

After a brief exodus at sea to fatten up, females lay in July–August, over a period of about six weeks. Eggs, incubated in daily shifts, hatch in September. Young continue to be brooded alternately by both adults for nearly two weeks, much longer than in other petrels, and they are fed nightly; indeed, it is common for both adults to visit their burrows every night throughout incubation and rearing. Most young fledge by the end of December in Australia, but are later elsewhere, from January to March in New Zealand and subantarctic islands.

OTHER NAMES
Diving-Petrel, Smaller Diving-Petrel.

IDENTIFICATION
LENGTH: *About 200 mm.*
ADULTS: *Sexes similar. Upper parts steel-black, shading to white on underparts; underwings, flanks and breast smoky. Eye brown. Bill black. Feet cobalt-blue, with webs black.*
IMMATURES: *Similar to adults, but secondaries more boldly edged with white; bill narrower.*
DOWNY YOUNG: *Mid-grey; head almost bare.*

VOICE
In colonies a moaning whistle ku, ku-aa – the pitch of each soft call rising on third syllable. Also loud nasal braying kuaka-did-a-did and variations, in display flight and on ground. Silent at sea.

NESTING
Breeds in colonies over spring–early summer, July–December, extending to March in subantarctic. Nest a short burrow sometimes up to 1 m, among tussocks or under forest on steep slopes or tops of islands. Egg: one; white; oval, about 38 x 30 mm. Incubation about 55 days, by both sexes. Young fledge in 47–59 days.

DISTRIBUTION
Circum-subantarctic and south temperate seas, breeding on many islands. Six races; two in southern Australian waters: one small, breeding on several islands in Bass Strait, off southern Tasmania and around North Island of New Zealand; the other large, breeding on subantarctic islands and visiting infrequently on winter dispersal.

The Common Diving-Petrel is a tubby, short-tailed little bird which breeds on several islands in Bass Strait.

Wandering Albatross *Diomedea exulans* (LINNÉ, 1758)

The Wandering Albatross builds a large bowl-shaped nest and lays a single egg. This is a female with finely vermiculated plumage.

THE LARGEST FLYING BIRD ALIVE today is the Wandering Albatross, with a wingspan of nearly three-and-a-half metres. True to name it wanders around the globe in southern latitudes, often following ships. Flight is an effortless, seemingly endless glide punctuated by occasional beats only on calmer days, traversing the ocean in the manner typical of all albatrosses. As it drops low, the bird turns into the wind to gain lift but little forward movement. Reaching sufficient height — five–20 metres — it turns downwind, sweeping away over the sea until forced to turn into the wind. To rest, it sits on the sea and feeds there, eating mainly squid and cuttlefish, augmented by crustaceans, fish and offal from boats.

Wandering Albatrosses may live for more than 40 years, and rarely breed until nine years old. Each breeding cycle lasts almost 11 months and so most adults (80 per cent) nest only every second year. The birds arrive at their breeding colonies, on subantarctic islands, in September and begin elaborate courtship rituals of bowing, bill-fencing with loud clappering, and dancing with wings oustretched; at the peak of the dance, both partners throw the head back with beak pointing skywards and bray loudly. From one to six or more pairs of birds of different ages take part in these ceremonies which can form pair bonds for life.

Eggs are laid in mid-November, the female returning to the nest site of previous years if successful. The male takes the greater share of incubation, and may sit for 38 days in a shift. Usually the sexes change every two to three weeks, losing about 17 per cent of their weight at a sitting. Metabolic rates differ between the sexes, the larger male having the lower rate so that he can sit for longer without losing any more weight. As soon as a sitting bird is relieved it flies straight out to sea to feed and regain weight. On land it is ungainly, able only to waddle slowly with neck held low in line with its swaying body. So the albatross needs a bare ledge or hill top with an up-draught from which it can take off directly by just spreading its wings.

Chicks take three days to break out of the egg at hatching, and far longer to fledge — 270 to 280 days; next year's adults have sometimes returned to breed before young have left the nest. Parents feed their chicks through the entire winter, daily for the first 20 days and then gradually less often but bringing larger amounts of food. It is an energetically demanding period for adults, and chicks of parents whose shifts in incubation were not evenly shared — particularly where the brunt fell on the female—have less chance of survival. Otherwise mortality at nests is low, involving only the occasional trampling of an egg or its predation by skuas.

By the next September the young bird is finally fledged and sets out for the ocean. After its departure, the parents also wander off and somewhere at sea undergo their moult.

OTHER NAMES
Snowy Albatross, White-winged Albatross.

IDENTIFICATION
LENGTH: *Up to 1350 mm; wingspan up to 3250 mm.*
ADULTS: *Sexes similar; male slightly larger. From a distance completely white but at close range fine brown edges of body feathers give a scalloped effect, strongest in female. Back of wing changes over ten years from black with two white spots to heavy blotches, then to white. Underwing white except for black tip and edges. Tail white. Some adults have flush of pink around ear and side of neck. Eye brown. Bill pink. Feet, toes and webs fleshy white.*
IMMATURES: *Black except for white face and underwing, but whiten rapidly in first three years and then more slowly. Brown breast band and grey plumage with wavy lines often remain up to seventh year. Black band at tip of tail. Bill and feet greyish. The change to adult plumage is gradual and takes about 10 years.*
DOWNY YOUNG: *White-downed.*

VOICE
Hoarse braying whistles in dancing display; coughing grunts when fighting over food. Clappering of bill during courtship. Chicks pipe, whistle and gurgle. Silent in flight.

NESTING
Begins early September; single brooded. Nest a large muddy bowl on the ground, reinforced with plant material. Egg: one; white, speckled with red-brown; oblong-oval, about 131 x 78 mm. Incubation nine–11 weeks, by both sexes. Young fledge in 270–280 days.

DISTRIBUTION
Throughout southern oceans. Found in southern Australian waters north to Perth in west and southernmost islands of Great Barrier Reef in east; greatest numbers off southeastern Australia in winter. Breeds on subantarctic islands, including Macquarie Island. Two races, both reaching Australia: one small and breeding on north subantarctic islands; the other large and breeding on south subantarctic islands.

Royal Albatross *Diomedea epomophora* LESSON, 1825

A female Royal Albatross about to settle on her egg. She has a band around one leg which will help track her movements around the Southern Hemisphere.

BIGGER THAN THE MOLLYMAWKS, the Royal Albatross is as large as the great Wandering Albatross, with a wingspan of over three metres. It can be distinguished from the Wandering Albatross, nonetheless, by its white-plumaged immatures, black eyelids, and even longer bill with a black stripe along the cutting edge and more widely protruding nostrils. Breeding only on islands around New Zealand, Royal Albatrosses rarely wander further east than South America or west of Australia, but do travel north to Polynesia and may use the Tasman Sea as an important wintering ground and feeding area when breeding. Their diet consists mainly of fish, cuttlefish and squid.

Long-lived and usually nesting only once every two years, the birds converge on their breeding islands in October, led by the males. They go through the same courtship rituals as the Wandering Albatross before settling down to laying and incubation in late November–early December. Displaying reaffirms the bonds between pairs mated for life or unites others that have lost their partners through misadventure: widowed males rebuild nests in their territories of previous years and advertise themselves while females do the choosing.

Both sexes incubate in shifts of up to a fortnight or so, the male sitting the longest in a series of about 12 shifts overall. Hatching chicks take one–four days to break out of the egg, ultimately emerging in daylight. They are brooded by both parents in shifts of one–seven days, which become shorter as the chick grows and cease after about five weeks. Both parents feed the chick but again the male often shoulders the brunt; and although they may stay on the

breeding grounds all day, parents only feed the young bird once or twice, most often in the mornings. Royal Albatross chicks reach peak weight at about 200 days, 25 days earlier than Wandering Albatross chicks, and fledge in 235–245 days. They are fed right up to the time of fledging.

OTHER NAMES
None.

IDENTIFICATION
LENGTH: *1150–1250 mm; wingspan 3000–3150 mm.*
ADULTS: *Sexes similar; female slightly smaller or with darker upper wings. Predominantly white, very thin black edges on underside of wings, black under tip. Back, tail and upper wing to last joint near tip white. Becomes whiter with age. Eye black or dark brown. Bill pale pink, upper mandible edged black. Feet, toes and webs pale grey. Northern race has upper surface of wings black in both sexes.*
IMMATURES: *Similar to adults, often brown or black flecks on wings and head.*
DOWNY YOUNG: *White-downed.*

VOICE
Hoarse, guttural calls when feeding and courting, with skywards whistled brays and bill-clappering.

NESTING
If successful, only breeds every two years, over summer; if unsuccessful new attempt made within 12 months. Nest a large, dished mound of mud, placed about 150 m above sea level on steep slopes in sheltered position in tall tussock of grass. Egg: one; white, often with pink-brown blotches; ellipsoidal, about 124 x 79 mm. Incubation about 79 days, by both sexes. Young fledge in 235–245 days.

DISTRIBUTION
Seas of southern temperate and subantarctic latitudes; frequents coastal waters of New Zealand, breeding there and on Chatham Islands, Campbell Island and Auckland Islands. Straggles to east and west coasts of southern Australia. Two races; one smaller and dark-winged, the other larger and white-winged, breeding mainly on Campbell Island where 4400 nesting pairs in 1969.

Black-browed Albatross *Diomedea melanophrys* TEMMINCK, 1828

FOR MOST OF THE YEAR, this thick-necked, robust bird is the most common albatross in southern Australian waters, whether alone or following ships or congregated at flushes of food in flocks of several hundreds. Most come in winter months after breeding, and they usually arrive several weeks ahead of the Wandering Albatross off the New South Wales coast and then leave earlier. Coming close inshore, Black-browed Albatrosses are often seen clearly from land.

Like other albatrosses, the Black-browed roams vast areas of ocean searching for food by effortless gliding, circumnavigating seas south of the subtropical convergence and even crossing the equator infrequently into the Northern Hemisphere. It accepts refuse and carrion thrown out by ships, but at sea usually eats squid, crustaceans and fish. Alighting on the water to feed, it planes down with legs spread forward and head back to skate forward on its feet for several metres before settling and folding its great wings. The birds will dive for food, plunging down until only the tips of their wings show.

Black-browed Albatrosses return to their breeding islands to nest each September–October. Ceremonial pair-bonding displays are elaborate. During nest building, the female stands on the nest while the male collects mud and brings it to her. As he does so, he bows his head to the ground, spreads his tail and brays, exposing a stripe of pink skin at the gape. The female bows and brays in return, arranges the mud, and then the two nibble one another, bow and bray again. There are other displays as well: nodding, bill touching and quivering, head turning and mutual head nibbling. In threat, adults gape and peck, while chicks, like all young albatrosses, protect themselves by vomiting smelly stomach oil.

Eggs are laid by late October and hatch by early January. Parents take shifts in brooding the clutch in its first month, both feeding it at intervals. It fledges in four–five months when both it and adults quit the breeding islands.

OTHER NAMES
Black-browed Mollymawk.

IDENTIFICATION
LENGTH: *About 880 mm; wingspan 2200 mm.*
ADULTS: *Sexes similar; male slightly larger. Body white. Back and upper wings slate-black; underwings white with broad black edges. Tail grey, appearing black, with conspicuous white feather shafts. Face white; dusky smudge over eye. Eye brown. Bill flesh-yellow, tipped pale red. Feet, toes and webs blue-grey to flesh-pink.*
IMMATURES: *Similar to immature Grey-headed Albatross, but with lighter grey suffusion on head and neck and often distinct grey-brown collar. Upper and underwings duller dark brown. Bill grey-green, with dusky ridge and tip, changing to orange-yellow with adulthood.*
DOWNY YOUNG: *Grey-downed with bare white mask on fore-face; bill black; feet flesh.*

VOICE
Guttural gruntings and cackling calls when squabbling for food. Whistled braying notes when displaying. Chick peeps. Silent in flight.

NESTING
Breeds in colonies September to late April or early May. Nest a large muddy bowl on steep bank or ledge, or slope, reinforced with plant matter or feathers. Egg: one; dull white, with pink tinge and dark red-brown markings towards larger end; oblong-oval, about

103 x 66 mm. Incubation about 71 days, by both sexes. Young fledge in four–five months.

DISTRIBUTION
Throughout oceans of Southern Hemisphere, south of subtropical zone. Breeds on subantarctic islands including Heard and Macquarie. Two races; one widespread with dark brown eye, the other with pale yellow-brown eye and breeding only on islands south of New Zealand. Both races visit Australia.

Black-browed Albatrosses on their breeding grounds in the Falkland Islands. This species is the most common albatross in Australian waters.

Grey-headed Albatross *Diomedea chrysostoma* FORSTER, 1785

SAILORS CALL THE GREY-HEADED, Black-browed and other small albatrosses mollymawks — from the Dutch word *mallemok,* which literally means 'foolish gull'. They may have won this name because they can be caught on hooks baited with meat or fish, or — when they are glutted with food and are too sluggish to rise from a calm sea — they can be caught easily with a net or a spear.

The Grey-headed Albatross is more often seen singly than in groups in Australian seas, usually in winter. It follows ships and attends fishing boats but not very closely. Although it roams far at sea, it does not seem to wander as widely as the Black-browed Albatross, keeping to the more southerly waters of the subantarctic and often resting back on its nest mound on breeding islands throughout the year. Fish, squid, crustaceans, galley scraps and carrion, including dead seabirds, make up the diet of the Grey-headed Albatross. To take them it has to land on water, and in coming in will lower and spread its huge webbed feet like 'flaps' to brake flight, as do other albatrosses.

In September, Grey-headed Albatrosses converge on their breeding islands to nest. Courting birds stretch their bills towards one another and hold them motionless with the sides touching. They then bow and bray, and fan and tilt their tails, preen one another and the males parade around the females. They nest in colonies, often in association but somewhat later than Black-browed Albatrosses. Although eggs may hatch in late December, young — which are fed by both parents — may not fledge until mid-May, up to a month later than Black-browed fledglings.

In appearance, Grey-headed Albatrosses resemble Buller's Albatross, a local species of New Zealand seas that only rarely wanders to the southeast coast of Australia. The Grey-headed, however, has an all-grey head as its name suggests, lacking the white front of Buller's, and showing a broad black edge around its underwing almost as wide as that in the Black-browed Albatross.

OTHER NAMES
Flat-billed Albatross, Grey-headed Mollymawk, Gould's Albatross.

IDENTIFICATION
LENGTH: *About 910 mm; wingspan up to 2150 mm.*
ADULTS: *Sexes similar; female smaller. Head and nape grey; back warm black. Upper wings warm black; underwing white with black edge, broader on leading edge; tail grey. Throat grey. Breast and belly white. Eye brown; dark line through and just over eye, white crescent behind eye. Bill black with brilliant golden stripe along upper and lower ridges, faintly red at tip. Feet, toes and webs light blue-grey.*
IMMATURES: *Head leaden grey, darker than in adults; upper wings browner; underwing grey with very broad black edges. Bill appears black, gradually whitening then yellowing on upper and lower ridges with increasing age; bill tip remains dark for some years.*
DOWNY YOUNG: *Light grey with dark ear patches and dull white face; beak black, feet flesh.*

VOICE
Braying whistles in display, and guttural sounds when fighting for food. Chicks twitter and clap bills in alarm.

NESTING
Breeds in summer, probably every second year. Nest a cup of mud and plant matter on windswept ridge or slope. Egg: one; white with band of brown spots towards larger end; oblong-oval, about 107 x 67 mm. Incubation about 70 days, by both sexes, the male taking the first shift. Young fledge in about five months.

DISTRIBUTION
In Australian seas immature birds perhaps more common than adults in eastern Australia; adults more common in Great Australian Bight and westwards. Rare north of Shark Bay, WA; rare in New South Wales waters. Ranges widely in Southern Hemisphere, more common from latitude 40°S southwards to pack ice. Breeds on Macquarie Island, Campbell Island, Kerguelen Island and other subantarctic islands. No races.

The Grey-headed Albatross spends most of the year at sea, but visits the subantarctic islands to breed. This bird is on Campbell Island.

Yellow-nosed Albatross *Diomedea chlororhynchos* GMELIN, 1789

The Yellow-nosed Albatross ranges around the coast of southern Australia.

WHEN THE YELLOW-NOSED Albatross is seen in the company of other albatrosses it looks very small, and this serves to emphasise its comparatively large bill. Its wings span just over two metres.

The islands where the Yellow-nosed Albatross breeds in summer are along the northern limit of the subantarctic zone, but while in Australian waters it is a bird of temperate to subtropical seas. The temperatures of the surface of the sea, and perhaps the surrounding air, probably play a significant part in determining seasonal and perhaps daily dispersal. In the seas off western South Australia and the southern and central coasts of Western Australia it is probably the most common of the mollymawks.

Yellow-nosed Albatrosses follow ships as do most of the other species of albatrosses, but they attend fishing boats to the point where they sometimes become a nuisance. When they haunt boats engaged in long-line fishing, some are drowned through taking baited hooks and others are shot to prevent loss of bait. Their natural diet consists of squid and fish.

The birds converge on their breeding islands each August to nest. During courtship, the male stretches out his neck, raises his wings, erects his feathers and utters high-pitched, rapidly repeated calls resembling a shrill laugh. Putting his head against the female's, the two rub bills and then the female responds with an identical display. Both sexes build the nest.

OTHER NAMES
Carter's Albatross, Yellow-nosed Mollymawk.

IDENTIFICATION
LENGTH: *810 mm; wingspan 2100 mm.*
ADULTS: *Sexes similar. Head white with grey-smudged cheeks in newly moulted plumage; back and upper wings dull to glossy brown-black. Tail black. Underparts white; underwing white with narrow black edge all around, slightly broader on leading edge. Eye brown or black. Slender hooked bill black with chrome-yellow strip along upper central ridge. Feet, toes and webs dull blue-grey.*
IMMATURES: *As adults, but no yellow on bill at first; later a straw-yellow line along top. Smaller than adults.*
DOWNY YOUNG: *Grey-downed, white on face with bare chin and throat; bill black, feet pale leaden.*

VOICE
Guttural coughing when squabbling for food and during courtship; also bill-clapping, a call with head tilted back, and a bleating cry, all in display.

NESTING
Breeds in summer; egg-laying begins mid-September. Nest a solid mud bowl on ground, reinforced with plants. Egg: one; white marked with brown, mainly at larger end; ellipsoidal, about 96 x 62 mm. Incubation about 78 days, by both sexes in shifts. Young, fed by both parents, fledge in about 18 weeks.

DISTRIBUTION
Breeds on Tristan da Cunha group in Atlantic Ocean and Prince Edward, Saint-Paul, and Amsterdam Islands in Indian Ocean. Occurs from South Atlantic east to Indian Ocean and Tasman Sea. No races.

Shy Albatross *Diomedea cauta* GOULD, 1841

SEABIRDS ARE BEST SEEN from cliffs or boats in winter and spring and the Shy Albatross is no exception. Although rarely following larger ships, it crowds around fishing vessels and often approaches the coast, gliding and banking low over the sea. Fish, squid and cuttlefish, crustaceans and carrion are its food. It is the largest of the mollymawks, approaching the Wandering Albatross in size, and is often the most abundant of them in southeastern Australian waters, tailing off westwards across the Bight.

The Shy Albatross is the only albatross to breed in Australian waters. It converges on its breeding grounds — rocks and rubble on the windswept tops of inaccessible islands — to nest in loose colonies each September–October. Mated birds sit together in courtship, fencing with their bills, cackling, and fanning their tails from side to side. To defend the nest, they stand erect, stretch the neck forward and gape, shaking their heads from side to side, *baa*-ing and clappering. Both parents bring food to their young. As each approaches, they often bow, perhaps to help the chick to recognise them. The chick then begins to peck at the parent's bill, first at the tip then along its length, while often *cheeping*. Soon the parent starts to pump food up from its stomach and this the chick scoops up by inserting its bill crosswise in the parent's. Young are fully grown and fledge about mid-April.

The Shy Albatross, like other albatrosses, settles on the sea to feed.

OTHER NAMES
White-capped Albatross, Mollymawk.

IDENTIFICATION
LENGTH: *990 mm; wingspan 2250 mm.*
ADULTS: *Sexes similar; male slightly larger. Body white. Back and upper wings ash-grey; underwing white with narrow black edges and tip. Face and neck with grey bloom, cut off from white or greyish cap by dark brow. Eye dark brown. Bill leaden with pale yellow tip and black-edged nasal groove. Feet, toes and webs blue-grey.*
IMMATURES: *Similar to adults but bill and feet darker; sometimes darker on nape and ear coverts.*
DOWNY YOUNG: *Grey-downed; bill black, feet flesh.*

VOICE
Hoarse gurgling and guttural calls when feeding and fighting; bill clappering and soft throat calls when courting.

NESTING
Breeds late September or early October. Nest a muddy bowl, reinforced with plant matter or feathers, maintained by chick. Egg: one; white often flecked with red towards larger end; oblong-oval, about 106 x 67 mm. Incubation about 60–70 days, by both sexes. Young fledge in 18–19 weeks.

DISTRIBUTION
Wide ranging in oceans of Southern Hemisphere. In Australia breeds on Albatross Island in Bass Strait, and on Mewstone and Pedra Branca, off southern Tasmania. Two races in Australia; one resident, the other a greyer-headed, darker-billed visitor from New Zealand.

Sooty Albatross *Phoebetria fusca* (Hilsenberg, 1822)

This Sooty Albatross has made its nest, a bowl of mud and plants on a steep hillside, on Marion Island in the southern Indian Ocean.

THE SOOTY AND GREY-MANTLED Albatrosses look so similar that they are often difficult to identify at sea. A dark back and a yellowish, not bluish stripe along the mandible distinguishes adult Sootys but not their immatures. Young Sootys, however, have mottled buffy collars that are missing from Grey-headeds. The two albatrosses also have rather different breeding and foraging ranges, the Sooty keeping more to the temperate seas and islands just north of the subantarctic belt where it feeds on squid and crustaceans.

Sooty Albatrosses have a superbly balanced gliding flight and can make slow wheeling turns using the outspread webs of their feet as brakes. The webs are virtually transparent and when the birds glide close overhead the blood vessels in them can be seen. With ease and grace they may sweep and bank within metres of a ship, wings stiff and every part of their body motionless except their heads which swivel slowly from side to side. Wings are trimmed to the changing wind currents by a myriad of minute flexions and their pointed tails may be fanned into a wedge to aid steering.

The life cycle of the Sooty Albatross is similar to that of the other small albatrosses. They nest in summer on subantarctic islands, usually in very narrow gullies or on ridges overlooking the sea or above a steep drop. Arriving in late July, they pair and occupy nest sites by late August and lay during late September. The nest site, often reoccupied in successive seasons, is usually overhung with heavy vegetation. The nests can be solitary or in loose association but Sooty Albatrosses probably do not nest in colonies unless sites are limited. Chicks hatch about mid-December, and are first brooded and later fed by both parents. When threatened, they regurgitate the oily remnants of their meal in foul-smelling defence. By mid-May they are fully grown and fledge.

OTHER NAMES
None.

IDENTIFICATION
LENGTH: *640–760 mm, with pointed tail; wingspan about 2000 mm.*
ADULTS: *Sexes similar. Generally sooty brown; chocolate-brown on head, slightly paler across nape; breast paler than head. White crescent behind eye. Eye dark brown. Bill slender, glossy black, with razor-sharp edges; stripe of yellow to red tissue along side of lower mandible. Feet, toes and webs fleshy grey.*

IMMATURES: *No white quills to flight feathers; bill stripe less pronounced, otherwise similar to adults.*
DOWNY YOUNG: *Ash-grey with mask of paler grey down on face; bill black.*

VOICE
On nesting sites a wild double-note call pee-oo to birds overhead, probably to signal occupied territory. Bill clappering in display.

NESTING
Breeds over summer. Nest a deep cup or bowl of mud and plants. Egg: one; white with grey-brown speckles; ellipsoidal, about 101 x 66 mm. Incubation about 10 weeks, by both sexes. Young fledge in five months.

DISTRIBUTION
Ranges during winter to Australian seas from Brisbane to Fremantle, WA, but not common. Most records in or south of Great Australian Bight. Breeds on Tristan da Cunha, Gough Island, Marion Island, and Saint-Paul Island in subantarctic. No races.

Light-mantled Sooty Albatross *Phoebetria palpebrata* (FORSTER, 1785)

LONG, NARROW WINGS, a large wedge-shaped tail and pale grey back help to identify the Light-mantled Sooty Albatross, which ranks with the Sooty Albatross as the most graceful of all the birds of the southern oceans. Like the Sooty Albatross, it will fly close to ships and virtually hang-glide motionless in midair in strong winds and up-currents. It may feed mainly at night, on squid and crustaceans — krill — which are more numerous at or near the surface then. The albatrosses capture all their food while swimming on the surface, accepting fish, penguins and prions as well, and sometimes waste from ships.

Squid-eating albatrosses take prey of varying size and species. Wandering and Light-mantled Sooty Albatrosses consume a greater variety of squid than the Grey-headed Albatross, and more squid and less crustaceans and fish than the Black-browed and Shy Albatrosses.

Light-mantled Sooty Albatrosses are thought to have a lifespan of 20 years or more. Their life cycle is similar to that of the Wandering Albatross, but the breeding season is shorter. Like the larger species, they do not breed each year.

In courtship, pairs of Light-mantled Sooty Albatrosses wheel and fly almost in unison, their long tails and wings giving the utmost flexibility to their aerial manoeuvres. On the ground, courting birds sit facing each other and repeatedly reach forward, snapping their bills, exposing their pink mouths in each movement. Mutual billing and preening precedes copulation which takes place at the nest site, usually a high ledge on a steep hillside.

Light-mantled Sooty Albatrosses are solitary nesters and signal their small territory with a heart-rending two-note scream, standing with bill pointed skyward at any bird passing overhead.

A new nest is built each year and eggs are laid in early November. Both sexes incubate in turn in irregular spans of several to 19 days. Young hatch in early January and are guarded by one or other parent for about three weeks. Both adults also feed the chick, regurgitating about 700 grams of liquid material—a mixture of water and oil from the digestive breakdown of krill—twice a day. To catch the food, the chick inserts its slightly open bill sideways into the gaping mouth of its parent. Chicks fledge and fly out to sea in about May.

OTHER NAMES
Grey-mantled Albatross, Light-mantled Albatross.

IDENTIFICATION
LENGTH: *600–700 mm, with pointed tail; wingspan about 2100 mm.*
ADULTS: *Sexes similar. Body pearly brown, shading to chocolate on head. Mantle pale ash-grey dividing dark brown wings. White crescent behind eye. Eye brown. Bill glossy black with mauve to pale blue stripe along side of lower mandible. Feet, toes and webs fleshy-grey or pink.*
IMMATURES: *Resemble adults but lack white quills to flight feathers.*
DOWNY YOUNG: *Powder grey with lighter facial mask.*

VOICE
Wild, double-note territorial call pee-aa at breeding grounds. Bill clapping during courtship and as defence sign. Ghostly trumpeting when squabbling for food at sea.

NESTING
Breeds over summer. Nest a tall mud and plant cup on ground. Egg: one; white with a zone of red spots; ellipsoidal, about 102 x 66 mm. Incubation 63–67 days, by both sexes. Young fledge in 16–18 weeks.

DISTRIBUTION
Wide-ranging across oceans of subantarctic, south to pack ice and north into southern temperate waters. Not very common in Australian seas; most records are of beach-washed birds thought to be immatures. The few birds seen have been in Great Australian Bight. Breeds on many subantarctic islands, including Heard and Macquarie Islands. No races.

A pair of Light-mantled Sooty Albatrosses and their downy chick. When courting, the birds face each other in this way, lean forward and snap bills.

Southern Giant-Petrel *Macronectes giganteus* (GMELIN, 1789)

IN SIZE AND SHAPE the Southern Giant-Petrel resembles an albatross; in flight, however, it has a distinctive, rather hunchbacked appearance. Its big, pale, tube-nosed bill adds to the difference. The Southern Giant-Petrel is a fast glider in high winds; with a drop in wind speed it increases its wing-flaps. It takes off from water after pattering across the surface, and launches itself more easily when it has help from the wind. Feet are often used as rudders in flight and as brakes when landing.

On land, giant-petrels walk fairly well, in a waddling fashion with head erect. They gorge on offal and will gather in squabbling parties to tear into the rotting carcass of a beached whale or seal. There is a definite peck-order and an individual asserting its right of access spreads its wings, ruffles its neck feathers, and fans out and tilts its tail to the vertical. Although these birds are basically scavengers they sometimes prey on smaller petrels and even penguins — especially chicks. At sea they usually pick up food from the surface — mostly squid, crustaceans and fish — but will plunge their heads in deep to retrieve morsels and can dive. In common with the fulmars, giant-petrels of all ages will spit an evil-smelling fluid at a would-be attacker. The material consists of oily stomach juices or sometimes of the bird's last meal, and can be ejected over quite some distance.

Most giant-petrels are thought to breed from about five years of age. Males are appreciably larger than females — a sexual difference which is rarely so marked in other members of the petrel family. They gather to breed in traditional colonies each spring, courting birds facing one another or sitting side-by-side to reach forward nibbling one another, touching bills and waving their heads. Eggs are laid in early October. Both sexes incubate, sitting for two–twelve days in a shift and changing over without ceremony; the relieved bird flies off to feed. Young, tended by both parents, hatch during December and are guarded and brooded in their first two–three weeks. They reach adult weight in about 50 days and fledge in March. Although the female sometimes lays two eggs, no pair fledges more than one young.

After leaving the nesting colonies, giant-petrels scatter over a wide area, generally dispersing downwind with the prevailing westerlies. Younger birds may spend some years wandering the southern oceans and almost all the giant-petrels that reach Australia belong to this age group. Breeding adults are probably rather sedentary, and in winter those belonging to the subantarctic island colonies visit them regularly. However, birds with breeding sites well to the south avoid the rigours of the Antarctic winter by moving well northwards.

The more common dark-plumaged form of Southern Giant-Petrel.

OTHER NAMES
Giant Fulmar, Mother Carey's Goose, Nelly, Stinker.

IDENTIFICATION
LENGTH: *900 mm.*
ADULTS: *Sexes similar; male larger. Two colour types: one entirely white-plumaged, save for a few scattered dark feathers; the other much more common — dark-plumaged, birds of which with age develop a paler head and neck and have the leading edges of the wings mottled with pale feathers. Very pale individuals in this phase have light grey-brown, rather mottled body plumage and almost white* foreparts. *Eye dark brown to pale grey. Bill pale pink-ochre to horn, with tip pale green. Feet, toes and webs dark grey; in some white-plumaged birds they are pale pink-grey.*
IMMATURES: *Dark-plumaged birds entirely glossy dark brown, becoming paler with age. White-plumaged birds are white as immatures. Eye, bill and feet as in adults.*
DOWNY YOUNG: *Medium grey or white; bill ivory-horn, feet greyish.*

VOICE
Deep, guttural, rather raucous whinny hu-hu-hu-hu in threat; cat-like mewings in display. Chicks pipe, gulp, rasp and squawk.

NESTING
Breeds August–March. Nest a depression surrounded by heap of dried vegetation, about 60 cm in diameter. Nests on exposed sites which allow the birds to come and go with the help of the wind, often on western sides of subantarctic islands. Egg: one; chalky-white; ellipsoidal, about 104 x 66 mm. Incubation about 60 days, by both sexes. Young fledge in 105–108 days.

DISTRIBUTION
Southern Giant-Petrels — mostly immatures — occur regularly, particularly in winter, in all southern coastal waters of Australia. They breed at several places along coastline of Antarctica, Antarctic Peninsula and islands of Scotia Arc to South Georgia; also on Falklands, Marion, Crozet, Heard and Macquarie Islands. No races.

A white-plumaged Southern Giant-Petrel and white chick on Macquarie Island.

Northern Giant-Petrel *Macronectes halli* MATHEWS, 1912

A PINK-TIPPED BILL in immature as well as adult birds is the main feature distinguishing the Northern Giant-Petrel from the Southern Giant-Petrel, with its green-tipped bill. The Northern Giant-Petrel has no white plumage either; its face may become pale but never the whole head. Otherwise, the two species are similar in their habits and voices and seek the same food.

That they are in fact two species has only recently been dis- covered by finding colonies of both nesting within sight of one another without interbreeding. Even so, their breeding seasons do not coincide precisely, Northern Giant-Petrels going to nest at least six weeks earlier than the Southern.

The two species are also somewhat separated in their foraging ranges, the Northern feeding and breeding on and north of the Ant- arctic Convergence and the Southern keeping to the south.

OTHER NAMES
Hall's Giant-Petrel, Giant Fulmar, Stinker, Mother Carey's Goose, Nelly.

IDENTIFICATION
LENGTH: *900 mm.*
ADULTS: *Male larger. In most respects similar to Southern Giant-Petrel, but there are no white-plumaged birds. General plumage sooty-brown or dark grey. With increasing age face becomes paler and leading edges of wings mottled with paler feathering. Eye brown or white. Bill similar to that of Southern Giant-Petrel — pale pink-ochre to horn — but tip darker pink, not green. Feet, toes and webs dark grey.*
IMMATURES: *Glossy black-brown, like those of Southern Giant-Petrel, but bill*

pink-tipped as in adult.
DOWNY YOUNG: *As Southern Giant-Petrel.*

VOICE
Deep, guttural, rather raucous whinny hu-hu-hu-hu ... in threat; cat-like mewing in display.

NESTING
Breeds early summer, July–February. Nest a rough heap of dry plant matter surrounding a depression. Has a tendency to nest alone in sheltered area, rather than in a colony; sometimes mixes with colonies of Southern Giant-Petrels. Egg: one; chalky white; ellipsoidal, about 102 x 61 mm. Laid late August–September. Incubation

about 60 days, by both sexes in shifts. Chick, tended by both adults, fledges in about 110 days.

DISTRIBUTION
Occurs regularly in southern waters of Australia, particularly in winter. Immatures are most often seen, but adults also move into Australian waters outside the breeding season. This species replaces the Southern Giant-Petrel above the Antarctic Convergence during summer months. Breeds on Gough, Marion, Crozet, Kerguelen, Stewart, Macquarie, Auckland, Campbell, Antipodes and Chatham Islands; also South Georgia in Antarctic. No races.

The Northern Giant-Petrel looks similar to the dark plumaged Southern Giant-Petrel. It can be distinguished by the pink, rather than green, tip of its bill.

A Southern Fulmar sounds its cackling cry on its breeding island near Antarctica. These fulmars often nest in colonies and are noisy at nesting sites.

Southern Fulmar *Fulmarus glacialoides* (SMITH, 1840)

A THICK-SET, CHUNKY BODY and delicate pale-grey plumage distinguish the Southern Fulmar from other sea birds of the Southern Ocean. It flies well, sailing on straight narrow wings alternating with swift wing-beats. Rapacity is another characteristic: fulmars follow ships for galley refuse and quarrel much when feeding on flushes of krill — crustaceans, squid and fish. A common bird among the summer Antarctic pack ice, they keep to cold waters and follow the currents north in winter, particularly off the west coast of South America.

On land Southern Fulmars are awkward, especially when approaching the nest with the wind: they literally tumble out of the air. Birds arriving at the breeding grounds do so in large groups in October and nest in dispersed colonies. Most of them fly directly to past nest sites and begin territorial defence and courtship at once. Only minutes may elapse between the time of arrival and pair-formation. In display, pairing birds sit together, gape and wave their open beaks about, tail-shiver, preen one another and cackle in a duet. During copulation, about 17 days before laying, the male strops his bill on the female's, as do giant-petrels.

Fulmars are noisy at the nest site which, usually on the edge of a drop, allows the birds to hobble a few steps and take flight by simply falling into the air. On warm days they patrol the cliffs of the colony, flying back and forth in the updraughts and eddies. At the nest both adults and chicks defend themselves by spitting putrid stomach oils with accuracy for a metre or more.

Eggs are laid late November to mid-December, and many are lost by thaw-floods and rolling from the nest, when they are eaten by skuas. After hatching, the chick is first guarded by its parents in shifts over 15–18 days and is fed by both at the nest. It fledges by mid-March and leaves the colony then with the adults.

OTHER NAMES
Antarctic Fulmar, Silver-grey Petrel.

IDENTIFICATION
LENGTH: *About 450 mm.*
ADULTS: *Sexes similar. Pale silver blue-grey above from nape to tail, with upper surfaces of wings darker, especially flight feathers. Head, neck and underparts, including underwings, white. Paler patch towards outer part of each upper wing, clearly visible in flight. Bill pink with black tip and blue nostrils. Feet, toes and webs pale flesh with irregular darker patches.*

IMMATURES: *Similar to adults but bill more slender.*
DOWNY YOUNG: *Creamy white; bill and feet as adults.*

VOICE
Loud, guttural cackle in threat, based on aark-ag-ag-ag-ag ... arrr, *but with much variation and changing of intensity. Soft droning or guttural croaking in courtship.*

NESTING
Breeds summer months, October–March, in scattered colonies. Nest site usually on a cliff edge or in a crevice in rock outcrops from sea level to the tops of cliffs. Little nest material is used. Egg: one; white; ellipsoidal, about 74 x 50 mm. Incubation about 44 days, by both sexes in shifts. Young fledge in six–eight weeks.

DISTRIBUTION
Occasionally reaches southern Australian waters in winter and spring. A petrel of Antarctic seas mainly south of Antarctic Convergence and particularly in pack-ice zone, but follows cool water currents towards subtropics, especially Humboldt current. Breeds only around Antarctica and on adjacent islands. No races.

Cape Petrel *Daption capense* (LINNÉ, 1758)

OTHER NAMES
Cape Pigeon, Pintado Petrel.

IDENTIFICATION
LENGTH: *About 400 mm.*
ADULTS: *Sexes similar. Head and mantle black-brown, rest of upper parts and wings white with black spots and patches; large white patch at base of dusky primaries. Tail white with broad dusky tip. Underparts white, except for dusky chin and dark border to underwing. Eye brown. Bill, feet and toes black.*
IMMATURES: *Like adults; bill thin.*
DOWNY YOUNG: *Slate-grey with bare cheeks.*

VOICE
Harsh cackling from feeding flocks at sea. Greeting call at breeding grounds a prolonged, trilled cooo.

NESTING
Breeds over summer, September–April. Nest a shallow scrape in debris, usually on a rocky ledge or in a crevice. Egg: one; white; rounded-oval, about 63 x 43 mm. Incubation 41–50 days, by both sexes. Young, tended by both adults, fledge in seven weeks.

DISTRIBUTION
Cool inshore and ocean waters from Antarctic ice northwards to 25°S. Breeds along shores of Antarctica and at nearly all islands south of 45°S. Disperses north in winter; common visitor to southern Australian seas then. Two races in Australia; one larger with finer rump spotting.

THERE IS NO MISTAKING the plump little bird with the checkered plumage known as the Cape Petrel, or pintado—an anagram which gave rise to its generic name *Daption*. It is a gregarious and quarrelsome feeder, gathering noisily to gorge on offal and waste thrown out by ships and at ports. At sea it captures its main food—krill and squid—in a variety of ways: it dives into the water from flight or while swimming or paddles about pecking food from the surface, stirring with its feet to bring plankton to the top. Its bill is furnished with a pouch and tiny serrations.

On land Cape Petrels are helpless, but nesting in colonies on steep ledges they can literally land straight onto the nest and fall off it into air. They return to breed in August–October each year; then and during incubation they pull up just a few pieces of stone and gravel. Like other fulmars, Cape Petrels are swift, direct flap-glide fliers and day-active at their nesting colonies.

Arriving birds greet their mates in courtship—first one, then the other stretching its neck and trilling, and then swaying their heads in unison. Once pair bonds and nest site have been established, they leave for several weeks at sea before returning to lay in November–December.

The Cape Petrel is recognised by its black and white plumage. It is also called pintado, Portuguese for 'painted'.

Great-winged Petrel *Pterodroma macroptera* (SMITH, 1840)

THE GREAT-WINGED PETREL is a distinctively long-winged, stubby-billed gadfly petrel. The gadflys (genus *Pterodroma*) are medium-sized petrels resembling shearwaters, but are plumper with shorter, more pointed wings which they hold bent at the wrist to carry them in more erratic, stronger flap-glide sweeps over the ocean, often rising in high wheeling arcs.

At sea, Great-winged Petrels are solitary, avoid ships, and forage silently mainly at night. Neither swimmers nor divers, they cover vast areas of ocean on the wing, picking and scooping krill—squid and crustaceans—off the surface. Immatures probably wander farthest; breeding adults perhaps rarely move very far from breeding islands that they occupy for up to 10 months a year, spanning winter; chicks are particularly slow-growing.

Activity at the breeding colonies builds up during autumn, when noisy aerial chases occur at dusk and during the night. Pairs and groups of birds dash about or wheel up and down in the air currents, often close together and calling continuously.

On the ground, courting pairs fence with their bills, preen one another's heads and necks, and bray and whistle in greeting.

Great-winged Petrels are night-active and noisy at their breeding colonies. Although pairs are reunited in February–March, eggs are not laid until May. Incubated in shifts of about 11 days each, eggs hatch through July. Young are fed and brooded by day and night in their first two–three days, then abandoned and fed only at night. From August on, the colonies quieten down as breeders arrive silently and ever more briefly to feed krill to their chicks and then leave. By early December the chicks have fledged, and the colonies are deserted. Mortality is often high, due to skuas and particularly feral cats. Survival is 30 per cent higher on cat-free islands.

OTHER NAMES
Great-winged Fulmar, Grey-faced Petrel.

IDENTIFICATION
LENGTH: *400–420 mm.*
ADULTS: *Sexes similar. Plumage entirely brown to black; face tending lighter. Eye brown. Bill and feet black.*
IMMATURES: *Similar to adults.*
DOWNY YOUNG: *All sooty; bill black, feet flesh to dark grey.*

VOICE
Staccato and squeaky jit-jit-jit-jit *in display flight, often preceded by mellow whistle; sibilant* si-si-si *and* ee-aw *bray in greeting and courtship on ground. Young chirrup, whistle when older, and hiss in threat.*

NESTING
Breeds over winter; forms loose breeding colonies February–November. Nest in a shallow depression in the ground, under shelter of rocks, grass or bushes; often in a chamber at end of a burrow up to 1.5 m long; varying amounts of dry plant material used to line nest chamber. Egg: one; white; minutely pitted; swollen oval, about 66 x 47 mm. Incubation about 53–56 days, by both sexes. Young, tended by both parents, fledge in about 130 days.

DISTRIBUTION
Widespread in offshore, rare in inshore seas around southern Australia. Two races, both in Australian waters: one dark-faced and breeding on islands between Albany and Recherche Archipelago, and on Tristan da Cunha, Gough, Crozet, Marion and Kerguelen Islands; the other creamy grey-faced and breeding in northern New Zealand and offshore islands.

Tahiti Petrel   *Pterodroma rostrata* (PEALE, 1848)

The stocky Tahiti Petrel has a massive, down-sloped bill. It rarely visits land and has only recently been seen in eastern Australian waters.

OTHER NAMES
Peale's Petrel.

IDENTIFICATION
LENGTH: *380–440 mm.*
ADULTS: *Sexes alike, with stocky body. Head, foreneck, upper breast and all upper parts — including long upper wings and tail — uniformly dusky-brown. Lower breast, belly and crissum white. Underwings uniformly dusky-brown. Eye dark brown. Bill black, massive and down-sloped. Feet flesh-coloured; toes and webs black.*
IMMATURES: *Similar to adults.*
DOWNY YOUNG: *Probably dark grey.*

VOICE
Details not recorded. Noisy squawks and sibilant trills and wheezes at nesting colonies at night.

NESTING
Breeds January–May in tropical southwestern Pacific; in loose colonies on slopes and mountains close to sea. Nest a natural hollow under rocks or a burrow excavated by the petrels. Egg: one; white.

DISTRIBUTION
Two widely separated populations, one centred on Mascarene Islands in Indian Ocean, the other in the tropical South Pacific where it nests on islands between the Bismarck Archipelago, New Caledonia and the Marquesas. Four races; the large form breeding on New Caledonia is the only one recorded with certainty in Australian waters.

ONE OF THE TROPICAL GADFLY PETRELS, the Tahiti has only recently been found to visit the seas along coastal eastern Australia within the past decade. It is also one of the least known, the breeding grounds of one of its races being still undiscovered. It nests on no more than a handful of islands in the South Pacific and Indian Oceans over summer and autumn, and probably disperses more widely at sea in winter and spring. Most inshore Australian records,

however, have been between December and May, perhaps when the petrels are shifting to and from their breeding grounds.

The Tahiti Petrel visits land only when nesting and then at night. At sea it is a tireless flier, swooping and soaring like a Great-winged Petrel but lower on windy days, and flap-gliding leisurely in calm weather. It probably picks its food — crustaceans, squid and small fish — off the surface of the ocean in flight.

White-headed Petrel

Pterodroma lessonii (GARNOT, 1826)

OTHER NAMES
White-headed Fulmar.

IDENTIFICATION
LENGTH: *400–420 mm.*
ADULTS: *Sexes similar. Head almost white, except for an oblong dark patch below the eye. Upper parts shade to pale grey on nape and mid-grey on the back, then pale grey again on rump and tail. Upper wings much darker grey with flight feathers dusky black. A faint M-pattern is visible in flight, extending across upper wing surfaces. All underparts white; underwings very dark grey, appearing almost black in flight at sea. Eye brown. Bill black. Feet flesh-pink with dusky on outer toes and outer parts of webs.*
IMMATURES: *Similar to adults.*
DOWNY YOUNG: *Uniformly grey, developing white from chin to belly; bill dusky, feet flesh-white, darkening gradually.*

VOICE
As that of Great-winged Petrel. Display song is a rapid wi-wi-wi *or* tew-i, tew-i, *interspersed with braying* oooo-er, kukoowik, kukoowik.

NESTING
Breeds in summer; present at breeding islands August–May; egg-laying occurs in November to December. Nest a pile of matted vegetation on a chamber at the end of a burrow up to 2 m long. Burrows are in soft soils with short plant cover and are loosely grouped into small colonies. Egg: one; white; rounded-oval, about 72 x 51 mm. Incubation about 60 days, by both sexes in shifts. Young fledge in 100 days.

DISTRIBUTION
A petrel of the subantarctic waters, visiting southern Australian waters usually in late summer and during winter. Ranges south to Antarctic pack ice and east to Pacific coast of South America. Breeds on Crozet, Kerguelen, Macquarie, Auckland and Antipodes Islands. No races.

The dark eyepatch and white head distinguish the White-headed Petrel.

THE DARK EYEPATCH AND white head, body and tail, contrasting with the dark upper and underwings, identify the White-headed Petrel at sea. It is usually seen alone, skimming the water on bent M-shaped wings and towering high in wide circles. It picks its food from the surface in flight, mainly squid, but also crustaceans and fish. Although breeding on only a handful of islands in the subantarctic, it is a great wanderer and regularly follows cold currents north each winter as far as Australia and New Zealand.

This night-active petrel has much the same habits and calls as the Great-winged Petrel, but breeds over summer. Signalled by noisy aerial chases, breeders return to their nesting islands in August to nest in burrows that they dig out at night. They tunnel straight into a slope for one–two metres to a chamber; the same site is often used in successive years.

Young hatch over January–February and are brooded for two–three days, then deserted and only fed at the nest at intervals by both parents. In April they begin to leave the burrow at night, exercising their wings, and finally fledge during the next few weeks.

To defend themselves, both chicks and adults lunge aggressively with their hooked black bills and may even spit putrid stomach oil—something that the Great-winged Petrel does not do. It does not go far to deter predation by skuas and feral cats, however.

Like some other gadfly-petrels, the White-headed begins its yearly moult during breeding, replacing most of its body feathers while incubating. These accumulate in telltale tufts around the entrance to the burrow. Flight and tail feathers are changed later and more slowly when the adults are feeding young and at sea.

Providence Petrel *Pterodroma solandri* (GOULD, 1844)

OTHER NAMES
*Brown-headed Petrel, Solander's
Petrel, Bird-of-Providence.*

IDENTIFICATION
LENGTH: *400–420 mm.*
ADULTS: *Sexes similar. Head brown-
grey with scaly-white face caused by
pale feathers with dark edges at base of
bill and on chin. Upper plumage dark
grey, mottled slate-grey across back;
paler grey on underparts. Underwings
dark, with large and distinctive pale
patches, formed by cream bases to outer
flight feathers and pale outer coverts
with dark tips. Eye brown. Bill black.
Feet and toes usually black, but
occasionally irregularly patterned with
pale grey flesh, especially on inner webs
and some of the leg.*
IMMATURES: *Similar to adults, but back
edged whitish and bill thin.*
DOWNY YOUNG: *Dark ash-grey.*

VOICE
*In courtship flight a loud, rapidly
uttered screech* kir-rer-rer, kik-kik-kik-
kik. *Birds on the ground at the breeding
colony give a more trilling version,*
ker-er, kuk-kuk-kuk ... ker-rer, *in
display and greeting.*

NESTING
*Breeds at Lord Howe Island from late
February until November. Often a
substantial nest of a pile of dried leaves
and shredded palm fronds in a chamber
at the end of a burrow about 1 m long.
Burrow entrance is often surrounded by
a crescent-shaped mound of excavated
soil; when occupied, burrow often
blocked by a plug of dried leaves and
fronds. Nests are often densely spaced in
a colony. Egg: one; white; ellipsoidal,
about 65 x 48 mm. Incubation about
seven weeks, by both sexes in shifts.
Young fledge in four months.*

DISTRIBUTION
*Rare inside continental shelf: only a few
sightings reported in eastern Australia.
Now known to breed only at Lord Howe
Island — 575 km east of Australia —
but formerly bred at Norfolk Island. Its
oceanic range is still unknown, though
it does extend to northern Pacific.
No races.*

The Providence Petrel breeds only at Lord Howe Island. It used to nest on Norfolk Island, but is now extinct there.

THE NAME OF THIS petrel commemorates the bird's involuntary contribution to the food supply of Norfolk Island colonists during. the first hungry years of settlement, shortly after the arrival of the First Fleet at Sydney Cove in 1788. It soon came to the notice of the colonists that Mount Pitt, the highest point of the island, was riddled with burrows, and that during the winter months these were occupied by enormous numbers of birds — the 'Mount Pitt birds', or 'Norfolk Island petrels'.

Lieutenant Ralph Clark, Quartermaster General and Keeper of the Public Stores, recorded that in 1790 the petrels slaughtered on the island totalled 171 362. In the same year Captain John Hunter recognised the bird's importance in the settler's diet by referring to it as the 'Bird of Providence'. As well as hunting the birds, the colonists introduced stock animals and these left the surviving petrels with no safe place to dig their burrows. On Norfolk Island, the bird of providence became extinct.

In flight at sea the Providence Petrel looks generally brown toned. Its head is clearly dark and in favourable lighting conditions contrasts strongly with the paler, almost buff tones of its underparts. The underwings also look darker than the under body. A distinctive white wing patch combined with the mottled face and grey tones of the back are the important features which help to distinguish this petrel from several other similar-looking large petrels in the gadfly group (genus *Pterodroma*).

Today it is only occasionally sighted in the western Pacific, and its oceanic range remains a mystery. The petrels may nonetheless shift regularly into the central northern Pacific where they have been seen east of Japan and the Ryukyu Islands, and near Hawaii. At sea they are leisurely fliers, beating their wings slowly and banking and sweeping easily and low in long glides over calm seas, picking their food off the surface. They eat mainly squid, crustaceans and small fish. Some of the crustaceans, which the birds swallow whole, are 100 millimetres or more long.

There is only one known breeding site, Lord Howe Island — but on that island, the Providence Petrel survives in thousands. Its colonies, totalling at least 20 000 pairs, nest throughout all of the forested upper slopes of the precipitous Mt Lidgbird and Mt Gower. A few lower colonies persist, and others may well have occurred prior to settlement on the island and the introduction of animals such as goats and pigs.

On a clear winter's afternoon, masses of calling petrels fly in courtship chases close above the forest canopy on the mountain tops of Lord Howe, diving and wheeling in the sharp upcurrents around the mountainsides. These gatherings begin in March and continue until August. The Providence Petrel maintains a territorial space around its burrow by aggressive defence against intruding members of its own population. Eggs are laid in mid-May in grass-lined chambers at the end of a burrow, or in a cavity among rocks, anywhere from near sea level to 80 metres above it, and hatch in July. After this, the daytime activity over the colony begins to diminish, probably because the immature birds leave the area in much the same way as happens in the Great-winged Petrel colonies. By September, the birds are seldom heard calling at night, because the adults return only briefly to feed the growing chicks. Some birds sleep quietly on the ground during the night, but resume calling when they depart before dawn. The chicks are fledged by November.

The rare woodhen *Tricholimnas sylvestris,* which survives only within the range of the Providence Petrel on Lord Howe Island, takes some petrel eggs early in the year, but these are probably eggs laid by the inexperienced. Such birds often lay an egg on the bare ground before establishing a proper breeding site.

Gould's Petrel *Pterodroma leucoptera* (GOULD, 1844)

THERE IS ONLY ONE KNOWN breeding colony of Gould's Petrels in Australia — on the steep western slopes of Cabbage Tree Island at the entrance to Port Stephens, NSW. There, mostly under cover of the palm forest, the birds make their nests in rock piles or in the hollowed-out trunks of fallen trees without digging a burrow. A few birds nest at the forest edge, under boulders almost at sea level, and others occupy rocky crevices on the upper slopes of the more exposed eastern side of the island.

Gould's is a small petrel that should be recognised at sea by its white, black-striped underwing, white underparts and dark upper parts — particularly the contrasting pattern of a pale face and throat against a dark head. Its flight is typically swift, of rapid wing-beats interspersed with steep banking and arcing, the wings bent back at the wrist. To feed, it skims low over the sea, pecking up small squid and, less often, crustaceans and small fish.

Gould's Petrels stay at sea until their summer breeding season comes around. They arrive off their nesting islands in October and fly in each night after dark. Coming in at a great height, they circle overhead, calling and performing the paired chases typical of gad-fly petrels. They tumble down through the forest canopy to reach their nest sites, and move about among the trees with a fluttering flight. To leave — well before first light — they scramble up the trunks of palms and forest trees to launch into the air, or simply flutter out through a gap in the canopy from a ground takeoff. On land they are clumsy and can only waddle awkwardly. Egg-laying takes place usually from late November to early December; the chicks hatch in January. Both parents brood and feed them.

The total breeding population of Gould's Petrels on Cabbage Tree Island has been calculated at no more than 500 pairs. Even allowing for immature birds, the entire world population may be no more than 1000–2000. The greatest threats to the birds' continued existence on Cabbage Tree Island would be interference with their colony, and the introduction of predators such as cats and rats. As it is, a number of birds are lost by being trapped on the sticky seeds of the *Pisonia* tree. Competition from other seabirds for nesting sites is not a problem, for shearwaters that nest there burrow in soft ground avoided by the rock-hole breeding Gould's Petrels.

OTHER NAMES
White-winged Petrel.

IDENTIFICATION
LENGTH: *About 300 mm.*
ADULTS: *Sexes similar. Head dark sooty brown above with forehead strongly freckled with white. Dark upper parts extended to the sides of the neck and eye, with clear demarcation from white face and foreneck. Back noticeably greyer than head, and rump darker. Tail grey with sooty brown tips to central feathers and paler peppered outer tail feathers. Underparts white from face and chin to undertail. Dusky wash on sides of neck almost forms a collar across the throat. When wings are open, an indistinct M-pattern is seen across upper wing surfaces, created by the grey back, inner leading edges, and frosty-grey secondaries contrasting with the sooty brown wing coverts and outer flight feathers. Most of underwing is white, but tips and outer edges of flight feathers are dark. A sooty black sash extends along the leading edge of the bend in the wing diagonally inwards across the inner wing, reaching the axillars. Eye brown. Bill black. Feet flesh-coloured; most webs and outer toes dark.*
IMMATURES: *Similar to adults.*
DOWNY YOUNG: *Dark grey, some white on undersurface.*

VOICE
In courtship flight over colony a thin, cicada-like tit-tit-tit-tit *...On the ground or at nest site variations on a squeaky, high-pitched* pee-pee-pee-peeoo *in greeting and display; also a low, often tremulous growl* cr-r-r-r-ow.

NESTING
Breeds in colonies on islands over summer, October–April. Nest often within a rock pile, with fallen palm fronds as the only cover; occasionally in a short natural burrow or the hollowed-out trunk of a fallen palm tree. Little nesting material, usually no more than a few dry chips of palm frond. Within the colony the occupied nest sites are arranged into groups here and there under sheltering vegetation. Egg: one; white; swollen-oval; about 50 x 37 mm. Incubation about seven weeks, by both parents in shifts. Young fledge in about three months.

DISTRIBUTION
Tropical–subtropical southwestern Pacific; breeding on Fiji, Samoa(?), New Caledonia and Cabbage Tree Island, NSW. Three races; two in Australian waters: one small with incomplete breast collar, breeding only on Cabbage Tree Island; the other larger, breeding in New Caledonia and only visiting eastern Australian seas.

Gould's Petrel breeding on Cabbage Tree Island at the entrance to Port Stephens, NSW. It makes its nest in rock piles under cover of the palm forest.

Kermadec Petrels occur in light, dark and intermediate plumages. This bird is light-plumaged.

Kermadec Petrel *Pterodroma neglecta* (SCHLEGEL, 1863)

ONLY RARELY DOES THE Kermadec Petrel wander from its westernmost breeding grounds on Lord Howe and the Kermadec Islands to Australian waters. When at sea it usually keeps to the subtropical-tropical zone of the southern Pacific, patrolling the ocean with unhurried flight, its deep wing-beats alternating with steep barking and gliding; characteristically, the wings are held bent at the wrists. Like other gadfly petrels, the Kermadec dips in flight to pick its food—mainly crustaceans and squid—from the water's surface and rarely dives or swims after it. In pale phase it is unmistakable in tropical seas, but in dark and intermediate plumages it can be confused with other gadfly petrels.

Kermadec Petrels converge to breed in colonies on their more tropical nesting islands haphazardly through the year, but mostly over summer and autumn. In the Kermadecs they seem to do so in two main shifts: the first arrives in August, lays in November–December and leaves in April–May; the second comes in December, lays in March–April and quits in July–August. Although the Kermadec Petrel is a surface-nester like the Herald Petrel, it is strictly nocturnal at its colonies. Incoming birds circle the colony just after sunset, calling plaintively. Incubating birds are relieved then but do not go to sea to feed until just before sunrise. Before laying but after pairing and choosing the nest site, mated birds leave for a two–three week 'honeymoon' at sea. Young are fed by both parents for over three months then deserted, fledging on their own 10–14 days later.

OTHER NAMES
None.

IDENTIFICATION
LENGTH: *About 380 mm.*
ADULTS: *Sexes similar but variable, from pale to dark. Palest birds are dusky above with almost pure white heads and white underparts. Darkest birds are uniformly dusky, except for a few flecks of grey on forehead and face. All stages of intermediate plumages occur. In all, a large pale area at base of underwing primaries, formed by off-white shafts and inner webs. Eye brown. Bill black, stubby. Feet black or flesh-white, often with tips of webs and toes black, and base flesh.*
IMMATURES: *Resemble adults but bill narrower.*
DOWNY YOUNG: *Variably light to dark grey, as adults.*

VOICE
Characteristic, loud and explosive yuk-ker-a-ooooo-wuk in courtship; initial, rather resonant, hoot-like part of call ends with explosive, strongly accented final note.

NESTING
Breeds summer–autumn; probably January–July at Lord Howe Island. Nest a depression in the ground, lined with a few leaves and twigs; placed in bushes, often on steep cliffs. Large colonies also on flat coral sand islands in central Pacific. Egg: one; white; rounded-oval, about 64 x 46 mm. Incubation about 51 days, by both sexes. Young fledge in about 15 weeks.

DISTRIBUTION
Subtropical and tropical waters of South Pacific, spreading across equator in winter, and reaching the eastern Australian coast. Breeds on Balls Pyramid at Lord Howe Island, the Kermadecs and Austral, Pitcairn, Easter, Tuamotu and Juan Fernandez Islands. Two races; one, small, in Australian–New Zealand seas.

Herald Petrel

Pterodroma arminjoniana
SALVIN, 1888

OTHER NAMES
Trinidad(e) Petrel.

IDENTIFICATION
LENGTH: *370–400 mm.*
ADULTS: *Sexes similar but variable, from dark to light. Darkest birds entirely dusky-brown on upper and underparts, including underwings. Lightest birds uniformly mid grey-brown from head to tail and upper wings dorsally; whitish ventrally from chin to crissum with white freckling on forehead and grey-brown flecking across breast and down flanks; underwing grey-brown with white band along base of flight feathers. Intermediate phases are brown-breasted and mottled white-and-brown on the belly. Eye dark brown. Bill black. Feet, toes and webs black (dark phase birds) to pink-white mottled black (lighter phase birds).*
IMMATURES: *Similar to adults.*
DOWNY YOUNG: *Dusky-grey to light grey, perhaps reflecting phase; bill black; feet dusky to pale flesh-white, apparently reflecting phase.*

VOICE
Rapidly repeated ki-ki-ki ... up to 20 times, followed by extended series of melodic, oscillating k-lu, k-lu, k-lu in aerial display. Harsh kree-kree-

kree ... and tern-like chattering when bickering on breeding grounds.

NESTING
Breeds sporadically all year, in small dispersed colonies; nest unformed on island surface, usually a bed of gravel and stones sheltered under ledge or in open crevice or hole. Egg: one; white; rounded-oval, about 59 x 43 mm. Incubation about 52 days, by both sexes in shifts. Young, fed by both parents, fledge in about 100 days.

DISTRIBUTION
Rather sedentary around breeding islands: Trinidad(e) and Martin Vaz Rocks in southern Atlantic; Mascarene Islands in southern Indian Ocean; Easter Island and Marquesas west to Chesterfield and Raine Islands in tropical southern Pacific. Two races; the smaller with complete white wing bar in pale phase reaching Australia.

The Herald Petrel nests without making a burrow.

FIRST FOUND IN AUSTRALIAN WATERS in 1959, the Herald Petrel has just recently been discovered breeding on Raine Island in the Great Barrier Reef. It is one of the smaller, subtropical gadfly petrels that seems to stay close to its breeding islands for much of the year. During that time it may land occasionally to rest, as well as to nest, in shallow stony shelters on bare rocky knolls. It flies silently in graceful swoops and banks close to the sea, with wings bent at the wrist, scooping up its food: squid, mostly, and fish.

Herald Petrels nest sporadically throughout the year, in gravel-lined holes and hollows on the surface of their breeding islands. Over the colonies, adults keep up noisy display flights all year round. Activity peaks early each morning, one of a pair chasing the other and uttering a rapid, high-pitched series of melodic chords, sounding rather like a soft, weird laugh. Male and female greet one another at the nest with the same call, giving it alternately face to face and then billing and preening one another.

Soft-plumaged Petrel *Pterodroma mollis* (GOULD, 1844)

A Soft-plumaged Petrel on Antipodes Island. These rather solitary and shy petrels are sometimes washed up on southern Australian beaches.

RISING AND FALLING low over the sea, with rapid wing-beats and long glides, the Soft-plumaged Petrel flies like a typical gadfly petrel, swinging about in great arcs. Unlike the Kerguelen Petrel, however, it rarely flies high nor does it float in the air. This and its dark M-pattern across the wings in flight, dark crown, paler rump and tail, white underparts and plain slaty underwings distinguish it from other petrels. At sea it picks its food—mainly squid with some crustaceans and fish—from the surface of the water, and, although usually solitary and shy, it will gather in small groups and follow ships for galley waste.

Soft-plumaged Petrels are colonial tunnel-breeders and stay in the vicinity of their breeding islands for about 10 months of the year, arriving in August and not leaving until next May. Individual burrows are often branched, and their arms occupied by separate pairs of birds. Not only do the adults court in flight after dark but in their burrows as well. It is a long process, with time spent at sea, and eggs are not laid until November–December, hatching in January–February; young do not fledge until May. This long season, later than the Kerguelen Petrel's, exposes the Soft-plumaged Petrel to heavy predation from Great Skuas and feral cats.

OTHER NAMES
None.

IDENTIFICATION
LENGTH: *About 350–360 mm.*
ADULTS: *Sexes similar. Forehead freckled grey and white; face and throat white with black patch before and below eye. Upper parts slate-grey. Upper wings dark grey-brown. Underparts white, usually with partial or complete grey band across breast. Undersides of wings plain dark grey. Eye brown. Bill black. Feet flesh-coloured; outer toes and webs black. Occasional birds dusky with white areas freckled or streaked grey; grey breast band strongly marked.*
IMMATURES: *Similar to adults.*
DOWNY YOUNG: *Dark grey above, lighter below; bill and feet black.*

VOICE
Courtship call in flight a shrill, fluting treee-pi-pieee; also moaning cries in aerial chases.

NESTING
Breeds colonially August–May, over summer. Nest a vegetation-lined chamber at end of 1.5 m long burrow in dense cover on coastal hill-slope. Egg: one; white; oval, about 58 x 43 mm. Incubation about 50 days, by both sexes. Young fledge in about 91 days, tended by both parents.

DISTRIBUTION
Widely distributed in temperate South Atlantic and southern Indian Oceans south to 50°S and regularly north to waters off western South Australia. Breeds on Tristan da Cunha, Gough, Marion and Crozet Islands, and on Antipodes Islands in South Pacific; also in North Atlantic. Three races; one only in austral oceans.

Kerguelen Petrel *Pterodroma brevirostris* (LESSON, 1833)

AT SEA, THE GREY KERGUELEN PETREL often flies high with rapid wing-beats. Sometimes it floats in the wind; sometimes it soars; sometimes, in a light wind, it weaves close above the sea. Occasionally it will briefly approach a passing vessel in the Roaring Forties, for it is a petrel of subantarctic and temperate oceans. Kerguelen Petrels are mostly solitary at sea but sometimes gather to rest on the water in small flocks. To catch their prey — squid, crustaceans and occasional small fish—they not only dip into the surface of the sea but also dive, both from flight and while swimming.

Kerguelen Petrels congregate in August or September on their subantarctic nesting islands to breed in colonies. They occupy permanent up-sloping burrows tunnelled into steep marshy banks, laying their eggs on a mound of soil and vegetation in a chamber hollowed out at the end. Surrounding the mound is a channel that drains seeping water out through the mouth of the burrow. Eggs are laid from mid-September into October, and young hatch in late November. Brooded for the first two days, the nestlings are fed by both parents which bring in about 75 grams of squid a day, augmented by crustaceans and fish. Only about half the year's brood survives to fledge in January–March, due to predation by skuas and feral cats, and nest abandonment.

The Kerguelen Petrel breeds colonially on subantarctic islands.

OTHER NAMES
Little Black Petrel, Short-billed Petrel.

IDENTIFICATION
LENGTH: *About 330–350 mm.*
ADULTS: *Sexes similar. Upper parts slate-grey. Face mottled lighter grey, darker about the eyes; underparts grey shading to lighter grey on belly. Primaries narrow with pale shafts. Underwings pale grey; scalloped white edge to inner forewing differs from other soft-plumage petrels. Eye brown. Bill black, noticeably narrow and compressed, as well as stubby. Feet, toes and webs dull black.*
IMMATURES: *Similar to adults, but supposedly thicker-billed.*
DOWNY YOUNG: *Sooty-brown.*

VOICE
Courtship calls not recorded. A high-pitched screech in alarm, like those of other gadfly petrels.

NESTING
Breeds in colonies September–March, over summer. Nest a 1–2 m long curved or branched burrow in steep slope. Egg: one; white; oval, about 57–59 x 45–46 mm. Incubation 47–51 days, by both sexes. Young fledge in about 61 days.

DISTRIBUTION
Subantarctic and temperate South Atlantic and Indian Oceans, south to pack ice and north as far as southern Australian seas in winter; occasional in South Pacific. Breeds on Tristan da Cunha, Marion and Kerguelen Islands and the Crozets, remaining offshore much of the year. No races.

The Blue Petrel differs from prions in its bill and mottled forehead.

Blue Petrel

Halobaena caerulea (GMELIN, 1789)

OTHER NAMES
None.

IDENTIFICATION
LENGTH: *About 300 mm.*
ADULTS: *Sexes similar. Forehead white mottled slate; crown, nape and eye patch dark slate and distinctly darker than blue-grey back, upper wings and tail. Faint dark M-pattern across spread upper wings and back. Square tail broadly tipped with white. Underparts white; pale grey collar across breast. Eye brown. Bill black, tinged blue on sides. Feet and toes pale blue; webs flesh-coloured.*
IMMATURES: *Similar to adults; bill narrower.*
DOWNY YOUNG: *Grey-blue above, white below.*

VOICE
Three short coo-s *followed by two longer ones* kuk, kuk, kuk, coo-coo, *in courtship.*

NESTING
September–February; in colonies. Nest a vegetation-lined chamber at end of 1–2 m long sharply curved burrow in soft soil, among plants. Egg: one; white; oval, about 50 x 37 mm. Incubation about 46 days, by both sexes.

DISTRIBUTION
Regular visitor to southern Australian seas in winter and spring. Pan-subantarctic, breeding on Marion, Crozet, Kerguelen and South Georgia Islands. No races.

RESEMBLING A PRION, the subantarctic Blue Petrel nonetheless has the freckled white face, long wings, and black, uncombed bill of a gadfly petrel; and it differs from all petrels in its white-tipped tail, making it easy to identify when specimens are washed up occasionally on southern Australian beaches. Its flight is not as agile or as erratic as a prion's, and the Blue Petrel glides more, low over the water, following ships as well as whales. Blue Petrels commonly flock at sea, and swim, dive and dip in flight for their food: krill, small squid and occasionally small fish. They alight awkwardly on water and take off only after pattering over the surface.

Blue Petrels are colonial summer nesters but come and go from their breeding burrows only at night, often later than other petrels. Their arrival in September is usually signalled by much pigeon-like coo-ing in courtship at burrows and by ringing flight calls overhead. The birds flit hither and thither around the burrows before choosing one, and then both of a pair will occupy it constantly until laying in September–October; after that, activity and calling tails off.

Young hatch in November–December and, fed by both adults, fledge through February, earlier than most southern petrels.

Black-winged Petrel *Pterodroma nigripennis* (ROTHSCHILD, 1893)

NOT LONG AGO, ornithologists considered the Black-winged Petrel a rare bird, breeding only in the Kermadec group of islands, northeast of New Zealand.

Then a large colony was discovered at the Three Kings off northern New Zealand and the bird was seen regularly in summer at Norfolk Island. It soon became apparent that colonies might occur at several places on Lord Howe Island and breeding was finally confirmed in 1971. Lately Black-winged Petrels have been found breeding at the Chatham Islands, New Zealand, and in New Caledonia. Small groups are also prospecting for breeding sites along the eastern coast of Australia each summer.

All this suggests that in recent decades the birds have been expanding their range, or perhaps simply recolonising breeding grounds lost to the tremendous impact of European settlement over the past two centuries.

This gadfly petrel is easy to identify, and unlike most of the smaller petrels it often flies over its breeding colonies during broad daylight. Its flight is fast with sudden rapid changes in height, birds swooping, often wheeling in steep arcs and inclined loops, with frequent rolls from side to side. Rapid, fairly deep wing-beats are followed by banking and gliding with the wings swept back. They dive for their food—shrimps, fish, squid and cuttlefish.

Pairs giving shrill peeping calls often circle and dip in wild courtship chases across their colony. They are also easy to observe landing and entering their burrows before dark. In contrast, the birds visiting their colony on South-East Island in the Chathams land only after dark.

Breeding birds arrive at the breeding colonies in November to clean out their burrows, at night. Egg-laying starts in December but varies with the individual pair. Chicks hatch from January onwards and depart usually by the end of April.

OTHER NAMES
None.

IDENTIFICATION
LENGTH: *About 300 mm.*
ADULTS: *Sexes similar. Slate-grey upper parts from crown to tail, except for a blacker area across rump. Upper wings dark sooty. Grey tail broadly tipped with sooty. Forehead freckled white; dark stripe through eye. Grey smudges extend down sides of neck to form an incomplete collar around throat; otherwise underparts white from chin to crissum. Underwing pattern strongly marked with black and white: a broad, sooty-black leading edge and a diagonal stripe tapering inwards on the inner wing combine with dark tips of flight feathers to produce a strong contrast against the white central wing areas and axillaries. Eye brown. Bill black. Feet flesh-coloured with dark patches at ends of webs and toes.*
IMMATURES: *Similar to adults.*
DOWNY YOUNG: *Dove-grey with chin to belly white.*

VOICE
In flight a high-pitched peet *repeated four–six times, occasionally interspersed with* peet, pee-ur. *On the ground a similarly repetitive* pee, *often on an ascending scale.*

NESTING
Breeds in summer, November–May. Nest an almost bare chamber at end of a short burrow usually less than 1 m long, dug in soft soil. Nest colonies are often among low bushes on high ground along cliff faces. Egg: one; white; oval, about 51 x 37 mm.

DISTRIBUTION
Frequents northern Tasman Sea and areas extending eastwards into central southern Pacific Ocean. Has also been found ashore at Heron Island and other islands within the southern Barrier Reef and recently at Mutton-bird Island off Coffs Harbour, south to Eden, NSW. Breeds on New Caledonia and Lord Howe and Norfolk Islands, and Kermadecs and Three Kings off northern New Zealand. Probably also breeds at Rapa in Austral Islands and at South-East in Chatham Islands. No races.

The Black-winged Petrel frequents tropical and subtropical Pacific waters.

Broad-billed Prion

Pachyptila vittata (FORSTER, 1777)

The heaviest-billed race of the Broad-billed Prion, from the Chatham Islands.

LARGEST AND MOST northwards ranging of the Southern Hemisphere prions is the Broad-billed. Its broad head, proportioned to hold its massively wide bill, and steep forehead give it a frog-like appearance which distinguishes it from other blue-grey petrels on the wing. Like all prions, the Broad-billed is blue-grey above, white below, with a dark band running across the wings and back that forms the letter M in flight; and the tail is wedge-shaped with a terminal black band. Flight is also typical of prions. These dashers of the ocean, both dumpy in body and rather short in wing, are fast erratic fliers when on the move. Often travelling in flocks—and avoiding ships — they skim the sea, rising and falling and twisting from side to side, all gleaming white breasts showing one moment, then grey backs lost against the ocean the next.

Finding concentrations of their food—krill, squid and plankton at places of mixing and up-welling ocean currents—prions will gather to feed day and night, often associating with whales harvesting the same bonanza: hence their other name, 'whale-birds'. With its bill edged with comb-like plates for sieving plankton, the Broad-billed Prion has its own particular method of feeding. It hydroplanes. Holding out its wings for balance, it rests its breast on the surface of the water, and kicks its feet to propel it rapidly along. The bill is plunged open into the water, and scoops up food and water into an extendable chin pouch around the tongue. When the pouch is full, the bill is closed and the pouch contracted to squeeze the water out through the bill's plates, trapping the food. The birds will also swim and dive adeptly for their prey.

Broad-billed Prions converge in vast numbers to nest on their southern ocean breeding islands from July to October. Many remain in the vicinity throughout the year, even roosting in their burrows through early winter, perhaps to maintain ownership. Like other prions, they are burrow-nesters and usually night-active at their colonies. Some of the colonies are enormous, that on South East Island in the Chathams, for example, spreading over vast areas of forest floor and numbering many thousands. These great numbers and the occasional daytime visits by adults make the prions easy prey to skuas and gulls, giant-petrels, and even rats.

On land, Broad-billed and other prions are nonetheless not as helpless as other petrels, able to take flight directly even on calm days. Although fighting actively among one another to take and hold nest holes, they do not spit stomach oil in defence and will tolerate another pair in the same burrow. Such burrows are compound, with separate chambers or branches for each pair. Males hold the sites in the one–two weeks that females spend at sea prior to laying, in August–November. Young hatch within another two months and, tended by both adults, fledge in December–March, after being deserted for the last week or so.

Adults moult under rocks onshore in February–March and then take to sea in the vicinity of their islands. Fledgling immatures disperse further north, and it is these that are occasionally wrecked on southern Australian and New Zealand beaches by winter storms.

OTHER NAMES
Broad-billed Dove Petrel, Medium-billed Prion, Lesser Broad-billed Prion, Whale-bird.

IDENTIFICATION
LENGTH: *About 280–300 mm.*
ADULTS: *Sexes similar. Upper parts from head to wings and tail pale leaden; darker line through eye and conspicuous whitish eyebrow and lores. Tail tip and line along shoulders of wing and mantle narrowly dusky. Underparts from chin to crissum pure white. Eye brown. Bill leaden, very broad and bowed, with small hook, and conspicuous yellow lamellae (plates) along maxilla; chin pouch mauve. Feet and webs leaden blue.*
IMMATURES: *As adults; bill narrower.*
DOWNY YOUNG: *Smoky grey, whiter below, almost bare on face; becoming bluer above and whiter below.*

VOICE
In courtship, a crooning, rather rasping call with rhythmical alternating stress on second and fourth syllables: ku-a, ku-a, kuk. This phrase is repeated rapidly with variations several times in succession. Chicks cheep and squawk harshly in alarm.

NESTING
Breeds July–March, over summer, in large colonies. Nest a burrow over 1 m long, with leaf-lined egg chamber at end, in soft soil in variety of sites under cover of cushion plants and shrubbery. Egg: one; white; oval, about 50 x 36 mm. Incubation about 56 days, by both sexes. Young fledge in about seven weeks.

DISTRIBUTION
Subantarctic and temperate oceans of Southern Hemisphere, ranging north to southern Australian coasts and even tropics of Indian Ocean in winter. Three races, all reaching Australia: one large, with very broad steel-grey bill, breeding in southern New Zealand and adjacent islands and Tristan da Cunha group; another medium, with slightly narrower steel-grey bill, breeding on St Paul and formerly Amsterdam Islands; a third smaller, with narrower bluish bill, breeding in the Crozets, Prince Edward and Marion Islands.

The narrowest-billed race of the Broad-billed Prion still has a wide bill.

Fairy Prion *Pachyptila turtur* (KUHL, 1820)

THE ONLY PRION TO BREED in Australia, the Fairy Prion has several colonies on islands in Bass Strait and off Tasmania. It is common in Bass Strait in summer and is frequently washed up on beaches in southeastern Australia. Birds found on Western Australian beaches probably come from Marion Island in the Indian Ocean.

Fairy Prions appear at their colonies in late August, their arrival signalled by much courtship calling in the air and from their burrows at night. Established breeders—birds more than four or five years old—may return to the same burrow each year and become reunited. Egg-laying peaks in early November, the birds not only nesting in close-packed burrows, but in crevices under rocks as well. First male, then female incubate in six–seven-day spells until the eggs hatch in late December.

Newly hatched chicks are brooded for a day or so by each parent,

then abandoned by day and fed only at night. Adults return to the colony an hour or so after dusk and flutter about silently as if to get their bearings. Then they go to their burrows, kicking out any drifting debris, and greet the chick with a faint coo-ing. By dawn they have left again. Most young are deliberately deserted one–six days before they fledge, in February, so that they lose weight and fly at only 80–90 per cent of adult weight.

At sea, Fairy Prions are swift erratic fliers like the Slender-billed Prion, and feed by day on plankton, crustaceans and squid in the same way: by hovering and pattering this way and that to pick out each morsel from the surface of the sea with their bills. They can be identified from Slender-billed Prions, however, by their smallness, broader and wider black tail bands and stubbier bills with an enlarged hook.

OTHER NAMES
Fairy Dove Petrel, Whale-bird.

IDENTIFICATION
LENGTH: *About 230 mm.*
ADULTS: *Sexes similar. Upper parts pale leaden; darker eye-stripe and pale whitish eyebrow. Underparts white. Tip of tail a broad dusky band. Eye brown. Bill more blue than in other prions; short, curved hook of upper mandible robust, with little space between it and nasal tubes. Feet and webs blue.*
IMMATURES: *Similar to adults; bill narrower.*
DOWNY YOUNG: *Clear blue-grey.*

VOICE
Soft evenly phrased cooing kuk-kuk-coo-er, *uttered quickly and several times in quick succession in courtship; also canary-like calls; harsh cries in alarm.*

NESTING
Breeds in colonies over summer, August–February. Nest a leaf-lined chamber in burrow in soft soil among low vegetation or within a rocky crevice. Egg: one; white; rounded-oval,

about 45 x 34 mm. Incubation about 56 days, by both sexes. Young fledge in 44–55 days.

DISTRIBUTION
Temperate southern oceans but centred off New Zealand and southern Australia where common in Bass Strait and frequently found washed up on beaches in southeastern Australia; uncommon in southwestern Australia. Breeds on a few islands in Bass Strait, Chatham Islands, Antipodes Islands, Marion and Falkland Islands. No races.

Fairy Prions nest under overhanging rocks, in crevices or in burrows.

A White-chinned Petrel crouches in its nesting burrow in moist soil.

White-chinned Petrel

Procellaria aequinoctialis LINNÉ, 1758

OTHER NAMES
Cape Hen, Spectacled Petrel, Shoemaker.

IDENTIFICATION
LENGTH: *About 500 mm.*
ADULTS: *Sexes similar. Entirely sooty black with a conspicuous pale bill and, usually, a clear white chin; chin patch usually absent in birds breeding in New Zealand region. Birds with more white about face and head are usually referred to as 'spectacled'. Eye brown. Bill yellow or light green-horn with black areas at base of nasal tubes and along ridge on upper bill. Feet and webs black.*
IMMATURES: *Similar to adults.*
DOWNY YOUNG: *Sooty-black, becoming smoky grey; bill greenish grey; feet dark grey.*

VOICE
In courtship, a loud, deep, rapidly uttered clacking clop-clop-clop... *can become more rasping, machine-gun-*

like rattle. Also a piercing trill, both in mutual display and territorial advertisement by day. Silent at sea.

NESTING
Breeds in summer; present at colonies September–May. Nest a bulky pedestal of mud lined with vegetation at the end of a 1–3 m long burrow, often in sloping marshy pasture and tussocks and occasionally flooded. Egg: one; white; long-oval, about 84 x 55 mm. Incubation about 55–60 days, by both sexes. Young fledge in 95 days.

DISTRIBUTION
Ranges widely within colder southern oceans and even moves well north in Humboldt Current off western South America. Often seen in Great Australian Bight and southern Tasman Sea. Breeds on many subantarctic islands; spectacled race breeds at Inaccessible Island, and white- or black-chinned race on all others, reaching Australian waters.

THIS LARGE AND CHUNKY-LOOKING petrel with a pale, heavy bill is one of the most common petrels of the southern oceans and is often seen in the Great Australian Bight and the southern Tasman Sea. With its leisurely, languid flight, it resembles more a small albatross than the stiff-winged shearwaters to which it is related; wing-beats are slow, deliberate and graceful and keep the petrel close to the surface of the sea. It often flocks in small groups to feed, sometimes settling after ships and squabbling over the waste. Squid is its main prey, supplemented by fish and crustaceans, and these are taken in shallow dives from the air or while swimming.

Colonial burrow nesters like so many other petrels, the White-chinned Petrel varies its breeding season according to latitude, laying as early as October around New Zealand and as late as Jan-

uary on South Georgia and Kerguelen Islands further south. At the beginning of the season the birds come ashore at night searching for old burrows and pair soon after landing. Those without burrows dig new ones, using their beaks as a pick, then scratching the dirt out with their feet. Courtship continues noisily, both members of a pair croaking and trilling shrilly to the accompaniment of mutual billing and preening. At a distance, it sounds like a chorus of frogs. By day, the trill is used territorially, a sitting bird giving vent to it whenever its burrow is approached. Hence the name 'Shoemaker' given to this petrel by whalers: it 'sits in its shop and sings'.

Slender-billed Prion

Pachyptila belcheri
(MATHEWS, 1912)

OTHER NAMES
*Narrow-billed Prion, Thin-billed
Prion.*

IDENTIFICATION
LENGTH: *250–270 mm.*
ADULTS: *Sexes similar. Upper parts
pale leaden with eye-stripe darker;
eyebrow and sides of face white. Narrow
dusky M-band across wings and back
and at tip of tail. Underparts white. Eye
brown. Bill blue, darker on upper ridge,
slender, with rudimentary, invisible
lamellae. Feet blue, paler on webs.*
IMMATURES: *Similar to adults; bill
weaker.*

VOICE
*Coos in courtship; harsh grating in
alarm.*

NESTING
*Breeds colonially in summer months,
October–March. Nest one or more
chambers in a burrow. Egg: one; white;
oval, about 48 x 35 mm. Incubation by
both sexes.*

DISTRIBUTION
*Circumpolar at subantarctic latitudes,
following cold currents north in winter
to New Zealand and southern
Australia, particularly southwest where
often washed up on beaches. Breeds only
at Falkland Islands, the Crozets and
Kerguelen Island where predation by
rats is disastrous. No races.*

The Slender-billed Prion's bill and narrow black tail tip distinguish it from the similar Fairy Prion.

FIRST COLLECTED AT SEA and drawn off Cape Horn on Captain James Cook's first voyage to Australia in 1769, the Slender-billed Prion was long confused with the Fairy Prion. Not until 1912 was it recognised—from a specimen washed up at Torquay, Victoria—as differing in its very slender bill and narrow black tail tip and described as a new species.

On its limited breeding grounds, the Slender-billed Prion nests over summer in large colonies like other prions, and builds compound burrows, where several pairs occupy separate chambers along the one tunnel. In flight at sea, however, it is much more erratic, impetuous and agile, and flocks less. Lacking a broad, comb-plated bill, it also feeds differently on the wing, dashing helter-skelter over the ocean's surface, pattering on the water with its feet and vibrating its wings to hover at one spot. Food—luminous plankton, small squid and crustaceans—is picked from the water, mostly at night.

Antarctic Prion

Pachyptila desolata (GMELIN, 1789)

OTHER NAMES
Dove Prion, Snowbird, Whale-bird.

IDENTIFICATION
LENGTH: *270–290 mm.*
ADULTS: *Sexes similar. Upper parts
leaden, darker on head. Bold dark eye-
stripe; less pronounced white eyebrow
than other prions. Narrow dark band
across shoulders and back, and at end of
tail. Sides of neck slaty, creating partial
collar. Underparts white. Eye brown.
Bill leaden, straight-sided, with
lamellae just visible near gape. Feet
blue, paler on webs.*
IMMATURES: *Similar to adults;
narrower-billed.*
DOWNY YOUNG: *Smoky leaden above,
whiter below; face rather bare.*

VOICE
*In flight over colony or from within a
burrow a cooing call* kur-ur-kuratcha
or tutter-da-der-da-da *in courtship.
Piping whistle from female during
copulation and from begging chicks.*

NESTING
*Breeds October–May over summer, in
vast colonies, visiting at night. Nest a
burrow among low plants or cavity in
rocks and screes; often several pairs to
one system. Egg: one; white; oval, about
47 x 35 mm. Incubation about 45 days,
by both sexes in three–four-day shifts.
Young, brooded in first three–five days,
fledge in 45–55 days.*

DISTRIBUTION
*Circum-antarctic and subantarctic
oceans except central South Pacific.
Breeds at Kerguelen, Macquarie and
Auckland Islands, South Orkney,
South Georgia and Heard Island, and
at Cape Denison, Antarctica. Three
races; probably all reaching Australian
seas in winter.*

The Antarctic Prion is commonly washed up on the beaches of southern Australia. It has a moderately large bill and a slaty collar.

AT ITS MORE SOUTHERLY BREEDING SITES, this prion is often forced to dig through deep snow to clear a way into its burrow. The eggs are not usually laid until December, and the chicks hatch into February. Tended by both parents, the young fledge in late March.

This is one of the prions most commonly washed up on beaches on Australia's southern coastline, especially after winter storms. At sea, as on its breeding islands, it resembles the larger Broad-billed Prion in its habits. The birds flock in thousands to feed by day on krill, scooping it up by hydroplaning, and filtering the morsels out through the reduced sieve plates on their bills. They also swim, flutter and dive like the Broad-billed, but with greater agility. After breeding, adults go to sea for their annual moult.

Streaked Shearwater *Calonectris leucomelas* (TEMMINCK, 1835)

ONLY IN THE PAST DECADE has the Streaked Shearwater been found in Australian waters. It is, in fact, a regular visitor to the seas around the north coast on migration over the austral summer. A big petrel, it is easy to identify by its contrasting dark grey upper and white underparts, its dark streaked face, and slender, horn-coloured bill.

At sea it often gathers in great, loose flocks, following warm-water tuna to pick up small fish, squid and crustaceans in shallow dives on the wing. It flies low and more gracefully than other shearwaters, its easy wing-beats broken by very long glides on down-curved wings bent at the wrists.

Streaked Shearwaters return to their breeding islands in March to nest in vast colonies. They breed in close-packed burrows dug out by both sexes in April, lay from late June to mid-July, and hatch young in later August. Young fledge by late November, the adults leaving several weeks earlier. The birds are strictly nocturnal at the colonies, flying in from the sea in noisy swarms after dusk, and climbing trees in line to take off in turn before dawn.

OTHER NAMES
White-faced Shearwater.

IDENTIFICATION
LENGTH: *450–480 mm.*
ADULTS: *Sexes similar. Upper surface from crown to tail and upper wings dusky grey, with white edging on mantle. Forehead, fore-crown and face white, flecked dusky, giving streaked effect. Undersurface from chin to crissum white with fine dusky streaking on sides of neck. Underwing white, tipped and fringed dusky on trailing edge (flight feathers).*

IMMATURES: *Similar to adults.*
DOWNY YOUNG: *Grey-downed, whiter below.*

VOICE
Probably asthmatical croonings and wailings in courtship and greeting at nesting colonies, both on ground and on wing. Silent at sea.

NESTING
Breeds March–October, over northern summer; in large colonies. Nest 1–2 m burrow. Egg: one; white; long-oval, about 68 x 45 mm. Incubation 64 days, by both sexes. Young fledge in 66 days, on sea shore.

DISTRIBUTION
Trans-equatorial migrant in subtropical and tropical waters of western Pacific Ocean, reaching Philippines, Arafura Sea, Coral Sea and northern Australian coast southeast to Sydney–Eden in austral summer. Returns to breeding islands off Japan, Korea and northern China in austral winter. No races.

Streaked Shearwaters are regular visitors to northern Australian waters. Their flight is low and graceful, with very long glides on down-curved wings.

Short-tailed Shearwater *Puffinus tenuirostris* (TEMMINCK, 1835)

AT SEA THE SHORT-TAILED SHEARWATER is recognisable by its sickle-shaped wings and dashing purposeful flight in which a few rapid wing-beats alternate with stiff-winged glides. On windy days it follows a corkscrew course at an angle to the wind, rising on upcurrents, then banking and side-slipping away over the sea before turning into the wind for more lift. It usually travels in flocks and will converge to feed in rafts, swimming in a group and diving from there or from flight a metre or more under water after krill, and occasional small fish and squid.

Shearwaters appear to be remarkably uniform in their breeding behaviour—allowing for some differences in timing—so many of the following habits of Short-tailed Shearwaters apply generally in the group.

Adults return to their nesting colonies in late September; immature birds and non-breeders follow some time afterwards. An adult generally reunites with its partner of the previous season and the pair occupy their previous burrow or one nearby. The burrow is prepared during nightly visits, though some birds remain ashore during the day.

When Short-tailed Shearwaters return to the colony their body weight is about 500 grams but rises before egg-laying and falls during incubation. Early in the season there is much noise in the colonies at night, particularly during the evening arrival. Their calls presumably serve to establish and strengthen the pair bond and announce that a burrow is occupied. In courtship and greeting, mated birds duet, arc their heads and preen one another.

After mating at the burrow there is an exodus of adults from the colony for about three weeks before egg-laying. When females return, eggs are laid within a remarkably short and constant period, unvarying throughout the range of the Short-tailed Shearwater, from about 20 November to 2 December each year. Peak egg-laying always occurs between 24 and 26 November.

The male undertakes the first incubation shift of about 12 to 14 days, after which the female takes over for another long spell. The male and female alternate twice more until incubation ends.

The chicks hatch from mid-January onwards, the date depending on the date the egg was laid and on minor variations in the incubation period. The chick is deserted by day when it is about three days old, but fed nightly for the first week of its life. After this, visits by adults become less and less frequent.

At first, a thick grey down covers the chick. This is replaced at about 10 days by a smoky-brown second down. The nestling grows at a prodigious rate; it often reaches double the adult weight just before losing its down through the rapid growth of feathers.

Chicks remain in the nest for about 94 days and receive their last feed about 14 days before they venture out of the nest. They swim out to sea to fledge on their own.

The fledglings leave the colony in late April to early May. Probably 50 per cent of them die within the first year. During the breeding season immature birds return to their natal colonies, the length of their stay increasing with age. It seems that the birds rarely breed until five years of age, and may take longer to acquire a mate.

In late afternoon during breeding, large flocks of shearwaters build up close to the colonies, resting on the sea in rafts after feeding, waiting for nightfall. Rafting is common in the Short-tailed Shearwater, which never visits colonies during the daylight hours. It may be an adaptive behaviour that minimises predation.

The annual migration of the Short-tailed Shearwater from its Australian breeding islands takes the adults and young birds to the North Pacific. A figure-of-eight pathway was once suggested for this migration to and from the north. Starting out in the Tasman Sea towards New Zealand it was thought that the birds move clockwise into and around the North Pacific, eventually returning to the breeding islands by crossing the equatorial waters of the central Pacific and making a landfall on the coast of Australia before moving on to Bass Strait. It is now considered doubtful this migration 'loop' actually occurs.

It is likely that many young Short-tailed Shearwaters do not return to Australia in their first year, but remain in the north. It is also certain that many of the adults move into the northwestern portion of the Pacific and return by the most direct route. Between July and August there are large concentrations of Short-tailed Shearwaters in Arctic seas above the northwestern Pacific.

The birds moult their head and body feathers at the breeding colonies but the flight feathers are replaced at the winter quarters before the long haul south.

The Short-tailed Shearwater is the most common shearwater in the south and southeast of Australia throughout the summer months. Its regular passage south along the east coast of Australia in spring is spectacular. In some years enormous numbers perish along this coastline; between October and January masses of emaciated birds are sometimes found dead or dying on the beaches anywhere from southern Queensland to the far south coast of New South Wales. The reasons are not entirely clear, but starvation and exhaustion are often evident.

The muttonbirding industry of Bass Strait islands involves a limited commercial harvesting of the Short-tailed Shearwater. Today the annual harvest is taken between 27 March and 30 April. The fat nestlings, or squabs, weighing almost one kilogram each, are killed, the down and feathers removed and the bodies gutted to extract the oily stomach content to be purified for pharmaceutical use. The cleaned bodies are sold fresh or pickled in brine.

Control of the harvesting ensures that there is no threat to the survival of the species. Indeed, without commercial interest, the breeding islands may have been used for other purposes, probably destroying the breeding colonies.

OTHER NAMES
Muttonbird, Short-tailed Petrel.

IDENTIFICATION
LENGTH: *About 400 mm.*
ADULTS: *Sexes similar. Plumage brown-black overall, with white mark under eye and dusky underwing; tail short and rounded. Both lighter and darker phases occur. Eye brown. Bill leaden-grey to olive-tinged. Feet and toes dark grey to black; webs paler.*
IMMATURES: *Similar to adults.*
DOWNY YOUNG: *Sooty grey; bill and feet black.*

VOICE
In courtship and greeting a crooning kooka-rooka-rah *repeated rapidly and evenly accented. The call runs to a* coo-roo-rah *as tempo quickens and pitch rises in frenzied repetition. Calls are given, as in most shearwaters, by birds on ground or from within burrows and rarely by birds in flight. Harsher cries in nesting disputes.*

NESTING
Breeds late September to early May. Nest a chamber lined with dead leaves in a burrow up to 2 m long under tussocks, often in densely packed colonies, one nest per sq metre. Egg: one; white; long-oval, about 71 x 47 mm. Incubation about 53 days, by both sexes. Young fledge in about 94 days.*

DISTRIBUTION
All known breeding colonies are in Australia, from St Francis Island, SA, to southern Tasmania and northeast as far as Broughton Island, NSW. Favours cool, temperate waters, with breeding concentrations in Bass Strait and Spencer Gulf. Migrates to North Pacific between breeding seasons. Non-breeders may summer off Antarctica. Infrequently seen in southwestern Australia. No races.

The Short-tailed Shearwater is the muttonbird of the islands in Bass Strait.

A Sooty Shearwater spreads its wings before takeoff; it can be identified by its silvery underwings. The birds come ashore to their colonies at night.

Sooty Shearwater *Puffinus griseus* (GMELIN,1789)

THE SOOTY SHEARWATER BREEDS around Australia only in colonies that it shares with the Wedge-tailed Shearwater or the Short-tailed Shearwater, or both, and it is not abundant at any of them. Else-where, however, the Sooty replaces its close relative, the Short-tailed, as a breeding species on the islands off New Zealand and the tip of South America. But for its larger size, longer bill and usually silvery underwing, it resembles the Short-tailed in appearance. Their habits are similar too. The Sooty nests in vast colonies on its southern islands over summer and masses in huge flocks to migrate to the cold waters of the Northern Hemisphere each autumn, returning in the same flocks-in-line sequence in spring. South American birds seem to travel up and down either coast of the Americas while Australian–New Zealand birds keep more to the edge of the western Pacific, reaching Japan.

At sea, it hunts by day for its food — plankton, crustaceans, squid and fish — in two main ways. One is a massed chase by swimming petrels after a shoal of prey, those left at the back leap-frogging over to get to the front so that the whole formation rolls forward across the water like a hoop. The other strategy is a shallow plunge-dive from flight, the birds literally flying under water, wings beating, to snatch food. In the air, Sooty Shearwaters flap swiftly and strongly, gliding gracefully for long distances on stiffly out-stretched wings, and adjusting the trim to rise and sweep.

Sooty Shearwaters are typically nocturnal and colonial in their nesting. They commonly gather in rafts of an afternoon before fly-ing ashore, where, early in the season, pairs greet and court with the same duetting, billing and preening as do Short-tailed Shear-waters. Burrows are dug out of rather hard soil on headlands or high ground often well inland, and are particularly long. Eggs are laid from late November into December over 21 days, and they hatch through late January. Chicks are brooded in their first two–three days, then abandoned by day and fed only at night, until one–three weeks before they fledge when they are deserted completely. Adults leave the nesting islands first, in March–April, and moult at their winter quarters, at sea.

At the extremely dense shearwater colonies on the Mutton Bird Islands off Stewart Island, southern New Zealand, the Maoris have long harvested Sooty Shearwater chicks, but never on as great a scale as that in Tasmania.

OTHER NAMES
Ghost Bird, King Muttonbird, Sombre Shearwater.

IDENTIFICATION
LENGTH: *About 450–460 mm.*
ADULTS: *Sexes similar. Dusky brown all over except for a pale silver area in centre of underwings. Eye brown. Bill leaden-grey slightly olive-toned. Feet and toes dark grey or black.*
IMMATURES: *Similar to adults; bill weaker; underwing darker.*
DOWNY YOUNG: *Grey, becoming smoky brown; bill and feet dark.*

VOICE
In courtship and greeting at nest and in the air a deep, evenly phrased, rhythmic repetition of der-rer-ah, *with first two syllables exhaled and last inhaled; deeper, half as rapid and not so hysterical-sounding as Short-tailed Shearwater's call. Often two birds duet, one giving a higher-pitched* coo-roo-ah *against a lower-pitched call. Bouts of calling increase in volume and emphasis, then die away. Brooding birds will croon on the nest by day. Silent at sea.*

NESTING
Breeds over summer, September–April. Nest a grass-lined chamber in a winding burrow 1–3 m long, on high ground either among coastal plants, tussocks or below a forest canopy. Egg:
one; white; elongate, about 77 x 48 mm. Incubation about 58–60 days, by both sexes in eight–14 day shifts. Young fledge in about 97 days, at night, flapping at the mouths of their burrows for several days before leaving.

DISTRIBUTION
Seas of southern Australia with small numbers breeding at Broughton Islands, Cabbage Tree, Boondelbah, Bird, Lion and Tollgate Islands off NSW coast; also at Tasman and Courts Islands off Tasmania, and Maatsuyker Islands and others in Port Davey. Vaster colonies on islands about and south of New Zealand (including Macquarie Island), Cape Horn and Falklands. Migrates to winter in northern Pacific, travelling off eastern Australian and both American coasts. No races.

Flesh-footed Shearwater *Puffinus carneipes* GOULD, 1844

A Flesh-footed Shearwater on Lord Howe Island; the usual nest is a burrow.

OTHER NAMES
Fleshy-footed Shearwater, Pale-footed Shearwater.

IDENTIFICATION
LENGTH: *About 480–500 mm.*
ADULTS: *Sexes similar. Plumage wholly dusky, almost black. Eye brown. Heavy bill straw-coloured with dark tip. Feet and toes flesh-pink.*
IMMATURES: *Similar to adults.*
DOWNY YOUNG: *Mid-grey, lighter below; bill leaden, feet flesh-grey.*

VOICE
In courtship, on ground and in air, a loud, repeated ku-kee-arh; often preceded by panting splutters. Also crooning cackles.

NESTING
Breeds late September to May. Nest a sparsely lined chamber in burrow 1–2 m long in soft soil, on grassy slope, among low vegetation or under forest. Egg: one; white; long-oval, about 69 x 46 mm. Incubation about 60–65 days, by both sexes. Young fledge in about 92 days.

DISTRIBUTION
Tropical-subtropical Indo-Pacific seas. Two races: one breeding from Cape Hamelin to Recherche Archipelago, WA; the other on Lord Howe Island and around northern New Zealand.

LARGEST OF THE AUSTRALIAN SHEARWATERS, the Flesh-footed resembles the Wedge-tailed Shearwater in flight, holding its wings even more stiffly in long glides low over waves. An all-dusky body and stout buff bill are its best identifying features at sea. The birds commonly congregate to feed, taking more fish and less crustaceans and squid than other shearwaters, and diving more frequently and adeptly, sometimes plunging as much as three–five metres. Often they accompany fishing boats, filching scraps.

Flesh-footed Shearwaters breed in two isolated groups on either side of southern Australia, one around the extreme southwest coast and the other on Lord Howe Island and islands around New Zealand where they are harvested by Maoris. The birds, led by older breeders, begin to appear on their nesting grounds in September, cleaning and digging out burrows until, by early November, the entire colony is ashore each night. The colonies are quiet by day, occupied only by birds deep in their burrows, the mouths of which are often covered with pulled-in vegetation. Each afternoon flocks gather on nearby water in rafts, but do not fly to their burrows till nightfall. As they approach they mew in flight, adding to the noisy chorus from territorial and pairing birds on the ground. Courtship occurs on open ground around burrow entrances. Male and female bill, preen and chase one another, necks outstretched, wobbling their bodies, swaying and crooning; action culminates in a loud squeaking duet.

Eggs are laid late November–early December and hatch through late January into February. Chicks are brooded in their first two-three days, then abandoned by day and fed only at night. As soon as brooding ceases they spend time by pulling debris and feathers from around them to line the nest. Parents visit and feed them about once every two nights in the first weeks, then less often as fledging approaches. In gathering food, adults will forage as far as 150 kilometres from the colony.

After breeding, Flesh-footed Shearwaters migrate in flocks north across the equator. The Western Australian populations apparently travel west across the Indian Ocean to the Mascarene islands, then north to the Arabian Sea and after wintering there, return in a great circle past the Maldives, Ceylon and Christmas Island. Eastern populations evidently move up the western side of the Pacific towards Japan, then swing east and south past Hawaii towards the Californian coast before circling back across the equator to Australasian seas. Both paths are laid and timed to make use of tailwinds and keep the birds in warm subtropical waters.

Fluttering Shearwater

Puffinus gavia (FORSTER, 1844)

OTHER NAMES
Brown-backed Petrel.

IDENTIFICATION
LENGTH: *About 320–330 mm.*
ADULTS: *Sexes similar. Upper parts very dark brown. Underparts white, with sides of neck, face and throat smudged grey-brown. Underwings mostly white; inner parts smudgy brown. Eye brown. Bill dark grey. Feet and toes flesh-coloured with brown outer sides.*
IMMATURES: *Similar to adults.*
DOWNY YOUNG: *Grey-brown.*

VOICE
Loud, staccato, rapidly repeated kahowoo, first two syllables strongly stressed and the inhaled oo soft and almost inaudible. Given in courtship.

NESTING
Breeds August–March. Nesting burrow dug in soft soil, with passage leading to chamber lined with dry plant matter and feathers. Egg: one; white; long-oval, about 57 x 40 mm. Incubation by both sexes.

DISTRIBUTION
Regular and common winter visitor to waters off Australia's east coast. Less common west of Bass Strait. Breeds on islands in New Zealand. No races.

The Fluttering Shearwater is a common winter visitor to eastern Australia.

THE FLIGHT OF THE Fluttering Shearwater is generally swift and low over the sea, with quick wing-beats and short stiff glides. The bird is closely related to Hutton's Shearwater and is difficult to distinguish from it in flight. The Fluttering Shearwater always looks whiter, especially on the underwings; Hutton's is rather more dusky, particularly on the neck, sides of body and underwings. The Little Shearwater is still smaller, and more strongly black and white with no grey on its face.

Fluttering Shearwaters are common visitors from New Zealand to the southeast coasts of Australia in winter. They flock at sea to swim or dive for their food: planktonic crustaceans and fish. They are not known to nest in Australia, so birds in the area in summer are presumably immature or non-breeders.

The birds return to their breeding colonies in New Zealand in August, and are nocturnal at their nests. Eggs are laid late September or early October. After hatching in late November, the chicks are first brooded for several days, then fed sporadically by both parents at night before fledging by early March. They call regularly in flight as well as from the burrows.

Hutton's Shearwater *Puffinus huttoni* MATHEWS, 1912

Hutton's Shearwaters at the entrance to their snow-covered burrows high in the Seaward Kaikoura Mountains of the South Island of New Zealand.

UNTIL 1965, IT WAS NOT KNOWN where this bird bred. Then breeding colonies were discovered high in the Seaward Kaikoura Mountains of New Zealand's South Island. The remarkable high-altitude colonies were found well inland on steep to very steep slopes covered with tussocks of snowgrass *Chionochloa*.

In the colonies, the shearwaters dig into loose soil to make burrows, which are often close together. Periodically, soil erosion and destruction of snowgrass seem to cause shifts in colony sites.

Although returning to their breeding colonies in August, the birds rarely lay until early November, much later than the allied Fluttering Shearwater, and will be delayed further if wintry weather persists and snow falls. Chicks also hatch and fledge late, often into late March and April.

At sea, Hutton's Shearwaters are rather sedentary, occurring around the year in and off Cook Strait and down the east coast of the South Island of New Zealand. There is some dispersal westwards over winter to the waters of eastern and southern Australia, and it is possible that some birds circumnavigate the continent then. The birds commonly flock at sea to feed on shoaling fish and crustaceans, swimming, flying and diving like Fluttering Shearwaters. They also gather in resting flocks on inshore waters close to their breeding grounds on late summer afternoons, waiting to fly in after dusk. At their colonies they are strictly night-active.

Hutton's Shearwater is closely related to the Fluttering Shearwater and the migratory Northern Hemisphere Manx Shearwater; and it resembles them both in feeding and nesting habits. Often the three are classified as races of one another. Hutton's Shearwater, however, can be identified by its slightly larger size and longer-tailed shape. Its bill is 34–40 millimetres long, compared with 28–36 millimetres in the Fluttering; and it is duskier, particularly along its underwings and sides of the neck. The duskiness on its underwings extends to the axillaries or armpit feathers which are long and round-ended.

OTHER NAMES
None.

IDENTIFICATION
LENGTH: *350 mm.*
ADULTS: *Sexes similar. Upper parts uniformly dusky brown from head to tail; sides of neck dusky, leaving a narrow white line on throat. Underparts white; outer undertail coverts edged with some dark brown. Axillaries long and dark brown. Eye brown. Long, slender bill very dark grey. Feet and toes flesh-coloured with brown outer sides.*
IMMATURES: *Similar to adults.*
DOWNY YOUNG: *Grey.*

VOICE
In display and greeting a deep, repetitive cackle, kow-wow-haw, *with first two syllables stressed and exhaled, and last strongly inhaled and wheezy.*

NESTING
Breeds colonially August–April, over summer. Nest a chamber at end of a burrow well lined with snowgrass leaves and roots. Egg: one; white; oval, about 60 x 41 mm. Incubation by both sexes in shifts.

DISTRIBUTION
All known breeding colonies occur at more than 1600 m above sea level in Seaward Kaikoura Mountains, in South Island of New Zealand. Disperses to eastern Australian seas over winter but less commonly than Fluttering Shearwater. Occurrence in Torres Strait, NW Australia and in SW suggests it may circumnavigate the continent on migration. No races.

Buller's Shearwater

Puffinus bulleri SALVIN, 1888

Buller's Shearwater has distinctive black and grey upper wings.

IT IS EASY TO RECOGNISE this large grey and white shearwater, with its long body and broad wings, its striking dark-capped head and its distinctive black and grey upper wings. Buller's Shearwater is a regular visitor to southeastern Australia in summer. It appears in small numbers over the deeper offshore waters, mostly beyond the continental shelf—but probably does not range widely inshore. Occasionally, however, it is found onshore in burrows among other large shearwaters, but evidently does not breed. It may get caught up in the activities of the local shearwaters and simply come ashore with them for the night.

After summer, dispersal from the only known breeding site—the Poor Knights Islands off northern New Zealand—takes the bird well into the Tasman Sea and south to Cook Strait, Banks Peninsula and Foveaux Strait. Some birds migrate to the North Pacific, where they have been reported east of Japan and off the west coast of North America. They also appear in the South Pacific off Peru. Birds present in the North Pacific in early summer and off South America throughout the summer must be non-breeders. Some birds visit New Zealand during the winter, so not all migrate.

In its breeding habits, Buller's Shearwater is similar to the Flesh-footed. It does not fly ashore to its colonies, however, until well after nightfall. The birds reappear off their islands in late August, court and clean out their burrows in September–October, and lay in late November–early December. Chicks hatch in January and, fed by both parents, fledge in late March.

At sea, Buller's Shearwater flies more leisurely than most shearwaters, flapping less and gliding more, like an albatross in calm weather. It swims and dives for its food—squid and a variety of crustaceans—and commonly forages in loose but cohesive flocks. Like most shearwaters, it pays no attention to ships.

There is some suggestion that the Buller's Shearwater's numbers are increasing in the Poor Knights Islands, and this could explain why more have been seen in Australian waters recently.

OTHER NAMES
Grey-backed Shearwater.

IDENTIFICATION
LENGTH: *About 450–460 mm.*
ADULTS: *Sexes similar. Crown and nape dusky grey, shading to paler grey on rump and back; brownish when worn. Tail dusky. Conspicuous dark M-pattern across upper wings with lighter secondaries in flight. Underparts and face white; underwing coverts white. Eye brown. Bill leaden-grey, darker at tip. Feet and toes pinkish white inside, black outside.*
IMMATURES: *Similar to adults.*
DOWNY YOUNG: *Light grey, paler below; bill and feet lighter than adult.*

VOICE
Mewing calls at nest.

NESTING
Breeds September–May in dense colonies. Nest a leaf- and twig-lined chamber in a burrow or rock crevice.

Egg: one; white; long-oval, about 66 x 43 mm. Incubation about 50 days, by both sexes.

DISTRIBUTION
Regular visitor in small numbers to western side of Tasman Sea in summer. Only known breeding site is Poor Knights Islands, northern New Zealand. Disperses widely within Pacific Ocean. No races.

Little Shearwater *Puffinus assimilis* GOULD, 1838

The Little Shearwater breeds on several Australian islands. It nests among plants.

STRIKING BLACK-AND-WHITE plumage, small size and relatively short wings make the Little Shearwater reasonably easy to distinguish in the air. It is a fast, low flier, beating its wings more rapidly than larger shearwaters and gliding for shorter distances on stiff wings. To feed it both swims and dives, often congregating in flocks and taking mainly squid, some fish and crustaceans. Although breeding off Australia, it keeps to southern waters.

The Little Shearwater never visits its breeding islands by daylight. It is a loosely colonial winter breeder and in Australia begins to return in February. Activity and noise at the colony increase nightly until egg-laying—over June–July—then tail off, with only occasional bursts from influxes of non-breeding or resting birds. Breeders defend their burrows by raising wings and growling. They court with much reciprocal billing, preening of heads and duetting, their napes arched, throats swollen and nostrils sometimes oozing reddish saline. Chicks hatch in August and, at first fed nightly by both parents, fledge in October–November. The shearwaters seem to be fairly sedentary around their colonies.

OTHER NAMES
Allied Shearwater, Dusky Shearwater.

IDENTIFICATION
LENGTH: *About 280–300 mm.*
ADULTS: *Sexes similar. Upper parts black; underparts chalky white, extending above eye. Underwings almost entirely white. Eye brown. Bill leaden, black on culmen. Feet cobalt-blue with irregular black markings on outer toes; webs flesh-colour.*
IMMATURES: *Similar to adults.*
DOWNY YOUNG: *Grey above, whitish below; bill dark grey, feet leaden.*

VOICE
Whistling preep-preep, scream, and dove-like coo in flight over colony. Courting and greeting birds give high-pitched, rapidly repeated asthmatic crooning, wah, i-wah-i-wah-ooo; Chicks chirrup.

NESTING
Breeds in large, often scattered colonies, February–November. Nest a burrow 1–2 m long with large chamber at end in soil or among rocks under low vegetation; lining of dry vegetation variable. Preferred sites are steep hillsides. Egg: one; white; long-oval, about 52 x 36 mm. Incubation 52–58 days, by both sexes. Young fledge in 70–75 days.

DISTRIBUTION
Temperate seas of Indian, Atlantic and southern Pacific Ocean, including waters of southwestern and southeastern Australia. In Australia, breeds between Houtman Abrolhos and Recherche Archipelago, WA, and at Lord Howe and Norfolk Islands. Seven races; two in Australia: one in east; the other smaller, in west.

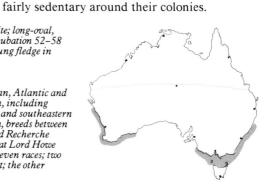

A pair of Wedge-tailed Shearwaters. These birds nest in burrows in bare soil, among low plants or on the surface of the ground under rocks or bushes.

Wedge-tailed Shearwater *Puffinus pacificus* (GMELIN, 1789)

EVEN WHEN THE WEDGE SHAPE of its large tail is not clearly visible, the Wedge-tailed Shearwater can be distinguished at sea from other similar dark petrels. Its more buoyant drifting flight, slim head and body accentuated by a long, folded tail, and broad straightened wings with the wrists held well forward when gliding, set it apart. The main reason this broad-winged shearwater of the tropical seas differs in its flight from its more southerly relatives is the lightness of its body: the more heavily built shearwaters of cooler regions flap faster. At sea, Wedge-tailed Shearwaters are solitary, or form small parties to feed, congregating in the afternoon to rest in massed rafts on the water only off their breeding colonies, waiting for nightfall before flying ashore. Like other shearwaters they eat squid, crustaceans and small fish which they catch while swimming or from shallow dives in flight.

The shearwaters return to their nesting islands to breed in close-packed colonies in September, apparently arriving a little earlier on Coral Sea islets than further south. Each bird may take up the nest burrow of previous years, which helps to avert conflict with other shearwaters — Short-tailed and Sooty — where they nest side by side on southeastern islands off the New South Wales coast.

Evenings early in the season are filled with the sound of courting birds. Pairing shearwaters preen and bill one another and duet in gasping croons around their burrows and copulate there. Before laying, however, they go to sea for a week or two, building up reserves of energy. Egg-laying is protracted, from late October into December and young hatch through January. On some islands birds lay in crevices and under bushes; and others without burrows deposit theirs on the open ground, usually to be taken by gulls.

Chicks, brooded for only a few days, are then fed by both parents at night at irregular intervals. They fledge from mid-April into May, earlier on tropical than subtropical islands, and are tended by their parents to the end, without desertion. In good years, the density of chicks raised approaches something like 2500 per hectare on islands off New South Wales.

After breeding, Wedge-tailed Shearwaters depart from the coastal waters of New South Wales, some travelling as far as the central western Pacific. Similar northward movements must occur in the Indian Ocean, because the bird is common there during the southern winter, particularly in the northwest.

OTHER NAMES
Wedge-tailed Muttonbird.

IDENTIFICATION
LENGTH: *About 420–440 mm.*
ADULTS: *Sexes similar. Entirely black-brown. Eye brown. Bill leaden-grey. Legs pale flesh-coloured with white toenails. Birds in fresh plumage are almost black but become browner with time, especially across the upper wing coverts, which then contrast strongly with the darker flight feathers. A form with white underparts blending into the dark upper plumage, and white underwings with darker borders and axillaries, is sometimes seen.*
IMMATURES: *Similar to adults.*
DOWNY YOUNG: *Ash-grey above, lighter below.*

VOICE
In courtship or greeting a wailing ka-whooooo-ahh. First syllable is soft, second forced and strongly exhaled and last a gasping, inhaled gargle. The phrase is repeated steadily in doleful manner, and with increasing frenzy reaches an abrupt and hysterical climax. Single mournful calls are frequent, but several birds calling together create a rhythmic, rising and falling sound. Cat-like cries accompany territorial clashes.

NESTING
Breeds September–May, over summer, in dense colonies. Nest usually a large chamber, sometimes lined with dry vegetation, at the end of a burrow 2 m or more long; but on some tropical islands under rocks or bushes. Colonies are usually in bare soil or among low plants, but some occur beneath forest canopies, such as those on Cabbage Tree Island, NSW. Egg: one; white; ellipsoidal, about 63 x 41 mm. Incubation about 50 days, by both sexes. Young fledge in about 70 days.

DISTRIBUTION
Inhabits subtropical and tropical waters of Pacific and Indian Oceans; most southerly known colony is on Montague Island off southern New South Wales. Common off coasts of Australia north of Cape Naturaliste and Cape Howe, but rare southwards, breeding on offshore islands. Subtropical colonies migrate towards equator in winter. Two races: one small, on Kermadecs, Norfolk and Kandavic Islands; the other large and breeding elsewhere throughout Pacific and Indian Oceans. Both races reach Australia.

Wilson's Storm-Petrels and a Cape Petrel (left) feeding in Hope Bay, Antarctica. This storm-petrel sometimes reaches Australia's continental shelf.

Wilson's Storm-Petrel *Oceanites oceanicus* (KUHL, 1820)

A GREAT WANDERER, this dainty little petrel with its dark plumage, square-tipped tail and white rump-band migrates from its breeding grounds in the Antarctic and subantarctic to winter in the northern Indian Ocean, western Pacific Ocean and North Atlantic. It is seen more often over Australia's continental shelf than any other storm-petrel, despite not breeding there.

Over the roughest seas, it flies like a butterfly, skipping and fluttering erratically, then gliding on. While feeding, it darts and hovers, wings held aloft, dangling its feet in the water and pattering about. Usually it picks its food—planktonic crustaceans, krill and oil — from the surface, but may occasionally plunge-dive for it. It often follows ships, and will investigate oily bait thrown overboard from fishing boats. At sea, it is commonly gregarious.

The birds return to breed in colonies in November, courting in high-speed aerial chases, and by mutual preening, bill-vibrating, and duetting on the ground. Nests and mates are located by sound, and occupants of nests often attract several prospective partners at a time by calling. The most aggressive of these wins out by a series of threat-hops, but itself may not be accepted by the nest-occupant; if so, it is quickly driven off with high-pitched squeaks and a jet of disgorged orange stomach oil.

Egg-laying, from early December to late January, is not synchronised among the colonies. Young hatch from mid-January to late March and, brooded in their first one–two days and fed irregularly at night thereafter, fledge from mid-March.

OTHER NAMES
Flat-clawed Storm-Petrel.

IDENTIFICATION
LENGTH: *About 180 mm, with square tail.*
ADULTS: *Sexes similar. Entirely sooty black except for white rump and pale diagonal bar across upper wing coverts. Eye brown. Bill black. Feet and toes black with yellow webs.*
IMMATURES: *Similar to adults.*
DOWNY YOUNG: *Dark grey; feet pink.*

VOICE
At nest, a soft, nasal several-syllable aark-aark in greeting, often repeated in long sequences. Chattering in courtship. At sea a faint rapid squeaking when feeding.

NESTING
Breeds in loose colonies in summer, November–May. Nest in short burrow or among rocks. Egg: one; white, usually spotted lightly with red-brown, especially at blunt end; oval, about 34 x 24 mm. Incubation 39–48 days, by both sexes in 48-hour shifts. Young, fed by both parents, fledge in about 60 days.

DISTRIBUTION
Occasionally seen in all coastal waters around Australia in winter. Breeds along coastline of Antarctica and on several Antarctic and subantarctic islands. Moves north from these breeding colonies to inshore waters around North Atlantic, northern Indian and western Pacific Oceans in April–June. Two races; one large, one small, both reaching Australia.

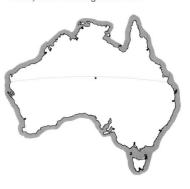

White-bellied Storm-Petrel

Fregetta grallaria (VIEILLOT, 1817)

OTHER NAMES
Vieillot's Storm-Petrel.

IDENTIFICATION
LENGTH: *180–200 mm, with square tail.*
ADULTS: *Sexes similar. Upper parts black; shoulders faintly paler; rump white. Throat and upper breast black; rest of underparts white. Occasional duskiness on rump and underparts. Central underwing white; broad black leading and trailing edge to wing. Eye brown. Bill black. Feet short, black.*
IMMATURES: *Similar to adults, scaled paler on back.*
DOWNY YOUNG: *Leaden above, white belly; feet black.*

VOICE
In courtship in nesting cavity, high-pitched whistling pee-pee-pee-pee... or peu-peu-peu-peu... often repeated 20 or more times in sequence; also high-pitched advertising whistle huuuuuuuu.

NESTING
Breeds December–May, in loose colonies; night-active. Nest in burrow or crevice or cavity among loose rocks with little nesting material. Egg: one; white with faint pink spots at blunt end; oval, about 35 x 26 mm. Incubation about 40 days, by both sexes.

DISTRIBUTION
In Pacific breeds on Lord Howe Island, Kermadecs, Austral Islands, and on Juan Fernandez; in southern Atlantic at Tristan da Cunha group. Populations in southwestern Pacific winter through Tasman to Coral Sea and probably central Pacific, occasionally off southeastern Australia. Four races; one off Australia.

A White-bellied Storm-Petrel at the entrance to its nesting burrow.

AT SEA THE WHITE-BELLIED and Black-bellied Storm-Petrels can be very difficult to distinguish from each other. They both fly close to the water, with bill pointed downwards and wings held stiffly out, either with dangled feet springing from side to side on the surface or with sustained glides into the wind. The flight may undulate, following the contours of the waves, before the bird flutters off downwind. In this way, the birds pick their food — planktonic squid and crustaceans—from the surface of the sea. So small are the food particles that they have to feed almost continuously, by night as well as by day. Congregations at sea are infrequent, the birds being rather solitary; but they will accompany ships, commonly flying ahead instead of in the wake.

Black-bellied Storm-Petrels have a black belly stripe missing from White-bellieds, but this is not easy to see at sea, and some White-bellieds—about 10 per cent of breeders at Lord Howe Island — have dusky underparts. In the hand, White-bellieds have much shorter feet and flatter, spade-like claws. White-bellieds breed in warm, cool-latitude waters and Black-bellieds in the subantarctic, but they overlap widely on northward migrations over winter and are alike in calls and breeding habits.

Black-bellied Storm-Petrel *Fregetta tropica* (GOULD, 1844)

OTHER NAMES
Gould's Storm-Petrel.

IDENTIFICATION
LENGTH: *180–200 mm, with square tail.*
ADULTS: *Sexes similar. Upper parts black; shoulders faintly paler; rump white. Throat and upper breast black. Belly white with dark stripe down centre to undertail. Underwings white, margined dusky. Eye brown. Bill and long feet black.*
IMMATURES: *Similar to adults, scaled paler on back.*
DOWNY YOUNG: *Dark grey above, white belly; feet black.*

VOICE
Thin, high-pitched advertising whistle huuuuuuuu at burrow; softer, whistled pee-pee... or peu-peu... in courtship.

NESTING
Breeds November–May. Nest a burrow or cavity among rocks. Egg: one; white, faintly spotted with red-brown to black; oval, about 37 x 27 mm. Incubation 38–44 days, by both sexes. Young fledge in 65–71 days.

DISTRIBUTION
Circum-subantarctic breeder; nearest colonies on Kerguelen, Auckland and Antipodes Islands. Straggles north over winter to near equator; common then off southeastern Australia. Two races; one in Pacific-Australian region.

A Black-bellied Storm-Petrel on an island in the Antipodes group, one of its breeding areas closest to Australia.

BLACK-BELLIED STORM-PETRELS fly, feed and look like White-bellied Storm-Petrels, and are distinguished with difficulty only by their black ventral stripe and longer, finer feet. But they breed further south and only visit Australian and other subtropical seas over winter. The birds return to their colonies in November–December, calling noisily at night. Long high-pitched whistles, lasting several seconds and given inside or outside the burrow, advertise nest sites and attract mates; and softer repeated notes are given by pairs in courtship flight as they glide down in unison, one behind the other.

Before laying December–January, females spend one–two weeks alone at sea while males keep the nest. Incubation is shared in shifts of three days, each bird losing about 12 per cent of its weight in that period. Eggs hatch in late January–February, but nestlings, although fed by both parents at night, are never brooded. They and the adults depart by mid-April, the latter moulting at winter quarters at sea.

Grey-backed Storm-Petrel *Garrodia nereis* (GOULD, 1841)

The Grey-backed Storm-Petrel is seldom seen in the seas around Australia.

OTHER NAMES
None.

IDENTIFICATION
LENGTH *170–180 mm, with square tail.*
ADULTS: *Sexes similar. Head dull sooty grey, grading to paler ash-grey on back, rump and tail, which has broad dark grey tip. Upper wings dark grey, with two faint pale grey bars along edges of upper wing coverts. Throat and breast dark grey, merging to thick, dark leading edge to underwing. Rest of underwing coverts white; trailing edge of underwing grey, much paler than leading edge. Belly and undertail white. Sides of rump and outermost undertail coverts flecked with grey. Eye brown. Bill black. Feet and toes black.*
IMMATURES: *Similar to adults.*

DOWNY YOUNG: *Pale grey, lighter on belly; feet black.*

VOICE
High-pitched crake-like twittering.

NESTING
Breeds in loose colonies October–April. Nest a small hollow in tussocky grasses or other low plants. Egg: one; white with rufous-red spots, mostly at blunt end; oval, about 33 x 25 mm.

DISTRIBUTION
Rare in Australian waters, most records coming from Tasman Sea and Bass Strait. Breeds on several subantarctic islands south and east of New Zealand and others in South Atlantic and southern Indian Ocean. No races.

A BIRD OF SUBANTARCTIC SEAS, the Grey-backed Storm-Petrel is a rarity in Australian waters—possibly because it appears to be a rather sedentary species that remains close to its colonies and visits them even outside the breeding season. Most records of its Australian appearances are from the Bass Strait and Tasman Sea areas.

Very little is known about the habits of this small, grey-backed bird with white underparts. At sea it skips and bounces almost frenziedly from side to side, wings extending low over the water, as it picks tiny planktonic particles—cephalopods, molluscs, crustaceans—from the walls of advancing waves.

The birds return to breed in loose colonies in late October–early November, calling at night in advertisement or courtship with high-pitched twittering. Eggs are laid mid-November to mid-December, and the chicks hatch in January and fledge by April.

White-faced Storm-Petrel *Pelagodroma marina* (LATHAM, 1790)

The White-faced Storm-Petrel, recognisable by its head pattern, breeds on islands around southern Australia.

OTHER NAMES
Frigate Petrel, White-breasted Storm-Petrel.

IDENTIFICATION
LENGTH: *About 200 mm.*
ADULTS: *Sexes similar. Crown dark grey; forehead, eyebrows and face white with black stripe through eye. Back grey; rump paler. Tail dusky brown; square. Shoulders grey-brown; flight feathers dusky. Underparts white; faint grey wash on breast; flanks sometimes dusky. Eye brown. Bill black. Feet black; webs buff.*
IMMATURES: *Similar to adults, pale edges to head, wing and tail coverts.*
DOWNY YOUNG: *Blue-grey; bald crown; bill and feet black.*

VOICE
In breeding colony soft, slightly tremulous peeoo-peeoo-peeoo, often repeated 10–20 times. Young purr at approach of adult.

NESTING
Breeds in colonies over summer, late October–early February. Nest a frail 50–120 cm long burrow in soft, sandy soil. Egg: one; white, peppered with red-brown at blunt end; oval, about 36 x 27 mm. Incubation 55–56 days, by both sexes. Young fledge in 55–65 days.

DISTRIBUTION
Temperate and subtropical waters of both hemispheres, wandering towards equator in colder, non-breeding months. In Australia, breeds in Houtman Abrolhos and Recherche Archipelago, WA, off Eyre Peninsula, in Bass Strait and up to Broughton Island, NSW. Six races; one in Australia.

ALTHOUGH THIS STORM-PETREL breeds on many islands around southern Australia, it is rarely seen close inshore or following ships. It feeds in parties or large aggregations on surface plankton beyond the continental shelf and visits its breeding colonies only after dark.

The distinctive head pattern of the White-faced Storm-Petrel makes it easy to recognise at sea. Its flight is exceedingly erratic, on broadly rounded wings. It dances from side to side, bouncing over the water on short, stiff-winged glides, long legs dangled to hit the water together, perhaps to aid balance or give thrust. On land, the bird walks awkwardly, placing its long legs almost flat on the ground and then raising them vertically with each step. The gait is rather hurried and accompanied by wing-fluttering to aid balance. Other storm-petrels walk similarly.

In their often dense breeding colonies, White-faced Storm-Petrels dig nesting burrows among low vegetation or, occasionally, under forest. Burrows may be straight or twisted in horizontal as well as vertical directions. A chamber at the end is lined with a bed of fine dry grasses. Occasionally there seems to be no exact nest site, because an incubating bird will shift its position over a small area beneath a tangle of matted plants. Nesters, which may not nest till three-five years old, lay from early October into November, earliest in the north. Chicks, hatching from December into January, are brooded in their first few days, then abandoned and fed only at night. They fledge in five weeks, without formal desertion by their parents.

The White-faced Storm-Petrel is absent from Australian seas between breeding seasons, probably moving into the northern Indian Ocean, where they moult their flight feathers before returning. New Zealand colonies may shift to the eastern Pacific area then.

Rockhopper Penguin

Eudyptes chrysocome (FORSTER, 1781)

OTHER NAMES
Crested Penguin, Jackass Penguin.

IDENTIFICATION
LENGTH: *450–600 mm.*
ADULTS: *Sexes similar; female slightly smaller. Small-to-medium sized, with glossy black head, back, upper flippers and throat. Face dull sooty black, often grizzled silvery. Feathers of back of crown protrude over nape in a fringe. Eyebrow stripe-crest of black and pale yellow to straw-yellow feathers extending over eye, and widening to hang out rakishly over the ears. Tail feathers stiff, black, almost spiny. Undersurface satin-white. Underflipper white with black edge and tip. Eye dark brown to carmine-red. Bill dull orange to very dark brown. Feet and webbed toes pale pink; nails and soles black.*
IMMATURES: *Similar to adults, but throat pale grey, stripe-crest smaller and paler.*
DOWNY YOUNG: *Dusky from head and throat over back; breast and belly dull white; feet, bill black.*

VOICE
Variety of guttural to shrill gurgling calls. Braying calls common, especially during courtship as duet, also shrill churring noises at nest sites, and single high-pitched shriek of alarm. Chicks beg food with a plaintive see-eep.

NESTING
Breeds in spring to early summer on subantarctic islands. Nest a scrape to well-formed, of stones, grass, feathers, built on rocky promontories or at base of rocky cliffs, in caves or beneath thick vegetation. Eggs: two, rarely three; dull white, green-tinged but become stained; ovoid, first averaging 64 x 46 mm, the second, larger, 72 x 53 mm. Incubation 32–34 days, by both sexes, female first. Young fledge in 67–72 days.

DISTRIBUTION
Visits waters of southern Australia. Elsewhere throughout all subantarctic seas. Most if not all birds reaching Australian waters are of the light-flippered race (with a rim of pink skin around the base of the bill) which breeds on the subantarctic islands south of New Zealand and Australia.

Rockhopper Penguins at their breeding grounds at Hut Hill, Macquarie Island. These penguins disperse north to southern Australian seas in winter.

BEACH-WASHED SPECIMENS OF the Rockhopper Penguin—both alive and dead—have been found around the most southern coasts of Australia. Most have been found in winter when the penguins wander north from their main fishing and breeding grounds around the subantarctic islands of the southern Atlantic, Indian and Pacific Oceans. They are extremely regular in their movements and return punctually to most breeding islands in mid-October

each year, thousands forming close-packed rookeries.

Males are first to arrive. True to their name, they move about, up and down steep slopes, by agile hops, even hopping feet first into water instead of diving in like other penguins.

The arrival of females is greeted with noisy displays as each pair settles down to nest. Male and female trumpet and bow to the nest in a variety of actions, and stand side by side, pointing their bills at each other. Males have a special head-shaking display, with bill pointed skywards and flippers raised while uttering pulsating brays. Copulation takes place at the nest, during which the male goes through the atypical procedure of tapping his mate's flanks with his flippers while grasping her nape in his bill. Nearly all eggs are laid in the first month after arrival. Usually only one chick is reared by each pair. It is first brooded by the male for 19–25 days, then crèched with the massing young of the rest of the colony and fed at the nest site by both parents until it leaves for the sea, 67–72 days after hatching. Adults then return to the breeding ground for their annual moult in February–April. By May all birds have left.

At sea, Rockhopper Penguins specialise in feeding on crustaceans—amphipods and copepods—but also take squid locally.

Erect-crested Penguins can be identified by their upturned brow crests.

THE ERECT-CRESTED PENGUIN belongs to a superspecies that includes the Fiordland and Snares Penguins, all of which breed in southern New Zealand and/or fringing islands and wander erratically into Australian seas.

The birds visiting Australia come mainly in winter, when they are dispersed at sea, feeding mostly on krill, cephalopods and fish. Over summer they gather to nest in colonies of up to hundreds of thousands on their breeding islands. The actual breeding grounds are usually nothing more than a steep, rocky shore rising above the sea and covered with thick white guano. September finds the birds arriving in numbers, and eggs are laid during October.

No nest is made, eggs being laid in scrapes and crevices and held in position by the sitting bird. Athough the penguins will lie down on their breasts to incubate, they often squat erect to do so. Feet are turned in to stop the egg rolling away, and a fold of feather-covered

Erect-crested Penguin

Eudyptes sclateri BULLER, 1888

OTHER NAMES
Big-crested Penguin, Macaroni Penguin.

IDENTIFICATION
LENGTH: *600–700 mm.*
ADULTS: *Sexes similar; female slightly smaller. Plain bluish-black above, including head, throat and upper side of flippers. Breast and belly satin-white; underside of flippers white with broad black base, tip and forward edge. Tail of long, stiff, almost spiny blue-black feathers. A broad golden-yellow eyebrow stripe extends from near gape to over ears, rising in brush-like crest on either side of the head. Eye brown. Heavy bill reddish brown, edged with a flesh-coloured strip of bare skin around the base. Feet and webbed toes pinkish white; nails and soles black.*
IMMATURES: *Resemble adults but crests much smaller and whiter and throat ashy-white.*
DOWNY YOUNG: *Head, throat and upper surface dusky brown; breast and belly white; bill and feet blackish, the former tipped white.*

VOICE
Shrill cries in defence and threat, and braying calls in display.

NESTING
Breeds early spring through summer. Nest an unlined scrape or crevice. Eggs: two; chalky bluish-white; round-ovoid, first about 77 x 48 mm, second larger, about 89 x 57 mm. Incubation about 35 days, by both sexes; first egg usually rejected. Young fledge in about 75 days.

DISTRIBUTION
Beach-washed birds on south coasts of Victoria, South Australia, Western Australia and probably Tasmania. Breeds on islands south of New Zealand. No races.

skin on the belly is lifted over the egg to keep it warm.

It is usual for only one young to be reared. After it hatches, it is first guarded alone and later crèched with other young and fed by both parents. As soon as they are freed from parental duties, adults come ashore to moult, not finally quitting the colony until April.

Little Penguin *Eudyptula minor* (FORSTER, 1781)

PENGUINS ARE BEAUTIFULLY ADAPTED to life at sea. They 'fly' through the water, flapping their modified wings or flippers. When at rest they lie belly-down on the surface with flippers outstretched for stability. Their bodies are shaped like torpedoes, with thick necks, and their body feathers are short and stiff, lying close like scales. Underneath, thick down covers the body and air trapped in it provides insulation. Their short legs are set far back on their body, enabling them to steer in the water, or to stand upright on land where they waddle along with a peculiar gait. Their toenails are long and the feet are webbed.

Smallest of all penguins, the Little Penguin is the only one to breed in Australia and the only one to wait till dark before coming ashore to roost. Leaving the surf, they form groups and cross the beach to sand dunes and cliffs where they roost in crevices and burrows excavated under tussocks.

The penguins' early morning departure is a reversal of the evening arrival. About an hour before dawn, the *yap-yap* call is heard from all parts of the colony. The birds converge on the paths to the beach and scurry silently to plunge into the water.

Although some penguins come ashore every night, the number varies according to the time of the year. After the end of the breeding season when the birds undergo their annual moult there is less activity, and usually April and May are fairly quiet months. After that the somewhat deserted appearance of the colony changes to one of bustling activity. Usually the male returns first, but a female soon joins him. She may be his mate from the previous season, although not necessarily. Most pairs occupy their old burrows or dig new ones nearby. Egg-laying usually begins in July.

Both parents share incubation, and while one parent sits the other feeds at sea. Shifts can last as long as 10 days. Change-over is signalled by a relief display at the nest, both birds leaning forward and dangling their flippers to a succession of throaty growls. If the first clutch fails, the birds may lay again. Some pairs raise two clutches successfully in a season.

As soon as the eggs have hatched, the parents exchange duties every night, one guarding, the other fishing. When the chicks are about two weeks old it is necessary for both parents to spend the day at sea, to catch enough fish to feed their offspring. With bulging stomachs they scramble up the beach and regurgitate the food straight into the chick's mouth.

Adults dive for fish and squid, usually returning to the surface to swallow it, later regurgitating it whole.

The two chicks in a clutch do not always grow at the same rate, but weigh about the same as an adult when they are ready to leave the land at about eight weeks. Young birds disperse widely in their first year at sea—for example from Phillip Island, Victoria, to Spencer Gulf, South Australia, 1100 kilometres by sea. After they fledge, adults go to sea to fatten up, then return to moult on any burrow they can find, over two to three weeks.

Mortality is greatest within three months of fledging but the life expectancy of breeding birds is six-and-a-half years. Some survive for over 20 years. They swim at about six kilometres per hour and usually dive up to 40 metres. Copulation appears to occur throughout the year, except during moult, and four-fifths of surviving pairs renew their bonds each breeding season. The sexes advertise with trumpeting displays, standing erect, with bills pointing skywards and flippers waving in arcs as they bray and breathe noisily. When mating, the male growls throbbingly, pushes against the female, beats on her back with his flippers, then nibbles her nape and, grasping it in his bill, mounts, causing her to sink to the ground.

OTHER NAMES
Fairy Penguin, Blue Penguin.

IDENTIFICATION
LENGTH: *330 mm standing.*
ADULTS: *Sexes similar; male slightly larger. Upper parts steely blue-grey; underparts white. Flippers blue-grey with white trailing edge. Eye silver-grey. Bill black. Feet pale flesh with black soles and claws.*
IMMATURES: *As adults, bill smaller. Moult to adult plumage begins in fifth week, completed by eighth.*
DOWNY YOUNG: *First down fine, grey; eye dark grey. Second down at 10 days grey-brown above, cream below.*

VOICE
Sharp yapping in contact. Hoarse loud braying in sexual display.

NESTING
Varies throughout range; on Phillip Island, Vic., July–March. Nest in rock crevice or burrow about 1 m long in sand, shorter in cliffs; excavated by both sexes and lined with plant matter. Eggs: up to three; white; ovoid, 50–60 x 38–44 mm. Incubation 35–42 days, by both sexes. Young fledge in about eight weeks.

DISTRIBUTION
Seas of southern Australia; roosts and nests along coast and islands off southwestern and southeastern Australia from Fremantle to northern New South Wales, Tasmania and islands in Bass Strait. Common endemic, thin-billed race. Also in New Zealand, including about five races in Chatham Islands.

Little Penguins usually come ashore at night. They form groups and then waddle off to their burrows.

Fiordland Penguin *Eudyptes pachyrhynchus* GRAY, 1845

A Fiordland Penguin, with its chick, at its New Zealand breeding ground. Fiordland Penguins are often washed up on beaches of southeastern Australia.

INCREASED BEACH SEARCHING by ornithologists has resulted in many finds of beach-washed living and dead Fiordland Penguins in Tasmania and the southern mainland in recent years. This is the only species of crested penguin regularly breeding in the mainland islands of New Zealand. It feeds around the coast during the breeding season, but this is followed by the annual body moult on land over summer, after which the birds disperse during autumn and winter. Most of the Australian finds have been in the winter months during this dispersal, or sometimes during January and February, when birds that do not get back to New Zealand in time to moult on land, come ashore on Australian beaches to seek refuge.

So many of the recorded finds are from the Victorian and Tasmanian coasts that it is possible the penguins may be concentrated immediately to the east of Australia, perhaps just beyond or along the edge of the continental shelf and extending eastwards to New Zealand. The birds' patterns of movement are probably determined by surface sea temperatures, the currents and the direction of food-bearing waters. The exact circuit of the migration is not known. Stragglers have reached Campbell and Auckland Islands,

the Snares Islands in the subantarctic, the far northern peninsula of the North Island of New Zealand, and even Western Australia.

The Fiordland Penguin's head adornments probably allow swimming birds to recognise individuals of their own species, the head normally being the only part of the body above the water. Facial signals are also important in courtship ceremonies and are reinforced by a waving of the black-edged undersurface of the flippers.

Fiordland Penguins breed in late winter and early spring, but if the season is extended chicks may leave as late as early December. The penguins often build their nests among roots of trees in the coastal forests, within small caves or under overhanging banks. Nests tend to be separate in rather loose groups. Conspicuous nesting colonies are known only on Big Solander and Open Bay Island. Fiordland Penguins lay two eggs, and both parents help with incubating, guarding and feeding the chicks. The birds feed on small fish and a variety of molluscs and small crustaceans.

Predators on the Fiordland Penguin are Giant Petrels, Southern Skuas, sea lions, fur seals, and perhaps sharks and killer whales. On land they might fall prey to cats, dogs, foxes and humans.

OTHER NAMES
Thick-billed Penguin, Crested Penguin.

IDENTIFICATION
LENGTH: *520–700 mm.*
ADULTS: *Sexes similar; female slightly smaller. Blue-grey to blue-black above; upper side of flippers blue-grey. Underparts satin-white; underflipper white with broad black base and tip. Tail of long, stiff, blue-black almost spiny feathers. Head and throat blue-grey to blue-black, dusky on cheeks, where there are often several conspicuous white stripes. Eyebrow stripe a white to straw-yellow crest, reaching bill and drooping far back behind ear region. Eye usually claret-*

red. *Massive bill red-orange or red-brown. Feet and webbed toes pale pink; nails and soles black.*
IMMATURES: *Similar to adults, but cheeks chocolate brown to black. Eyebrow stripe-crest of shorter feathers, paler. Chin and throat almost white.*
DOWNY YOUNG: *Dusky brown from head and throat over back; breast and belly dull white.*

VOICE
Variety of guttural to shrill gurgling calls, uttered during courtship, when fighting or as contact call when swimming in flocks.

NESTING
Breeds in late winter and early spring,

July–October, but sometimes longer. Chicks may be present till early December. Nest of debris, stones and feathers. Eggs: two; dull white with slight green tinge; ovoid, first averaging 67 x 52 mm, normally slightly smaller than second, 71 x 55 mm. Incubation by both sexes.

DISTRIBUTION
Many records from beaches in Tasmania and Victoria in recent years; also more than five from Western Australia, three from South Australia and two from New South Wales. Breeds in New Zealand. No races.

Great Crested Grebe *Podiceps cristatus* (LINNÉ, 1758)

GREAT CRESTED GREBES ARE aquatic birds, adept at diving and flying little except when migrating. With paddle-shaped toes set far back on their bodies, they sit low in the water, like the other grebes, with slender neck erect. At rest, the head is sunk on the shoulders and the bill often buried in feathers on one side. The silky, white underparts are displayed during preening as the bird rolls over on to its side.

The Great Crested Grebe, with its double-horned crest and chestnut frills about the head, has an elaborate courtship display. The most common display involves 'head-shaking' as head feathers are raised. In the 'discovery ceremony' one bird makes a far-carrying two-note call, while another bird spreads its wings and face-ruff partly. The first then approaches the other in a shallow underwater 'ripple dive', then rises up beyond it in a 'ghostly penguin' display. They shake their heads together and turn away. This is followed by a 'weed trick' and 'weed dance' with the birds diving and bringing up weeds, approaching each other, rising breast to breast nearly upright as they stretch their necks. They sway, paddle with their feet, and sink down again.

Like other grebes, the Great Crested Grebe dives for its food, staying under water for nearly a minute but usually for shorter periods. It can swim considerable distances underwater, moving both feet at once, and usually swallows its food there. Its diet includes fish, insects and larvae, crustaceans, snails, tadpoles, plant material and quantities of feathers. Fish figure prominently and these it secures by rapid pursuit.

Grebes build floating nests in sites that vary from reed-beds growing in a few feet of briny or brackish as well as fresh water by the shoreline to islands of weeds floating in deep water. The territories around the nest are strongly defended. Both sexes construct the nest out of water weeds, rushes and reeds, attached to emergent plants, and both incubate for three–four weeks. Weeds are pulled over the eggs when the incubating bird leaves the nest.

After the young hatch, they ride on the back of one parent while the other brings food for them to eat. Periodically there is a changeover. The parent carrying the brood rises up and flaps its wings; the young tumble into the water, swim to the other parent and clamber aboard using the parent's foot as a ramp.

OTHER NAMES
Crested Grebe, Tippet Grebe.

IDENTIFICATION
LENGTH: *About 500 mm.*
ADULTS: *Sexes similar. Very dark brown above, silky white below; flanks mottled with brown and dark grey. Crest on each side of crown black; cheeks and throat white. Feathers of side of head elongated into pair of tippets, or ruffs, chestnut near base and shading to black at tips. Wings have two white patches, one on secondaries and one on leading edge of forearm. Eye red. Bill brown above, carmine below. Lobed feet dark olive above, pale yellow below. Distinct non-breeding dress with shortened tippets, reduced crests and browner crowns.*
IMMATURES: *Some stripes on head remain in juvenile plumage. Flying young as adults but lack tippets and crests.*
DOWNY YOUNG: *Sooty brown above with white stripes on head, neck and back. Bare pink spot on crown turns red when young are excited.*

VOICE
Calls are thought to be similar to those of the European birds: loud, rattling, rather shrill trumpeting bark in threat; two-note advertising call row-ah; ticking note during head-shaking displays; copulation note; and begging calls by chicks.

NESTING
Usually breeds November–March. Nest a mat of water plants, often in loose colonies. Eggs: three to seven; pale green dulled with stain; oblong-oval, about 55 x 35 mm. Incubation 22-29 days, by both sexes.

DISTRIBUTION
On open sheets of water, mostly in east, but also southwestern Australia; vagrants occasionally seen inland, particularly in Lake Eyre basin and Murray–Darling drainage. One race in Australia–New Zealand. Elsewhere widespread in temperate parts of Eurasia and southern Africa.

The Great Crested Grebe nests on a raft of water plants, moored to reeds to prevent it drifting away. Both sexes incubate the eggs and feed the young, which are carried round on the back of one of the parents.

Australasian Grebe

Tachybaptus novaehollandiae
(STEPHENS, 1826)

AUSTRALASIAN GREBES usually nest among emergent water plants, where their frequent trilling may betray them. While in breeding dress their head pattern is quite distinctive, but in winter plumage they look remarkably like Hoary-headed Grebes, and may even be found together in the same flocks.

Poor, fluttering flyers, they keep to smaller, deeper stretches of fresh water with patchy rush cover in which they can hide. In territorial pairs or small groups when not breeding, they feed mostly at dawn and dusk, using a variety of deep dives and surface chases to capture their prey. Much of their food is mobile: mainly small fish and pond snails, assorted water insects and crustaceans, but little zooplankton. Like most grebes, Australasian Grebes eat their feathers and feed them to their young. Whether this plugs the stomach to prevent sharp bones entering the intestine is not clear, for the birds regurgitate all hard indigestible objects.

They are the most vocal of Australian grebes.

The Australasian Grebe builds a nest of floating water plants, usually on a small body of water.

OTHER NAMES
Little Grebe, Australian Dabchick, Red-necked Grebe, 'Diver'.

IDENTIFICATION
LENGTH: *250–270 mm.*
ADULTS: *Sexes similar; male larger and longer-billed. Sooty above; breast and flanks dappled with grey-brown; belly silky white. Head glossy black with pear-shaped patch of chestnut extending from eye backwards to side of head and neck. Oval patch of pale yellow bare skin at gape. Wing sooty with broad white band through middle remiges. Eye orange-yellow. Bill black with white tip. Feet dark green-grey. Non-breeding: head dull; throat and sides of face white; bill grey-brown.*
IMMATURES: *As adults in non-breeding plumage but have some stripes on head.*
DOWNY YOUNG: *Grey-black with patch of chestnut on crown and white stripes along sides of head, neck and back.*

VOICE
Rattling trill, sometimes as a duet. Single sharp note also reported.

NESTING
Breeds mostly September–March, rearing two–three broods a season. Nest of floating plant material, usually on a small body of water; solitary. Eggs: four to seven; chalky pale blue stained brown; ellipsoidal, about 35 x 25 mm. Incubation 21 days, by both sexes.

DISTRIBUTION
In sheltered ponds of fresh water throughout Australia. Also islands in southwestern Pacific, including New Hebrides, New Caledonia, Java, Timor and New Guinea. A few breed in New Zealand. Six or seven races; one large and rather pallid in Australia.

Hoary-headed Grebe

Poliocephalus poliocephalus (JARDINE & SELBY, 1827)

OTHER NAMES
None.

IDENTIFICATION
LENGTH: *270–300 mm.*
ADULTS: *Sexes similar; male somewhat larger and longer-billed. Mid-grey above, white below; neck and upper breast pale buff. Crown and throat black with overlying narrow white plumes on grey face. Wing grey-brown with broad white band through middle remiges. Eye golden yellow (male) or ivory (female) finely speckled with black. Bill black with pale tip. Feet and toes dull olive. In non-breeding season, top of head plain dark grey; throat and sides of head white; bill largely pale.*
IMMATURES: *Crown marked with black, buff and white; black spots and lines on sides of head. Eye brown.*
DOWNY YOUNG: *Not described.*

VOICE
Usually silent, but occasional soft guttural notes in flocks and copulation.

NESTING
Breeds November–January or after rains; one brood per season. Nest floating, of algae and other water plants; sometimes in groups of up to 400 nests, 1 m or so apart. Eggs: five to six; chalky pale blue becoming stained with brown; ellipsoidal, about 40 x 28 mm. Incubation by both sexes.

DISTRIBUTION
Sheets of open fresh or saline water throughout Australia; most numerous in southeast and southwest. Formerly endemic but now established in New Zealand. No races.

The Hoary-headed Grebe takes its name from its breeding head plumes.

THE HOARY-HEADED GREBE, like other small grebes, often sunbathes keeping its tail towards the sun, with feathers spread to allow the sun's rays to heat the black skin of the bird's back. The more heat received from the sun, the less needs to be generated metabolically from food.

Hoary-headed Grebes frequent open, unsheltered sheets of fresh or saline water. Adapted to the ephemeral nature of such waters inland, they are highly nomadic and often fly long distances at night despite their weak wings. They are also the most communal of all grebes, nesting in groups, clustering on open water, and clumping in loose rafts to roost. Like other grebes they dive for their prey, but in a stereotyped way that limits them to searching and gleaning for mainly stationary food — various aquatic insects, zooplankton and occasional crustaceans. Pairing is impermanent and courtship simple, involving ceremonies both in the water and on the nesting platform where copulation takes place.

Red-tailed Tropicbird *Phaethon rubricauda* BODDAERT, 1783

THIS BEAUTIFUL WANDERER of the Indo-Pacific tropical and subtropical seas feeds on squid and fish. As it searches for them, alone or in pairs, it flies with fluttering wing-beats which alternate with soaring glides. It swoops and dives on to its prey from heights up to 14 metres and often submerges for about 25 seconds. Most of its food, however, it snaps from the surface of the water, rough serrations on its bill holding prey fast.

Adult tropicbirds mate for life and return to traditional nest sites to breed every 12 months or so. Shaded sites on the edge of cliffs keep the brooding bird cool—for tropicbirds cannot cool themselves by throat-fluttering—and allow the birds to come and go easily; to depart, they just fall off into the air. Weak, fully webbed feet make tropicbirds almost helpless on land. A bird relieving its mate at the nest calls on approach, hovers overhead, then lands and greets its partner with the most perfunctory of bill-touching. Nest sites are held against competitors by fighting alone. The combatants eye one another off, then grapple with their bills, spreading wings and feet for balance and purchase. Daily aerial displays by courting birds are spectacular. Call-

ing pairs or groups of pairs circle the nesting area. One, followed by its mate, swoops up, then back-pedals on rapidly beating wings before fluttering on. Their tail-streamers undulate down and up, and their feet are spread on either side. Such flights may continue even after egg-laying. Mating takes place back in the nest.

Mated birds share incubation in daily shifts, often changing about midday. Chicks, which hatch covered with down, are brooded continuously in their first few days, but after a week or so, both parents return only briefly to feed them once a day. Responding to the chick's persistent shrill rattling, the feeding parent approaches and is lunged at by the chick. The adult inserts its beak into the chick's and, turning its head sideways, regurgitates partly digested fish into the chick's throat—the reverse of feeding techniques in boobies, cormorants and allies.

The young bird is fully feathered by 40 days, and heavier than adults, but it does not fledge for another four–five weeks. Departure is abrupt: the fledgling just flops off the nest into the sea or air and flaps off, never to return or be attended by its parents again.

OTHER NAMES
Red-tailed Bos'n-bird, Silver Bosun-bird.

IDENTIFICATION
LENGTH: *460–470 mm, excluding 300–530 mm tail-streamers.*
ADULTS: *Sexes similar. General plumage white with black stripes through eye, on innermost flight feathers, and on flanks. Rosy sheen of varying intensity on body plumage. Two long, red central tail feathers with black shafts. Eye dark brown. Bill red with black line along nostrils. Feet pale blue; webs and toes black.*
IMMATURES: *As adults but black bars on upper parts and no streamers.*
DOWNY YOUNG: *Silky grey-fawn from hatching; bill and feet black.*

VOICE
Main call a ratchet-like pirr-igh *in courtship flight. Loud defensive screaming at nest.*

NESTING
Around Australia breeds mainly over summer in subtropics and over winter in tropics. Solitary or in loose groups, each nest 20–30 m apart. Nest a scrape in the ground, in shade of a bush, or under rocky overhang on side of cliff. Some nests are inside caves. Eggs: usually one, sometimes two; colour variable—dark spots on light grey-brown or white base; long-oval, size varies, about 64 x 45 mm in northwestern Australia and 68 x 47 mm in Tasman Sea. Incubation 42–50 days, by both sexes. Young fledge in four–five weeks.

DISTRIBUTION
Tropical and subtropical waters of Indian and western Pacific Oceans. More common along northern than southern shores of Australia. Nests on cliffs and islands off western, northern and northeastern shores. Four subspecies, two in Australia: one smaller and whiter off west coast and the other rose-tinted and larger off east.

The Red-tailed Tropicbird, whose tail-streamers are prized as ornaments by South Pacific islanders, performs spectacular aerial displays during courtship. They are almost helpless on land.

White-tailed Tropicbird *Phaethon lepturus* DAUDIN, 1802

White-tailed Tropicbirds gather no nest material and lay an egg in a sheltered position such as this space between two rocks.

SMALLEST OF THE TROPICBIRDS, the White-tailed is much more agile in flight than its red-tailed relation, and its tail-streamers are more pliable. It plunge-dives for fish and squid on the open tropical and subtropical seas like the Red-tailed but, perhaps because of its smaller bulk, it rarely takes prey much below the surface of the water. Air cells under the skin of the fore-body cushion the impact of the dives.

On their breeding islands — all outside Australia — White-tailed Tropicbirds nest about every nine–ten months. As a result of this cycle, some birds can be found breeding in every month. They fight for nest sites, struggling in silence with interlocked bills, and court in brilliant aerial displays. Small tight groups of up to ten circle and weave above their breeding grounds, uttering a repetitive rattling, and drooping and undulating their tails. Often pairs break off, go into glides and zigzag about, one bird above the other, the top bird's wings swept down to the raised wings of the bird below. Then they swoop back to their nests to copulate.

Nest sites may be concealed in rocky holes, crevices, scrapes under overhangs, or, on Christmas Island, even a tree fork or tree hollow. No attempt is made to line it. The parents brood their single downy chick for only a few days but return daily to feed it for a couple of months before it is ready to fledge. When left alone by day, it may be killed by other adults seeking a nest hole.

Upon fledging, after 10–15 weeks, young birds fly straight out to sea unaided, where they wander around the tropics, returning only when they are ready to breed.

White-tailed Tropicbirds are nomadic and probably visit Australia, particularly the northeastern coast, regularly. Most of the White-taileds seen off the western and eastern coasts have been juveniles — identifiable by black bars on upper parts and lack of tail-streamers — and were probably blown there by cyclones.

OTHER NAMES
Golden Bosun-bird, Yellow-billed Tropicbird.

IDENTIFICATION
LENGTH: *About 400 mm, excluding 300 mm tail-streamers.*
ADULTS: *Sexes similar. Body generally white with black crescentic stripe through eye. Black line from upper wing to inner secondaries and scapulars, and on outer flight feathers. Two long white or yellow central tail feathers with black shafts. Thighs streaked black. Some birds seen off northwestern Australia have golden-yellow sheen on body plumage. Eye dark brown. Bill greenish yellow to orange. Feet and soles white tinged with blue; toes, including webs, black.*
IMMATURES: *As adults but thin black bars on upper parts; no tail-streamers.*
DOWNY YOUNG: *Silky grey-fawn from hatching; bill and feet black.*

VOICE
Rattling t-t-t-t *and* tick *calls in courtship flight. Loud, defensive screaming at nest.*

NESTING
Breeds throughout year. Nest in tree fork or hollow; a scrape in hole or crevice in rock face, sometimes tree fork or hollow on Indo-Pacific islands; no nesting material gathered. Egg: one; white, with many dark purple-brown spots; rounded- or oblong-oval, about 50 x 36 mm. Incubation about 41 days, by both sexes. Young fledge in 10–15 weeks.

DISTRIBUTION
Tropical and subtropical seas around the world. Visits waters off northwestern and northeastern Australia but does not breed in region; occasionally blown inshore in southeast by storms. Five races; three in Australia: one white from Cocos–Keeling Islands and another golden-toned from Christmas Island wanders to northwest coast; a third, white race wanders to northeast coast from its breeding grounds in central Pacific between Micronesia, New Caledonia, Polynesia and the Hawaiian islands.

Soaring magnificently on huge broad wings, a male Great Frigatebird displays its throat pouch, which is inflated during courtship.

Great Frigatebird *Fregata minor* (GMELIN, 1789)

WHOLLY ADAPTED TO LIVING in the air, the Great Frigatebird neither walks nor swims, except by accident. Its short legs are useful only for perching and its toes are not fully webbed. It takes off simply by raising its huge wings, and in flight its body hangs low like a gondola beneath the main plane of the wings. It can outmanoeuvre almost any other bird. Its long forked tail and broad, curving wings enable it to hover, soar, twist and glide with apparent ease in heat thermals and updrafts along cliffs and forest edges. Sometimes small groups hang-glide there for hours at a time, several hundred metres up.

Frigatebirds drink while skimming low over fresh or salt water, and are attracted to pools of rainwater in cleared areas. When sunbathing on land, they twist their outstretched wings upside down, airing their flanks. Frigatebirds feed at sea on flying fish, squid and other prey, which they pick up from the surface without landing; flying fish, caught and killed in the frigatebird's long, hooked bills, are often taken in midair as they break to the surface from underwater predators. Tuna are pre-eminent among such predators, and frigatebirds follow hunting shoals of these fish. The birds avoid landing in the water, however, where their plumage, poorly oiled from a small preen gland, becomes quickly waterlogged.

Frigatebirds are piratical by nature, and they snatch food and nesting material from other seabirds, mainly terns and boobies. It is a habit helped by their nesting among colonies of their victims. In a spectacular swoop, a frigatebird will dive on a booby or tern flying back to its rookery heavy with food. The incomer disgorges its meal which is promptly caught in midair by the harasser. Frigatebirds also steal eggs and unprotected chicks, eat carrion, and patrol beaches for hatchling turtles.

Great Frigatebirds nest about once every two years because their young spend so long gaining their independence. Pairing is impermanent. Males take up their nest sites in clusters, spread and turn their wings upwards on it, and inflate a small throat pouch of bare skin into a huge red balloon. When a female flies over, they try to attract her with violent shivering and rattling of bills and quills. Intermittent head waving and billing completes the ceremony.

Both parents accumulate material for the nest, incubate in erratic shifts and brood their naked hatchling in its first weeks until it is covered with protective down. Although young are fully feathered and fledge in four–five months, they mature slowly and remain dependent on their parents for another two–six months until they gain sufficient skills in hunting to fend for themselves.

Rather sedentary, most Great Frigatebirds spend their lives in the region of their nesting islands. Because of this, young frigatebirds are hand-reared on some Pacific islands and trained to return to perches to be fed. Such tame birds have been used to carry messages between islands.

OTHER NAMES
Greater Frigatebird, Man-o'-War Bird, Sea Hawk.

IDENTIFICATION
LENGTH: *860–980 mm; female larger.*
MALE: *General plumage uniformly black; light brown bar on shoulder. Naked throat red. Eye brown with black eye-ring. Bill black. Feet black or red-brown.*
FEMALE: *General plumage black; breast white, grading to grey on throat. Eye brown with red eye-ring; naked throat blue. Bill blue-grey. Feet pink to white.*
IMMATURES: *General plumage dark brown with light brown shoulder bars. Head and underparts mainly white with varying amounts of rufous, yellow and brown.*
DOWNY YOUNG: *First naked, then grey-white downed; bill and feet grey-white.*

VOICE
Male on nest warbles wah-ho-ho-ho-ho *and clappers a snore-like* torrrr. *When landing at nest male makes a repetitive yelp* tjew-tjew-tjew, *with individual variations.*

NESTING
Breeds January–October. Nest a substantial platform of sticks and vines, on branches of trees and bushes. Egg: one, glossy white; ellipsoidal, about 68 x 48 mm. Incubation about 50 days, by both sexes. Young fledge in four–five months.

DISTRIBUTION
In most tropical seas of the world, including seas off northeastern and northwestern Australia. Near Australia breeds only at northern end of Great Barrier Reef and in Coral Sea. Five races; two in Australia: one in northwestern seas; the other breeding northeast in Coral Sea.

Least Frigatebird *Fregata ariel* (GRAY, 1845)

LIKE THE GREAT FRIGATEBIRD, the Least Frigatebird is a superb aerial performer, but cannot walk or swim. It has the same piratical habit of harassing other sea birds and forcing them to disgorge food. Least Frigatebirds also take young turtles and crabs from beaches and squid from the surface of the sea, catching them by dipping with their hooked bills.

The Least Frigatebird lives on most of the tropical seas of the world and it is the frigatebird most commonly seen along the northern shores of Australia. It breeds on many islands nearby, and apparently disperses widely from there.

The birds have been dubbed 'rain brothers' by the Aborigines of Western Australia, for they have often heralded the approach of a storm by coming ashore to rest on mangroves with wings outspread over the leaves, disappearing again as soon as the storm has abated. On bright days, the birds sun their spread wings by turning them upside down — perhaps both to cool themselves and to get rid of the small parasites among their feathers.

Like other frigatebirds, the Least mates for the season and nests in colonies among other sea birds. Its males, wearing a ballooning red throat pouch, court in the manner of the Great Frigatebird. Often they fly circling the nest colony in display, their pouches inflated. Chicks are naked at hatching and are brooded by both parents in shifts for a week or two before growing down. The chick prostrates itself to beg for food from its parents. It stretches out its wings, cocks its tail, and makes sharp calls, wagging its head up and down behind lowered shoulders. Young birds defend their perches by pecking and gaping at a rival and also by calling sharply.

Bonds between parents often begin to weaken at this time, even though the young bird remains dependent for up to a year. As a result, few adults nest more than once every two years. Young birds themselves are not ready to breed until at least five years old. Rearing only one young at a time as well, frigatebirds have a low rate of productivity and recruitment, in keeping with their position as predators at the top of the food chain in tropical seas.

Male Least Frigatebirds can be identified from male Great Frigatebirds not so much by their smaller size as by their white flanks (armpits). Females have a black, not grey-white throat. Rusty-headed immatures cannot be picked other than by size.

OTHER NAMES
Lesser Frigatebird.

IDENTIFICATION
LENGTH: *700–800 mm; female larger.*
MALE: *General plumage uniformly black with white line or patch under base of wing on side of belly. Throat red, naked. Eye brown with black eyering. Bill black or dark grey. Feet black or brown.*
FEMALE: *General plumage black with grey-brown shoulder bars; breast and sides of belly white. Throat black. Eye brown with red eye-ring. Bill grey-pink. Feet pink-red.*
IMMATURES: *Upper parts dark brown with light brown shoulder bars; head and underparts mainly white with various amounts of rufous, yellow and brown. Eye brown. Bill and feet tinged blue.*
DOWNY YOUNG: *Naked, becoming white-downed; bill and feet whitish.*

VOICE
Male on nest grunts and rattles its bill. Both sexes cackle in greeting. Sharp drawn-out kikikik *from supplicant nestlings.*

NESTING
Breeds most months, peaking spring and autumn. Nest of sticks, grass and debris, in trees, on bushes and occasionally on the ground. Egg: one; limy white; ellipsoidal, about 64 x 44 mm. Incubation about 41 days, by both sexes in irregular shifts.

DISTRIBUTION
Occurs in most tropical seas except eastern Pacific. Breeds on many offshore islands in northern Australia. Three races; one in Australian seas.

A female Least Frigatebird with its chick. This member of the frigatebird family breeds on many islands off the northern coasts of Australia.

Large webbed feet propel the Black-faced Shag underwater.

OTHER NAMES
White-breasted Cormorant, Black-faced Cormorant.

IDENTIFICATION
LENGTH: *600–700 mm.*
ADULTS: *Sexes similar; male larger. Upper parts black. White below eye, on side of head and on underparts. Thighs black. Eye blue-green. Naked face, chin and bill black. Feet black. At start of breeding, dense cover of white nuptial plumes on back of neck, rump and thighs.*
IMMATURES: *General plumage dusky above and white below, patched brown. Naked face pale buff, naked chin pink. Eye brown. Feet brown.*
DOWNY YOUNG: *Grey mottled with white below; bill and feet grey; gular pouch flesh-yellow.*

VOICE
During courting male's voice loud and guttural; female's a soft, hoarse hissing. Males gargle to advertise.

NESTING
Breeds in colonies mainly September–January, also at other times of year. Nest a large mounded cup, 500 mm diameter of seaweed, other plants and debris; on the ground, usually on bare rock, also on man-made platforms at sea. Eggs: up to five, usually three; limy green; oval, about 57 x 36 mm. Incubation by both sexes.

DISTRIBUTION
Coasts of Tasmania and southern mainland, north to Fremantle in west and Montague Island in east. Common in Spencer Gulf, SA. Rather sedentary. No races.

Black-faced Shag

Leucocarbo fuscescens (VIEILLOT, 1817)

AUSTRALIA'S ONLY exclusively marine cormorant is the Black-faced Shag. Today it is restricted to southern coastal seas, never penetrating further inland than saline estuaries, inlets and the South Australian gulfs where it often hunts shoals of fish in flocks of thousands. A million or two years ago, however, it was more widespread, extending into the then Lake Eyre sea—according to fossil evidence. The rocky coastal islets that it now uses for roosting and nesting seldom have any fresh water. In keeping with its habits it has a larger nasal salt gland than any of the cormorants, enabling it to excrete excess salt from its body.

Like other cormorants, it leap-dives from the surface of the water in underwater pursuit of its prey—fish and squid. Few of the fish are important commercially. Each dive lasts from about 20 to 40 seconds, the birds darting along propelled by their fully webbed feet kicking together behind. Stiff tails of hard, spiky feathers assist the slightly opened wings in balance underwater. Prey is grasped and held in the slender, hooked bill, then carried back to the surface.

Shags and cormorants have permeable plumage which lowers their buoyancy underwater. Black-faced Shags may add to ballast in salt water by swallowing small pebbles. This may contribute to their laboured flight as well. Although flying in the direct flap and glide manner of other cormorants, they do so much more heavily, rarely rising much above wave tops, flapping almost continuously, and becoming airborne only after much effort with both feet kicking together many times in take-off. From time to time, however, they rise and hover at 20 metres or more.

At their nesting islands, Black-faced Shags breed on the ground in large colonies, and build their nests not out of twigs but of seaweed and leafy material. Other breeding habits are much as in all cormorants; males advertising themselves and their nest site for a mate, however, throw back their heads, gargle, and wave their wings rapidly at four or so beats a second.

The young hatch black and naked. As they mature they leave the nest and form crèches but are still fed by both parents. To beg they spread their wings, bend up the tail and distend their coloured gular pouches. Parents bend over and open their mouths, into which the young birds plunge their heads for food.

Black-faced Shags can be identified from other Australian pied cormorants by dark bills and face skin, giving a masked appearance.

Black-faced Shags breed in their thousands at Dangerous Reef, Spencer Gulf, SA. They make their nests of seaweed, grass, plant matter and debris.

Pied Cormorant

Phalacrocorax varius
(GMELIN, 1789)

OTHER NAMES
Black-and-White Shag, Yellow-faced Cormorant.

IDENTIFICATION
LENGTH: *660–840 mm.*
ADULTS: *Sexes similar; male larger. General plumage black above and white below; black-and-white border starts above eye. Outer part of thighs black. Conspicuous bare orange-yellow face patch on lores; chin skin bare, pale flesh, becoming purplish pink in breeding birds. Eye green with blue eye-ring. Bill dark grey. Feet black.*
IMMATURES: *General plumage dusky brown above and white below; irregular brown patches on underparts.*
DOWNY YOUNG: *First naked, later black-downed above, white below.*

VOICE
At nest male makes several loud greeting calls: such as rick-tick-tick-tick when landing; t-t-t-t before leaving nest and quog-wog-wog-wog on the nest.

NESTING
Breeds in colonies at any time, depending on food supply. Nest of sticks and debris in a tree, a mangrove, on a bush or man-made platforms at sea. Eggs: usually three; limy white with green tinge; oval, about 60 x 38 mm. Incubation about 30 days, by both sexes. Young fledge in about 50 days.

DISTRIBUTION
Circum-continental Australia, on coastal and subcoastal waters and larger river systems. One race in Australia.

The Pied Cormorant has a conspicuous orange-yellow face patch in front of its eye.

ALTHOUGH AT HOME IN BOTH fresh and salt water, the Pied Cormorant is more a bird of open coastal and subcoastal inlets and lakes than inland rivers. Off their coastal colonies they often congregate in thousands on shoals of fish, but inland they are more solitary. Adult males seem attached to their colonies, and even though females and young of the year are more dispersive, Pieds are the least nomadic of Australian cormorants.

Like all cormorants, they capture their food—fish augmented with crustaceans and molluscs—by underwater pursuit. The birds leap-dive headfirst from the top of the water and propel themselves swiftly underneath, their fully webbed feet pushing in unison. If wings are used, it is for braking and turning. Prey are grasped in the hooked bill and carried back to the surface for despatch. To protect their eyes and adjust focusing underwater, cormorants—and Darters—have a thick transparent nictitating membrane and a special muscle to squeeze the eye's lens convex in an instant. Nostrils are sealed and the birds breathe through valves at the corner of the mouth like gannets.

Out of the water, Pied Cormorants spend much time on perches

—dead trees, boats and poles—hanging out their wings to dry and oiling their permeable plumage from two large preen glands. They fly strongly and in a straight line, their regular flapping wing-beats punctuated with brief glides; groups will fly in V-formation like other water birds.

At their breeding grounds, males choose the nesting site and advertise by silently wing-waving for several seconds at a time. They throw back the head, point the bill skywards, spread and cock the tail, and flutter their part-opened wings at two flaps a second. If a female approaches, they drop the wings and give vent to a guttural scream. After pairing, the male gathers nest material while the female builds it into a platform. They cement their bonds by passing nest material between one another, bill fencing, intertwining their necks, and mutual preening. To the male's *wog-wog-wog* notes of greeting, the female hisses inaudibly. Both parents brood in shifts and both feed the young.

In early colonial times and during both world wars, guano—excreta—deposited by the dense colonies of Pied Cormorants at Shark Bay, WA, was mined for the fertiliser industry.

Great Cormorant

Phalacrocorax carbo (LINNÉ, 1758)

LARGEST OF AUSTRALIAN CORMORANTS, the Great Cormorant eats a wide variety of fish, also crustaceans and insects. These it takes in underwater dives in large inland lakes and rivers, and in bays and estuaries on the coast. It swims submerged for periods of up to half a minute or more, kicking along with both feet together; on the surface it swims with alternating leg strokes.

When nesting, males advertise themselves and their nest sites with a wing-waving display of less than two flaps per second that exposes their white flank patches. The yellow throat pouch is vibrated to help to cool the bird. Birds on nest guard lower their crests. Birds near nests raise their crests, except when alarmed. Both sexes contribute to nest building and share incubation.

OTHER NAMES
Black Cormorant, Black Shag.

IDENTIFICATION
LENGTH: *700–900 mm.*
ADULTS: *Sexes similar; male larger. General plumage black, with white or grey throat feathers. At start of breeding, dense patches of white nuptial plumes on sides of rump and upper neck; prominent erectile median crest on back of head. Yellow bare skin on face and throat. Eye green. Bill grey, buff at base. Feet black.*
IMMATURES: *General plumage sooty with irregular white flecks on underparts. Eye green; brown in juveniles.*

VOICE
During courting at nest, male loud and raucous; female has soft, hoarse hiss, but voice becomes male-like after egg-laying.

NESTING
Breeds in colonies throughout year, peaking autumn and spring. Nest of sticks and debris, in a tree, on a bush or on the ground; Eggs: four, sometimes five or three; chalky blue; oval, about 60 x 36 mm. Incubation about 28 days, by both sexes. Young fledge in about seven weeks.*

DISTRIBUTION
Mainly fresh, less frequently marine waters of eastern and coastal western Australia; rare in north. Six races; one in Australia dispersing irregularly to New Zealand, New Guinea, Indonesia and Macquarie Island.

The Great Cormorant is more common inland than on the coast.

A Little Black Cormorant (left) and a Little Pied Cormorant.

Little Black Cormorant

Phalacrocorax sulcirostris (BRANDT, 1837)

LITTLE BLACK CORMORANTS frequent inland lakes and rivers, as well as coastal estuaries and quiet marine inlets, often in company with Great and Little Pied Cormorants.

With its longer, thinner bill, the Little Black Cormorant takes a wider range of prey than the Little Pied, and commonly congregates communally on larger, deeper stretches of water. Co-operative rafts of hundreds will gather to herd shoals of fish, birds at the back leap-frogging those in the front and diving to swim fast underwater with their feet behind the body.

Out of the water, Little Black Cormorants sit about in flocks on banks or perch on dead trees, boats and cables to dry; they fly — with alternating flapping and gliding—often in line formation.

OTHER NAMES
None.

IDENTIFICATION
LENGTH: *About 610 mm.*
ADULTS: *Sexes similar; female smaller. General plumage black. At start of breeding, slight concentrations of white nuptial plumage on side of head. Bill grey-black. Feet black.*
IMMATURES: *General plumage dusky with some irregular white spots on underparts. Eye brown.*

VOICE
At nest female silent; male makes ticking sounds. Both creak kraa-kraa-kraa in nest relief.

NESTING
Breeds mainly spring–autumn, depending on food supply. Nest a platform of sticks and debris, in a tree, on a bush; often in same tree as Little Pied Cormorants and Darters. Eggs: up to six, usually four; chalky green; oval, about 48 x 32 mm. Incubation three–four weeks, by both sexes.*

DISTRIBUTION
More common on inland waters throughout Australia than on marine waters. Also in Java and Borneo, New Guinea, New Zealand.

Little Pied Cormorant

Phalacrocorax melanoleucos (VIEILLOT, 1817)

OTHER NAMES
Frilled Shag, Little Black-and-white Cormorant, Little Black-and-white Shag.

IDENTIFICATION
LENGTH: *610 mm.*
ADULTS: *Sexes similar. General plumage black above and white below, with white line extending over eye to bill. Thighs white. Eye ring and chin naked and dull yellow. Eye brown. Bill mostly dull yellow with dusky maxilla. Feet black. In breeding plumage a black tuft on forehead, and white frills on sides of black crown; bill and chin orange.*
IMMATURES: *Black feathers on thighs and above eyes. Irregular brown patches in plumage. Bill dusky, yellow at base.*
DOWNY YOUNG: *Naked, becoming black-downed with bare orange head; eye and bill black, grading to flesh-grey face; feet grey-black.*

VOICE
Males coo-oo when greeting prospective mates. Guttural uk-uk-uk by both sexes during nest relief, softer uk-uk-uk in greeting chicks. Croaks in alarm. Chicks croak continuously.

NESTING
Breeds in colonies, in spring and summer in south; autumn inland; late summer to winter in north. Nest a platform of sticks and debris, in trees, on bushes or on the ground. Eggs: usually three to five; pale blue or pale green, with limy coating; oval, about 46 x 31 mm. Incubation by both sexes.

DISTRIBUTION
On marine or fresh water throughout Australia. Also in eastern Indonesia, New Guinea, New Zealand, and on several southwest Pacific islands. Three races; one in Australia.

The extremely common Little Pied Cormorant on guard at its nest of sticks and debris.

ALMOST ANY BODY OF WATER in Australia, large or small, marine or fresh, is likely to be frequented by Little Pied Cormorants. Where food is plentiful, the birds form large flocks composed of hundreds of birds and often mix with Little Black Cormorants.

Little Pied Cormorants, with their blunt, hooked bills, prey more on crustaceans than other cormorants. Yabbies, in particular, are selected in inland waters, their claws shaken off before being swallowed. More fish are taken in marine waters where the birds' nasal salt glands enlarge to excrete any excess salt consumed.

Although Little Pied Cormorants chase fish deep underwater, their methods are best suited to taking more sedentary prey in shallow waters. They swim with feet kicking in unison out at the sides of the body. On the surface, the birds paddle with alternate leg strokes, and can flush straight up from the water.

After fishing, the cormorants rest on bare branches, stumps and banks around feeding pools, shaking water off, preening, and standing still with wings spread, sunning.

The birds accept a wider range of breeding sites—flooded timber and trees lining rivers, lakes and ephemeral swamps—than Little Black Cormorants. When courting, the male cormorant advertises for a mate by calling from a suitable nest site. Instead of wing-fluttering like other cormorants, he simply crouches or bows slowly up and down with wings and tail raised. A prospective mate is greeted by a deep bow, the male swinging his head right down, underside up, towards his feet, bill open and crest raised, coo-ing as he moves. After he has been chosen by a female, he gathers sticks and debris, which she builds into a platform nest. Both parents take turns at incubating; they warm the oval eggs with their webbed feet. When relieving one another, both stand erect on the nest and grunt, mouths open, crests raised, and heads swaying.

For the two or three days after the chicks have hatched they are brooded and fed on a liquid from the tip of the adult's lower mandible. When they are older, they put their heads inside the parent's mouth for bits of predigested food.

Darter *Anhinga melanogaster* PENNANT, 1769

WITH ITS BODY SUBMERGED and only its head and neck above the surface, the Darter resembles a snake rising from the water — hence one of its popular names, Snake-bird. It sinks to hunt its prey — small fish, insects and other small aquatic animals — underwater. Not always chasing it, the bird often stalks quarry or waits for it to come close. As it approaches, the bird holds back its S-shaped neck, then suddenly strikes, spearing the victim on its dagger-like bill. Special articulation of the cervical vertebrae similar to that in herons, enables the strike, and reversed serrations on the bill prevent the quarry from escaping.

Darters frequent smooth fresh or salty riverine waters and lakes inland from the coast for their feeding, submerging for up to a minute at a time and surfacing for a few seconds between each dive. Tiny prey such as insects are swallowed during swimming but a fish or small tortoise is carried back to the surface and moved about until it can be swallowed head first. Large items requiring up to 20 minutes of manipulation may be taken to a perch.

With eyes open or closed, Darters rest on branches, logs, islets or the nest, head pointed forward and neck in a sharp S. There they preen, scratch their heads and necks with foot raised under the wing and, like cormorants, hang out their wings to dry. Unlike most water birds, the plumage of Darters and cormorants is not waterproof; rather, its permeability is needed to lower the buoyancy of these underwater hunters. Out of the water, the birds remove water by squeezing the feathers through the bill and repel water with oil from their enlarged preen glands at the base of the tail. Much time and care is spent on this.

After a leaping takeoff, Darters fly well. Like cormorants, they alternate series of quick flaps with glides in a straight line, but they soar much more, often planing up in spirals with ibises or pelicans on thermal air currents. Their silhouette, with large, fan-shaped tail, is characteristic.

At the onset of nesting, males select a nest site, defend an area around it, decorate it with leafy twigs, and wave their wings alternately to attract females flying by. Nests tend to be solitary, and when gathered into small loose colonies of half a dozen or so, they are very well-spaced. Courtship, pairing, copulation and nest relief involves a variety of displays, male and female wing-waving, wing-flicking, rubbing necks and bills, and gaping. Then the male goes off to collect most of the twigs for the nest, from up to several hundred metres away. Both sexes defend their site, the sitting bird pointing with opening, shutting and sometimes hissing bill, and the other hopping about and snapping at the intruder.

The first egg is laid two or three days after pairing, and the rest at two- or three-day intervals. Incubation begins with the first egg, so the eggs hatch in the order of laying. Both sexes incubate and are relieved after regular shifts. At changeover, the arriving bird calls *kah* several times from nearby and the sitter replies. Then there is a brief greeting ceremony, and as the sitting bird stands, its mate pushes it aside to hop on to the nest. Both parents brood and shade the chicks, and feed them by regurgitation six–nine times a day. When begging, older chicks touch the bill of the adult, then take the food out of its throat. Disturbed chicks may regurgitate their meal and, if old enough, scramble over the rim of the nest and drop into the water. After an underwater swim they surface and scramble back to the nest or a nearby tree.

Darters are closely related to cormorants; they differ from them in that they have an S-shaped neck, and males and females have different plumages. Cormorants have a larger head and a strong hook at the tip of their upper mandible.

OTHER NAMES
Snake-bird, Diver.

IDENTIFICATION
LENGTH: *850–900 mm.*
MALE: *Almost entirely glossy black. Head marked with white stripes below eye extending along side of neck and fringing chin. Naked skin around eye and on chin yellow; front of neck black with rusty-brown patch decreasing with age. Grey-buff streaks on upper wing coverts. Eye brown, orange or yellow. Bill brown above, yellow below. Feet and webs cream to grey-brown.*
FEMALE: *Generally grey-brown above; white or pale buff below; stripe on side of head has dark edges. Upper wing coverts striped pale grey, forming a patch. During courtship upper mandible and tip of lower become light green in both sexes and feet become cream-white.*
IMMATURES: *Similar to female but stripe on head less distinct. Wing coverts shorter and less clearly marked. Naked skin around eye and on throat pale yellow to orange. Legs and feet pink, grey, light brown or dark brown.*
DOWNY YOUNG: *Naked but covered with pale buff down within several days; eye-ring white; eye black; bill pink, black inside; feet white.*

VOICE
Clicking sounds away from nesting area. During nesting harsh rolling kah *repeated up to 15 times, decreasing in volume after a few calls, more rapid and harsh in male than female; explosive pre-mating* khaah *by male and* tjeeu *by female;* krrr kururah *in or near nesting tree as well*

as hissing sound emitted by adults and immatures perhaps as threat.

NESTING
Breeds mainly spring and summer but breeding birds may be found every month. Nest a rough platform of coarse twigs, with droopy, leafy branches hanging from sides, lined with a few leaves, placed in tree above water. Nests may be used for several years. Eggs: usually four, sometimes five or six; chalky white tinged with green; oblong-oval to pyriform, 53–64 x 35–43 mm. Incubation 26–30 days, by both sexes. Young fledge in about 50 days.

DISTRIBUTION
Frequents lakes, rivers, swamps and sheltered coastal estuaries of mainland Australia. Also in New Guinea, Indonesia, India, Middle East, Madagascar and Africa south of Sahara. Three races; one in Australasia, distinguished by white-breasted females.

The Darter's plumage is not waterproof so here a male spreads its wings to dry them in the sun. This also helps to control skin parasites.

Red-footed Booby

Sula sula (LINNÉ, 1766)

THE PLUMAGE OF THIS smallest of boobies can be white or brown or a mixture of both, and this has led to problems in identification. Its red or pink legs, however, are a reliable guide, and so is its sleek, long-tailed body.

The Red-footed Booby is unusual in that it feeds both by day and by night—on squid, crustaceans and fish, including flying fish which it often catches in flight. Like other boobies, it plummets down in slanting dives on to its prey, but takes most from on or near the surface of the sea without plunging deeply in.

Red-footeds nest in large colonies in trees, often in company with frigatebirds which parasitise them. They display in trees, males advertising themselves and greeting females with nodding heads and raised tails and wings; and they copulate there, the males calling.

Males gather most nesting material while females weave it in. Both incubate the single egg in turns like all boobies, by covering it with their webbed feet. Over the hot tropical midday, they also stand beside the egg, shading it.

The Red-footed Booby nests on islands of the Great Barrier Reef and the Coral Sea.

OTHER NAMES
Red-footed Gannet, Red-legged Gannet.

IDENTIFICATION
LENGTH: *710–790 mm.*
ADULTS: *Sexes similar. Several colour forms. White birds have yellow sheen on head and neck; black primaries and secondaries; white tail; white underparts. Eye-ring blue; eye brown. Bill pale blue with brown tip and red or pink base rimmed with black. Feet red. Brown birds have all grey-brown* plumage. *Intermediates are brown on head and neck and white behind.*
JUVENILES: *Dull grey-brown, darker above than below; dark breast band. Face green-blue. Eye green-grey. Bill black. Feet grey-pink.*
IMMATURES: *Mottled white on brown with dark brown wing and tail feathers. Bill brown. Feet brick-red.*
DOWNY YOUNG: *White; bill black.*

VOICE
Harsh, repetitive karr-uck *at nest, by both sexes.*

NESTING
Breeds April–October. Nest of sticks and vines in tree or bush; in loose colonies. Egg: one; chalky white; oval, about 61 x 41 mm. Incubation about 45 days, by both sexes.

DISTRIBUTION
Throughout tropical seas. In Australia, breeds on northern islands of Great Barrier Reef and in Coral Sea, and islands off northwestern Australia. Three races; one in Indian–western Pacific Ocean.

Brown Booby

Sula leucogaster

(BODDAERT, 1783)

OTHER NAMES
None.

IDENTIFICATION
LENGTH: *750–800 mm.*
MALE: *Plumage dark brown except for white belly, underwing and undertail coverts. Eye white or grey. Naked face; eye-ring, base of bill and chin blue; rest of bill grey-cream. Feet, webs green-yellow.*
FEMALE: *Plumage as male. Face skin, eye-ring, base of bill and chin yellow-green; blue patch in front of eye. Feet and webs yellow.*
IMMATURES: *Dull brown where adult is dark; pale grey where adult is white. Face, base of bill, chin and feet green-yellow. Bill pale green.*

VOICE
Harsh quacking by female; soft hissing by male in displays at nest.

NESTING
Breeds colonially throughout year, with peak in autumn. Nest a scrape or platform of leaves and debris, on cliff edge, in clear spot among bushes or on coral pinnacle. Eggs: two; chalky green; oval, about 64 x 46 mm. Incubation 43–47 days, by both sexes. Young fledge in about 120 days.

DISTRIBUTION
Throughout tropical seas. Breeds on islands off northern shores of Australia. Four races; one in Australian seas.

The Brown Booby often perches on structures in northern harbours to rest. This is a female.

THE BOOBY MOST COMMONLY SEEN in Australia—the Brown—forages closer inshore than other boobies and readily enters harbours and river mouths to hunt for fish and squid. It is adept at pursuing prey underwater from its dives, swimming with both feet and wings for propulsion.

To attract a mate, a male Brown Booby at its chosen nest site will raise its bill and tail but not, unlike other boobies, its wings. Young are fed at least twice a day by their parents and never wander away from their nest site even when well grown.

Adults, although nesting on the ground, often perch to rest and sleep on trees, bushes and harbour markers.

A Masked Booby with its huge chick. Although two eggs are laid, usually only the first chick to hatch survives because it grabs nearly all of the food.

Masked Booby *Sula dactylatra* LESSON, 1831

BOOBIES ARE THE GANNETS of tropical waters, and the largest and most gannet-like of them all is the Masked. Yet its males have the simple bill- and wing-raising rituals of boobies when advertising for a mate, and they copulate without nape-biting or tramping. They also do not co-ordinate their fishing, patrolling alone well out at sea and plunging deeply from dives as high as 100 metres. Flying fish and the occasional squid are its prey. Like other boobies, the Masked differs from gannets in its bodily structures. It has a bare, unfeathered face; it lacks a bare concealed throat stripe; and it has reticulately scaled feet of a uniform, unstriped colour. All these birds have a protracted moult at sea, growing only three or four primaries a year. Moult is arrested during breeding.

On some tropical islands, two or three species of boobies sometimes breed near one another. Each, however, keeps to its own habitat. The Red-footed Booby builds its nest in trees and bushes; the Brown Booby on the edges of cliffs or in small clear spots among bushes; and the Masked Booby in large clearings on headlands and islands, where it can take off easily into the wind. The Masked Booby defends its nesting territory—up to 50 square metres—which is very large for a colonially nesting seabird.

Although Masked Boobies breed all year round, individuals have a 12-month cycle and do so only once. Males return roughly, not precisely to the same site of previous years and usually, but not always, attract the same mate; their nests are not permanent mounds like those of gannets. Young are much more faithful to the site, never wandering far or crèching.

The Masked Booby usually lays two eggs, about six days apart. Although both hatch, usually only the first chick survives. It is bigger by the time the second one hatches, and it grabs all or most of the food. The incubation period is about 43 days, with an extra day for the first egg. The second egg acts as an insurance in case the first one fails to hatch. About one fifth of the chicks in a colony are raised from second eggs.

The chicks exceed adult weight at two-and-a-half months and fly at four months, when their wings reach adult size.

OTHER NAMES
Blue-faced Booby, Masked Gannet.

IDENTIFICATION
LENGTH: *750–850 mm.*
MALE: *All white with black flight feathers and tail feathers. Eye golden yellow. Face, eye-ring, base of bill and throat naked and black; rest of bill bright yellow. Feet and webs light grey tinged with yellow, green or blue.*
FEMALE: *As male but bill dull yellow-green.*
IMMATURES: *Head, flight feathers and tail feathers brown. General plumage mottled white and grey-brown, with white patch around neck, on rump and on underparts. Bill brown; feet and webs black. Plumage whitens over three–four years.*
DOWNY YOUNG: *Naked at hatching, growing pure white down; bill and eye dusky.*

NESTING
Breeds throughout year with peak in spring and trough during summer cyclone season. Nest a scrape or of debris on ground in large clearing on a headland or an island. In colonies, but nests are farther apart than those of other ground-nesting boobies and gannets. Eggs: two; pale chalky blue; ellipsoidal, about 65 x 45 mm. Incubation 42–46 days, by both sexes in shifts. Young fledge in about four months.

DISTRIBUTION
Occurs throughout tropical seas. Breeds on islands off northwestern and northeastern Australia. Four races; one in Indian and western Pacific Oceans, where rather sedentary.

An Australasian Gannet glides over the sea on barely moving wings which may span two metres. Most gannets in Australia come from New Zealand.

Australasian Gannet *Morus serrator* (GRAY, 1843)

THE FISHING TECHNIQUE OF THE sea-going Australasian Gannets is spectacular. They patrol along, then suddenly plunge into the water from 10 metres or more, with their wings folded back to form a living arrowhead. Air sacs in the body cushion the impact of the sea, the nictitating membrane covers the eye involuntarily, and the nostrils are occluded to keep water out. Out of the water, gannets breathe through the corners of the mouth. Often they forage in small flocks, effectively herding the fish. Some birds will dive while others are rising and yet others are swimming. Shoaling fish are their quarry and they catch them not by spearing but by diving beneath, turning and grasping them on their sweep back to the surface. The margins of the bill have fine, reversed serrations for holding fish firmly. Gannets seldom stay underwater for longer than 10 seconds and usually swallow the fish in this time.

Alternating a few leisurely flaps with long glides, Australasian Gannets are graceful fliers and can wheel against the wind on barely moving wings. They sleep at sea and are silent there, which contrasts starkly with the cackling that rises as a daily roar from their dense breeding colonies. Like the boobies, they are day-active at their colonies, but they have rather different displays. When touching down, they crane up and down, bounce up in the air and land a metre or so away to inhaled bellows. As the pair greet, facing one another, they stretch and shake their heads from side to side, wings angled out and bills sometimes clashing, falling into a deep bow. Mutual preening and further bowing may continue until the relieved bird is ready to depart. Gannets pair for life, and in courtship the male raises its wings and points its bill skyward, in much the same way as male boobies do when advertising for a mate. Unlike them, however, male gannets nape-bite females in copulation and tramp with their feet.

In the colony nests are evenly spaced about a metre apart, signifying the extent of each pairs' territory. Eggs are laid through October and hatch over January–February. Young are first brooded by both adults in 12-hour shifts until well-downed, and fledge by desertion in late April–early May. They may return to the rookery from the age of three years, but are not able to begin breeding until six or seven years old.

OTHER NAMES
Australian Gannet.

IDENTIFICATION
LENGTH: *840–920 mm.*
ADULTS: *Sexes similar. General body plumage white with buff head and black primaries, secondaries and inner tail feathers. Concealed slate-blue throat stripe. Eye light grey. Bill blue-grey. Feet black with yellow-green stripes on toes and scutellate front of lower 'leg'; webs brown.*
IMMATURES: *General body plumage irregular mixture of white and grey-brown with dark tail. Upper parts of body mainly dusky, mottled white; underparts mainly white, greyish on neck.*
DOWNY YOUNG: *Naked, then white-downed.*

VOICE
Display call at nest a loud repetitive cackling urrah. *Voice of male has slightly higher pitch than that of female. Departing birds cackle* erk-erk, *and snort and quack in flight and fights. Young grunt and chirp.*

NESTING
Breeds October–May. Nest an earth mound of guano and debris about 250 mm high, on ground or on a man-made platform, in colonies. Egg: one; white; oblong-oval, about 78 x 48 mm. Incubation 43–47 days, by both parents in 27-hour shifts, clasping egg in their webbed feet. Young fledge in 93–105 days, fed by both parents.

DISTRIBUTION
Temperate waters along coasts of southern Australia including Tasmania; common. A few breed on islands off Victoria, such as Lawrence Rocks, and isolated rocks off Tasmania. Most of population breeds on rocks and headlands around main islands of New Zealand. General westwards dispersal in winter and by non-breeding birds, extending to Western Australia and rarely even Africa; breeders more sedentary. No races.

Australian Pelican *Pelecanus conspicillatus* TEMMINCK, 1824

A FLOCK OF AUSTRALIAN PELICANS swimming slowly in formation is one way in which they drive fish into the shallows. Never diving, they dip their bills into the water simultaneously to trap them. Any water engulfed is squeezed out through 'valves' at the corner of the mouth by pressing bill pouch to breast. Pelicans may also feed alone, and eat crustaceans as well.

Pelicans breed throughout Australia on lakes and swamps, fresh or briny. They congregate at isles where mature birds—at least four years old—develop red courtship colours on the bill. These colours fade quickly after pairing. The birds use their great bill in display, raising it, swinging and rippling its pouch, and throwing and catching objects. In threat, they thrust it forwards, head down and pouch bulging, snapping it open and shut.

When pairing begins, several males follow one female, either walking or swimming after it, until only one male is left. After a short courtship flight the female selects the nest site. Both birds collect sticks and plants and build these into a nest: a loose platform on a rough scrape in the ground.

Both parents feed the chicks, which fall into violent convulsions and collapse after picking their food from their parents' gullets. This lasts about one minute and may be an exaggerated form of begging. Soon after the chicks walk, they leave the nest and cluster together in crèches.

When in groups, pelicans fly in a loose V-formation or in line. Heads are rested back, wings are flapped leisurely several times, and then spread flat in long glides that can carry the birds in soaring circles as high as 3000 metres. During droughts, some have reached Indonesia, Solomon Islands and New Zealand.

Pelicans have lived in Australia for a long time. Their fossil remains have been found in deposits between 30 and 40 million years old. The prehistoric pelicans were very similar to the present-day ones, but probably had shorter legs and were slightly smaller.

OTHER NAMES
Spectacled Pelican, Australasian Pelican.

IDENTIFICATION
LENGTH: *1600–1800 mm, including bill.*
ADULTS: *Sexes similar; female smaller. General body plumage white; rump band, wings and tail black. Plumed shoulders and upper tail coverts white; underwing coverts white. Head and short crest white or grey. Naked skin around eye pale yellow; eye brown. Bill pale blue with pink ridge; edge and nail pale yellow; pouch pink-yellow with faint red stripe from base towards centre. Feet and webs leaden. During courtship naked skin around eye yellow-orange; front two-thirds of pouch scarlet; stripe on pouch dark blue; base of pouch rimmed dark blue; terminal quarter of bill and nail orange.*
IMMATURES: *Plumage brownish where adults are black. Plumed wing coverts short. Head and rump dull white; crest short. Bill and pouch flesh-yellow; naked skin around eye with or without blue tint. Feet brown-grey.*
DOWNY YOUNG: *Plain greyish white; bill and feet flesh.*

VOICE
Normally silent. Some grunt-like sounds away from breeding areas. During breeding, a guttural orrh, thu-thuh, ah-ah-ahah, oh-oh *and* uh-uhhr *in displays.*

NESTING
Breeds any time of year if sufficient rain or water; usually spring in south. Nests usually in dense colonies on ground on islands, occasionally on bushes. Eggs: two to four; pure white; ellipsoidal, about 90 x 59 mm. Incubation 32–35 days, by both sexes in shifts. Young fledge in about 100 days.

DISTRIBUTION
Throughout Australia; frequents fresh- and salt-water lakes, rivers, lagoons and swamps. Ranges to New Guinea; stragglers have been recorded in the Lesser Sundas, New Hebrides, Solomon Islands and New Zealand. No races.

The Australian Pelican lives in all parts of Australia where there are lakes and swamps, and by the sea.

The Pacific Heron forages in shallow waters and wet fields for insects.

Pacific Heron *Ardea pacifica* LATHAM, 1801

ADAPTED TO FLUCTUATING AND EPHEMERAL rivers and swamps inland, the nomadic Pacific Heron is uncommon around the Australian coast—often appearing only during drought.

Insects, crustaceans, tadpoles, frogs and fish are its food. These the herons take wading around shallow pools usually less than 10 centimetres deep and stalking through wet grass. Launching an attack every few minutes, a bird is successful in more than half its attempts and swallows large prey headfirst. The herons hunt from both upright and crouched positions, using the 'stand-and-wait' and 'walk slowly' techniques, and will even stir with the foot; all the time they watch, head back, ready to strike. Usually working alone, the herons nonetheless gather in small groups on flushes of food, without defending a feeding territory.

The Pacific Heron—like other herons—flies with its neck folded and its head held close to its body. Its long, slim legs trail beyond its blunt tail. Flight is a deep continuous flapping with little gliding. The birds perch, roost and nest in open or bare trees.

OTHER NAMES
White-necked Heron.

IDENTIFICATION
LENGTH: *About 910 mm.*
ADULTS: *Sexes similar. Body plumage grey-black. Long, thin maroon plumes on back. Head white; neck white with double row of fine black spots on front; breast white; belly and undertail dark slate streaked with white. Bend of wing white, conspicuous in flight; wing black. Naked face skin blue or yellow. Eye buff. Bill black. Legs and feet black. Non-breeding birds: vinous-grey wash on head and neck; more black spots in front of neck.*
IMMATURES: *Numerous black spots on front of vinous-grey neck. No plumes on back or breast.*

VOICE
Alarm call a loud croak; other guttural calls at nest.

NESTING
Breeds throughout year, depending on
food; usually spring and summer. Nest a loose platform of sticks in a tree up to 30 m above ground near or over water; solitary or in loose aggregations. Eggs: up to six, usually four; dull blue-green; oval, about 53 x 38 mm. Incubation by both sexes.

DISTRIBUTION
Inland or coastal waters and wet fields. Nomadic; rare vagrant in Tasmania, New Zealand and New Guinea. No races.

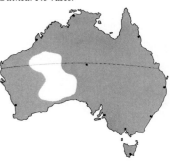

Great-billed Heron

Ardea sumatrana RAFFLES, 1822

OTHER NAMES
Alligator bird.

IDENTIFICATION
LENGTH: *About 1050 mm.*
ADULTS: *Sexes similar. General plumage uniform brown-grey; long silver-grey nuptial plumes on nape, back; persistent plumes on breast. Throat white. Naked skin in front of eye olive-yellow. Eye yellow. Bill black, yellow at base of mandible. Legs and feet dusky grey.*
IMMATURES: *General plumage uniform rust-brown. No nuptial plumes.*

VOICE
Guttural notes; loud croak in alarm; irregular resonant roaring at nest.

NESTING
Breeds throughout year, depending on food. Nest about 1.3 m in diameter by about 0.5 m deep, a platform of sticks built up to 6 m above ground in tree.

Eggs: two; pale blue-green; oval, about 69 x 48 mm. Incubation by both sexes.

DISTRIBUTION
Mud flats, estuaries, lagoons, rivers and dense mangroves of northern Australia, New Guinea, Indonesia and southeastern Asia. Rather solitary; nowhere common. No races.

When breeding, the Great-billed Heron has long nuptial plumes.

THIS GREAT SKULKING HERON keeps to the mangrove-lined waterways of coastal northern Australia. It stalks stealthily along the mud flats exposed by the tide and in the shallows of nearby lagoons, feeding on various aquatic animals as large as catfish and crabs. At high tide it rests perched in the mangroves, flying into them with the lumbering, head-retracted flight characteristic of all the herons.

The birds seem to pair permanently and hold a foraging territory of riverfront in which there may be three to seven nests, any one of which may be used for breeding and the others for roosting. Most nests are placed in mangroves inundated with up to one metre of water at high tide.

In what may be courtship, male and female fan and cock their short tails, puff up their neck hackles and raise a small crest. Drooping wings touch the ground as the pair strut around, bowing to one another, and dancing a few steps. At least one of the birds drums like a small engine. A resonant roaring, lasting several seconds, may be repeated irregularly by nesting birds. In alarm they croak. Although two eggs often form a clutch, one young is usually reared. Established pairs may not breed every year.

White-faced Heron
Ardea novaehollandiae LATHAM, 1790

THE HERON MOST COMMONLY SEEN in Australia is the White-faced — usually one or a pair, stalking about in shallow water or on pastures, occasionally shooting out its long S-shaped neck to catch prey. Herons have a special hinge at the sixth vertebra that allows them to strike with the neck. They also have tufts of powder down under plumage on breast and rump. These feathers disintegrate to produce a protective powder which the birds pick up with their bills to groom their plumage.

Among the herons, White-faced are generalists, both in their habitats and feeding. They forage over intertidal mud flats and rock pools, swamps, wet pasture, and even residential lawns. On mud flats the birds generally space themselves out, but more often flock loosely on pasture. Their prey is varied, mostly crustaceans, squid, fish, insects, amphibians, spiders, snails and worms. Their mode of hunting follows the usual wait-and-watch and slow stalk methods—and they will stir one foot in water—but they tend to walk further and more quickly than most larger herons.

In courtship, one bird follows another walking slowly along a branch, its head lowered and crest and scapulars raised, while pecking at sticks. Male and female relieve one another every 10 hours or less during incubation, with much bill-snapping, croaking and preening. Both parents brood and feed the young by regurgitation, the chicks characteristically inserting their bills crosswise in their parents'. If chicks are disturbed they freeze with up-pointing bills. After fledging they remain with their parents until chased off at the recommencement of nesting.

OTHER NAMES
White-fronted Heron, Blue Crane.

IDENTIFICATION
LENGTH: *About 650–690 mm.*
ADULTS: *Sexes similar; male larger. General plumage two-tone grey, with flight feathers darker than rest of plumage. Face and stripe on throat white. Long grey plumes on back, vinous on breast. Eye yellow; naked skin in front of eye slate with lemon eyelid. Bill black. Legs and feet olive-yellow.*
IMMATURES: *As adults, but little white on forehead and no nuptial plumes.*
DOWNY YOUNG: *Grey; bill and feet as adults.*

VOICE
Loud croak in alarm; guttural notes and aggressive grating graak *at nest.*

NESTING
Breeds most of the year, depending on food supplies; mostly in southern and inland Australia over summer, using northern wetlands more as dry season refuge. Nest a loose platform of sticks up to 20 m above ground, in a tree not necessarily near water. Nests sometimes in loose aggregations. Eggs: up to seven, usually four; pale blue; oval, about 48 x 35 mm. Incubation 24–26 days, by both sexes. Young fledge in 40 days.

DISTRIBUTION
Frequents lakes, swamps, estuaries, mangroves, dams, tidal mudflats and grasslands throughout Australia. Nomadic. Also in New Zealand, New Guinea, eastern Indonesia and some southwestern Pacific islands. Possibly two races: one small in New Caledonia and Loyalties; the other larger, everywhere else.

The White-faced Heron, sometimes erroneously called a blue crane, differs from some other herons in that it does not necessarily nest near water.

Pied Heron *Ardea picata* GOULD, 1845

PIED HERONS ARE EXCLUSIVELY TROPICAL and locally abundant on the coastal flood plains of northern Australia. They are dainty, gregarious birds and commonly gather in loose feeding groups of five to 30 or more on shallow freshwater and saline swamps, wet grassland and muddied ground churned by stock; even sewage ponds, garbage tips and meatworks are visited. Larger aggregations of several hundred or so sometimes congregate around drying lagoons in the dry season, but most of these are white-headed, white-bellied immatures of the year.

Adults tend to be more solitary, and sometimes defend feeding territories of about 50 square metres against others of their species. These are probably the more sedentary breeders. Their food includes crustaceans, small molluscs and fish, but insects, their larvae and nymphs, predominate. These the herons often find around buffalo, cattle, horses, pigs and even poultry.

Pied Herons capture their prey by walking quickly, gleaning low and floating vegetation with rapid pecks. Their strike rate is high. The birds move about more than most herons, pausing less to stand and peer, and pecking more frequently. When hunting in deeper water up to 15 centimetres deep they use the conventional 'stand-and-wait' and 'stalk slowly' strategies, lunging from upright or crouched positions.

Pied Herons roost and nest colonially. The sight of hundreds flying silently in random formation up-river to their roosting trees at dusk is impressive. Nesting colonies are usually smaller but often mixed with other species, such as the Intermediate Egret and Little Pied Cormorant. Most colonies have been found in pockets of estuarine mangroves that are flooded at high tide; nests are built two–five metres above mud level.

OTHER NAMES
Pied Egret, White-headed Egret.

IDENTIFICATION
LENGTH: *About 450–480 mm.*
ADULTS: *Sexes similar. General plumage blue-black with white cheeks and neck. Blue-black crest on back of head and long blue-black plumes on back; long white plumes hang down from base of neck. Eye yellow; naked skin in front of eye and on base of upper mandible dark blue. Bill yellow. Legs and feet dull to orange-yellow.*
IMMATURES: *As adults, but entire head, neck, breast and belly white; bend of wing white; no plumes; face skin yellow-grey. Adult plumage gained at end of first year moult.*
DOWNY YOUNG: *Patterned as immature, with dusky flanks; eye olive-grey; bill black.*

VOICE
Flight call a load ohrk. *Soft cooing at nest.*

NESTING
Breeding season over monsoonal summer, mainly January–May. Nest a platform of sticks and twigs, placed in tree. Eggs: three or four; blue-green; ellipsoidal, about 42 x 30 mm.

DISTRIBUTION
In saltwater and freshwater coastal swamps and adjacent grasslands in northern Australia; west to the Fitzroy River, WA, and east to the Burdekin system, Qld. During flood years a few vagrants reach southeastern Australia. Also in New Guinea and eastern Indonesia. No races.

A bird of the tropics, the Pied Heron forages for invertebrates in swamps and grasslands. They peck more frequently than most herons.

Cattle Egret

Ardea ibis LINNÉ, 1758

OTHER NAMES
None.

IDENTIFICATION
LENGTH: *480–530 mm.*
ADULTS: *Sexes similar. Plumage white. When breeding, crown, neck and back tinged orange-buff; face skin and eye-ring red. Eye yellow. Bill red with yellow tip. Feet red. Non-breeding: face skin green-yellow; bill pale yellow; feet yellow-olive.*
IMMATURES: *As non-breeding adults.*
DOWNY YOUNG: *Drab, whitish; bill, face skin and feet dull grey.*

VOICE
Chattering croaks at nest.

NESTING
Breeds throughout year, mainly early summer in north. Nest of sticks, built by male in a fork or upright branch of tree. Eggs: three to six; white tinged blue-green; oval, about 45 x 33 mm. Incubation 22-26 days, by both sexes. Young fledge in 25 days.

DISTRIBUTION
Coastal Australia since 1940s; also the Americas, Africa and Eurasia. Two races; one reaching Australia.

Cattle Egrets acquire orange-buff head plumes and a red bill when breeding.

CATTLE EGRETS ARE SO NAMED because of their habit of feeding around the feet of slow-moving cattle and buffalo. They even perch on them to rest and pick insects and parasites off their hides. The birds are communal and forage mainly in wet pasture in groups of two to twenty, feeding on a variety of insects and, less often, small aquatic animals. They strut along, heads nodding, make a quick dash and strike; small prey is swallowed at once.

Cattle Egrets roost and nest colonially in tens to thousands with other water birds, in trees and shrubs lining waterways, earlier than other egrets in northern Australia. Males choose each nest site, defend it, call, raise their plumes and wings, and brandish twigs to attract females.

Although Cattle Egrets were introduced in the 1930s–40s, their many thousands across far-northern Australia today suggest self-introduction from Asia then.

Great Egret *Ardea alba* LINNÉ, 1758

THE GREAT EGRET, largest of the white herons, is a solitary and territorial feeder which hunts in water up to 30 centimetres deep, deeper than other herons. There it often crouches slightly and stretches its neck to the side, holding the head horizontal, perhaps to offset glare. Hunting Great Egrets are masters of the wait-and-watch strategy, freezing motionless for long intervals and then stalking slowly and deliberately. Although taking insects, crustaceans and amphibians, they feed largely on fish.

Displays towards a prospective mate run to a mixture of snaps and stretches, with a fully extended neck sometimes bent backwards with bill pointing vertically up.

OTHER NAMES
Large Egret, White Egret.

IDENTIFICATION
LENGTH: *About 800–900 mm.*
ADULTS: *Sexes similar. General plumage white. Neck longer than body. In breeding plumage long white nuptial plumes only on back and extending beyond tail. Naked face blue-green, extending back in spur at gape. Eye yellow, red when courting. Bill yellow, black when courting. Legs and feet brown to black. In non-breeding plumage no nuptial plumes; face yellow.*
IMMATURES: *As non-breeding adults.*

VOICE
Low-pitched croak in alarm; at nest several guttural calls.

NESTING
Breeds mainly early summer in south, later in north, in colonies. Nest a platform of sticks in tree up to 15 m above ground, or sometimes in a reed bed. Eggs: three to six; pale green-blue; oval, about 53 x 38 mm. Incubation about 25 days, by both sexes. Young, usually two, fledge in six weeks.

DISTRIBUTION
Waters of lakes, swamps, rivers and dams throughout Australia; in other tropical and warm temperate regions. Four races; one, small, from India to Australasia.

The Great Egret hunts by standing and waiting, or stalking slowly.

The bill and legs of the Little Egret are black all year round.

Little Egret *Ardea garzetta* LINNÉ, 1766

DISTINGUISHED FROM OTHER EGRETS by their slender black bills and nuptial head plumes, the Little Egret forages, usually alone, mainly on mud flats. Rarely does it enter pasture or waters more than 10 centimetres deep. Its prey is small vertebrates—fish and amphibians—and various invertebrates.

When hunting the egret stands and waits motionless for much of the time, but on sighting prey, dashes after it with a quick high-stepping walk or run, often raising its wings. It may shuffle a foot in the water or feed in association with spoonbills for prey disturbed. The Little Egret has difficulty in handling fish longer than 10 centimetres and often loses them. It averages two or three attacks a minute and is successful about half the time.

Complex displays both before and after the pair bond has been established include cracking of the wings in flight and fanning of the nuptial plumes.

OTHER NAMES
None.

IDENTIFICATION
LENGTH: *About 560 mm.*
ADULTS: *Sexes similar. General plumage white. Naked skin of face yellow. Eye yellow. Bill black. Legs and feet black; soles yellow. Face and eyes turn red when courting. In breeding season two fine ribbon plumes on back of head; frayed plumes on back and breast.*
IMMATURES: *Similar to non-breeding adults.*
DOWNY YOUNG: *White; bill and feet dusky.*

VOICE
At nest utters several croaking and bubbling calls; also bill-clacking.

NESTING
Breeds throughout year, mainly spring and summer. Nest a platform of sticks in tree or bush; in some districts in reed bed or on rocky islet. In colonies with other colonially nesting water birds. Eggs: up to five, usually three or four; bright blue-green; oval, about

43 x 31 mm. Incubation 21–25 days, by both sexes. Young, fed by both parents by regurgitation, fledge in 45–50 days.

DISTRIBUTION
Coastal and inland mud flats around Australia and Tasmania, also New Guinea to southern Eurasia and Africa. Two races; one small and black-toed in Australia.

Intermediate Egret

Ardea intermedia WAGLER, 1829

LACY FILAMENTOUS PLUMES on back and breast grace the Intermediate Egret when it breeds. It frequents shallow waters, mud banks and dry pasture around freshwater lakes and rivers. Either alone or in small dispersed groups, it hunts slowly and methodically. The bird may make fewer than one jab a minute for food, but is successful in two out of three strikes. Occasionally it hovers to dive on to prey in deeper water. Small fish are staple diet, but frogs, insects and crustaceans are also taken.

Courtship combines flight, twig-shaking, snap and stretch displays, as in other egrets. Nesting colonially in trees, both sexes incubate, changing over with a spectacular fanning of plumes.

OTHER NAMES
Plumed Egret.

IDENTIFICATION
LENGTH: *620 mm.*
ADULTS: *Sexes similar. General plumage uniformly white. In breeding plumage long white nuptial plumes on back and breast, those on back extend beyond tail. Eye yellow. Naked face blue-green. Bill and legs red. Feet black. In non-breeding plumage no nuptial plumes; face green-yellow. Bill yellow-orange. Legs flesh-brown.*
IMMATURES: *Like non-breeding adults.*
DOWNY YOUNG: *Dull white.*

VOICE
Loud croaking in alarm; bi-syllabic croak and hoarse buzzing at nest.

NESTING
Breeds colonially, mainly spring in south, late summer in north. Nest a platform of sticks, in trees. Eggs: three

to six; pale blue green; oval, about 46 x 35 mm. Incubation 24–27 days, by both sexes. Young fledge in five–six weeks.

DISTRIBUTION
Eastern and northern Australia; also New Guinea to southern Asia and warmer Africa. No races.

Sunlight catches the nuptial plumage of an Intermediate Egret on its nest.

Eastern Reef Egret

Ardea sacra GMELIN, 1789

THE EASTERN REEF EGRET is an exclusively coastal bird and abundant on many Pacific islands. Coral reefs, tidal flats and rock platforms are its foraging grounds. A versatile hunter, it feeds mostly on small fish up to 15 centimetres long and occasional crustaceans and insects; it even pirates colonies of terns, picking off nestlings and deftly stealing fish brought to feed young.

Reef egrets forage in a business-like yet stealthy manner. Both day and night, as tide falls they fly out from their loosely colonial roosts or nests in trees on the edge of feeding grounds, and spread over exposed shore. Each bird hunts alone on a feeding area from which it excludes others. It crouches low on its short legs and creeps along, almost gliding over rocks and coral; and it hops from point to point in short flights as well, landing erect and peering about or crouching low.

When lunging after food, Eastern Reef Egrets may plunge into water and partly submerge. Because sea water is clear at most feeding sites, they commonly crouch to make themselves inconspicuous and exploit the element of surprise in a sudden strike. That this is effective is suggested by the high rate of capture: about half the strikes are successful. In pools with much seaweed, an egret may stir the plants with its foot, to uncover hidden prey; it also stirs silty water. When fish are surfacing in deep water, it sometimes flies, skimming the surface, to snatch them in its bill.

Eastern Reef Egrets occur in two forms—white, which is the more common in tropical zones, and dark or slate-grey, which is the more numerous in temperate regions. The two forms interbreed, and both white and dark birds can be found in the same brood. The inheritance of colour type is evidently controlled by a single set of genes, although occasionally complicated by the occurrence of pied birds.

The white phase of the Eastern Reef Egret is more common in the tropics.

OTHER NAMES
Reef Heron, Sacred Heron.

IDENTIFICATION
LENGTH: *About 600–650 mm.*
ADULTS: *Sexes similar; male larger. Slender plumes on nape, back and breast.* White form: *plumage uniformly white; bare skin on face green-yellow; eye yellow; bill yellow; sometimes with upper mandible slate-grey; short legs and feet yellow-green or -grey.* Grey form: *plumage slate-grey or blue-grey; white stripe on throat; bill slate-brown, tending at times to grey, upper mandible usually darker.*
IMMATURES: *Similar to adults but no plumes; grey phase paler.*
DOWNY YOUNG: *White or grey in phase of adults.*

VOICE
Loud croak.

NESTING
Breeds at any time, mostly August–April. Nest a simple platform of sticks in a tree, on low shrub or on ground; in loose colonies. Eggs: two to five; pale green; oval, about 46 x 35 mm. Incubation 25–28 days. Young fledge in five–six weeks.

DISTRIBUTION
Coastal Australia except southern Victoria and Tasmania; also Japan to New Zealand through western Pacific. Two races; one small in Australasia.

The grey phase of the Eastern Reef Egret is the more usual form in temperate areas. Both forms interbreed.

This Rufous Night Heron's fledglings will go through a phase in which their plumage is streaked brown and white before they acquire adult colours.

Rufous Night Heron *Nycticorax caledonicus* (Gmelin, 1789)

NOCTURNAL HABITS AND chunky, cinnamon-toned form set the Rufous Night Heron apart from other Australian herons. A higher percentage of them—up to 85 per cent—also carry the virus for Murray Valley encephalitis. Night herons camp by day in small groups or hundreds inside the cover of leafy trees close to water, dozing, heads on breasts. At dusk they fly out, croaking sporadically, to forage alone along shallows and shores, fresh or briny, in the early night and before dawn. There they hunt for fish, amphibians and crustaceans, as well as insects, chicks and eggs stolen from other birds. Night herons watch-and-stalk slowly along or stand-and-wait, at times vibrating their bills in water to attract prey; sometimes the birds plunge feet-first into deep water after quarry. Prey is caught with a quick bill jab.

At the beginning of breeding, males and females converge independently at colonies of tens to thousands. Males separate to stake out small nesting territories, the diameter of a bill-stab, and attract females with elaborate snap-stretch and wheezing song-dance displays. In the dance, they tread with their feet and jerk their heads down to their toes, raising crest and nape plumes with a hiccoughing *plup*. Each pair mates only for the season and usually raises a single brood. Males collect and present material to their mates to construct a flimsy platform of twigs. Eggs are laid at two-day intervals and hatch in sequence.

Both sexes feed their young by regurgitation, and later cough food into the nest for the chicks to pick up. After two weeks the young wander among neighbouring territories, returning to their nest only to be fed.

OTHER NAMES
Nankeen Night Heron, Night Heron.

IDENTIFICATION
LENGTH: 560–650 mm.
ADULTS: *Sexes similar; male larger. Upper surface from lower neck to wings and tail plain cinnamon-rufous. Crown slate-black, with two–three white nape plumes all year. Ventral surface white with cinnamon bloom at sides. Face skin dull lemon; cobalt-blue in courtship. Eye bright yellow; orange in courtship. Bill black. Legs and feet greenish yellow; pink-red in courtship; claws black.*
IMMATURES: *Brown above, white below, streaked dusky brown; wings spotted buff-white. Bill dull yellow. Legs and feet yellowish olive-grey.*
DOWNY YOUNG: *Mouse-grey; bill and feet dull olive-grey.*

VOICE
Guttural croak; rasps, buzzes and clacks at nest. Young screech.

NESTING
Breeds September to March–April, mainly in southwest and southeast. Nest a loose, leaf-lined platform of sticks in tree or shrub up to 25 m above water; also in ground crevices

on treeless islands. Eggs: usually two–three; chalky light turquoise; oval, about 51 x 37 mm. Incubation about three weeks, by both sexes. Young fledge in about seven weeks.

DISTRIBUTION
Permanent and semi-permanent fresh and brackish waters throughout Australia. Nomadic; breeding centred in Murray–Darling basin. Also Indonesia to Melanesia. Six races; one in Australia–New Guinea.

Striated Heron *Ardeola striata* (Linné, 1766)

OTHER NAMES
Green-backed Heron, Little Green Heron, Mangrove Heron.

IDENTIFICATION
LENGTH: *420–460 mm.*
ADULTS: *Sexes similar; slender back plumes in male. Mid-grey to dark grey-green above and light to dark cinnamon-grey below (grey form), or rufous above and brown-grey below (rufous form). Black crown. White line with dusky spots down throat. Bare face lemon. Eye yellow. Bill green-yellow with black ridge. Legs and feet brown or olive-grey, lined yellow to orange on back. During courtship, face and legs become red.*
IMMATURES: *Grey and white stripes on underparts; white spots on wings.*
DOWNY YOUNG: *Grey-downed on jade green skin; eye and feet as adults.*

VOICE
Squeaking at nest, harsh tch-aah, and explosive hoo. Nestlings croak.

NESTING
September-February/March; solitary. Nest a platform of sticks in fork of mangrove. Eggs: three or four; chalky green-blue; oval, about 42 x 31 mm. Incubation 21–25 days, by both sexes. Young fledge in four weeks.

DISTRIBUTION
Coastal and estuarine waters south to Shark Bay in west and Mallacoota in east. Sedentary. Also widespread throughout tropics and subtropics. Twenty-two races: two in Australia; one on east coast to Cape York; the other on north and west coast.

This is the grey-green form of the Striated Heron. There is also a rufous form, found on the Pilbara coast.

LIVING IN MANGROVES in Australia, Striated Herons roost within the shelter of low branches at high tide. From there they sometimes dive into water after prey, then swim back and climb on to branches to eat. When the tide retreats, the birds fly over the exposed tidal flats to forage, stalking stealthily along, body hunched. Crustaceans, fish, molluscs, insects, and particularly mudskippers are taken.

Striated Herons are solitary birds, roosting alone. Their territorial and courtship displays include bowing duets, flap-flight displays, crest-raising and tail-flicking. Young, brooded and fed by both parents, are tended mainly by the male after fledging if the female nests again.

There are two colour phases in Australia: one, greenish grey, everywhere; the other, rufous-toned, abundant only on the Pilbara coast.

Little Bittern *Ixobrychus minutus* (LINNÉ, 1766)

OTHER NAMES
Kaoriki, Minute Bittern.

IDENTIFICATION
LENGTH: *About 280–340 mm.*
MALE: *Black over crown, back, wings
and tail; neck rufous and shoulders
ochre-buff. Undersurface light
cinnamon-brown to white, with dusky
streaks on neck and sides of breast.
Face skin yellow. Eye yellow. Bill
green-yellow with black culmen. Legs
and feet green-grey, with yellow stripe
behind. Face skin, eye and base of bill
red during breeding.*
FEMALE: *As male, but back brown.*
IMMATURES: *Ochreish buff, heavily
streaked dusky; eye straw; bill light
brown; legs and feet yellow olive.*
DOWNY YOUNG: *Hairy rufous above,
white below.*

VOICE
*Deep repeated croaks and croons at
nest. Sharp bark in alarm.*

NESTING
*Breeds October–December. Nest 10–40
cm above the water, a flimsy pad of
reeds and rushes. Eggs: four to seven;
white; oval, about 30 x 25 mm.
Incubation 16–19 days, by both sexes.
Young fledge in about four weeks.*

DISTRIBUTION
*Freshwater reed beds in eastern and
southwestern Australia and New
Guinea. Regionally nomadic. Four or
five races; one in Australia.*

The Little Bittern is rarely seen outside the dense reed beds. This is an immature bird with streaked plumage.

THE RARELY SEEN Little Bittern lives in dense swampy reed beds, clambering about adeptly mainly at night for insects and small vertebrates. It feeds alone, defending its feeding territory, and freezes like a stick to conceal itself.

Males begin the nest, but both parents incubate, and greet each other with mellow calls and sparring, their crown feathers raised. Both also feed young by regurgitation. When disturbed young also 'freeze' with bills pointing upwards. Within eight days they begin to clamber out of the nest, and fly after several weeks.

The Black Bittern often nests in a tree over water.

Black Bittern

Ixobrychus flavicollis (LATHAM, 1790)

OTHER NAMES
Yellow-necked Bittern.

IDENTIFICATION
LENGTH: *550–650 mm.*
MALE: *Upper surface, wings and face
plain sooty-slate; patch of straw
plumes at sides of neck. Throat and
foreneck white, mottle-striped sooty-
brown. Underside brownish slate. Face
skin yellow-brown to dusky. Eye pale
yellow. Bill dusky above, yellowish
grey below. Legs and feet slate-brown.
Early in breeding, eye reddish, face
skin violet-pink, bill red-tinged and
feet dull yellow.*
FEMALE: *Browner and paler than
male; rufous flush on cheeks.*
IMMATURES: *As female but browner,
scalloped with buff on body.*
DOWNY YOUNG: *Plain white.*

VOICE
Cooing coo-oorh, *repetitive* eh-eh,
eh-he *at nest; boom from perch.*

Alarm croak when flushed.

NESTING
*Breeds September–March. Nest of
sticks, in tree over water. Eggs: up to
six; bluish white; rounded-oval, about
44 x 35 mm. Incubation by both sexes.*

DISTRIBUTION
*Forested fresh rivers and inlets of
eastern, northern and western
mainland coast; also New Guinea and
Solomons to China and India. Three
races; one large in Australia.*

LARGEST OF THE SMALL BITTERNS, the Black Bittern may also boom when breeding and fan the distinctive plumes at the side of its neck in display. Both sexes nest-build, incubate and feed young, and also forage and roost alone, holding set feeding and breeding territories. By day they rest in waterside vegetation and come out at dusk and dawn to hunt for fish, amphibians, molluscs and insects. If disturbed they fly to a perch and freeze like a stick.

Australasian Bittern *Botaurus poiciloptilus* (WAGLER, 1827)

BITTERNS ARE HERONS with a difference. They spend their lives in solitude and secrecy within the cover of rush- and reed-filled marshes, feeding, roosting and breeding there. They also have only ten instead of twelve tail feathers, two instead of three sets of powder downs, an inner toe that is longer than the outer, and a fused pelvic girdle. Still more distinctive is their habit of freezing like sticks, to escape notice if suddenly confronted. The birds become instantly rigid, feathers compressed to slim the body, eyes open, and bill and neck pointing stiffly skyward.

There are two groups of bitterns, large and small; the Australasian Bittern is Australia's representative of the world's four large ones and is the brownest of them. Despite its bulk, the Australasian Bittern is rarely seen. It keeps to the cover of dense reed beds, is solitary, and hunts mainly at night, stepping high but stealthily knee-deep in water and jabbing periodically at prey: amphibians, fish, crustaceans, snails, mice and various insects. Each bird keeps to its own foraging territory, through which it builds several roosting pads under shelter of brakes of reeds. There it rests, mainly by day, littering them with pellets that are the coughed-up indigestible parts of its meals: bones, crustacean carapaces and the like. If flushed, it lumbers off, legs trailing, broad wings flapping slowly and deeply, and head drawn down on to the body in the manner of all herons, only to drop back to cover shortly.

The booming so characteristic of the large bitterns announces breeding. Victorian Aborigines attributed it to the bunyip. Apparently only males give it to advertise themselves, expelling air through their throats while keeping the bill closed and held level or down and flaring their neck plumes. They may also give courtship flights which end in copulation. Although one male may usually mate with only one female, it is possible that he accepts several; as many as seven nests have been found in the same stretch of reeds. Females incubate and rear young unaided, feeding nestlings by the conventional method of regurgitation, often coughing food into the nest for older young to pick out.

OTHER NAMES
Brown Bittern, Australian Bittern.

IDENTIFICATION
LENGTH: *650–750 mm.*
ADULTS: *Sexes similar; male significantly larger. Upper surface deep brown, mottled with buff on wing coverts; face and eyebrow buff, with dark brown stripe running from bill to erectile plumes at sides of neck. Undersurface buff, striped with brown. Eye yellow. Face skin dull green. Bill dark brown; base of lower mandible green-yellow. Legs and feet dull, pale green.*
IMMATURES: *Paler than adults, with buff flecking all over back and finer, sparser brown striping ventrally.*

VOICE
Loud or soft braying or booming at night by males during breeding, carrying several kilometres; females and young babble at nest.

NESTING
Breeds October–January. Nest a

platform of trampled reeds and rushes over water in dense cover. Eggs: four to six; olive brown; oval, about 52 x 38 mm. Incubation about 25 days, by female. Young venture out from nest into surrounding reeds in several weeks and fledge in about four.

DISTRIBUTION
Temperate and subtropical reed-filled freshwater swamps in southwestern and southeastern Australia north to Fraser Island. Also in New Zealand and New Caledonia. No races.

In the swamps of southeastern and southwestern Australia the Australasian Bittern forages for small animals and booms its gloomy call mainly at night.

Black-necked Stork

Ephippiorhynchus asiaticus (LATHAM, 1790)

SOME STORKS ARE sociable birds, but the Black-necked Stork, Australia's only member, is usually seen by itself or in a loose pair. Sometimes, however, it may be seen in family parties, each bird hunting independently of each other, striding through shallow water, probing with its large, powerful bill as it goes. The storks are freshwater foragers where their main food is fish, but they also eat reptiles, frogs, crabs, rodents and carrion. When hunting active prey a bird may run a few seemingly disjointed steps and catch the food with a rapid forward thrust of the bill, swallowing it with a backward jerk of the head. Mostly, however, they stand and wait or stalk slowly, as herons do. On rare occasions, such as when a well-stocked pool is drying up, several family groups may congregate with other birds to feed on the massed fish.

As the adult pair seems to stay together during the non-breeding season, new pairs may not be formed each year. Social displays by the birds are rarely seen but occur both at the nest and away from it.

The nest is a substantial structure at or near the top of a tree or large bush often in a swamp. Constructed of fine sticks, sometimes over a metre in length, laid over one another, the top is tramped into a platform. A layer of dried reeds and grasses about 20 centimetres thick is placed on top with a hollow for the eggs. It is possible that the non-brooding bird will also rest on the platform at night.

Both male and female take part in building or repairing the nest and in incubating the eggs. The same nest may be used year after year. Both parents feed the young by regurgitating food on to the floor of the nest. On hot days the parents bring water to the nest and regurgitate it over the upward-pointing bills of the begging nestlings. From the age of about 30 days the young are often left by themselves in the nest, and by this time they have developed a defence display which involves bill clattering, standing erect and lifting their wings. When they are 100–115 days old they are ready to leave the nest.

Black-necked Storks start their flight with two or three running jumps, and fly with slow flaps of their wings alternating with short glides. The birds often soar as high as several hundred metres, heads stretched out in front and legs trailing behind.

'Jabiru' is a commonly popularised name for this bird in the mistaken belief that it is Aboriginal. The name is actually Portuguese and given elsewhere to storks in South America and Africa. The only rational alternative for the Australasian species is Black-necked Jabiru.

Yellow eyes show the Black-necked Stork above is a female. Below, a brown-eyed male.

OTHER NAMES
Jabiru.

IDENTIFICATION
LENGTH: *About 1100–1300 mm (stands about 1200 mm high).*
ADULTS: *Sexes similar. Head, neck, scapulars and tail and broad band extending across centre of both upper and lower wing surfaces glossy green-black. Rest of plumage white. Adult males have dark eyes, females yellow eyes. Bill black. Legs and feet red.*
IMMATURES: *Grey-brown with back rump, breast and belly dull white. Eye dark brown. Bill black. Legs and feet dusky.*
DOWNY YOUNG: *Off-white with grey crown; bill dusky; feet flesh-coloured.*

VOICE
Apparently none, but clattering sounds made by shaking bill up and down in threat and dancing display.

NESTING
Breeds February–June. Nest a large, bulky stick platform, up to 1.8 m wide and 0.9 m deep, built high (up to 25 m) on top of large tree. Eggs: two to four; white; oval, about 72 x 53 mm. Incubation by both sexes. Young fledge in 100–115 days.

DISTRIBUTION
Along north and east coasts, sometimes as far south as Sydney, but less common in southern part of range. Rare vagrant to Victoria. Frequents lakes, swamps, freshwater pools and mangroves. Also in New Guinea and southern Asia. Two races; one with bottle-green neck in Australasia.

Glossy Ibises feed in shallow water and mud flats. The smaller bird with white striations on the neck is immature.

Glossy Ibis *Plegadis falcinellus* (LINNÉ, 1766)

THE COSMOPOLITAN Glossy Ibis, the smallest ibis in Australia, looks black when seen from a distance. It is only when seen close up that its red-brown colouring and the metallic iridescent sheen on the wings become noticeable. In flight they resemble Black Cormorants, their regular flapping alternating with short glides, but they hold their necks lower, inclined towards the ground.

Glossy Ibises are gregarious birds and feed in small flocks of two–thirty or more in shallow freshwater swamps and mud flats, particularly where trees and bushes provide shelter. They walk along and probe their bills into the water and mud, searching for frogs, snails, spiders and aquatic insects. Sometimes they eat beetles and grasshoppers, which they peck off plants.

Nesting in small colonies of 10–20 pairs, Glossy Ibises may breed within colonies of Straw-necked and Sacred Ibises. They start breeding later than the other ibises and build their nests sometimes lower, just above water level or on the periphery. Egg-laying extends about five weeks, after the other ibises have completed their clutches.

Of the several eggs laid, most hatch but only one young may fledge. Brooding commences as soon as the first egg is laid which means that young hatch in sequence. The first chick to hatch may out-compete later hatchlings for food, and so the latter die.

Near the nest, Glossy Ibis mates bow to and preen each other. As they bow they make guttural cooing sounds.

About two weeks after hatching the young begin to roam over the nesting bushes and mix with the young of Straw-necked Ibises. They differ from the latter in having two flesh-coloured bands on their black bills. The young are able to fly at about one month and can feed themselves. They feed with their parents during the day and roost with them very late at night, settling in the trees with other species of ibises, spoonbills and herons.

Glossy Ibises may be more specific in their food requirements than other ibises, particularly the Straw-necked. Wandering nomadically in search of feeding grounds, they do not use regular breeding sites. Their core breeding range, however, seems to be the Murray–Darling basin, from which they disperse autumn and winter to seek refuge in the wetlands of coastal northern Australia.

OTHER NAMES
Black 'Curlew'.

IDENTIFICATION
LENGTH: *About 490–550 mm.*
ADULTS: *Sexes similar; males have longer bills. Both dark red-brown when breeding with metallic, iridescent green sheen on wings. Head dusky, streaked white in non-breeding birds. Naked face blue-grey with white rim in breeding birds. Bill olive-brown. Legs, feet and eye brown.*
IMMATURES: *Duller in colour than adults with dusky breast and belly and bill less curved. Head and neck patchy white.*
DOWNY YOUNG: *Dusky with white crown band; bill black, with two flesh-coloured bands.*

VOICE
Croaking thu-thu-thu-u *call during flight; grunting* arrh *and* eh-eh-eh-h *during breeding displays.*

NESTING
Breeds September–April. Nest a platform of sticks, generally with a lining of aquatic plants. Nest built between upright branches of bushes or trees growing in water in secluded areas. Breeds together with other ibises in small colonies. Eggs: up to six, most frequently three; green-blue; elongate-oval, about 52 x 35 mm. Incubation by both sexes; both feed young, by regurgitation.

DISTRIBUTION
Frequents swamps, lake margins and flats, and fields near water throughout mainland Australia. Nomadic or migratory. Seen only occasionally in eastern Victoria, northern Queensland, and central Australia. Occurs also in North and Central America, Africa, southern Eurasia and New Guinea. Vagrant in Tasmania and New Zealand. No races.

Sacred Ibis

Threskiornis aethiopicus
(LATHAM, 1790)

OTHER NAMES
White Ibis, Black-necked Ibis.

IDENTIFICATION
LENGTH: *680–750 mm.*
ADULTS: *Sexes similar; males have longer bills. Both white, except for black tips of primary and plumed outer secondary feathers; spiny white plumes on breast. Head and neck naked and black with pink bands on nape. Naked scarlet stripe on underwing and on each side of breast. Eye dark brown. Bill black and caruncled. Legs pink; feet purple-brown.*
IMMATURES: *Similar to adults but head and neck feathered spotty black and white, no breast plumes.*
DOWNY YOUNG: *White, with black crown and neck; bill and feet pink-flesh.*

VOICE
Flight call a grunting urk; koaha, taw-taw *and* taw-aw *when breeding.*

NESTING
Breeds in colonies September–April. Nest a platform of sticks, built on low plants, generally in secluded places. Eggs: two to five; dull white; oval, tapered, about 66 x 45 mm. Incubation 20–25 days, by both sexes. Young fledge in about four weeks.

DISTRIBUTION
Swamps, irrigated pastures and shallow lake margins in north and east; small but increasing colonies in southwest since 1950s. Nomadic. Also Africa, southern Asia to New Guinea and Solomons; vagrant in Tasmania, New Zealand. Six races; one in Australia.

The Sacred Ibis has no feathers on its black head and neck, which it sometimes immerses while feeding.

IN THE AIR, SACRED IBISES often fly in groups strung out in a stepped or V-formation, like the Straw-necked Ibises with which they often associate. All birds in the formation flap their wings at the same time, then all glide together. At times they soar, spiralling upwards on thermal air currents to almost 3000 metres, often accompanied by spoonbills and pelicans.

On the ground, the Sacred Ibis forages only in swampy or water-covered ground. In the water it moves its head from side to side continuously probing with its sensitive bill for food — crustaceans, especially freshwater crayfish, water insects, fish, snails and frogs. It also eats crickets, earthworms and, occasionally, small snakes. Sometimes it holds its head and the upper part of its neck under-water when feeding. When an ibis feeds on mussels, it holds the mussel by one foot on a hard surface and breaks the shell open with hard blows of its bill.

Sacred Ibises do not begin breeding until their nesting grounds are flooded to a particular depth, usually at least a metre. It is a safeguard against failure, for breeding grounds on inland swamps undergo great fluctuations of inundation and, when drying rapidly, are virtually deserted by the birds.

At the start of breeding, flocks of males select a breeding site — generally the site used in previous years. Each bird establishes a display territory on a nearby tree branch and becomes very noisy and aggressive towards other males, raising his feathers, snapping his bill and displaying the scarlet bare patches under his wings.

Once a male has secured a display territory, he flies down to the bushes below and tramples a small area for a future nest site. When the females arrive, the males attract them by deep bows from their branches. A female lands as close to a male as possible. Then the male flies down to the nest territory, where he grasps a twig in his bill and performs several bows until the female flies down. Pairing is forged when both grasp the twig and preen one another.

After copulation the male collects nest material by removing branches from bushes, and brings them to the female which constructs a platform nest. Both birds incubate the eggs in shifts and greet each other with deep bows when changing over. Both also care for the young, one standing guard while the other gathers food.

Young ibises solicit food by calling insistently and flapping whichever wing is closest to the adult. Wrapping this wing around the parent's head, it pulls it down to reach in for food regurgitated from the capacious crop in the adult's throat. Parents do not feed young indiscriminately, not commencing until they have established vocal contact. The young stay together after leaving the nest, settling on bushes for a further two weeks before they begin to fly, and afterwards congregate on trees nearby where they are still fed by the parents.

Once independent, young ibises may disperse over distances as far as 1200 kilometres. The longest journey recorded is from southern Victoria to New Guinea, more than 3000 kilometres. Movements appear to be north–south rather than east–west.

Straw-necked Ibis *Threskiornis spinicollis* (JAMESON, 1835)

STRAW-NECKED IBISES ARE THE most abundant and widespread of Australia's ibises, gathering to breed in colonies of up to 200000 birds and dispersing over dry plains as well as marshy wetlands to forage. Crucial to their survival is the maintenance of suitable breeding habitat inland, particularly in the Murray-Darling basin.

At the start of breeding, large flocks search for nesting islands and swamp thickets, often returning annually to the same areas. When courting, the birds display on each side of the breast and behind the eye a red patch of skin which fades as soon as pairing has been completed at the nest site. They bow to each other, sometimes with their wings partly open, after which mutual preening signifies pairing. With the straw-like feathers on their necks raised, they start pecking at neighbouring single birds; those that are unsuccessful in attracting a mate are chased away.

The male brings sticks, and the female works and pushes them into the nest. Copulation occurs several times, and when the eggs are laid the birds incubate in shifts, bowing deeply to each other when changing over; they also bow to the young before feeding them. Three weeks after hatching, young wander from their nests and they are able to swim, although with some difficulty. In five weeks they can fly, but are fed by both parents for a further one or two. They may spend long hours resting on the shores or pastures near water and at night they roost in trees near the breeding area. Full maturity, however, is not reached for two years.

Straw-necked Ibises feed in both wet and dry pasture, eating not only water insects, molluscs, frogs and snakes, but also caterpillars and grasshoppers. An influx of the birds into an area may be associated with plaguing of locusts or other insects. They move seasonally between breeding areas over inland southern Australia and permanently wetter, coastal areas depending on rainfall in the drier regions; during the non-breeding season they usually roost in trees close to their evening drinking site.

OTHER NAMES
Dryweather-bird, Farmer's Friend.

IDENTIFICATION
LENGTH: *680–750 mm.*
ADULTS: *Sexes similar; male longer billed. Back and wings black with bronze-green sheen. Head and throat bare and black; upper neck buff with dark mottling; black band across upper breast in females, and stiff yellow straw-like feathers on lower neck of both sexes. Breast, belly and tail white. Naked yellow patches under wings and on each side of breast. Eye brown. Bill black and caruncled. Legs red; feet black. In courtship, breast skin and behind eye red.*
IMMATURES: *Dull; straw-like feathers absent; head feathered downy black-white. Bill short, straight.*
DOWNY YOUNG: *White with dusky head and neck; bill and feet black.*

VOICE
Long grunting u-u-urh in flight; orh-orh and urh-urh in display.

NESTING
Breeds in large colonies any time depending on flooding, mainly spring–summer. Nest a platform of sticks, sometimes lined with leaves, on rushes and shrubs, occasionally on ground. Eggs: up to five; dull white; oval, about 67 x 46 mm. Incubation 20–25 days, by both sexes. Young fledge in five weeks.

DISTRIBUTION
Swamps, lake margins, dry and wet pastures, sea shores. In all suitable situations, except Tasmania where it is nomadic or migratory. Also a vagrant in New Guinea. No races.

Male and female Straw-necked Ibises take turns incubating. They bow deeply to each other when changing shifts. They also bow before regurgitating food for the young, which are fed by the parents for six or seven weeks. Straw-necked Ibises breed in noisy colonies of as many as 200000 birds.

Royal Spoonbill

Platalea regia GOULD, 1838

OTHER NAMES
Black-bill Spoonbill.

IDENTIFICATION
LENGTH: *750–800 mm.*
ADULTS: *Sexes similar; male has
slightly longer bill. Both have white
plumage with long nuptial plumes on
crown and upper nape. Red spot on
forehead. Front of head black and naked
with warts. Naked areas under arms
yellow. Face and throat naked black. Eye
red; eyelids and a small patch above
and sometimes below eye yellow-ochre.
Bill straight with spoon-shaped tip,
black with caruncled central area slate.
Legs and feet black.*
IMMATURES: *Some black patches on
flight feathers, otherwise as adults; lack
nuptial plumes on crown, red patch on
forehead and yellow-ochre patches on
face. Bill rather smooth.*
DOWNY YOUNG: *White; bill and feet
flesh; face dusky.*

VOICE
*Single chew and cho calls and also
clapping of bill.*

NESTING
*Breeds October–May. A shallow nest of
sticks built on bushes or in trees up to
9 m, generally above water, nests singly
or in loose colonies together with ibises,
darters and small cormorants. Both
birds build nest. Eggs: up to four; dull
white with brown spots or streaks;
oblong-oval, about 65 x 45 mm.
Incubation by both sexes.*

DISTRIBUTION
*Frequents any shallow body of water,
large or small, marine or fresh. Occurs
in mainland Australia — mainly over
east and north — and Indonesia, New
Guinea and New Zealand. Vagrant in
Tasmania. No races.*

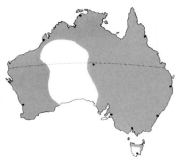

The Royal Spoonbill broods its chicks — as many as four — in a nest that is generally built over water.

AS THE ROYAL SPOONBILL WADES through the shallow waters of lagoons and marshes, or along the shore, it moves its partly open, vertically held, spoon-shaped bill from side to side. Each of the movements consists of slow sweeps or quick strokes. It grasps prey in the spoon-shaped tip of the bill and then, with an upward flick of the head, throws the food back and swallows it. In fresh water, fish is their main food, though spoonbills sometimes snatch insects off plants. They also eat crustaceans, after crushing them with the prominent knobs at the base of the bill.

When breeding begins the female Royal Spoonbill selects a branch on a tree near the nesting area. A male tries to obtain a place near the female, but at first she responds aggressively, flapping her wings and opening her large bill. She then pecks in his direction and both birds bob their heads. The male tries to nibble the female's bill and when he succeeds in doing so the pair bond has been formed. If any other bird comes near, the pair raise their nuptial crown feathers into a fan, causing the intruder to retreat.

Once the pair has formed, the female walks or flies towards the nest site where she starts to tug on some branches. The male follows her and while mounting her he grasps the same branch or twig that she is nibbling. The male then collects sticks, which the female arranges into a nest. Before and after the eggs are laid the birds spend much time on the nest or on the display branch, clapping their bills and preening each other.

The eggs are incubated by each bird in turn, while the other feeds or watches from the branch. Royal Spoonbills breed in loose colonies together with other spoonbills and ibises. At all times at least one bird is on guard duty. When disturbed this bird utters warning calls which prompt most sitting birds to flee the nest until the danger has passed. In the early stages of incubation, birds that are disturbed may desert their nests and eggs permanently.

When food is scarce in winter, or when adults are feeding their young, spoonbills will feed at any time of the day or night. They are nomadic birds and are usually found on shallow water, both fresh and briny. Between feeding grounds, they fly in formations similar to ibises and roost on the bare branches of trees.

Yellow-billed Spoonbill *Platalea flavipes* GOULD, 1838

FRESHWATER SWAMPS AND WATERWAYS are the habitat of Yellow-billed Spoonbills where they are much more solitary than Royal Spoonbills. They feed in shallow water both day and night, slowly side-sweeping their partly open bills through the water. Each sweep covers an arc of about 120 degrees. If the bill touches prey, the pattern of search changes to short rapid side-to-side strokes. The birds probe about water plants or submerged logs in this way, in contrast to the Royal Spoonbill which probes up and down.

Yellow-billed Spoonbills grasp anything that touches the inside of the spoon-shaped tip and use the teeth-like knobs in the bill to filter the food. Their bill is longer than that of the Royal Spoonbill with less prominent knobs and this probably accounts for the differences in food taken. Yellow-billed Spoonbills prey mainly on water insects, but also eat crustaceans, fish and molluscs; more than 700 items have been found in a bird's full stomach. When feeding, they walk through the water with a slow, deliberate tread, stirring debris and organisms from the bottom.

Yellow-billed Spoonbills go back to the same breeding areas year after year, as long as water is present. Their behaviour in courtship and mating is similar to that of the slightly smaller Royal Spoonbill and the two species are often seen in the same areas. In defence of nest sites male Yellow-billed Spoonbills become aggressive towards one another. They open their wings and bills and jump up, pushing each other with their long-toed feet like fighting cocks.

The young leave their nests after about four weeks and roam over nearby bushes and trees. When they are about seven weeks old they are able to fly and will follow the adults to the feeding places. The young congregate in large flocks to roost in trees above water.

OTHER NAMES
Yellow-legged Spoonbill.

IDENTIFICATION
LENGTH: *800–900 mm.*
ADULTS: *Sexes similar; male has longer bill. Both have white plumage with black tips to inner flight feathers. Face naked and fleshy with narrow black border. Eye yellow. Bill pale yellow, straight and spoon-shaped with fine transverse caruncles. Legs and feet pale yellow with black joints. Birds in breeding condition have blue tinge on face and spiny white nuptial plumes on breast. When feathers are new the white has a pink tinge. Base half of upper mandible and all of lower have narrow black lines running out from central ridge to bill edge.*
IMMATURES: *Face flesh-yellow without border line. Bill flesh-yellow.*
DOWNY YOUNG: *White; bill, face and feet flesh.*

VOICE
Single chhee *calls, and clapping of bill in threat and display.*

NESTING
Breeds September–April. A large nest up to 20 m above water or ground, of sturdy sticks on trampled-down rushes, bushes and in trees, usually but not always growing in water. Nests singly or in loose colonies, sometimes in mixed flocks with other species. Eggs: up to four; matt white; tapered-oval, about 68 x 45 mm. Incubation by both sexes. Young are fed by regurgitation from both parents and stay in nest until four weeks old.

DISTRIBUTION
Endemic to Australia, breeding mainly in south and inland areas, and only refuging on northern flood plains; vagrant to Tasmania, New Zealand, Lord Howe Island and southern New Guinea. Frequents freshwater swamps, dams and shallow lake and river margins. Nomadic and moderately common. No races.

The Yellow-billed Spoonbill retains its long nuptial plumes until the end of the breeding season.

Osprey *Pandion haliaetus* (LINNÉ, 1758)

DARK BROWN UPPER PARTS contrasting with white underparts and head distinguish the Osprey from other coastal birds of prey. In flight it can be identified by its bowed—rather than upswept—wings, and by a thin brown 'necklace' across its upper breast.

Ospreys are fishers and keep to coasts and the inlets of the larger rivers around Australia, except in the extreme southeast. Singly or in dispersed pairs, they are usually seen patrolling up and down the in-shore waters that make up their feeding and breeding territories, usually five–20 kilometres of coastline. The birds sail along at 15–30 metres above the water with a kite-like flap-flap-flap glide on long but round-tipped wings. Sighting prey they either swoop low over the surface to snatch it like a sea-eagle, or hang, drop and then plunge feet-first into the water with a great splash. Their plumage is compact, which reduces wetting.

Some dives are made from cliff tops or high vantage perches. Ospreys may submerge completely when seizing prey, but they soon reappear, flapping and gripping a fish headfirst in their talons; about 90 per cent of dives are successful. To eat their catch they fly back to a set perch or roost, usually grasping their prey with one foot behind the other. Sharp spicules on the soles of their feet help in holding slippery items.

Fish up to two kilograms are the Osprey's main food, but the birds also take occasional sea snakes. The water birds, mammals, crustaceans and amphibians that are sometimes eaten by Ospreys in the Northern Hemisphere have not been recorded in the diet of Australian birds.

Like other birds-of-prey, pairs of Ospreys perform spectacular aerial dives and swoops in courtship, at 100–300 metres above the nest. They climb upward on beating wings, the male hovering briefly at the top, and then both plunge down with wings closed and tail spread. The pair may also soar together, the male pursuing the female. At times he turns on his tail in midair near the nest, flapping heavily and even backwards, screeching, his feet sometimes holding a fish. Apart from during displays, calls are infrequent and feeble. Copulation usually takes place on the nest or at a perch near it, the male flapping to keep balance on his mate's back.

Nests, never colonial in Australia, can be huge. Not only are they added to year after year by the resident pair, but also throughout each nesting. Both male and female share building and nest repair, but the male brings most of the material while the female works it into the nest. Incubation begins with the laying of the first egg. The female shoulders the brunt of the brooding — although her mate may occasionally relieve her briefly—and she becomes completely dependent on him for food. He brings fish to the nest or a nearby tree and often starts to eat in sight of her before she solicits food from him, emitting a high-pitched *preek-preek,* and leaves the nest to take it and feed. Her appetite is reduced during incubation and she is brought only one–two fish per day.

Young hatch at intervals, yet despite bullying by the elder, the younger are rarely killed; rather they die if food is short. Feathers do not begin to grow through their down until about their 30th day, and during this time they are brooded and shaded constantly by the female. The male continues to bring all the food, stepping up the rate to three–five fish per day, according to the size of the brood. Peak hunting times are early morning, midday and evening.

It is the female, however, which passes the food on to the young. She tears up morsels of fish, starting with the head and continuing to the tail, and feeds the chicks rapidly, giving them up to 10 pieces a minute. Her calls to the male may spur him to bring another fish. Parental duties are clearly divided throughout breeding, the male doing all the hunting and the female staying at the nest to incubate, brood and care for the young. She continues to feed them for up to six weeks and irregularly thereafter, even after they have left the nest some eight weeks after hatching.

Young Ospreys return to the nest to roost for a week or so after fledging and use it as a feeding platform for some weeks. They learn or are taught to fish within a week of leaving the nest.

OTHER NAMES
White-headed Osprey, Fish Hawk.

IDENTIFICATION
LENGTH: *500–630 mm.*
MALE: *Head white to cream, occasionally sparsely flecked with dark brown on forehead and back of neck, with a broad dark brown stripe from eye to back of neck. Rest of upper parts brown with most feathers edged indistinctly with light brown or cream. Wings dark brown above; outermost flight feathers with black tips; underside white, indistinctly barred with black and cream, with dusky patch on bend of wing. Tail brown with white tip; paler and indistinctly barred below. Underparts white with fine band of light brown on lower throat and upper breast. Eye pale cream-yellow to yellow. Bill black with blue-grey base to lower mandible; cere blue-grey sometimes tinged blue. Feet bone to pale grey.*
FEMALE: *Similar, but crown and breast band more heavily marked with brown, forming a 'necklace'.*
IMMATURES: *Similar to adults but crown and neck band with darker brown flecks; tips of feathers of upper parts, broadly spotted white or buff. Upper parts, bill and feet lighter.*
DOWNY YOUNG: *First down smoky brown above, cream-white below, head and stripe down back sandy buff; second down speckled brown on undersurface.*

VOICE
Contact call a rather short, quavering whistle, pee-ee, pee-ee *or* tchip-tchip-tchip *or* chewk-chewk-chewk. *Shrill cheeping alarm cry,* kyick-kyick-kyick *or* kiweek-kiweek. *Female, when soliciting fish from her mate, emits high-pitched* pseek-pseek.

NESTING
Breeds August–November in south and July–September in north. Nest a bulky structure of sticks, roughly lined with grass and seaweed; on rocky foreshores and islands, cliff faces, trees and occasionally transmission towers; up to 30 m above ground. Eggs: two or three, occasionally four; matt white to buff-brown, blotched with chocolate- to purple-brown, at times with underlying purple-grey; oval, about 60 x 44 mm. Incubation about five weeks, by female.

DISTRIBUTION
Thinly distributed around coast, apparently more abundant in north. Single, white-headed subspecies in Australia, Pandion haliaetus cristatus, *is probably sedentary and ranges from Indonesian Archipelago southeastwards. Four or five races; one in Australia. Northern subspecies are migratory, breeding in North America, Eurasia, North Africa and Philippines, wintering in South America, South Africa and southern Asia east to Greater Sundas.*

A pair of Ospreys with their nestlings in their large bulky nest. The larger, darker-breasted female has her wings raised.

Pacific Baza *Aviceda subcristata* (GOULD, 1838)

A male Pacific Baza at its nest. It has darker breast bands than the female and a richer rufous crissum.

OTHER NAMES
Crested Hawk, Pacific Lizard-Hawk.

IDENTIFICATION
LENGTH: *350–430 mm; female longer-tailed than male.*
MALE: *Upper parts medium to dark grey-blue, tinged brown on back and shoulders; head darker, with lighter face; crest black. Wings broad and rounded; flight feathers mid to dark blue-grey above, paler below, with darker bars. Tail dark blue-grey above, paler below with a dusky bar near tip. Throat and upper breast mid-grey; chin lighter. Belly white to cream, with distinct black-brown bars; vent and undertail coverts rufous. Eye golden yellow; skin around eye yellow-green with blue tinge. Bill black above, with two-notched hook, lower mandible blue-grey with black tip; cere and gape blue-grey. Feet pale grey; claws dusky.*
FEMALE: *As male except crown, mantle and rump browner. Throat slightly whiter; upper breast lighter grey, occasionally tinged cinnamon. Breast bars chestnut-brown; vent and underwing coverts lighter rufous; tail has narrower subterminal bar.*
IMMATURES: *Head dark brown; crest black; back mottled brown and grey, each feather rufous-edged. Tail light silver-grey below, barred with four distinct dark bars. Chin white; throat and upper breast mottled light rufous, tinged with grey-blue. Belly rufous-cream, with slightly narrower bars than in adults; crissum sandy. Eye light yellow. Cere yellow-green to grey.*
DOWNY YOUNG: *Whitish.*

VOICE
A hoarsely whistled double call wee-choo *or* ee-chu, *commonly heard during breeding months; other calls include a double note* ke-i, ki-i *or* ki-o, ki-o *and short whistles and trills.*

NESTING
Breeds September–March, usually October–December. Nest a flimsy, slightly cupped structure of sticks, lined with twigs and a layer of green leaves, 280–380 mm across and 130–200 mm deep; egg cavity 130–150 mm across and 30–50 mm deep; may be used for more than one season. Usually set in a horizontal limb at 15–30 m above ground, rarely lower. Eggs: two or three, rarely five; rough to fine in texture with faint sheen; plain white with blue tinge, occasionally stained and blotched; rounded-oval, about 43 x 34 mm. Incubation about 33 days, by both sexes. Young fledge in 32–35 days.

DISTRIBUTION
Forests of coastal northwestern Australia from Fitzroy River to McArthur River, NT, possibly around Gulf of Carpentaria, and in east from Cape York Peninsula to about 280 km south of Sydney and inland to western fringes of Great Dividing Range. Also occurs from Moluccas through to Lesser Sunda Islands and in New Guinea and adjacent islands to the Solomons. About 12 races, one in Australia. Northwestern Australian populations slightly smaller than in the east.

QUIET AND UNOBTRUSIVE HUNTERS of the tree tops, Pacific Bazas live along the edges of eucalypt and rainforest, particularly the galleries of trees lining watercourses. They patrol the outer foliage, weaving through and around tree crowns, snatching their food—grubs, frogs, reptiles but mainly large stick insects (Phasmatidae) — from the leaves. Sometimes they crash into foliage, presumably to disturb prey; and they have been seen hanging upside down on branches, searching for food. Some insects are even caught in midair, the birds wheeling and somersaulting to take them.

Flight is slow, of leisurely flapping and gliding on broad, rounded wings, allowing the birds to manoeuvre easily and acrobatically. Pacific Bazas hunt at any time of the day, but mostly through the morning and later afternoon.

Although infrequently gathering in groups of up to nine—maybe family parties—Bazas are rather solitary birds; even though they are rather sedentary and probably permanently paired, they consort closely with their mates only when breeding. Nesting is heralded by spectacular aerial displays. The pair soar and circle often to considerable heights, and swoop and tumble while calling loudly. Flight then often undulates excessively, the birds plunging down then drawing up with vigorous flapping, and somersaulting and rolling over in midair.

Male and female share not only nest-building but also incubation and the brooding and feeding of young. Both protect the nest, raising their crests in threat or swooping in attack.

As young grow, the female spends much time attending the nest while the male concentrates on hunting. She brings fresh eucalypt leaves to the nest, cleans away all refuse and often intercepts food brought by the male, dismembering it and passing it to the young herself.

Letter-winged Kite *Elanus scriptus* GOULD, 1842

Letter-winged Kite nestlings, which are sometimes reared in loose colonies, are brought food by both parents.

CYCLES OF 'BOOM-AND-BUST' control the rarely seen Letter-winged Kite. For its food, the kite relies almost completely on one of the native Australian plague rats, *Rattus villosissimus,* which lives along the river channels of the Georgina–Diamantina–Cooper Creek river systems in northeastern central Australia. When, in good seasons, the rats plague, the kites thrive and breed prolifically, following the advancing hordes of rodents on whatever route they take through the inland basins.

Then, when drought ends the plagues, the populations of kites crash. Many birds die. Some hang on in desert pockets, partly on native and marsupial mice, to become the nucleus of the next boom. Still others disperse to all quarters of the continent where they live, for a time, on other rodents, reptiles and insects, including house mice, *Mus musculus.* One such group of almost a hundred reached Werribee near Melbourne in the summer of early 1977 after a crash inland at the end of 1976, but by the end of winter only a handful of birds were still alive. The direction of dispersal often seems to follow the direction in which rat plagues move, which may explain why so many kites reach Victoria.

To exploit the rats the kites hunt nocturnally, and roost and breed in colonies. By day they rest quietly in groups among leafy branches of trees, at times nestled against one another. As dusk approaches they become restless and emerge to sit out on exposed branches, and then, as soon as night falls, they fly out to hunt on their own. Rounder-winged than Black-shouldered Kites and gliding along with wings at shallower slope, they course and circle slowly and buoyantly, at 10–30 metres above the ground. Sighting prey, they hover slowly, almost hanging in the air, then drop silently on to it, talons first and wings stretched up above their heads. Captured animals are carried back in talons to a perch to be eaten.

Nesting colonies of Letter-winged Kites wax and wane with the supply of food, and the birds will raise brood after brood for as long as it lasts. Pairing is only for the season. In courtship, the male flies high, circling his mate on steeply raised, quivering wings. Then he descends to her and both circle together, quivering their wings and eventually mating on top of a bare branch in the nest tree. Both help to build a new nest each season, or to renovate an old one, first lining it with green leaves and later with the cast fur of prey.

Females incubate, brood, and dismember and pass food to the young while males do all the hunting until young are almost full-grown. Often when arriving with prey—at night, when the colony awakes to noisy activity—the male calls to his mate and she flies out with quivering display flight to take it from him in midair with her feet. Young acquire adult plumage within two–three months of fledging and may breed then, contributing to the Letter-winged Kite's ability to recover its numbers quickly.

OTHER NAMES
None.

IDENTIFICATION
LENGTH: *340–380 mm.*
ADULTS: *Sexes similar; female slightly larger. Face white merging to light grey on crown; black patch around eye. Nape, back and rump light to mid-grey. Primaries rounded, mid-grey with broad black 'shoulder patch'. Tail white with pale shafts. Underparts white with broad black line along underwing coverts and axillaries. Eye orange-red; skin around eye black. Bill black; cere green to yellow-grey or horn. Legs flesh-cream; claws black.*
IMMATURES: *Rusty grey-brown from crown to rump, mottled white on* scapulars, and broadly tipped white on flight feathers and wing coverts; reduced black 'shoulders' edged white. Cream-white centrally with mottled rusty breast band. Eye brown.
DOWNY YOUNG: *First cream-white, cream-grey; bill and feet black.*

VOICE
When breeding, rapid sharp whistles, similar to Black-shouldered Kite, but louder and harsher: kack-kack-kack, chirp-chirp-chirp or chip-chip-chip; repeated harsher kar; also screeches. Females and young call at nest wee-er, wee-er.

NESTING
Breeding opportunistic and sporadic, continuous when food ample; colonial. Nest a cup of light sticks and twigs, lined with leaves and often wool or rodent's fur; 400–800 mm in diameter; placed in upright fork, usually in thick foliage 1–12 m above ground. Eggs: three to six; matt white to cream, spotted and blotched with red-brown, concentrated at larger end; oval to rounded-oval, about 44 x 32 mm. Incubation 25–36 days, by female. Young fledge in 30–35 days.

DISTRIBUTION
Fluctuating range, centred in channel country of southwestern Queensland and northeastern South Australia, in Cooper, Warburton, Georgina and Diamantina river basins. Disperses erratically to all coastal districts. Hunts in open savanna near tree-lined watercourses; roosts and nests in trees along watercourses. No races.

The raised wing of the Letter-winged Kite shows the black pattern.

The Black-shouldered Kite hunts mainly at dawn and dusk.

Black-shouldered Kite

Elanus notatus GOULD, 1838

THIS ELEGANT RAPTOR IS Australia's representative of a worldwide group of 'black-shouldered' kites. From its relatives overseas it differs in many subtle ways: a *small* black spot under each wing; a short, square, all-white tail with dark shafts; and dark-tipped, more pointed wings which promote rapid, fluttering flight.

Its methods of hunting, however, are similar. From bare vantage perches on the top of trees or poles, the kite sails out over its grounds, fluttering and gliding on upswept wings, mainly after dawn and towards dusk. Sighting movement on the ground below, it hovers on its tail, then silently drops down on to the victim, dangling talons outstretched and wings swept up above its head. Rodents, reptiles, amphibians and insects are main prey.

In courtship a pair will soar and flutter together; and the male will sometimes dive at the female, which, turning in the air to present and lock claws, carries him whirling down. Breeding alone, they build a new nest each year; the male hunts, while the female passes food to the young until they are about two weeks old.

OTHER NAMES
None.

IDENTIFICATION
LENGTH: *330–380 mm.*
ADULTS: *Sexes similar; female larger. Upper parts pale grey. Primaries painted, dark grey; black patch at 'shoulder' of wing (lesser wing coverts). Head and neck white except for small black patch in front of eye. Tail white, square-cut. Underparts white except for small black patch under bend of wing. Eye orange-red. Bill black; cere yellow. Feet bright yellow; claws black.*
IMMATURES: *Darker on upper parts, with white edging. Crown, neck and breast mottled buff-brown. Wings mottled white and brown. Eye brown.*
DOWNY YOUNG: *Creamy white.*

VOICE
Rapidly uttered whistling chip-chip-chip *in display; hoarse wheezing* kair-kair *in defence.*

NESTING
April–October. Nest of sticks, lined with leaves, 20–25 m above ground. Eggs: three or four; white, blotched red-brown; oval, 40 x 30 mm. Incubation about 30 days, by female. Young fledge in five weeks.

DISTRIBUTION
Throughout mainland in woodlands and wetter savannas; irregular in Tasmania. Nomadic. No races.

Black Kite *Milvus migrans* (BODDAERT, 1784)

OTHER NAMES
Fork-tailed Kite, Allied Kite.

IDENTIFICATION
LENGTH: *480–550 mm.*
ADULTS: *Sexes similar; female slightly larger. Upper parts dark brown, edged paler. Flight feathers black. Tail dark brown with black bars, shallowly forked. Head and neck paler brown-grey with dark streaks. Rest of underparts rufous-brown with black shaft streaks. Eye brown. Bill black, grey at base; cere yellow. Feet yellow; claws black.*
IMMATURES: *Paler than adults, with upper and underparts spotted cream.*
DOWNY YOUNG: *Cream to pale fawn.*

VOICE
High-pitched quavering kwee-errr; *staccato* keee-ki-ki-ki *whistles.*

NESTING
Year-round; mainly September–November in south, March–May in north. Nest, a rough platform of sticks, about 60 cm in diameter up to 30 m above ground; also renovates old nest of

a crow or hawk. Eggs: two or three; white with sparse red marks; rounded-oval, about 51 x 42 mm. Incubation about 35 days, by female. Young fledge in 38–42 days.*

DISTRIBUTION
Tropical and dry northern inland Australia, occasionally large irruptions in southern Australia; in woodland and savanna. Also Europe and north Africa through southern Asia to New Guinea. Six races; one small and dark brown from Indonesia to Australia.

The Black Kite, seldom seen alone, is more scavenger than predator.

BLACK KITES ARE RARELY solitary, most often congregating in flocks of several hundred. They scavenge carrion and refuse, feeding on the ground, but also dive on to live rodents, reptiles and insects that may be flushed by a grass fire. Prey are caught in the talons and, if small enough, passed to the bill to be swallowed in flight. In hot weather, the kites may perch together in trees near a water hole, resting there with wings spread and beaks agape. Although foraging communally, the kites disperse to nest in pairs.

Both sexes build, but only the female incubates and tends the young, brooding them in their first week or so and later standing guard nearby for long periods. The male rarely feeds them but does most of the hunting. He brings food to the nest, carrying it in his talons, but he often transfers it to his bill before passing it to his mate. She tears off morsels to feed the young.

Black Kites fly leisurely with slow wing-beats and glides, stabilised by a constantly moving and twisting tail.

Brahminy Kite *Milvus indus* (BODDAERT, 1784)

SCAVENGING AROUND GARDENS and crops overseas, the Brahminy Kite lives only along mangrove-lined coastal inlets and bays on northern Australia and feeds mainly on fish. Only rarely does it take live prey, relying instead on fish and other marine animals stranded or cast up by the tide. Offal and scraps are part of its diet as well, and also frogs, crabs, snakes and insects which, if small enough, it catches alive, even in midair. Most prey are taken on the ground and eaten there but, if small, they are carried to a perch for despatch. The kite is incapable of killing live animals of large size.

To find food, Brahminy Kites soar in low tight circles, quartering their foraging grounds at usually less than 50 metres altitude. Their wings are held straight out horizontally and this — with their short, square tails—gives the birds a bat-like appearance. In Australia they are solitary, pairing only to breed, and never gathering in flocks or roosting communally as they do in India. Each bird seems to patrol its own stretch of shore, using high exposed perches in living or dead trees for resting and to survey.

Courtship and copulation may begin several months before nesting. Displaying pairs soar over the nest site and perch in tall trees, calling at intervals; occasionally they also join to clasp feet in midair and come whirling down for 100 metres or more. The female does virtually all incubating and brooding while the male hunts and brings food to her, calling her off the nest to feed and pass food to the chicks. As the young grow and learn to feed themselves, from about three weeks of age, both parents hunt, returning only briefly to drop food at the nest.

The handsome Brahminy Kite can be found near rocky shores and beaches around northern Australia.

Whistling Kite *Milvus sphenurus* (VEILLOT, 1818)

Whistling Kites about to touch down, their long rounded tails and longer 'fingered' wings outspread. The Whistling Kite looks similar to the Little Eagle, but the feet of the latter are feathered right down to the toes. Whistling Kites are found in open woodland throughout Australia.

GLIDING SLOWLY AT LOW ALTITUDES, or soaring high into the sky, the Whistling Kite is a graceful bird. It flaps with slow wing-beats, and when gliding holds its wings horizontally but bowed downwards at the tips. As it flies it sometimes utters its loud whistling call but does not twist its tail when manoeuvring.

The Whistling Kite is found throughout Australia, but it is most common in open wooded country near swamps, rivers, or the coast, avoiding the settlements and slaughter yards frequented by the Black Kite. Although rather sedentary, it will shift about, congregating on irruptions of prey in the inland and leaving during famines. It is also somewhat communal. Small groups commonly gather on large kills, but just as often the kites forage alone; large loose flocks of 100 or more are rare.

Like other kites, it sails about searching for living or dead prey on the ground, swooping down and feeding on it there if it is too large to be carried. Although taking live animals—small mammals, reptiles, birds, fish, crustaceans and large insects—it is as much a scavenger, feeding on carrion of any sort including animals killed by traffic on roads.

Whistling Kites are opportunistic breeders, pairs sometimes courting in groups and tolerating one another's nests in the same tree. Courting birds soar about the nest tree without spectacular aerial manoeuvres but call much, both from high exposed perches and in flight. Most pairs return to use the same nest—of sticks lined with fresh green leaves—year after year, or even twice a season, adding to its bulk each time.

Like other kites, the female incubates and broods while the male hunts, and passes on all food to the chicks when they are young.

OTHER NAMES
Carrion Hawk, Whistling Eagle.

IDENTIFICATION
LENGTH: *500–550 mm.*
ADULTS: *Sexes similar; female larger. Head and neck plain pale buff-brown with little streaking. Back and upper wing coverts mid-brown; flight feathers dusky. Tail pale grey-brown. Underparts buff, faintly streaked brown. Underwings with buff-brown coverts and inner primaries, forming bar between outer primaries and secondaries. Eye brown. Bill and cere dusky brown. Feet whitish grey; claws dusky.*
IMMATURES: *Darker; head, neck and underparts brown strongly streaked buff; back, shoulders and upper wing coverts thickly spotted buff. Spots disappear and head becomes paler at end of first year.*
DOWNY YOUNG: *Buff-white, darker on head and back.*

VOICE
Vocal. Call a long shrill down-slurred whistle followed by four–six rapid ascending short notes.

NESTING
Apparently breeds any time of year in warm regions where food supply is abundant; in southeastern Australia breeds in spring. Large nest of sticks, about 600–700 mm across, lined with fresh green leaves, 15 m or more above ground often in a dominating tree, usually by a river. Eggs: two or three; rough textured; pale white-blue, sparingly marked with red-brown blotches; oval, about 57 x 44 mm. Incubation by female. Young fledge in about six weeks.

DISTRIBUTION
Most common in open woodland near swamps, rivers, lakes and coast; avoids dense forest and treeless desert. Also in New Guinea, Solomon Islands and New Caledonia. No races.

Square-tailed Kite *Lophoictinia isura* (GOULD, 1838)

THIS LONG-WINGED, LONG-TAILED kite is harrier-like in its hunting. But unlike harriers which quarter fields and steppe, it skims and circles the tree tops. Its prey is mainly live small birds, insects and reptiles. These the kite spots and picks off from the outer foliage, particularly the nestlings of honeyeaters. It is an expert nest-robber, dipping and swooping to pluck young from their nests as it flies past. Fewer prey are taken on the ground and carrion rarely, if ever.

Flight is buoyant and manoeuvrable, the kites gliding smoothly on slightly upswept wings, flexing and turning their wing tips and constantly twisting their square-cut tail from side to side. Sometimes they soar high on thermal air currents; when they do flap for momentum, the movement is deep and leisurely. Dull whitish 'windows' towards the tip of each wing aid identification.

Although ranging over much of Australia, Square-tailed Kites are not abundant anywhere. Even in their preferred habitat — open eucalypt forest and woodland — they are solitary or well dispersed in territorial pairs. Pairing is probably permanent and the same nest may be used year after year. Both sexes participate in building and incubation but the female carries the main burden. She may leave the eggs only to hunt, the male relieving her then.

She also tends the young constantly, brooding them and passing on food brought by the male when they are young and, as they grow older, staying to roost at the nest and bring fresh green leaves each morning for lining. At first she may eat food brought by the male but later, as nestlings learn to feed themselves, leaves briefly to hunt on her own.

The male does most of the hunting and rarely stays long at the nest, simply dropping the food and departing quickly. As he flies off to hunt, alarm calls go off from other birds which may harry him if he enters their territories. Within a radius of some 200 metres of the nest, however, the kites are free of attack. Birds that they prey on also nest within that zone, in mutual tolerance.

Although resembling a kite in appearance and a harrier in its hunting, the Square-tailed Kite seems to be related instead to the eagle-like Black-breasted Buzzard. Like the buzzard, its juveniles are russet streaked with dusky, its eggs are heavily marked, and its feet are covered with distinctively fine reticulate scales.

OTHER NAMES
None.

IDENTIFICATION
LENGTH: *500–560 mm.*
ADULTS: *Sexes similar; female larger. Upper parts mottled brown-black. Crown, neck and all underparts rufous-brown streaked with black, blotched on breast; hind crown with short crest. Chin, face and forehead off-white. Upper wing grey-brown marked and barred dusky; underwing russet with rear half light grey barred dusky; outermost tips of primaries barred black and grey, with an off-white patch or 'window' towards end of each wing. Square tail light grey tipped black. Eye yellow. Bill brown-yellow, tipped black; cere buff. Feet and talons yellow-brown, unfeathered; claws black.*
IMMATURES: *Generally russet-brown over body. Head and underparts more finely streaked with black; upper parts tinged brown; rump off-white. Eye hazel to brown.*
DOWNY YOUNG: *Whitish.*

VOICE
Quick quavering call; also a yelp; usually silent.

NESTING
July–October. Nest 600 mm–1 m in diameter, of sticks brought by both birds; usually lined with eucalypt leaves. Generally placed on thick horizontal bough in eucalypt 12–26 m above ground. Eggs: two or three; coarse-grained, off-white boldly spotted and blotched with red-brown, purple-red or pale purple-grey; rounded-oval to oval, about 53 x 38 mm. Incubation 35–42 days, mainly by female. Young fledge in eight to ten weeks.

DISTRIBUTION
Thinly distributed through the open eucalypt forests, woodlands and sandplains of coastal and subcoastal mainland Australia. Least rare in southwest, north and northeast; more irregular in southeast and inland. Nomadic, but established pairs may be sedentary. No races.

When perched, this kite is distinguished by its pale face and eyes. Its folded wings are longer than its tail.

Black-breasted Buzzard *Hamirostra melanosternon* (GOULD, 1841)

In a situation never before recorded, this Black-breasted Buzzard is rearing a number of kestrel chicks. It is one of Australia's largest birds of prey.

THE PIONEER OF AUSTRALIAN ORNITHOLOGY, John Gould, reported that Aboriginals told his collector John Gilbert that the Black-breasted Buzzard was in the habit of breaking and eating the eggs of emus, brolgas and bustards. Despite rumour, the tale has never been substantiated. The main food of the Black-breasted Buzzard is live animals — reptiles, grasshoppers, a great variety of birds, and small mammals, including rabbits and sometimes wallabies. The buzzard does not molest sheep and seldom touches carrion. Like the Square-tailed Kite, it is an inveterate nest-robber and young snatched from the nests of other raptors are common fare for its chicks.

It takes most of its prey on the ground, often by a low swoop from a perch, and kills and usually eats it there. Sometimes it remains on the ground but usually it flies to a nearby exposed perch to digest the food. There it will remain, quiet and motionless, for hours. It spends much of its time soaring like an enormous bat in high, wide circles on thermal updraughts, with only an occasional laboured flapping of the wings. At other times it floats with peculiar side-slipping actions low over the treetops in search of prey. In flight the Black-breasted Buzzard is unmistakable. It is large and dark, the tail is short and square-cut, and the long round-tipped wings are held up at an angle to the body in glide, revealing a pair of large, round, white 'windows' at the base of the flight feathers.

Solitary birds, the buzzards are usually found alone or in pairs, whether in the open woodlands and savannas of northern Australia or along the eucalypt-lined watercourses of the inland. Groups are rare and usually comprise one or more family parties. Adults probably mate permanently and hold or return to the same breeding ground year after year. In courtship, the pair first soars slowly and silently in parallel, then separates by 100 metres or more, one bird slightly higher than the other. Then the higher bird — evidently the male — swoops towards its mate which rolls over on its back and presents talons. Without touching, the birds pass and separate to repeat the manoeuvre several times. Copulation takes place in a tree near the nest.

Both sexes may incubate, with the female bearing the brunt, and both evidently share hunting, brooding and feeding of the young almost equally. Whichever is hunting at the time brings prey to the nest and skins and tears it up to feed to the brooding or incubating adult. Only after it has fed does the brooding bird pass mor-

sels to the young. Although two eggs are the usual clutch, they are laid several days apart, so that one chick hatches first and takes the major share of food early in growth; often it is the only one to fledge, even in good years. Young remain dependent on their parents for several months after fledging, and may use nests for feeding and roosting platforms.

OTHER NAMES
Black-breasted Kite.

IDENTIFICATION
LENGTH: *550–600 mm.*
ADULTS: *Sexes similar, male slightly smaller. Head and back dusky black, edged russet-brown, with broad rufous ruff. Wings dusky black above with broad, almost circular, white 'windows' at base of flight feathers; shoulders edged with red-brown and pale grey. Tail short and square; grey-brown above, paler below. Throat, breast and upper belly varies from pale red-brown with black shaft streaks to rich coal-black, according to colour phase. Flanks, lower belly and undertail coverts red-brown. Underwing coverts pale rufous with black and white mottling; underwings grey with white 'windows'. Eye light to deep brown. Bill pale grey to flesh grading to black at tip; cere pale leaden to dirty white. Feet and toes pale grey to flesh coloured. Scaly legs.*
IMMATURES: *Red-brown to fawn above and below, like adults of pale birds, with dusky shaft streaks to feathers of back and undersurface.*
DOWNY YOUNG: *White for first two weeks, then russet. Eye light brown; cere pale blue. Feet and toes white.*

VOICE
Short, sharp two- or three-syllable cry, between a whistle and a scream, often repeated rapidly; uttered most frequently during breeding. Also short, rasping yelp repeated at intervals of one or two seconds, in alarm.

NESTING
Breeds in July to December, laying mostly September–October, earlier in north. Nest a large coarse platform of sticks 700–1200 mm in diameter in fork of tree, 6–20 m above ground. Uses same nest year after year if not disturbed, lining it with green leaves. Eggs: one to four, usually two; matt white to pale buff, finely freckled to boldly blotched with rust-red, purple-red, chocolate and lilac; rounded-oval, about 62 x 50 mm. Incubation about 40 days, by both sexes. Young fledge in about 60 days.

DISTRIBUTION
Throughout northern interior and along adjacent coasts. Nests on eucalypt-lined inland watercourses. Occasionally wanders south to Darling Range, WA, eastern Australian mallee and Darling Downs, Qld. Nomadic; vagrant in Melbourne and Tasmania. No races.

Brown Goshawk *Accipiter fasciatus* (VIGORS & HORSFIELD, 1827)

OTHER NAMES
Australian Goshawk, Chicken-hawk.

IDENTIFICATION
LENGTH: *Male of southern forms 400–430 mm; female 470–560 mm. Male of northern forms 370–400 mm; female 430–460 mm.*
ADULTS: *Sexes similar. Upper parts grey-brown, occasionally tinged blue, especially on head; sides of face paler. Rufous collar around neck. Tail brown finely barred with darker brown, round-tipped. Throat pale grey flecked white. Underparts finely barred cream and pale to rich russet. Thighs have rufous tinge with fine barring. Eye and naked eye-ring yellow. Bill blue-grey with darker tip; cere green-yellow. Feet yellow; claws black.*
IMMATURES: *Upper parts mottled and off-white; shoulders dark, feathers edged rufous. Throat and upper breast white with broad brown streaks. Rest of underparts coarsely barred cream and dark chestnut-brown. Eye changes from brown to yellow between 75 days and three months; eye-ring yellow-green. Bill blue-grey with darker tip; cere blue-grey. Second-year plumage, kept for about a year, differs from adults in that head is slightly darker, collar is absent or tinged grey; bars on underparts are darker and broader; throat and breast have a blue-grey suffusion; tail bars more pronounced.*
DOWNY YOUNG: *Creamy white; eye dark; cere and feet pale blue.*

VOICE
At most times silent, but utters shrill chatter when approached, in defence of nest or when disturbed or excited in display; si-si-si-si *or* kek-kek-kek *from female and* wit *or* weet *from male. Also slow, repeated* swee, swee swit, seep *or* sceep.

NESTING
Breeds August–January. Nest up to 70 cm in diameter and 30 cm deep, of sticks and twigs, lined with green leaves; usually in horizontal fork 7–31 m above ground. Eggs: one to five, usually two or three, laid at two–four day intervals; smooth, matt white or blue-tinged, sparingly blotched with red-brown, dark brown or lavender; swollen oval, about 46 x 37 mm. Incubation, beginning with second egg, 29–33 days, mainly by female. Young fledge in four-five weeks.

DISTRIBUTION
In a wide range of woodland and open forests throughout Australia, but particularly along tree-lined watercourses and water holes. Pale northern race Accipiter fasciatus didimus *appears to be sedentary and restricted to subcoastal northern Australia. Larger southern forms A. f. fasciatus and rufous A. f. cruentus in southern Western Australia mostly found south of Tropic of Capricorn during August–January, but are nomadic and migratory and immatures scattered throughout northern range in winter months. Also in New Guinea, Lesser Sundas and New Caledonia–New Hebrides where another nine-ten races.*

LIKE MOST GOSHAWKS, the Brown Goshawk is a skulking predator that hunts by stealth. Silently and secretively it works from tree to tree in short flights, landing briefly within cover to look about and then flying on or diving sharply on to surprised prey. Most prey — not only birds from wrens to domestic fowl, but also mammals up to the size of a rabbit, and reptiles, frogs and large insects—is stationary and usually snatched from the ground or a perch. That, however, does not stop the goshawk from occasionally pursuing flying birds. These it often hunts at dusk when they are settling to roost.

Although appearing solitary, Brown Goshawks are fairly abundant throughout their habitat—drier open eucalypt forests and woodlands and tree-lined watercourses inland. Rarely do they move out of cover on to open grass plain and heath. Established pairs are sedentary and breed in the same area—and often the same nest—year after year. Young birds looking for territory disperse much further, those in southern Australia even migrating to the far north in winter.

The farthest distance so far recorded of banded goshawks is 900 kilometres. Flight is slow and usually low, of a series of quick wing-beats broken by long, flat glides. At times the goshawks also soar in circles above the trees.

As breeding approaches, mated pairs re-establish territory aggressively, calling much and flying in display together to considerable height where they circle in unison and dive and chase one another.

Nests can be a kilometre apart if food is abundant. Both sexes build, males as well as females working material they have gathered into the structure. Building is finished within two to four weeks, and thereafter the nest is re-lined with fresh leaves early each morning until young are well grown.

The female shoulders the brunt of incubation and brooding but is relieved by her mate for an hour or so on most mornings when she leaves to hunt or feed on prey brought by the male. The male does most of the hunting for the brood, giving his catches to the female at a perch near the nest. These she carries to the chicks, apportioning them evenly.

Young are brooded until about 15–16 days old and continue to be fed by the female for another week or so. After that they learn to feed themselves but remain dependent on their parents for food for at least three weeks after fledging.

This female Brown Goshawk, moulting into second-year plumage, has coarser bars than an adult.

Grey Goshawk

Accipiter novaehollandiae (GMELIN, 1788)

A BOLD AND PERSISTENT HUNTER, this goshawk flies directly in pursuit of prey, striking suddenly at speed, and taking unwary birds by surprise or in ambush. It usually preys on small birds, mammals up to the size of a rabbit, reptiles, grasshoppers, cicadas, beetles and other insects. The female is larger than the male and can take bigger prey. The birds attack their victims in the air and on the ground, and will even chase them into dense undergrowth to capture them in their talons. Occasionally they soar to great heights, particularly in circling display flight, and then can be readily identified by their grey-white tones, broadly rounded wings, and long rounded tail.

Except for their more powerful talons and thicker-set bodies, Grey Goshawks are the same size as Brown Goshawks and take the same range of prey in the same way. Direct competition between them, however, is averted by preferences for different habitats. Grey Goshawks keep to heavy, humid forests, occupy rainforests wherever they are found and spread into eucalypt and paperbark woods only where they are dense or form tall galleries along streams. There the goshawks are rather sedentary, established pairs holding the same home range year after year; only birds looking for territory of their own wander beyond.

There are two colour phases of Grey Goshawks in Australia—one pure white, the other grey-backed. The distribution of the phases seems to be connected with habitat. Along the subtropical forests and jungles of the east coast, the grey phase is the more common. In the more open eucalypt forests of Tasmania, southeastern Australia and the northwest, however, the white phase predominates. Yet white and grey phases interbreed freely.

Pairing seems to be permanent, and both male and female build the nest, often using the same structure in successive seasons. Repairs may spread over several months. The female undertakes most of the incubation and brooding, but her mate will relieve her for an hour or so each morning while she feeds. He also assists in bringing fresh leaves to line the nest. After young hatch, he does all or most of the hunting for the brood, bringing food which the female takes, tears up with her bill, and passes on to the young.

In its grey phase, the Grey Goshawk is found mainly in heavy forests.

The white phase of this goshawk is common in open forested areas.

OTHER NAMES
White Goshawk, Grey-backed Goshawk.

IDENTIFICATION
LENGTH: *340–540 mm.*
ADULTS: *Sexes similar; female distinctly larger. White phase: plumage completely white. Grey phase: upper parts light to mid blue-grey; outer webs of flight feathers mid blue-grey, inner webs light with slight barring. Tail firmly barred above; light grey and indistinctly barred grey-brown below. Underparts white; neck, upper breast and sides of belly lightly barred light grey-brown; some birds lack breast bars. Both phases: eye vermilion to red-brown, with lemon-yellow skin around eye. Bill black; cere golden yellow. Feet golden yellow; claws black.*
IMMATURES: *Those of grey phase similar to adults, except for a light grey-brown neck, the feather edges tinged light rufous. Underparts have broader grey-brown bars; throat is slightly mottled. Maturity reached in two years.*
DOWNY YOUNG: *White-phase chicks covered with white down; eye brown-yellow, bill dusky, cere yellow, feet pale yellow. At 14-15 months eye changes to apricot, especially at centre. Grey-phase chicks covered with white down, growing light slate-grey wings and slightly barred tail. Eye dark brown, bill dusky, cere and legs yellow.*

VOICE
Musical call rising in pitch, repeated many times; loud ku-wit, swee-swit; soft, repeated queet; repeated contact call weep-weep when breeding; shrill chatter when aggressive. Male's call is more rapid than female's. All calls given mainly during nesting and courtship; otherwise silent.

NESTING
Breeds July–December in southeast, January–May in northwest. Nest up to 500 mm in diameter, a solid construction of sticks lined with twigs and green leaves, usually in high fork in a tree 9–30 m above ground. Eggs: two to four, usually three; almost lustreless white with occasional pale blue to green tinge, or with red to purple-brown markings; oval, about 48 x 40 mm. Incubation about 35 days, mainly by female; usually only one brood raised per season. Young fledge in five–six weeks.

DISTRIBUTION
Heavy timber around coastal and subcoastal northern and eastern Australia, from the Kimberley Division to southeastern South Australia, Kangaroo Island and Tasmania. Sedentary or regionally nomadic. Also New Guinea, Moluccas, Lesser Sundas, northern Melanesia and Solomon Islands. As many as 19 races; one in Australia, grey- or white-breasted. All races on islands north of Australia are russet-breasted, with or without bars, plus white and sooty phases in New Guinea.

Collared Sparrowhawk *Accipiter cirrhocephalus* (VIEILLOT, 1817)

AN ACTIVE CHASER OF small birds, the Collared Sparrowhawk hunts by stealth. It watches from cover of leafy branches, then flashes out to snatch its unsuspecting victims mostly in midair but also from perches and on the ground. Rarely are attacking flights longer than 50 metres. Striking and seizing prey in its talons, the sparrowhawk carries it back to a sheltered perch to pluck and dismember with its bill. Although mammals, reptiles and large insects are taken occasionally, birds are primary prey.

The sparrowhawk's predatory technique determines its habitat: open forests and woodlands throughout Australia where there is cover from which it can hunt without being seen. Only open heaths, grass plains, steppes and the denser rainforests are shunned. In most areas, it overlaps the similar-looking but larger Brown Goshawk. Female sparrowhawks are particularly difficult to distinguish from male goshawks, and both fly in much the same way, interspersing quick flapping on rounded wings with long glides and circling. Sparrowhawks, however, have disproportionately longer and squarer-tipped tails and much longer middle toes. The two species avoid competing with each other for food by hunting in different ways for different prey—the Collared Sparrowhawk is more a pursuer of flying prey.

The female sparrowhawk incubates, broods and cares for young while the male does all the hunting. She often calls to him for food and when he brings it to a nearby tree, she flies out to take it from him, chatters briefly, and then flies back to the nest to feed it equally to all young. As a result most young are usually reared to fledge. The female tends the nest constantly, sits tightly and, with the male, defends the territory aggressively.

OTHER NAMES
Australian Sparrowhawk, Chicken-hawk.

IDENTIFICATION
LENGTH: *Male 280–330 mm; female 360–390 mm.*
MALE: *Upper parts grey-blue; sides of face lighter. Rufous collar round neck. Flight feathers duskier, with inner webs barred white to cream-brown towards base. Tail square-tipped, barred darker above, pale silver-grey with distinct barring below. Underparts and underwing coverts finely barred mid-rufous and white, washed greyer on throat; thighs rufous with finer barring. Eye and skin around eye bright yellow. Bill dark blue-grey to* black, lighter below; cere cream-lemon. Feet yellow; claws black.
FEMALE: *Upper parts browner grey.*
IMMATURES: *Upper parts grey-brown; mottled white on collar. Outer edges of feathers on back, rump and shoulders scalloped light rufous; flight feathers and tail darker than in adults, with more conspicuous tail bars. Throat and breast white to cream mottled brown or red-brown, lighter on throat and more barred on belly, thighs and vent. Skin around eye green-yellow. Bill lighter than adults; gape pale blue.*
DOWNY YOUNG: *White; eyes pale grey.*

VOICE
Aggressive swee-swee-swee; *loud, insistent* kee-yow; *typical repeated* see; sweep-sweep-sweep; *and shrill chatter* ki-ki-ki-ki-ki *in display.*

NESTING
Breeds July–December, mainly September–October. Nest a shallow 300 mm diameter platform of fine twigs, usually in a horizontal or vertical tree fork, 6–31 m above ground. Eggs: two to four, usually three; smooth, usually lustreless cream to blue-white tinged, at times sparsely speckled or smeared with light red-brown; oval to rounded-oval, about 39 x 31 mm. Incubation about three weeks, apparently by female only. Young fledge in about four weeks.

DISTRIBUTION
Woodlands and open forests; sedentary or regionally nomadic. Two or three races; one in Australia.

An adult Collared Sparrowhawk and its two chicks peer from their nest, a rough platform of sticks lined with green leaves, built each year.

A Little Eagle of the light phase with its white chick. Throughout the wide range of the species the light phase is more common than the dark phase.

Little Eagle *Hieraaetus morphnoides* (GOULD, 1841)

IN BOTH LIGHT AND DARK COLOUR PHASES, the Little Eagle is a rather sedentary bird, each pair spending much of the day soaring over their wooded terrain alone or together. On sunny days it will spiral tightly on thermal air currents, sometimes rising to great heights. In flight, both phases can be distinguished from the similar-looking Whistling Kite by their stouter build, short square tail and broader, more rounded wings which are turned slightly up at the tip, not drooped. Little Eagles have a short, erectile crest and are the only eagles other than the Wedge-tailed to have fully feathered 'legs' down to the toes.

The Little Eagle is a leisurely hunter which prefers live prey, but will occasionally eat carrion, including dead rabbits. It searches for prey by flying and gliding over wooded country, or by watching from a commanding position in a nearby tree where it rests for long periods. Its prey includes small mammals, reptiles, large insects and occasionally other birds. In country infested with rabbits, their young, about one-third grown, are its chief food. Little Eagles usually kill and eat their prey on the ground, or carry it up to a stout tree branch so escaping the attention of piratical and scavenging birds such as kites, crows or ravens. They pluck and eat alternately, anchoring prey in their talons and pulling it apart with the bill.

Pairs probably mate for life. Before and during breeding, the male performs steeply undulating display flights over his territory, calling loudly, and circles with the female, diving down at her from above while she rolls to present claws. Occasionally a pair will also perch near one another or in adjacent trees, face each other and bow and peer; the purpose of this display is not known. At the nest, the female does nearly all incubating and brooding and she feeds the young with prey brought by the male; the male provides for the family and early each morning brings fresh leaves for the nest.

OTHER NAMES
None.

IDENTIFICATION
LENGTH: *Male about 480 mm; female about 550 mm.*
ADULTS: *Sexes similar. Two colour phases. Light-phase birds are light and dark brown above with black flight feathers and paler band on wing coverts. Head, neck and upper breast russet; small erectile crest with black-tipped feathers; black streak below eye. Tail square-cut grey-brown above with dark brown bars; nearly white at tip. Underparts mainly white or pale buff, with few chestnut streaks. Dark-phase birds have upper parts chiefly dark brown with paler band on wing coverts. Underparts mainly dark brown with black streaks. In both phases eye brown; bill dark brown or grey with grey cere; feet feathered down to pale blue-grey toes; claws dusky.*
IMMATURES: *Underparts chestnut in light-phase birds; darker brown than adults in dark phase.*
DOWNY YOUNG: *Snowy white; eye pale brown; cere yellow; feet flesh.*

VOICE
Normal call a soft whistling note of two or three syllables with the second and third syllables shorter and lower in pitch. Also a longer series of whistles, starting slowly and ending rapidly, falling in pitch. Trilling screams in display flight; peeping notes with prey.

NESTING
Breeds August–November in southern Australia. Builds or reuses a large stick nest about 800 mm diameter lined daily with green leaves, placed high in a tree, 10–45 m above ground. Eggs: one or two; white tinged with blue, with red-brown streaks and blotches; rounded-oval, about 55 x 44 mm. Incubation about 30–35 days, mostly by female. Usually only one young fledges, in about 50 days.

DISTRIBUTION
In wooded country over much of mainland Australia. Sedentary or nomadic. Two races: one in Australia; the other, smaller, in New Guinea.

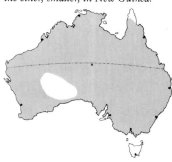

Red Goshawk *Erythrotriorchis radiatus* (LATHAM, 1801)

OTHER NAMES
None.

IDENTIFICATION
LENGTH: *450–580 mm.*
ADULTS: *Sexes similar; female longer. Head and neck white, heavily streaked dusky with russet cast on crown. Shoulders, back and rump mottled dusky and russet, with broad russet scalloping on wing coverts. Flight feathers grey barred black, lighter below; underwing coverts russet. Tail mid-grey clearly barred black, paler below. Chin and throat white streaked dusky, becoming flushed with russet on streaked breast and belly; flanks, thighs and undertail coverts richer russet, without dusky streaks. Eye yellow. Bill black, becoming greyer at base; cere pale grey. Feet heavy, yellow; claws black.*
IMMATURES: *Evidently more russet than adults, with entire undersurface cinnamon-rufous streaked dusky. Either that or Red Goshawks are dimorphic with a rufous-breasted phase. Eye brown.*
DOWNY YOUNG: *Snow-white; bill dusky with yellow gape.*

VOICE
High-pitched chatter skeep-skeep-skeep-skeep-skeep *when alarmed, otherwise not as rapid or as shrill as in other goshawks.*

NESTING
Breeds April–November during dry season in north; possibly only August–November in east. Nest of sticks and twigs and green leaves in vertical or horizontal fork 7–25 m above ground. Abandoned nest of crow or another hawk sometimes rebuilt. Eggs: one or two; slightly coarse; dull white to blue tinged, sometimes sparsely blotched with brown; swollen-oval, 53–57 x 42–46 mm. Incubation by female. Young fledge in seven–eight weeks.

DISTRIBUTION
Tropical open woodland, forest woodland, edges of rainforest, and dense riverine vegetation of coastal and subcoastal north and northeast, from the Kimberleys, WA, almost to Hunter River, NSW. No races.

The Red Goshawk is a secretive and solitary bird in its northern habitat.

THE RED GOSHAWK is Australia's rarest and least-known raptor. Despite its imposing size and powerful talons as big as a small eagle's, it is a secretive and solitary bird in its hunting and breeding habitat: the taller woodlands, open forests, and stream-side galleries of trees in northern Australia. Like other goshawks it hunts by stealth through and beneath the canopy of its woods, working from tree to tree and snatching unsuspecting prey from a perch, on the ground or even in midair. Birds are main targets—honeyeaters, parrots, kookaburras, nestlings, herons and other waterbirds—but it also takes occasional mammals, reptiles and large insects. Much hunting is done at dusk and dawn.

Established pairs seem to occupy the same large territory and use the same nest year after year. Often they hunt at least three kilometres from the nest. The female builds alone, taking about three weeks to refurbish the nest and lining it daily with green leaves. She also seems to incubate and brood unaided, but leaves once or twice a day to be given food by the male, usually in the morning. She eats it then and there and is rarely off the nest for more than 20 minutes.

The male does all the hunting until young are well grown and calls the female off the nest to take his catches. After plucking and pulling them apart, she passes them on to the young. Only in the last weeks before fledging will the male drop food at the nest while the female is also away hunting.

Spotted Harrier *Circus assimilis* JARDINE & SELBY, 1828

The Spotted Harrier is the only tree-nesting harrier. It is also the most brilliantly coloured of any Australian raptor.

LIKE ALL HARRIERS, the Spotted Harrier hunts by hedge-hopping. Replacing the much browner Swamp Harrier on the dry, open grass plains and shrub steppes of inland Australia, it patrols the countryside methodically with slow flapping and long glides on upswept wings, usually within five metres of the ground. Beating a few times to wind, it then soars low, side-slipping to leeward, repeating the tacks over and over with precision. Surprising prey, the harrier plummets down on to it—whether a small mammal (rabbit, rat, mouse) or ground-dwelling bird, a reptile or large insect. All prey is captured on the ground and the harriers rest and roost there, taking shade under bushes on hot days.

Spotted Harriers are solitary and nomadic and irrupt on booms in their prey. It is then that they find temporary mates. In display they fly to a great height, then descend in slow spirals and side-slips, occasionally plummeting with half-closed wings. Both sexes build a new nest every year and bring fresh green leaves throughout breeding. The male may also help with incubation and brooding while the female assists him in hunting. Although most of a clutch are often reared, there is a definite pecking order among the chicks. The dominant cows the rest, some of which may starve or be pecked to death if food is short. The old nest serves as a flying platform and roost for young in their first few days of fledging.

OTHER NAMES
Allied Harrier, Jardine's Harrier.

IDENTIFICATION
LENGTH: *Male 530 mm; female 600 mm.*
ADULTS: *Sexes similar. Upper parts mid blue-grey; wing-quills tipped black, and brown bars on upper wing coverts. Head grey with red-brown lines and red-brown ruff. Underparts and underwing coverts red-brown with white spots. Tail barred boldly dusky and grey-white. Eye yellow. Bill black; cere green-grey. Feet long, lanky, yellow; claws black.*
IMMATURES: *Upper parts grey-brown tipped buff-brown, rump pale, underparts russet-buff streaked dusky, tail grey with dull dusky bars.*
DOWNY YOUNG: *Ash-grey; eye dark; bill and cere as adult.*

VOICE
Alarm call a rapid kit-kit-kit-kit; *food call a loud whistling* seep; *also quieter* kitter, kitter, kitter.

NESTING
Breeds mainly July–October. Flat, bulky nest of sticks in low tree 2–15 m above ground. Eggs: two to four; white or blue-tinged; rounded-oval, about 48 x 40 mm. Incubation 32–34 days. Young fledge in four–six weeks.

DISTRIBUTION
Sparse and nomadic in inland and subcoastal regions. Possibly two races; one only in Australia.

Swamp Harrier *Circus approximans* <small>PEALE, 1848</small>

TRUE TO ITS NAME, the Swamp Harrier is usually seen singly or in pairs coursing low over the pasture of an open marsh, reed bed or rank field near water. It glides along on long upswept wings, flapping only sporadically. Surprise is a crucial element of its hunting, as it suddenly looms over its prey: water birds of all kinds, as well as small mammals, frogs, and reptiles and large insects. Like all harriers, it has an incomplete owl-like facial disc which improves its hearing, and long lanky talons for plucking its victims from thick growth while it stands clear. Swamp Harriers rest, roost, and feed on the ground, sometimes using a low stump, and often building platforms of weed in brakes of reeds for these purposes.

In Australia, Swamp Harriers are partly nomadic and migratory, southern birds shifting north in winter and back to breed in summer. As breeding approaches they display on the wing at great height, manoeuvring about, side-slipping and plummeting down and rising up on half-closed wings while whistling loudly. Several birds may display at the same time, and each ends its flight with dives over its own territory.

Both sexes build new nests each year in traditional territories, but only the female incubates, broods and feeds the young. The male does all the hunting while the female is sitting; he calls her off the nest to give her food in midair in a talon-to-talon pass near the nest. This procedure continues until young are about a week old, from which time both parents hunt and drop food at the nest. Most young fledge although the elder will kill and eat the younger if food is short; eggs are laid at several day intervals and hatch in that order. By four weeks, young are fully feathered and they fledge in another two, returning to the nest to rest and feed in the first week or two after taking their first flight.

Adult Swamp Harriers resemble immature Spotted Harriers but can usually be distinguished by their plainer grey tails. All Swamp Harriers show a whitish band on the lower rump in flight.

OTHER NAMES
Marsh Harrier, Gould's Harrier, Swamp Hawk.

IDENTIFICATION
LENGTH: *500–580 mm.*
MALE: *Mottled and streaked dark brown above, grading to plainer grey on tail and mid-grey dully barred dusky on flight feathers; a conspicuous off-white band across upper tail coverts. Underparts buff streaked dark brown, grading to plainer off-white on belly, flanks and crissum. Eye yellow. Bill dusky; cere dull lemon. Feet yellow; claws black.*
FEMALE: *Larger than male. Browner, with heavier streaking extending over belly, flanks and crissum.*
IMMATURES: *Dusky brown above, dark russet-brown and unstreaked below; pale area in underwing. Eye brown.*
DOWNY YOUNG: *White-grey; eye dark; bill and cere as adult.*

VOICE
Generally silent. Food call during breeding a high-pitched whistle, psee-uh. In courtship a short, loud, whistled kee-a or kee-o.

NESTING
Breeds September–January. Nest a 600 mm diameter platform of light sticks, reeds and weeds, lined with grasses; hidden in brakes of reeds or rushes over water, less often on ground among bushes or grain crops. Eggs: three to six, often four; dull plain white with blue tinge; rounded-oval, about 50 x 38 mm. Incubation 32–34 days, by female. Young fledge in about 42–46 days.

DISTRIBUTION
Flooded reed beds and wet pastures around coastal Australia, Tasmania, and inland river systems. Nomadic and migratory, Tasmanian birds wintering on mainland. Also New Zealand, southern New Guinea and islands in southwestern Pacific. Two races; one, large, in Australia.

Reed stalks and sticks over water make up the nest of the Swamp Harrier, a fairly common bird in swamps or open country near water. The nest is usually well hidden, and only the female incubates and takes care of the young.

The White-bellied Sea-Eagle builds a huge nest of sticks, often on a cliff. Here a female feeds her young. Both sexes defend the nest.

White-bellied Sea-Eagle *Haliaeetus leucogaster* (GMELIN, 1788)

OTHER NAMES
White-breasted Sea-Eagle.

IDENTIFICATION
LENGTH: *Male 760 mm; female 840 mm.*
ADULTS: *Sexes similar. Wings, back and base of tail dark ash-grey, broad tip of tail white. Head, neck and underparts, including undertail, white, often with faint dark grey shaft streaks. Eye brown. Bill blue-grey, black at tip; cere grey. Feet and toes off-white; claws black.*
IMMATURES: *First-year birds have all upper parts light brown with pale buff feather tips; tail light brown with white base; breast brown with buff*
edges to feathers; belly mottled brown and buff. Second-year birds mostly slate-brown above and light brown below; head and tail almost all white. Full adult plumage acquired at three to four years.*
DOWNY YOUNG: *White.*

VOICE
Loud clanging or cank-cank-cank, goose-like, call; sustained duets performed, with heads pointing skywards. More vocal during breeding season.

NESTING
Breeds May–October. Nest a huge structure up to 4 m deep of sticks,
30 m or more above ground, used annually for long periods. Nest also found in smaller trees in inland swamps, on coastal cliffs, or on the ground or rocks on treeless islands. Nest lined with stems of green leaves which are added throughout breeding. Eggs: two; plain white; oval, about 71 x 53 mm. Female does most of incubating and brooding but male relieves for periods during the day. Incubation about six weeks, mainly by female. Young fledge in 9–10 weeks.*

DISTRIBUTION
Found throughout coastal Australia, along coast and large lowland rivers and lakes. Also extends to inland lakes

and waterways along Murray River and its larger tributaries. Ranges from India and southern China through Indonesia to New Guinea. Sedentary or nomadic. No races.

GRACEFUL FLIGHT AND attractive grey-white tones belie the aggressiveness of this large, huge-taloned sea-eagle. It spends its time soaring and sailing over and adjacent to surface waters and bays, its long broad wings upswept, or perches on rock or exposed branches on prominent trees beside water. Pairs are permanent and hold the same hunting range year round, and have a few favoured perches where they rest, roost and often duet together morning and evening. In flight, wing-beats are slow and powerful.

The sea-eagles hunt from their perches or in flight, commonly diving on to fish, snatching them from the surface in a sweep of the talons, or picking up tortoises, sea-snakes, waterfowl, nestlings from rookeries, and even rabbits on land. Carrion is also eaten at

times, the birds landing on the ground to feed. They occasionally harry terns and ospreys as well, robbing them of their prey.

At the onset of breeding, displaying pairs soar and call much, loop the loop, drop fish from a great height, then dive to catch it in midair. There may be from one to several nests in a territory, and one is used each year, both sexes helping in reconstruction and adding to them until they become huge. Eggs are laid several days apart, but incubation begins with the laying of the first so giving the first hatched a head start. It takes all the food and cows the later young so that they eventually die. The female feeds her young with food brought by the male and broods and incubates with but brief relief from him (about 10 per cent of the time).

Wedge-tailed Eagle *Aquila audax* (LATHAM, 1801)

WITH A WING-SPAN OF UP TO 2.5 metres, the Wedge-tailed Eagle is the largest bird of prey in Australia. A lanky bird, it hunts by high soaring flight, circling up on thermal air currents for hundreds of metres and sailing out over the countryside, covering wide areas on upswept wings, its tail fanned and diamond-shaped. Sighting prey, it sweeps down onto it in a long, slanting swoop, but is more often unsuccessful than not when chasing live prey: rabbits, wallabies, small kangaroos and, where these are scarce, various ground-dwelling and swamp birds and reptiles. Nearly all prey is taken on open ground, and the eagles usually feed there.

Much carrion is taken too, the eagles sometimes congregating vulture-like in 20s and 30s at kills. Only rarely do more than two eagles feed on a carcass at a time, the others standing or perching nearby, digesting or waiting their turn. When, earlier this century, eagles were found on dead sheep or lambs, it was thought that they had killed them. Bounties were paid for their destruction. In one year in Queensland 10000 bounties were paid and between 1927 and 1968 in Western Australia another 150000. The practice has ceased since it has been realised that the eagles usually attack only poor, dying or dead lambs and have little effect on the sheep industry. Today they are protected in all states.

Most eagles congregating at kills are nomadic young birds. Adults mate permanently and hold to the same home range throughout the year, breeding there. They usually spend the hours around sunrise and sunset quartering part of their territory at tree-top level. For the rest of the day they either sit about on exposed perches or circle and glide, soaring for as much as 90 minutes at a time. Little time is spent maintaining territory but the eagles advertise occupancy by high aerial flights and may glide along presumed boundaries.

Acrobatic display flights herald breeding. The male dives down at speed at the female, pulls out and rises on part-opened wings. She ignores him or turns on her back to present claws, and they may loop the loop, calling much. Often in mid-morning and mid-afternoon they perch together and preen one another. They usually have several nests in their territory, one of which is used each season. Both sexes repair it, bringing in sticks in bill or feet, and the male lining it daily with fresh leaves when the female is incubating and breeding. He also relieves her on the nest occasionally, and does all the hunting until the chicks are too old to brood, bringing food to a perch near the nest and passing it to the female there. Prey, commonly rabbits, is roughly skinned and shredded by the female, and she passes morsels to the young, dripping with saliva at early stages. Brooding ceases at about 30 days when the pins of mature plumage begin to show through the chicks' down. Then both parents leave to hunt and bring food and leaves to freshen the nest. In a good season, two chicks may be reared, but mostly only one survives by killing its sibling. In arid, drought-affected regions, the birds may not breed at all for several years at a time.

OTHER NAMES
Eagle-hawk.

IDENTIFICATION
LENGTH: *Male 900 mm; female 1000 mm.*
ADULTS: *Sexes similar. General plumage black. Nape, wing coverts and undertail coverts dark russet-brown. Tail long and wedge-shaped. Eye hazel-brown. Bill dull white with dark tip; cere very pale yellow. Claws black.*
IMMATURES: *Upper parts brown; nape yellow to golden brown. Underparts dark brown with pale edges to feathers. Become gradually darker with age, but not blackening until five–six years old.*
DOWNY YOUNG: *White; eye grey; cere and toes pale yellow; bill dusky.*

VOICE
Repeated double whistle, pee-yaa; *also loud cat-like screech, especially when disturbed from nest; slurred* yessir *in aggression; loud mating screeches of double notes with rising inflection. Commonly silent.*

NESTING
Most eggs laid in June–August in southern Australia, earlier from April in the north. Nest a very large platform of sticks, 1–2.5 m diameter, lined with green leaves; fresh leaves are added regularly through breeding. Re-used and added to year after year. Usually placed in fork of tree, 1–30 m above the ground, sometimes on cliffs. Eggs: one to three, usually two; white to pale buff-grey, sparsely splotched with purple and brown; one egg invariably more lightly marked than other, and occasionally pure white; rounded-oval, about 73 x 58 mm. Incubation about 45 days, by female. Young fledge in 70–90 days.

DISTRIBUTION
Fairly common over forest and open country on plains and mountains throughout mainland Australia and Tasmania. Also in southern New Guinea. Two races: one on mainland; the other naped and large-taloned in Tasmania.

A Wedge-tailed Eagle feeding on a wallaby. Despite its imposing size, it is as much a carrion feeder as a hunter.

Grey Falcon *Falco hypoleucos* GOULD, 1841

The rare Grey Falcon.

OTHER NAMES
None.

IDENTIFICATION
LENGTH: *Male 340 mm; female 430 mm.*
ADULTS: *Sexes similar. Upper parts pale blue-grey with faint black shaft streaks; tail feathers barred darker grey. Primaries have black tips. Face and underparts grey-white with thin dark, shaft streaks; inconspicuous dark streak below eye. Eye brown. Bill dark grey. Eye-ring and cere bright yellow. Feet yellow; claws black.*
IMMATURES: *Darker grey than adults on upper parts. Head dark grey with more conspicuous dark streak below eye;*

underparts with thicker dark streaks. Cere and eye-ring blue-grey. Feet dull yellow.
DOWNY YOUNG: *White.*

VOICE
Rapidly repeated kek in agitation; also a cluck-cluck, probably in contact.

NESTING
Breeds July–November. Lines old nest of another species of hawk or crow with animal hair or bark. Eggs: two to four, usually three; pink-buff heavily spotted with red-brown; blunt-oval, about 51 x 37 mm. Incubation 32–35 days, by female. Young fledge in 42–45 days.

DISTRIBUTION
Lightly timbered plains of mainland Australia. Occasionally seen farther east and southwest than indicated on map. Nomadic. No races.

THE TIMBERED PLAINS OF THE dry interior are the home of the Grey Falcon, one of Australia's rarest raptors. Singly or in pairs, they work mainly along eucalypt-lined river channels, perching motionless in the shelter of tree branches looking about, or flapping easily along. In flight they may circle slowly, soaring with fanned tails, but when hunting they move at great speed. Most of their prey—birds, small mammals, reptiles and insects—is snatched in surprise from the ground. Larger birds are swooped upon in midair.

Nests are poorly defended, the adults doing little more than flapping slowly around the nest tree. Although, in usual falcon-fashion, the female broods and cares for the young while the male hunts, he may relieve her on the nest when she leaves to eat prey he has brought. Not only will he brood then, but also feed the young. As young mature, both parents share hunting.

After fledging, young falcons may stay with their parents for another six or more months before dispersing.

Brown Falcon

Falco berigora VIGORS & HORSFIELD, 1827

The Brown Falcon, a common bird, is often seen quietly perching.

OTHER NAMES
Brown Hawk, Cackling Hawk.

IDENTIFICATION
LENGTH: *Male 450 mm; female 500 mm.*
ADULTS: *Sexes similar. Six basic forms, with intergrades: (a) wholly dusky brown; (b) dark brown above and deep rufous below with fine dusky shaft streaks; (c) wholly dark brown with cream-white spotting on underparts; (d) deep russet above and lighter rufous below; (e) mid-russet above and white below; (f) deep brown above and cream-white below. All these forms have a dusky tear stripe below the eye, dark thighs, finely spotted or barred flanks, dark grey-brown flight feathers with buff spots or bars beginning on the fourth to sixth inwards, and grey-brown tails with close rufous bars. Eye dark brown. Bill blue-grey with black tip; cere and orbital skin usually grey-white. Distinctively long feet and toes pale grey; claws black.*
IMMATURES: *All brown-backed and cream-breasted in first year, with coarsely blotched flanks and incompletely barred tail. Older birds resemble their adult phase but have more coasely marked flanks.*
DOWNY YOUNG: *White, with grey bills and feet.*

VOICE
Loud, cackling calls uttered frequently on the wing, particularly in display.

NESTING
Breeds opportunistically June–November in south and through to

March and later in north. Usually appropriates an old nest of another species of hawk; occasionally nests in open tree hollow; sometimes builds its own large nest of sticks, lined with finer material and green leaves. Eggs: two to five, usually three; pale buff, with many red-brown spots and blotches; oval, about 50 x 38 mm. Incubation just over 30 days, by both sexes. Young fledge in 40–45 days.

DISTRIBUTION
Throughout Australia. Also on islands off northeastern coast and in New Guinea. Sedentary, locally nomadic, or a partial migrant in Tasmania. Two races: one consistently brown-and-white in Tasmania and mixing with other colour forms across southern and eastern Australia; the other consistently brown-and-rufous in New Guinea and mixing with other forms across northern Australia. All other colour types endemic to mainland Australia.

THE FLIGHT AND HUNTING methods of the Brown Falcon differ markedly from those of other falcons. Both its wing-beats and flight are relatively slow. It is usually seen quietly perched or flying, alternately beating its wings and gliding with wings held up in a shallow 'V'. It sometimes hovers rather inefficiently, but it can soar to great heights.

The Brown Falcon rarely hunts by chasing its prey on the wing. Its main method of searching for its food is to sit quietly on a high perch, such as a branch of a dead tree or telegraph-pole and watch the ground. It drops down on the victim and grabs it with its talons. It also does some searching while gliding low.

It eats small mammals, including house mice and occasionally young rabbits; some small birds, lizards and snakes; and a variety of invertebrates, particularly caterpillars, grasshoppers, crickets and beetles. It has been seen chasing grasshoppers on the ground and catching them with its bill as well as with its talons.

The Brown Falcon is usually seen alone or in pairs, but in the non-breeding season several may be seen within sight of each other. One of the most widespread and abundant Australian raptors, it is primarily a bird of open grassy woodland and is well adapted to agricultural areas and towns. It is also found in open forested country. Around inhabited areas it sometimes becomes rather tame.

So variable is the Brown Falcon in its plumages that it has often been mistaken for more than one species. It has six main colour forms, ranging from all dusky like a Black Falcon to light rufous-and-white like a kestrel. Although most colour types can be found together in all places except Tasmania and New Guinea, light rufous birds prevail inland. This suggests genetic selection in response to environment, known as 'balanced polymorphism'.

Brown Falcons perform display flights as breeding approaches.

The courting pair, and perhaps an interloping male, fly rapidly around in circles and perform a variety of aerial manoeuvres, including gliding with wings held in a high V-shape, while uttering a loud cackling call.

Both sexes incubate and brood, although the female shoulders most of these duties while the male hunts. When he brings food, she leaves the nest to take it from him in midair or at a perch nearby, eating it there or carrying it back to the nest to apportion among her young. Small prey—mice, small birds and insects — may be carried in the bill but larger items are clasped in the talons. Young become independent within days of fledging and leave their parents soon after.

Australian Kestrel *Falco cenchroides* Vigors & Horsfield, 1827

A female Australian Kestrel brings a rodent to its young in their nest. Small mammals and insects are the main food of the Australian Kestrel.

Lacking the speed of the typical members of the falcon family, the Australian Kestrel usually preys on creatures that live on the ground. To find them it hovers expertly, literally hanging in midair at one spot, 10–20 metres up, for minutes at a time. From that vantage point it watches the ground, wings quivering and tail fanned. If it sights prey, it drops, hovering lower and lower in steps until finally plummeting head first on to the victim.

Although catching mostly insects, kestrels rely on small vertebrates—rodents, rabbit kittens, ground birds and reptiles — for the bulk of their diet. They are common and nomadic, following flushes of their prey and appearing in numbers in pastoral areas when mice or insects plague. Adaptable birds, they can exploit small urban parklands—and will even nest on high-rise buildings—avoiding only dense forest which prevents their hunting. They commonly shift north in winter and south over summer along the eastern seaboard, even reaching New Guinea on migration. Mostly young of the year move, while older established pairs hold territory year round in productive areas.

In good seasons, kestrels rear successive broods. Displaying pairs fly, dive and hover close together near the nest site, calling much. Only the female incubates and the male does the hunting until young are well grown, passing prey to her for herself and the chicks. In the week or so before fledging, however, both parents bring food independently.

OTHER NAMES
Nankeen Kestrel.

IDENTIFICATION
Length: *Male 310 mm; female 350 mm.*
Male: *Upper parts pale rufous with fine sparse black spotting on back; head rufous tinged pale blue-grey. Face white with thin black tear stripe from front of eye down side of throat. Outer flight feathers almost black with buff-white bars to inner vanes. Rump and tail plain pale grey with black bar near tip; tip white. Underparts white, sometimes with faint rufous wash on breast and flanks, and some dark streaks on breast.* *Eye brown; eye-ring and cere yellow. Bill blue-grey. Feet yellow; claws black.*
Female: *Like male but more heavily spotted with black above and streaked below; tail pale rufous with black bars and narrow black bar near tip.*
Immatures: *Similar to female but prominently marked with black.*
Downy young: *White.*

VOICE
A high-pitched shrill, repeated ki *or* twitter, *in alarm or when nesting.*

NESTING
Breeds July–December, peaking September–October. No nest built; uses tree hollows, recesses in cave entrances, ledges on city buildings or cliffs, and nests of ravens and other birds. Eggs: three–seven, usually four; very pale buff or pink with blotches of brown-red; round, about 38 x 31 mm. Incubation 26–28 days, by female. Young fledge in about 26 days.

DISTRIBUTION
Most common in open woodland and agricultural land. Nomadic and fluctuates in numbers. Straggles to Norfolk and Lord Howe Islands and New Zealand. Another race in montane western New Guinea.

Australian Hobby *Falco longipennis* SWAINSON, 1837

An Australian Hobby of the grey-backed race.

OTHER NAMES
Little Falcon, White-fronted Falcon.

IDENTIFICATION
LENGTH: *Male 300 mm; female 340–350 mm.*
ADULTS: *Sexes similar. Upper parts slate-grey to black, with black shaft streaks and greyer edging to back and wing coverts. Flight and tail feathers dusky grey with hidden buff bars. Sides of face and sometimes crown black. Forehead, throat and collar at sides of neck buff-cream. Rest of undersurface rufous-brown, streaked black on breast and thighs and grading to black mottling on belly and flanks. Extreme southeastern, southwestern and Tasmanian birds much the darkest. Eye dark brown; eye-ring bluish white. Bill light grey with black tip; cere dull yellow. Feet dull yellow; claws dusky.*
IMMATURES: *Above, including crown, generally grey-brown with buff edges to feathers. Underparts rufous-brown with indistinct streaks. Adult plumage acquired after first year.*
DOWNY YOUNG: *Off-white; bill and cere flesh-pink.*

VOICE
Shrill twittering call repeated. Shrill harsh chatter in defense.

NESTING
Breeds September–November in southern Australia. Uses old nests of magpies, crows, and others high in trees and lines them with leaves or bark; sometimes uses hollows. Eggs: two or three, occasionally four; pale buff, thickly sprinkled with red spots and blotches; oval, about 46 x 34 mm. Incubation about 30 days. Young fledge in five weeks.

DISTRIBUTION
Throughout Australia where there are trees, particularly open wooded country. Nomadic and migratory, particularly in south, reaching southern New Guinea, New Britain, Moluccas and Lesser Sundas in winter. Two races: one black-backed in coastal southeast, extreme southwest and Tasmania; the other grey-backed everywhere else.

A FIERCE AND DASHING HUNTER, this small falcon preys chiefly on birds, capturing them in midair from direct pursuit or in power dives from above. Birds up to its own size are taken, and sometimes even larger ones are struck and knocked to the ground. The hobby will pluck and eat its kill there, or more usually carry it in its talons to a perch. Most perches are high, exposed branches of trees where the hobby rests or watches for the movement of prey, bobbing its head as it focusses. It searches much on the wing, dashing about swift-like at tree-top level, surprising small birds feeding on the ground below, and catching stragglers before they reach cover. Occasionally it soars and circles higher, looking about, and will even hover awkwardly. Often it hunts at dusk, when it takes bats or snatches large flying insects such as grasshoppers,

dragonflies and winged ants, eating them on the wing. Although not uncommon and often visiting urban parks, Australian Hobbys are usually solitary and wary, except when nesting.

A breeding pair will occupy the abandoned nest of another bird and defend it fiercely and noisily. The female appears to incubate, brood and care for the young unaided while the male does most of the hunting, particularly until the cessation of brooding. He calls the female off the nest to take his catches, either passing them to her in midair or in a nearby tree, and she carries them to the nest, to be plucked, dismembered and fed to the young.

Brooding ceases as pin feathers appear and both adults begin to drop food at the nest, leaving the young to obtain possession and feed themselves. Most young fledge.

Peregrine Falcon *Falco peregrinus* TUNSTALL, 1771

FOR MANY CENTURIES the Peregrine Falcon has been a symbol of speed and audacity in nature. One of the swiftest of all hunting hawks, it swoops on its panic-stricken prey at speeds of more than 300 km/h. It will attack and kill any small to medium-size bird that flies in the open, and sometimes it swoops on birds larger than itself, even a Black Swan. It regularly kills racing pigeons, though many of these victims are probably birds that have become lost or exhausted. It also kills rabbits and a few other mammals that are found in the open during daylight hours.

The Peregrine Falcon swoops on its prey from above and catches it with the talons or strikes it with a foot so that the bird is stunned and drops to the ground. Sometimes it will hang on to large birds and drop to the ground with them. The Peregrine Falcon plucks its prey and, if it is not too large, carries it to a sheltered place to eat. Pairs of Peregrine Falcons sometimes hunt co-operatively.

Peregrines mate for life and occupy a home range of about 20–50 square kilometres throughout the year, often resting and roosting on cliffs and high exposed branches close to the nest site. The same nest site is used year after year. As breeding approaches, unmated males make circling display flights or established pairs dive, swoop and tumble over one another. Although the female undertakes most

of the incubation and caring for the young, the male will relieve her. He does most of the hunting early in breeding, dropping food to the female on the nest, giving it to her at a nearby perch, or passing it in midair. Later they both hunt and dump prey at the nest for the young to tear up.

A most successful predator, the Peregrine Falcon is widespread on all continents. Rarely common anywhere, it has become much rarer in recent years because of the thinning and breaking of its egg shells caused by volatile insecticides.

OTHER NAMES
Peregrine, Black-cheeked Falcon.

IDENTIFICATION
LENGTH: *Male 380 mm; female 480 mm.*
ADULTS: *Sexes similar. Generally deep blue-grey above with dark cross-bars. Outer flight feathers dusky with hidden grey-white bars; underwing coverts buff barred black. Barred tail tipped grey-white. Head, nape, sides of head and cheeks black. Throat and breast pale cream-buff; a few black spots on lower breast; rest of underparts greyish buff crossed with numerous fine black bars. Underparts of females are more russet buff. Eye brown; eye-ring yellow. Bill bone with black tip; cere yellow. Feet pale yellow; claws black.*

IMMATURES: *Dusky above with buff or rufous edges to most feathers. Underparts rufous-buff, paler on throat, streaked with dusky from breast to crissum.*
DOWNY YOUNG: *White; eye black; bill and cere grey-white; feet yellow.*

VOICE
Loud, shrill, repetitive screams hek-ek-ek in alarm, lower pitched in female; longer-drawn double-note shrieking in display and soliciting. Sharp calls in flight.

NESTING
Breeds August–December. Does not build nests but lays eggs in recesses in cliffs, hollows in large trees, or abandoned large nests of other birds. Eggs: three, sometimes two or four; pale buff with heavy red or red-brown blotches; oval to rounded-oval, about 53 x 40 mm. Incubation about 30 days, mainly by female. Young fledge in five–six weeks.

DISTRIBUTION
All parts of Australia, particularly cliffs, watercourses, open timber and urban high-rise, but not common anywhere. Also in Eurasia, Africa and North and South America. About 18 races; one in Australia.

The Peregrine Falcon is one of the swiftest and deadliest birds of prey.

Black Falcon *Falco subniger* GRAY, 1843

The Black Falcon does not build its own nest. Here the female is seen with her young at the disused nest of another bird of prey.

SLENDEREST OF THE AUSTRALIAN FALCONS, the Black Falcon is also one of the most agile. In appearance it resembles the longer-legged Brown Falcon in dark phase, but in habits it is much different. When searching for prey it watches from the top of bare vantage perches or flies and glides on pointed wings low to ground with leisurely purpose or even circles high in the sky. Prey is warm-blooded. Sighting it, the falcon sweeps into a stooping dive or weaves along behind the intended victim, snatching it in midair or off the ground.

Falcons also fly at bushes to flush their quarry. Birds up to the size of galahs, ducks and native hens are taken, and also small rabbits on the run and rats. These the falcons pluck and eat at the site of the kill or carry off to a perch to consume.

Black Falcons are solitary nomads of the open, sparsely treed plains of inland Australia. In good seasons, when food is plentiful, they breed there in numbers, and then when drought comes they disperse to more coastal districts, frequently the same open habitat.

Mating seems to be temporary and displaying birds evidently soar to great heights and chase and stoop at one another, screaming much. Territory does not seem to be well-marked and nests, newly usurped for each breeding, are not defended until they have young. In typical raptor fashion, the female bears the brunt of incubation, brooding and feeding the young while the male hunts. Most of his kills are passed to her at a perch near the nest. Even after young fledge she may continue to feed them for several weeks.

OTHER NAMES
None.

IDENTIFICATION
LENGTH: *Male 450 mm; female 550 mm.*
ADULTS: *Sexes similar, appear black, but most of body plumage is dark sooty-brown. Upper throat and forehead off-white; underside of flight feathers sparsely barred white. Eye brown. Bill dark blue-grey; cere and eye-ring blue. Feet blue-grey; claws black.*
IMMATURES: *Similar to adults, but blacker, without white marks on throat, forehead and underwings.*
DOWNY YOUNG: *White.*

VOICE
Loud, deep repetitive gak-ak-ak... *also a soft whistling call, or a drawn-out moaning* karrrrr. *Silent when hunting.*

NESTING
Breeds June–December. Builds no nest but uses old nest of other species of hawk, raven or crow. Eggs: two to four, usually three; pink-buff heavily spotted with red-brown; rounded-oval, about 54 x 40 mm. Incubation about 32–34 days, by female. Young fledge in about six weeks.

DISTRIBUTION
Mostly in sparsely timbered plains and steppes of interior, often around waterholes. Sometimes visits southeastern coastal districts. Nomadic. No races.

Magpie Goose

Anseranas semipalmata (LATHAM, 1798)

The knob on the head of the Magpie Goose develops with age and is usually larger in males than females.

THE LARGE, NOISY, BOLDLY MARKED Magpie Goose is a bird of the sub-coastal plains of northern Australia, where it is still numerous and widespread. However, the bird has completely disappeared from southern Australia, brought to extinction by the effects of human settlement, combined with a couple of disastrous droughts. The birds were poisoned or shot because they grazed crops, and their breeding swamps were drained, or the plants in them destroyed by wading cattle. Similar influences — such as agricultural development and grazing of the swamp vegetation by the introduced water buffalo — now pose a threat to the geese even in the north; there, too, their numbers are declining.

The Magpie Goose differs from most waterfowl in having feet that are only half-webbed and strong hind toes, in common with its other relatives, the South American Screamers, *Anhimidae.* The bird is further characterised by a conspicuous knob on its head, usually larger in males than in females. But the size may vary from one individual to another, so that the knob is really a more reliable gauge of age than it is of sex — the older the bird, the larger the knob. In adult males, which are generally larger than females, the windpipe loops down under the skin, extending over the breast. It does not reach beyond the breastbone in female or juvenile birds, but old females have a very small loop close to the neck.

Both sexes honk resonantly, the male at a higher pitch than the female. In flight and on the ground, a call by a male is answered immediately by females. A male often mates with two females, but the birds also breed in pairs. At the start of the wet season the geese move to nearby swamps. As the season progresses and the swamps fill to sufficient depth, they separate off in their breeding pairs and trios and start building floating platforms by bending and trampling clumps of spike-rush. The male does the greater share of the work. As the swamp plants grow, the birds weave the clumps into a more substantial platform. These platforms are used for courtship and resting. Each platform is used only once; a new one is built next time they visit the swamp.

Shortly before egg-laying, the birds make the platform more elaborate and break or uproot shoots of spike-rush until a substantial pile is formed. Finally an egg is laid and the platform becomes a nest. Each day the birds add more material to it, forming a thick, deep cup. Usually the two females of a breeding trio lay on one nest and together with the male share the incubation duties, often standing over the eggs to shade them from the tropical sun rather than warming them. Each female lays six to nine eggs.

After hatching, the chicks remain in the nest for a day, and are then led away by their parents, to feed on the shoots and seeds of the swamp grasses *Panicum, Paspalum* and wild rice *Oryza.* The adults help the young by bending seedheads down with their feet so that they are within reach of their offspring. In water too deep for the young, the adults will upend and submerge their long necks to bring up food.

The birds moult at the end of the breeding season, when the

In the Fogg Dam Sanctuary, near Humpty Doo, southeast of Darwin, NT, Magpie Geese feed in the company of other waterbirds.

swamps are drying out. They moult their wing feathers gradually and, unlike all other waterfowl, have no flightless period. As the swamp waters decline, the families wander from place to place, often covering long distances to follow water. If all the water goes before the young are fledged, they perish.

At 11 weeks the young can fly. With their parents they join other family parties, congregating in loose flocks. Each flock has a favourite roosting place, at the edge of a swamp or in a paperbark grove, where they often perch for the night on surprisingly thin twigs. At dawn they fly out to feed on the plains, where they mingle with the flocks from other roosts. Individuals may return to their original roost, or travel with a group to another one. Their flight is heavy and laboured, but strong.

As the dry season intensifies, from May onwards, the geese feed on the bulbs of spike-rushes, which they dig up from the bare, sun-baked mud of the plains with their strong, hooked bills. They become quite nomadic at this time, shifting from one drying swamp to another until they become concentrated around the most permanent. The young birds stay with their parents until the following wet season. If they survive their first year, they may live for another 20 years or more.

Dingoes have been seen to charge from cover into feeding or roosting flocks and kill or maim several birds. This may be one reason why the geese prefer feeding in open places, far from cover, where they are safer from sudden attack.

OTHER NAMES
Pied Goose, Wild Goose, Semi-palmated Goose.

IDENTIFICATION
LENGTH: *Male 750–920 mm; female 710–815 mm.*
ADULTS: *Sexes similar. Head, neck, wings, tail and thighs black. Back and undersurface white; in dry season stained red-brown. Eye brown. Bill and bare skin of face flesh-grey; nail bone-grey. Feet and part-webbed toes yellow; claws slate.*
DOWNY YOUNG: *Head and neck cinnamon-red; dark grey stripe on upper neck, dark grey on back and sides of body. Underside white; pale grey under tail and wing. Bill and legs claret but yellow at three to five days.*

VOICE
Loud resonant honk, higher pitched in male; uttered singly or in rapid repetition; often birds concert together.

NESTING
Begins October–November; nest building and egg laying delayed until water depth reaches 25–90 cm and vegetation in swamps is suitable,

March–April. Nest a deep, floating cup of spike-rush Eleocharis, about 1.5 m in diameter and 0.5 m above water level. Eggs: about 16 (six to nine from each female); cream, usually becoming nest-stained; oval, 64–80 x 46–63 mm. Incubation 24–25 days, by both sexes.

DISTRIBUTION
Breeds around coastal northern Australia, mainly between Fitzroy River, WA and Bowen, Qld; occasionally south to Clarence River, NSW. In dry season wanders throughout Australia, also New Guinea. No races.

FAMILY ANSERANATIDAE magpie geese   137

Wandering Whistling-Duck *Dendrocygna arcuata* (HORSFIELD, 1824)

A FEEDING FLOCK OF Wandering Whistling-Ducks seems to roll forward across the water in a dense, constantly moving mass, as the ducks at the rear fly forward to the front. The birds fill the air with a shrill, whistling sound made with the wings as well as the voice box. They remain still only in the heat of the day or if alarmed, when they stretch their necks fully to check the disturbance.

Whistling-Ducks jump from the water and fly with neck craning distinctively forward. They beat their rounded wings slowly and whistle; extend their long necks and lower their heads so that their shoulders appear to be hunched; and trail their long legs out behind. As they alight they lower their necks further and drop their legs before they hit the water.

Wandering Whistling-Ducks seldom leave the water to feed. They prefer the deepest and most permanent of tropical lagoons where aquatic plants, insects and other animals are plentiful. Although they can walk well, they seldom come ashore except to roost in camps on the edge. The birds can dive and swim underwater with ease. They feed by stripping seeds and flowers of surface water plants or by dabbling in deep water, where they also dive to the bottom to get plants. The food of Wandering Whistling-Ducks is 99 per cent vegetable: aquatic grasses, waterlilies, sedges, gentians, and other aquatic or submerged swamp plants.

Wandering Whistling-Ducks sometimes travel long distances, but their main movements are local, determined by the availability of feeding habitat. In dry weather they concentrate in better-watered places near the coast and disperse inland in the wet season when dry swamps fill.

With the coming of the summer monsoon their sexual activity increases and courtship and fighting among males becomes more frequent and intense. Rainfall affects the timing and length of the breeding season because of its influence on vegetation; young must be produced when the swamps are full of aquatic plants and insects. In exceptionally dry years many birds do not breed at all. Wandering Whistling-Ducks make their nests by lining scrapes in the ground with a thin layer of grass, generally some distance from the water, perhaps avoiding the danger of sudden floods swamping their nests. Both male and female, which mate for life, choose the

nest site, share incubation, and care for their young. Ducklings from more than one nest may amalgamate in rafts on the water.

These ducks are numerous in the tropics, and widespread, but their habitat is vulnerable to agricultural development which, if extended, will decrease their numbers.

OTHER NAMES
Water Whistling-Duck, Whistling Tree Duck, Wandering Tree Duck.

IDENTIFICATION
LENGTH: *Male 550–610 mm; female 550–575 mm.*
ADULTS: *Sexes similar. General plumage above, including crown, dusky. Face buff brown. Dusky line extends down back of neck; feathers of back and scapulars bordered with rich chestnut. Primaries and outer wing coverts black; inner wing coverts deep chestnut; underwing dusky. Central tail coverts black; outer tail coverts buff; tail black. Throat white; front of neck and breast rufous with sparse black spots; belly chestnut; undertail white. Plumes on flanks buff with broad dusky edges. Eye red-brown. Bill black. Feet and webs dark grey.*
IMMATURES: *Duller than adults.*
DUCKLINGS: *Crown, neck, back and tail dusky. Face light grey with dusky stripes through eye and behind back of cheek. Throat white; breast and flanks dusky; belly pale grey. Bill olive-grey, buff-pink below. Feet olive-grey.*

VOICE
Shrill, high-pitched whistle, uttered as a single note or a multisyllabic twitter, on the ground or in flight.

NESTING
Breeding occurs during and after tropical wet season January–July. Nest

a scrape in the ground with a thin layer of grass in it, usually sheltered by tall grass or a bush, some distance from water. Eggs: six to 15, usually seven or eight; hard, vitreous, cream; oval, 47–53 x 35–39 mm, distinctly pointed at small end. Both parents share nesting duties. Incubation 28–30 days, by both sexes.

DISTRIBUTION
Tropical freshwater wetlands from Kimberleys, WA, to Mary River, Qld. Vagrants wander as far south as Victoria. Species ranges to New Guinea, Fiji, New Britain and Philippines. Two races: one large in Australia and southern New Guinea, grading smaller northwest to Philippines and east to Fiji; the other, in northern New Guinea and New Britain, is still smaller, and darker rufous with finer spotting on breast.

Wandering Whistling-Ducks frequent lagoons and dams, seldom coming ashore. They feed almost entirely on grasses, waterlilies and other aquatic plants.

Plumed Whistling-Duck _Dendrocygna eytoni_ (EYTON, 1838)

OTHER NAMES
_Plumed Tree Duck, Grass
Whistle-Duck._

IDENTIFICATION
LENGTH: _Male 435–615 mm; female
415–560 mm._
ADULTS: _Sexes similar. General
plumage above from crown to wings
mid-brown, with yellow edges to
feathers of upper back. Upper tail
coverts buff, tipped darker; tail dusky.
Face and fore-neck pale brown; breast
rufous with conspicuous black bars at
sides; belly and undertail pale buff.
Long lanceolate plumes on flanks, each
buff with a broad black edge.
Underwing brown. Eye orange-yellow.
Bill pink, mottled black. Feet and webs
pink._
IMMATURES: _As adults, but paler and
breast marking not as distinct._
DOWNY YOUNG: _As Wandering
Whistling-Duck, but russet wash to
crown, back and breast, and pale stripe
on fore-wings and sides of back._

VOICE
_Shrill high-pitched whistle as single
note or multisyllabic twitter, both at rest
and in flight._

NESTING
_Breeds in tropical wet season,
February–April. Clutches are begun
in February–June, but most breeding is
February–March. Nest a scrape in the
ground, usually lined with a little grass
and sheltered by a bush. Eggs: eight to
14; white; oval, 44–51 x 33–38 mm.
Incubation 28 days, by both sexes._

DISTRIBUTION
_Wetlands from Kimberleys, WA, across
north and down east coast to Murray
River basin; rare vagrant in southern
part of range. Greatest numbers in wet
grasslands of central Queensland and
Barkly Tableland. Vagrant to New
Guinea and New Zealand. No races._

The Plumed Whistling-Duck stays near water during the day. At night, it grazes on surrounding grassland.

UNLIKE ITS RELATIVE, the Wandering Whistling-Duck, this bird is quite at home on land. It walks gracefully for a duck, with body upright and head held high, but appears clumsy on water, where it floats high and swims slowly. It can dive but does so rarely, probably only to escape danger, never to feed. It perches awkwardly and seldom roosts in trees. In flight, which is slow and buoyant, its posture and the whistling sound made by its wings are typical of the whistling-ducks.

The Plumed Whistling-Duck is a bird of tropical grasslands, and has benefited from European settlement. Its essential needs are simple: a dam or lagoon on which to camp and short, green grass to graze. The cattle industry has increased the number of possible camp sites for the birds in dry country by providing stock watering places, and the animals have kept the tall, coarse grasses of the tropics down to the short sward that Plumed Whistling-Ducks can graze. In the Northern Territory in the dry season, when the plains are dry and dusty, the birds remain close to swamps and feed on sedges and spike-rushes. In the wet season, they disperse more widely, and their food changes to the blades and seeds of grasses, legumes and herbs.

As the birds feed mainly on land, water is not the most important element in their habitat, and camps may form on muddy pools far out on dry plains, or on the banks of brackish estuaries. During the day the ducks cluster densely on the ground near water and at night stream out in groups to feed elsewhere on the plains. Small groups may travel 30 kilometres and more to feed, and are often joined on favourite feeding grounds by flocks from other camps, perhaps attracted by their constant whistling and twittering. At dawn, the birds return to their camps; they spiral down to the water to swim to the shore and run rapidly to the communal daytime roost.

Plumed Whistling-Ducks move towards the coast or other well-watered regions in the dry season, and over wider inland areas in the wet season. During the dry season the birds are gregarious, gathering in flocks on traditional camping grounds from which they make local foraging flights. The best camping sites are occupied by flocks each year. Individual members of a flock have been known to return to the same place year after year, but the overall permanence of the composition of a flock is not known.

The birds breed in the tropical wet season. Sexual activity, and fighting between the males, increases greatly within two weeks of the first storms. In exceptionally wet years the breeding period is extended and the whole population breeds. Dry years limit the breeding season or restrict the part of the population which breeds. Non-breeding birds remain in flocks.

Mated pairs stay together for long periods—probably for life. Both male and female share in the selection of the nest site, hatching and care of the young. When the young are hatched, both parents lead them to water which can be two kilometres away.

Black Swans and their downy cygnets can be seen in any month, but they usually breed February–May in the north and May–September in the south.

Black Swan Cygnus atratus (LATHAM, 1790)

THE EXPLORER GEORGE BASS, commenting on the call of the Black Swan, wrote: 'That song, so celebrated by the poets of former times, exactly resembled the creaking of a rusty ale-house sign on a windy day'. Yet many people find the Black Swan's trumpeting musical. The male or cob has a deeper voice than the female (pen) and its calls last longer. The birds trumpet to one another in contact; and they also exploit the contrast of white on their black plumage to signal intentions. If alarmed, they swim rapidly downwind or to a position giving maximum manoeuvrability for flight. The neck is held erect, and head and bill are raised to trumpet an alarm call. The first beat of the wings, exposing their flash of white, is the signal for a flock to take flight, pattering across the water into the air on heavily beating wings, necks outstretched, and rising on long skeins or Vs. They fly about much at night.

At the beginning of breeding, pairing arises out of aggressive behaviour, usually kindled by a female inciting a male to parade towards an intruder. The female follows him and then they face in a greeting display in which, with wings lifted, necks extended and bills raised, they call repeatedly. With repetition, the pair bond is reinforced and the tempo increases, terminating sometimes with two or three rapid wing-beats by the male. Before copulating a pair may display for up to 20–25 minutes in a 'wave-like' ducking activity, usually in water 30 centimetres or more deep. The head, neck and body are held parallel to the water's surface and, in succession, are rapidly and briefly immersed several times. Following a break of several minutes the sequence is repeated. Copulation follows when the female ceases display and collapses outstretched and immobile, often after manoeuvring herself beneath the male.

Black Swans are ready to breed at the age of 18 months, and most breed before the end of three years. Young birds about to breed for the first time may form a pair only temporarily—if a clutch is produced, either partner may leave the other to incubate the eggs and raise the young alone. The deserting partner usually mates again to rear another brood. In this way there may be as many as four broods in the one year from clutches laid by one female. Among older birds pair formation is generally permanent.

The nest construction may begin just before or, if the nest is on an island, soon after the first egg is laid and may continue for at least three or four weeks during egg-laying and incubation. Depending on the supply of material, the size of the nest will vary from a simple ring of plant matter to a large mound. On islands where swans breed in colonies, nests are often destroyed as the swans pilfer one another's nest material. As eggs are deserted and scattered, neighbouring swans scrape them into their nests and incubate them. Dominant pairs defend the largest territories and obtain the most favoured roosting and nesting sites. When cygnets hatch, birds frequently graze elsewhere but continue to defend a distance of about five metres from the vicinity of the brood.

Each year between September and February Black Swans moult, becoming flightless, and then they often gather on open lakes in flocks that may number thousands. They are good swimmers, and feed on vegetation mainly in water, dabbling for surface aquatic plants and upending in deeper water to pull up shoots and growth from the bottom. Pasture is also grazed if close to water.

OTHER NAMES
None.

IDENTIFICATION
LENGTH: *Male about 1300 mm; female about 1200 mm.*
MALE: *Entirely black, often stained with brown. Wing black with varying white outer flight feathers. Eye changes from white to red in breeding season. Bill varies from orange to dark red with a white bar near the off-white, horny tip, or nail. Feet dark grey.*
FEMALE: *As male but bill and eye usually lighter. Slightly shorter neck in proportion to body.*
IMMATURES: *At fledging, plumage is mottled grey and brown. White wing feathers all black-tipped. Eye red-brown. Bill dull red with traces of grey; nail and bar at tip of bill light grey. First complete moult occurs at about one year; in the time before this, general plumage changes slowly to black to become identical with adult. Some adults may have only one or two entirely white primary and secondary feathers.*
CYGNETS: *Downy, light grey. Eye grey-brown; bill dark grey-black with light grey nail; legs and feet dark grey. Light brown feathers appear after three or four weeks. Process continues up to fledging. Eye and bill begin to colour from 60 days onwards.*

VOICE
Used for contact in flight and in display, but males have deeper, longer 'trumpet' than females.

NESTING
Breeding may occur in all months of the year, but in north is often limited to late wet season and immediately after, around February–May. In south, mostly May–September. Nest a mound of vegetation about 0.35 m in height and 2 m in diameter, built on reeds, small islands, or among tall bushes. In one year a nest may be used three or four times by the same bird or several in turn. Eggs: three to nine, usually four to six; pale blue-green when fresh but later turning brown with nest-staining; ellipsoidal, 96–115 x 60–73 mm. Incubation 39–43 days, by both sexes; females take greater share. Young fledge in 113–160 days.

DISTRIBUTION
Freshwater and briny swamps, rivers, estuaries and lakes. Predominantly in southeast and southwest and north along eastern coast to Townsville, Qld; vagrants have been recorded in most parts of Australia. Nomadic. Introduced in New Zealand. No races.

Mute Swan *Cygnus olor* (GMELIN, 1789)

MUTE SWANS ARE NOT AS SILENT as their name suggests, for they snort and hiss when annoyed and occasionally trumpet loudly. However, the legendary 'swan song'—said to be sung by a dying swan—has no foundation in fact.

There is no record of when this decorative white swan was introduced into Australia, but it was presumably in the early years of European settlement. Mute Swans are now found in most cities and many towns, where they live in a semi-domesticated state in ornamental ponds. A few have been seen in the wild, but these were most likely wanderers, for the bird shows no inclination to live and breed in Australia's natural swamps. Their native Northern Hemisphere range is in Denmark, southern and central Sweden and in a sweep through Germany, Poland, Romania, central Russia, Asia Minor and Asia to Mongolia.

Mute Swans pair for life. Unlike Black Swans, which often nest in colonies, they are very pugnacious and keep to themselves in the breeding season. The female does not start breeding until she is two or three years old. She builds her nest—a large sturdy heap of plant matter, usually on a small island or among plants in shallow water—without any help from the male, though he savagely defends the area. She probably produces three to five eggs in her first year of breeding, up to seven in the second, and nine to 11 in subsequent years. The eggs resemble the Black Swan's in colour and shape but are larger. Both parents incubate the eggs and tend the cygnets, which leave the nest one or two days after hatching but remain with their parents. They can fly after about four months.

Both the Black and the Mute Swans are beautiful birds, but it is a pity the Mute Swan has been more widely used as a decorative bird than the native Black Swan, for the latter could survive equally well on a properly managed ornamental lake.

Mute Swans feed chiefly on water plants, and also eat some small frogs, fish and insects.

OTHER NAMES
White Swan.

IDENTIFICATION
LENGTH: *1300–1600 mm.*
ADULTS: *Sexes similar. All plumage white; fleshy knob on forehead larger in cob (male) than pen (female), and skin at base of bill black. Eye brown. Bill red-orange. Feet and webs grey-black.*
IMMATURES: *All plumage white, mottled grey-brown; bill black but changes to orange in first year; grey plumage replaced in first winter but some grey feathers remain until two years of age.*
CYGNETS: *Uniformly light grey.*

VOICE
Savage hiss when disturbed; loud trumpet call occasionally.

NESTING
Breeds late winter and spring in Australia, but in parks where birds are sheltered and fed, breeding can take place at any time. Nest a sturdy heap of vegetation. Eggs: three to 11; coarse green, usually coated with lime; oblong-oval, about 116 x 80 mm. Incubation 35 days, by both sexes, particularly the female. Cygnets leave nest after one or two days but remain with parents, and can fly after about four months.

DISTRIBUTION
Introduced into towns in parts of Southern Hemisphere, including Australia. Frequents ornamental ponds, lakes and rivers in parkland areas. Established in Perth and surrounding areas such as Northam, Coolbellup and Bridgetown, northern Tasmania and possibly other areas. Natural range southern Scandinavia to Asia Minor and Mongolia. Migrates in winter to southeastern Europe, north Africa, and southwestern Asia. No races.

The introduced Mute Swan is established in parts of southwestern Australia and Tasmania, and is widely used as a decorative bird.

Freckled Duck

Stictonetta naevosa
(GOULD, 1841)

OTHER NAMES
Diamantina Duck, Speckled Duck.

IDENTIFICATION
LENGTH: *Male 520–590 mm; female 480–540 mm.*
MALE: *Upper parts dark grey-brown to almost black, uniformly freckled with off-white or buff spots, usually 2–3 mm long and 1–2 mm wide. Throat and front of neck as back, but lighter. Breast dark grey with freckles as back. Rest of underside pale grey freckled with white and, rarely, buff. Eye brown. Bill slate-grey, distinctly dished above and heavy at the base. Feet and webs slate-grey. In breeding season base of bill vivid red.*
FEMALE: *Lighter than male, and more faintly freckled. Bill slate-grey at all times.*
IMMATURES: *Similar to female but ground colour light brown, freckles deep buff.*
DUCKLINGS: *Upper parts uniform light grey suffused with brown. Crown dark grey, above eye inconspicuously freckled with darker grey. Upper wings as back. Underside paler grey, lower belly light grey, almost white. Underwing pale grey with darker trailing edge. Bill blue-grey, pink spot on nail. Feet blue-grey; webs buff; claws brown.*

VOICE
Usual call of both sexes is a harsh hiss. Not very vocal. Male gives a peculiar soft squeak during his simple display. Ducklings make shrill chirrup, like noise of a cricket.

NESTING
Nest bowl-shaped, of well-woven fine sticks and lignum, lined with a moderate amount of very pale down; built in lignum or other bushes at water level or in tangled flood rubbish at base of flooded tree. Eggs: five to 14, usually seven, larger numbers due to more than one female laying; smooth; shell thicker and softer than other ducks' eggs; glossy cream or ivory; oval, 60–65 x 45–48 mm. Incubation 28–36 days, by female.

DISTRIBUTION
Most parts of Australia, but as vagrants. Withdraw to breed in Murray–Darling, Lake Eyre and Bulloo basins and around central coastal southwest of Western Australia. Nomadic. No races.

A female Freckled Duck on its bowl-shaped nest, firmly constructed of woven sticks and lignum with a little down.

RECENT RESEARCH ON THE Freckled Duck—one of the rarest waterfowl in the world—relates it more closely to swans than other ducks. It is now thought to be a primitive form closely related to the ancestors of waterfowl that differentiated into swans, geese and ducks. It is similar in shape to the dabbling ducks but its windpipe is outside the breastbone, like the Magpie Goose, and it resembles swans in the shape of its voice box and the scales on its legs as well as in several of its skeletal characteristics. Like swans, plumage colouring is simple, without speculum—a distinctive patch of colour on the wing—and its downy young are plain grey; its calls and courtship and threat displays are also swan-like.

Its preferred habitats are freshwater swamps or creeks rich in plankton with a heavy growth of cumbungi, lignum or tea-tree. Its life depends on the availability of such an environment, although it does visit and sometimes breeds in, more temporary and open waters.

Freckled Ducks usually gather in small parties of five or six. Occasionally, especially in drought, large concentrations, sometimes hundreds, occur. During the day birds rest in dense cover, usually in deep water. At night they fly silently out to the shallows to feed.

They feed in a similar manner to dabbling ducks, cruising and wading heads down in shallows, but spend more time filtering food just above the surface of the mud. They also run their bills along submerged logs and posts encrusted with algae.

Some Freckled Ducks have been found with tiny fish, minute shells, midge larvae and other small insects in their stomachs, as well as the seeds of smartweeds, docks, nardoo, aquatic grasses and sedges. But their main food appears to be crustaceans, zooplankton and algae.

During breeding, male Freckled Ducks develop bright red at the base of the upper mandible. It disappears after breeding is finished. The timing of the breeding season is not fully understood, as few of the birds' nests have been recorded. In the southwest of Western Australia, where rain falls regularly in winter, the breeding season varies little, and nests are found between October and December. The season is more variable in inland New South Wales where rainfall and changes in water levels are more unpredictable. In years of great floods, nesting booms in January and between June and September. In other years, few nests have been found, and only between September and November. Freckled Ducks evidently breed out of season when conditions are favourable

Only the female appears to incubate, and climbs down rather than flying from the nest when leaving, reversing the process when returning to recommence incubation.

The Freckled Duck's survival depends on dense vegetation in expansive shallow swamps for breeding and on permanent waters for refuge in drought. Its future is not secure. Some districts in South Australia and Western Australia have been subjected to vigorous drainage programmes, and wetlands in New South Wales are threatened by water conservation schemes. The Freckled Duck will not survive without active management programmes.

Cape Barren Goose *Cereopsis novaehollandiae* LATHAM, 1801

CAPE BARREN GEESE are not typical geese. They have reticulate scaling on their feet, their syrinx or voice box lacks a bulla, and their skeleton has much in common with the shelducks. Nonetheless, they live on land and graze like geese, picking grasses, sedges, clovers, herbs and their seeds—even the fleshy fruits of *Myoporum insulare*—from the swards and heaths of their coastal and island habitats; water is rarely entered. Nasal salt glands secrete any excess salt taken in with their food. When not breeding the geese usually congregate in small groups. They fly strongly, necks outstretched, but only after a lumbering run to take off.

Pugnacious and intolerant of others, males fight particularly strongly to establish their small territories at the approach of breeding. Nests are rarely closer than 20 metres to one another. Both male and female build, carrying up twigs and grass, and siting their nests among tussocks and rocks from which they have a clear view; and in thickets of *Atriplex cinerea*. Some nests are built up to six metres above the ground, in bushes and tea tree.

Males defend their territory while the females brood, and later both parents guard their young fiercely. The birds keep to their own territories, feeding there, until the young are about six weeks old. By this time young, abandoned by the adults, gather into crèches of up to 50 or so. Larger nomadic groups are formed as soon as they can fly. Sexual maturity comes in about three years. After breeding, the adults moult and for a short time become completely flightless.

These distinctive geese are unique to Australia, and are among the least numerous waterfowl in the world. They have been hunted and eaten since George Bass first saw them on islands off the Victorian coast in 1797. After that, a sealing industry developed in Bass Strait, leading to a great destruction of the birds and their eggs. They are now fully protected.

OTHER NAMES
Pig Goose.

IDENTIFICATION
LENGTH: *750–1000 mm.*
ADULTS: *Sexes similar; female slightly smaller. General colour ash grey. Crown with broad white stripe; mantle and scapulars edged white; wing coverts spotted black; primaries grey with black tips. Upper tail coverts, crissum and tail black. Eye hazel. Bill black; cere green-yellow over maxilla. Feet pink or yellow; webs black.*
GOSLINGS: *Boldly marked. Top of head, back of neck and rest of upper parts dark brown. Face grey with broad black-brown stripe extending through eye. Broad light grey stripe on each side of back. Wing dusky with pale grey leading edge. Underparts light grey. Eye black. Bill black with green cere. Feet and webs grey-green.*

VOICE
Females have low-pitched grunt; males also grunt but have fairly high-pitched, rapid, multisyllabic honk or trumpet. On the ground both sexes are usually quiet except when alarmed or displaying, but in flight very vocal.

NESTING
Probably mates for life. Breeding is usually May–August. Nest a heap of whatever material is at hand, built into shallow cup about 90 mm deep, often on west side of islands off south coast. Nest lined with grey down, with which female covers eggs when she leaves nest. Nest may be hidden in tussock grass, or by loose material. Eggs: one to seven, usually four-five; white with coarse lime layer over shell; ellipsoidal, 73–92 x 44–59 mm. Incubation about 35 days, by female.

DISTRIBUTION
Breeds on islands off southern coast of Australia, from Furneaux Group, Tas., to Recherche Archipelago, WA, dispersing seasonally to adjacent mainland out of breeding. Inhabits pasture, heathy headlands, strand and shores of swamps. Two races: one with yellow feet and narrow white crown stripe in Recherche Archipelago, WA; the other with pink feet and broad white crown stripe from Eyre Peninsula, SA, to Bass Strait.

Cape Barren Geese probably mate for life, and share the rearing of young until they are about six weeks old. The young then join a flock of juveniles.

Australian Shelducks are grazers, and feed on plants in shallow water or on land. The male is on the left.

Australian Shelduck

Tadorna tadornoides
(JARDINE & SELBY, 1828)

OTHER NAMES
Mountain Duck, Chestnut-breasted Shelduck.

IDENTIFICATION
LENGTH: *Male 590–720 mm; female 550–680 mm.*
MALE: *Head and neck black, often glossed green; broad, clear white ring at base of neck. Breast and mantle pale cinnamon brown. Back and scapulars black with faint white vermiculations; rump and tail black. Belly dusky with light vermiculations; undertail black. Upper wing coverts white, forming conspicuous white shoulders; primaries black; secondaries glossy green for half of length; black at base; tertiaries rich chestnut. Eye dark brown. Bill black. Feet and webs dusky. In non-breeding eclipse plumage breast yellow-brown and neck ring less clearly defined.*
FEMALE: *As male but breast bright chestnut. Ring of white around base of bill and around eye; in some birds two white areas continuous.*
IMMATURES: *Similar to adults but duller in colour. White shoulder patches flecked with grey. Most juveniles have white flecks between bill and eye.*
DUCKLINGS: *Crown, neck and back brown, with white stripe down either side of back. Face brown above eye, pure white below eye. Underside pure white, with brown thighs. Wing brown with white band. Eye brown. Bill and feet blue-grey.*

VOICE
Identity call a loud, low-pitched honk; pitch much higher in females than in males. Commonly given in flight. During displays honk of male is wavering and uttered in pairs of syllables, one long, one short.

NESTING
Breeds June–October over winter, mostly July–August. Nest usually in hollow limb of tall tree, 2–25 m above ground, but also on ground, floor of cave and rabbit hole. Eggs: five to 15; close-grained, lustrous cream; oval, 62–74 x 45–51 mm. Incubation 30–35 days, by female.

DISTRIBUTION
Marshes and pastures of southern Australia. Breeds in southwestern Australia throughout wheat belt and on some offshore islands. In east main populations are in Tasmania, southeast of South Australia, western Victoria and southeastern New South Wales. Nomadic. Vagrants occasionally wander as far as Cape Leveque in west and Darling River in east in summer. No races.

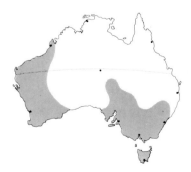

CONTRARY TO ITS POPULAR name, Mountain Duck, Australian Shelducks live in the lowland areas such as the large brackish lakes of the coast, which are their preferred habitat. They also congregate in deep freshwater lakes, large lagoons and billabongs. When in saltwater habitats, they sometimes fly long distances to fresh water and gather in large numbers to drink.

Australian Shelducks often flock in 100s or 1000s when they are not breeding. They rest in loose groups on the water's edge by day, and in the late afternoon fly out in long, honking skeins to feed. They do not often perch in trees, except by nest holes. They swim strongly, high on the water, but seldom dive except to escape danger during the flightless moulting period. They can walk fast and well, and when disturbed rise quickly and utter a harsh *chank-chank* call. Flight is strong and direct. If on a small lake the birds leave the area entirely, but on a larger expanse of water they settle in the centre in a large raft, later swimming back to their former resting place.

Their movements are regular. The shelducks concentrate to feed and moult in large rafts on large lakes and estuaries in the summer, and then disperse to widespread breeding areas in autumn and winter. Some of these journeys are very long. Banded birds from the southeast of South Australia move throughout Victoria and Tasmania after the breeding season, and birds from near Canberra reach Tasmania and the southeastern tip of South Australia. These movements all go on at the same time, so the movement pattern of the population is complex.

Australian Shelducks graze green plants on land or in shallow water. In western Victoria they often do considerable damage by eating cereal crops and vegetables. They also graze many grasses, clovers, *Medicago* species and herbs, as well as duck-weed, sedges, pondweed, ribbon weed and algae. Insects and molluscs are also part of their diet. These include adults and larvae of beetles, water boatmen, dragonflies, mayflies and midges, and a few small freshwater mussels. Brine shrimps are important food on Rottnest Island, WA.

As in other shelducks, the pair bond is probably for life. In southeastern New South Wales, the birds move to a breeding area in March, separate, and become very pugnacious during April and May, when they define their territories. The breeding territory may be a small pool, or a portion of the shoreline of a large lake. The pair select the nest site, often returning to the same nest-hole year after year. While the female is incubating the eggs the male establishes a separate territory, where the young will be reared, and defends it against other shelducks. This territory can be two kilometres or more from the nest and is visited by the female when she leaves the nest to feed. On return to the nest the pair fly back together, the male usually leading. Their flight may take them across other males' territories but flying birds are not attacked by the owners. At the nest site the female lands in the tree and enters the nest-hole. The male may pause to perch too but more usually brakes, banks, and returns quickly to his territory. When the young are hatched they are led overland to the male's territory and the family is united there. Although pairing when subadult, young birds do not breed until they are at least 22 months old.

Australian Shelducks moult twice a year, changing their body plumage in autumn before breeding and then shedding it again, with their wings and tail, after breeding in late spring. During the post-breeding moult, body plumage is changed over 90 days, followed by the flight and tail feathers over the next 60 days. The birds are flightless for about a month until their new flight feathers grow.

Radjah Shelduck *Tadorna radjah* (Garnot, 1828)

Radjah shelducks utter a harsh rattling cry, as they fly weaving through timber or low over the water. They keep mainly to brackish waters, mud banks and the mangrove-fringed mouths and lower reaches of tropical rivers, but visit freshwater swamps and lagoons further inland during the wet season. Although dispersed in pairs on their territories the shelducks become more gregarious afterwards as the dry season progresses, occasionally gathering in several hundreds in paperbark swamps or on large, drying lakes. Most groups, however, remain rather isolated and, numbering only six–twelve birds, are probably family parties. They swim well but spend more of their time wading on the edge of pools or resting there quietly on mud banks, in cover, or on limbs in green trees, mangroves or paperbarks; seldom do they move more than 10 metres from water's edge. Before feeding in the later afternoon, they become active—flying about, squabbling, fighting and gathering in small groups near the edge of the cover, ready to move off. Their flight is strong and direct and they are very vocal in flight. After feeding through parts of the night, they return to their daytime roosts during the morning.

Each pair of Radjah Shelducks has a feeding territory—a small pool or a stretch of swamp edge, often many kilometres from the roosting place. The birds feed on the water's edge, walking rapidly, swinging the bill from side to side in the mud, sieving for food or stamping the mud with alternate feet, forcing worms to come to the surface. Their food includes various molluscs and large insects, algae and sedges.

Pairs of Radjah Shelducks mate probably for life and take up breeding territories when the monsoonal rains set in each January or February. Intruders are challenged by the male which rushes forward with neck outstretched and feathers erect. Sometimes the female participates, trumpeting as she does so. The pair selects the nest site together, a shallow hollow in a tree trunk or on a limb near water. Eggs are laid on bare wood and covered with a little down. While the female is incubating the eggs, the male remains nearby and may defend a pool, or a section of swamp edge near the nest. When the young hatch, the male assists in their rearing. The family may move away from the breeding territory as the water dries up, and join the increasing flocks on the larger pools. Where the breeding territory has sufficient food to last through the dry season, the family may stay there until the next breeding season.

Restricted by habitat and rarely abundant anywhere, Radjah Shelducks have declined over many parts of their range around northern Australia. Reclamation of coastal swamplands and indiscriminate shooting have contributed to this. The largest concentrations in Australia today survive on the coastal plains of western Arnhem Land and eastern head of the Gulf of Carpentaria.

OTHER NAMES
Burdekin Duck, White-headed Shelduck.

IDENTIFICATION
length: *Male 500–555 mm; female 485–610 mm.*
adults: *Sexes similar. Head, neck, breast and belly pure white; dark chestnut band across upper breast. Upper back and scapulars rich chestnut with fine transverse black lines; lower back, rump and tail black; undertail black. Upper wing coverts white, crossed by fine black line near tip of feathers; primaries black; secondaries white, innermost chestnut-black; speculum through outer secondaries bright glossy green bordered with black. Eye white. Bill, feet and webs pink or pale flesh; claws brown.*
immatures: *Plumage similar to adults but duller, white parts sometimes flecked with grey or brown, back duskier, breast band incomplete.*
ducklings: *Crown chestnut; back of neck, back and upper tail dark brown; face, throat, front of neck and underside pure white. Broad dark brown or black line from bill through eye to back of head. White forehead spot, white bar on wing and white spot on either side of back. Bill and feet pink.*

VOICE
Male, a loud hoarse whistle; female, a harsh rattling note in contact.

NESTING
Most clutches begun May–June. Nests in large hollow trees or large limbs close to water; eggs laid on bare wood and covered with grey down. Eggs: six to 12; smooth, lustrous cream; rounded oval, 55–61 x 39–45 mm. Incubation 30 days, by female.

DISTRIBUTION
Brackish waterways of major tropical river systems, from northern Kimberleys, WA, to Fitzroy River, Qld; also New Guinea, Moluccas. Two races; one in Australia.

Strong but reluctant swimmers, Radjah Shelducks are seldom seen on the water. They rest and feed on the water's edge, rarely venturing far inland.

Green Pygmy-Goose *Nettapus pulchellus* GOULD, 1842

AN AGGRESSIVE DUCK, the Green Pygmy-Goose is actually a perching duck closely related to the Maned Duck. The name 'goose' is probably derived from the bird's short, strong bill — an adaptation to grazing — which resembles the bill of the true geese. Of the three pygmy-geese in the world, the Green Pygmy-Goose is the only one restricted to Australasia. All three are colourful, similar in shape and habits, and live in the tropics.

The Green Pygmy-Goose is sedentary in its habits. In the dry season it forms flocks of several hundred on the most permanent lagoons. In the wet season — when water areas are more extensive — it spreads out across the subcoastal plains to breed in the deepest swamps and ponds. It is among the most water-loving of ducks, and is usually found in small groups among the blue waterlilies of the tropical freshwater lagoons — one of the most attractive waterfowl scenes in Australia. Green Pygmy-Geese sometimes rest on the water's edge, but on land they are awkward and walk with difficulty. Sometimes they crawl out of the water to rest on partly submerged fallen trees. When flushed or flying from pond to pond, the birds spring from the water at a low angle and fly swiftly, low down, in direct lines, whistling incessantly.

The Green Pygmy-Goose feeds on aquatic vegetation. Usually it cruises among waterlilies, grazing the buds and heads of emergent plants. It dives, remarkably like a Eurasian coot, to get submerged plants as much as 500 mm below the surface. It can also filter floating seeds and flowers from the surface of the water. Pygmy-Geese eat vegetable food — and a few insects, by accident. In the Northern Territory nearly half their food is the seeds and buds of waterlilies. About 30 per cent is the seeds and leaves of grasses and the rest is pond weeds and other emergent and subemergent plants.

Green Pygmy-Geese are always seen in pairs, keep to themselves in flocks, and presumably mate for life. In courtship, a male swims round the female, raising and lowering his head. Both birds stretch their necks in mating displays. The male finds potential nest sites but the female makes the final selection. When the female is brooding, the male defends the nest area; when the eggs are hatched he helps rear the young. To escape danger, young dive and 'freeze' under waterlilies until parents return to call them out.

So far this colourful bird has survived human settlement well.

Although some of its habitat has been destroyed, water storages for stock and irrigation in the tropics quickly develop deep water plants, providing suitable feeding grounds.

OTHER NAMES
Green Goose, Goose-teal.

IDENTIFICATION
LENGTH: *Male 305–360 mm; female 300–345 mm.*
MALE: *Crown dark green crossed with fine brown bars; back and scapulars dark glossy green; rump and tail freckled glossy green and grey-white. Wings grey-green with white panel through secondaries. Conspicuous white patch on face below eye. Chin grey; neck glossy green. Breast, belly and flanks grey-white, each feather having crescents of dark green or brown; undertail dark brown. Eye dark brown. Bill dark green-grey above, pink below and on tip. Feet and webs green-grey.*
FEMALE: *Crown less green and less distinctly barred than male's. Back of neck green, but rest white flecked with green. Area below eye, extending to back of neck and chin, pure white, with some dark grey flecks.*
IMMATURES: *Resemble female, but face, chin and neck heavily spotted with dark brown. By two months males begin to acquire solid green neck. Non-breeding males may go into eclipse with white flecking on face, chin and foreneck.*
DUCKLINGS: *Crown and back dark grey-brown, face light grey-white with dark eye stripe and less white above eye than in White Pygmy-Goose. Wing dark grey-brown above, whitish below, with white trailing edge. Two whitish spots on either side of back. Undersurface pale grey-white. Eye dark brown. Bill pink with yellow-green upper ridge. Feet yellow-green with yellow webs.*

VOICE
Musical whistles and trills, pee-whit pee-yew *and* whit *in alarm; rapid high-pitched trill in threat and fighting by males.*

NESTING
January–March near Darwin, NT, and in northern Queensland. Nests found in swamp vegetation, on the ground, or in hollows of trees standing in water. Eggs: eight to 12; hard-shelled, smooth; lustrous, cream or white; blunt-ellipsoid, about 44 x 32 mm. Incubation 26 days, by female.

DISTRIBUTION
On deep lily-covered freshwater lagoons across northern Australia, between Fitzroy River, WA, and Rockhampton, Qld. Also in southern New Guinea, Buru and Seram. No races.

A male Green Pygmy-Goose. The male is aggressive and fights often and savagely, using its short, strong bill as a weapon.

Cotton Pygmy-Goose Nettapus coromandelianus (GMELIN, 1789)

The Cotton Pygmy-Goose lives in deep, tropical lagoons and usually only enters shallow water to feed on plants and seeds. This is a male.

THE COTTON PYGMY-GOOSE lives in settled districts within its range, provided deep freshwater lagoons in those areas are not drained. Its habits are similar to those of the closely related Green Pygmy-Goose, and it is completely aquatic, seldom leaving water except to rest on logs. It spends most of its time floating among waterlilies in deep water in pairs or small family groups and comes near shore only to feed in the early morning and evening. It flies very fast, and usually quite low. Pairs probably mate for life.

The Cotton Pygmy-Goose has a wide range: from India and Southeast Asia through parts of Indonesia and New Guinea to northern Australia. The Australian race is found in coastal and subcoastal districts from the tip of Cape York Peninsula to the Clarence River in New South Wales. The bird is now rare in the southern part of this range and birds seen there are probably vagrants from farther north. The main populations now survive between Rockhampton and Ingham, Qld. Although characteristic of deep permanent freshwater lagoons where waterlilies grow, they are also sometimes found in large freshwater lakes and along the edges of quiet rivers and creeks fringed with waterlilies but never in streams, shallow swamps or water covered with vegetation.

Cotton Pygmy-Geese seem to be sedentary and make only local movements. In the wet season they disperse some distance inland to breed, but in the dry season, as inland waters dry, they fly back to the permanent lagoons closer to the coast.

In feeding behaviour the Cotton Pygmy-Goose is similar to the Green Pygmy-Goose; it cruises among waterlilies, stripping seeds and seedheads from aquatic plants, dabbling the surface and darting at an occasional insect. On the coast more than half of its diet is pond weeds, and seeds and aquatic grasses. In more inland swamps, it eats less pond weed and more sedges.

The Cotton Pygmy-Goose's breeding season seems timed to occur at the end of the main rainy season. In the southern part of its Australian range, most nests are found between September and November. In northern Queensland most breeding probably occurs between January and March. The bird selects an elevated hollow, up to a metre from entrance to nest, in a dead tree not far from water. Eggs may be laid on bare wood but if the hollow has been used by another species, material may still be there.

The Cotton Pygmy-Goose is not in any immediate danger of extinction because, in its range, dams impounded for stock and other purposes soon develop deep water plants and become suitable habitat. Extra areas are easily created. But its range is more restricted than that of any other Australian duck and its numbers are few. Any change in local land use could affect it.

OTHER NAMES
White Pygmy-Goose, White-quilled Pygmy-Goose, Cotton Teal.

IDENTIFICATION
LENGTH: *Male 350–380 mm; female 330–380 mm.*
MALE: *Crown brown; face white; back of neck white with some brown feathers; back glossy green; upper tail coverts and tail brown. Wing coverts glossy green; primaries dark brown with a broad white bar near tip, diminishing through secondaries. Chin white, neck white with some brown feathers; black collar between neck and belly. Breast and belly white, freckled with brown; undertail dusky. Eye bright red. Bill black. Feet olive-green.*
FEMALE: *Less green on back than male; lacks black collar and white bar across wings; brown eye-stripe; breast barred with fine brown marks. Eye brown.*
IMMATURES: *Similar to female but have no green gloss; dark eye-stripe more distinct. Males in eclipse resemble female but keep white wing bar.*
DUCKLINGS: *Crown dark grey-brown; face light grey with dark brown eye-stripe. Back of neck, back and tail dark grey-brown; underside light grey; underside of tail dark grey to black at tip. Wing dark brown above and grey below with white trailing edge. Two white spots on either side of back. Bill yellow with dark grey ridge. Feet dark grey; webs yellow.*

VOICE
Male makes loud staccato cackle or trumpet in flight; female a soft quack.

NESTING
In south of range breeding seems to be September–November, and in northern Queensland January–March. Nests in tree holes up to 10 m above ground, usually within 20 m of water. Eggs: usually six to nine; pearly white; oval, about 48 x 35 mm. Incubation by female.

DISTRIBUTION
Coastal eastern Queensland, from Cape York Peninsula to Clarence River, NSW. Main population between Rockhampton and Ingham, Qld, with greatest numbers in Ayr, Townsville and Charters Towers districts. Locally nomadic. Also in India, Sri Lanka, Burma, Malaya, Thailand, south China, Philippines, Indonesia and northern New Guinea. Two races; one large, endemic to Australia.

Maned Duck *Chenonetta jubata* (LATHAM, 1801)

THE MANED DUCK IS ONE OF THE 'perching' ducks, and related to the pygmy-geese. It is better adapted to walking than swimming and is most often seen grazing like a goose near open fresh water; it usually takes to water only for bathing, copulation or refuge. During the breeding season birds perch in trees, looking for tree holes in which to nest. They have well developed claws on the end of their half-webbed feet and these help purchase.

The Maned Duck is a generalised grazer, and although concentrating on green herbage, will also take insects. This versatility has made them a pest in some areas where they eat crops such as rice and lucerne. They also eat any grain that is available, and during drought capitalise on any hand-feeding of stock.

Flocks of up to 100—sometimes even 1000—commonly gather in southern districts through autumn and winter. These comprise pairs of birds, which appear to be independent of one another, and the flock is seldom constant for more than a few days. The ducks wander about much at night. Flocks disintegrate to some extent during the breeding season, when the pairs disperse and settle on the edge of local waters to nest. Because they nest in holes in trees, there is a preference for water in open wooded areas at this time.

Courtship is rarely seen because it is usually confined to younger ducks that have not paired previously; Maned Ducks mate for life. It usually involves a number of males in a shake display around a female. The female responds by neck-swaying away from the preferred male, inciting him. If other ducks approach too close to the pair, the female will react towards the intruders and even attack. Mating occurs on the water and is preceeded by a number of ritualised displays, usually performed only by the male. Following mating, the pair bathe-display and sometimes dive.

Breeding occurs in spring in southern districts, but its onset and extent depends on rain. Ducklings jump out of the nest hole soon after hatching, called out by their parents from below. As soon as all regroup on the ground, they are led to the nearest water and, unless disturbed, remain there until they can fly, about 50 days later. Ducklings graze as soon as they hatch and they also take any available insects.

Both parents care for the young. The male initially watches for predators while the female eats to regain the weight lost during incubation. She in turn protects the young against inclement weather, brooding them. Both parents perform distraction displays when alarmed, shamming injured wings in their attempt to divert intruders. At other times they lead the young off or freeze with necks outstretched. Young remain with their parents for at least two weeks after fledging, then all amalgamate in local flocks.

OTHER NAMES
Wood Duck, Maned Goose.

IDENTIFICATION
LENGTH: *Male 420–590 mm; female 420–550 mm.*
MALE: *Head and neck dark brown with mane of elongated black feathers; mantle and scapulars grey, edged black; lower back to tail black. Upper wing coverts grey; primaries dusky; secondaries white with dusky bases, bordered on top with white bar; iridescent green speculum on inner secondaries. Underwing white. Breast white, mottled grey edged black; belly and undertail black; sides of breast and flanks pale grey with fine, wavy black lines. Eye brown. Bill, feet and webs dark olive-brown to black. Eclipse: A few white feathers around eye, chin and belly in male.*
FEMALE: *Upper parts brown to grey; lower back, rump and tail and edges of scapulars black. Wing as in male. Head and neck pale brown, with mottled white line above and below eye, and white flecking on throat. Breast and flanks white, mottled with brown edged black on breast; belly and undertail white.*
JUVENILES: *As female, but lighter and with streaky breast.*
DUCKLINGS: *Grey-brown above with two white spots on either side of back, white trailing edge to wing. Off-white underside and face, with conspicuous black line through eye and below it. Eye dusky. Bill black-brown. Feet grey-brown.*

VOICE
Drawn out, nasal mew. Shorter and higher-pitched in male than female. A shortened mew by female during courtship. A high-frequency cluck and shortened mew are also restricted to the female.

NESTING
Spring in south, when there is regular rainfall; irregularly inland, after heavy rain. Nest a bed of wood chips in hollow spout in living tree, sometimes far from water; eggs covered with down. Eggs: nine to 12; smooth; white or cream; oval, about 58 x 43 mm. Incubation about 28 days, by female; male stands guard. Young fledge in 50 days.

DISTRIBUTION
Better-watered coastal and subcoastal woods and swamps of east and west. Regionally nomadic. No races.

The male Maned Duck has a brown head and neck with a mane of elongated black feathers. Maned Ducks nest in holes in trees, in open wooded areas, and spend much of their time on land in 'camps' near water, leaving them to feed on grass and herbs.

Pink-eared Duck *Malacorhynchus membranaceus* (LATHAM, 1801)

The Pink-eared Duck is easily recognised by its zebra-striped plumage and shovel bill. These ducks are nomadic, and are found across the continent.

AN EXTREME NOMAD WHICH WANDERS the residual floodwaters of inland Australia, the Pink-eared Duck is one of the world's most aberrant and distinct ducks. It is small and feeds in water, as the 'dabbling' ducks do, and it head-shakes and preens behind the wing in the same way. On the other hand its feather proteins and the structure of its voice box or syrinx, with tapered trachea and poorly developed bulla, have more in common with those of 'perching' ducks and pygmy-geese. And its barred plumage and displays when pairing and threatening are distinct. This and its adaptation to ephemeral inland waters suggest that the Pink-eared Duck may have an evolutionary history as old as arid Australia.

With flaps of skin flanking its bill, to form a broad scoop, the duck is specialised to feed in plankton-rich shallow stagnant fresh water. So it concentrates in big flocks on flood sheets and claypans, rarely gathering on deeper lagoons and swamps where feeding is uneconomic except temporarily to sit out droughts. Pink-eared Ducks seldom leave the water except to roost on the edge, and they are able to stay on dwindling pools long after other ducks have left.

They cruise the water with bill immersed up to the eyes. Water is drawn in through the slightly opened tip of the bill and then pumped out at the sides, where a dense layer of fine lamellae or plates filter and catch particles of food. Like shovelers, groups of Pink-eareds often forage in arrowhead formation. At other times a pair will rotate clockwise or anticlockwise up to 50 times. Although this resembles the ritualised feeding display given by shovelers, its purpose may simply be to stir up food in a vortex. Pink-eared Ducks also immerse heads and necks to trawl along the bottom, and even, on occasion, stand on the edge and dredge. Plankton, which include tiny insects, waterfleas, copepods, ostracods, freshwater algae, augmented by floating seeds and a few larger plants, is their food.

To adapt such specialised feeding habits to unpredictable flooding in inland Australia, Pink-eared Ducks are nomadic and able to breed at any time, whenever conditions are right. They are swift fliers, beating their wings more slowly than teal and holding their heads higher. Often when flushed they fly in dense clouds and are noisy, chirruping continually. They wander in search of feeding grounds mainly at night.

Their sexual cycle may be triggered by rising floodwaters, but breeding is commonly held back behind that of other ducks until the flood has begun to subside. Males have nodular gonads, which may hold sperm at any time. Their pair-forming display — an uplift call — is similar to their threat display. The bill is tossed up and then dropped quickly, accompanied by a drawnout whistle. In threat, males may rush at an intruder, bills swinging up and down and trilling. Males remain with their mates throughout, defending the nest during incubation and helping to raise the brood, but new pairs are formed at each breeding.

OTHER NAMES
Pink-ear, Zebra Duck, Whistling Teal.

IDENTIFICATION
LENGTH: *Male 380–450 mm; female about 400 mm.*
ADULTS: *Sexes similar. Top of head grey; neck, back and wings mid-brown. Side of head white with fine light brown bars; dark brown mask surrounds eye and extends to back of neck; small pink patch behind eye and narrow white ring around it. Rump white; tail dusky; white band at tip. White trailing edge to wings. Front of neck and undersurface white barred dusky. Undertail buff. Eye brown. Bill leaden-grey, with membranous flaps on edges near tip. Feet and webs leaden-grey.*
IMMATURES: *Resemble adults, but generally duller with pink patch smaller and less distinct.*
DUCKLINGS: *General plumage above light grey-brown. Sides light brown with white-grey patch behind wing; wing light brown with white-grey band. Top of head and neck dark brown; face white-grey with single dark patch surrounding eye. Throat and underside of body light grey or white. Bill with spatulate flaps at hatching.*

VOICE
Musical chirrup; when fighting a continuous trill commonly a whistled whee-oow call is given by males. Both sexes give fluty chirrups as well as purrs.

NESTING
Breeds at any time of year, provided floodwaters are high enough. Nest a rounded mound of very sticky grey down 250 mm in diameter and 150 mm high, that envelops eggs; placed on logs, limbs or in bushes a few centimetres to 10 m above water; often the old nests of other water birds are used. Eggs: five to eight, usually six or seven; smooth and with greasy feeling; white or cream; oval, pointed at smaller end, about 49 x 36 mm. Incubation about 28 days, by female. Both adults care for brood.

DISTRIBUTION
Nomadic and moves over whole continent; more common in floodwaters, though can exist in any freshwater or brackish habitat. Core breeding area is Murray–Darling basin. Endemic but fossil in New Zealand. No races.

Grey Teal *Anas gibberifrons* MÜLLER, 1842

AT HOME IN ALMOST ANY WATERY habitat, the Grey Teal can be found all over Australia in fresh, brackish or salt water. It lives in the mangrove estuaries of the coast, the deep cold lakes of the highlands, as well as the flood pans of the desert and coastal and inland lakes and swamps. It is found in greatest numbers in the tree-lined billabongs of the Murray-Darling River system.

Grey Teal are highly nomadic and most swamps and lagoons support a few at any time. But the mass of birds wander the whole continent according to the distribution of rain and flood. Soon after a flood the teal begin to arrive in numbers to breed; as the waters dry up they disperse or die. It is a cycle of boom-and-bust. In drought, dispersing individuals from one swamp will wander straight across the continent in all directions. Apart from such dramatic irruptions, Grey Teal also make more regular small-scale nomadic movements. In winter, southern inland waters are often extensive, and most teal stay there to breed. Then, as waters decline in summer, some leave and move to the coast.

Typical dabbling ducks, Grey Teal feed by upending and dredging, or by stripping seeds from plants in or overhanging water. They feed on both plant and animal material. Inland, most of their food is the seeds of smartweeds, sedges and grasses. Animal food is mostly insects including beetles, water boatmen and the larvae of midges, dragonflies, caddis flies and mosquitoes; also mussels and small crustaceans, particularly on tidal swamps. When water levels are steady the birds remain in the billabongs or lagoons, cruising the edges and eating aquatic insects, plants and seeds. If levels rise and flood adjacent areas, teal move with it,

feeding on the invertebrates forced out of burrows, as well as on the seeds of grasses, clovers and other herbs. This flexibility allows the birds to use almost any kind of water for feeding.

Just as opportunistic in their nesting, Grey Teal can breed at any time of the year. The sexual cycle is triggered by an increase in water level, provided the birds are adequately nourished at the time. They respond rapidly and can lay eggs in less than two weeks after waters begin rising. The extent of the breeding season varies greatly from year to year. In droughts there is little or no breeding; in years of flood all teal breed. If the flood is prolonged the breeding season continues for many months, the birds rearing brood after brood. They will nest anywhere: on the ground, in rabbit burrows, crevices in rocks and in hollow trees. In the inland, tree holes are the most common nest site. The hollow is fairly steeply inclined and more than a metre deep. Newly hatched young jump-and-grab up to the entrance from which they explode like a cork from a bottle, and waft down to the water, often three metres or more below, where they are gathered together by the female.

The rate of population turnover is high. Although some birds live for eight years, most juveniles survive only one year and few live longer than 20 months. When there is a flood, the rate of replacement is high. Young birds take almost a year to reach adult plumage; adults themselves moult twice a year, once before breeding and immediately after breeding. Post-breeding moulters hide away on their own and remain flightless for 13–27 days.

The Grey Teal depends on the flooding of inland rivers for breeding, and on permanent coastal swamps for drought refuges.

OTHER NAMES
Slender Teal.

IDENTIFICATION
LENGTH: *Male 410–480 mm; female 370–440 mm.*
ADULTS: *Sexes similar. Top of head and back of neck black-brown, speckled with lighter brown. Feathers of back dark brown with paler edges; rump and tail dark brown. Upper wing and coverts dark brown; upper secondaries and their coverts white, forming a band; lower secondaries glossy black with green sheen, forming a speculum with white band above and below. Side of head, throat and chin almost white. Underparts dark brown, scalloped with broad pale feather margins of each feather. Underwing dark grey-brown with triangular patch of white on lower*

coverts. Eye bright red. Bill and feet slate-grey.
IMMATURES: *Similar to adults but paler, particularly on head and neck. Eye brown.*
DUCKLINGS: *Smoky grey-brown on back and head with white spots on wing and sides of back; grey-white on face and underneath. Two conspicuous brown stripes on head, one through eye and one below it.*

VOICE
Female has loud, penetrating quack repeated rapidly up to 20 times like a hoarse laugh, with pitch falling successively. Male has loud burp gdeeu. Used for contact and advertisement. Very similar to calls of Chestnut Teal. Variety of other soft calls.

NESTING
Breeds at any time of year provided water level is suitable and food available. The birds nest anywhere—on the ground, in rabbit burrows, crevices in rocks and tree holes up to 10 m above water. Eggs laid on bare wood or on ground and covered with grey down plucked from female's breast. Eggs: four to 14, usually seven or eight; cream, becoming stained; oval, 54 x 39 mm. Incubation 24–26 days, by female.

DISTRIBUTION
Throughout Australia, but greatest numbers in lagoons and billabongs of Murray–Darling basin. Dispersing birds reach New Guinea, New Caledonia, Macquarie Island and New Zealand. One race—large, light-

coloured, and with sloping forehead— in Australia; three other races in Lesser Sundas, Andamen Islands and Rennell Island in Solomons.

Grey Teal are nomadic and range across the continent, following the rains and floods on which they depend for food.

The male Chestnut Teal has a glossy green-black head, chestnut underparts, white patch at the side of rump, and a black tail.

Chestnut Teal _Anas castanea_ (EYTON,1838)

FOR MANY YEARS OBSERVERS took the Chestnut and Grey Teal to be one species — all Grey Teal were thought to be female Chestnut Teal. Chestnut Teal commonly associate with Grey Teal in mixed flocks, but careful observation distinguishes them. Female Chestnut Teal are darker than Grey Teal and lack their characteristic white throat. In flight they are particularly difficult to distinguish, both rising abruptly from the water, flying off with the same rapid direct beating, and showing identical wing patterns. Only the male Chestnut's white flank spots distinguish it. Both species occur together in many areas where they breed in southern Australia, but hybrids are very rare.

Chestnut Teal keep more to southern coastal surface waters than Grey Teal, and are equally or more at home on brackish lakes and mangrove-lined estuaries than on freshwater swamps. They never congregate in vast flocks of hundreds either, except at times in Tasmania, their stronghold. Most non-breeding flocks rarely number more than 10–20 birds, as they cruise and feed in surface water or rest together on mud banks, logs or rocks in or on the water's edge.

Much more sedentary than Grey Teal, Chestnut Teal do move locally in response to changing water conditions and food supplies. In autumn and winter they gather in flocks on larger lakes and estuaries and in spring they disperse to breed. Many breed in the same area in which they passed the winter. Juvenile birds wander more widely. Birds banded in Tasmania have been found 500 kilometres away in Victoria. In drought years a few birds travel great distances and some have reached Darwin 3000 kilometres from their usual range, after travelling with the highly mobile Grey Teal.

The Chestnut Teal is a dabbling duck, and feeds, typically, by dabbling on the water's edge, upending, filtering the water surface or stripping seeds from plants. Its diet in saltwater habitats is mainly widgeon grass, sedge seeds, a variety of molluscs and crustaceans, and a few insects and worms. In summer, the habitat of Chestnut Teal is invaded by vast numbers of nomadic Grey Teal from the inland. The two species select different items, however, Chestnut Teal taking more plant material than Grey, as well as different animal species within the same classes that both birds feed on. More importantly though, the Chestnut Teal takes larger prey items, which suggests that the two species do not compete for food, at least when food is relatively abundant.

Chestnut Teal breed regularly each year over spring, but begin as early as July around Melbourne and finish as late as January on the South Australian Coorong. Males first gather in small groups to whistle and puddle about to attract a mate. The pair-bond formed, drake and duck cruise the water's edge for a nest site, paddling ashore to inspect holes among rocks and even low hollows in trees. The female broods unaided but her drake remains attached to her and commonly accompanies the brood with her until they can fly and fend for themselves. Hatchlings stay in the nest for only about a day before leaving. Full adult plumage is not gained for a year, after several moults.

OTHER NAMES
Chestnut-breasted Teal, Mountain Teal.

IDENTIFICATION
LENGTH: _Male 410–480 mm; female 380–460 mm._
MALE: _Head and neck glossy green-black; back dark brown, each feather with a chestnut fringe; rump and upper side of tail black. Wing dark brown; speculum in secondaries dark glossy green with broad white band on top and narrow one underneath. Underwing dark grey-brown with triangular patch of white on lower coverts. Breast and underside chestnut, each feather with conspicuous dusky central blotch; undertail coverts glossy black; on flanks a conspicuous white patch. Eye crimson. Bill blue-grey with black nail. Feet and webs olive-grey. In eclipse plumage, resembles female very closely._
FEMALE: _Dark brown above; each feather, except those of rump and tail, edged pale brown. Crown dark brown; face fawn with black streaks. Throat and underside generally pale brown, each feather with dark centre. Wing marks as in male._
IMMATURES: _Resemble female._
DUCKLINGS: _Similar to those of Grey Teal but darker and dusky over back._

VOICE
Drake and duck have same calls as Grey Teal, but are slightly deeper and harsher in tone.

NESTING
Breeds July–January, laying peaking in October. Nest a scrape in the ground, in long grass, rushes, crevices in rocks or tree holes close to water; often on small islands. Eggs: usually seven to 10; shell close-grained and smooth; cream; ellipsoidal, 52 x 37 mm. Enveloped in brown-grey down. Incubation 27 days, by female. Both adults care for ducklings.

DISTRIBUTION
Most common in brackish coastal lagoons, saltwater estuaries and the lower reaches of creeks with mangroves around coastal southern Australia. Also found in freshwater swamps inland and on high mountains of southern tablelands. Tasmania is its stronghold. No races.

Pacific Black Duck *Anas superciliosa* GMELIN, 1789

EVERY COASTAL STREAM and lagoon, every mountain lake and inland swamp has its quota of Pacific Black Ducks. They are probably more widely distributed in Australia as a breeding species than any other. They can be found in any habitat, and often mix with Grey and Chestnut Teal. Their flight is strong, swift and direct. When disturbed, they form a compact flock, gain height rapidly and generally leave the area. The teal, on the other hand, usually circle or make several passes and then settle on the other side of the swamp or pool.

In habitats where the Pacific Black Duck occurs together with Grey and Chestnut Teal, there are differences between the three in their diurnal activities. Pacific Black Ducks spend the most time feeding—more than a quarter of the day—and the Grey Teal the least. All three ducks feed in much the same places, but the black ducks keep more to the deeper permanent freshwater pools and lagoons. The three species also differ in both bill structure and size, the Pacific Black Duck having the largest bill and Grey Teal the smallest, so that they may take different food items. Most of the ducks feed in the early morning and evening, spending much of the day sitting, the Pacific Black Duck and Grey Teal preferring the ground while Chestnut Teal more often select dead trees and logs.

A typical surface-feeding duck, the Pacific Black Duck takes both plant and animal food from the water by dabbling, dredging and upending. It also strips seeds from emergent plants and growth along the edge of the water and adjacent pasture, preferring to eat the larger seeds, but capable of collecting and living on the smallest items. The most important seeds in its diet are from aquatic and ditch grasses like barnyard millet, water couch, summer grass and cultivated rice. Aquatic insects account for about half of its animal food. Other important items are crustaceans, yabbies, and fairy shrimps. Young ducklings feed almost exclusively on aquatic insects.

Although Pacific Black Ducks are randomly nomadic, following floods and evacuating drought-stricken areas, they are nonetheless rather sedentary on permanent waters, particularly around coastal eastern and northern Australia. In southeastern Australia there are also general—but not complete—seasonal shifts in the populations, north over winter and south in spring and summer. Across northern Australia, the birds concentrate on coastal waters during the winter-spring dry season, and then disperse inland with the break of the summer monsoon.

The breeding season is timed to occur when water areas are at their most extensive and aquatic plants are mature. Most breeding takes place in spring in southern Australia, where the rains fall in winter. In the tropics, with summer rainfall, the bird breeds in autumn. Where rainfall is erratic, it breeds when the rivers flood, and where uniform it breeds all year round.

Pair-forming displays that prelude breeding usually begin in April–May everywhere, irrespective of the time of local nesting. The sequence and postures in display seem to be generally Mallard-like, and include sterile copulation. By spring most adults are mated and courtship intensified. Females, which carry the brunt of incubation, lay their eggs in a wide variety of situations. The nests range from scrapes in the ground to well-woven cups in grass or reeds, and are also found in tree holes, on stumps, in deserted nests of water birds or on the flat surfaces of staghorns. When leaving the eggs to feed, the female covers them with down. On her sorties she is accompanied by the male.

In some seasons Pacific Black Ducks visit irrigated rice fields in large numbers and farmers fear they do significant damage to crops. But the overall losses caused by the bird are small; it is not an agricultural pest. It is the most popular game bird in Australia and in coastal districts makes up around 70 per cent of the bag. It is able to survive controlled hunting, but cannot maintain its numbers unless its habitat is preserved.

The Pacific Black Duck is one of the most widespread and abundant ducks in Australia.

The introduced Mallard is closely related to the native Pacific Black Duck, with which it interbreeds and competes for food.

Mallard *Anas platyrhynchos* LINNÉ, 1758

CONSERVATIONISTS ARE CONCERNED by the Mallard. It was introduced to Australia late last century from the Northern Hemisphere and is now found in many city parks and gardens throughout the country, and on many farms close to swamps. These Mallards are both pure-bred and in varying degrees of hybridisation with domestic ducks, most strains of which have been developed from the Mallard, and with the closely related native Pacific Black Duck.

In dry weather wild black ducks visit city parks and some of them mate with the tame Mallards. In some coastal districts female Mallards are allowed to swim in swamps and become impregnated by wild black ducks. There have been a few records, mostly from the Riverina, in New South Wales, of apparently pure-bred Mallards flying with wild black ducks.

Such a spread of the Mallard presents a particular danger to the Pacific Black Duck. It has similar food and habitat needs and can compete with the black ducks. When the two species interbreed the Mallard strain is dominant and in successive generations the characteristics of Pacific Black Ducks can be lost. In addition, the Mallard may impart unfavourable characteristics to the hybrids. It is sedentary and its crosses are probably not able to survive the erratic climate of Australia as successfully as does the thoroughly adapted native species, which is nomadic in times of drought.

Some authorities say that if the drift of Mallard genes is not to endanger the populations of Pacific Black Duck, the most important game species in Australia, Mallards in the wild should be shot.

Elsewhere, in North America and New Zealand, Mallards have interbred with the local black ducks and have swamped them genetically in many areas.

OTHER NAMES
None.

IDENTIFICATION
LENGTH: *Male 550–680 mm; female 520–580 mm.*
MALE: *Head and neck rich iridescent green with white collar at base of neck. Back grey. Rump and curled-up tail glossy black; side of tail white. Wings brown-grey; speculum in secondaries purple-blue bordered at both sides with black and white bars. Breast rich purple-brown; rest of underside white with fine dark lines; underside of tail black. Eye brown. Bill lemon. Feet and legs orange. In non-breeding plumage resembles female but has dull green bill.*
FEMALE: *Head and neck buff with brown streaks; dusky line through eye. Body mottled and streaked with dusky and dull buff-brown. Tail whitish. Wings dark brown; speculum as in males. Bill dusky orange. Feet dull orange.*
DUCKLINGS: *Similar to Pacific Black Duck, but feet more orange.*

VOICE
Similar to Pacific Black Duck.

NESTING
No information on breeding season in Australia. Nests on the ground, often on islands in ornamental ponds. Eggs: usually eight to 12; smooth and glossy; light green-buff or grey-buff; oval, 48 x 42 mm. Incubation 26–28 days, by female.

DISTRIBUTION
Introduced into city parks and gardens. Wild Mallards have occasionally been sighted in southeastern and southwestern Australia, particularly in Murray-Murrumbidgee basin. Native to arctic and temperate regions of Eurasia, all North America, northern Pacific, and northwestern Africa. Winters south to southern USA, Mexico, North Africa, southern China and India. Seven races; one from northern North America and Europe introduced to Australia and New Zealand.

Australasian Shoveler *Anas rhynchotis* LATHAM, 1801

A SLIM DUCK WITH A distinctively broadened blue-grey bill, the Australasian Shoveler has apparently declined in numbers over the past 50 years. In severe droughts, flocks of up to 500 Shovelers are sometimes seen, but this may give a false idea of their abundance. Such flocks are concentrations of birds drawn from wide areas and at the time are under considerable stress. Usually Shovelers are found in twos and threes, dispersed among other ducks, swimming characteristically low in the water or flying swiftly and directly overhead on rapidly winnowing wings. In flight their wings appear somewhat backswept and pointed.

Shovelers keep mainly to permanent, sheltered freshwater swamps, lakes and waterways where there is much floating growth to provide food. Once established in such waters they seldom shift and stay to breed, often using the same site year after year. Local movements do occur but widespread wandering is rare and forced only by drought. On their feeding grounds, Shovelers are quiet and unobtrusive. During the day they rest quietly on the water in dense cover, rarely on the shore, and are highly alert. They react quickly to an observer, and are usually swimming restlessly to and fro, ready to take off long before other ducks. On taking off they spring vertically into the air with a characteristic whirr of the wings.

The Shoveler is specially adapted to feeding off the surface of the water, neither dabbling nor stripping seeds like other ducks. Its broad bill is fringed with fine, hair-like structures, or lamellae, through which it strains water or mud. The lamellae retain small items of food. The feeding Shoveler swims quickly, sunk low, bill immersed and chattering rapidly, filtering water as it goes. Although Shovelers commonly feed in pairs, communal feeding sometimes occurs. The birds arrange themselves in an arrowhead or echelon formation and each keeps its bill close to the flank and feet of the one ahead. The paddling feet of the birds in front stir up the mud and aquatic animals and these are filtered by the others. Like other dabbling ducks, they can upend, and they sometimes stand in shallow water dredging mud.

Aquatic animals make up most of the food harvested in this way: water insects — mostly beetles — mussels, shrimps, other crustaceans and large quantities of zooplankton. Itinerant seeds are taken as well from a variety of plants — whatever happens to be floating on the water.

Breeding mainly on perennial waters with a permanent food supply, Shovelers breed consistently over spring in most districts. The birds court on the water, usually far from shore. The female swims along followed by one or more chattering and grunting males. Sometimes a male darts in front, turning the back of his head to the female, feathers raised. The female raises and lowers her bill with increasing rapidity, then takes wing, to be followed by a male or two and they twist and swoop through the air. The mated pair copulate on the water, after which the male swims in circles, grunting and chattering and swinging his head up and down. Both drake and duck select the nest hole together, choosing a site on the ground more commonly than any other Australian duck.

The Shoveler is now more common in the inland than on the coast, because coastal habitats have been destroyed by flood mitigation and swamp drainage. The birds' feeding habits make rich permanent waters essential to its survival.

OTHER NAMES
Shoveler, Blue-winged Shoveler.

IDENTIFICATION
LENGTH: *Male 450–530 mm; female 460–490 mm.*
MALE: *Forecrown, foreface and chin brown-black; rest of head and neck blue-grey with green gloss. White stripe on face in front of eye. Back and rump black; scapulars plumed black and white; scapulars plumed black and white. Upper wing coverts powder-blue; speculum on secondaries dark green with broad white band on front. Front of neck and breast speckled dark brown; rest of underside deep chestnut; conspicuous white patch on each side of tail. Eye yellow. Bill olive-grey. Feet and webs bright orange. In eclipse plumage resembles female, but feet orange or yellow-brown.*
FEMALE: *Duller than male. No white face crescent; wing patch duller. Chin and sides of head mottled brown-buff, crown and nape dark brown. Rest of upper parts dark brown, each feather edged with light brown. Underparts pale chestnut, each feather with dark brown centre. Eye brown. Bill dusky. Feet green-grey*
IMMATURES: *Resemble female but paler. By four months yellow of eye and legs apparent in male.*
DUCKLINGS: *Dark brown above; yellow tinged with brown below. Broad yellow stripe above eye and conspicuous dark brown band from bill, through eye to back of head; dark mark on cheek. Trailing edge of wing yellow; yellow spot on each side of back. When just hatched bill no larger than that of other ducklings, but by 14 days is distinctly spoon-shaped and large in proportion to bird. Bill and feet olive-brown.*

VOICE
Usually silent, but male has soft 'club-it' call and guttural grunt; female has soft, husky quack. Soft chatter in flight.

NESTING
Breeds August–December over spring in coastal districts; in semi-arid interior also breeds out of season when rivers flood. Nests on ground or on top of low stump 1–2 m above water. Nest usually a depression lined with a little grass and down in shelter of tussock or in tall grass usually close to water's edge. Eggs: nine to 11; cream with pale green tinge; oval, 54 x 38 mm. Incubation about 24 days, by female.

DISTRIBUTION
An aquatic habitat, in most parts of Australia. Prefers deep, heavily vegetated swamps such as cumbungi swamps inland and tea-tree swamps at coast. Main breeding range is in Tasmania, Murray-Darling Basin, along southeast coast and southwest of Western Australia. Normal nomadic range includes most of eastern Australia south of Townsville, Qld and in Western Australia it wanders inland for 300 km and as far north as Point Cloates. One race in Australia; another, more brightly coloured, in New Zealand.

A pair of Australasian Shovelers; the male is on the left. Shovelers are usually found in groups of two to six, dispersed among flocks of other ducks on coastal or inland waters.

Hardhead *Aythya australis* (EYTON, 1838)

Only the male Hardhead has a white eye. Hardheads swim swiftly, low in the water, and often dive, getting food inaccessible to other ducks.

FAST-BEATING WINGS with a white bar and an audible whirr identify the swift-flying Hardhead. A duck of deeper waters, it seldom comes to land and never perches in trees. It is most common in the still reaches of large swamps and lagoons, but equally at home in deep turbulent waters where flooding inland rivers flow through lignum creeks and channels. It swims swiftly, low in the water, diving frequently with a smooth and effortless action. When disturbed, it rises vertically and flies off, gaining height rapidly.

Hardheads feed exclusively in water, sometimes dabbling at the edge, upending and stripping seeds from surface aquatic plants but commonly diving as well. They belong to a worldwide group of partly white-eyed diving ducks called pochards. Submerging by springing forward under the water without a ripple, they may travel for up to 30–40 metres before surfacing, staying down for a minute or so. Hardheads are able to get at deep food inaccessible to other ducks. Aquatic insects, molluscs, shrimps, yabbies and small fish form a major part of their diet, but they also eat emergent sedges, docks and grasses, and submerged plants.

Hardheads are more sedentary than Grey Teal but probably more mobile than Pacific Black Ducks. They are thought to be nomadic in normal seasons. As swamps dry in inland New South Wales, the ducks move south and west along the Murray River and its tributaries to the southeast of South Australia. When winter rains fall in New South Wales, they reappear there. Congregations of arriving or departing birds may number a thousand or more and form huge rafts floating out on open water. In drought they wander more widely, many appearing in the north and inland, and some reaching Indonesia, New Guinea, New Zealand and various Pacific islands; colonies established by these vagrants are impermanent.

Hardheads have a spring-based breeding cycle that is influenced by rains. In southwestern Australia they usually breed from October to November, at much the same time as in inland New South Wales, between September and December; but the season can be extended when flooding is extensive. Needing deeper water for feeding, they often begin later than Grey Teal and Pacific Black Ducks. They have declined in numbers on the east coast, but are still common in the inland.

OTHER NAMES
White-eyed Duck, Brownhead, Coppertop, Punkari.

IDENTIFICATION
LENGTH: *Male 415–490 mm; female 420–545 mm.*
MALE: *Head and neck coppery brown; back, rump and tail rich dark brown. Wing deep brown; outer two–four primaries brown, inner white with brown tips; secondaries white with narrow brown tips. Underwing white with brown forward and trailing edges. Throat and neck rich dark brown; breast dark brown, deeply suffused with rufous; lower breast and upper belly white, mottled with brown; lower belly dark brown; undertail coverts white. Eye white. Bill black with slate-blue bar at tip and black nail. Feet grey; webs slate-grey.*
FEMALE: *Similar to male but generally lighter, with narrower and paler bar on bill and more mottled white ventrally. Eye brown.*
IMMATURES: *Similar to female but paler; white parts on underside more extensive, reaching throat. Eye hazel-brown.*
DUCKLINGS: *Light brown above suffused with pale yellow. Pale yellow on face and below. Fine brown line behind eye, buff line on wing and two buff spots on either side of back. Eye pale brown. Bill blue-grey above, pale pink with blue edge below. Feet blue-grey.*

VOICE
Usually silent, but female has soft, harsh croak and male soft, wheezy whistle.

NESTING
Breeds in wet months, but mainly spring, especially when flooding extensive. Nest a cup of neatly woven reeds, sedges and sticks, built in dense reeds, tea-trees, lignum or cumbungi in water about 1 m deep. Eggs: usually nine to 12; glossy cream, become covered with grey-brown down; oval, about 57 x 41 mm. Incubation about 25 days, by female.

DISTRIBUTION
Stronghold is Murray-Darling Basin; usual breeding range is in better watered parts of eastern states and in southwest of Western Australia. Has strong preference for extensive areas of deep water with emergent plants, particularly lignum and cumbungi. Ranges throughout Australia at times of drought, reaching Indonesia, New Guinea, parts of inner Melanesia, and formerly New Zealand. No races, unless population in Banks Islands and New Hebrides proves permanent, darker and smaller.

Blue-billed Duck *Oxyura australis* (GOULD, 1837)

THE COURTSHIP DISPLAY OF THE Blue-billed Duck is spectacular, though rarely seen because of the bird's wary nature. The male splashes water backwards with both feet; springs erect to stand on his tail, jerks his bill up and down; rushes across the surface with flailing feet and wings; and dives and rocks his body back and forth with his stiff tail feathers held erect as a fan. Copulation follows a vigorous chase, the male pursuing his mate at speed, often under water. They surface frequently in a flurry, then submerge and rush on. Eventually, the male overtakes and copulates with the female, completely submerged. Separating, they preen vigorously.

The distinctive blue bill of the male only develops during breeding; in winter it fades to slate grey. The bird is a member of a small but worldwide group of diving ducks that have spiny erectile tail feathers, inflatable neck skin for display, and no bulla on the trachea. It is completely aquatic and helpless on land. While it flies well, it is tail-heavy and laboured in takeoff, pattering over the surface for several metres before rising. In the water the Blue-billed Duck swims swiftly, and at the first hint of danger dives with scarcely a ripple to travel 50 metres or more before surfacing.

Blue-billed Ducks live on deep, permanent fresh waters and come and go regularly with the seasons. Over spring and summer pairs disperse widely to quiet, sheltered pools and backwaters in swamps to breed. In autumn and winter, many gather in rafts of sometimes a thousand or more on open sheets of water. The greatest concentrations occur along the central Murray River. There they do much of their moulting, twice a year.

Blue-billed Ducks get most of their food from the bottom of swamps by diving and swimming underwater, for up to 30 seconds at a time. They also swim beneath overhanging vegetation, stripping seeds and dabbling the water surface. Vegetable items include seeds, buds and leaves of a wide variety of emergent and submerged plants; most of their animal food comprises larvae of chironomid midges.

Unlike many Australian ducks, the Blue-billed has a precise breeding season over spring and early summer. The female builds her nest alone in dense vegetation over water and occasionally in the deserted nest of other water birds. She tramps plants into a platform and fashions a deep, cup-shaped nest, often covering it with a roof of bent-over reeds. Intruding coots and other birds are driven off; she fluffs her head feathers and, with darting head, swims swiftly at the offender, hissing.

After hatching, the young remain in the nest for a day and are then led away by the female. They feed at once by diving and dabbling and gain adult plumage in about six months.

OTHER NAMES
Stiff-tail, Spinetail, Diving-duck.

IDENTIFICATION
LENGTH: *Male 350–440 mm; female 365–440 mm.*
MALE: *Head and neck glossy black, sometimes tinged with chestnut. Back rich chestnut, upper tail coverts dusky flecked with chestnut; upper side of tail black. Wings dark brown. Upper breast and flanks chestnut; rest of underside brown flecked with black or dark brown; undertail black. Eye dark brown. Bill slate-blue. Feet and legs grey. In eclipse plumage, head speckled black and grey; chin grey with some black speckles; breast dark grey, each feather edged with pale brown. Upper neck speckled with black and grey; back and scapulars dark brown, each feather fringed with light brown. Bill slate-grey. Feet grey.*
FEMALE: *General colour above black-brown, each feather barred with narrow bands of light brown. Upper tail black. Chin and throat brown speckled with black; breast and belly mottled light brown and black—each feather black with light tip. Eye brown. Bill grey-brown. Feet grey-brown.*
IMMATURES: *Resemble female but are paler. Bill grey-green.*
DUCKLINGS: *Top of head, neck, back and tail dusky; light brown line extends backwards from eye. Underside light brown, except for dusky neck and upper breast. Wings dark brown above, pale brown below. Bill and feet dark grey.*

VOICE
Usually silent, but male emits low-pitched rattle in display and female low quack *in alarm.*

NESTING
Breeds regularly in spring–summer, September–February, mostly September–November. Deep cup-shaped nest of vegetation, 250 mm in diameter and 80 mm deep, built on platform of trampled plants and often covered with bent-over reeds. Eggs: usually five or six or up to 12; large, coarse-grained; light green; oval, about 68 x 49 mm. Incubation 26–28 days, by female.

DISTRIBUTION
In deep, densely vegetated freshwater swamps of southeast and southwest. Most numerous in Murray-Darling basin. Regionally and seasonally nomadic. No races.

The Blue-billed Duck owes its name to the male whose slate-grey bill turns bright blue in the breeding season; the female's bill is grey-brown.

Under its bill the male Musk Duck has a large pendulous lobe which is distended during courtship display.

Musk Duck

Biziura lobata (SHAW, 1796)

OTHER NAMES
Diver, Diving Duck, Steamer.

IDENTIFICATION
LENGTH: *Male 600–730 mm; female 470–600 mm.*
MALE: *Upper parts dusky black overall, crossed with numerous fine lines of cream-white; flight feathers and tail almost black. Head, neck and upper breast dusky black. Head, neck and upper breast dusky, sides of face and neck mottled with white; lower breast, belly and undertail white, mottled grey. Eye dark brown. Bill black with large pendulous black lobe under it. Feet and webs dark grey.*
FEMALE: *As male, but lobe under bill small and rudimentary, never more than 10 mm deep.*
IMMATURES: *Resemble female; front half of lower mandible yellow.*
DUCKLINGS: *General colour above, head and neck uniform dark grey-brown; rest of underside off-white. Wings dark brown. Eye brown. Bill dark grey with yellow mandible. Feet dark grey.*

VOICE
In display, male gives rumbling grunt followed immediately by shrill whistle and also signals by noisy splashing of water and deep plonk, made by the feet. Whistle does not develop till bird several years old. Otherwise silent.

NESTING
Breeds regularly in spring. Most clutches start in September–October, though male sexual cycle begins in March and displays begin soon after. Nest well concealed, a rough cup of broken-down stems on clump of reeds or swamp plants over or almost on water, lined with a few leaves and a little down; nest can be so flimsy that the eggs rest in water. Some nests sheltered by canopy of broken-down reed stems; others built in low hanging branches of tea-trees in water, on top of low stumps, or on the ground on small islets. Eggs: usually one to three, sometimes more; smooth, glossy; pale green quickly stained brown; ellipsoidal, slightly pointed, about 80 x 53 mm. Incubation by female.

DISTRIBUTION
Southern mainland and Tasmania, from Fraser Island, Qld, to North West Cape, WA, wherever there are large and permanent swamps. Avoids arid regions. In winter sometimes assembles in saltwater estuaries. Nomadic. No races.

CAPTAIN GEORGE VANCOUVER of HMS *Discovery* was the first to draw attention to the Musk Duck while replenishing his larder in Western Australia in 1791. He wrote: 'A very peculiar one (duck) was shot, of a darkish grey plumage, with a bag like that of a lizard hanging under its throat, which smelt so intolerably of musk that it scented nearly the whole ship'. The musky odour is confined to the males — a secretion from the oil or preen gland on the bird's rump. The odour becomes intense during the breeding season. At the same time, the lobe of skin under the male's throat enlarges. While the male is displaying to the female, this lobe becomes turgid and further enlarged, and an inflatable sac below the tongue is distended, causing the cheeks and throat to swell.

In courtship the male Musk Duck stages a remarkable display. He sails out into a clear pool with deliberate kicks, throwing jets of water behind; staying in one spot on the pool he keeps kicking jets of water two metres and more behind him. He raises his head, blows his neck and cheeks out and expands a bladder under his bill to a diameter of 100–150 mm. He then raises his tail feathers and spreads them fan-like over his body. Sinking lower in the water he revolves, uttering his piercing whistle.

This flamboyant water display attracts females. As one approaches, she is submerged in copulation, and then leaves to begin a clutch on her own. No pair bond is formed and a male may mate with several females. Musk Ducks have a regular breeding season, helped by their permanent habitat. The male begins his sexual cycle in March and starts courtship displays soon after. Most females reach breeding condition by August and most clutches are begun in September and October. Rainfall and swamp level do have an effect, and the breeding season contracts and extends as water levels fall and rise.

Usually Musk Ducks are seen spaced out in ones and twos floating motionless in their preferred habitat: deep and often sheltered permanent freshwater lakes and swamps. One of the stiff-tailed diving ducks, they are completely aquatic and almost helpless on land. They dive silently and smoothly and swim great distances underwater to surface under cover. To rest, they doze on the surface, with tail spread. They fly seldom in dense swamps, but more often on lakes. They need a long take-off run and labour into the air, and once airborne they fly heavily. Their landing is more like a crash.

Musk Ducks feed almost entirely by diving. They can dive deep and remain submerged for at least a minute, bringing larger items back to the surface to dismember and eat. Ducklings do not dive until they are several days old, and until then the female brings them food from the bottom and they cluster around her to be fed and even carried on her back. Adults eat mainly animal food, including insects such as adult and larval water boatmen, beetles, dragonflies, mayflies, midges and caddis flies. They also eat large numbers of freshwater mussels, snails, crayfish and frogs, and a few aquatic plant seeds.

The movements of the Musk Duck are regular. In inland swamps of New South Wales there is an exodus of young birds after the breeding season. Between April and July most young birds gather on the Murray River and on big clear lakes farther south. They return to the breeding swamps in August. In winter, they have been seen out at sea. They also move extensively to exploit favourable flood conditions. They turn up in Lake Eyre when it fills, and isolated birds arrive at ground tanks in very dry country. Much of their movement is by night.

Like the Blue-billed Duck, Musk Ducks moult twice a year, once in April–June and again in October–December. It is not well synchronised with breeding and there are no differences in the seasonal plumages.

and departs. The number of eggs that she lays in one breeding season is not known; average clutch-size is estimated at 18–24 eggs. The interval between the eggs and the length of the laying period is doubtless controlled by the weather, as with the Malleefowl. Many

1–1.5 m high. Eggs: usually 18–24; pure white; long-oval, about 92 x 64 mm. Laid in holes dug in the mound. Incubation about 50 days.

Orange-footed Scrubfowl *Megapodius reinwardt* DUMONT, 1823

SMALLEST OF THE AUSTRALIAN MOUND-BUILDERS, the Orange-footed Scrubfowl builds the largest mound. The masses of decaying days apart. In dry weather, eggs are placed in a damp part of the mound and in wet, a higher better-drained section is chosen. They

A male Malleefowl digs at the nesting mound of sand, sticks and leaves, in which the female lays up to 30 or more eggs.

THE MALLEEFOWL IS FACED WITH a life of toil from the moment it hatches underground. The chick must struggle up through a metre of loose sand to the surface of the nest mound. When it emerges, it is completely on its own, very weak and barely able to tumble down to shelter. Within 24 hours it can fly, for although its body is downy at hatching, its wings are well-feathered.

Malleefowl mate for life, yet are usually solitary; the male is bound to maintaining the nest mound almost year round while the female wanders locally in search of the food needed to sustain her production of eggs. So the two seldom meet away from the nest. Each pair occupies a permanent territory of 40–70 hectares of natural mallee and in it may have up to four or five scattered nest mounds, only one of which is used in a season.

Beginning in autumn, both birds may build the mound, first scraping out an old one, unhatched eggs and all, to a depth of one metre and diameter of three–four metres. Into the hole they then scrape leaf litter, twigs and bark, radiating up to 25 metres out from the nest, working the material into windrows then kicking it backwards in powerful strokes. An egg chamber is then dug into the top of the heap and, after rain has wet it, the whole is covered with sand, forming a mound some five metres in diameter and 1.5 metres high. At this stage, after about four months of intermittent work, the mound is ready for eggs.

The female visits the mound only to lay eggs from then on, depositing them one per visit early in the morning in holes dug for her and then filled in by the male. The number of eggs that she lays in a season is related to the interval between eggs and the length of the laying period, both of which are affected by rainfall. In drought, the interval between eggs increases, from about two days to over two weeks, and the laying period decreases. And if autumn

Malleefowl

Leipoa ocellata GOULD, 1840

OTHER NAMES
Lowan, Gnow.

IDENTIFICATION
LENGTH: *About 600 mm.*
ADULTS: *Sexes similar. Crown and
nape streaked dusky, with slight crest.
Back of neck and upper back grey,
grading into heavy black, white and
buff-brown mottlings and ocellations
over back, scapulars and wing coverts.
Flight feathers and tail mid-brownish
grey barred dusky and tipped off-white
on outer tail feathers. Face mid-grey
with white line under eye; chin russet.
Throat buff and foreneck grey, with
central black streaking coalescing in
broad black stripe to centre of breast.
Lower breast and belly cream-white;
flanks barred black; crissum cream-
buff. Eye orange-brown. Bill slate-grey.
Feet and toes leaden; claws dusky.*
DOWNY YOUNG: *Grey-brown, finely
freckled and peppered with black and
buff on upper parts.*

VOICE
*Territorial call a loud booming; in
threat a sharp grunt. When pair is
together, a soft, drawn-out* cluck.

NESTING
*Begins mound construction in autumn;
lays September to following March–
April. Nest a mound of decomposing
vegetable litter covered with sand to
1.5 m high and 5 m in diameter, swept
into a hole in the ground 1 m deep and
3–4 m in diameter, with an egg
chamber 500 x 500 mm filled with wet
rotting litter in the top. Eggs: five to 33,
but usually 15–24; delicate pink but
soon stained brown; long-oval, about 92
x 61 mm, but variable. Incubation
about 49 days, depending on
temperature of mound. Young
independent and free-running in
hatching.*

DISTRIBUTION
*Throughout dry inland of southern
Australia, from Pilliga, NSW, to west
coast. Mostly found in mallee and other
dry scrubs in semi-arid zone, but enters
wetter mallee heaths at southern edge of
range. No races.*

and winter are dry during nest building, the mounds are abandoned altogether.

Throughout the breeding season, the male maintains the nest mound and defends the area around it. It is his responsibility to keep the egg chamber of fermenting vegetation at the constant temperature of 33°C. Early in the season, the eggs are incubated by the heat of fermentation and, later, as fermentation wanes, by the heat of the summer sun. The male tests the temperature of the mound with the inside of his mouth, first pecking rapidly once or twice, and then driving his partly open bill into the sand up to his eyes for a few seconds. Both sexes have this capacity but the male does it the most frequently. If heat generated from fermentation early in the season is too intense, the male kicks out material from the egg chamber to release it; and if the summer sun is too hot later on, he piles insulating sand on top, and periodically opens the mound up for a short time in the cool of the very early morning. In the autumn, the male scoops out the mound each morning to expose the interior to the sun's rays—and then rebuilds the mound in the afternoon. If opening the mound in unsuitable weather is likely to alter the correct internal temperature, the male will drive the female away even when she is ready to lay an egg.

The Malleefowl is a quiet, unobtrusive bird that feeds on seeds on the ground—principally acacia—and the buds of herbs and some insects. Although it will drink if water is at hand, it normally lives without it. A powerful runner, it rarely flies but does flap up into low trees to roost or take refuge.

Today, Malleefowl are moderately abundant only in remnant pockets of mallee. Although foxes dig out mounds for eggs and sheep graze the Malleefowl's seed plants, the real cause of the decline seems to be the clearing of its habitat for crops and grazing.

California Quail *Lophortyx californicus* (SHAW, 1798)

A male California Quail. This introduced species has disappeared from mainland Australia and survives only on King Island, Bass Strait.

THIS NORTH AMERICAN GAME BIRD was first released in the wild in Australia in the 1860s, in southern Victoria. Further introductions soon followed at Rottnest Island in the mid-1870s, Pewsey Vale in South Australia in the late 1870s, at Bathurst in 1880, and in Queensland sometime before 1919. But all failed, and it is doubtful if any wild California Quail are established on the mainland now, even from some of the more recent attempts at acclimatisation.

Curiously, colonies have been established successfully on two islands—King Island in Bass Strait and Norfolk Island—where they have adapted to rather different habitat from the open grass-lands and stubble in which they live in North America. On the islands, where they are common, they prefer shrubby ground dotted with clumps of shrubs among short grass and open space.

Social organisation is highly developed. In winter, they gather into coveys of up to 30 birds, over which one male stands sentry on a vantage perch. With the coming of spring, the birds pair up, the male guarding his mate aggressively. He spends much time standing motionless while she feeds, builds the nest, and incubates.

OTHER NAMES
Californian Quail.

IDENTIFICATION
LENGTH: *About 240 mm.*
MALE: *Conspicuous black crest on dusky brown crown. Long white eyebrow. Forehead pale grey-brown streaked with black. Nape grey with black scallops and white spots. Back and upper side of tail dark grey-brown. Wing coverts dark grey-brown, some feathers edged with fawn; flight feathers dark grey-brown. Throat black with conspicuous white border to eye; breast dark grey. Lower breast and belly cream with sharp black edges to feathers, giving scaled appearance. Flanks dusky streaked cream. Eye brown. Bill black. Feet and toes flesh.*
FEMALE: *Small black crest on crown.*

Forehead, crown and neck grey-brown, finely flecked with black and white; rest of upper parts grey-brown with very fine fawn wavy lines. Wing-coverts as male. Face and throat grey streaked with black; upper breast grey with very fine fawn wavy lines; lower breast and belly white scalloped conspicuously with grey; flanks grey streaked with white.

VOICE
In California 14 calls recorded, most important being a contact call ut ut *and an assembly call* cu-ca-cow, *the threat whistle* meah, *and the territorial crow* kah-ah *heard in the breeding season.*

NESTING
Breeds September–January. Nest a shallow depression in the ground, lined with grass or leaves and usually sheltered by a shrub, rock or log. Eggs: eight to 22, usually 10–15; buff or cream, irregularly marked with dull brown spots and blotches; pointed oval, about 32 x 24 mm. Incubation 22-23 days, by female.

DISTRIBUTION
Confined to King Island in Bass Strait. Also introduced into New Zealand and Norfolk Island. In North America range extends naturally from Oregon south to California on western seaboard. Four races; one in Australia.

Stubble Quail *Coturnix pectoralis* GOULD, 1837

THE BEST KNOWN AUSTRALIAN QUAIL, the Stubble is widespread in most pastoral districts, replacing the Brown Quail in the drier, more open grassfields there. Human settlement has had a mixed effect on its abundance. In coastal regions, the clearing of forest and woodland for pasture and crops has increased its habitat; but inland the savanna and grass plains that were—and still are—core shelter have been degraded by sheep and rabbits.

Despite its abundance, the Stubble Quail is seldom seen. One reason is its cryptic behaviour. Like all quail, it is a plump, round-winged, stump-tailed bird that lives on the ground and prefers to squat in grassy cover rather than fly or run when disturbed. There its mottled plumage camouflages it effectively. Only when almost trodden on will it burst from the grass in a clatter of wings and dash swiftly away in direct whirring low flight for 50 metres or more before dropping and running off quickly at an angle.

Another reason why Stubble Quail are not often seen is their nomadism. Although they do eat some insects and caterpillars, their staple diet is seeds, particularly waste grain in stubble fields and those from annual pasture weeds. These the quail follow around most of southern and eastern Australia as they become ripe, and moving inland whenever rain brings on herbage there; banded birds have been recorded travelling at least 1300 kilometres, from near Adelaide to Gunnedah, NSW. The quail do not travel in flocks but individually, building up in an area and then dispersing again as the food supply dwindles. Much feeding is done at night.

Centred around southern Australia, Stubble Quail breed mostly in spring when the ripening of the seeds of annuals peaks, and may raise several broods in succession. To begin, the female scratches out a shallow scrape for the eggs while her mate calls or crows to advertise their nesting territory. He does this mostly at dawn and dusk, but also during the day and on moonlight nights for hours at a time. Eggs are laid at 48-hour intervals.

As soon as young hatch, they leave the nest to be guarded closely, brooded, and led by parents in scratching for food. In about six weeks they are fully feathered and about two-thirds grown, and they can fly well. From then on, parents force them to leave, which they often do in male or female groups. Pairs form in the following spring, probably for life.

OTHER NAMES
None.

IDENTIFICATION
LENGTH: *About 180–190 mm.*
MALE: *Upper parts generally fawn-brown with dusky blotches and clear cream stripes in centre of each feather. Head and nape dusky, a white line down centre of head and a white stripe above each eye extending to nape. Throat and face light chestnut. Black centre on breast; rest of breast and belly white, streaked black. Eye red-brown. Bill grey-horn. Feet yellow-buff.*
FEMALE: *Differs from male in throat off-white, and face and neck pale buff with dark flecking; dusky-flecked breast without black centre.*
IMMATURES: *Like female.*
DOWNY YOUNG: *Buff, with central black dorsal stripes from crown to tail and a lateral pair on sides of back.*

VOICE
Three-syllable clear whistle cuck-ee–whit *or sharp, clear* too-weep, *by breeding male; also deep purring.*

NESTING
Breeds mainly August–February; year-round in northern inland if rain continuous. Nest a scrape in the ground lined with a little grass; in fairly thick cover. Eggs: seven to 14; pale creamy buff, uniformly covered with irregular freckles and blotches of umber or dusky; oval to pyriform, about 30 x 23 mm. Incubation about 21 days, by female.

DISTRIBUTION
In open country and better-watered parts of southern Australia north to the Pilbara, Alice Springs and central Queensland. Nomads appear at times in upper Northern Territory and elsewhere beyond their normal range. Formerly in Tasmania, but now extinct. No races.

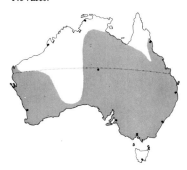

A female Stubble Quail on its well-hidden nest, which is simply a scrape in the ground lined with grass.

Brown Quail *Coturnix ypsilophora* BOSC, 1792

A male Brown Quail in the type of habitat it prefers, dense grass on the edges of swamps and creeks around coastal Australia.

AS LARGE AS A STUBBLE QUAIL, feeding on the same range of seeds and insects, and often living side by side with it in crops and grass-fields, the Brown Quail nonetheless keeps to denser, taller, ranker pockets of tussock and sedge-land often in low-lying swampy ground, along creeks and around lakes. It can survive there in very small pockets of less than a hectare. Despite this, drainage and the development of close-grazed pasture have reduced its habitat and numbers in many southern coastal districts.

Brown Quail seem to be neither as active nor as mobile as Stubble Quail, even though they are nomadic in Torres Strait islands and may cross back and forth to southern New Guinea. On the mainland, movements are usually more local as birds shift about a district following food supplies. Squatting closer to the ground, it is more difficult to flush than the Stubble Quail, and

when it does burst from cover, does not fly as swiftly or as far. It can be identified in flight by its more uniformly russet-brown or slate-brown back, without distinct whitish streaks.

Brown Quail are found in pairs or loose non-breeding coveys of up to 30. They usually nest when grasses are tall and seeding, and may rear up to three successive broods per season.

In the past, two species of Brown Quail have been recognised in Australia: one in Tasmania (Swamp Quail) and one on the mainland. This has been caused by misunderstanding the sexual plumages and phases in males. Tasmanian birds differ from those on the mainland only in their slightly larger size and pale yellow, not reddish eyes, a trait also found in montane New Guinea Brown Quail. There are no confirmed records of the Tasmanian race from the mainland opposite, nor of the mainland race from Tasmania.

OTHER NAMES
Swamp Quail, Silver Quail.

IDENTIFICATION
LENGTH: *180–205 mm.*
MALE: *(1) Brown-phase, common: upper surface mid-brown with fine black flecking and faint creamy shaft streaks; crown duskier with pale centre line; face plain; undersurface buff with close black chevrons. (2) Red-phase, common: like brown phase but distinctly more reddish in tone generally, and with finer dusky markings above and below. (3) Blue-grey-phase, rare in eastern Australia, common in eastern New Guinea: uniformly slate-grey with dull brown*

wash generally. Eye orange-to-brown-red or yellow (Tas). Bill blue-black. Feet orange-yellow; claws dusky.
FEMALE: *No phases; as brown-phase male but with distinct heavy black blotches on back and heavier black marks below.*
DOWNY YOUNG: *Rather uniform brown, buffer on face, with pair of faint dusky lines on sides of back.*

VOICE
Loud whistling crows, ff-weep and gop-war both rising high in pitch, repeated by male at deliberate intervals.

NESTING
Breeds August–March in south, April–

May in north. Nest a small depression in the ground, lined with grass and leaves and placed in dense cover under tuft of grass or bush, often near water. Eggs: seven to 11 (-20); creamy, finely freckled dusky brown; rounded-oval to pyriform, about 28 x 23 mm but varying with latitude. Incubation about 20–22 days, by female.

DISTRIBUTION
Wetter coastal and subcoastal regions; also New Guinea and Lesser Sunda Islands. Two races in Australia: one larger with yellow eye in Tasmania; the other smaller with reddish eye on mainland and offshore islands, grading smaller and duller northwards.

King Quail *Coturnix chinensis* (LINNÉ, 1766)

KING QUAIL PREFER THE densest of grassland habitats and are most common in tall rank grass in boggy country, in heaths, or on swamp edges. They are rarely found in crops—which are too open for them—except dry corn with a heavy weed growth. They often visit lucerne paddocks, especially those partly overgrown with paspalum and other weeds, and will nest there.

King Quail are usually found in pairs or small coveys of five or six, though groups of 40 have been reported. They are secretive. When disturbed they prefer to squat rather than fly or run. If King Quail do rise, their flight—on silent wings—is weak and decidedly tail-heavy. They often fly as little as 20 metres and seldom more than 40 metres before dropping into cover. To flush them a second time is difficult.

Although King Quail feed on the seeds of seasonal grasses and insects, there is no evidence of large-scale movement to follow seeding. Local rises and falls in their numbers have been linked with the seasons, but this could be the result of breeding. They can reproduce rapidly, rearing a series of broods in good years.

The survival prospects of the King Quail in coastal northern Australia are still largely unaffected, but in the southeast they have suffered two serious blows. One is the draining and clearing of their habitat for pasture and crops; the other has been the string of wild releases of the Chinese race begun by the Victorian Acclimatisation Society in the 1860s. The releases have the potential for interbreeding and exterminating the genetic integrity and uniqueness of the native Australian populations. Already the natural King Quail isolated in the Mt Lofty Ranges, South Australia, may have disappeared.

OTHER NAMES
Chinese Quail.

IDENTIFICATION
LENGTH: *120–130 mm.*
MALE: *Upper surface brown, toned russet on the sides, mottled with black and shaft-streaked faintly with cream; crown with central cream streak. Wings grey-brown. Upper face, sides of neck, upper and sides of breast plain slate-blue. Lower face and throat white, bordered by an outer black line and a second black line dividing throat and chin. Lower breast, belly, undertail and flanks dark rufous. Eye brownish red. Bill bluish black. Feet and toes dull yellow; claws grey.*
FEMALE: *Upper surface plain deep brown, flecked black and with strong cream shaft-streaks. Face buff, clear cream-white throat. Rest of undersurface cream-buff marked with close, short dusky bars. Eye browner.*
IMMATURES: *Flying young like female but more spotted, less barred dusky ventrally.*
DOWNY YOUNG: *Buff-brown, with pair of strong dusky lines on sides of back.*

VOICE
High-pitched crowing whistle of three descending notes, uttered rapidly, and given by male day or night, particularly dusk.

NESTING
Breeding, sometimes twice each season, seems to coincide with seasonal flushes in grass growth and seeding; in eastern New South Wales most nests found September–March, in Northern Territory mostly February–April. Nest a small depression in the ground, lined with fine grasses, placed in very dense cover. Eggs: four or five, occasionally as many as 10; smooth, lustrous light brown, covered with black-brown dots and spots; oval, about 25 x 19 mm. Incubation about 20 days, by female.

DISTRIBUTION
Coastal wetlands of northern and eastern mainland Australia, west to Kimberleys and isolated outlier in Mt Lofty Ranges, SA; possible gap at head of Gulf of Carpentaria. Also through Indonesian archipelagos to Philippines, SE Asia, India and China. Two possible races in Australia: one small in northwest, the other slightly larger throughout east. Both are browner and more heavily mottled with black on the back than any of the Asian races, and are not as uniformly slaty as New Guinean and Philippine males.

A male King Quail at its nest. The male can be distinguished from the female by the distinctive slate-blue on the sides of its head, chest and body.

Common Peafowl *Pavo cristatus* LINNÉ, 1758

NATIVE TO THE JUNGLES of India and Sri Lanka, Common Peafowl have led a semi-domesticated existence in other parts of the world. The male's splendid plumage, and the train which rises in a shivering fan during the mating display, have won the bird a place as an ornament in many Australian parks and gardens. Attempted introductions into the wild, however, have generally failed. Of releases in southeastern Queensland, the Capricorn Island group, Riverina in New South Wales, Melbourne districts, Bass Strait islands, South Australian gulfs and environs of Perth over the past 100 years, only the colony on Rottnest Island, WA, has settled in. It was introduced in 1912 and by 1960 numbered over 50 birds.

In the wild, Common Peafowl are shy and elusive, and when disturbed, burst upwards and fly off strongly, the males trailing their long tails. Although ground-living, feeding mainly on seeds and insects, they flap up into trees to roost away from predators. Males are polygynous and each may mate with four or five females during breeding. There is no pairing—the two sexes lead separate lives—and females incubate and rear young alone.

OTHER NAMES
Peacock, Peahen, Indian Peafowl.

IDENTIFICATION
LENGTH: *Male 1800-2300 mm; female 900-1000 mm, including tail.*
MALE: *Head, pompom crest, neck and upper breast metallic blue; white stripes of skin above and below eye. Back and rump metallic green, each feather edged blue-black and shaft-streaked blue. Wings with outer flight feathers russet and inner metallic green; scapulars white, barred black.*
Lower breast and belly black-green, thighs grey. Tail elongated, the feathers frayed bronze-green, terminating in large blue eye-spots with pale brown surround. Eye dark brown. Bill, feet and claws mid-grey. By second year, males resemble adults but have shorter tails without 'eyes'; train not full-grown until fifth or sixth year.
FEMALE: *Crest, crown, eye-stripe, nape and all neck dull metallic green; eye brown, face and throat white. Rest of upper parts, wings and tail brown. Breast buffy grey, grading to white belly and undertail. Eye dark brown. Bill and feet horn-grey.*

VOICE
Loud, harsh, braying crow, kay-ow, rising in scale, and usually repeated several times by male, with pumping action. Particularly vocal at dusk.

NESTING
Nest a scrape in the ground, under thick cover. Eggs: three to five; cream or buff; oval, about 69 x 51 mm. Incubation about 28 days, by female.

DISTRIBUTION
Common in city garden enclosures in Australia. From time to time there have been populations of birds living in the wild in several parts of Australia, but most have been short-lived. Only large free-living colony at present is on Rottnest Island near Perth, WA. Native range is in jungles of India and Sri Lanka. No races.

The Peacock raises its train in a fan to attract a mate. Peacocks are polygynous, and mate with four or five Peahens each breeding season.

Common Pheasant *Phasianus colchicus* LINNÉ, 1758

The Common Pheasant was first introduced into Australia in 1864, but efforts to establish it have been largely unsuccessful. This is a male.

THE FIRST ATTEMPT TO ESTABLISH hybrid stocks of this Eurasian game bird in the Australian wild was at Phillip Island, Victoria, and around Melbourne before 1855. Further releases followed there and in other parts of Australia: in Tasmania about 1882 and 1950, on King and Flinders Islands in Bass Strait in the 1950s and '60s, in the Hawkesbury district of New South Wales in 1944, in the Mt Lofty Ranges and adjacent areas of South Australia in the 1960s, and on Rottnest Island near Perth in 1928. Island locations have been preferred because they lack predatory foxes.

Even so, few of the introductions survived, not even the hundreds released by the Upland Game Association in the Mt Lofty Ranges with the approval of state fauna authorities in the 1960s. Today, the only firmly established colonies appear to be in Tasmania, on islands in Bass Strait, and Rottnest Island.

Hunters who prize the pheasant as quarry are still privately releasing hand-reared birds for game. This is of concern because there has been no research into its possible effects on native birds and the environment. Australia has already been greatly damaged by the introduction of animals and other birds from overseas—the rabbit and the Common Starling for example.

Mainly grain-eaters, Common Pheasants spend most of their time on the ground—including egg-laying and incubating in a bowl-shaped nest of loose grass—but they take clumsily to the trees to roost, and sometimes to escape danger by day. Disturbed on the ground, they either steal away or 'freeze'. If pursued or surprised, they flush, rising suddenly with a whirr of wings and then glide away. Their flight is slow and laboured.

OTHER NAMES
Ring-necked Pheasant.

IDENTIFICATION
LENGTH: *Male about 800 mm; female 600 mm.*
MALE: *Crown metallic green with green ear-like crests; neck metallic blue with or without white collar. Rest of upper parts copper-red, the feathers of the mantle marked black and of the back and scapulars white. Wings greyish brown streaked russet on shoulders. Tail copper-brown barred sparsely black. Face of bare scarlet skin. Breast copper-chestnut scalloped black. Lower breast and flanks copper-red marked black. Lower belly and undertail black. Eye red-brown. Bill green-yellow. Feet and claws deep grey.*
FEMALE: *Upper parts buffy brown barred and mottled with black from crown to wings and tail (barred only). Underparts paler buff-brown, scalloped black on sides of breast and flanks. Bill horn. Feet grey-brown. Above descriptions apply to Australian introductions; many races with marked colour differences through Eurasia.*

VOICE
Territorial call of male is loud three-syllable crow ko-koro. Also soft clucks and a squawk.

NESTING
Nest a loose bowl of grass, lined with finer material; 200 mm in diameter and 70 mm deep; placed on the ground in grass, or sheltered by a bush. Eggs: up to 17, but usually eight to 14; smooth, lustrous, cream or pale brown; oval, about 44 x 35 mm. Incubation about 23–24 days, by female.

DISTRIBUTION
Australian colonies on Rottnest Island, WA, King Island in Bass Strait and Tasmania. Natural range from Japan, China and Korea across Asia to Caucasus Mountains and Black Sea, Bulgaria and Turkey and eastern Greece. Has been established as game bird in North America, Europe, Great Britain and New Zealand. Over 40 races; Australian releases seem to be of hybrid origin.

Red-backed Button-quail *Turnix maculosa* (TEMMINCK, 1815)

The female Red-backed Button-quail, the more brightly coloured bird, leaves the male to incubate the eggs and rear the young.

THE FEMALE OF THIS SPECIES — as of other button-quail—is polyandrous, mating with itinerant males each breeding season and never pairing with any. She is also larger and more richly coloured than the males and, true to the group, dominates courtship. Males take on incubation and the rearing of young unaided. Young are precocial and mature quickly, running from the nest straight after hatching and flying within a week or two; some reach sexual maturity in four months.

Button-quail have arisen from rail- and crane-like ancestors and resemble true quail only through evolutionary convergence, by adapting to the same life style. Like true quail, they are small, plump, short-tailed birds that live and nest on the ground in rank herbage and grass-fields and have dappled, autumn-toned plumage that camouflages them well. With seven species, they are also more diverse in Australia than anywhere else in the world. Despite their superficially quail-like appearance, button-quail have a number of structures and behaviours that reveal their true ancestry. Apart from the form of their nostrils, palate and leg bones, they have — unlike true quail—no hind toe, no crop and only a single row of scales down both faces of the tarsus. Conventional sexual roles are also reversed in breeding; the female booms in courtship and there is no crowing from males.

Red-backed Button-quail are the smallest of Australia's button-quail and among the least frequently seen. Either in pairs or family coveys of five–eight, they live in damp rank grassland and dense herbage, whether in small pockets or extensive stands. Such habitat lines the edges of water channels and covers swamps and seasonally flooded pans. Where it is permanent, the button-quail are fairly sedentary, but where it is subject to seasonal fluctuations, the birds seem to be nomadic. Across coastal northern Australia they are still moderately abundant year round, but on the east coast they appear to have come and gone much over the years. A population around Sydney in the late 1800s seems to have disappeared, but since then the birds have appeared erratically in numbers in eastern Queensland and bred as far south as Finley in the Riverina, NSW. Transient individuals from islands in Torres Strait indicate movement to New Guinea and cast doubt on races described from that island.

Although a seed- and greens-eater like other button-quail, the Red-backed has a particularly fine and acute bill and takes a higher proportion of insects. Unobtrusive in habits, it hides or 'freezes' when approached and flushes only when close-pressed. Then it rarely flies far, on fluttering wings, before dropping to cover.

OTHER NAMES
Red-backed Quail, Black-backed Quail.

IDENTIFICATION
LENGTH: *Male 120–130 mm; female 130–140 mm.*
MALE: *Crown dusky with paired blackish stripes separated by central white line. Rest of upper surface grey-brown, each feather clearly marked with black and edged buff. Wings grey-brown, the shoulders tawnier with black flecking. Face buff. Throat white, grading to tawny over breast and flanks, then white on belly; sides of breast and flanks barred with short black scallops. Eye cream-white. Bill dull grey. Feet bright yellow; claws horn. Old or breeding birds tawnier to light rufous up on to throat and hind neck; upper parts deeper, duller and 'smoother'.*
FEMALE: *Like male but upper parts deeper and duller with less distinct black marks and buff edges to feathers. Breast more extensively tawny, extending over throat, sides of neck and flanks with rufous tone. Old or breeding birds deeper russet over throat, and around neck, breast and flanks; bill turns yellowish.*
IMMATURES: *Similar to adults; paler; eyes duller.*
DOWNY YOUNG: *Dusky above with central and lateral pairs of cream stripes; buff-brown below.*

VOICE
Female repeats loud oom *rapidly for considerable periods of time, may serve to attract male and advertise breeding territory. Male usually silent.*

NESTING
Breeds October–July, when there is maximum amount of insect life to feed young. Nest a hollow depression under tuft of grass, lined with fine grass; surrounding grass stems are bent and woven to form a canopy or dome with entrance on one side. Eggs: usually four; dull white, minutely speckled and marked with brown and sometimes grey; oval to pyriform, about 22 x 17 mm. First eggs in clutch usually larger than others. Incubation about 14 days, by male.

DISTRIBUTION
Common in coastal northern Australia. In eastern Australia it occurs sporadically along coast and near inland and may be highly nomadic according to food supplies. Occasionally ranges south to south coast of New South Wales, Riverina and central Victoria. Also occurs from Philippines to New Guinea and Solomons. No races in Australia.

Painted Button-quail *Turnix varia* (LATHAM, 1801)

UNLIKE MOST QUAIL-LIKE BIRDS, the Painted Button-quail frequents open shrublands and dry woodlands and forest, particularly where a layer of twig and leaf litter is mixed with patchy tussocks of grass on stony ridges, slopes and hillsides. Cleared or grazed areas and open grass-fields are shunned. Throughout their range, Painted Button-quail are still moderately abundant in this habitat, although not in the numbers of over a century ago.

Some birds are sedentary, but others are nomadic, particularly young dispersed from parental territory southwards to breed in spring in the extreme southeast.

Thinner-billed than the other large button-quail, Painted seem to be as much insectivorous as granivorous. They uncover most of their food from leaf mulch, scratching alternately with each foot and clearing characteristically circular scrapes. Mostly they occur in pairs and sometimes small coveys. When disturbed, they run to hide, only flushed when hard-pressed and then bursting up and off low with rapidly whirring wings for 50 metres or more.

Females are the larger and more brightly coloured sex; they defend territory, dominate courtship, and mate with several males each season, leaving them to incubate and rear the young.

OTHER NAMES
Painted Quail, Butterfly Quail, Scrub Quail, Varied Quail.

IDENTIFICATION
LENGTH: *Male 170 mm; female 200 mm.*
MALE: *Crown of broad pair of rufous stripes mottled black. Rest of upper parts mid grey-brown washed rufous on mantle and sides of neck, and coarsely mottled with black and feather-edged white to rump. Wings and shoulders mid-grey, mottled white and black on wing coverts. Face and throat freckled white. Breast and flanks mid olive-grey coarsely spotted cream, grading to plain cream on belly and undertail. Eye red. Bill horn-grey.*

Feet dull yellow; claws horn.
FEMALE: *As male but more dully and smoothly marked, with more rufous crown stripes, more extensive rufous on mantle and sides of neck, and finer spots on breast.*
IMMATURES: *More clearly marked white and black on upper parts, no rufous wash; larger breast spots.*
DOWNY YOUNG: *Dark grey-brown above with central and lateral pairs of cream stripes, creamier below.*

VOICE
Female has low display booming call, resembling that of a courting Emu or a Bronzewing Pigeon. Given standing on tip-toe with chest inflated, often at night. Male usually silent.

NESTING
Breeds August–March, also other months in northern part of range. Nest on ground at base of shrub or tuft of grass, well lined with grass and leaves, and sometimes partially domed. Eggs: usually four; glossy white, minutely speckled with light brown, with large blotches of black and sepia; round to pyriform, about 27 x 20 mm. Incubation 14–15 days, by male.

DISTRIBUTION
Frequents lightly forested country around southern Australia north to the Atherton Tablelands. Two races: one on mainland; the other—smaller and more brightly marked—on the Houtman Abrolhos, WA.

The male Painted Button-quail does most of the nest building. After the female has laid her eggs, he is left to incubate them and to rear the young.

Little Button-quails are widespread through Australia's arid inland.

Little Button-quail

Turnix velox (GOULD, 1841)

OTHER NAMES
Little Quail, Butterfly Quail, Dotterel Quail, Swift-flying Quail.

IDENTIFICATION
LENGTH: *Male 130–140 mm; female 140–150 mm.*
MALE: *Crown of pair of dusky brown stripes separated by cream line. Rest of upper parts cinnamon-brown, each feather faintly barred black and edged cream. Wings grey, the shoulders cinnamon flecked black. Face to throat buff to cream, grading into cinnamon-brown breast and flanks with faint dusky barring. Belly and undertail white. Eye cream. Bill grey-horn. Feet flesh. Deeper cinnamon-rufous over breast when breeding.*
FEMALE: *As male, but less patterned and more cinnamon-rufous dorsally, uniformly so on crown; breast plainer, deeper cinnamon rufous, particularly in breeding birds.*
IMMATURES: *As male, but more strongly patterned with black and white dorsally; breast whitish, with dusky streaking changing to barring at two months; eye dark till then. Sexually mature in three months.*

VOICE
Repeated, moaning oop, *uttered by female when nesting, often at night. Chipping alarm call.*

NESTING
Breeds in all months except cold winters, after rains have brought seeding. Nest a shallow depression at base of grass clump; lined with fine grass, usually with part dome and entrance at one side; built by both sexes. Eggs: three to five; slightly glossy off-white, finely spotted with light brown, and thickly splotched with browns and slate-grey; oval to pyriform, about 23 x 18 mm. Incubation 13–14 days, by male.

DISTRIBUTION
Widespread throughout inland Australia, reaching coasts erratically; usually in areas of rainfall less than 500 mm a year. No races.

THE LITTLE IS AUSTRALIA'S only button-quail centred in the arid zone. Like many arid zone birds, it is highly nomadic, adapted to flying long distances to find food in a capricious environment. In good seasons it arrives in abundance, breeds rapidly and then disappears as the food supply wanes.

Its movements take it to most of the continent except the wet tropical north and extreme southeast. There is also a seasonal bias, the birds shifting into southern districts over most summers to take advantage of seeding grasses. Good seasons coincident with droughts inland bring vast numbers.

One of the small button-quail, it can be distinguished by its pervadingly cinnamon plumage. It also has a much thickened bill, reflecting its granivorous diet; insects are eaten also but are not the staple item that seeds of native grasses are. These the bird finds in all natural rangelands, even the driest spinifex desert, and, at times, crops and stubble. Like other button-quail, it is fairly solitary or in small coveys, and it has the habit of standing and rocking forwards and backwards on its feet, its body horizontal. Females are bigger and brighter than males, dominate breeding, but hold smaller territories than other species and defend them less vigorously.

Chestnut-backed Button-quail *Turnix castanota* (GOULD, 1840)

OTHER NAMES
None.

IDENTIFICATION
LENGTH: *Male 160 mm; female about 180 mm.*
MALE: *Crown with pair of dull rufous stripes edged faintly black and divided by central white line. Rest of upper* parts cinnamon-rufous, with blurred black mottling, white spotting, and dull cream edges to feathers from mantle to mid-back; rump plain. Wings pale grey, grading to cinnamon on inner flight feathers and shoulders; wing coverts spotted finely white. Face and sides of cinnamon-rufous neck speckled finely white. Throat white, grading into mid olive-grey breast and flanks spotted coarsely cream in centres of feathers. Belly and undertail whitish. Eye rich yellow. Bill cream-grey. Feet yellow; claws dark horn.
FEMALE: *Like male but markings duller and finer. Crown almost plain rufous with white speckled eyebrows. Rest of upper parts plain cinnamon-rufous finely speckled cream-white on mantle. Olive-grey of breast and flanks more extensive, with tiny cream shaft streaks. Eye orange.*
IMMATURES: *Resemble adult male but more clearly marked with black and cream edges to feathers; crown stripes blacker; wing coverts spotted coarsely white; face and neck more coarsely spotted white; cream spots in centres of breast and flank feathers larger. Eye cream.*
DOWNY YOUNG: *Brown-rufous above, with central and lateral pairs of cream stripes; paler cream below.*

VOICE
Low, moaning oom *probably for contact and to advertise territory, by female.*

NESTING
Breeds December–May, corresponding with wet season when insects and seeds are most abundant. Nest a slight depression in the ground, at base of shrub or grass clump; oval and sometimes domed or partially domed, woven with grass and leaves, with side entrance. Eggs: usually four; glossy white, finely speckled with light brown, blotched all over with brown, blue-grey and black; round to pyriform, about 25 x 19 mm. Incubation 14–15 days, by male.

DISTRIBUTION
Kimberleys and Arnhem Land; not uncommon; sedentary in open, dry savanna woodland and on sandy or rocky ridges. No apparent races.

WELL-GRASSED GRAVELLY RIDGES, slopes and tablelands in eucalypt woodland are the preferred habitat of this button-quail in northwestern Australia, where it replaces the Buff-breasted and Painted Button-quail of the east. All three are large birds, occuring in shrubby grasslands; and the Chestnut-backed, living in the seasonally driest habitat, is the most uniformly cinnamon in tone. This reflects Gloger's Rule, that brown-toned birds in arid habitats are paler and more rufous than their relatives in wetter areas. So the name 'chestnut-backed' is not very appropriate.

Chestnut-backed Button-quail gather in non-breeding coveys of six–20, appear to move about locally without being highly nomadic, and feed on the seeds of grasses, other vegetation and occasional insects. When disturbed they tend to run off rather than fly, but will flush with a typical quail-like clatter and dash off five metres or more on buzzing wings before dropping back to cover. Flight is fast and direct. When birds in a group are separated they utter their low moaning *oom* to re-establish contact.

Like other button-quail, males incubate the eggs and rear the young. Each may brood up to three times a season.

Red-chested Button-quail *Turnix pyrrhothorax* (GOULD, 1841)

ALTHOUGH PARTLY OVERLAPPED by the Little Button-quail, the Red-chested tends to replace that species in the better-watered grasslands of eastern and northern Australia. Much of that habitat has been affected by grazing, but Red-chested Button-quail are still moderately abundant, occur in small coveys, and wax and wane in numbers according to the season. Although the birds are somewhat nomadic, many of their fluctuations seem to reflect rises and falls in local breeding. In any area, some individuals are present year in year out. Overall there seems to be a northward shift in winter and a southern one in spring to breed.

Red-chested Button-quail breed when insect-life and seeding peaks, and may nest more than once in a season. The female solicits various males and advertises her territory by booming, and also defends her ground against other females. Often she begins nest-building, then lays her clutch, and leaves the male to attend to the rest. He feeds the precocial young first on insects and later leads them in search of seeds.

OTHER NAMES
None.

IDENTIFICATION
LENGTH: *Male 130 mm; female 150 mm.*
MALE: *Crown of pair of brown-black mottled stripes separated by cream line. Rest of upper surface grey-brown with black mottling and white edgings to feathers. Wings grey, the wing coverts tawny-brown flecked white. Face and sides of neck coarsely freckled white. Throat and belly white, grading into rufous breast with black-and-white barring at the sides. Eye cream. Bill pale blue-grey. Feet flesh. Breeding birds duller.*
FEMALE: *Non-breeding birds as eclipse male. Breeding birds dark grey-brown on upper parts with only faint dusky,* cream and buff markings. Face finely spotted white, extending on to crown. Undersurface plain rich rufous.
IMMATURES: *As eclipse males, but breast whiter with extensive dark bars. Eye duller.*
DOWNY YOUNG: *Grey-cream.*

VOICE
Female utters rapidly repeated oom *during breeding season. Soft, whistling churps when flushed.*

NESTING
September–March or May in north. Nest a shallow depression at base of grass tuft, lined with fine grass and usually domed. Eggs: usually four; matt buff-white, thickly splotched with chestnut, purple-brown and slate-grey; pyriform, about 23 x 18 mm. Incubation 13–14 days, by male.

DISTRIBUTION
In grasslands of coastal and near inland northern and eastern Australia. Nomadic. Occasionally occurs as far west as Kimberleys, Alice Springs and Adelaide. No races.

A female Red-chested Button-quail. The male is less rufous underneath, even duller when breeding.

Buff-breasted Button-quail *Turnix olivei* ROBINSON, 1900

FROM THE MOMENT OF its recent discovery at the turn of the century, this Button-quail has suffered from confusion with the Chestnut-backed Button-quail which it replaces on Cape York Peninsula. It is a still larger bird, with a much stronger bill and much less marked plumage grading to a completely plain undersurface.

Only a handful of ornithologists have seen it alive and next to nothing is known of its habits. The fringes of swampy grasslands and heathy uplands appear to be preferred habitat, where the button-quail form coveys of six–eight birds when not breeding. Their thick, heavy bills suggest a primarily granivorous diet. Incubation and the rearing of young are borne by males.

OTHER NAMES
Olive's Button-quail.

IDENTIFICATION
LENGTH: *Male about 180 mm; female 200 mm.*
MALE: *Crown grey with pair of plain dull rufous stripes. Rest of upper parts uniform cinnamon-rufous, with faint black mottlings and cream fringes to feathers of mantle and upper back;* rump plain. Wings pale grey, grading to cinnamon on shoulders; wing coverts mottled and marked cream-white. Face freckled white. Throat cream, grading to plain cinnamon on sides of neck. Breast and flanks plain, lustrous olive-cream. Belly and undertail whitish. Eye mid-yellow. Bill buff-brown, thick and long. Feet yellow; claws horn.
FEMALE: *As male, but still more faintly marked. Crown plain grey; mantle* plain cinnamon-rufous; wing coverts more finely spotted white; face plain cream-buff. Eye, bill and feet as male.
IMMATURES: *Slightly more clearly striped on crown and mottled on upper back; faint black bars on (sides) breast.*

VOICE
Low moaning oom, *probably for contact and to advertise territory, by female.*

NESTING
Breeds December–May, corresponding with late wet season when seeds and insects most abundant. Nest in slight depression in ground (10–15 mm deep), at base of shrub or clump of grass; oval and sometimes partially domed, with side entrance, of loosely and sparsely woven grass and leaves, about 130 x 140 mm outside and 70–80 mm high. Eggs: three to four; glossy white, finely speckled and blotched with light brown, grey-brown and black all over; round to pyriform, about 27 x 23 mm. Incubation probably 15 days, by male.

DISTRIBUTION
Restricted to wooded grasslands, heaths and grassed fringes of forest and swamps on upper Cape York Peninsula, probably south to Laura and rarely, if ever, reaching Cooktown. Sparse. No races.

Black-breasted Button-quail *Turnix melanogaster* (Gould, 1841)

RAREST OF THE BUTTON-QUAILS, the Black-breasted Button-quail is also one of the largest. Its favoured habitat is the edge of dry rainforest, in small grassy clearings, or in tangled vines with thick overhead cover supplied in some instances by introduced lantana. There it is sedentary, singly, in pairs or parties of up to four or five.

This button-quail is strong and stocky, with powerful legs and feet. Like other members of its family it scratches in the leaf litter to find most of the seeds and insects on which it feeds. While it scratches with one foot it pivots on the other foot so that it rotates in a half-circle. Then it shifts feet and rotates back on the other, forming a characteristic saucer-shaped depression. In this way it moves methodically over the forest floor.

The female is larger and brighter than the male. It advertises its territory with its repeated booming call, holds it against other females, and mates with any males it can entice into its area. The males alone incubate the eggs and rear the young, though females have been observed as part of a family flock. The young are fed by males for the first few days after hatching. They grow rapidly and are sexually mature at five or six months.

Black-breasted Button-quails are heavy, clumsy fliers, usually running and freezing when disturbed and appearing to fly only with great reluctance.

Two other species resemble the Black-breasted Button-quail in appearance, behaviour and habitat: the Madagascar Button-quail, which is found only on Madagascar, and the Ocellated Button-quail, found on Luzon, in the Philippines.

OTHER NAMES
None.

IDENTIFICATION
LENGTH: *Male 150–160 mm; female 170–180 mm.*
MALE: *Crown fawn-brown with black-mottled stripes at side. Rest of upper surface deep russet-brown, the feathers barred black and lined cream. Wings grey-brown, wing coverts dull chestnut, flecked cream. Face and throat freckled cream with black edging. Breast and flanks coarsely spotted cream with black edging to feathers. Belly and undertail buffier grey with fainter spotting. Eye cream-white. Bill mid-grey. Feet dull yellow; claws darker.*

FEMALE: *As male but crown, face, throat and whole breast black, with faint white flecking on eyebrows and lower cheeks, and coarse white spotting across breast to sides of neck and nape. Belly darker fawn-grey.*
IMMATURES: *As male, but eye dark and feet greyish.*
DOWNY YOUNG: *Russet-brown above with central cream stripe on crown and central black stripe on back flanked with pair of cream lines; buff-grey below. Eye brown; bill sepia; feet flesh.*

VOICE
Female utters rapidly repeated boom. *Male utters soft clucking when with young.*

NESTING
Breeds in any month, but usually September–March. Nest a shallow depression in ground at base of shrub or grass clump, lined with grass and leaves. Eggs: three or four; glossy with dirty white ground, finely speckled light brown, moderately covered with splotches of dark brown, black or grey; rounded-oval, about 28 x 21 mm. Incubation 16 days, by male.

DISTRIBUTION
Scattered clearings and on edges of rainforests in eastern Queensland and northern New South Wales. No races.

A pair of Black-breasted Button-quails; the female is the darker bird. Black-breasted Button-quails live on the edges of rainforests in eastern Australia.

Red-necked Crake *Rallina tricolor* GRAY, 1858

OTHER NAMES
Scrub Rail.

IDENTIFICATION
LENGTH: *260–290 mm.*
ADULTS: *Sexes similar. Head, neck, breast and upper shoulders bright red-chestnut; throat paler. Back and wings plain dusky olive-brown. Belly, flanks and undertail coverts dusky brown, each feather tipped with a narrow buff-white band. Wing feathers on underside spotted and barred with an irregular white pattern. Eye red. Bill greyish yellow-green. Feet olive.*
IMMATURES: *Upper parts uniformly mid brown-grey; underparts paler mid grey-brown, whiter on throat. Flight feathers dark brown, barred white.*
DOWNY YOUNG: *Plain black; eye brown; bill black; feet flesh-grey.*

VOICE
Loudly repeated, harsh naak, nak-nak-nak, with emphasis on first syllable, then in a descending pattern, which may go on for a minute or more, in which case calls remain on same note. Often given in chorus by territorial pairs at dusk. Also call like tock, tock, tock or plop-plop-plop, which may go on for hours; contact noises like piglets grunting. Abrupt cluck when disturbed.

NESTING
Breeds November–April. Nest a few leaves between buttresses of a tree, or more substantial cup-shaped structure up to 2 m above ground in heart of small pandanus palm or bird-nest fern. Eggs: three to seven, usually five; glossy white, soon becoming discoloured; rounded-oval, about 30 x 28 mm. Incubation 18–22 days, mainly by female.

DISTRIBUTION
Restricted to rainforests on eastern Cape York Peninsula, south to Ingham on Herbert River. Also in New Guinea, nearby islands, outer Bismarck Archipelago and islands in Banda Sea. Four races; two in Australia: one nomadic in northern Cape York Peninsula; the other larger and sedentary from Ingham to Cooktown.

The Red-necked Crake is largely nocturnal and seldom leaves the rainforests of northern Queensland.

THE RED-NECKED CRAKE is Australia's only rainforest-inhabiting rail. Found only in coastal northeastern Queensland, it lives on the forest floor within the cover of rainforest and vine scrub, usually in damp pockets along streams. There it rests and sleeps through much of the day, probably on roosting platforms in rock crevices, the crowns of palms and in tree buttresses. At dusk it comes out to feed, remaining active well into the night. Strutting along upright, its blunt tail erect and flicking, it works methodically along shallow stream beds and adjacent banks, raking over pebbles and leaf litter with bill and feet, and probing for frogs, tadpoles and crustaceans in water or insects, amphipods, snails and worms on land. Seeds of plants are also taken but less often. Searching for food, the birds occasionally venture along tidal channels.

When disturbed, they are quick to take cover under roots and banks, darting off with head hunched and wings partly spread. They cross creeks readily by swimming, both above and under water. Flight is floppy and noisy but the crakes can fly silently, as nightjars do. Much of the Australian population is sedentary, particularly pairs with established prime territory in the Cooktown-Ingham area of northeastern Queensland. The northern Cape York Peninsula population, however, seems to be more fluid, and many birds, including probably the young of the year, appear to disperse to southern New Guinea and fringing islands each winter.

In northeastern Queensland, adult pairs of Red-necked Crakes seem to hold territory year round. Nesting is heralded by mutual duelling choruses from dusk monotonously on into the night. The nest may be a leaf-lined scrape on the ground at the base of a tree or, more usually, a saucer of dry leaves in a plant or fork of a tree, on sloping ground near water. The female lays on consecutive nights until the clutch is complete, and only then sits to incubate. This ensures that the eggs hatch together. She carries out the bulk of brooding, at least during the day, but her mate may assist at night. At this time, the birds are bolder towards intruders and, if disturbed, may squat, fluff their feathers and flutter in a shivering manner, as if to distract the intruder from the nest.

Chicks, open-eyed and strong in leg at hatching, are soon out and about, although they still return to the nest to sleep for the first few days. They begin to feed themselves in three–five days, and are assisted by their parents for another week or two. Normal feathering replaces their down in four–six weeks.

Chestnut Rail

Eulabeornis castaneoventris GOULD, 1844

OTHER NAMES
Chestnut-bellied Rail.

IDENTIFICATION
LENGTH: *430–440 mm.*
ADULTS: *Sexes similar. Head grey, merging down back of neck to olive-chestnut or olive-grey over back. Throat pink-grey, shading to chestnut on breast and rest of underparts. Eye scarlet. Bill dirty yellow-green with grey tip. Feet yellow-green.*
IMMATURES: *Not known.*

VOICE
Loud, raucous trumpeting—erratic whack, whacka, wak-wak repeated at steady pace. Also grunting note.

NESTING
Breeds October–February. Nest a large, flat or saucer-shaped structure of twigs lined with bark, seaweed leaves and grass, on platform of mangrove roots or leaning tree trunk, or fork among outer foliage of mangrove tree, 1–3 m above
ground. Eggs: four–five; pink with fine chestnut spots; oval, about 53 x 36 mm.

DISTRIBUTION
Coastal northern Australia from western Kimberleys to eastern side of Gulf of Carpentaria. Restricted to mangroves. Also found on islands off north coast of Australia, and Aru Islands, Indonesia. No races in Australia.

The Chestnut Rail is a wary bird, often heard but rarely seen.

FOR SUCH A LARGE BIRD, this moorhen-sized rail is remarkably shy and secretive. They are usually located in tall mangroves along tidal waters but if these are not available they will inhabit the lower, bushy mangrove scrub. They are very strong-legged birds and when frightened they almost always run to escape into the mangroves; they are seldom seen to fly.

The best time to observe the birds is at low tide, when they come out on mud flats to feed. In the open, they seem to lose their wariness. They strut along, flicking their tail and sometimes calling as they peck in the mud for small crabs or other crustaceans.

They appear singly or in pairs, or, when the young first leave the nest, as a family party. Their large nest is probably used more than once, as, built on mangrove crotches above high tide, the structure could last for many years. The birds easily climb up to the nests, rather than fly. They also have well-defined territories and vigorously defend them.

Chestnut Rails are said to inhabit the coastal mangroves of Cape York, but because of the difficulty in penetrating such habitats there is a lack of confirmation.

Lewin's Rail *Dryolimnas pectoralis* TEMMINCK, 1831

Lewin's Rail weaves grass and rushes into a nest, sometimes pulling the surrounding plants down to form a roof.

OTHER NAMES
Water Rail, Slate-breasted Rail.

IDENTIFICATION
LENGTH: *200–230 mm.*
ADULTS: *Sexes similar. Crown and nape chestnut-brown with black flecking. Rest of upper parts dark brown with black streaks. Wings dusky, coverts barred white. Throat and breast slate-grey washed brown; belly black with fine white bars. Eye brown. Bill pink or red-brown with black tip. Feet pink-grey.*
IMMATURES: *Duskier on upper parts with heavier black streaks; duller and browner below with belly more spotted white.*
DOWNY YOUNG: *Black.*

VOICE
Alarm call a loud, staccato jik-jik-jik or tree-eek, tree-eek, lasting up to 30 seconds; also a pig-like grunting call and a whining oo-err.

NESTING
Breeds August–December in Australia. Nest of grass or rushes woven into a cup about 120 mm across internally, sometimes with a well-defined approach runway. Eggs: four to six; cream with blotches of red-brown and purple-grey; oval, about 35 x 26 mm. Incubation about 20 days, by female.

DISTRIBUTION
Uncommon; in coastal southern and eastern Australia, rarely inland. Eight or nine races; two in Australia: one in east; the other, long-billed, in southwest.

RARELY SEEN because it spends so much time skulking in dense vegetation, Lewin's Rail lives on the ground in brackish and freshwater marshes, wet heaths and swampy grasslands around coastal southern and eastern Australia. It is more abundant than the few observations suggest, except in southwestern Australia where it may be extinct.

With a longer, more slender bill than other Australian rails, Lewin's Rail probes into cracks and holes in the ground for its food — insects, molluscs, crustaceans and plant matter. It holds its stumpy tail erect and flicks it as it goes. Most feeding is done at dawn and dusk. The birds make their own runways beneath marshy vegetation, and use them to escape when disturbed, flushing only as a last resort. They fly awkwardly, with legs trailing, and rarely flutter far before dropping back to cover. They also swim readily, both on and under water.

Only females have been recorded brooding. They lay eggs on successive days, often around midday. Typically precocial, young chicks leave the nest within hours of hatching.

Buff-banded Rail *Gallirallus philippensis* LINNÉ, 1766

IN AUSTRALIA, THE BUFF-BANDED RAIL is very much a coastal and subcoastal bird, rarely if ever venturing far inland. Its habitat is dense tussocky vegetation and shrubberies around swamps and lagoons, among mangroves, along watercourses and on islands. Despite these restrictions, Buff-banded Rails are great nomads. Local groups may be fairly sedentary in lush stable habitat, as in eastern Queensland; elsewhere they seem to move around seasonally, flying across the continent and reaching southern and western New Guinea. Across southern Australia the rails are most abundant from late winter through spring, breeding then.

Like all rails, the Buff-banded Rail is ground-living and uses wet tussocky vegetation to shelter its feeding activities, roosting and nesting. Singly or in twos, it pecks its food—insects, small molluscs, and other invertebrates, seeds and a little vegetation matter—from damp ground and may even hoard it in caches.

It walks about nimbly, short tail held erect, and flicked in alarm. If frightened, it usually runs through cover rather than flushes to escape. It is usually silent, but during breeding, territorial birds shriek harsh braying notes day and night; these may develop into choruses if the nesting population is dense.

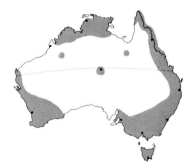

OTHER NAMES
Banded Land Rail, Land Rail, Painted Rail, Little Tarler Bird.

IDENTIFICATION
LENGTH: *300–330 mm.*
ADULTS: *Sexes similar. Crown russet-olive flecked dusky; nape plain light rusty. Rest of upper surface mid-brownish olive, mottled black and spotted white on mantle and shoulders. Wings dusky with broad rusty-buff bars grading whiter. Face with grey-white eyebrow, broad rusty stripe through eye to nape and grey cheeks. Chin white, grading to mid-grey foreneck. Breast, flanks and crissum barred black and white with broad rusty band across centre breast. Centre belly plain mid-grey. Eye red. Bill flesh-brown. Feet and claws light brown.*
IMMATURES: *Duller, without russet on hind neck or on breast band; eye brown.*
DOWNY YOUNG: *Sooty black.*

VOICE
Usual call, generally at dusk, a loud creaky swit swit. *When surprised or agitated, utters loud throaty* krek. *At nest, soft, low* kik-kik-kik.

NESTING
Breeds September–January in Australia, although probably at any time of year if conditions suitable. Nest of grass or reeds pulled down and woven into cup under tussock; a scrape under rocks and logs on some islands. Eggs: usually five to eight, but up to 11; biscuit coloured, lightly blotched with red-brown and purple-grey; swollen-oval, about 36 x 28 mm. Incubation 18–19 days, by both sexes.

DISTRIBUTION
Patchy around coastal Australia except dry sectors; also in Tasmania where rare and erratic. Widely distributed on islands of eastern Indian Ocean through Celebes, New Guinea and neighbouring islands to Philippines. Also on islands of southwestern Pacific to New Zealand and formerly Macquarie Island. Over 20 races; two in Australia: one throughout mainland and Tasmania; the other, darker, on islands in Coral Sea.

The Buff-banded Rail is common in swamps, lagoons, wet grasslands and along watercourses, but it is seldom seen because it stays under cover.

Australian Crake *Porzana fluminea* GOULD, 1843

A foraging Australian Crake.

OTHER NAMES
Spotted Crake, Water Crake.

IDENTIFICATION
LENGTH: *180–200 mm.*
MALE: *Upper parts olive-brown mottled with black and speckled with white. Underparts deep blue-grey from face to belly. Flanks barred with black and white; undertail coverts pure white. Eye deep red. Bill green, with orange-red at base of upper mandible, particularly in breeding season. Feet olive-green.*
FEMALE: *Paler than male, with red at base of upper mandible paler and less extensive.*
IMMATURES: *Duller and lighter. Bill grey-green, with little red at base of upper mandible. Feet grey-green.*
DOWNY YOUNG: *Sooty black.*

VOICE
Large repertoire of notes such as gloo-ik; high-pitched, rapid chatter-chatter-chatter and trinnick-trinnick-trinnick; and note like distant yelp of a puppy.

NESTING
Breeds August–February. Nest an open saucer or cup of green weeds lined with soft grass and with a ramp of weed stems leading up to it; often covered by canopy of leaves and stems of aquatic plants, in large tussock of grass or near water. Eggs: three to six, usually five; glossy green-olive or brown-olive, blotched and spotted mainly at larger end with shades of red-brown and purple-brown and underlying lavender-grey, some marked all over with small red-brown spots; oval, about 31 x 23 mm.

DISTRIBUTION
Shallow swamps, lagoons and drains of inland river systems of southeastern and southwestern Australia. Nomadic. Vagrants reach northeastern Queensland and Kimberleys. No races.

LIKE SO MANY WATER BIRDS centred in the Murray–Darling–Cooper basin wetlands, the Australian Crake is a nomad. It wanders the ephemeral waters of the southern inland, appearing in numbers wherever flood pans, swamps and channels fill, and disappearing as quickly when they dry. Only when reaching the more permanent swamps of coastal districts and along the Murray–Darling waterways does it become rather sedentary.

Australian Crakes inhabit the muddy edges and very shallow part of still waters, both fresh and brackish, wherever they are interspersed with a patchy cover of tussocks of reed, clumps of lignum and stands of rush. These pockets of vegetation the crakes use for shelter, roosting and resting there and feeding out in their shadow. Quiet and furtive like other small rails, the crakes work hesitantly over the mud, creeping here, darting there, picking up their food—aquatic insects, hatching-flies, molluscs, tadpoles and plant matter—from the surface. The tail, its pure white underside a good field guide, is held erect and flicked all the while. They often forage further out from cover than other crakes, and flutter-bathe in open water, but dash back at the first hint of danger. Flight, a laboured fluttering with dangling legs, is infrequent and used more for moving between feeding grounds.

Australian Crakes are day-active and apparently form no permanent pair bonds. Although foraging alone, they will form loose aggregations of up to 15–20 at concentrated food sources.

White-browed Crake
Poliolimnas cinereus (VIEILLOT, 1819)

The White-browed Crake has distinct facial markings and long toes.

OTHER NAMES
Marsh Crake, Little Crake.

IDENTIFICATION
LENGTH: *160 mm.*
ADULTS: *Sexes similar. Upper parts generally light orange-rufous. Crown and nape streaked with black. Mantle, back, upper tail and wing coverts have feathers with dusky centres, and underlying off-white streaks and spots. Flight feathers dark brown. Face to above eye, sides of neck and chin to belly light blue-grey. Flanks and undertail coverts barred black and white. Eye ruby-red. Bill grey-green. Feet grey-green.*
IMMATURES: *Paler than adults and less distinctly marked; face and neck mottled brown; centre throat, breast and belly white.*
DOWNY YOUNG: *Black with glossy green on head, throat and upper parts.*

VOICE
Calls chut, krek and utters a rapid falling trill usually when alarmed.

NESTING
Breeds September–February. Nest about 13 cm in diameter, an open saucer or cup of leaves and stems of aquatic plants in tussock or clump, in shallow water, often with hood and approach ramp. Eggs: four to eight, usually five or six; glossy olive-brown marked all over with fine darker specks; oval, about 28 x 20 mm. Incubation about 21 days, by both sexes.

DISTRIBUTION
Coastal and near-inland freshwater marshes and water channels across southern Australia. Nomadic and shifting as far as north coast and New Guinea in winter. Accidental in Tasmania. Also central Eurasia, southern Africa, Borneo and New Zealand. Six races; one in Australia.

FEET THAT ARE SLENDER with a middle toe 35 mm long equip the White-browed Crake to run on waterlily pads and other floating vegetation of its habitat—a lake, a dam, a stream with still pools, or the edges of swamps. These crakes are most active in the early morning and evening, though they will also feed in the open throughout the day. In pairs or small loose groups they dash in stop-start manner over and among the matted vegetation, rarely venturing into thicket on dry land or swimming, but often running up the branches and roots of floating limbs and fallen trees. Adept at catching insects flying past, they nonetheless eat mainly leeches, frog spawn, worms, slugs, water spiders and vegetable matter. A common ploy is to float quietly, neck extended, snapping up prey with short sudden thrusts of the bill. Individuals in feeding parties may rest for half an hour or more behind a clump of leaves while others around continue to forage. All will chatter noisily, responding readily to a loud clap, or to a bird flying up a few metres to a new spot. Flight is fluttering, with legs dangled.

Although some birds may remain on permanent waters year round, most of the Australian population is nomadic or migratory. Many of the crakes, it seems, cross Torres Strait to New Guinea from April to November when the swamps dry out, and then return in December to breed through the wet season.

The Spotless Crake pulls surrounding vegetation over its nest into a canopy.

Spotless Crake

Porzana tabuensis (GMELIN, 1789)

OTHER NAMES
Leaden Crake, Tabuan Crake.

IDENTIFICATION
LENGTH: *About 180 mm.*
ADULTS: *Sexes similar. Back, wings and tail dark olive-brown, with a sheen in good light. Head and underparts dark blue-grey, paler on throat. Undertail coverts have a little white barring and spotting. Eye ruby-red, with a red lid. Bill dark olive-brown. Feet deep pink.*
IMMATURES: *Lighter and duller than adults. Throat almost white.*
DOWNY YOUNG: *Black; green tinge.*

VOICE
Call variable. A sharp kik; *a mechanical sound* bop-bop-bop *starting slowly and running together rapidly as the call trails off; dove-like low* crroo.

NESTING
Breeds September–January. Nest an open cup or saucer shape, of dry leaves and stems of aquatic plants about 1 m above water, in reeds, a tussock or clump of aquatic plants. Approach ramp is up to 1 m long and slopes down towards the water. When birds are sitting, they pull stems and leaves over the nest to form a canopy. Eggs: three to six; glossy pale cream-brown, finely freckled all over with dark brown, occasionally forming cap at larger end; oval, about 30 x 23 mm. Incubation 19–22 days, by both sexes.

DISTRIBUTION
Brakes of reeds and rushes of swamps and water channels across southern Australia and Tasmania, breeding north to about Brisbane in east and Perth in west. Nomadic. Ranges seasonally north to north coast and New Guinea. Also New Zealand, many islands in southwestern Pacific and Philippines. Three races; one, large, in Australia.

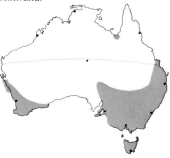

FEW WIDE-RANGING RAILS are as unobtrusive and rarely seen as the Spotless Crake. The Australian race, centred in the deeper, rush-covered swamplands of coastal and near-inland southern Australia, is somewhat nomadic and may shift north in winter, quitting Tasmania altogether then. Some birds reach the far north coast and even montane New Guinea, flying at night.

This crake spends nearly all its time—foraging and resting—within the cover of brakes of reeds and rushes, over both mud and shallow water. It almost never comes out to feed on the edge as Aus-

tralian and Baillon's Crakes do, from which it can be identified by its plain, blackish-looking plumage and pink feet. Only in New Guinea and some Pacific islands does it work out into more open grassland and brackish thicket.

Like all crakes, the Spotless pokes along with flicking tail, feeding mainly on molluscs, insects and plant matter. It swims gracefully and will dive if disturbed. Precocial young are brooded in the nest —in the shallow water of a swamp, billabong or stream—at least two days after hatching.

Baillon's Crake

Porzana pusilla (PALLAS, 1776)

OTHER NAMES
Marsh Crake, Little Crake.

IDENTIFICATION
LENGTH: *160 mm.*
ADULTS: *Sexes similar. Upper parts generally light orange-rufous. Crown and nape streaked with black. Mantle, back, upper tail and wing coverts have feathers with dusky centres, and underlying off-white streaks and spots. Flight feathers dark brown. Face to above eye, sides of neck and chin to belly light blue-grey. Flanks and undertail coverts barred black and white. Eye ruby-red. Bill grey-green. Feet grey-green.*
IMMATURES: *Paler than adults and less distinctly marked; face and neck mottled brown; centre throat, breast and belly white.*
DOWNY YOUNG: *Black with glossy green on head, throat and upper parts.*

VOICE
Calls chut, krek *and utters a rapid falling* trill *usually when alarmed.*

NESTING
Breeds September–February. Nest about 13 cm in diameter, an open saucer or cup of leaves and stems of aquatic plants in tussock or clump, in shallow water, often with hood and approach ramp. Eggs: four to eight, usually five or six; glossy olive-brown marked all over with fine darker specks; oval, about 28 x 20 mm. Incubation about 21 days, by both sexes.

DISTRIBUTION
Coastal and near-inland freshwater marshes and water channels across southern Australia. Nomadic and shifting as far as north coast and New Guinea in winter. Accidental in Tasmania. Also central Eurasia, southern Africa, Borneo and New Zealand. Six races; one in Australia.

LONG TOES ENABLE THE BAILLON'S CRAKE to walk on the plants in the swamps, marshes, lagoons and waterholes where it lives. The bird is also an accomplished swimmer and diver. It feeds on small molluscs, insects, tender pieces of water plants, and seeds.

It is also the smallest of Australia's rails, which is evident wherever it shares its habitat with the Australian Crake and Spotless Crake. A

The Baillon's Crake usually lays five or six glossy olive-brown stippled eggs.

barred undertail and mottled brown back help to identify it as well. Like the Australian Crake, it often comes out to forage by day on the edges of cover, poking along marshy ground and shallow waters with tail erect and flicking. It keeps, however, almost entirely to fresh waters patchily covered with shorter and more open brushes of reed and sedge. Over short distances, Baillon's Crake flies with dangling legs, its flight looking weak and fluttery. On long flights, mostly at night, its legs are drawn up more in line with the body and its wing-flaps are rhythmically stronger.

Baillon's Crake seems to undergo seasonal south–north movements, ranging sporadically to coastal northern Australia in winter, returning to breed across the south in spring and summer.

Bush-hen *Amaurornis olivaceus* (MEYEN, 1834)

STRANGE CALLS IN THE NIGHT — donkey-like sounds ending in a shudder, a monotonous *tok-tok-tok,* or an assortment of clicks and grunts—announce the presence of Bush-hens. The secretive birds are much more often heard than seen even by day, feeding, resting and roosting almost entirely within the cover of their habitat: moist stands of deep rank grass with pockets of dense shrubbery along the banks of permanent running streams, often on the edges of rainforest. Thickets of lantana are favoured in eastern Australia. In that environment they are fairly sedentary, although Bush-hens in drier parts of Cape York Peninsula and Arnhem Land may shift to southern New Guinea when creeks dry up in the dry season (April–November).

Bush-hens are mainly nocturnal, but remain active by day if the sky is overcast. Usually they are alone or in territorial pairs, but family parties are frequent in summer and autumn because young stay with their parents until full-grown. Keeping to shade and often wading, they stalk about hunting for a wide range of insects, worms, seeds and shoots. Despite their long slender toes, they do not walk on floating vegetation and rarely fly on being flushed. By day they rest much on coarse, nest-like roosting platforms built up in grass tussocks and shrubs.

Vocal all year, particularly during rain, Bush-hens become very noisy morning and afternoon early in breeding. Pairs then duet alternately in shuddering wails, often out of sight of one another. The precocial young leave the nest to forage soon after hatching, but return to roost for up to 10 days.

OTHER NAMES
Brown Rail, Rufous-tailed Moorhen.

IDENTIFICATION
LENGTH: *About 260 mm.*
ADULTS: *Sexes similar; female smaller. Crown, nape, back and wings olive-brown. Throat grey; breast darker grey with brown wash. Brown tinge increases towards sides of lower breast, which is sharply demarcated from soft rufous lower belly and undertail coverts. Eye deep brown. Bill yellow-olive with small orange frontal shield. Feet olive-yellow.*
IMMATURES: *Duller than adults; chin white.*
DOWNY YOUNG: *Black with black bill.*

Head still black when body brown in five–six weeks.

VOICE
Prolonged, shrieking knee-you, repeated eight–10 times, and in quick muted shuddering of five–six notes, given by both sexes, sometimes antiphonally. Also single tok or click not repeated for long periods. Single chuck in alarm.

NESTING
Breeds October–April. Nest a shallow bowl of crisscrossed green and dry grass blades, some bent from surrounds and moulded into a cavity by the bird's body, or made by trampling down part of tussock into a platform, to which more plant material added; about 23 cm across, 12 cm deep. Placed in tall clump of grass or shrubbery through which grass grows, up to 2 m above ground. Often a rudimentary roof is made from bending down surrounding stems. Eggs: five to seven; creamy white with irregular marks of red-brown and lavender; round, about 40 x 29 mm. Incubation by both sexes. Lays again if first clutch lost.

DISTRIBUTION
Coast and nearby ranges of Arnhem Land, from Daly River to Cape Arnhem and northeast coast from Cape York to Clarence River, NSW. Also Philippines, Moluccas and New Guinea to Solomons. Four or five races; one in Australia.

The Bush-hen lives in deep, stream-edged grass and at the edge of rainforests. It has large, slender feet with a middle toe about 50 mm long.

Tasmanian Native-hen *Gallinula mortierii* (DUBOIS, 1840)

The Tasmanian Native-hen makes its nest by trampling part of a tussock.

OTHER NAMES
Native Hen, Water Hen.

IDENTIFICATION
LENGTH: *450–480 mm.*
ADULTS: *Sexes similar. Upper parts brown tinged with green; tail duskier, short, held erect. Underparts grey with blue tinge, grading to black on belly and tail; white patch on flank. Eye bright red. Bill pale dirty yellow. Powerful grey feet with blue tinge.*
IMMATURES: *Dull form of adult plumage with grey tinge. Eye brown.*
DOWNY YOUNG: *Black with white spot on flanks; bill black, pink upper base.*

VOICE
Most frequent call is loud, hoarse see-saw in territorial defence. Also high-pitched alarm call; various low-pitched grunts.

NESTING
Breeds July–December, rearing two broods in good years. Nest a cup of grass or reeds, sometimes slightly roofed, in thick cover close to water. Eggs: four–nine; buff-grey or greenish, marked with fine and coarse spots of red-brown and sepia; oval, about 55 x 39 mm. Incubation, by all of group, begins when clutch complete. Chicks attended for about eight weeks.

DISTRIBUTION
Tasmania, up to 1100 m, but mainly from sea level to 700 m on north and east coast. Grassy situations. No races.

FOSSIL REMAINS SHOW THAT the Tasmanian Native-hen once lived on mainland Australia, but this plump, dull-coloured bird is now found only in Tasmania. It is almost twice as big as its closest relative, the Black-tailed Native-hen of the mainland. It is flightless, but it can run extremely fast, aided by stubby wings which it uses as balancers when pursued. When alarmed, it flicks its erect, stubby tail, which lacks any white underneath. It lives in swampy short-sword grassfields—on which it grazes — intermingled with creek-side tussocks and thickets in which it shelters. Resting in cover much of the day, the hen emerges at dawn and dusk to feed on plant shoots and various insects.

The Tasmanian Native-hen is sedentary—individuals rarely move more than three kilometres from their parent's nest; the recorded maximum is 40 kilometres. The hens live in small groups of one female with one or two males, occasionally more, plus the young of the previous season. Pairs and trios occur in about equal proportions; the males of one nesting group are often brothers. The group works as a unit, establishing a permanent territory that can grow from 5000 square metres to 15 000 square metres, defending it, building the nest, incubating and rearing the chicks. Warning of an approaching intruder is announced by single, sharp knocking notes. Then the defenders run forward, heads and necks lowered, only to stop short, parade with feathers fluffed and utter a loud, *see-saw* call antiphonally between them, rising in crescendo. If that fails to repel the intruder, fighting ensues. Through such competition, old established groups hold the largest territories in the best habitat, forcing younger groups to space out in new ground.

Females initiate courtship; but in song both sexes duet, heads aloft, in a crescendo of repeated shrieks. Nests are made by birds sitting at the site, thrusting material beneath them, and then revolving on their breasts to mould the material. Another nest is also built solely for brooding the chicks at night.

Black-tailed Native-hen

Gallinula ventralis GOULD, 1837

OTHER NAMES
Black-tailed Water Hen, Bantam.

IDENTIFICATION
LENGTH: *340–350 mm.*
ADULTS: *Sexes similar. Upper parts dark plain green-brown. Large black tail held cocked and flattened side-on like a bantam's. Underparts dark grey with slight blue tinge, grading to black under tail and a few large white flecks on flanks. Eye bright golden-yellow. Bill: upper mandible bright pea-green, lower red. Feet coral-pink.*
IMMATURES: *As adults but duller.*
DOWNY YOUNG: *Greenish black; bill as adult.*

VOICE
Almost silent, but sharp call sometimes given in alarm; also single cackle.

NESTING
Probably breeds at any time of year, depending on rainfall. Nest a cup of plant matter on or near ground, close to water, usually under cover in thicket, occasionally with partly woven roof of reeds. Eggs: usually five–seven; glossy pale green with red, brown or purple blotches and small spots; oval, about 44 x 30 mm.

DISTRIBUTION
Throughout inland Australia, centred in areas of uncertain rainfall for breeding. Highly nomadic. Rare vagrant in Tasmania and New Zealand. No races.

The Black-tailed Native-hen, like many of its relatives, has black chicks.

LOOKING LIKE A BANTAM with its cocked, flattened tail, the Black-tailed Native-hen is usually seen in loose flocks of five–fifty dashing among clumps of lignum on inland swamps. It shelters in lignum and cane grass and comes out to graze on the flat mud-pans between and along the edge of surface water, keeping more to dry open ground than other rails. There it feeds both day and night on vegetable matter, augmented with snails, insects and seeds.

Unlike the Tasmanian Native-hen, the Black-tailed is communal and nomadic. And it flies well if heavily, with steady silent wing-beats, taking off and landing with a run. Having no need to adver-tise and hold territory, it is rather silent and has no pronounced agonistic displays. Rather, it follows the uncertain rains and floods in inland Australia, appearing on newly filled swamps in hundreds one day and leaving as soon as they dry out. Their travelling is done by night.

A good season in the Great Artesian Basin brings the birds to breed in thousands, in almost every clump of lignum. If it is followed by a drought, the birds disperse. This results in the sporadic but spectacular irruptions of hundreds or thousands that occasionally reach the coast and once even New Zealand.

Dusky Moorhen *Gallinula tenebrosa* GOULD, 1846

THE DUSKY MOORHEN, larger, plain darker, and red-legged when breeding, is Australasia's representative of the Eurasian moorhen. It feeds by day both in fresh water by swimming and on land by walking, and so lives on swamps, lakes and waterways where rather deep reed-margined waters abut grassy banks for grazing. It eats land and aquatic plant matter, as well as insects, fish, molluscs and worms. On land, Dusky Moorhens will use their feet to anchor food and in water will up-end to find it. They drink and bathe regularly, often preening one another. At night they retire to grouped roosting platforms up to two metres above water in reeds and shrubs, each bird selecting its own and standing to sleep. The birds also use the platforms for resting by day and even mating.

Dusky Moorhens are sedentary and territorial, and form groups of two to seven birds comprising one to three males to a female. During breeding, the group defends its territory by threat display, calling and even fighting in border disputes. Females initiate courtship and will mate with all males in their group. All of the group build the nest, pulling down nearby stalks and pressing them into shape by turning the body.

Eggs are laid daily until the clutch is complete, and then the group takes turns in incubation. Newly hatched young are taken to a second, nursing nest over deeper water and brooded there for about three days. After that they are led on foraging forays by one adult at a time. For the first four weeks they are fed intensively and taken back to the nursery to sleep, brooded, at night. Parental feeding ceases at about nine weeks.

OTHER NAMES
Black Gallinule, Black Moorhen.

IDENTIFICATION
LENGTH: *340–380 mm.*
ADULTS: *Sexes similar. General plumage sooty, washed brown on back. White lines on each side of tail show clearly when tail flicked up and down. Occasional white flecks on flanks. Red frontal shield on forehead. Eye brown. Bill red with yellow tip. Feet green, with red knees, all reddish when breeding.*
IMMATURES: *Much duller than adults, with white wash on breast and belly, yellow-green bill and frontal shield and green feet.*

DOWNY YOUNG: *Black, no white under tail. Bill red. Bare patch of orange-yellow skin on leading edge of wing.*

VOICE
Territorial raucous crowing call; soft mewing call before sexual behaviour; raucous squawks if alarmed; miscellaneous staccato calls; contact clicks by adults to chicks; short descending whistles or shrill piping calls by chicks.

NESTING
Breeds August–February, often two broods a season. Nest a substantial, slightly dished platform of aquatic vegetation, usually among rushes or at base of tree growing in swamp. Eggs: five to eight per female in group; off-white, with red-brown and grey blotches and spots; oblong-oval, about 53 x 36 mm. Incubation 19–24 days, by group.

DISTRIBUTION
Freshwater swamps and parkland lakes in eastern Australia north to foot of Cape York Peninsula, far southwestern Australia and, recently, northeastern Tasmania. Vagrants reach Arnhem Land. Also in New Guinea and Indonesian region. Three races; one large with narrow frontal shield in Australia.

This moorhen has no connection with moors; its name is a form of 'merehen', or bird of the lakes. It is common on city lakes, and in swamps.

Purple Swamphen *Porphyrio porphyrio* (LINNÉ, 1758)

The Purple Swamphen is common in dense reeds along freshwater lakes, swamps and streams in the better-watered coastal regions, and in park lakes.

CLAMBERING THROUGH SWAMP VEGETATION, the Purple Swamphen supports its weight by gripping several reed stems at a time with its big feet. It can swim, but rarely does so, and can run fast on land. During much of the day swamphens keep to denser reed beds, wading among them or resting on roost platforms, but it also moves out into adjacent wet pasture and sward to graze.

It will eat herbs, seeds, fruit, eggs, small vertebrates, insects, spiders and molluscs, but its diet centres on young reed stems. These it bites off at the base with its pincer-like bill and then grips in one foot to eat them, often discarding much. All the while it jerks its stubby tail up and down, flashing the white undertail.

Although swamphens in marginal or seasonal habitat wander widely, those on permanent swamps are sedentary and live in territorial groups of two–ten of both sexes year round. The dominant males defend the territory and mate more successfully, displaying in front of females holding plants in the bill, bowing and chuckling. All construct a single nest in which several females may lay, and all incubate, the dominant birds most. A nursery nest is also made for chicks, where they are brooded at night and from which they are led to forage, mostly by subordinate adults.

OTHER NAMES
Purple Gallinule, Bald Coot.

IDENTIFICATION
LENGTH: *440–480 mm.*
ADULTS: *Sexes similar; male larger with bigger frontal shields. Upper parts and wings dusky, with dark blue collar in east; fore-bend of wing deep blue or turquoise. Face dusky; neck, breast and upper belly deep blue in east, all turquoise in southwest; lower belly black; undertail pure white. Eye red. Massive bill and frontal shield bright red. Feet pink-red with dusky joints.*
IMMATURES: *Duller in all parts;*
frontal shield small.
DOWNY YOUNG: *Black, with silver tips on head and back; bill lemon-cream with pink base and red frontal spot.*

VOICE
Loud, harsh screeching calls resemble kee-oww, *frequently heard at night. Soft* chuck-chuck *notes between group members while feeding.*

NESTING
Recorded as breeding in every month, mainly August–February. Nest large platform of reeds trampled down to form dished nest sparsely lined with grasses, up to 30 cm across, 4–10 cm
deep. Eggs: three to eight; buff to pale green, spotted and blotched with red-brown and purple; oval, about 50 x 36 mm. Incubation 23–29 days, by group.

DISTRIBUTION
Banks of freshwater and sometimes saline swamps, lakes and streams, throughout eastern Australia northwest to the Kimberleys, and an isolated population in southwest. About 10–12 races; two in Australia: one in east and northwest; the other paler, more turquoise, with square-cut shield in southwest.

Eurasian Coot *Fulica atra* LINNÉ, 1758

EURASIAN COOTS ARE THE ONLY Australian rails more at home in water than on land. Although often coming ashore to graze on short pasture, even in large groups, they spend most of their time on open sheets of deep fresh water, well out from the cover of reed banks frequented by Dusky Moorhens. Communal birds, they often gather there in flocks of hundreds, forming dense rafts. Most of their feeding is done on open water, much of it by diving. They have been recorded diving deeper than seven metres and remaining underwater up to 15 seconds. Equipped with broad lobes (not webs) on their toes, they swim well, with heads rocking forward and back as in other rails. In common with diving ducks and grebes, coots can squeeze air from their feathers to help them dive and forage on the deeper underwater plants.

In Australia, Eurasian Coots are primarily vegetarians, taking much less of aquatic insects, molluscs, worms, amphibians and fish than the Eurasian race. Rather, they forage on a whole range of aquatic algae, shoots and seeds from the surface and under water. Underwater material is brought to the surface and sorted out before eating. They will not only eat but also sleep on the water, both day and night.

When breeding, Eurasian Coots select territories on swampy ground with much calling and fighting, using feet, beak and beating wings in defence. Opponents approach with heads lowered and wings raised, and will walk parallel to one another. Non-breeders are chased off by both sexes.

Mating displays on open water involve much pursuit, calling, and striking of the water with the wings, followed by pair formation. Mutual feather-nibbling and greeting postures occur and may strengthen the pair bond. The coots are aggressive to other species at mating time and there are a number of reports of them killing ducklings and young grebes.

Sometimes coots nest in loosely associated colonies; threesomes, involving two females and a male, have been observed. Both sexes share in nest-building, incubation and feeding of the young; the males often build separate nests in which they roost after the females have laid the eggs. Eggs are laid on consecutive days and incubation commences before the completion of the clutch. Young coots are inexpert feeders, unable to dive until about three weeks old, and are partially dependent on their parents for food until about seven weeks.

Australia's coots are opportunistic in their movements. If food and breeding sites are available they will probably stay to breed; if not, they become nomadic, and large numbers suddenly appear where in the past they have occurred only sporadically; there seems to be some segregation of the sexes outside the breeding season. The birds often moult at this time, losing their tail and flight feathers simultaneously.

Eurasian Coots are capable of sustained flight. Taking off from the water, they rise slowly, pattering with their feet along the surface and then flying with neck and legs outstretched; and they land on water breast first, feet dragging. Long-distance movements appear to take place at night.

OTHER NAMES
Australian Coot, Toorie.

IDENTIFICATION
LENGTH: *320–390 mm.*
ADULTS: *Sexes alike; male slightly larger, with broader frontal shield. All slate-black with white frontal shield and bill. Eye red. Legs and lobed toes grey.* IMMATURES: *Throat dull white; rest of plumage paler and duller than adults.* DOWNY YOUNG: *Orange-red head; blackish, flecked body; bill red; distal third white, black tip.*

VOICE
Single, quite loud kowk *most common call. Other calls also shrill and abrupt. Some call notes sometimes strung together, as* kow-kow-kow, kok-kowk, kik-kowk.

NESTING
Usually breeds August–February, but at other times when conditions are good. Nest a loose clump of sticks and twigs or leaves and stalks of various waterweeds; 260–390 mm in diameter, with average cup size 220 x 230 mm. Nest, often approached by a ramp of nesting material, is placed among leaves or plant matter, or floats on water or occasionally is built on stumps or logs surrounded by water. Eggs: four to 15; sandy-grey to bright clay-coloured, thickly and uniformly covered with grey-violet speckles and spots; oval, about 52 x 35 mm. Incubation 21–26 days, by both sexes.

DISTRIBUTION
Open fresh or brackish surface waters throughout Australia, rare in north and deserts. Elsewhere across Eurasia to Indonesia, New Guinea and New Zealand. Three or four races; one in Australia.

The Eurasian Coot, identified by white bill and lobed toes, is the only rail to flock and feed on open water.

Kori Bustard

Ardeotis kori (BURCHELL, 1822)

OTHER NAMES
Plains Turkey, Wild Turkey, Australian Bustard.

IDENTIFICATION
LENGTH: *Male 1100–1200 mm, with 2.3 m wingspan; female 800 mm, with wingspan of almost 2 m.*
MALE: *Crown black. Back, wings and tail freckled greyish brown; wing coverts black with fine white edging. Face, all neck, breast and belly white, with faint black flecking on neck and thick black pectoral band; flanks and thighs dusky. Eye cream-white. Bill bone-coloured. Legs and feet dull yellow to olive.*
FEMALE: *As male but crown brown, white edging on wing coverts extensive, neck and undersurface plain cream with obsolete pectoral band, and cream thighs.*
IMMATURES: *Resemble female.*
DOWNY YOUNG: *Stippled buff and brown; dark stripes on head and neck.*

VOICE
Usually silent, but a low booming in breeding and loud roar during display.

NESTING
May be any month depending on season; in north mostly January–March. In south breeds predominantly in spring, September–November. No nest; eggs are laid on bare ground among grass. Eggs: usually one, occasionally two; olive-brown to light olive-green, with irregular spots and blotches of olive-brown; oval, about 78 x 55 mm. Incubation by female.

DISTRIBUTION
In open wooded grass plain and shrub steppe. Numerous only in central and northern Queensland and Kimberleys. Scanty populations on Nullarbor Plain. Also occurs in eastern and southern Africa, northwestern India and southern New Guinea. Three races; one in Australia and New Guinea.

The stately Kori Bustard used to be common almost anywhere in open country; nowadays it is seldom seen.

THE MATING DISPLAY OF the male Kori Bustard is spectacular. His foreneck inflates and the long neck feathers spread out into an apron or fan which he sways from side to side. His wings droop to the ground, tail spreads and rises over his back, the head is thrown backwards—and in this majestic posture the bird struts about, roaring and booming loudly. Males do this on a small display ground, to attract itinerant females.

Once, this large and striking bird could be encountered almost anywhere in open country. In 1896 flocks of 50–60 were found near Moree, NSW; in 1897, a flock of more than 1000 birds was seen near Hay, NSW. It was also common in Victoria. But like the rest of the world's 20 species of bustards, the Australian bird has not fared well in the last century or so of expanding human population. In Australia it has disappeared from all closely settled as well as many of the more sparsely settled districts in the south.

Alteration of its grassland habitat by the grazing of sheep and rabbits, predation by the fox, and widespread and continuing illegal shooting have brought about its decline. Today Kori Bustards are found in some abundance only in drier parts of northern Australia. Flocks of up to 200 may be seen in the Kimberleys, but they are usually alone or in small groups, often of one sex.

Kori Bustards roost in clumps or trees or, in treeless country, on the ground, usually on some high vantage point. At dawn they fly out to the plains to feed and spend the day in the open, or rest in the midday heat and come out again to feed at dusk. Their diet includes grasses, the seeds and fruits of native plants, and large numbers of grasshoppers, crickets and other insects, small mammals like mice, and reptiles. In northwestern Australia a favourite food is the moonflower.

Kori Bustards are nomadic, their movements apparently governed by rainfall. In places where there has been heavy rain to bring on growth their numbers increase, and in drought there is a movement to better-watered coastal districts. Though they are usually seen on the ground, their flight, while heavy, is strong—with neck and legs outstretched—and can be sustained over long distances. When disturbed they first 'freeze', then stalk slowly away and if pursued break into a run and take wing. When taking off, they first fold their legs up under the body before trailing them out behind. A female disturbed when brooding or incubating the eggs will creep away in a crouched attitude. She incubates and rears young unaided. Flightless young squat motionless when surprised, their mottled plumage making them inconspicuous.

The graceful Brolga is most abundant throughout coastal tropical Australia, close to swamps. It is renowned for its elegant, elaborate dancing.

Brolga *Grus rubicundus* (PERRY, 1810)

THERE IS PERHAPS NO MORE stately Australian bird than the pale grey, long-legged Brolga. When dancing, Brolgas line up roughly opposite each other before starting the movements: they step forward on their long, stilt legs with wings half-open and shaking. Bowing and bobbing their heads they advance and retire. Now and then a bird will stop and, throwing back its head, trumpet wildly. They sometimes leap into the air a metre or so and parachute back to the ground on their broad black and grey wings. Pieces of twig and grass are thrown into the air. These elaborate dances may be part of the courtship display but the birds do dance outside the breeding season. The dance may help maintain pair bonds.

Out of breeding, family groups of Brolgas, led and protected by the dominant male, often join others in flocks of several hundreds.

They may wander widely then for food, dispersing around coastal northern Australia and even reaching the Simpson Desert. Flight is graceful, on steadily up-flicking wings, with outstretched neck and legs; the birds soar and will spiral almost out of sight on thermal air currents. On the ground they roost in groups on residual surface water at night, and move out to feed by day, mainly on the tubers of sedges which they dig from up to 15 centimetres underground with their bills. They also take grain, molluscs and insects and can be a pest in cereal crops.

In the wet season, Brolgas return to their breeding grounds in shallow swamplands and space themselves out in pairs to nest. Both sexes incubate and care for young which can run and swim within hours of hatching and are tended for a year or more.

OTHER NAMES
Australian Crane, Native Companion.

IDENTIFICATION
LENGTH: *Male 1050–1250 mm; female 950–1150 mm.*
ADULTS: *Sexes similar. Pale grey, with primary wing feathers duskier, rump paler grey. Naked crown green-grey; ear coverts grey; dewlap under chin hairy black. Rest of head orange to bright red skin. Eye yellow. Bill long, straight, green-grey. Legs and feet dark grey to black.*
IMMATURES: *Similar to adults.*

DOWNY YOUNG: *Grey with paler markings; head covered with buff down; eye dark brown; feet pink-grey.*

VOICE
Single trumpeting garooo *in contact. Duetting pair call* kaweee-kreee-kurr-kurr-kurr-kurr-kurr. *Chicks* peep.

NESTING
Breeds September–December in south and February–June in north. Nest a platform of dry grasses or sedge, 1.5 m in diameter, in or beside swampy

grasslands. Eggs: usually two; cream with reddish-brown and lavender markings; tapered-oval, about 92 x 61 mm. Incubation about 28–30 days, by both sexes.

DISTRIBUTION
Open swamplands of coastal and subcoastal tropical Australia, ranging to eastern interior; small local populations through Murray–Darling basin to western Victoria. Also southern New Guinea. Vagrant to New Zealand, Coral Sea and southwestern Asia. No races.

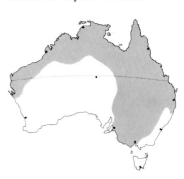

Sarus Crane *Grus antigone* (LINNÉ, 1758)

IDENTIFICATION
LENGTH: *Male 1300–1400 mm;
female 1100–1300 mm.*
ADULTS: *Sexes similar. Generally
uniform pale grey, the outer flight
feathers quite dusky and the innermost
much paler (but not white), forming a
rudimentary bustle in males. Head
and upper neck bare, with ellipse of
grey feathering on chin, a large spot of
grey feathering over ear, and black
hairs on foreneck; crown skin olive-
grey; face and all upper neck skin
orange-red. Eye orange-yellow. Bill
olive-grey. Legs and feet greyish pink.*
IMMATURES: *As adults but bustle
shorter and darker grey; face skin
paler orange.*
DOWNY YOUNG: *Rusty buff, grading to
white in centre of breast and belly;
lines of dark brown down centre of
back, enclosing paler brown median
stripe; buff-white spot opposite base of
both white-tipped wings on sides of
back.*

VOICE
*Trumpeting garrraww in contact in
flight, especially on take-off — more
grating than Brolgas. Duet in
courtship and advertising territory a
trumpeting krrr-kwerrr-krrr-krrr by
male and tuk-tuk-tuk-tuk-tuk in
unison by female. In alarm a
trumpeting blast. Chicks solicit with a
shrill, trilled peeep.*

NESTING
*During late wet season, January–
March, sometimes just before or after.
Nest a rough platform of stems, sticks
and vegetable matter, about 2 m in
diameter, often in shallow water with
base on mud in densely grassed
swamps. Eggs: usually two; glossy
bluish white to cream, lightly spotted
and dotted with brown, mauve and
sepia; mainly oval, about 100–105 x
65 mm. Incubation by both sexes.
Usually only one young reared; chick
begins to walk, swim and feed itself
after two days and is almost self-
sufficient in a week.*

DISTRIBUTION
*Cape York Peninsula, south to
Burdekin Valley and west around
head of Gulf of Carpentaria towards
Roper River; withdraws to nest
around eastern head of Gulf. May
occasionally straggle further west to
Kimberleys, but records suspect due to
confusion with Brolga. Also peninsula
India, and southeastern Asia to
Philippines where virtually extinct.
Three races; one endemic in Australia.*

EASILY CONFUSED WITH the Brolga, the Sarus Crane was not recognised in Australia until the late 1960s. That it has been present for much longer is indicated by its isolated occurrence in northeastern Queensland, far from any likely point of invasion from Asia, and from its distinctive features: an all-grey lower neck and large all-grey ear coverts, as large as those of the Brolga. From the Brolga itself the Sarus Crane can be identified by its bare red upper neck, pink legs, and ellipse of normal grey feathering on the chin in place of a black-haired dewlap.

Out of breeding, Sarus Cranes spread out across Cape York Peninsula and will congregate in loose flocks of up to several hundred on feeding grounds: shallow, grass- and sedge-covered swamps and adjacent pasture. By day they work out in pairs or families over feeding grounds, picking up a range of shoots, grain, tubers, insects (grasshoppers) and small vertebrates. At night they congregate in tighter groups standing to roost in shallow water. Brolga-like dancing is frequent in and out of breeding.

Nesting pairs space themselves out in territories of 50–80 hectares. These they defend by ritual, the male leading the female against intruders, walking up first, then preening vigorously, and, if that fails, arching and pointing the bill and jumping forward, wings outstretched. Courting and advertising pairs duet in unison standing close together, both with necks upstretched and bills pointing skywards, and the male's wings flared. Both sexes build the nest, and incubate and feed the young, which remain with them until the next season's breeding. Sarus Cranes live for 60 years or more.

The Sarus Crane looks similar to the Brolga, but has more red on its head and neck.

Comb-crested Jacana *Irediparra gallinacea* (TEMMINCK, 1828)

AN EXCEPTIONALLY LONG hind toe (about 75 mm) helps the Comb-crested Jacana to walk on waterweeds—a habit that gives it the popular names of Christbird or Lilytrotter. The bird is one of a family of seven waders which are distinguished by long legs, fairly long wings, extraordinarily long toes and claws, and—with one exception—short tails. Its long legs appear to hamper its flight initially, and its wings seem to work overtime before it can gather speed and extend its legs behind. As awkward as they appear in the air, they are agile in running and walking over floating vegetation, where they spend their whole life. As they walk, their heads nod forward and back and also bob when alert.

Jacanas are, in many ways, similar to rails. Both have long toes and frontal shields, both flick their tails as they walk along, and both build a number of extra nests for roosting at night. They also fly similarly. When startled they launch low into the air like a coot, rapidly beating their wings and stretching their legs, but soon land again. In moments of excitement the bird can change the colour of its comb from red to yellow; the blood is drained out.

Solitary or in pairs, feeding birds forage along the edges of pools and among floating leaves, probing and pecking among the vegetation. They probably eat mainly aquatic plants, including seeds and insects. Most feeding is done by day, and the birds often sunbathe then, lying on their sides on top of pond plants.

Comb-crested Jacanas become aggressive in the breeding season when a mated pair will defend their territory vigorously against other birds of the same species. They usually nest between September and January in eastern Australia. They nest later, from January to May, in the north of Australia, presumably because of the monsoonal rains. Their sheltered platform nest of plant matter is usually in water more than one metre deep.

Both parents look after the young birds. Adults become extremely wary when nesting. When disturbed off a nest or threatened by a predator, both young and adult birds are able to dive and swim under water, even though their feet are not webbed. They can remain motionless under water, with just nostrils and bill above the surface for up to half-an-hour. When adults with young are disturbed they may perform a distraction display, floundering and flapping as though they had a broken wing. Adult birds have been seen moving both eggs and downy young—fluffy creatures with disproportionately long legs and toes—by carrying them under their wings. This unusual habit becomes crucial for survival if the water level rises or falls suddenly.

OTHER NAMES
Lotus-bird, Lilytrotter, Christbird.

IDENTIFICATION
LENGTH: *200–240 mm.*
ADULTS: *Sexes similar; female up to half again as big as male. Forehead comb fleshy, red or orange or yellow. Crown, back of neck, breast band, tail and flight feathers black. Back and upper wing coverts deep olive-brown. Neck and belly white. A black line extends from base of lower bill to eye; sides of face and lower neck washed golden yellow. Eye yellow. Bill flesh-yellow, tipped with brown. Legs, feet and toes olive-green.*
IMMATURES: *Head and nape rufous; comb vestigial breast white without black band. Later stages have black and rufous on breast band, head and nape; otherwise as adults.*
DOWNY YOUNG: *Stippled buff above with dark lines on back and sides of face; underside white.*

VOICE
Shrill trumpet-like alarm call; and a squeaking contact call, pee-pee-pee.

NESTING
Breeds September–May. Nest a fragile but sometimes substantial raft of sedge, grass and aquatic plants, supported by aquatic vegetation. Eggs: three or usually four; glossy bright tan, thickly covered with black squiggles and fine wavy brown lines; pyriform, about 30 × 23 mm. Incubation by both sexes.

DISTRIBUTION
Coastal and subcoastal northern and eastern Australia, west to Kimberleys and southeast to Hawkesbury River, NSW, where irregular. On deeper, permanent, still freshwater swamps, ponds and billabongs; moderately abundant. Three races; one, brown-backed, in Australia, reaching Trans-Fly of New Guinea across Torres Strait.

The Comb-crested Jacana builds its platform nest on plants in water. Both parents look after the young.

The Painted Snipe lives in swamps and marshes inland. It is most active at night, and walks furtively, with head held low. This is the smaller male.

Painted Snipe *Rostratula benghalensis* (LINNÉ, 1758)

ALTHOUGH A BRILLIANTLY PATTERNED BIRD, with wings marked like a huge butterfly, the Painted Snipe is seldom seen and often regarded as a rare species. Viewed from above, the birds look dark and blend with their surroundings; from the side they are camouflaged by their alternating dark and light plumage, which breaks up their body outline.

They are also more active at night than during the day and they live in boggy swamps which are hard to reach; and that, perhaps, is the real explanation for the scanty records.

Painted Snipe prefer shallow freshwater swamps; in the southern part of their range they favour samphire, a succulent herb growing in salt marshes. When an area begins to dry up, becomes flooded or too cold the birds move away. They are most active at night, dawn and dusk. During the day they sit quietly under grass or reeds. Usually living alone, they mostly eat aquatic insects, grasshoppers, crickets, earthworms, and some plant seeds, skulking along like a rail. The bill is adapted to probe in soft mud.

Sex roles are unusual in the Painted Snipe. The female is the more brightly coloured, takes the initiative in courtship and mates with any available male. The male builds the nest, incubates the eggs and rears the young which hatch covered with dense down and are soon able to run about, swim and pick up food. The female, meanwhile, is left free to seek another itinerant mate.

The Painted Snipe stages a remarkable defence display when cornered. It fans out its wings and tail, facing the predator, presenting a body area four times normal size, and sometimes hisses like a snake or growls like a dog. At other times a bird will 'freeze' in whatever attitude it has when disturbed. Birds also 'tail bob' when alerted, dipping the tail.

OTHER NAMES
None.

IDENTIFICATION
LENGTH: *Male 220 mm; female 250 mm.*
MALE: *Resembles female, but duller. Head and neck mottled grey-brown, with buff stripe down centre of crown and through eyes. Wings and back barred black, buff and white. Breast has broad black band. Upper wing coverts spotted buff.*
FEMALE: *Head, neck, upper breast and back chestnut-bronze. Back has a conspicuous buff 'V' in centre. Wings metallic bronze-green, with bands of black, buff and chestnut on flight feathers; upper wing coverts finely barred; scapulars conceal long pure white feathers. Broad white band between the neck and wings; buff central streak down crown; broad white horizontal band through eye. Belly and vent white. Eye brown. Bill long, pink-orange darkening towards tip. Feet and legs bluish-green.*
IMMATURES: *Resemble male, but lack continuous black band on lower breast.*
DOWNY YOUNG: *Fawn, striped black above, with central strip of tan.*

VOICE
Female growls like a dog when threatened; also hisses like a snake. Also a sharp repeated alarm call

cuck...cuck. Male near nest gives soft click-click call.

NESTING
Breeds October–December in south, March–May in north, in small colonies. Nest 15 cm in diameter, a slight depression in a raised area of mud, surrounded by shallow water and usually partly shaded; lined with grass, reeds and roots to form simple platform. Eggs: usually four; quite glossy light buff, heavily splotched with dark olive, slate-grey and brown; pyriform, about 36 x 25 mm. Incubation 19–20 days, by male.

DISTRIBUTION
Eastern and northern Australia, mainly inland in muddy, freshwater swamps in Murray–Darling and Great Artesian basins. Nomadic. Occurs on many Pacific islands, throughout Indonesia, Asia and Africa. Two races; one in Australia.

Pied Oystercatcher *Haematopus longirostris* VIEILLOT, 1817

The Pied Oystercatcher lays its two brown-spotted eggs in a shallow scrape in sand well above the high-water mark.

BRILLIANT PIED PLUMAGE makes this large, chicken-sized wader one of the most unmistakable birds of Australian beaches and sandy-shored bays and estuaries. Against this pattern, its stout pink legs and long, scarlet chisel-shaped bill stand in contrast. The form of the bill, flattened side-on, is adapted to the bird's particular manner of feeding on its staple food: molluscs, both bivalved and coned. Foraging oystercatchers work alone or in dispersed pairs along wet sandy flats and bars exposed at low tide, walking sedately and probing and pecking deeply with the bill.

Finding prey, they dig it out and open it by one of two methods: hammering and stabbing. To hammer, the bird lays a bivalve on solid ground, strikes one valve until it breaks, then inserts the scissor-like tip of bill to cut the mollusc's adductor muscles and extract the body. To stab, the bird inserts its bill, head on side, into the already-gaping bivalve and, cutting the adductor muscles and other attachments, pulls out the body. Individual birds tend to use one or other method which they learn from their parents. Worms and crabs are eaten too.

Oystercatchers are noisy birds, quite sedentary, and sociable when not breeding. They commonly roost and rest in small groups on neutral, non-territorial sand bars, often standing on one leg, heads turned and bills tucked into the back. Their flight is usually low, strong and direct, with regular shallow wing-beats.

Pairs, which mate for life, defend territories throughout the year but may temporarily join flocks of non-breeding birds. Pairs and trios or more give 'piping' displays that are much the same for all sorts of breeding behaviour: courtship, aggression, territorial defence. All members involved thrust the neck forward, depress the bill, and run here and there, side by side, uttering long, piping trills, or sometimes flying to do so. Copulation is synchronised by call and accompanied by much wing flapping from the male: The precocial young leave the nest within one–three days of hatching but are still fed by both parents for several weeks. They and the eggs are defended by elaborate injury-feigning and mock-brooding displays, and by aerial attack. Young also hide, or enter the sea where they swim and dive strongly.

OTHER NAMES
None.

IDENTIFICATION
LENGTH: *About 480–520 mm.*
ADULTS: *Sexes similar; female slightly larger. Upper parts including wings and tail all black except narrow white bar in secondaries only and narrow white band on upper tail coverts. Head to upper breast black; rest of underparts white. Eye and bare skin scarlet. Bill orange-red. Legs and feet pink.*
IMMATURES: *First year birds have black-brown plumage; shoulder feathers tipped buff-brown. Eye brown. Bill tip dusky. Legs grey-brown. Full adult colouring reached in three years, before which no breeding occurs.*
DOWNY YOUNG: *Dusky stippled buff-and-white with black lines on back, sides of face and wings; belly white.*

VOICE
CALL: *Clear, penetrating he-eep.*
SONG: *Sharp pic notes gathering into prolonged chorus of high-pitched kervee-kervee-kervee and ending in short, lower trilling phrase, by both sexes in display and courtship.*

NESTING
Breeds August–January. Eggs: two or three; grey-olive with dark brown spots; long-oval, about 59 x 41 mm. Laid in a shallow scrape in sandy beaches well above high water. Incubation about 28–32 days, by both sexes but mainly female. Young fly in five–nine weeks.

DISTRIBUTION
Common on beaches and in estuaries in Tasmania, otherwise thinly scattered around seashore of Australia ranging to New Guinea. Closely related forms occur throughout the world, from which Pied Oystercatcher differs in large size, reduced white wing and rump bar, and no eclipse plumage. One or two races; one in Australia.

Sooty Oystercatcher *Haematopus fuliginosus* GOULD, 1845

BLACK AGAINST A DUSKY BACKGROUND, the Sooty Oystercatcher commonly frequents exposed rocky shores, wave-cut platforms, headlands, coral reefs and stony beaches, replacing the Pied Oystercatcher there. It does occur on sandy beaches, but much more rarely. Why the two species separate themselves out this way is not clear, but it probably reflects different preference for feeding habitat and types of food. Sooty Oystercatchers eat mainly limpets, periwinkles and mussels picked off rocks; some shells are hammered against a stone. Bivalves are also eaten, the birds hammering or stabbing them open with the same method that Pied Oystercatchers use.

Sooty Oystercatchers are like the Pied in most of their habits. They gather in small groups when not breeding, roost and rest together on rocky heads, and space themselves out when feeding. They also court and pair in the same manner and perform the same distinctive piping display. Injury-feigning, mock death and mock brooding are tactics, too, that are used to draw intruders from young and nest. Young, typically, run to an object for cover and freeze or squat at a call from their parents. Unlike Pied Oystercatchers, however, Sootys usually fly out to offshore islands to breed, adjacent to non-breeding foraging grounds. These pairs take up and hold what are probably traditional territories.

OTHER NAMES
Black Redbill, Wee-ardoo.

IDENTIFICATION
LENGTH: *480–520 mm.*
ADULTS: *Sexes similar; female slightly larger. Sooty-black plumage. Eye scarlet; eye-ring orange. Bill bright orange-red. Legs and feet coral pink.*
IMMATURES: *First year birds have grey feathers on back, belly and flank tipped buff. Eye brown. Bill dusky. Legs grey. Older immatures have dull red eye and pale pink legs.*
DOWNY YOUNG: *Head dusky, back brown, stippled buff and lined with black, belly white.*

VOICE
Loud, carrying kleep *or* hu-eep *in contact. Piping display calls.*

NESTING
Breeds August–January. Nest a shallow depression in sand above the high-water level, or a cleft in rocks which may be built up with pebbles, shells or seaweed. Eggs: two to four, usually two; olive-grey, suffused with dark brown and purple blotches; oval, about 64 x 43 mm. Incubation about 25–27 days, by both sexes.

DISTRIBUTION
Rocky shores, beaches and estuaries; often offshore islands and rocky islets. Two races: one roughly south of Tropic of Capricorn; the other north, with enlarged fleshy red eye-ring.

A Sooty Oystercatcher at its nest, a rock cleft lined with shells. It is seen on rocky or stony shores more often than the Pied Oystercatcher.

Plains-wanderer *Pedionomus torquatus* GOULD, 1840

WITHIN THE PAST DECADE it has been suggested that this quail-like bird was really related to American seed-snipe and plovers. It emerged from a review of the bird's structure and hybridisation of its DNA — the genetic material in animal cells—with that of other birds. Outward clues are there too: its plover-like head, green and pointed wader-like eggs, and slow, fluttering flight—like that of a thick-knee—showing buff wing bars.

Only its patterned brown plumage and plump, tail-less form is quail-like, camouflaging it on the open, sparsely grassed plains and steppes that it inhabits. Old stubble, fallow and grazed pasture are now occupied as well as short-grassed natural rangelands.

Often thought rare and declining, Plains-wanderers are still probably fairly abundant. This is indicated by the banding of over 100 of them in three months in one grazing paddock near Deniliquin, NSW, in 1982-83. Rather, it is their cryptic behaviour that explains rarity of observation. Throughout their range—central and southern Victoria, western New South Wales, and the southeastern section of South Australia—Plains-wanderers are sparsely dis-

tributed in ones, twos or small groups of up to five. They are also nomadic. Although they may stay sedentary in pockets of permanent habitat with sufficient food, they commonly wander, often quite widely.

As well, Plains-wanderers are nocturnal. By day they sleep flat-down in shallow scrapes on the ground where, even in open fields, they are impossible to see. So tight will some sit that they have been picked up by hand. At night they emerge to feed, usually solitarily, on a range of seeds and grass. Unlike quail, they walk upright and often stop and crane on tip-toe. When running they are more hunched and will 'freeze' in a squat if alarmed.

The roles of the sexes when breeding are the same as those of button-quail and some waders. Females, the larger and more brightly coloured, dominate courtship and may mate with more than one male in a season. Although participating in nest-building and part of incubation, they leave most of the duties to each male which rears the young unaided.

Young, downy and able to walk off at hatching, are reared first on soft insect material and later weaned on to seed.

OTHER NAMES
Collared Plains-wanderer, Plain-wanderer Quail, Turkey-quail, Collared Hemipode.

IDENTIFICATION
LENGTH: *Male 150 mm; female 170 mm.*
MALE: *Upper parts from crown to short, obsolete tail uniformly pale brown with fine black barring and scalloping and cream fringes to feathers; nape paler creamy-buff with black and brown flecking; rump almost black. Wings dusky brown with cream-buff bands along trailing edge and along base of flight feathers next to wing coverts; wing coverts buff-brown scalloped and barred finely black. Underwing cream-grey with broad central cream-white wing stripe. Face and underneck buff flecked black. Throat plain cream-white. Breast sandier-buff, with black scallops spreading across it and down flanks. Belly and undertail plain cream. Eye cream-white. Bill pale yellow with browner nostrils. Feet cream-yellow; claws browner.*
FEMALE: *As male, but plainer brown dorsally. Collar of black chequered white. Rich chestnut bib below collar on breast. Yellow almost orange with breeding.*
IMMATURES: *As male but upper parts more heavily scalloped black and streaked cream; breast and flanks spotted dusky, not scalloped black. Young females develop black-and-white chequered collar and rufous breast patch within several months of hatching.*
DOWNY YOUNG: *Tawny on upper parts, peppered and lined dusky; underparts and face plain cream-buff.*

VOICE
Mournful bovine moo, possibly by female only. Male utters soft chuck, often repeated, when calling chicks if danger threatens.

NESTING
Breeds May–February, mainly September–December, but opportunely if food abundant. Nest a 6–8 cm diameter, 1–4 cm deep scrape in ground, lined with grass and vegetable material. Eggs: two to five, usually four; smooth, matt pale green, heavily blotched and freckled with brown, olive and grey; pyriform, about 30 x 23 mm. Incubation 23 days, mainly by male.

DISTRIBUTION
Flat, short- and sparsely grassed plains, steppes, fallow and stubble fields in southeastern Australia inland of Great Dividing Range and throughout Murray–Darling basin where still abundant. Ranges south to coast at Yorke Peninsula, near Adelaide, and plains around Melbourne, and north to Darling Downs, Qld, and fringes of Simpson Desert. Now rare and erratic on south coast and on southern tablelands of New South Wales to Sydney. No races.

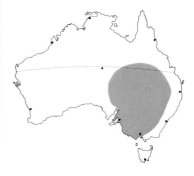

A female Plains-wanderer, larger and more colourful than the male. The female also dominates courtship, and leaves most of the duties of caring for the young to the male.

The Black-winged Stilt builds its nest mainly around the muddy edges of lakes, in water or amid the damp vegetation in swamps.

Black-winged Stilt *Himantopus himantopus* (LINNAEUS, 1758)

THE SPINDLY LEGS OF THE Black-winged Stilt not only give the bird its apt name, they also control its feeding. Longer than those of other waders and only vestigially webbed, they enable the bird to wade out into shallows to find its food but not to swim or submerge for it as Banded Stilts and avocets do. As a result, it is limited to foraging in wet mud and shallow water up to 15 centimetres deep in still, fresh water and brackish swamps. There it stalks gingerly along, spaced out in ones, twos and threes, picking up its food from the surface and in mud with jabs and probes of its needle-like bill: molluscs, flies and aquatic insects, diatoms and brine shrimps. Its mouth is tiny, allowing only minute organisms to be ingested. Adults are more adept feeders than juveniles, walking more slowly

and pecking more actively; in family parties they may defend their feeding area from other birds.

Often appearing sedentary, Black-winged Stilts nonetheless seem to be nomadic, often travelling to new feeding grounds at night, their movements traced by their characteristic yelping barks. Their flight, on short-pointed triangular wings, is not fast, on deliberate pushed wing-beats; long trailing legs may help in manoeuvring. They may be gregarious and gather in loose feeding assemblages of several hundred, but they never form compact flocks and nest in dispersed aggregations, each pair with its own moderate territory. Young hatch together, are precocious and leave the nest within hours. While still small they are brooded at night.

OTHER NAMES
Pied Stilt, White-headed Stilt, Longshanks, Dog-bird.

IDENTIFICATION
LENGTH: *360–390 mm.*
ADULTS: *(Australian race) Sexes similar, without eclipse plumage. Back of head and nape black, separated from black back and wings by white collar. Rest of body white. Eye red. Bill black. Legs and feet pink.*
IMMATURES: *Back of head dull grey; dark grey patch around eyes; wings and back grey-brown.*
DOWNY YOUNG: *Pale ochre above, dotted black that develops into two pairs of broken lines down back and flanks; hind neck, underparts white.*

VOICE
Single yelping, or puppy-like barking call, persistently repeated, in contact, sharper in alarm; higher-pitched warning piping notes in flight.

NESTING
Breeds August–December. Nest a depression in mud at water's edge, or on an island in a swamp among damp vegetation, or at times a built-up structure in shallow water. Leaves and stalks of swamp plants, grasses and small twigs added for lining, often forming platform. Eggs: usually four; dull green or stone-coloured, heavily marked with purple-brown and black with underlying lavender lines; pyriform, about 45 x 29 mm.

Incubation 22-25 days, by both sexes in short spells.

DISTRIBUTION
Edges of still, shallow, muddy surface waters, both fresh and brackish, throughout Australia, with outlying populations in southern New Guinea and Sunda arc to Philippines (Australian race, with white head and mantle, and black hind-neck). Nomadic. Self-introduced in New Zealand where hybridises and intergrades with endemic Black Stilt. Other races, sometimes regarded as separate species, in Afro-Eurasia (one), the Americas (three) and the Hawaiian islands (one); those that meet intergrade.

The Red-necked Avocet has a long, upcurved bill and stilt-like form. Avocets nest in a depression in the ground which they line with plant matter.

Red-necked Avocet
Recurvirostra novaehollandiae VEILLOT, 1816

AN UPTURNED BILL WHICH has been likened to a cobbler's awl distinguishes the Red-necked Avocet from its close relatives the stilts. It has long legs, like stilts, but its toes are over half-webbed which enable it to swim readily. In flight — which is fluttering, on quickly and shallowly beating wings — its legs stretch beyond its tail.

Avocets feed mainly by wading and sweeping their part-opened bills from side to side through shallow water or soft mud; sometimes they even stir with the bill. In clear water they also pick off prey, jabbing at it from an upright position. Young feed in this way when learning to forage, but as their bills lengthen and up-curve, they change to sweeping. A variety of tiny crustaceans, aquatic insects, worms, molluscs, and even occasional seeds are taken.

The birds nest in dispersed aggregations. In pre-mating displays, the birds bow, trample, bill-dip and preen. At length the male springs on to the female's back and sinks, wings outstretched, while the female leans forward and jerks her head to and fro. Both sexes incubate, and young, which hatch almost together, soon leave the nest; they are brooded at night when small.

Outside breeding, avocets usually feed, roost, rest and fly in compact flocks of up to 100 or more. They frequent salty and brackish marshes and tidal inlets, and range further inland only when rains have filled the pans.

OTHER NAMES
Australian Avocet, Cobbler, Trumpeter, Painted Lady.

IDENTIFICATION
LENGTH: *400–450 mm.*
ADULTS: *Sexes similar. Head and neck bright chestnut, with white eye-ring; head washed greyer in female. All body and tail white; inner scapulars dusky, outer white. Wings with outer flight feathers dusky, inner white; lesser wing coverts white, median and greater coverts dusky. Eye red-brown. Bill black. Legs pale leaden.*
IMMATURES: *As adults but head and neck pallid chestnut-white.*
DOWNY YOUNG: *Pale grey above, sparsely speckled with black, forming pair of broken lines down upper back and mid line down lower; white tinged buff below.*

VOICE
Various trumpeting whistles toot-toot *in contact and alarm at nest colonies.*

NESTING
Breeds August–December but influenced by climatic conditions. Nest a depression in ground, lined with scraps of swamp vegetation. Placed on small islands in lakes or flooded ground, or at edge of swamp. Eggs: usually four; olive-brown to pale brown heavily spotted and blotched with dark brown and grey; oval to pyriform, about 48 x 33 mm. Incubation probably 3–4 weeks, by both sexes.

DISTRIBUTION
Centred on brackish and saline surface waters across southern and central Australia west of Great Dividing Range; rare on east and north coasts and vagrant in Tasmania and New Zealand. Nomadic. No races.

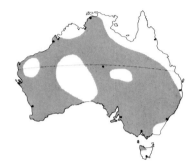

Banded Stilt
Cladorhynchus leucocephalus (VEILLOT, 1816)

OTHER NAMES
Bishop Snipe, Rottnest Snipe.

IDENTIFICATION
LENGTH: *380–410 mm.*
ADULTS: *Sexes similar. Breeding: Head and body white with broad chestnut band across breast and extending down to black belly. Wings black with white trailing edge. Eye brown. Bill black. Legs and feet pink.*
NON-BREEDING ADULTS, IMMATURES: *No breast band; legs duller.*
DOWNY YOUNG: *Plain grey-white.*

VOICE
Yelping notes chowk-chowk *similar to Black-winged Stilt, but quieter. Also some wheezing calls, resembling plaintive whistle.*

NESTING
Breeds erratically in massed colonies of thousands May–December but predominantly July–September; also at other times after heavy rains. No nest built; eggs are laid in small depression in soft ground. Eggs: three or four; deep fawn to white, with spots or blotches of brown and black and underlying markings of grey, or with twisted black lines all over or concentrated at larger end; oval, about 55 x 40 mm.

DISTRIBUTION
Salt lakes and brackish estuaries and inlets in southwestern and central southeastern Australia. Some stragglers to central-eastern New South Wales and Tasmania. Nomadic. No races.

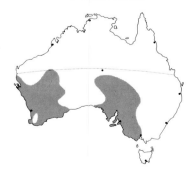

Flocks of Banded Stilts can contain several thousand birds, and nesting colonies on inland salt lakes may be larger.

ENIGMATIC DESCRIBES THE Banded Stilt. It appears in dense flocks of thousands on saline swamps and inlets round the South Australian gulfs and southwestern Australia, yet it was not found nesting until 1930 and only a few colonies have been found since. The large numbers of birds without breast bands in the flocks have traditionally been assumed to be newly bred juveniles, but most are almost certainly adults in a previously unrecognised non-breeding eclipse plumage. And despite its stilt-like appearance, some ornithologists relate it to the flamingos instead, because of some structural traits, its colonial habits and plain grey-white chicks.

In their nomadism, Banded Stilts follow a seasonal trend. Through winter and early spring many tend to move inland on any newly filled salt lakes, breeding if flooded pans evaporate sufficiently slowly to expose flat nesting islands while maintaining the food supply. Then as the lakes dry up through summer and autumn, the birds shift back to tidal swamps and inlets on the coast. They feed almost exclusively on brine shrimps and related crustaceans, swimming for them with their half-webbed feet, wading, and even submerging their heads as they probe and peck in the water. On occasions the stilts form close-packed rafts of hundreds or more to round up their food.

Banded Stilts are colonial at all times. In groups of a dozen or so to tens of thousands they feed together, rest standing on the edges of salt pans in close-packed masses, nest in vast colonies, and fly in compact flocks. Their flight is fluttering, like an avocet, on quickly and shallowly beating wings, with legs trailing behind.

Bush Thick-knee *Burhinus grallarius* (LATHAM, 1801)

EERIE WAILING CALLS AT NIGHT are often the only sign that Bush Thick-knees are about. Not only have they become very rare in southern pastoral areas due to disturbance and predation, but they also come out—to feed—only at night. They live in open-grassed woodlands and sparsely treed rangelands, roosting by day on broken ground with which their plumage blends. At rest they squat down on their feet, head out and legs stretched forward, under the body. If disturbed, they prefer to crouch or to stalk stealthily off, then 'freeze', rather than fly.

At dusk they emerge, often in loose groups of up to 10 or 20 when not breeding, and walk or fly out to foraging grounds, sometimes travelling 20 kilometres or more. Taking off with fluttering wings and taxying to land, they fly on leisurely beating wings and can cover long distances. Even so, they are sedentary birds and rarely wander far throughout the year. All feeding is done on the ground or by wading, the birds puttering along, hunch-shouldered, on spindly legs, turning over litter and picking up a variety of insects with their bills. In deeper water, they up-end.

As breeding begins, the groups disperse, and pairs of birds return to traditional territories. These they advertise with much duetting at night, repeating their wailing at intervals which can end in an hysterical jumble of sound. Courting males lead females in a dodging follow-the-leader chase; and in defence of ground or young, they strut and face the intruder with wide-spread drooping wings and raised, fanned tails. Eggs, laid on ground that matches their colour, are laid at two-day intervals and, pointing the same way, are brooded by paired brood patches on the parents' bodies. Young hatch together and can walk in a few hours. Parents teach them to feed by dropping food in front of them and, as with eggs, will carry them off under their wings if danger threatens.

OTHER NAMES
Bush Stone-curlew, Southern Stone-curlew, Weeloo, Willaroo.

IDENTIFICATION
LENGTH: *500–580 mm.*
ADULTS: *Sexes similar; male slightly larger. Upper parts mid grey-brown, streaked lightly to heavily black, and washed variously russet in northern populations. Forehead buffy white, running back in white eyebrow; dusky stripe through eye down side of neck. Outer flight feathers dusky with off-white band through mid vanes; shoulders patterned, with dusky-grey upper coverts often washed russet and whitish black-streaked median coverts forming a band. Tail barred black-and-white on outer feathers. Throat* plain whitish; breast, belly and flanks white to buff, heavily streaked black, most strongly on breast; undertail white to cinnamon. Eye yellow. Bill wholly black. Legs and feet olive-brown; claws black.
IMMATURES: *As adults but paler and more lightly marked.*
DOWNY YOUNG: *Sandy stippled salt-and-pepper with black dorsal stripes: one splitting on centre of hind crown, another through each eye down sides of neck to run in parallel down back to rump, another from tail up either side of body to wings, and a last short, thick pair on either side of underneck.*

VOICE
Common call loud, mournful, high-pitched, wailing wee-loo *or* wer-loo *lasting about two seconds, usually at night; during breeding repeated quickly. Harsh wheeze in defence.*

NESTING
Breeds July–January; usually single-brooded. Nest a scrape or small clearing on bare ground, often near bush or tree, or beside a fallen dead limb. Eggs: two; light stone to buff, spotted and blotched with shades of brown; oblong-oval, about 59 x 39 mm. Incubation 28–30 days, by both sexes. Young full-grown in about 50 days.

DISTRIBUTION
Open wooded rangelands, edges of forest and watercourses inland throughout Australia and offshore islands, avoiding sandy or treeless deserts and heavy forest; accidental in Tasmania. Now rare in southern settled area where flocks of hundreds once occurred. Also southern New Guinea. No races.

The Bush Thick-knee lives in grassy woodlands throughout Australia. Its nest is a small clearing on bare ground.

Beach Thick-knees, living on beaches and worn inshore reefs of northern Australia, have conspicuously patterned faces.

Beach Thick-knee *Esacus magnirostris* (VEILLOT, 1818)

THE DEEP, HEAVY BILL of the Beach Thick-knee, larger than that of any other thick-knee, seems to be fitted for taking crabs and other hard-shelled marine invertebrates. These it feeds on mostly at night, puttering along on its spindly legs over wet sand, shallow reef pools, and low rocks, following the line of incoming and outgoing tides. Prey is snapped up, cracked, softened by bashing and eaten as the bird proceeds. During the day the thick-knees rest, squatting on feet placed forward under the body or just standing around, often on one leg, on shaded foreshores or the fringes of mangroves. Throughout their range they keep to sandy seashores and worn reefs, each pair or small group of up to half a dozen or so occupying their own stretch of beach. To escape intruders these wary birds first run, but can be pushed to fly rather easily, taking off in slow, stiff-winged beats, with legs trailing.

Breeding pairs are vocal at night, giving a similar but more subdued duetting of *wee-loos* to that of the Bush Thick-knee. The birds also display by nodding and tail-wagging, but the function of these performances is not clear.

Chicks, heavy-billed from hatching, are downy, open-eyed and can totter off within hours. To shelter, they walk up to stand on their parent's feet; to hide they press themselves flat on the sand, legs tucked forward under the body and head stretched out; and to rest, they flop belly down on the sand with legs splayed out behind as do young of some waders.

In these traits, and their permanent pairing, sharing of incubation, salt glands, a tufted preen gland, and partly webbed feet, thick-knees resemble wading birds such as stilts and plovers. In other ways, thick-knees resemble bustards, not only in their broad heads and cranial structure, but also in their three-toed feet with reticulate scaling and their habit of squatting with legs forward under the body, and their aggressive displays with wings spread out and down and tails raised and fanned. Thus thick-knees may lie on the evolutionary tree somewhere between bustards and waders. This dilemma is reflected in the contradictory names given to them: stone-curlew or stone-plover or shore-plover. So the name 'thick-knee' at least has the advantage of neutrality.

OTHER NAMES
Beach Stone-curlew, Reef Thick-knee.

IDENTIFICATION
LENGTH: *530–580 mm.*
ADULTS: *Sexes alike. Upper parts plain grey-brown. White stripe from over eye down side of head flanked with narrow black line above and broad black stripe below through eye. Black patches at sides of lower base of bill. Wings mid-grey, marked on shoulder with broad black stripe (lesser coverts), edged with narrow white line. Throat white. Breast mid grey-brown faintly striped dusky, grading to white belly and under tail. Eye pale yellow. Bill dusky with dull yellow base. Legs and feet dull lemon.*
IMMATURES: *As adults but markings duller.*
DOWNY YOUNG: *Sandy, stippled salt-and-pepper, with obsolete head marks and stripes limited to broken lines of dusky spots.*

VOICE
Mournful territorial wee-loo, *harsh in tone, often repeated; soft* peet-peet *when alarmed.*

NESTING
Breeds October–February. Nest a hollow scratched on a beach just above high-water mark, either in shingle or sand, *often among flotsam washed up by the tides. Eggs: one, occasionally two; cream, irregularly spotted and blotched with brown, black and underlying inky-grey marks; oval to oblong, about 64 x 45 mm. Incubation by both sexes.*

DISTRIBUTION
Beaches and worn inshore reefs of northern Australia, south towards Northwest Cape in west and the Manning River, NSW, in the east; avoids long exposed beaches and mangrove mud. Stragglers reach Mallacoota, Vic. Also New Caledonia, Solomons, New Guinea and Indonesian islands to Philippines, Andamans and Malay Peninsula.

Oriental Pratincole *Glareola maldivarum* J. R. FORSTER, 1795

The Oriental Pratincole at its nest on bare ground among dry mammal droppings. The birds nest on the plains of eastern Asia.

EVERY OCTOBER AND NOVEMBER huge flocks of Oriental Pratincoles, varying erratically from a few hundred to tens of thousands, spread into the northwestern quarter of Australia on migration from their breeding grounds in Asia. Most move inland from the coast, staying along the southern fringe of summer monsoonal rains, from the inland Kimberleys to the Gulf Country of Queensland. There storms are sufficient to bring out the swarms of insects on which they feed, but not enough to flood or grass the bare pans and flats that they need for resting and roosting. Some groups wander east, over Cape York Peninsula, and still others straggle infrequently southwards, even reaching the Nullarbor Plain. Everywhere the flocks are on the move, rarely remaining for more than a week in any area, and finally leave to breed in April.

Although related to waders, pratincoles are quite differently shaped, with short, wide-mouthed bills, long-pointed wings, forked tails, and short, weak feet on which the middle claw is combed. These are traits that fit the birds for a different way of life — that of catching insects aerially. They fly gracefully and swiftly, manoeuvring like a swallow, and mass in dense noisy flocks to feed on swarming beetles, termites, grasshoppers and crickets.

On the ground, they are nonetheless far from helpless, walking with a tripping gait to catch swarming locusts, holding their bodies horizontal, or craning and head-bobbing if alerted. When at rest, usually squatting close together on bare ground near water, their brown backs provide excellent camouflage.

OTHER NAMES
Grasshopper-bird, Swallow-plover.

IDENTIFICATION
LENGTH: *About 230 mm.*
ADULTS: *Sexes similar. In non-breeding plumage upper parts plain dusky olive. Deeply forked tail black; upper tail coverts white. Wing black; underwing black with chestnut-red axillars. Throat buff edged with broken black line of short streaks. Breast and upper belly dusky grey. Lower belly and undertail coverts white. Eye dark brown with pale eye-ring. Bill black with a little red at gape. Feet dark olive. Breeding plumage similar to non-breeding, but throat light buff, edged with a complete black line; gape of bill brighter red.*
IMMATURES: *As non-breeding adults but upper parts lighter with thin buff edges to wing coverts. No throat line.*

VOICE
Noisy chick-chick *and plover-like* too-wheet, too-wheet *in flight.*

NESTING
Breeds May–July in eastern Asia. Nest on bare ground or on dry mammal droppings on plains near rice fields, lakes, rivers. Eggs: two to three; grey-yellow or cream with blotches, patches and spots in various dark browns and greys; rounded-oval, about 31 x 24 mm. Incubation of eggs and care of young probably by both sexes.

DISTRIBUTION
Erratic non-breeding migrant across northwestern Australia, south to Shark Bay in west and Gulf Country, Qld, in east; vagrant further south. Breeds on Asian mainland from India to China, and migrates to Sunda arc as well. No races.

Australian Pratincole *Stiltia isabella* (VEILLOT, 1816)

THE AUSTRALIAN PRATINCOLE blends the traits of coursers and pratincoles. Like the pratincoles, it has attenuately pointed wings and broad mouth, with bicoloured bill and forward nostrils, all adapted to catching insects in the air. And like the coursers, it has a short square tail, erect stance and long legs with no hind toe, all fitted for catching insects on the ground. As well, it lacks a comb on the middle claw.

It is an elegant bird in flight, rising and dipping buoyantly about on its long wings, whistling sweetly — and no less graceful on the ground as it runs about, stopping now and then to rock its body slowly up and down, or darting forward to snatch an insect. Living in small, loose groups of up to 20 on bare plains and fields, the pratincoles are both nomadic and migratory. From February to April they shift, flying high, into far northern Australia and the Papuan and Indonesian islands beyond for winter, then wander back into central and southeastern inland Australia to breed in September–October; few colonies nest north of 20°S. On hot days they do not seek shade but pant to regulate body temperature; water is drunk often, the birds tolerating brackish fluids by excreting excess salt through salt glands above the nostrils.

In display, both male and female run, head down, towards or parallel to one another, and head-pump and trill in greeting. Then, facing each other, they tilt their bodies forward, heads touching and bills to ground, and half-open their upward pointing wings. Both select the nest site, taking it in turns to shuffle on the ground at various points before making the final choice.

Both sexes incubate, for about 90 minutes at a time. Even on very hot days they sit covering the egg, their backs to the sun, keeping as cool as possible by opening the wings and back feathers and panting. Changeover is marked by calling, pebble throwing and sometimes a brief display in greeting.

On hatching, young are quickly led by their parents to the shade and shelter of a clump of vegetation or burrow. When insects are brought, the chicks emerge for long enough to take the food, then scramble back to their hideout.

OTHER NAMES
Australian Courser, Swallow-plover.

IDENTIFICATION
LENGTH: *200–230 mm.*
ADULTS: *Sexes similar. In breeding plumage, upper parts uniformly light buff-brown, greyer on lower back and redder on shoulders. Tail square, white with black subterminal band. Wings pointed, projecting beyond tail when folded; flight feathers dusky black, becoming browner on inner secondaries; underwing coverts black. Chin and throat buff-white, shading to sandy on breast. Flanks dark chocolate, the colour washing over upper belly; lower belly and undertail coverts white. Eye dark brown. Bill red with black tip. Legs and feet dark grey. In non-breeding plumage, centre belly white with chocolate paler and restricted to flanks; bill sepia with darker tip.*
IMMATURES: *As non-breeding adults, upper parts faintly scalloped dusky.*
DOWNY YOUNG: *Pale cinnamon-buff speckled dusky above, whiter below.*

VOICE
Sweet, whistled weeteet *or* weeteet peee, *rising slightly in pitch as flight call, but falling in pitch as contact call.*

NESTING
Breeds August–January, mostly October–November. No nest; eggs are laid on bare flat patch of ground, in loose colonies on open gibber plains, bare gravelly areas, usually within 2 km of water. Eggs: two; pale buff or yellow-tinged, with dark spots, blotches or short streaks; rounded-oval, 28–34 x 22–25 mm. Incubation by both sexes.

DISTRIBUTION
Widespread in summer in eastern inland Australia south to Hay and Adelaide plains, and sparsely west to Port Hedland. Migrates to far northern Australia, Papuasia, Sulawesi and Borneo in winter. No races.

The Australian Pratincole lives on bare plains and fields. It runs on long legs, stands bobbing its body, or darts about, catching insects in its wide gape.

Banded Lapwing *Vanellus tricolor* (VIEILLOT, 1818)

DRY, SHORT-GRASSED PASTURE and bare plains and mud flats are the habitat of the Banded Lapwing; nearby water is not an essential ingredient as is the case with the Masked Lapwing. Its proportionately shorter legs are better fitted for such open ground. The Banded Lapwing is also more communal than the Masked, living in small groups of five to a dozen or more birds. They feed on surface-living invertebrates, seeds and green shoots picked from the ground in short, crouching runs from foraging walks, and, like Masked Lapwings, they will shuffle a foot to flush prey from damp ground. Invertebrates are staple food, vegetable matter becoming a large component only during drought and cold periods.

In their exposed environment, they seek shade in the hot hours and will fly kilometres to find it, on steady, staccato wing-beats, showing white bars in the wings missing from Masked Lapwings. Much movement is at night, the birds calling sporadically, presumably to keep contact. They are much more nomadic than Masked Lapwings and tend to follow the rains in Australia's arid zone, converging on areas brought on by the erratic falls.

Rains also influence breeding, falls in summer bringing an autumn nesting over and above spring breeding. Pairs leave the groups to take up breeding territory and defend nest and young with strident calling and aerial attack; injury-feigning with a 'broken wing' is another tactic used to lure off intruders. Young, fed and guarded by both adults, leave the nest within a day or so of hatching; they squat to freeze in cover at a call from the adults. The eggs of Banded Lapwings are relatively larger than those of Masked Lapwings. As a result, young hatch bigger and stronger, and are able to cope with larger prey of a greater variety.

OTHER NAMES
Banded Plover, Black-breasted Plover.

IDENTIFICATION
LENGTH: *About 250 mm.*
ADULTS: *Sexes similar. Crown black, with white stripe through eye around side of head. Back and shoulders mid-brown with maroon cast. Flight feathers black with broad white stripe through secondaries. Upper tail coverts and tail white with subterminal black band. All underparts white with broad black band from side of face around over breast. Eye and eye-ring yellow; round red wattles over lores. Bill pale yellow with dusky tip. Legs and feet purple-red.*
IMMATURES: *As adults but flecked brown on black crown and breast band; face wattles small.*
DOWNY YOUNG: *Brown peppered black and with white underparts and white collar subtended by black band.*

VOICE
Musical chime-like call a-chee-chee-chee in contact and alarm, plaintive and falling in pitch; given by both sexes.

NESTING
Breeds usually July–December but also following local rains. Nest a

scrape in the ground lined with dry grass and debris; sometimes built on an old cow pat. Nests are usually sited in open area; sometimes forming small colonies. Eggs: three to five, usually four; brownish yellow to pale olive-brown, with dark brown and dusky blotches all over; pyriform, 38–40 x 30–35 mm. Incubation about 28 days, by both sexes.*

DISTRIBUTION
Open plains and bare ground across southern Australia and Tasmania, north to Pilbara and fringes of Barkly Tableland; centred in inland regions. Sporadically reaches southern Kimberleys and southern Gulf of Carpentaria. No races.

The four eggs of this Banded Lapwing are on the right in a scrape in the ground. It defends them with strident calling and aerial attack.

Masked Lapwing

Vanellus miles <small>(BODDAERT, 1783)</small>

OTHER NAMES
Masked Plover, Spur-winged Plover.

IDENTIFICATION
LENGTH: *330–380 mm.*
ADULTS: *Sexes similar. Crown black. Back and shoulders mid to deep brown. Flight feathers black. Upper tail coverts and tail white, with black subterminal band. Yellow, lappet-like wattles cover face. Eye mid-yellow. Bill pale yellow with dusky tip. Legs and feet reddish purple. A buff, black-tipped spur on each shoulder.* Northern race: *smaller, with white collar and sides of neck, mid-brown back and large face wattles covering head over eye.* Southern race: *larger, with black collar and sides of neck, deep brown back and smaller face wattles not extending over eye.* Intermediates: *blend of both races.*
IMMATURES: *As adults but crown and back flecked black and buff; wattles and wing spur reduced.*
DOWNY YOUNG: *Brown peppered black and buff, with white underparts, a white collar subtended by black band and yellow wattle in front of eye.*

VOICE
Main contact and alarm call by both sexes a strident, staccato kekekekekek, *each syllable much shorter and sharper than in Banded Lapwing, and in same pitch. Notes more spaced out in attack; also a single piercing* kek. *Running trills given in display.*

NESTING
Breeds July–December in south, November–June in north, but also throughout year after local rains. Nest a scrape on low ridge, mound or depression on ground, lined with bits of grass, straw, rootlets—or unlined. Eggs: three to usually four; yellowish green to olive-brown, blotched all over with dark brown, black and sepia; pyriform, about 43 x 32 mm in northern race and 49 x 36 mm in southern. Incubation about 28 days, by both sexes.

DISTRIBUTION
Eastern and northern Australia and Tasmania, west to all Eyre Peninsula and central Australia in south and Kimberleys in north, including Dampier Land. Common on shores of swamps and lakes, but non-breeding visitor to most northern inland regions. Also New Zealand (self-introduced), New Guinea and eastern Indonesia; vagrants reach Christmas, Lord Howe, Norfolk and Campbell Islands, and southwestern Australia. Two races in Australia: one across north, south to Townsville and Alice Springs; the other in southeast, north to a line between Ceduna and Rockhampton. Areas between occupied by hybrids and vagrants of both races.

The Masked Lapwing from the southeast has black on its neck. All races have a prominent wing spur.

THE STRIDENT STACCATO CHATTER of Masked Lapwings is a familiar warning signal in the eastern Australian marshes and wet pastures. This call, given both from the ground to warn and in flight to keep contact, alerts other birds as well. Masked Lapwings, with their longer legs, frequent wetter, more lush short pasture, crops and marshy ground than the Banded Lapwing, and are rarely found far from water. Clearing for pasture and irrigation has increased their habitat in many regions and they have exploited it well, even entering parklands in southeastern cities and roosting and nesting on the tops of high-rise buildings. Yet despite such close contact with man, they have remained wary birds.

In pairs or occasional non-breeding groups of up to a dozen or more, they pick up a range of surface-living invertebrates—insects, spiders, small crustaceans, and worms—from the ground and grass, even venturing on to beaches and tidal flats exposed at low tide. Their manner of foraging is typical of lapwings. They stalk watchfully along, shoulders hunched and head forward, in much the same way as they run. Sighting prey, they dart the bill down and poke into tussock often at the end of a short run. Seeds may be eaten when insects are scarce in dry or cold weather.

Masked Lapwings are fairly sedentary birds, and although wandering locally, mainly at night, rarely travel far between roosting and feeding grounds. Flight, although not fast, is of rather quick staccato wing-beats below the horizontal, on round-tipped wings. When not breeding, they travel more widely and may form temporary flocks of several hundred. At night and by day the flocks roost or rest standing in shallow water or on small islands.

As breeding approaches, flocks break up into pairs that establish territory, returning to traditional grounds if they are still suitable and rearing more than one brood if the season is good; only non-breeders hang on in small groups. Both sexes co-operate in nest-building—from stray material close by—and in incubating. Eggs are laid at slightly more than 24-hour intervals. The bird not incubating may remain in the nest territory or move outside to feed. Chicks quit the nest within a few hours of hatching, not always together, to be led away by their parents to the shelter of rough pasture and dry ditches; the vacated nesting territory may be taken over by another pair. The young are brooded by both parents at night and during rain, and are defended vigorously; their parents dive at intruders with a daunting screaming chatter.

Masked Lapwings from the north have large wattles and white necks.

Lesser Golden Plover *Pluvialis dominica* (MÜLLER, 1776)

GOLDEN SPOTS AND WASHES suffuse the non-breeding plumage of this Holarctic breeding migrant, more so than in its black-breasted and black-bellied breeding dress. They are tones, nevertheless, that are visible only at close quarters, the plovers otherwise appearing dull grey-brown at a distance. The race reaching Australia breeds from northern Siberia to western Alaska in the northern summer and migrates down the west side of the Pacific and through eastern Asia to winter from India and southeast Asia to Australia, New Zealand and Oceania in the southern summer. They trickle into Australia from September into October, some birds crossing the continent but many spreading down along the east coast. Many arriving adults are still in black-breasted nuptial plumage, but this moults out within several weeks, along with flight and tail feathers.

At their winter quarters, the plovers frequent rocky coasts, mud flats, estuaries and marshes, mostly around the coast but also sporadically inland. Between favoured areas there is much commuting, single birds and small groups flying from one to another, mainly at night. Their daily routine at any one coastal site is simple. At low tide they spread out to feed on exposed mud flats, walking, head-bobbing occasionally, and up-tipping to pick up small molluscs and crustaceans, augmented with insects and vegetable matter. As the tide comes back in, they regroup into flocks, sometimes of a hundred or more, to rest or roost on higher ground. The same resting grounds are used repeatedly, usually isolated rocks in water or debris-strewn beaches against which their plumage blends in camouflage, but sometimes dry pasture and cultivated paddocks several kilometres inland. To these they fly swifly in compact, co-ordinated groups, their pointed wings beating with easy grace.

During April the plovers lay down much fat preparatory to return migration which begins by May, as breeders start to gain nuptial plumage. Occasionally birds stay to winter in Australia.

OTHER NAMES
Eastern Golden Plover, Pacific Golden Plover.

IDENTIFICATION
LENGTH: *About 250 mm.*
ADULTS: *Sexes alike. Non-breeding plumage: upper parts mottled brown and golden-buff. Faint wing stripe; underwing and axillaries grey. Face, sides of neck and over eye pale buff, with broad buff eye-brow. Breast mottled with grey-brown and suffused with pale buff; belly white. Eye dark brown. Bill black. Legs and feet dark slate. Breeding plumage: upper parts darker with conspicuous golden spangling. Underparts black, including face and most undertail coverts. Broad white stripe from forehead, over eyes to flanks.*
IMMATURES: *Similar to adults in non-breeding plumage, but more buff.*

VOICE
Too-weet *in alarm. Occasional squealing notes* queeble *in greeting.*

NESTING
Breeds June–July in eastern Siberia and western Alaska. Nest a shallow depression sparsely lined with grass, moss or leaves; on open tundra. Eggs: three to five; cream, pale buff or cinnamon, well covered with black blotches and spots; pyriform, about 48 x 33 mm.

DISTRIBUTION
Locally abundant around north, east and southeast coast between October and April, some remaining through winter; scarce around west coasts. One race; small and brightly marked, reaching Australia and possibly a distinct species: Pluvialis (dominica) fulva.

The Lesser Golden Plover in non-breeding plumage, the way it is usually seen in Australia. This Northern Hemisphere migrant arrives in spring for the summer and usually keeps to tidal inlets around the north, east and southeast coasts.

Grey Plover *Pluvialis squatarola* (LINNÉ, 1758)

OTHER NAMES
Black-bellied Plover.

IDENTIFICATION
LENGTH: *About 290 mm.*
ADULTS: *Sexes similar. In non-breeding plumage upper parts grey-brown with light grey flecking overall; crown darker; pale grey eyebrow stripe; rump white; tail white barred with dark brown or black; broad white wing stripe above; underwing pale with conspicuous black axillaries. Underparts white, grading to grey on breast with dark blotches. Eye dark brown. Bill black. Feet dark grey. In breeding plumage upper parts dark brown or black, well covered with white mottling. Rump white; tail white barred with dark brown. Broad white stripe from forehead over eye down side of neck around bend of wing. Underparts black from face to belly. Feet black.*
IMMATURES: *Similar to non-breeding adults but more ash-brown and spotted cream above.*

VOICE
Long-drawn, plaintive pee-oo-ee, pee-ee-ee in contact; other similar notes on breeding grounds.

NESTING
Breeds in northern USSR, Alaska and Canada, June–July. Nest a shallow depression in the ground on open tundra, with a sparse lining of short pieces of plant matter. Eggs: four; grey-brown to light brown, well marked, particularly at larger end, with blotches and spots of dark brown or black; pyriform, about 52 x 36 mm.

DISTRIBUTION
Common breeding species in Arctic areas of America and Eurasia. Migrates to coasts of Australia in northern winter. No races.

A Grey Plover in winter plumage. When breeding, its underparts are black.

FROM BREEDING GROUNDS ON THE holarctic tundra, the Grey Plover migrates to winter on all southern continents. The Australian contingent arrives during September, mainly on the northwest coast and presumably from Asian stocks. From there some fly across the continent to the south coast but most seem to follow the coastline, concentrating on the west coast and in the Gulf of Carpentaria. Those that will breed return to their Northern Hemisphere breeding grounds in the austral autumn.

In Australia, Grey Plovers keep to tidal sands and mud flats of the coast and estuaries without going inland. They feed there on crustaceans, marine worms and other invertebrates, hunting prey in a typical stop-run-peck manner; at high tides they gather singly or in small groups with other waders on higher, often shrubbed banks, flying to resting grounds swiftly with graceful, even wing-beats. Most feeding is by day but the plovers also forage at night at low tide, perhaps taking advantage of nocturnal marine worms. Hunting on moonlit nights can be as active as by day.

Grey Plovers resemble Lesser Golden Plovers but are greyer in tone, bulkier, and have white wing stripes and rumps with a striking patch of black showing in the 'armpit' of the wing in flight.

Red-kneed Dotterel
Erythrogonys cinctus GOULD, 1838

OTHER NAMES
None.

IDENTIFICATION
LENGTH: *About 180 mm.*
ADULTS: *Sexes similar. Crown, nape and sides of face black, rest of upper parts olive-brown. Flight feathers black with broad white trailing edge. Broad black band across breast; rest of underparts white; flanks chestnut, edged white. Tail white, with dusky centre stripe. Eye dark brown. Bill pink with black tip. Feet deep grey, with pink around 'knee' and tibia.*
IMMATURES: *Plain mid-brown above, white below with faint brown breast band; bill and feet dull.*
DOWNY YOUNG: *Grey above mottled gold and black, with white crescent around hind head; white below.*

VOICE
Staccato chet-chet in contact and flight. Soft trilling in threat, display.

NESTING
Usually September–December but any month depending on rain. Nest a small depression in ground, near edge of swamp or lake, often sheltered by low shrub; lined with dry herbage. Eggs: two to four; dull ochre-yellow, speckled with dark brown and black hair-like markings and blotches; pyriform, about 30 x 22 mm. Both sexes incubate.

DISTRIBUTION
Throughout inland on shallow swamps and flood sheets with vegetation. Also coastal areas but rare in east. Nomadic. No races.

The Red-kneed Dotterel occurs around inland swamps.

LIVING ON THE INUNDATED MUDS of temporary flood-lands inland, Red-kneed Dotterels are nomadic, loosely gregarious, and among the most aquatic of waders. They follow shallow floodwaters, in loose groups of up to 50 or more, and feed mostly in shallow water, probing and even submerging their heads into the mud and swimming adeptly. Even chicks swim. With their long legs, the dotterels run with great swiftness, picking up beetles and other invertebrates. When alerted, they bob the head and even the body if alarmed, then flush to fly off low, weaving swiftly.

Defended breeding territories are small and nesting pairs toler-ate others nearby. Threat posturing, with crown flattened and nape raised, may nevertheless be followed by fighting among both sexes. Courting males tilt the body forward, fluff the feathers and trill from the nest site. In a chase, the female may stop, body horizontal and wings partly spread, and allow the male to mate. To protect the nest, both adults respond with a variety of distraction displays, from rodent-run and flutter-jumps to distinctive false-brooding and injury-feigning.

Red-kneed Dotterels are unusual among plovers in having a hind toe, no salt-secreting glands, and boldly marked precocial chicks.

FAMILY CHARADRIIDAE plovers and dotterels

Black-fronted Dotterel

Elseyornis melanops (VIEILLOT, 1818)

A DIMINUTIVE PLOVER OF THE shingle beds and firm wet edges of freshwater streams, dams and swamps, the Black-fronted Dotterel ranges throughout Australia inland from the coast. Short legs and short bill fit it for running and pecking its food — aquatic insects, crustaceans and seeds — from the surface of damp ground at the edge of the shoreline, without wading much for it. In many areas it lives on temporary waters and is accordingly nomadic. Its flight is buoyant rather than swift, with deep, erratically staccato wing-beats on long, round-tipped wings.

Although many dotterels may be scattered through a swamp, they are not communal, feed alone or in pairs, and nest in solitary territories. Copulation seems to be co-ordinated by soft *chizzing* calls by both male and female, and both share incubation equally; the off-duty parent rests or feeds nearby. Temperatures at the nest can get so hot that birds will stand to shade the eggs or wet their feathers to cool them. If disturbed, both sexes feign injury to distract intruders, turning their backs to the threat to display their bright dorsal pattern and flapping their wings or raising one wing, then the other, from the ground.

The V-patterns on the breast, white band on head of chicks, and buoyant, flapping flight suggest that the Black-fronted Dotterel may be more closely allied to lapwings than typical plovers.

Since 1954 the bird has been found in increasing numbers in New Zealand, and is even breeding there.

The Black-fronted Dotterel exposing its brood patch over its eggs.

OTHER NAMES
Black-fronted Plover.

IDENTIFICATION
LENGTH: *160–180 mm.*
ADULTS: *Sexes similar. Black on forehead, extending through eye to across nape; broad black breast 'V' joins forehead band. White line over eyes extends back to nape and divides forehead from dark grey-brown crown. Back and wings grey-brown, streaked lighter; shoulders chestnut; flight feathers black. Rump rufous; tail black with white edges. Rest of underparts* white. *Eye brown with bright red eye-ring. Bill orange-scarlet with black tip. Feet dull pink.*
IMMATURES: *Paler than adults; lack breast band.*
DOWNY YOUNG: *Grey-brown blotched black above, with white band encircling crown; white below.*

VOICE
In contact a simple tip *in flight; rapid* chizzing *in alarm or threat.*

NESTING
September–December in south, May–September in north; any time inland after rain. Nest a small depression, at times on bare, caked mud or on a small bank, or often among stones in a riverbed; lined with mud pellets, stones, shells or broken twigs. Eggs: two to three; dull green-grey or stone-coloured, speckled dusky; oval to pyriform, about 29 x 20 mm. Incubation about 26 days, by both sexes.

DISTRIBUTION
From shores of fresh waters throughout Australia; self-introduced to New Zealand. Nomadic. No races.

The Inland Dotterel lives on the claypans and gibber plains of the inland.

ONE OF THE WORLD'S MOST PERFECTLY camouflaged ground birds, the Inland Dotterel is almost impossible to see on the open, sparsely scrubbed gibber plains and claypans where it lives. In the open the chunky birds turn their back on an intruder and crouch motionless, their flecked plumage merging with the background. Behind bushes they turn face on, the black lines on their chest blending with plant stems. Only if pressed do they take flight, flying off low with swift, even wing-beats for a kilometre or more.

By day, Inland Dotterels stand about in small loose flocks of up to about 20, resting in the shade of shrubs to cool and preen, and browsing sporadically on the leaves of succulent chenopods and composite flower heads. All members of the flock move in unison — feeding, preening, stopping, and running together. The leaves

Inland Dotterel

Peltohyas australis (GOULD, 1841)

OTHER NAMES
Desert Plover, Australian Dotterel.

IDENTIFICATION
LENGTH: *200–220 mm.*
ADULTS: *Sexes similar. In breeding plumage rich buff above, boldly streaked with dusky. Flight feathers plain dusky. Tail dusky with pale sides. Forehead, face, throat and chest sandy-buff. Bold black line across crown to above eyes; short black line vertically below each eye. Black collar on back of neck extends forward to meet in 'Y' on lower breast, then extending as black stripe to meet broad rufous-brown band across belly. Crissum and undertail coverts white. Eye dark brown. Bill dull yellow-horn with black tips. Feet dull grey-yellow. Non-breeding plumage similar to breeding but body paler and black bands on head, neck and chest absent.*
IMMATURES: *Similar to non-breeding adults, but with shorter streaks on back giving more dappled effect.*

VOICE
Contact call a sharp quik; *take-off and alarm call, deeper* kroot.

NESTING
February–November. Nest a deep scrape on open flat ground, such as claypans, gibber plains and fallow fields. Scrape lined with any loose material available (soil, small stones, sticks and sand), which parent bird kicks over eggs when disturbed from nest. Eggs: usually three; brown or rich buff, marked sparingly black; oval to pyriform, about 37 x 27 mm. Incubation by both sexes.

DISTRIBUTION
Chenopod steppes of all arid inland Australia south of main summer rainfall zone. Nomadic. No races.

are probably the birds' main source of water, the salt content of which is excreted by large salt glands through the birds' nostrils. At dusk the flocks become more active as the birds disperse to feed at night, this time on insects: beetles, ants and grasshoppers.

The Inland Dotterel's habit of covering its eggs with soil when leaving the nest is unique among plovers. This conceals the eggs and may also protect them from the sun.

Double-banded Plover *Charadrius bicinctus* JARDINE & SELBY, 1827

DOUBLE-BANDED PLOVERS ARRIVE in Australia during January and February after breeding in New Zealand. Few are in breeding plumage when they arrive, but most assume it later in the year just before returning to New Zealand, from June to August. Many of the first-comers are immature birds, which can be distinguished by a suffusion of pink-buff about the sides of the head and on the upper breast, and also by the light edging on the plumage of the upper parts. Adult plovers arrive later, and during March and April the birds spread along the coasts of the mainland northwards as well as westwards. Some stragglers range as far north as Cairns.

In Australia, the Double-banded Plover is found both along coastal shores, bays, estuaries and inlets, and well inland on flats surrounding large lakes, particularly those with salty or brackish water. They are usually seen in small groups of two to 20 birds, but occasionally in flocks of up to 1000 resting on bars and paddocks when high tide prevents feeding. They forage on shores and damp ground, picking up insects and other invertebrates.

Between August and January, Double-banded Plovers fly back to New Zealand to breed. They nest in depressions in the ground beside lakes, in fields, and on sandy beaches and river-beds.

OTHER NAMES
Banded Dotterel, Double-banded Dotterel.

IDENTIFICATION
LENGTH: *180–190 mm; male a little larger.*
ADULTS: *In non-breeding plumage upper parts plain brown-grey. Forehead, lores and eyebrow white with light brown tinge. Underparts off-white, sometimes with two indistinct, pale grey breast bands. In flight a light wing bar and white around sides of tail, mainly near sides of upper tail coverts. Eye dark. Bill dusky. Feet grey-green, sometimes with a slight yellow tinge. In breeding plumage upper parts grey-brown. Forehead and eye-stripe white; lores black. Underparts white. Two wide bands across breast: upper black and lower, wider band deep rufous or chestnut.*
IMMATURES: *Similar to adults in non-breeding plumage, but upper parts more scalloped due to feathers of wing coverts having broader buff edges. Face and sides of neck have a pink-buff suffusion.*
DOWNY YOUNG: *Peppered dark grey, brown and black above; underparts white.*

VOICE
Loud chip, chip-chip, *or these notes* repeated. *Also a loud, rising and falling trill almost a squeal at times, with some shorter notes resembling a musical* kreep *or a loud, sharp* prrip.

NESTING
Breeds August–January. Nest a slight depression in the ground, near a lake, ploughed field, sandy beach or among river pebbles. Eggs: three; green- or grey-tinged, well marked with black streaks and blotches; oval to pyriform, about 35 x 25 mm.

DISTRIBUTION
Breeds in New Zealand, and migrates to eastern and southern Australia, its main non-breeding refuge, from late summer to winter. Coastal beaches and estuaries; also salt- and freshwater lakes inland. No races.

A Double-banded Plover tends its chick in its breeding ground.

Large Sand Plover *Charadrius leschenaultii* LESSON, 1826

THOUGH IT CAN BE FOUND right round the coast of Australia between October and January, the Large Sand Plover is little known to most bird-watchers. These plovers breed in central Asia and those that migrate to summer in Australia keep mainly to the northwest coast. Some stragglers reach more southern parts in small groups of five or six but rarely stay long.

The Large Sand Plover feeds mainly on small crustaceans and molluscs on tidal sand and mud flats; crabs and shrimps are staple diet. Individual birds feed over a small area; if disturbed they fly off swiftly, low down, uttering loud, long, trilling alarm calls and often return to the same place a few minutes after.

Some birds attain breeding plumage while still in Australia, in March or April. They develop black markings across the front of the crown and about the eyes and ear coverts; the upper parts become paler with a rufous wash over the crown and nape; and a narrow orange-red breast band develops. Most leave by April but a few non-breeding birds may remain year round.

In southern Australia, the birds are less common than the Mongolian Plover with which they frequently associate. The Large Sand Plover is slightly bigger, has a paler appearance — whiter below and paler grey above — longer, paler legs and a longer, stouter bill. Its calls are louder than the Mongolian Plover's.

A Large Sand Plover with a crab.

OTHER NAMES
Large-billed Dotterel, Large Sand-dotterel.

IDENTIFICATION
LENGTH: *210–230 mm.*
ADULTS: *Sexes similar in non-breeding plumage. Upper parts including shoulders mid grey-brown. Forehead and area over eye white; lores and small area below and behind eye grey-brown. Underparts white with light grey at sides of breast. In some birds grey areas almost meet, forming breast band. In flight a pale wing bar; white along sides of tail and upper tail coverts. Eye dark. Bill black. Feet grey or olive-grey. In breeding plumage upper parts grey. Forehead white, edged black; lores and ear coverts black. Narrow orange-red breast band, colour suffusing into nape and crown; rest of underparts white. Male brighter than female.*
IMMATURES: *Similar to adults in non-breeding plumage but with some light scalloping of the upper parts.*

VOICE
Short or prolonged trilling, in contact and alarm.

NESTING
Breeds May–July in central and eastern Asia. Nest a slight depression in the ground, sparsely lined with pieces of grass stems and thin twigs. Eggs: three, occasionally four; dull yellow or green tinged, marked all over with spots, streaks and scribbles of brown or black with underlying markings of light and dark grey; oval to pyriform, about 40 x 29 mm.

DISTRIBUTION
More common in northern coastal Australia, somewhat rare in south. Breeds from Turkey, Armenia, Transcaspia and Russian Turkestan east to Mongolia. Winters over austral summer in Africa, Madagascar, southeastern Asia, Taiwan, Philippines, Sunda Islands, New Guinea, Solomons, Australia and, rarely, New Zealand. Beaches, sand banks and estuaries. Three races; one reaching Australia from Mongolia.

Red-capped Plover *Charadrius ruficapillus* TEMMINCK, 1821

A female Red-capped Plover at its nest. The male is more richly coloured with black edging on the face and more rufous crown.

THE COMMON SMALL PLOVER OF beaches, estuaries and fresh and salty lake shores, the Red-capped Plover is Australia's representative of the almost worldwide Kentish or Snowy Plover. It usually occurs in pairs or small loose groups of up to six or more after breeding on bare, often salty sands and mud flats, frequently in company with other waders. There it feeds on small insects, worms and molluscs picked from the surface, taking them in the erratic stop-swift-run-peck manner of some other plovers; seeds of aquatic plants may be eaten too. When alerted they head-bob; in flight they dash along low on pointed, evenly beating wings.

Breeding pairs hold their own territory. The male scrapes several potential nest sites, squatting on them with tail high and breast on the ground and then breaks off to chase his mate. He parades around her in a high-stepping gait before copulation, mounts, and then drops off backwards, dragging her on top of him, his bill gripping her nape. Eventually she chooses one of the sites and seems to bear the brunt of incubation and brooding until newly hatched young dry. As chicks dry, the male leads each one off to brood, and the family begins to forage throughout their area as a unit from then on. Red-capped Plovers rear up to three broods a year.

If disturbed, brooding birds run from the nest, collect their mates, and together crouch-run erratically, stopping erect now and then to display their white fronts. In more extreme distraction, they also rodent-run and feign injury, often chirring noisily.

OTHER NAMES
Red-capped Dotterel.

IDENTIFICATION
LENGTH: *140–160 mm.*
MALE: *Crown and nape rufous; forehead white, bordered by fine black line; lores black and continuing behind eye; eyebrow white. At sides nape a broken black collar. Rest of upper parts pale grey-brown. Tail dusky-brown with white outer feathers. Flight feathers dusky-brown with white bar. Underparts all white. Eye brown. Bill black. Feet black.*
FEMALE: *Lacks sharp black face markings and crown paler; feet paler.*

IMMATURES: *Like female but duller.*
DOWNY YOUNG: *Upper parts grey-buff, speckled black, with buff collar; underparts white.*

VOICE
Main call sharp plaintive twink *but also faint* wirr-wit-wit; *flute-like* pooo-eet, *soft long trill; and shrill alarm call* kittup.

NESTING
Breeds mainly September–January although may nest any time. Nest a depression in soil or sand, usually lined with pieces of shell, small stones or dried plant leaves; often sheltered by a plant or tidal debris, on sandy hillocks near seashore, or bordering salt-marshes on inland lakes. Eggs: two to three; pale green or stone-grey, liberally spotted and dotted with dusky, with numerous underlying markings of lavender; oval to pyriform, about 29 x 21 mm.

DISTRIBUTION
Well dispersed along coast and tidal inlets. Inland, occurs in good numbers at permanent or temporary water, especially salt lakes. Away from coast range is distinctly patchy. Sedentary or nomadic. Doubtful records from New Guinea; straggler to New Zealand, and resident on Timor. No races.

The Oriental Plover is slenderer and longer-legged than other plovers.

Oriental Plover

Charadrius veredus GOULD, 1848

DESPITE THE IMMENSE NUMBERS that winter every summer across northern Australia, the Asian-breeding Oriental Plover is little known. It arrives in strength along the northwestern coast in October each year, but soon disperses to remote areas inland, settling on bare plains, the edges of roads, and the flat edges of lakes and lagoons as well as sea shores. Only stragglers reach southern Australia. A great wanderer, it rarely stops for more than a few days at any one place. Dry ground seems to be an important element of its habitat, and falls of rain may cause the plovers to move on. Through March and April, nearly all return to their breeding grounds, leaving very few to over-summer in Australia.

On its feeding grounds, the Oriental Plover is a wary, slenderly built bird, rather like a courser in appearance. It bobs its head, often rests on one leg, and its slender wings cross above the tail. Flight is strong and graceful, or erratic with swift turns.

OTHER NAMES
Oriental Dotterel.

IDENTIFICATION
LENGTH: *230–250 mm.*
ADULTS: *Sexes similar. Dark olive brown above with crown to mantle brighter. Forehead, eyebrow and face pale buff to white; cheeks grey-buff. Chin, throat and belly to undertail coverts very pale buff to white. Breast with light grey-brown band, lower edge darker. Flight feathers plain dusky, underwing all grey. Tail dusky, edged white. Eye dark brown. Bill black with* paler base to lower mandible. Legs light brown, yellow or green tinged; feet darker. In breeding plumage upper parts dark brown. Forehead, eye-stripe and face white with dark brown line behind eye. Chin, throat and belly to undertail coverts white. Breast has broad red-brown band with black lower edge.
IMMATURES: *Similar to non-breeding adults but more buff; pale edges to upper wing coverts.*

VOICE
Loud chip or chip-chip-chip in flight. Also musical trills and piping.

NESTING
Breeds in summer in Northern Hemisphere. Nest a slight hollow in the ground. Eggs not described.

DISTRIBUTION
Non-breeding summer migrant, wintering from Sunda Islands to northern Australia, rarely New Guinea and New Zealand between October and April. Breeds Mongolia to Manchuria. No races; forms superspecies with Caspian Plover, C. asiaticus.

Mongolian Plover *Charadrius mongolus* PALLAS, 1776

ON ARRIVAL FROM breeding grounds in eastern Siberia in September–October each year, the Mongolian Plover spreads out along tidal sands and mud flats in bays, inlets and estuaries around the Australian coast. It is most abundant in the north, but some stragglers have been known to reach Tasmania. The birds usually group in small loose parties of twos and threes but sometimes gather in flocks of a hundred or more at staging areas or favoured feeding sites.

Their feeding is unobtrusive. Working quietly over wet sand and mud, they make a quick short run here and a sloping dip there for their prey: crabs, amphipods, worms and molluscs. Worm holes are approached with stealth, the plovers carefully putting down one foot after the other before tugging at the worm. When disturbed the birds rise with short trilling notes and fly low to another feeding spot away from the intrusion. When roosting at high tide, they often gather in flocks with other waders. Most, but not all, return to their breeding grounds in early April.

In Australia, Mongolian Plovers are often seen beside two other similar-looking and -flying plovers in non-breeding plumage. One is the Double-banded Plover which is buffier-brown on its face and upper parts, has lighter legs and a slimmer bill. The other is the Large Sand Plover which is slightly taller, has lighter grey upper parts, and has a much longer and stouter bill.

Two of these Mongolian Plovers — left and centre — are in the non-breeding plumage.

OTHER NAMES
Mongolian Dotterel.

IDENTIFICATION
LENGTH: *190–210 mm.*
ADULTS: *Sexes similar. Upper parts all deep mid-grey-brown. Forehead and stripe above eye white. Lores and small area below eye dark brown. Underparts white with a broad broken grey-brown breast band. In flight a narrow, pale wing bar and white on sides of tail and upper wing coverts. Eye large, dark brown. Bill stout, black. Feet deep grey. In breeding plumage, upper parts as* before; forehead white; lores, ear coverts and line above forehead black. Breast has broad rufous-red band edged with black; rest of underparts white. Males brighter than females.
IMMATURES: *Similar to adults in non-breeding plumage, with some light scalloping on upper parts.*

VOICE
Call a short drrit on flushing; protracted trilling at times.

NESTING
Breeds June–July in Siberia. Nest a slight depression in sand. Eggs: three; cinnamon-ochre to almost olive, with blotches of dark cinnamon to dusky; oval to pyriform, about 36 x 27 mm.

DISTRIBUTION
Non-breeding summer migrant, nesting from central Asia to eastern Siberia. Populations reaching Australia are from two races in eastern Siberia. In Australia spreads around coast from north, with local concentrations; only stragglers reach south coast and Tasmania.

Hooded Plover *Charadrius rubricollis* GMELIN, 1789

FOUND ONLY ON THE COASTS of southern Australia, the tubby Hooded Plover seems to have declined over the past 50 years, perhaps as a result of increasing use of beaches by man. In the east it is confined to long stretches of sandy shore, backed by tussock- and creeper-covered dunes, with inland lakes close by. There pairs return to traditional breeding territories to nest, often under the sand hills, and later flock and wander locally in groups of up to 30–40 after young are reared, in autumn and winter. Hooded Plovers feed among the drift at the high-tide levels on the beaches, picking up insects and other invertebrates trapped on the wet sand. They run swiftly, stopping and starting with hunched posture and, like other plovers, bob the head when alerted by intruders. Their flight is direct and swift on evenly beating wings.

In the west, the plovers often range well inland on to the shores of salt lakes, and may congregate in flocks of several hundred when not breeding. Stray birds, probably younger adults or birds seeking new territories, occasionally range north to Shark Bay and Sydney.

Hooded Plovers scratch out their nest on sandy shores between high-tide mark and the top of the beach. It is usually placed next to an object — such as a piece of driftwood or stone — or among a dense patch of shells. Lake-side nests in Western Australia, however, may be placed closer to water.

OTHER NAMES
Hooded Dotterel.

IDENTIFICATION
LENGTH: *190–210 mm.*
ADULTS: *Sexes similar but head of female duller. Head, throat and nape black; lower nape has broad white band; upper back and lower sides of neck black; rest of upper parts, including shoulders and wing coverts, pale pearl-brown; rump duskier and centre tail black. Flight feathers dusky with broad white bar showing in flight. Underparts white from breast to crissum. Eye brown with crimson eye-ring. Bill maroon with black tip. Feet buff-pink; claws dusky.*
IMMATURES: *Lack all black parts. Upper parts pale brown; broad white nape patch; underparts white; eye patch dusky.*
DOWNY YOUNG: *Sandy flecked black, with black crescent behind head; white underneath.*

VOICE
Rather silent. Deep barking fow fow; *also short, peevish piping. Guttural flock calls in flight.*

NESTING
Breeds August–January. Nest small circular depression in sand, above high-tide line; sometimes scantily lined with small stones, dried seaweed, stems and leaves of plants. Eggs: two or three; pale buff-brown or light stone, blotched dusky and lavender; oval, about 39 x 27 mm.

DISTRIBUTION
Scattered over entire southern coast of Australia, including offshore islands. Ranges north to Geraldton, WA, and Jervis Bay, NSW. No races.

The Hooded Plover lays two or three eggs in a depression in sand or earth. Pairs may hold territories for long periods.

Ruddy Turnstone

Arenaria interpres
(LINNÉ, 1758)

OTHER NAMES
Turnstone, Beach-bird.

IDENTIFICATION
LENGTH: *220–240 mm.*
ADULTS: *Sexes similar. In non-breeding plumage, upper head, mantle and shoulders deep brown with dusky shafts and lined white through scapulars; lower back white, rump band black; tail with white base and broad dusky tip. Flight feathers dusky with clear white bar through centre. Face grey-brown flecked white; upper throat white grading to blotched dusky over breast. All lower underparts and underwing pure white. Eye dark brown. Bill black, tinged olive. Feet deep orange. In breeding plumage upper parts have similar pattern to non-breeding plumage but are covered with patches of russet and black, giving a tortoiseshell effect. Crown and nape white with short streaks of black. Lores, ear coverts, throat and rest of underparts pure white, except for a black mark on forehead extending to eye, down cheek and across side of neck, and broadening to form a black patch across the breast. Male brighter than female.*
IMMATURES: *Similar to non-breeding adults but browner with buff edging on upper parts.*

VOICE
Rattling kutta-kutakut, ketetetet *in contact; single, sharp* tuk *to alert; other calls when nesting.*

NESTING
Breeds June–July in Northern Hemisphere. Nest a slight depression in the ground, scantily lined with pieces of dry plant matter; in an exposed position or sometimes close to a rock or small shrub. Eggs: four, rarely three; shiny green or brown with underlying patches of grey and marked with well-defined dark blotches; oval to pyriform, about 40 x 29 mm. Incubation 22–24 days.

DISTRIBUTION
Non-breeding migrant around coast of Australia, September–April, mainly in north, with a few birds remaining all year. Also migrates to New Zealand and other southern continents from breeding grounds fringing Arctic Circle. Two races; one breeding in eastern arctic Canada, the other slightly larger and duller everywhere else. The latter, A.i.intrepres, usually or only reaches Australia, from breeding grounds in eastern Siberia and Alaska.

When feeding, the Ruddy Turnstone dashes about flipping over seaweed and stones, and snatching at prey.

THIS TUBBY LITTLE BIRD IS AMONG the most animated of the shore-frequenting waders. When feeding it is almost constantly on the move, walking or running from one feeding spot to another on its short, orange legs. Sometimes two or more turnstones quarrel noisily over a choice feeding patch, or ownership of a morsel.

The turnstone is named for its habit of flipping over stones and other objects, such as seashells, pieces of wood and seaweed, in search of the animals concealed beneath. Its sharp, stout bill is well adapted for this activity. At times the bird resembles a tiny bulldozer as it dashes about, pushing up heaps of seaweed with its bill and head, snatching at food as it becomes exposed.

Ruddy Turnstones use other techniques to broaden their diet. They break open barnacles with several rapid blows of the closed bill, prise limpets off rocks and open mussels with vigorous chiselling thrusts. Insects of many kinds, marine worms, sea urchins, small fish and even seeds, carrion and garbage scraps are taken by these voracious birds.

Turnstones are non-breeding migrants in Australia. Most fly from their breeding quarters in eastern Siberia and Alaska in August–September each year, arriving on the northwest coast and across Torres Strait soon after. From there they spread round the coast, some flying across the continent to points on southern shores, frequenting beaches where shingle and masses of seaweed are mixed with stretches of sand. Singly or in loose groups of 20–100 or more they are more abundant in the north than south.

By March–April, those birds returning to breed don their brilliant nuptial plumage and depart. A few birds—probably non-breeding immatures—stay behind to winter in Australia.

Bar-tailed Godwit *Limosa lapponica* (LINNÉ, 1758)

Bar-tailed Godwits visit Australia during the northern winter. Large waders, they can be recognised by the white rump and black and white barred tail.

SALINE AND TIDAL MUD FLATS and sands of coastal inlets, estuaries and nearby salt pans are the habitat of Bar-tailed Godwits in Australia. They arrive from their breeding grounds in August–September each year, the Australian contingent — representing the large, dark-backed race *baueri* — coming from northeastern Siberia and perhaps Alaska. Landing in large concentrations on northern beaches, they seem to spread around the coast without crossing the inland. As a result they are more abundant in the north, groups of up to 30 or more mingling there with the numerous non-breeders — probably juveniles — that seem to remain each year. Both for feeding and as staging grounds for arriving and departing migrants, the Eight-mile Beach between Broome and Port Hedland seems crucial; tens of thousands gather there.

Bar-tailed Godwits feed on sands and muds exposed by the tide, and in shallow water, the larger females wading further out than males. Molluscs, crustaceans, marine worms and other invertebrates are eaten. These the birds find beneath the surface by frequent shallow probes of their long, sensitive, slightly upcurved bills, by sweeping from side to side, and by deep thrusts and bill-turning. Sometimes they wade to the depth of their legs, but rarely do they swim. Feeding continues at low tide on moonlit nights.

Breeding godwits depart for nesting quarters from April into May, many of them donning nuptial dress in the weeks before leaving; males are resplendently rufous. While in Australia, the birds fly steadily and evenly in close flocks, rising, falling and banking together and sometimes strung out in echelon. Only on landing does unity break, each bird gliding and side-slipping about before landing on its own chosen patch of mud flat.

OTHER NAMES
Bar-rumped Godwit.

IDENTIFICATION
LENGTH: *Male 380–420 mm; female 420–450 mm.*
ADULTS: *In non-breeding plumage, sexes similar. Upper parts from head to shoulders mid grey-brown with faint darker centres to feathers; eyebrow white. Lower back and rump white with variable brown scalloping; tail white barred brown. Underparts cream-white, washed grey-brown over breast. Eye dark brown. Bill dusky at tip, grading to flesh-pink at base. Legs and feet dusky to olive-grey. In breeding plumage, males rich rufous-brown from head and neck to mantle and whole undersurface; rest of upper parts richly mottled grey, brown and black, washed rufous. Female has duller russet cast restricted to head, neck and upper breast beneath.*
IMMATURES: *Resemble non-breeding adult, but darker brown more clearly edged buff on upper parts.*

VOICE
Sharp, muted kewit *in alarm;* kip-kip-kip *in excitement; extended calls on breeding grounds.*

NESTING
Australian migrants breed in northeastern Siberia and Alaska, probably in June and July. Nest a shallow depression in moss, almost devoid of lining or well lined with plant matter. Eggs: four; olive-green or brown-green blotched with dark olive-brown, particularly at large end; pyriform, about 54 x 37 mm. Incubation 20–21 days, by both sexes.

DISTRIBUTION
Non-breeding migrant throughout coastal Australia, also New Zealand, New Guinea and Indonesian archipelagos to southern Asia and Africa. Breeds from Norway east to Alaska inside Arctic Circle. Two races; only larger eastern race visiting Australia.

Black-tailed Godwit _Limosa limosa_ (LINNÉ, 1758)

AUSTRALIA'S OTHER MIGRATORY GODWIT — the Black-tailed — is much the rarer and more dispersed at its non-breeding quarters. Arriving from its northern Eurasian breeding grounds during September along the north coast of Australia, it seems to spread inland rather than round the coast, and some birds may cross the continent to summering grounds in southeastern Australia. Most, however, stay in the north. The flocks of a hundred or more that gather at staging beaches on the northwest coast and Gulf of Carpentaria on arrival — and before departure in March — often disperse in ones and twos or groups of 10 or so. Ranging inland as well, they frequent shallow open muddy lagoons and swamp, whether fresh or brackish, as well as the coastal mud flats, tidal estuaries and spits to which Bar-tailed Godwits are restricted. It is only there that the two species sometimes occur together. They are easily distinguished, however, the Black-tailed being smaller and plainer grey over the back and showing a broad white wing bar in flight and a broadly black-tipped tail contrasting with a white rump.

In the manner of godwits, the Black-tailed feeds by probing its long, sensitive bill deep into mud in search of crustaceans, molluscs and worms, often immersing its head completely. Insects, their larvae, spiders, tadpoles and plant matter are taken as well. Often wading up to their bellies, the birds feed in deeper water than Bar-tailed Godwits, and in a more leisurely way. Usually they probe with the bill vertical, exploring gently, then suddenly thrust it deeply to grasp prey and pull it out, swallowing it at once.

At non-breeding quarters, Black-tailed Godwits fly in a swift, dashing manner and may perform spectacular aerial acrobatics. They twist and zigzag, suddenly dart skywards, then loop-the-loop while almost barrel-rolling simultaneously.

On their breeding grounds, the godwits still associate in compact feeding flocks. In display flight, the male rises sharply, calling, changes to slow, clipped wing-beats, tail spread, twisting and tilting from side to side, and then glides in silence to suddenly nose-dive and then side-slip in all directions to alight with wings vertically aloft. He also struts around the female and scrapes nest sites ceremonially, screwing his breast against the ground and kicking backwards. To copulate, he floats on to her back in flight.

The female chooses the nest site, but both sexes share incubation and rear the young with great care, brooding them at night even after they leave the nest.

OTHER NAMES
Eastern Black-tailed Godwit.

IDENTIFICATION
LENGTH: _360–430 mm._
ADULTS: _Sexes similar. In non-breeding plumage upper parts plain grey-brown; eyebrow white. Rump white; tail black. Dusky wing has broad white stripe; underwing linings and axillaries white. Breast washed grey; rest of underparts white. Eye dark brown. Bill long and straight with little upcurve, pink on base half, rest black. Legs and feet dark olive-green. Breeding plumage rarely seen in Australia: crown, nape and mantle red-brown with black streaking; rest of upper parts darker than non-breeding plumage, with much mottling in black, browns and grey. Throat pale; neck and breast rich red-brown, with dark brown scalloping on breast extending to otherwise white flanks. Male brighter than female._
IMMATURES: _A little browner than non-breeding adults, with some dark mottling and pale edging on upper parts._

VOICE
Sharp witta-witta _in flying flocks;_ kip-kip-kip _in alarm or scolding._

NESTING
Breeds May–July in northern Eurasia. Nest a small, shallow depression in the ground, lined with a little grass; amid sparse grass and other low plants in open marshy areas. Eggs: four; olive-green or brown-olive with dark brown blotches, underlying grey patches, particularly at larger end; pyriform, about 55 x 37 mm. Incubation 22–24 days, by both sexes.

DISTRIBUTION
Non-breeding migrant, sparse on coastal and inland mud sheet round Australia, and sparsest in southeast. Also migrates to Africa, southern Asia and Indonesian archipelago to New Guinea. Breeds round northern Eurasia south of Arctic Circle. Of three races, small L.l. melanuroides, which breeds from Mongolia and eastern Siberia to Saklin, reaches Australia.

This Black-tailed Godwit is in breeding plumage — the way it is seen in the Northern Hemisphere. In non-breeding plumage it is paler and greyer.

Whimbrel *Numenius phaeopus* (LINNÉ, 1758)

OTHER NAMES
None.

IDENTIFICATION
LENGTH: *400–430 mm.*
ADULTS: *Sexes similar. All upper parts mid-brown, finely streaked on head and neck with pair of duskier stripes on crown, mottled on back, wings and tail; rump white with brown bars. Throat and breast streaked brown; rest of underparts white barred brown on flanks. Eye black-brown. Bill down-curved and dark brown. Legs and feet olive-grey.*

VOICE
Shrill, tittering ti-ti-ti-ti-ti in alarm.

NESTING
Breeds in Arctic in June. Nest a hollow, usually pressed into moss or other soft surface, often lined with plant matter. Eggs: three to five; olive-brown to blue-green variously spotted and streaked with dusky; oval to pyriform, about 58 x 40 mm. Incubation 27–28 days, by both sexes. Young leave nest within an hour of hatching but continue to be cared for by both parents. They fly after 35–40 days.

DISTRIBUTION
Breeds in Arctic Circle, migrating to all southern continents for austral summer. Common around northern Australian coast, rare in south. Four races; only one, N.p.variegatus reaching Australia from eastern Siberia.

The Whimbrel looks similar to the Eastern Curlew, but it is smaller with a pair of dusky stripes on its crown.

RARE ON AUSTRALIA'S southern coasts, the Whimbrel is more abundant round the north, where it sometimes occurs in small flocks of up to 50. It is a non-breeding migrant, arriving for the austral summer in late August and early September from its breeding grounds on tundras inside the Arctic Circle.

The birds come in a broad wave, from the northwest coast to Cape York, some flying over glacial mountains in New Guinea. On their journey south they visit berry and rice fields and lakes through eastern Asia and fly to beaches to rest. When returning to breed, in late April–May, they keep more to the pebbly or sandy shores of the Asian coast. A few—mainly immatures—stay behind, especially in northern Australia.

In Australia, Whimbrels frequent estuaries and mangrove mud flats along the coast, feeding there and roosting on islets, coral reefs and meadows nearby. They forage by probing for worms or molluscs in mud or sand, and pick up crustaceans and insects among rocks, coral and seaweed. They may also eat vegetable matter, particularly seeds and fruits. Whimbrels have a light fast flight. Carrying the head up, they rise without a run, turn in tight circles, and land with a quick flutter.

Little Curlew *Numenius minutus* (GOULD, 1841)

FROM BREEDING GROUNDS in central and northeastern Siberia, Little Curlews migrate to summer in Australia in September–October and return to nest in March–April. On route they fly along the east coast of China, and through Japan, the Philippines and Sulawesi. Some stop at winter quarters in the Lesser Sundas and Moluccas, but most—almost the world's entire population—fly on to Australia, the majority funnelling through Darwin and nearby coastal plains on the journey south. It is then that they can be seen walking and flying through the streets of the city. On return, they depart on a broader front, much fewer passing through Darwin; virtually none stay behind.

On reaching Australia Little Curlews fan out in flocks of sometimes thousands around the northern Australian coast, not along the beaches but on the bare, dry subcoastal plains, and even air fields and suburban lawns. There they feed by picking and probing in cracks in the soil, taking seeds, caterpillars and other invertebrates. When the wet season comes and the plains flood, the birds flock together and spread out further inland, staying on dry ground. Many shift southeast, thousands congregating around the head of the Gulf of Carpentaria over summer, and some wandering to southern Australia if rains are particularly widespread.

The Little Curlew stands more erect than the large curlews, particularly in alarm. Flying with languid, short, yet deliberate beats, it manoeuvres gracefully. On the ground the birds patter across grass plain with a free, tripping gait. Their nearest relative is the near-extinct Eskimo Curlew.

OTHER NAMES
Pygmy Curlew, Little Whimbrel.

IDENTIFICATION
LENGTH: *300–330 mm.*
ADULTS: *Sexes similar. Upper parts mottled dark brown and light buff. Crown and head dark brown with buff centre stripe and eyebrow. Rump and tail buff, heavily barred dark brown. Flight feathers dusky. Underparts buff, lightly marked with dark brown streaks. Eye dark brown. Bill slightly down-curved, dark brown with dull yellow base to lower bill. Legs and feet grey-brown.*
IMMATURES: *Similar to adults.*

VOICE
Chattering communication call chee-chee-chee, while birds are foraging in flocks. When startled, birds fly off uttering harsh tcheu-tcheu-tcheu.

NESTING
Breeds in Siberia in June–July. Nest a depression in the ground. Eggs: three;

olive-buff with brown and slate-grey markings; oval to pyriform, about 50 x 35 mm.

DISTRIBUTION
Non-breeding migrant, breeding in Siberia and Mongolia and summering from Indonesia to mainly subcoastal northern Australia. No races.

The Little Curlew inhabits bare plains at its winter quarters in Australia.

Eastern Curlew _Numenius madagascariensis_ (LINNÉ, 1766)

EASTERN CURLEWS MIGRATE FROM far northeastern Asia to Australia during August and September, and return from late March to early May. Their southward migration over Asia is not very noticeable— perhaps the birds move at night—and only small groups have been reported. The northwest coast is the main staging ground for arrivals; few come through Torres Strait. The return passage, however, is quite conspicuous and large numbers may be seen flying northwards to Indonesia and on.

Most of the curlews spending the northern winter in the Australian summer seem to concentrate on the east coast, where they may occur in their hundreds. In Western Australia and the Northern Territory the birds are present in much smaller numbers— usually single individuals or flocks of up to 30 birds. There are a few inland records, enough perhaps to suggest that the birds migrate overland—probably non-stop and at night. There are always a few birds that do not return to Siberia each year to breed—probably mostly immatures—and many of these seem to shift north to over-winter around northern Australia.

The breeding range of the Eastern Curlew is poorly known, but the few areas reported are all in eastern Siberia and Manchuria. There the bird is found on extensive mossy marshes, burnt-out bare patches in reed grass thickets, or on grassy or peat marshes. In April and May courtship and pair formation take place. The male performs a display flight, rising 10–15 metres above the ground and flying with slowly beating wings. Meanwhile it whistles a gentle _tyui, tyui, tyui,_ which becomes more rapid towards the end of the display, when the bird stops with outspread wings and slowly descends, as whistling fades.

In Australia, Eastern Curlews prefer estuaries, mud flats and soft, sandy beaches. They feed alone or in dispersed groups by probing the mud or sand with their long bills—probably eating mostly worms and small crabs. In Siberia, insects, particularly the larvae of beetles and soldier flies and amphipod crustaceans called sand fleas, are important food items, and there are also records of the birds eating small frogs and crabs and berries.

The Eastern Curlew can readily be distinguished from the Whimbrel and Little Curlew by its much greater size and its disproportionately long bill. When these three species cannot be compared together, an easy way to tell the birds apart is to estimate how many times the length of the bill can be divided by the length of the head—the bill of the Eastern Curlew is four or five times as long as its head.

OTHER NAMES
Sea Curlew, Australian Curlew.

IDENTIFICATION
LENGTH: _580–620 mm, including 180 mm bill._
ADULTS: _Sexes similar. Pale fawn-brown above and below, finely streaked with black-brown over head, neck and breast and mottled and barred with black-brown on shoulders, back, flight feathers and tail; belly and undertail coverts plainer, creamier buff. Eye brown. Bill long, sickle-shaped, dark brown with pink lower base. Legs and feet olive-grey. In breeding plumage (not seen in Australia) centre of back and upper tail coverts tinged with cinnamon._
IMMATURES: _Not described._

VOICE
Mournful karr-er _and a higher-pitched rising_ ker-lee, ker-lee _in alarm. Short bursts of bubbling trills. Calls often._

NESTING
Breeds May and June in Siberia. Nest usually a scrape on a small mound, lined with dry grass. Eggs: four; olive-green spotted with green-brown; oval to pyriform, about 70 x 48 mm. Incubation probably 27–29 days.

DISTRIBUTION
Non-breeding migrant around Australian coasts, spring to autumn, when probably world's entire population present; a few birds remain year round. Most abundant around east and north coasts. Passage migrant through inland; occasional birds reach eastern New Guinea and New Zealand. Breeds in eastern Siberia and Manchuria. No races.

The long bill of the Eastern Curlew is four or five times the length of its head. With it the bird probes mud for worms and crabs.

A recently recorded visitor to Australian shores over the summer months, the Asian Dowitcher feeds along flat expanses of tidal sands and mud.

Asian Dowitcher *Limnodromus semipalmatus* (BLYTH, 1848)

LARGEST OF THE SNIPE-LIKE dowitchers, the Asian has only been recorded visiting Australian shores since 1971. Since then it has been recorded regularly in groups of up to 100 or more on northern beaches, suggesting that it is a regular non-breeding migrant along the north and northwest coast each austral summer. It seems to arrive in force each September along the Eighty Mile Beach and points north and from there spreads around the coast in small numbers without proceeding inland, occasionally reaching Moreton Bay in southern Queensland, and even the region of Port Phillip Bay in Victoria.

In Australia, Asian Dowitchers frequent flat expanses of tidal sands and muds on the coast. Looking like small, tubby godwits on short, part-webbed feet and with down-pointing bills, they feed in a characteristic manner, walking jerkily along and plunging the bill continuously deep into the mud with a sewing-machine action. Legs are used as a pivot for tilting the whole body — and the bill, on rigid neck, is thrust in up to its hilt; prey is pulled out slowly and with effort. Often the whole head is immersed as the birds work through still partly inundated flats, and sometimes they swim. When there are several or more in an area, the dowitchers group together, foraging, flying and resting on banks in compact flocks with other waders at high tide. Flight is swift and steady, with bill down-pointing; flying flocks may perform high evolutions.

The birds probably depart for their breeding grounds in central eastern Asia through April, arriving in May. There they nest in small colonies on marshes, damp meadows and grassy floodlands, often in company with other waders. The dowitchers are monogamous and both sexes incubate.

The relationships of the dowitchers are problematic among waders. On one side they have the appearance of snipe and have skull characters to match, and the tips of their long straight bills are soft and tactile, helping the birds to feed by touch. On the other side, they have anatomical and biochemical features of tringine sandpipers, particularly the godwits, and godwit-like rufous breeding plumage. The colour pattern on their downy young has been

more vigorously argued, some observers contending that it is snipe-like and others that it is a simple form of the godwit pattern, with puffs present only as a wide stripe down each side of a dark midline and as wide circles on each thigh.

OTHER NAMES
Asiatic Dowitcher.

IDENTIFICATION
LENGTH: *320–350 mm, including 80 mm long bill.*
ADULTS: *Sexes similar. In non-breeding plumage, crown, upper neck, upper back and shoulders deep greyish brown flecked and edged white; lower back to upper tail coverts white, spotted and barred dusky; tail white barred dusky. Outer flight feathers plain dusky, secondaries browner, edged white. Face, underneck and upper breast white flecked mid grey-brown; eyebrow whiter; lores browner. Rest of underparts white, becoming flecked dusky on undertail coverts. Eye dark brown. Bill black with flesh-grey base to lower mandible. Legs and feet black. In breeding plumage, russet over head and all underparts and russet-brown over back and shoulders with dusky centres to feathers; faint whitish eyebrow.*
IMMATURES: *As non-breeding adults, but white-buff edging to feathers of upper parts more pronounced.*

VOICE
Quiet nondescript chewsk *or plaintive, mewing* miau, *probably in contact. Usually silent on non-breeding grounds.*

NESTING
Breeds in central eastern Asia, end

May–August, in small colonies. Nest a loose cup-shaped platform of plant stems in small sheltering tussocks in shallow water, or small depressions in ground nearby, lined with a few grass blades. Eggs: two to three; light olive to sandy-buff, blotched and lined with brown, rufous and cinnamon, often concentrated at larger end; oval to pyriform, about 50 x 33 mm.

DISTRIBUTION
Non-breeding migrant, summering regularly from eastern India, eastern China and Philippines to the Indonesian arc and northwest coast of Australia; vagrant down eastern Australian coast. Breeds from western Siberia and Mongolia to Manchuria. No races.

Wood Sandpiper *Tringa glareola* LINNÉ, 1758

A REGULAR BUT UNCOMMON MIGRANT, the Wood Sandpiper is more solitary than most waders and keeps to itself on shallow freshwater swamps and the muddy edges of water holes inland from the coast. Only rarely does it gather in small flocks of up to 50, probably at staging grounds on migration. It arrives from its northern Asian breeding grounds through September and leaves again to nest in April.

Like other tringine sandpipers, Woods are nervously active, probing with erratic rapidity in mud, sometimes with head immersed, or sweeping the bill from side to side. Worms, beetles, bugs, flies, spiders, molluscs, occasional fish and even vegetable matter are eaten. They even pick insects off the surface and from plants or chase them into the air. In alarm, they bob head and tail up and down, then take off abruptly, climbing steeply and weaving about at speed, on bursts of rapid wing-beats. At rest they will perch on dead branches and fence posts. Rarely are they found away from small, reed-sheltered bodies of fresh water.

Arriving on the marshy tundra of their breeding grounds, they pair immediately and begin nuptial display flights and mating songs. Both sexes rise, then glide down around their territory, whistling and trilling. They also display on the ground: pairs walk with their wings raised for short distances, trilling softly.

OTHER NAMES
None.

IDENTIFICATION
LENGTH: *200–230 mm.*
ADULTS: *Sexes similar. In non-breeding plumage upper parts deep brown spotted with white. Flight feathers plain dusky. Rump white; tail white, heavily barred with dark brown. Face and neck mottled white and grey-brown, with white eye-ring and eye-stripe. Breast grey; chin and belly white. Underwing light grey. Eye brown. Bill black. Legs and feet yellow to olive-green. Breeding plumage more boldly marked.*
IMMATURES: *Similar to adults.*

VOICE
Sharp whistled tee-tee-tee *in alarm or loud, repeated* chiff. *Musical whistles and trills during display on breeding grounds.*

NESTING
Breeds May–July. Nest usually a hollow in the ground lined with plant matter. Eggs: three to four; pale green to buff, blotched with dark purple-brown; oval to pyriform, about 38 x 26 mm. Incubation 22–23 days.

DISTRIBUTION
Non-breeding migrant, on sheltered fresh waters in austral summer. Breeds from Scandinavia to Siberia, Manchuria and Kurile Islands on either side of Arctic Circle. No races.

The Wood Sandpiper is a regular but solitary migrant of freshwater swamps. It can be identified by its white-spotted upper parts and white rump.

Greenshank *Tringa nebularia* (GUNNERUS, 1767)

A CONSPICUOUS WHITE RUMP AND BACK and a ringing alarm call make the Greenshank—which is large for a wader—easy to identify. It is also one of the most widely dispersed of Australian migratory waders, frequenting fresh, brackish and saline waters, from coastal mud flats, estuaries and mangrove inlets to sand bars, river edges, samphire swamps and flood-sheets inland. Nowhere, however, is it abundant. Not flocking like other waders, it is usually well dispersed in ones and twos; only when overwintering during the boreal summer does it sometimes flock. Its flight is fast with clipped wing-beats.

Wading in mud and water up to the depth of their legs—and rarely swimming—Greenshanks feed mainly on aquatic invertebrates (insects, crustaceans, worms and molluscs) and also take tadpoles, frogs and small fish. They search for prey by sight and probing touch, but more often peck, often on one side then another, while walking, running or standing. Versatile in their techniques, they catch insects in the air, chase fish with a dash and a lunge, sweep the bill from side to side in inundated mud, or charge here and there, probably to flush insects or fish. Fish are manipulated before swallowing, but other large prey may be taken to dry land to be shaken and crushed first.

Greenshanks come south in late August and September each year, and apart from a few non-breeders remaining behind, fly back to their northern Eurasian breeding grounds through April into May. First to return on the breeding grounds are the males. Meeting and pairing takes place abut fresh surface waters, and previous partners often re-pair. Courtship flights signal the beginning of breeding. Male chases female, the birds twisting low, turning and sometimes swerving high before returning to the start point. After touring the territory, the female chooses the nest site and copulation then follows ardent displays of wing-waving, goose-stepping, bowing and tail-fanning from the male. Males usually defend the territory and help with incubation. Greenshank chicks run about soon after hatching and are then taken to a lakeside up to two kilometres away. They can fly when 26–31 days old.

OTHER NAMES
None.

IDENTIFICATION
LENGTH: *320–350 mm.*
ADULTS: *Sexes similar. Mid grey-brown from crown to upper back, shoulders and wings, crown and neck streaked white. Lower back to tail white, with faint brown bars on sides of tail. Forehead and all underparts white; lores dusky. Eye brown. Bill deep olive-brown. Legs and feet yellow-green. Breeding plumage — sometimes attained before birds leave Australia— richer with dusky spots over foreneck and breast.*

VOICE
Loud, ringing tu-tu-tu *in alarm; also a staccato whistling* chip-chip-chip. *Rich, flute-like song in flight at breeding grounds.*

NESTING
Breeds May–August in Northern Hemisphere. Nest a scrape in the ground, lined with plant matter. Eggs: three to four—rarely more unless more than one female is laying in nest; smooth and glossy, pale buff to red-ochre, with markings ranging from bold blotches and streaks of brown to fine streaks and irregular marks; oval to pyriform, about 51 x 35 mm. Incubation 23–26 days, by both sexes. Young fly in 26–31 days.

DISTRIBUTION
Non-breeding migrant, summering from Mediterranean and Africa through India and southeastern Asia to New Guinea, Australia and occasionally New Zealand. Widespread on all shallow surface waters. Breeds around northern Eurasia just below Arctic Circle. No races.

The Greenshank frequents coastal flats, lakes and estuaries. It eats mainly aquatic insects, but worms, molluscs and crustaceans also feature in its diet.

The Marsh Sandpiper often feeds by waving its bill back and forth in water.

Marsh Sandpiper

Tringa stagnatilis (BECHSTEIN, 1803)

OTHER NAMES
Little Greenshank.

IDENTIFICATION
LENGTH: *210–220 mm.*
ADULTS: *Sexes similar. Forehead, back, rump and underparts white. Crown, nape, mantle and upper wings grey faintly mottled brown and edged with white. Tail white, lightly barred with brown. Eye dark brown. Bill long, thin and pointed, olive-brown with pale yellow-green base. Legs and feet yellow-green. Breeding plumage is generally darker, brighter and spotted with sepia on throat and sides of the breast. Patch at base of bill and feet brighter.*
IMMATURES: *As non-breeding adults.*

VOICE
Soft, musical tee-oo, or a succession of sharp tchicks in alarm. In the breeding season a soft trilling song in flight; similar trills at times in Australia.

NESTING
Breeds May–July in Eurasia. Nest a scrape in the ground, sometimes in a hummock surrounded by water, generally lined with plants. Eggs: usually four; buff to green-tinged with brown blotches and streaks; oval to pyriform, about 37 x 27 mm. Incubation by both sexes.

DISTRIBUTION
Non-breeding migrant, summering in Africa, India, the Indonesian chain, Australia (mainly in east), and occasionally New Zealand. No races.

RESEMBLING A DIMINUTIVE GREENSHANK, with which it sometimes associates, the Marsh Sandpiper migrates to Australia in small numbers each year. The birds begin to arrive on the northwest coast through September, probably from central Asian colonies, and from there disperse in ones, twos and small loose groups around the coast as well as southeast across the continent. More restricted than Greenshanks, they frequent the still edges of extensive shallow open sheets of water. In their feeding they wade busily in the shallows up to the length of their legs and even swim, probing and pecking prey off the surface. Often they sweep their bills from side to side in the water, or dart back and forth and around in half-circles, capturing prey in their thin bills. Their diet is chiefly of aquatic insects, crustaceans and molluscs.

Marsh Sandpipers begin to leave Australia at the end of summer, as early as late February and on into April; or they may quit southern Australia then and congregate on the monsoon-filled flood plains of northern Australia before leaving to nest. Very few stay behind over the austral winter. Flight is fast, with clipped wing-beats.

At their northern Eurasian breeding grounds, the birds often nest in loose colonies, sometimes in company with other waders and terns, but always space their nests at least five–ten metres apart. The birds begin their courtship displays within a few days of their arrival at the breeding grounds. The male flies up from the ground at regular intervals, singing and fluttering his wings like a lark. After about five minutes he alights, with legs stretched down and wings folded back, and runs towards the female, singing and fluttering his wings around her. He then runs beside her, and flies into the air singing. The male continues this performance right up to the start of egg-laying.

Both parents share incubation and guard the eggs and young, flying out to meet an intruder and circling around with loud cries. Broods stay in the breeding area at first, then move to more open areas and band together before leaving on migration.

Common Sandpiper *Actitis hypoleucos* (LINNÉ, 1758)

OTHER NAMES
Summer Snipe.

IDENTIFICATION
LENGTH: *200–210 mm.*
ADULTS: *Sexes similar. In non-breeding plumage upper parts dark olive-brown with fine, short, dark streaks; eye-stripe white. Tail dark with sides white, barred dark brown. Underparts white with grey-brown patches on sides of breast shading into sides of neck. Broad white stripe in dark brown flight feathers. Eye brown. Bill dark brown. Feet grey-green or subdued yellow. In breeding plumage darker, with bronze tinge on upper parts. Breast patches also darker.*
IMMATURES: *Similar to non-breeding adults but upper parts with white edging.*

VOICE
High-pitched, swallow-like twee-wee-wee in contact alarm.

NESTING
Breeds May–August in northern Eurasia. Nest a shallow hollow in the ground among or near low plants, often on hill slopes near water. Eggs: four, sometimes five; glossy blue-grey to variously buff, spotted and blotched with dark russet, and underlying grey; oval to pyriform, about 36 x 26 mm. Incubation 21–22 days, by male.

DISTRIBUTION
Non-breeding migrant, summering sporadically across Australia, and from southern Europe and Africa across southern Asia to New Guinea and Solomons; vagrant in Tasmania and New Zealand. Breeds from northern Europe to eastern Siberia, close under Arctic Circle. No races.

Common Sandpiper, in mangroves.

ITS SOLITARINESS CAN GIVE THE IMPRESSION that the Common Sandpiper is much less abundant in Australia than its name implies. Rarely forming compact flocks or associating with other waders, it is nonetheless rather common, if widely dispersed, across the north, only becoming rarer southwards, particularly in the east. It arrives from its Eurasian breeding grounds as early as August and on into September, coming on to the northwest coast and from there both following the coast around and crossing the continent to the southeast; many probably remain on inland waters all summer.

Everywhere its habitat is the same: steep-sided banks of mud or rocks on dams, creeks, channels, pools, swamps, mangrove-lined inlets and even roadside puddles inland or on the coast, but rarely the open shore. There it fossicks actively about in ones and twos, feeding. It walks up, over and between rocks and mud piles with great dexterity, its body teetering up and down all the while, pecking and creep-snatching food from among stones, cracks, leaves and even animal droppings; probing is rare. Small insects are staple diet. At rest, Common Sandpipers habitually perch on streamside objects like rocks, snags, mangrove roots, boats and jetties. Flying from point to point, they skim straight and low over the water, their rapid flicking wing-beats alternating with glides on down-bowed wings. Then they land and start teetering again.

Most birds leave for their breeding grounds in March–April, without congregating noticeably at staging sites; some, probably immatures, remain behind, mostly in the north.

Grey-tailed Tattler *Tringa brevipes* (VIEILLOT, 1816)

The Grey-tailed Tattler is found along the coast on large expanses of exposed mud flats. At high tide it often rests on mangrove branches or rock platforms.

ONE OF THE MOST COMMON waders visiting Australia, the Grey-tailed Tattler summers in considerable numbers around the north. It becomes less common farther south, appearing only sporadically in Tasmania and South Australia, and is fairly rare in Victoria, although small numbers occur regularly in Western Port Bay and on Mud Island, in Port Phillip Bay. The birds begin to leave their breeding grounds, in northeastern Siberia, in mid-August, apparently arriving in Australia during September and leaving again through April. The exact dates of arrival and departure are not clear because some birds — mainly immatures — stay in Australia throughout the year. They seem to come and go over a broad front, from the northwest coast to Cape York, and from there they spread round the coast southwards, rather than fly over land. Those reaching the South Australian gulfs may come around the southwest corner, rather than from the east coast.

Singly, in flocks of up to 50 or more, or mixed with other waders, Grey-tailed Tattlers frequent tidal mud flats at the mouths of estuaries and adjacent rock piles, reefs, and muddy mangrove-lined inlets in Australia; sandy beaches are visited much less regularly and often only for roosting. Just as often, the birds roost on bare mangrove branches at high tide, or on rock platforms. They feed actively and nervously, walking quickly along bobbing the head and wagging their rear body up and down, probing here and there in the mud for food: crustaceans and other intertidal invertebrates. If flushed, they usually fly off low with clipped wing-beats and on landing, stretch their wings vertically before folding them.

Their breeding grounds are in the most remote and mountainous parts of Siberia, and it was not until 1959 that the first nest with eggs was found. Birds arrive to nest from mid-May to early June and begin courting from the first day. Their displays and call-ing resemble those of the Greenshank and, like that species, they often perch in the dead branches of trees. Both male and female share incubation and caring for the young.

OTHER NAMES
Grey-rumped Tattler, Grey-rumped Sandpiper, Siberian Tattler.

IDENTIFICATION
LENGTH: *260–270 mm.*
ADULTS: *Sexes similar. Plain light grey above; white below with a white eyebrow and dusky lores. Eye brown. Bill black. Legs and feet yellow-olive. Non-breeding plumage looks identical to Wandering Tattler, but bird smaller, has a shorter nasal groove in the bill, larger leg scales, slightly different two-note call. In breeding plumage underparts are barred with dark brown, except for white centre of belly and white undertail coverts.*
IMMATURES: *Like adults in non-breeding plumage, but with pale edges to feathers of back and upper surfaces of wing.*

VOICE
Fluty to strident troo-eet, troo-et *in alarm.*

NESTING
Breeds June and July in Siberia. Eggs: four; pale buff with dark blotches, mainly at larger end; oval to pyriform, size not yet reported.

DISTRIBUTION
Non-breeding migrant, on tidal muds of coastal Australia — most abundant in north — and Southeast Asia to Solomon Islands; vagrant to New Zealand. Breeds in mountains of eastern Siberia and Kamchatka. No races.

Wandering Tattler *Tringa incana* (GMELIN, 1789)

SMALL NUMBERS of Wandering Tattlers migrate to summer in Australia each year, arriving in September–October. In keeping with their breeding east of Grey-tailed Tattlers in the Northern Hemisphere, Wanderings apparently visit mainly the eastern Australian coast, from Cape York south to about Sydney. They regularly reach Norfolk and Lord Howe Islands, and New Zealand too. Most, however, travel down the western coast of the Americas, as far as Peru and out into Pacific islands.

Wandering Tattlers bob head and body up and down as they run around rock pools and over wet shingle, probing here and there in their feeding and swimming adeptly through deeper water. Crabs, molluscs and worms are staple diet in Australia where the birds forage more on rocky and coral reefs than the Grey-tailed Tattler; mud flats and sand bars are visited less often. In flight over short distances they flick their wings like Common Sandpipers.

When feeding on their breeding grounds, the tattlers wade along the gravelly beds of streams, submerging the bill — and even head — as they probe under pebbles for insect larvae. They are adept at catching flying insects with rapid thrusts. They arrive at their breeding grounds from mid-May to June, immediately performing *Tringa*-like sexual displays that combine flights with rapid, high, whistling calls. They call from perches on the end of tree twigs and from the tops of boulders as well. Both sexes incubate and care for the young, but from the age of two weeks, chicks accompany one parent alone. Wandering Tattlers are almost indistinguishable from Grey-tailed Tattlers in their eclipse plumage in Australia, but their legs are more finely scaled, the nasal groove is three-quarters the length of the bill, and the birds themselves are larger and darker.

OTHER NAMES
American Tattler.

IDENTIFICATION
LENGTH: *280–290 mm.*
ADULTS: *Sexes similar. In non-breeding plumage plain grey above and almost white below; white eyebrow. Eye brown. Bill black. Legs and feet greenish yellow. In breeding plumage, entire underparts conspicuously barred dark brown.*
IMMATURES: *Similar to adults in non-breeding plumage, with paler edges to feathers of upper parts.*

VOICE
Six to 10 notes in rippling alarm trill whee-we-we, *on same pitch in rapid succession, each shorter and softer than the last. Sometimes clear flute-like two- and one-syllable calls.*

NESTING
Breeds June and July along mountain streams in alpine zone. Nest a scrape in the ground lined with rootlets; in a rocky or gravelly area. Eggs: usually four; green, heavily blotched and spotted with brown; oval to pyriform, about 43 x 32 mm.

DISTRIBUTION
Non-breeding migrant summering along South American coasts as far south as Peru, and throughout Pacific islands to New Zealand and eastern Australia. Breeds from far eastern Siberia to Alaska and British Columbia. No races.

The Wandering Tattler feeds more on rocky and coral reefs than the similar Grey-tailed Tattler. It also has a longer nasal groove and a rippling trill in alarm.

Terek Sandpiper *Xenus cinereus* (GÜLDENSTÄDT, 1775)

Two distinguishing features of the Terek Sandpiper are an upturned bill and a high, white forehead. The bird migrates to Australia from northern Asia.

BRIGHT ORANGE PART-WEBBED FEET and long upturning bill readily identify the Terek Sandpiper among migrant waders, although in its fast flicking flight and bobbing and teetering actions it does resemble the Common Sandpiper. The birds arrive along the north Australian coast from late August through September, rarely filtering far southwards, and return to their boreal breeding grounds in late March and April. Some, probably immatures, remain behind for the austral winter, especially in the coastal Northern Territory.

In Australia Terek Sandpipers stay on the coast, frequenting flat expanses of tidal muds along shore and estuaries and around mangroves. Visits to rock pools, coral reefs and the muddy shores of brackish lakes close inland are rarer. The birds form loose aggregations, flocking together to roost perching on mangrove stems or on banks with other waders at high tide, then spreading out in ones and twos to feed out over mud flats as they become exposed. Their darting manner of feeding is characteristic. Although sometimes stopping to probe rapidly at one spot, they commonly dash for several metres in one direction to snap up a morsel, then stop and charge off to another. With body held low and horizontal, and head and long bill forward, the birds often seem to be in danger of toppling over. Worms, crustaceans, small molluscs, flies and their larvae, beetles and water bugs are staple prey.

On their breeding grounds, Terek Sandpipers keep to marshes in forest, tundra and steppe, nesting on the banks of slow rivers and marshy lake shores overgrown with shrubs and sedge. Monogamous birds, they nest in loose colonies, often with other waders. Display begins soon after the birds arrive at their breeding grounds, when males start uttering insistent calls. The male takes off obliquely, hovering and fluttering briefly then swooping to the ground with wings held motionless. On the ground the birds display by fluttering their wings, raising their tails and singing vigorously with bill wide open. The female lays one egg a day and may or may not share incubation with the male. It usually takes more than a day for the chicks to hatch, all breaking out close together.

OTHER NAMES
None.

IDENTIFICATION
LENGTH: *220–260 mm.*
ADULTS: *Sexes similar. In non-breeding plumage plain mid grey-brown over all upper parts and sides of neck, with darker centres to feathers; eyebrow white. Underparts all white. Flight feathers dusky, with broad white trailing edge from inner primaries across secondaries. Eye brown. Bill long and upcurved, dusky with dull orange base. Legs and feet orange. Breeding plumage greyer on upper parts with sharper dark centres to feathers.*
IMMATURES: *As non-breeding adults but feathers of upper parts whiter-edged.*

VOICE
Variety of melodious trills, tee-oo, tee-tee-tee *and* weeta-weeta-weet, *or rippling* du-du-du-du *in contact in flight and on ground. Resounding song sung during nuptial display.*

NESTING
Breeds June–August around northern Russia. Nest a cup-shaped depression in the ground, often abundantly lined with plants. Eggs: two to five, usually four; cinnamon-yellow with dark brown dots and dashes; pyriform, about 38 x 27 mm. Incubation about 23 days, mainly by male.

DISTRIBUTION
Non-breeding migrant, summering from eastern Africa and Persian Gulf to Southeast Asia, New Guinea and Australia. Breeds around all northern USSR, east to eastern Siberia, just south of Arctic Circle. No clear-cut races.

Red-necked Phalarope

Phalaropus lobatus (LINNÉ, 1758)

When breeding, the Red-necked Phalarope's neck becomes bright fox-red.

OTHER NAMES
Northern Phalarope.

IDENTIFICATION
LENGTH: *170–200 mm; male smaller.*
ADULTS: *In non-breeding plumage sexes similar. Forehead and much of crown white; back of crown dusky; nape and upper parts generally pale grey. Dusky grey stripe from front of eye to ear coverts. White above eyes and down sides of neck. Wing coverts dark grey, edged white. Two white wing stripes; dusky flight feathers. White at sides of upper tail coverts; tail black with grey sides. Underparts pure white. Eye dark brown with white eye-ring. Bill black. Legs and feet dark blue-grey. In breeding plumage female brighter than male, otherwise similar. Upper parts sooty grey; buff tips to wing coverts; broad yellow-orange stripe down scapulars. Broad rufous-red band from behind eyes down sides of neck to circle upper breast. White eye-ring split.*

Throat white; lower breast dusky grey; belly, undertail coverts white; along sides some dark bars and scales.
IMMATURES: *As non-breeding adults; duskier on upper parts; more mottling.*

VOICE
Calls chick *or rapid* chick-chick-chick, *in alarm and in flight.*

NESTING
Breeds June–July in arctic-subantarctic marsh and scrub. Nest a hollow in a tussock of marsh grasses, lined with grass and other plant matter. Eggs: three–four; light brown or olive, blotched darker; oval to pyriform, about 30 x 21 mm. Incubation 17-21 days, by male. Young fly in 20 days.

DISTRIBUTION
Rare non-breeding migrant on near-coastal surface waters. Breeds right around Arctic Circle. No races.

BREEDING AROUND THE ENTIRE RIM of the Arctic Circle, Red-necked Phalaropes migrate to three isolated tropical coasts for the austral summer each year: off Peru, southern Arabia, and the Philippines–New Guinea arc. There they spend most of their time far out at sea, feeding in nutrient-rich tropical waters. Only a few trickle on to Australia each year, arriving temporarily on freshwater and saline lagoons, ponds, marshes and bays around the coast in September and leaving by April. The first was not recorded until 1962, near Melbourne.

Unlike other waders, the phalaropes spend most of their time swimming for food, and for this have lobed flanges on their toes and dense ventral feathering that cushions them high on the water; seldom do they come ashore to mix and feed when not breeding. Swimming an erratic course, they bob their heads and dab quickly from side to side, picking prey off the surface or lunging forward to snatch prey underneath. At times they quickly up-end, to peck insects on water plants, and at others they rise from the water with a fluttering leap and short flight to chase flying insects. Spinning—at about 50 turns a minute—is one of their ploys that may stir up prey and it is used much.

Close inshore they also wade and walk, pecking up prey or collecting food with scything movements of the bill. Out at sea, the birds flock to follow shoals of fish or marine mammals and fossick over rafts of floating seaweed and driftwood. Insects, of a great range, are staple diet, augmented with molluscs, crustaceans, spiders, worms and some plant matter.

Conventional sexual roles are reversed in phalaropes. The female is larger and more brightly coloured than the male in breeding plumage. She conducts displays and initiates courtship and establishes the breeding territory. The male builds the nest—in a tussock of marsh grasses, lined with plant matter— and incubates and rears the young on his own.

A Red-necked Phalarope in almost complete non-breeding plumage. Phalaropes spend much of their time swimming after food, mainly water insects.

Red Knot *Calidris canutus* (LINNÉ, 1758)

DUMPY SANDPIPERS, Red Knots are as easily recognised by their squat posture and head-down feeding in close-packed flocks as by any marks in their rather nondescript grey-and-white eclipse plumage. They breed high within the Arctic Circle and large numbers—those nesting from far northeastern Siberia to northwestern Alaska—migrate down the western shores of the Pacific Ocean in August–September each year to Indonesia, Australia and New Zealand.

Movement south, and probably on return migration in May, is by long non-stop flights to two or three staging estuaries en route, where the flocks rest briefly to lay down fat reserves to keep them going. Perhaps split by New Guinea, groups coming to Australia may arrive on two separate fronts: one on the beaches of the northwest coast where they may remain in thousands all summer, without filtering south along the west coast in any great numbers; and the other along the northeast coast of Queensland from which they disperse further. Even so, the Red Knots rarely reach the central north and south coasts in large numbers.

On their non-breeding grounds, the birds keep to extensive open coastal and estuarine sand and mud flats, rarely moving to swamps inland. They group to feed in compact flocks, small or large, at low tide. Progressing slowly but together on their short legs, they often resemble a moving carpet. Bent heads are bobbed as bills are thrust methodically deep into the mud like a sewing needle, searching for crustaceans, worms, insects and molluscs. Sometimes they push the bill forward through the mud or peck on the surface. Such engrossed feeding allows easy approach, but when at rest on nearby bars and banks at high tide, Red Knots are much warier. If disturbed, a flock will rise rapidly in unison and fly swiftly, sweeping this way and that on steadily beating wings, to settle together some distance away.

On their breeding grounds — glacial gravels, tundras and bare marshy slopes — the birds are more insectivorous and herbivorous. Males display in a song-flight, rising obliquely to a great height, circling widely on quivering wings, then sliding slowly down and up on rigid wings and spread tail before dropping to earth. Several nest hollows are scraped out before one is selected. Nesting duties are shared between the sexes, but the male takes the greater burden, seeing the young through to fledging on his own.

OTHER NAMES
Knot, Lesser Knot, Grey-crowned Knot.

IDENTIFICATION
LENGTH: *About 250 mm.*
ADULTS: *Sexes similar. In non-breeding plumage upper parts mid-grey with feather-tips paler, giving indistinct scalloping and streaking. Rump and upper tail coverts almost white with light grey bars; tail slightly darker. Wing stripe white. Eyebrow off-white. Underparts white with dusky spotting and barring on breast and flanks. Eye dark. Bill black. Legs and feet olive-green. In breeding plumage upper parts marked with buff, black and brown; face and underparts rich rufous, paler in female.*
IMMATURES: *As non-breeding adults, but browner and striped on crown and more boldly patterned above.*

VOICE
On migration and locally, contact call low knut, *or* kloot kloot. *Usually a quiet bird. Piercing shrill calls in flight,* wah-quoi, we-a-wit, *and a long drawn-out* coo-a-hee, *soft and flute-like in display; also sharp, querulous* whit-whit-whit, *often repeated at nest site.*

NESTING
Breeds June–August in Arctic Circle. Nest a small hollow in dry ground plants amid rubble and gravel. Eggs: four, occasionally three; olive-buff, spotted and scrawled with umber-brown, more thickly at larger end; ellipsoidal, about 43 x 30 mm. Incubation 21–22 days, by both sexes.

DISTRIBUTION
Non-breeding migrant, on tidal mud and sand flats around Australian coast. Breeds high within Arctic Circle, from where it migrates to all southern continents and most islands. Three or four races; one—pale—reaching Australia from northeastern Siberia and Alaska.

Red Knots, dumpy waders with short legs, feed in soft tidal mud. They bob their heads and bills rapidly as they feed, walking forward slowly.

Great Knot

Calidris tenuirostris (HORSFIELD, 1821)

LARGEST OF THE SANDPIPERS, Great Knots are thick-set, low-slung birds that resemble eclipse-plumaged Red Knots but for their longer bills, more boldly mottled plumage, striped crowns and white rumps. In breeding plumage they are more distinct.

Their remote breeding grounds, in far northeastern Siberia, were not discovered till 1929. These they leave each August and, passing south through Japan and coastal China, migrate to winter from India to the northern Australian coast, arriving into early September. Flocks of thousands summer on the Eighty-Mile Beach, around Arnhem Land and in the Gulf of Carpentaria, far fewer straggling on to eastern and southern coasts. Return migration to breed follows the same course, in April–May; some birds remain behind.

Great Knots feed in the manner of Red Knots on tidal mud and sand flats, taking minute gastropods and other invertebrates.

The Great Knot resembles the Red Knot, but has a longer bill.

OTHER NAMES
Japanese Knot, Stripe-crowned Knot, Great Sandpiper.

IDENTIFICATION
LENGTH: *280–300 mm.*
ADULTS: *Sexes similar. In non-breeding plumage upper parts mid-grey with dark feather centres; distinct streaking on crown. Rump white; tail-tip grey. White wing stripe. Indistinct white eyebrow. Underparts white sometimes with dark spots on breast and flanks. Eye dark. Bill straight and dusky. Legs and feet olive-grey. In breeding* plumage, black and chestnut markings on back. Underparts white, heavily scalloped black on breast and spotted on flanks.
IMMATURES: *Like non-breeding adults, but darker, more mottled above and on wings; breast tinged with buff; spotting of underparts is thicker and duller.*

VOICE
Double-noted rather soft whistle, nyut nyut, *in flight. Usually silent.*

NESTING
Breeds June–July in northeastern Siberia. Nest a depression in the ground, amid moss, on a high gravelly ridge. Eggs: usually four; grey-yellow liberally speckled with red-brown markings; ellipsoidal, about 51 x 37 mm.

DISTRIBUTION
Non-breeding migrant, centred on tidal sand flats in northern Australia; also New Guinea, Indonesian archipelago and southeastern Asia to India. Straggles to Tasmania and New Zealand. Breeds in northeastern Siberia. No races.

Pectoral Sandpiper

Calidris melanotos (VIEILLOT, 1819)

OTHER NAMES
Pouter Shorebird.

IDENTIFICATION
LENGTH: *200–230 mm.*
ADULTS: *Sexes similar; male larger. In non-breeding plumage upper parts mottled brown, with dusky feather centres. Crown dark to warm brown; eyebrow pale, variable. Flight feathers dusky, with obscure pale stripe. Tail and upper tail coverts dark with white sides. Throat white; lower throat and breast washed brown, streaked dusky. Belly white, cut off contrastingly from brown breast and giving a bibbed look. Eye dark. Bill dark grey with green-yellow to dull yellow base. Legs and feet green-yellow to dull yellow. In breeding plumage colours a little more intense and washed russet.*
IMMATURES: *Similar to adults in non-breeding plumage, but rustier.*

VOICE
Sharp, rasping krrrt *or* chreep *in alarm when flushed; other notes when breeding.*

NESTING
Breeds June and July along Arctic Circle. Nest a depression in the ground in grassy tundra, lined with grasses, small leaves or moss. Eggs: four; light grey-green or green-buff, blotched with browns, especially at larger end; ellipsoidal, about 37 x 25 mm. Incubation 21–23 days, by female.

DISTRIBUTION
Uncommon non-breeding migrant on muddy surface waters around most of Australia, particularly southeast; migrates mainly to South America and Pacific islands, less frequently southeastern Asia, yet common vagrant through Europe. Breeds between central northern Siberia and northern Canada, along Arctic Circle. No races.

The Pectoral Sandpiper has yellower legs than the allied Sharp-tailed Sandpiper. Its yellower-based bill is also slightly longer.

SO EASILY IS THE PECTORAL Sandpiper confused with the Sharp-tailed that it was not recognised as a regular, albeit uncommon, migrant to Australia until the 1950s. Overall, it can be identified by its yellower feet, slightly longer, yellower-based bill, browner head, sharply cut-off breast-streaking from the belly, and short rasping alarm note.

From their breeding grounds in far northern Siberia, Alaska and Canada, most Pectoral Sandpipers travel down the eastern edge of the Pacific Ocean and through northern America in August–September each year to summer in South America. Some, however, probably from Siberia, pass through the western Pacific, reaching mainly Australia on its east coast; and from there they disperse inland and to Tasmania in small numbers. A few find the west coast, but whether from the north or east is not clear.

Often associating with groups of Sharp-tailed Sandpipers, the Pectoral Sandpiper — in ones and twos — frequents muddy edges of shallow, open swamps and streams, whether fresh or saline, and on the coast or inland; rarely does it visit the seashore. It walks, then stands for long periods, sometimes wading but rarely swimming. When feeding — on small crustaceans, insects, worms and plant matter in shallows — it works methodically, head-down, probing with a sewing-needle action. If disturbed, it may crane or freeze flat in the marsh, then flush and zigzag off like a snipe.

Most if not all birds return to their breeding tundras in March and April. The male's courtship-flight is distinctive. He fills a pouting sac under his throat and breast with air, then chases the female and flies into the air, flapping and hovering like a small balloon, booming musically. Females incubate and rear young unaided.

Sharp-tailed Sandpiper *Calidris acuminata* (HORSFIELD, 1821)

The Sharp-tailed Sandpiper gets its name from its acutely pointed tail feathers.

ONE OF THE MOST ABUNDANT waders migrating to Australia each year, the Sharp-tailed Sandpiper is still hardly known at its limited breeding grounds on the northeastern Siberian tundra. It travels south in large numbers from late July to September, the males leaving first. Passing over Mongolia and eastern China and down the Asian coast past Japan, the birds strike out over the western Pacific through the Philippines and Micronesia to their non-breeding quarters from Melanesia to Australia and New Zealand. The bulk of the world's population seems to come to Australia, landing in a broad front along the north coast into September and travelling on across the continent to concentrate in greatest numbers in the southeastern quarter. Although some remain behind each year, most return to breed by the same route, in April–May.

In Australia, Sharp-tailed Sandpipers frequent most wader habitats: tidal mud and sand flats around estuaries, the muddy shores of open freshwater or brackish swamps and lakes inland, and, less frequently, nearby fields and the sea-shore. Freshwater and brackish habitat is preferred to saline; in general the birds keep to mud flats interspersed with sparse, low herbage among which they can rest and take cover.

Often mixing with other species of feeding and roosting waders, Sharp-tailed Sandpipers forage and rest in small groups of two or three to flocks of hundreds. They eat polychaete worms, gastropods, crustaceans, insects and some aquatic plants, picking and probing diligently for them, heads bent, while paddling through shallow water. If flushed, the birds rise with a soft metallic *pleep* and quickly compact in a close flock, flying swiftly in unison before splitting up and alighting again. In flight, the *pleep* notes may be interspersed with shrill twitterings.

Immature birds arriving in Australia are much more colourful than adults: they have rufous-pink breasts, bright rufous crowns and brightly variegated upper parts. Adults become colourful in breeding plumage in Siberia, with bright rufous crown, rufous-pink breast and white throat, belly and undertail.

Sharp-tailed Sandpipers look like Pectorals, but the brown wash and breast-markings are not as sharply demarcated from the belly.

OTHER NAMES
Sharp-tailed Stint, Siberian Sandpiper.

IDENTIFICATION
LENGTH: *190–220 mm.*
ADULTS: *Sexes similar; male larger. In non-breeding plumage upper parts mottled dark and grey-brown, with pale buff edges to most feathers. Crown warm brown to rufous; eyebrow pale, variable. Wings dusky, with obscure off-white stripe. Tail and upper tail coverts dusky with off-white at sides. Underparts white on throat and belly, with ill-defined pale brown wash across breast faintly marked dusky. Eye dark brown. Bill dark grey, paler at base. Legs and feet grey-green to olive-yellow. In breeding plumage upper parts darker, more richly mottled and washed with rufous. Underparts strongly spotted and streaked.*
IMMATURES: *Similar to adults in breeding plumage, but no spots on lower underparts. Breast pink-rufous; throat, belly and undertail white.*

VOICE
Sharp metallic pleep *on flushing; shrill* trrrt-trrrt-trrrt *in flight.*

NESTING
Breeds on tundra in northeastern

Siberia, laying in June. Nest a scrape in the ground, protected by grass, lined with small willow leaves; in damp area covered with mossy grasses. Eggs: four; olive-brown or green finely peppered with dark brown spots and larger end sometimes covered with patch of dark brown; ellipsoidal, about 39 x 27 mm. Incubation by female.

DISTRIBUTION
Abundant non-breeding migrant on shallow waters and shores throughout Australia; also Melanesia to New Zealand and vagrant to southeastern Asia. Breeds inside Arctic Circle in northeastern Siberia. No races.

A Sharp-tailed Sandpiper (the larger bird) feeding with Red-necked Stints in sparsely vegetated swamp. It eats tiny crustaceans, molluscs and insects.

Red-necked Stint   *Calidris ruficollis* (PALLAS, 1776)

BELIEING ITS NAME AT non-breeding quarters, the grey-white Red-necked Stint is one of the smallest and most abundant waders migrating to Australia. Only when deep salmon suffuses the face and neck of nesters preparing to return to their breeding grounds in March and April each year does the meaning of the name become clear. Leaving the coasts of eastern Siberia through August after nesting, the birds fly south through Mongolia, China and Japan, partly inland, partly along the coast, to swing in a huge arc on to their summering grounds, from southeastern Asia to Australia. They arrive in a broad front across the northern Australian coast. Some stop there, while others continue across the continent to centres along the south coast, to gather in tens of thousands.

Although some spread out on shallow mud-edged waters and swamps inland, most Red-necked Stints keep to saline or brackish sand flats and tidal muds along the Australian coast. They often mix in with other waders there, running about, bodies hunched, and feeding both on partly inundated muds and just above the waterline by jabbing and probing busily into the substrate. Worms, tiny crustaceans, snails and insects are taken. In flight they form close-knit flocks, wheeling swiftly this way and that, landing together and often to rest on banks and bars above highwater mark.

Once birds reach their non-breeding grounds, they are rather sedentary, rarely wandering far until return migration. Many — mostly first-year birds—remain behind.

OTHER NAMES
Red-necked Sandpiper.

IDENTIFICATION
LENGTH: *About 150 mm.*
ADULTS: *Sexes similar. In non-breeding plumage upper parts mid brownish-grey, finely streaked black, giving mottled effect. Rump and tail black; outer tail feathers and sides of rump white. Flight feathers dusky, with white mid bar. Underparts white with grey wash on sides of breast. Eye dark brown. Bill black. Legs and feet black. In breeding plumage deep salmon-pink on head and nape suffusing into pink on mantle and wing coverts. Darker above and more mottled than in non-breeding plumage. Chin pale; lores, face, ear coverts, throat and upper breast rufous-red with black peppering across lower breast. Rest of underparts white.*
IMMATURES: *Similar to non-breeding adults but browner. Crown dull rufous. Clearer white edging to feathers of back, shoulders and wing coverts.*

VOICE
High, squeaky week; *abrupt rolled* chirp. *Constant low twittering when feeding; trills or sharp* chit-chit-chit *in alarm-contact when flushed.*

NESTING
Breeds June–July inside Arctic Circle. Nest of dry vegetation in a tussock of grass on low tundra. Eggs: four; yellow-tinged, with rufous-cinnamon spots, particularly at larger end; pyriform, about 28 x 20 mm.

DISTRIBUTION
Common non-breeding migrant in coastal Australia, mainly August–April, rarer inland. Some birds remain in winter. Breeds in coastal northeastern Siberia and occasionally in western Alaska. Migrates to southeastern China, Taiwan, Japan, Philippines, Indo-China, Nicobar Islands, Sunda Islands, New Guinea, Solomons, Australia and New Zealand. Occasionally wanders to South Africa. No races.

The Red-necked Stint is one of the smallest waders. It runs about as it feeds, twittering softly.
The Long-toed Stint (the bird side-on) is similar but darker and lemon-legged.

Long-toed Stint   *Calidris subminuta* (MIDDENDORFF, 1851)

REACHING AUSTRALIA IN VERY SMALL numbers at the very limits of its migratory range, the Long-toed Stint is even smaller than the tiny Red-necked. It can be identified readily, however, by its taller, slimmer stance, darker brown upper parts, obscure white wing bar, and longer yellow legs which trail past the tail in flight. Until the 1960s it was known in Australia from one record in 1886 in the Kimberleys; but since then records have shown that it regularly visits all parts of the continent in ones and twos or parties of up to about 10 every summer. Large aggregations of up to 100 are rare.

Leaving their breeding grounds in the central eastern Siberian uplands in July–August, they travel south over Mongolia and past the Soviet Maritime Territories, Manchuria and Japan to converge through China and out over their non-breeding quarters through southeastern Asia in August–September. Australia lies at the end of this track, and picks up little more than an overflow.

In Australia, Long-toed Stints keep to open, sparsely grassed swamps and shallow mud banks of fresh, rarely brackish waters, crossing the continent and avoiding the tidal flats of the coast. Muddy margins of drying pools or flood sheets are favoured, the birds arriving just before the water evaporates and moving on immediately after. To feed they probe and peck for insects and aquatic invertebrates, working along slowly and mouse-like or actively with darting runs. If disturbed they crane or freeze flat; and on flushing fly off with fast, bat-like twisting on rapidly beating wings, often calling as they go.

OTHER NAMES
Long-toed Sandpiper, Middendorff's Stint.

IDENTIFICATION
LENGTH: *140–150 mm.*
ADULTS: *Sexes similar. In non-breeding plumage crown and forehead grey-brown with some fine, pale streaks. Nape and upper parts brown-grey with dark centres and bright buff edges to feathers. A pale buff stripe above eyes from lores to ear coverts; ear coverts brown. Tail dark; sides of upper tail coverts white. Throat and belly to undertail coverts almost white; broad brown area across breast of short dusky streaks, paler in centre of breast. Eye brown. Bill black; a little lighter at base. Legs and feet yellow-grey to green-yellow. In breeding plumage upper parts darker, mottled chestnut; crown rufous with dark streaks. Underparts whiter; brown area of breast usually more conspicuous.*

VOICE
Sharp chirruping trerp. *Ringing* chee-chee-chee, *singly or repeated;* tring. *More prolonged trilling when in disturbed flight.*

NESTING
Breeds June–July in mountain tundra and taiga of Siberia. Nest a shallow depression among plants or on raised ground in marsh. Eggs: usually four; grey-green with underlying streaks and spots of light brown and marked with larger, darker spots, mostly at larger end; pyriform, about 31 x 23 mm.

DISTRIBUTION
Non-breeding migrant scattered across Australia in summer; main non-breeding range Bangladesh to Philippines and Sulawesi. Breeds in central eastern Siberia. No races.

Curlew Sandpiper *Calidris ferruginea* (PONTOPPIDAN, 1763)

A long, downcurved bill distinguishes the Curlew Sandpiper from its relatives. This is one of the most common waders visiting coastal Australia.

AS MUCH A COASTAL SANDPIPER as the Red-necked Stint, the Curlew Sandpiper is one of the most numerous of the migratory waders visiting Australia, and among the first to arrive from its breeding grounds north of the Arctic Circle in Siberia. Able to lay down reserves of fat quickly after feeding, the birds can migrate rapidly, seemingly moving in one long, continuous flight as they spread along various routes to their non-breeding grounds from Africa to Australia. The birds arrive about the end of August, and are among the last to leave, some staying until the first week in May and a few — probably mostly immatures — remaining over winter.

On reaching Australia each year, along the northwestern shores, Curlew Sandpipers probably disperse around the coast and overland to quarters in the south. There they are rather sedentary, especially while moulting their wings in early summer; indeed,

banded individuals have been found on the same grounds year after year. Although ranging sporadically inland on shallow swamps and flood sheets, they keep in the main to estuarine and tidal mud and sand flats around the coast, gathering there in flocks of tens to tens of thousands. The birds often feed in company with Sharp-tailed Sandpipers and Red-necked Stints, but forage along the shore in deeper water, often wading up to their bellies. With their longer bills, Curlew Sandpipers exploit different depths of sand or mud for the same food: polychaete worms, molluscs, insects and crustaceans. These they take while walking busily along in groups, bodies hunched and bills pecking or probing deep.

Curlew Sandpipers have the same swift, easy-beating flight as other calidrine sandpipers, forming compact flocks that wheel this way and that before splitting up to alight.

OTHER NAMES
Curlew Stint, Pygmy Curlew.

IDENTIFICATION
LENGTH: *200–210 mm.*
ADULTS: *Sexes similar. In non-breeding plumage upper parts plain grey-brown; eyebrow and upper tail coverts white. Flight feathers dusky grey, with clear white wing stripe. Underparts white with grey wash on breast. Eye dark brown. Bill, legs and feet black. In breeding plumage head, neck and mantle dull red; colour suffuses into brown- and buff-mottled wing coverts. White upper tail coverts scalloped dusky. White around base of bill. Chin to belly dull red with some pale edging.*

Undertail coverts white with sparse, dark flecks.
IMMATURES: *Similar to non-breeding adults, but darker and more mottled above, occasionally green-tinged. Breast grey, pink-tinged.*

VOICE
Soft, twittering chirrup *or* chirreep *on flushing. Chipping and trilling calls on chasing flights.*

NESTING
Breeds June–July in coastal high Arctic tundra. Nest a slight depression amid grass and other plants pressed flat, on sides of slopes; lined with small pieces of plant matter. Eggs: four; light

olive with underlying grey-violet areas and marked with brown patches, particularly at larger end; almost pyriform, about 36 x 26 mm. Incubation by both sexes.

DISTRIBUTION
Common non-breeding migrant in coastal Australia August–May; rarer inland. Some over-winter. Breeds in far northern Siberia above Arctic Circle. Migrates to Africa, islands in Indian Ocean, India, Indo-China, Celebes, Sunda Islands, Moluccas, Australia and New Zealand. No races.

Sanderling *Calidris alba* (PALLAS, 1764)

OTHER NAMES
Beach-bird, Whitey.

IDENTIFICATION
LENGTH: *180–200 mm.*
ADULTS: *Sexes similar. In non-breeding plumage, upper parts plain pale grey, almost white on head; rump and tail white with black centre stripe. Shoulders and flight feathers dusky grey, with broad white wing bar. Underparts and eyebrow white. Eye brown. Bill and feet black. In breeding plumage, upper parts, throat and breast spotted black and washed russet.*
IMMATURES: *As non-breeding adults but striped dusky on crown and spotted black on back.*

VOICE
Soft-liquid wik-wik, ket-ket-ket *in flight; twittering when feeding.*

NESTING
Breeds June–August in Arctic. Nest a depression in gravel on ridge, lined with dead plant material. Eggs: three to four; pale yellow, marked brown and black; pyriform, about 36 x 25 mm. Incubation 24–27 days, by both sexes. Young fly in 17 days.

DISTRIBUTION
Non-breeding migrant in small numbers around coastal beaches; rarest on northeast coast. Also New Zealand. No races.

Sanderlings, here in mottled immature plumage, feed on sandy beaches, darting after tiny invertebrates.

SANDERLINGS, NON-BREEDING migrants from inside the Arctic Circle, are waders of sea beaches and sandy ocean shores, rarely ranging further inland than bare, open coastal lagoons. During storms they may congregate at sheltered sites in flocks of up to a hundred or more, but in good weather they spread out along open beaches in small groups. Wherever they mingle with other waders, they can be picked out by their pale tubby form and restless, non-stop feeding. Hurrying along with heads down, they dart after insects and other small invertebrates in the sand as the waves ebb; running, pausing and probing, they dodge back quickly as the next wave floods in. High tide forces them into the debris on dry higher sand to rest. Their sturdy bill still allows them to probe in dry sand, and they also skim food from pools while running along. If flushed, they rise together with a hub-bub of shrill, liquid notes and fly swiftly, easily and directly low over the water.

From their breeding grounds, Sanderlings fly to all southern continents, often on protracted loop migrations. Those reaching Australia — during September — probably arrive on the northwestern beaches and disperse around the coast; most may travel south along the western coast, then east along the southern, for they are most abundant in the south. The birds depart for their breeding grounds in April, leaving a few — probably immatures — behind. Unlike other sandpipers, they have no hind toe.

Broad-billed Sandpiper *Limicola falcinellus* (PONTOPPIDAN, 1763)

A BROADENED AND DOWN-TIPPED BILL, stocky feet and striped head identify the Broad-billed Sandpiper from other small waders. A non-breeding migrant, it flies south from its arctic nesting grounds each July–August to the northern coast of Australia in small numbers. Although some straggle south erratically, most remain in the north, before departing again through April–May.

Soft brackish muds and ooze are frequented by the birds, on coastal lagoons, estuaries, tidal flats or swamps rarely far inland; mud banks on the seaward side of mangroves are favoured feeding grounds. The sandpipers walk fast, sometimes running, pecking to right and left at the surface, and occasionally stopping to peck repeatedly at one place or to probe delicately. Beetles, flies, grass-hoppers, ants, marine worms, crustaceans, molluscs and even seeds are eaten, the larger items being washed before swallowing.

A Broad-billed Sandpiper on its nest on the edge of the Arctic.

OTHER NAMES
None.

IDENTIFICATION
LENGTH: *170–190 mm.*
ADULTS: *Sexes similar. Non-breeding: upper parts mid grey-brown with light feather edging; crown browner. Broad white eyebrow, branching with thinner stripe to sides of crown. Rump and tail dusky with whitish sides. Flight feathers dusky with faint white stripe through secondaries. Underparts white, flecked faintly dusky across breast. Eye dark brown. Bill, legs and feet deep brown-olive, or feet paler green. Breeding plumage mottled darker brown above, washed russet; breast more heavily flecked brown.*
IMMATURES: *As non-breeding adults, but browner, with buff wash on breast.*

VOICE
Dry nasal chrreet, *often in flight; also scolding* chetter-chetter-chetter-chit-chit *and soft trills.*

NESTING
Breeds June–July in arctic bogs and peats, in loose colonies. Nests of grass in tussocks. Eggs: three to four; pale buff, heavily blotched with red-browns; oval to pyriform, about 32 x 23 mm. Incubation about 21 days, by both sexes.

DISTRIBUTION
Non-breeding migrant around northern Australian coast. Breeds along Arctic Circle. Two races; one, brighter plumaged, reaches Australia.

Ruff *Philomachus pugnax* (LINNÉ, 1758)

The Ruff looks similar to other waders when not breeding, and is about the size of a Red Knot. In breeding plumage the male develops an elaborate mane.

THE FEW RUFFS THAT REACH Australia each year from their northern breeding grounds are little more than stragglers from the main migration routes south to Africa and the coasts of India. They were not recorded in Australia until 1962; since then they have been found scattered around the continent in ones and twos each year, from September to April.

In Australia, Ruffs frequent the muddy or sedgy edges of shallow freshwater lagoons, sewage ponds, salt marsh and estuarine mud flats, near but not on the coast. They feed there, walking deliberately through the water margins, erect or hunched, probing here and there with their rather short bills or picking items from the surface of the water or vegetation. A variety of insects, their larvae, spiders, crustaceans, frogs, molluscs, fish, worms and even seeds are taken, both by day and at night. Although rising steeply if disturbed, Ruffs fly with a loose, seemingly lazy action, often depressing their wings deeply on the down-stroke; they also glide in full flight and always do so when planing in to land.

On their breeding grounds, males alone develop the showy mane around their necks that gives them their name. To court and mate, they congregate at a communal display ground or 'lek'. The lek, about 20 metres square, comprises a number of bare patches or 'residences' about 30 centimetres in diameter and about a metre apart. Each is the property of an occupant male, which, in colourful displays, defends his ground from other resident males; satellite males with no ground, however, may be tolerated. Females approach the lek by air, drawn by conspicuous displays by the males. As soon as one lands, all resident males squat and freeze. She then steps on to a chosen residence, mates with the occupant male, and leaves. To the females are left the exclusive tasks of nest-making, incubation and the rearing of young.

OTHER NAMES
Reeve (female).

IDENTIFICATION
LENGTH: *Male 290–300 mm, including 36 mm bill; female 240–270 mm, including 32 mm bill.*
ADULTS: *In non-breeding plumage sexes similar. Upper parts mid grey-brown, with dusky centres and cream-buff edges to feathers of back and wing coverts giving scaly appearance; forehead and around neck often white and flecked; crown often streaked dusky. Rump and tail dusky with white sides to upper tail coverts. Flight feathers dusky brown, with faint white bar. Underparts dull white with brown wash on breast. Eye dark brown. Bill brown with yellow base. Legs and feet yellow-green to grey-brown. Only male develops display plumage: upper parts heavily patterned brown, buff and black; yellow warts on bare face; conspicuous erectile ruff around neck and two ear tufts. These differ in colour from bird to bird; no two are completely alike. The ruff or mane can be white and the ear tufts black, or both can be same colour or red; sometimes they are uniform, sometimes barred or spotted. Breeding female darker on upper surface, more mottled, and washed russet on back; heavily barred and mottled dusky from lower throat to breast and flanks.*
IMMATURES: *Resemble non-breeding adults but plumage washed with evanescent buff and neck all dark.*

VOICE
Ruff usually silent; breeding reeve utters curious double note resembling quack, kack-kack-kick-kack. *When flushed utters low* tu-whit.

NESTING
Breeds May–August in arctic–subantarctic marshes and wetlands. Nest usually a hollow in grass tussock, neatly lined with dried plants and grass stems; well hidden. Eggs: four; pale green to grey, boldly blotched with dark brown and purple-grey; pyriform, about 44 x 31 mm. Incubation 20–23 days, by female. Young fly in 25–28 days.

DISTRIBUTION
Rare non-breeding migrant, on muddy surface waters in all parts of Australia, September–April. Breeds in northern Eurasia, from Scandinavia to far northeastern Siberia, and migrates mainly to Africa and coasts of western Europe to India over austral summer. No races.

Latham's Snipe *Gallinago hardwickii* (GRAY, 1831)

OTHER NAMES
Japanese Snipe, Australian Snipe.

IDENTIFICATION
LENGTH: *270–290 mm, including 70 mm bill.*
ADULTS: *Sexes similar. Upper parts and shoulders buff-brown barred, streaked and blotched black; pair of broad dusky stripes over crown. Flight feathers dark brown. Tail black with broad ochre band tipped white; 16–18 feathers. Undersurface cream-white, washed brown and flecked black on throat and upper breast to flanks and crissum. Eye dark brown. Bill olive-brown. Legs and feet olive-grey.*
IMMATURES: *Similar to adults.*

VOICE
Sharp zhak in flight; greater repertoire in breeding season in Japan.

NESTING
Breeds June–July in Japan. Nest a depression lined with grass and often a little moss; in grasslands, peat bogs and cultivated fields. Eggs: four; yellow or brown, spotted and blotched with black, olive-brown and yellow-brown, particularly at larger end; oval to pyriform, about 43 x 31 mm. Incubation about 20 days, by female. Young fly after about 20 days.

DISTRIBUTION
Non-breeding migrant along coast and tablelands of eastern Australia south to Tasmania; some straggle inland, reaching Lake Eyre basin. Breeds in uplands of Hokkaido and Honshu, Japan. No races.

AFTER THEIR ANNUAL nesting in northern Japan, Latham's Snipe gather in large numbers on the shores of local lakes there. These are their staging grounds before their long migration south to Australia. They begin to leave in August on into September, flying down through the Japanese islands, Taiwan and eastern New Guinea, to funnel through to Australia at Cape York. Almost the entire world's population enters Australia there after mid-August. By mid-September they have reached Tasmania. It is there and on the adjacent southeastern mainland that the bulk of them spend the austral summer. Their return journey to breed in March and April is not marked by any flocking, the birds evidently departing in ones and twos.

On their Australian grounds, the snipe disperse singly through favoured habitat: wet treeless tussocky grassland, short-grassed marshes, and low brakes along freshwater streams and channels; saline estuaries and mud flats are rarely frequented. They are wary birds and perhaps partly nocturnal. By day they spend much time squatting under cover of tussocks and low shrubs, sometimes far from water. Often they do not flush until almost trodden on; then, bursting up with a harsh croak, they weave away low on swift-beating wings, only to drop back to cover in a hundred metres or so. This quail-like manoeuvre makes them a favoured game bird.

When feeding, often at dawn and dusk, they walk rapidly along probing in soft ground. Beetles, other insects, and invertebrates and plant material are eaten. Drainage and flood mitigation may have brought a decline in the numbers of Latham's Snipe in recent years, destroying its habitat. In Japan, the problem is not so serious because any loss of habitat is offset by the clearing of highland forest, creating open plantations. Snipe often perch there on posts or in trees; in display, they fly high in the sky, drumming. Rough pastures, rice stubble, and larch and fir forests on mountainsides, often far from water, are their breeding grounds.

Latham's Snipe visits Australia from its breeding grounds in Japan. Swinhoe's Snipe looks like it but is smaller, and has more tail feathers.

Swinhoe's Snipe *Gallinago megala* SWINHOE, 1861

BREEDING WEST OF LATHAM'S SNIPE in northeastern Asia, Swinhoe's Snipe also migrates south on a more westerly meridian. Passing through China, it spreads out to non-breeding quarters from India and southeastern Asia to western Micronesia, the Indonesian arc and the northwest coast of Australia from the Kimberleys to Arnhem Land and possibly Gulf of Carpentaria; records from Queensland have still to be confirmed.

The birds rarely arrive on the coastal plains of northwestern Australia until November, when storms begin to open the wet monsoon; even then they do not remain long, leaving by March. On the plains they disperse singly or in twos, frequenting short-grassed marsh land and shallowly inundated tussock-covered freshwater flood pans. There they hide and rest by day, standing or crouching under a concealing tussock. Rising rapidly if flushed, they zigzag off fast, twisting this way then that before dropping to cover again; sometimes they croak when flushed, but not often. At night they come out to feed, probing soft ground and mud for worms, caterpillars, crustaceans and plant matter.

On their breeding grounds, Swinhoe's Snipe frequent wooded steppes and river valleys. Males perform elaborate aerial displays, flying swiftly back and forth and swooping suddenly to land. They utter a loud call during this display and make a loud drumming by vibrating their tail feathers as air rushes through them.

Swinhoe's Snipe is virtually indistinguishable from Latham's Snipe in the field. Claims in Australian literature that it is larger, has yellow central tail feathers or a more broadly white-tipped tail are misleading. Indeed it is smaller, and has the same ochre band and narrow white tip on the tail. Apart from size, the only sure guide is the greater number of tail feathers (18–24), the outer ones of which are needle-like and much narrower.

OTHER NAMES
Chinese Snipe, Marsh Snipe.

IDENTIFICATION
LENGTH: *240–260 mm, including 60 mm bill.*
ADULTS: *Sexes similar. Upper parts and shoulders dull buff-brown barred, streaked and blotched black; pair of broad dusky stripes over crown. Flight feathers dark brown. Tail black with broad ochre band tipped white; 18–24 feathers, the outermost needle-like. Undersurface cream-white, washed brown and flecked on throat and upper breast to flanks and crissum. Eye dark brown. Bill olive-brown; tip duskier. Legs and feet olive-grey.*

VOICE
Very occasionally a guttural grunt.

NESTING
Breeds in June in northeastern Asia. Nest a depression in the ground, lined with grass. Eggs: usually four; cream or pale ochre spotted red-brown or grey; oval to pyriform, about 41 x 29 mm. Incubation about 20 days. Young fly in about 20 days.

DISTRIBUTION
Non-breeding migrant, on coastal plains of northwestern Australia from Kimberleys east to Gulf of Carpentaria at least; also India to western Micronesia, Indonesian arc and southwestern New Guinea. Breeds from central Siberia to northern Mongolia. No races.

Southern Skua *Catharacta antarctica* (LESSON, 1831)

Southern Skuas nest in a bowl of plant matter on subantarctic islands. Both sexes take turns at incubating. Here one of the birds displays aggressively.

POWERFULLY BUILT AND PREDATORY, the Southern Skua is equipped for life as both pirate and scavenger with a strong hooked upper bill of four horny plates. On the subantarctic islands where it nests over summer, it kills the smaller, burrowing petrels and on some islands, rabbits, rats and mice. It also gorges itself on carrion—dead whales, seals, penguins and other birds—and at every opportunity steals eggs from penguins and other seabirds nesting in the open. At sea it follows ships, singly or in loose groups for refuse thrown from galleys, squabbling over it in the water; and it pursues gannets, terns, gulls and cormorants, forcing them to disgorge food. Commonly the skuas quarrel among themselves over prizes. In addition, they swallow stones which, stored in the gizzard, help to grind ingested food.

In November, each bird returns to its traditional territory on the subantarctic islands to re-mate and breed. Non-breeding and younger birds congregate on the beaches, while breeding birds nest in a loose association of solitary pairs. Territory, nests and chicks are all defended ferociously, the adults flying and screaming at intruders and issuing continuous challenges. In aggressive posture, the head is lowered and neck extended as the birds raise their wings and neck feathers threateningly; when soliciting, male and female raise their tails and throw the head back until it almost touches the back, then shake the part-opened bill from side to side.

Juveniles leave their islands after fledging and do not return for three years, remaining at wintering quarters on southern temperate and subantarctic seas. Adults mix with them there out of breeding. Sometimes they enter large bays but rarely come ashore; they will perch on moored ships but seldom approach wharves.

That skuas are related to gulls is obvious from their form, flight and displays. They also have similarly structured webbed feet, but sharper, taloned claws. The Southern Skua belongs to the bulky, dark, blunt-tailed group of skuas which breed mainly in the subantarctic-antarctic and have a distinct sequence of body moult. The group probably comprises three or four species, among which the Southern Skua stands out in its greater size, all dark plumage, very broad and rounded wings, and lack of neck hackles.

OTHER NAMES
Sea Hawk, Great Skua.

IDENTIFICATION
LENGTH: *620–650 mm.*
ADULTS: *Sexes similar; female larger. Plumage dark brown, becoming paler towards end of breeding season. Base of flight feathers white, forming patch on outspread wings. Eye brown. Bill black. Feet black.*
IMMATURES: *Similar to adults; marginally smaller. Legs and feet partly coloured grey or black.*
DOWNY YOUNG: *Plain buff.*

VOICE
Single gull-like shrieks; also crowing staccato calls, often uttered as a duet between male and female, and in asserting dominance. Plaintive alarm call in nest. Usually silent at sea.

NESTING
Breeds usually December–March on subantarctic islands. Nest a well-formed bowl of plant matter, on the ground on exposed vantage point. Eggs: usually two; olive-brown or green with many dark spots and blotches; long-oval, about 76 x 52 mm. Incubation

about 32 days, by both sexes.

DISTRIBUTION
Regular winter visitor in small numbers off southern Australian coast, north to Shark Bay in west and Sandy Cape in east. Widespread migrant to subtropical seas around Southern Hemisphere, autumn to early spring. Breeds on subantarctic islands, including Macquarie, late spring–summer. Three races; one visits Australia.

Pomarine Jaeger *Stercorarius pomarinus* (Temminck, 1815)

JAEGERS ARE SMALL, SLENDER, attenuately tailed skuas that breed on arctic tundras and are more adept at pirating food from other seabirds than foraging on carrion. The Pomarine Jaeger is no exception. Diving, turning and careening swiftly in the air, it harries terns, shearwaters, gannets and gulls, its greater bulk enabling it to attack and steal disgorged food from larger victims than the more agile Arctic Jaeger. It does, however, catch some food of its own, including fish, small birds, molluscs and crustaceans.

Pomarine Jaegers migrate south through the seas well off all northern continents each October–November after breeding. For those following the eastern Asian coast, the seas around Australia and New Guinea are the main summer quarters. There they remain off ocean coastlines out to the continental shelf—rarely coming into harbours and bays—before heading north in late April. Their behaviour when nesting is typical of skuas; although nesting in loose colonies, pairs are aggressively territorial and defend both nest and young vigorously.

There are two main colour phases — dusky-bellied and blotchy light-bellied; light birds are more common in Australia.

An immature Pomarine Jaeger.

OTHER NAMES
Pomatorhine Skua.

IDENTIFICATION
LENGTH: *480–540 mm.*
ADULTS: *Sexes similar; female larger. Dark form: uniformly dusky brown, shafts and bases of primaries white in crosswise wing patch. Light form: upper parts, tail and wings as dark form, with lighter collar often suffused yellow; underparts white, finely flecked brown at sides to form band across breast, underwing coverts greyer. Protruding central tail feathers broadened at tip and twisted over one another. In breeding plumage, throat and neck flushed yellow, crown black, and protruding tail feathers longer. Eye dark brown. Bill dusky grey, hook-tipped. Webbed feet black; claws taloned.*
IMMATURES: *As adults; barred dusky brown and grey-white; tarsus greyer.*

VOICE
Low kek; *quavering* wawawawa; *yelping* which-yew *in alarm.*

NESTING
Breeds June–July on holarctic tundra, in loose colonies. Nest a shallow, often unlined depression in ground. Eggs: one to three, usually two; warm brown to olive, spotted and blotched dark brown; ellipsoidal, about 64 x 45 mm. Incubation 25–27 days, by both sexes. Young fledge in 31–32 days.

DISTRIBUTION
Non-breeding summer migrant off all Australian ocean shores, most commonly off southeast; also tropical and southern temperate seas off all other continents. Breeds round entire inner Arctic Circle. No races.

Arctic Jaeger

Stercorarius parasiticus
(Linné, 1758)

OTHER NAMES
Arctic Skua, Sea Hawk, Parasitic Skua.

IDENTIFICATION
LENGTH: *460–500 mm.*
ADULTS: *Sexes similar, in light, dark and intermediate colour forms; female larger. Dark form: uniformly dusky brown, with often paler collar, cheeks and throat; feather shafts and bases of underprimaries white in dull crosswise wing patch. Light form: upper parts, tail and wings as dark form, with pale collar often suffused pale yellow; underparts all white, mottled variably dusky along flanks and across breast. Protruding central tail feathers (absent in moulting birds) pointed and straight. In breeding plumage, throat and neck flushed yellow, underparts plainer white in light form, and protruding tail feathers longer. Eye dark brown. Bill dusky grey, hook-tipped. Webbed feet black; claws taloned.*
IMMATURES: *As adults but marginally smaller, and heavily barred brown and white on body and wing coverts.*

VOICE
Variety of shrill staccato calls when in pursuit of other birds; challenging caterwaul in breeding territories; single gull-like shriek when alarmed.

NESTING
Breeds May–July in holarctic tundra, alone or in loose colonies. Nest a well-formed bowl of grass or other plant matter, on ground in exposed position in vigorously defended territories. Eggs: usually two, sometimes one to four; olive-green or brown with dark spots and blotches; oval, about 57 x 40 mm. Incubation 25–28 days, by both sexes. Young fledge in 25–30 days.

DISTRIBUTION
Non-breeding migrant on inshore Australian seas, most common in southeast but rare south of Tasmania; also tropical to southern temperate seas off all other continents. Breeds round entire Arctic Circle. No races.

A PIRATICAL PREDATOR LIKE all skuas, the Arctic Jaeger chases other seabirds—terns, gannets and shearwaters—in the air, forcing them to disgorge or drop their food. In flight, it is free and agile, gliding, swooping and dipping on quickly beating wings. It also finds its own food—fish, molluscs, windblown insects and carrion—and follows ships in numbers for refuse thrown overboard, often entering bays and harbours. Rarely does it come ashore, however, settling rather on waters offshore to rest and sleep.

From their holarctic breeding grounds, Arctic Jaegers migrate south in September–October each year to summer in tropical and southern temperate waters. Those passing down the eastern Asian coast reach Australian seas, where they come further inshore and in larger numbers than the Pomarine Jaeger. Loose groups of up to six or seven remain until return migration in April.

Like the Pomarine Jaeger, the Arctic has colour phases ranging from light to dark in variable proportions, but can be identified by its acute central tail feathers, and slighter size.

An Arctic Jaeger on its nest in the arctic tundra. This one is of the dark colour form.

Pacific Gull

Larus pacificus LATHAM, 1801

OTHER NAMES
Jack Gull, Molly Gull.

IDENTIFICATION
LENGTH: *600–650 mm.*
ADULTS: *Sexes similar. Body all white except slaty black upper back. Wings slaty black with white trailing edge to flight feathers. Tail white with black subterminal band. Eye red in western race, white in eastern; red rims. Bill yellow; tip red on lower mandible and edged black on upper in western race, both tips plain red in eastern. Feet pale yellow; claws black.*
IMMATURES: *Uniformly dusky brown with faint mottlings. Eye brown. Bill and feet dark flesh-grey, the tip of the bill black in western race.*
DOWNY YOUNG: *Cream with dark grey flecks.*

VOICE
Loud, honking oww, oww *in alarm; muffled* auk auk auk. *Often silent.*

NESTING
Breeds spring to early summer. Nest on the ground, a solidly woven bowl of grass, seaweed and debris. Eggs: three; grey-brown with dark brown spots and blotches; long-oval, about 74 x 51 mm. Incubation about 29 days. Young fly in five-six weeks.

DISTRIBUTION
Southern Australian coasts. Two races: western race breeding north to Shark Bay and east to South Australian gulfs; eastern race breeding in Tasmania and around Westernport, Vic., dispersing west to Portland, Vic., north to Sydney.

The Pacific Gull feeds along shorelines. It eats molluscs, crabs, squid, small fish—sometimes diving after prey.

LARGE AND HEAVIER BILLED than any other gull, the Pacific Gull is a rather solitary and strictly coastal bird. Frequenting beaches, headlands and offshore islands, it rarely strays further inland than saline coastal lakes and estuaries, but occasionally to rubbish dumps in Tasmania. Adults, permanently paired, are rather sedentary, keeping to the same stretch of shore year round. Young birds, however, disperse widely after fledging, travelling several hundred or more kilometres—often northwards up the east and west coast —before returning to breeding grounds a year or two later. Non-breeders from Tasmania range in small groups to the coasts of Victoria and New South Wales, where the bird no longer nests.

Using their deep bills with uniquely rounded nostrils to advantage, Pacific Gulls feed on fish and squid caught at sea; crabs, molluscs and sea-urchins are picked up on reefs and beaches, and carrion and eggs and young are seized from colonially nesting seabirds such as shearwaters, petrels and gannets. These the birds take while swimming, while walking with their characteristically sedate gait, or from shallow dives while flying, plunging in and sometimes completely submerging. Hard-shelled prey are carried up in the air and dropped on rocks to be broken open, the birds often using the same bouldery points for many years, so accumulating 'middens' of broken shells.

The flight of the Pacific Gull is graceful and leisurely, on deeply and slowly beating wings, broken by majestic soaring. To rest and roost the gulls perch on spits, reefs, beaches and wharves.

Pacific Gulls nest alone or in small loose colonies on high points on headlands and islands. Their many courtship signals resemble those of other large gulls. The pair bows, 'laughs' with heads thrown back, and, after approaching with lowered heads, one seemingly attacks the other, grasping its wing. The chicks leave the nest within a few days but take refuge in shrubbery nearby.

Immature Pacific Gulls often travel over 200 km from the breeding colony.

Kelp Gull *Larus dominicanus* LICHTENSTEIN, 1823

ALTHOUGH FIRST RECORDED IN 1943, at Botany Bay, the Kelp Gull has probably been present in Australia for rather longer, because of confusion with the similar-looking Pacific Gull. Its adults, nonetheless, have plain unbanded tails and white tips to the wings, its immatures are paler around the hind neck, and both are slightly smaller and noticeably slenderer-billed, with slit nostrils.

That the Kelp Gull is a recent arrival and expanding its numbers and range is indicated by its increased breeding. Since the first nest found in 1958, it now breeds, singly or in small loose groups, at three separate islands off the southeast mainland and on another five in eastern Tasmania. From there, both adults and juveniles disperse much more widely than Pacific Gulls. So far, it has kept to coastal beaches, inlets, lakes and islands, in ones to fours or fives. The source of the original colonisation is probably New Zealand.

Kelp Gulls are more versatile and aggressive foragers than Pacific Gulls but take much the same range of food: carrion, shellfish, the chicks and eggs of other seabirds—even young Pacific Gulls—crustaceans, sea urchins and fish. Molluscs are broken by being dropped on to rocks from a height in flight. Frequently the gulls feed on water, upending or leaping forward into the air to dive in. When fishing in this way they smack the water with both feet to propel the leaps.

Courtship begins with male and female turning their heads away from each other, then preening and relaxing. The female then begs food and the male regurgitates on to the ground. The birds toss their heads before copulation and often preen each other afterwards. Young gulls leave the nest after a few days and they become self-sufficient by seven weeks.

OTHER NAMES
Dominican Gull, Southern Black-backed Gull.

IDENTIFICATION
LENGTH: *550–590 mm.*
ADULTS: *Sexes similar; female smaller. Head, body and tail all white except slaty black back. Wings slaty black, with white trailing edge and small white 'windows' at tip. Eye white; rim red. Bill cream-yellow, red spot near tip of lower mandible. Feet greenish yellow; claws black.*
IMMATURES: *In first year, dark brown mottled buff, marked whitish on head, neck and underparts; eye and bill dusky, feet flesh-brown. In second year, mottled white on shoulders and tail; bill greyer, feet bluish white.*
DOWNY YOUNG: *Cream; grey flecks.*

VOICE
Hoarse laughing notes, mainly in display; loud gor-ah, gor-ah *when relaxed; chattering* uh, uh, ee-ah-ha-ha-ha *in alarm and defence; wailing* waaaah *in courtship; choking* wo-wo-wo *in aggression; fluted* kle-oo, kle-oo *when begging.*

NESTING
Breeds September–December. Nest a bulky structure of dried plant matter, about 120 mm high, with egg cavity at top. Built on the ground, often sheltered by tussock or rock ledge. Eggs: two or three; green-grey, heavily speckled and blotched with red-brown, dark brown and black; ellipsoidal, about 70 x 51 mm. Incubation 28 days, by both sexes. Young fly in five-six weeks.

DISTRIBUTION
Coasts of southern Australia north occasionally to Cairns in east and Jurien Bay in west; vagrant elsewhere. Breeds off New South Wales central coast and Tasmanian east coast. Also New Zealand, South America, South Africa and subantarctic islands. No races.

The Kelp Gull was not found nesting in Australia until the 1940s. As its population increases, it may compete with the endemic Pacific Gull.

Silver Gull *Larus novaehollandiae* STEPHENS, 1826

THIS ADAPTABLE BIRD THRONGS beaches, bays, city parks and even rubbish dumps, and also ranges far inland along river systems and lakes, both permanent and temporary, fresh and salty. Its adaptability has led to an increase in its numbers, and it is one of the few birds to have benefited from European man.

Its diet varies with locality. Rafts of gulls float on the sea, feeding on plankton, or scavenge behind boats, hovering and diving. They mass along the seashore, feeding on crustaceans in washed-up seaweed, or working along the edge of waves and shallow pools, paddling their feet up and down and snapping up invertebrates drawn to the surface. Many feed inland on paddocks, on insects, larvae and worms thrown up behind ploughs. They may gather at dusk to fly about in flocks, taking insects such as crickets and swarming termites on the wing. They congregate on rubbish dumps in their hundreds; and people feed them in droves in parks and on beaches.

Any group of gulls establishes a hierarchy of dominance, older birds prevailing over the younger with constant attempts to drive them from feeding territory. They hunch, arch and run forward, squawking, in a variety of aggressive postures, or beg in submission. Each night they fly from their feeding grounds in long skeins to sleep on bare flat islands, spits and city lawns in a circular mass, the outer birds taking watch and changing position with the inner in frequent swirling flights.

Silver Gulls usually nest in colonies on islands and spits with low vegetation, which gives them good visibility. They can breed at two years of age, but usually breed at three. A male establishes or reclaims a small territory and is joined by a female—usually his previous mate. The birds nest at different times around the continent. In southern Australia the main season begins in July and August; in New South Wales breeding usually starts only in September, continuing until January; and in the southern part of Western Australia the birds can breed twice a year—in spring and autumn. Along the east coast of Australia the shortage of suitable breeding sites has extended the breeding season. The nesting duties are shared by both birds. While the chicks are growing primary wing feathers, they seek shelter under plants within the nest territory. By six weeks they are independent. Should they wander from their territory too soon, they are often killed by other gulls.

Gulls are nomadic birds, but the distances they travel vary from one individual to another. Breeding flocks usually contain weakly and strongly nomadic birds in varying proportions. For example, the gulls breeding on Five Islands, off the New South Wales south coast, disperse mainly to Sydney, whereas those on the inland lakes of Victoria spread more widely, from Woomera, SA, to beyond Brisbane, following the coast. Silver Gulls become regular residents of beaches, leaving only to breed.

OTHER NAMES
Red-billed Gull, Red-legged Gull, Seagull.

IDENTIFICATION
LENGTH: *400–450 mm.*
ADULTS: *Sexes similar, but male has slightly stouter bill. Plumage white with grey back, shoulders and under flight feathers; outer primaries black with white tips and 'mirrors'. Eye white with red eye-ring. Bill and feet brilliant scarlet to purple-red.*
IMMATURES: *As adults but mottled brown on shoulders and back; with brown subterminal tail band; outer primaries with reduced 'windows' and* longer white bases; eye, bill and feet dusky to buff-brown.
DOWNY YOUNG: *Sandy brown, mottled and spotted black.*

VOICE
Common call is drawn-out, harsh kwarr; *varies considerably with behaviour. Young have peevish squeal often accompanied by submissive behaviour towards adults.*

NESTING
Breeds in various months around Australia. In southwestern Australia may breed twice a year, in spring and autumn. Nest a shallow cup of fine plant matter; in shrubs or dead trees when no bare ground available. Eggs: two or four; blotched with olive and marked with black or brown; long-oval, about 53 x 38 mm. Incubation 21–27 days, by both sexes. Young leave nest site after about four weeks.

DISTRIBUTION
All Australian coasts, inland waters, and urban parks; most abundant around south, no breeding across north coast. Also New Zealand, Chatham and Snares Islands. Four or five races; one throughout Australian mainland, another in Tasmania with larger wing 'windows'.

The Silver Gull nests in plant matter. Only adults have white eyes with a red eye-ring and red bill and feet; immatures have dark eyes, bills and feet.

Silver Gulls are the best-known seabirds in Australia. They are found on beaches, far inland and in city parks. These are on Flinders Island, Bass Strait.

Caspian Tern *Sterna caspia* PALLAS, 1770

A pair of Caspian Terns with their two chicks. Caspian Terns are the largest terns with a wingspan of 1400 mm and a huge scarlet bill.

A MASSIVE SCARLET BILL AND GREAT SIZE at once identify the Caspian Tern. It is the largest of the terns and as big as a Kelp Gull but more streamlined. Usually solitary or in pairs, it frequents sea coasts, coastal lagoons and estuaries and also ranges erratically far inland on the larger lakes and rivers. Although some adults may be rather sedentary on prime stretches of permanent feeding territory, others and immatures seem to be nomadic. One banded bird was recorded travelling a minimum of 1600 kilometres in three years, from Mt Isa, Qld, to Murray Bridge, SA.

Like other terns, the Caspian hunts on the wing and dives for its food—mainly fish up to 18 centimetres long—in shallow fresh or saline water. It patrols long transects at 10–20 metres above the surface, bill pointing down and wings beating more slowly and deliberately than those of other terns. Sighting prey, it closes its wings and plummets headlong into the water, reappearing moments later; or sometimes it hovers before dropping.

The courtship flight of Caspian Terns is spectacular. The pair dives downward from on high and at speed and, without losing formation, twists and turns repeatedly before alighting on their strip of sand. There they preen one another for a time before copulating. Chicks remain brooded in the nest for only a few days before being led off to cover in low vegetation. In their defence, parents dive and skim past intruders, screaming.

OTHER NAMES
None.

IDENTIFICATION
LENGTH: *540–580 mm.*
ADULTS: *Sexes similar. Crown, forehead, nape black to below eye. Back, shoulders, upper wings and shallowly forked tail silver-grey; tips of outer primaries dusky. Underparts and underwings white; dusky tips to outer flight feathers. Eye dark brown. Bill scarlet; tip black. Feet black. In non-breeders, crown streaked white.*
IMMATURES: *As non-breeding adults but upper parts freckled buff-brown; bill dull orange.*
DOWNY YOUNG: *Upper parts light buff, speckled sparsely brown; underparts cream; bill and feet deep orange.*

VOICE
Deep, throaty scream, kraah or kaah, in warning or alarm. Usually silent.

NESTING
September–December in south; any time in north; singly or in small colonies. Nest a bare scrape on ground. Eggs: one or two; matt stone-grey or light brown, blotched sparingly grey-brown and black; long-oval, about 64 x 45 mm. Incubation 20–22 days, by both sexes.

DISTRIBUTION
Shores, islands and fresh inland waters. Also in Eurasia, Africa, North America and New Zealand. Four races; one, large, in Australia.

Gull-billed Tern *Sterna nilotica* GMELIN, 1789

A nesting Gull-billed Tern warns off intruders with a harsh alarm call. It breeds on inland lagoons.

ESSENTIALLY BIRDS OF surface waters on land, Gull-billed Terns range from most of the Australian inland to coastal swamps, flood sheets and inlets, whether fresh or brackish, but rarely visit marine shores. They are about the size of a Crested Tern, but can at once be identified by their short black bills and squarer tails. Everywhere they are nomadic and migratory. Each spring and summer they shift south across southern inland swamps, fresh or saline, to breed locally in varying numbers; at the same time, an Asian race migrates to estuaries on the northwest coast in small numbers. Through winter, the Asian race leaves and many southern birds wander north. On many lagoons, one or two terns may be present at any time of the year.

The terns fish from the air, hawking long tran-

sects over open waters and mud flats at five–30 metres above the surface, and even skimming out low over flooded saltbush plains in the south; never are they far from shore. Sighting prey, they turn and glide swiftly down, tail fanned and bill tilted down, to pluck from the surface. Inland they eat fish, crustaceans and a variety of insects—grasshoppers, blowfly maggots, centipedes and lizards; on the coast they are more limited to fish and crabs.

Often in ones and twos when not breeding, the terns gather erratically in colonies of tens to hundreds to nest, mostly on remote inland lagoons after rain or flooding. Depending on plant cover, they nest on the ground on bare, flat islets, or in the tops of bushes in samphire. Nests may be as close as 40 centimetres or four metres apart.

Whiskered Tern *Chlidonias hybrida* (PALLAS, 1811)

The Whiskered Tern builds a fragile nest of grasses and rushes on the water.

WHISKERED TERNS BELONG to a small group of terns that don black ventral plumage when breeding, build floating nests, and have deeply incised webbed feet with a long hind toe. Widespread throughout Afro-Eurasia, they are both nomadic and migratory in Australia. Avoiding the coast, they move south to breed erratically in colonies of tens to hundreds on inland and subcoastal swamps, flood sheets and lakes, fresh or salty, across southern regions over summer. In winter they shift north, spreading over the swamps in coastal areas and wandering as far as Java and the Philippines.

The terns hunt on the wing, often gathering in loose groups of up

to 100 or more, but beat, bank, hover and circle lower into the wind than other terns, on tighter, more varied transects. They usually dip to the surface to pick off prey—aquatic insects, amphibians, small fish, and crustaceans—but sometimes dive and submerge briefly; insects may be taken on the wing or from ploughed fields.

In display, the terns fly together into a 'tower', side by side and above one another, standing on their tails and hovering for up to a minute before dispersing. The male feeds the female and newly hatched young at the nest but as soon as young scramble off— within a week—both parents hunt and simply drop food to them.

White-winged Tern *Chlidonias leucoptera* (TEMMINCK, 1815)

An immature White-winged Tern; adult's body is black when breeding.

OTHER NAMES
White-winged Black Tern, White-tailed Tern.

IDENTIFICATION
LENGTH: *220–240 mm.*
ADULTS: *Sexes similar. In breeding plumage all body and underwing coverts velvet-black; upper wings grey; tail and leading edge of wings white, showing as white shoulder patch when wings folded. Eye dark brown. Bill bright red. Feet orange-red. In non-breeding plumage crown and nape black; upper wings and back grey; rump and tail white. Forehead and all underparts white. Bill black.*
IMMATURES: *As non-breeding adults, with duskier mantle and primaries, greyer shoulders.*

VOICE
Chattering in feeding flocks includes high-pitched alarm note kreek-kreek *and threat calls of* kek-kek-kek.

NESTING
Breeds in eastern Eurasia during austral winter, in large colonies. Nest is small platform of plant material on a tussock in water or on floating debris.

Eggs: three; brown boldly marked with black and ash-grey; long-oval, about 33 x 24 mm. Incubation about 20 days, by both sexes.

DISTRIBUTION
Breeds in eastern Europe, tropical Africa and central Asia. Visits freshwater swamps and brackish estuaries around north coast Australia; vagrant elsewhere. No races.

AT NON-BREEDING QUARTERS in Australia, the White-winged Tern frequents both freshwater and brackish swamps, lagoons and estuaries around the coast. It is a summer migrant, arriving in a broad front across the north coast of Australia each November–December, from its breeding grounds in eastern Eurasia. Most remain along the north coast through summer, in flocks of tens to several hundreds, or even thousands before returning in late March–early April; but some groups trickle down east and west coasts to about 30°S, and there are occasional irruptions, perhaps fueled by cyclonic weather, that reach the south coast and Tasmania.

Gregarious birds and sometimes associating with other terns, they perch to rest on driftwood, small rocks and posts in water and roost on the ground on spits and islands. When feeding they wheel and hover in loose to tight groups low over water, skimming for insects both in the air and on the surface. Dragonflies, butterflies, moths, flying ants and others are taken.

In Australia, White-winged Terns only begin to don black breeding plumage at the end of summer. At other times they are in non-breeding dress or a state of change, their grey-and-white plumage mottled with dusky. Apart from the marks, they can be identified from Whiskered Terns by their whiter rump and tail, shorter and thinner bill, more thickset build, and more leisurely wing-beats.

On their breeding grounds, White-winged Terns nest in colonies on freshwater marshes. In display, feeding groups rise in high soaring flight on thermal air currents, and in greeting, pairs stand erect close to one another, pointing their bills skywards.

Bridled Tern *Sterna anaethetus* SCOPOLI, 1786

THE MOVEMENTS AND ECOLOGY of Bridled Terns vary with the seasons in Australia. In non-breeding months, mainly winter, they move northwards from their breeding grounds far out to sea, feeding and sleeping there, and reaching the seas around Indonesia and New Guinea, even across the equator. In spring many return to breed in colonies of tens to several thousands, on islands off the central west and northeast coasts. There they roost at night on land, on the ground or low bushes and posts, and then fly well away from the colony to feed at sea by day. At their nightly roosts they call often and carry out typically tern-like movements—stretching one wing and leg over a fanned tail, preening, rubbing their heads on their shoulders and scratching their faces. Flocking in groups, they hover over the water and dip down to pick up or plunge for small fish. Flight to and from feeding grounds is swift and graceful.

In display flight, a pair will climb and swoop in unison; or one bird, giving a special *mer-er-er* call, triggers a 'dread' flight, inciting itself and neighbours to tear swiftly seawards, canting violently from side to side. Courting pairs on the ground drop their shoulders, step in circles around one another, wave, fence and peck with their lowered bills and pick up twigs and stones. They display near potential nest sites by day, eventually sleeping by the chosen one.

The long white eyebrow stripe and black cap identify the Bridled Tern.

OTHER NAMES
Brown-winged Tern, Dog Tern.

IDENTIFICATION
LENGTH: *400–420 mm.*
ADULTS: *Sexes similar. Crown and nape black; all back, upper wings and tail sooty-brown. Forehead white, lined narrowly over eye. Eye dark brown. Bill and feet black.*
IMMATURES: *As adults; upper parts flecked buff-white, crown brown grading to white over front of head, lores freckled.*

DOWNY YOUNG: *Sandy-grey, peppered dusky above; feet grey.*

VOICE
Staccato, barking wup-wup; *grating cries* karr *or* kr-arr; kuak *in display.*

NESTING
Breeds September–January most areas, with second autumn nesting April–June off Kimberleys and Arnhem Land. No nest; egg laid on sand or shingle under shelter of ledge or bush. Egg: one; white to pink-buff, sparsely spotted and blotched chestnut and sepia; long-oval, about 46 x 35 mm. Incubation about 30 days, by both sexes.*

DISTRIBUTION
Breeds on offshore islands from Cape Leeuwin, WA, northwards along coast, round to central Queensland coast and on Great Barrier Reef; one dated record in southeast South Australia. Also widespread in tropical and subtropical Indian, Pacific and Atlantic Oceans. Three subspecies; one in Australia.

A White-fronted Tern in breeding plumage. Most White-fronted Terns seen are less than a year old and have a grey-streaked cap with white forehead.

White-fronted Tern

Sterna striata GMELIN, 1789

IN AUSTRALIAN WATERS, the White-fronted Tern is a marine species, never found inland; but in New Zealand, where it breeds, it forages in the estuaries of the larger rivers. It is often in the company of the Crested Tern, but it is the more streamlined and can always be distinguished by its smaller size and black bill. The White-fronted Tern eats only fish, which it catches in the surf and clearer water further offshore. It is gregarious, feeding and roosting with others of its kind. As resting and roosting places it favours offshore rocks and reefs, but also settles on the sea. It is graceful and buoyant on the wing, swooping for prey on and just below the surface from heights of six–ten metres, or from lower over shoals.

Apart from several small foundling colonies in the east Bass Strait islands, all White-fronted Terns in Australian waters are non-breeding trans-Tasman migrants from New Zealand, where they nest amid tussock grass and similar low plants. They arrive along the southeast coast in May and depart again in October–November, leaving, nonetheless, a few non-breeders behind each year. Most migrants are immatures of the year, but about five per cent are adult; the remaining adults stay around New Zealand all year.

In the non-breeding plumage seen in Australia, White-fronted Terns are easily confused with Common Terns. They can be identified, however, by their slenderer bill and a black line restricted to the outer web of the outermost primary.

OTHER NAMES
Black-billed Tern, Southern Tern.

IDENTIFICATION
LENGTH: *400–420 mm.*
ADULTS: *Sexes similar. In breeding plumage, crown and nape black; forehead, lores and cheeks white. Back and upper wings mid-grey, the outermost primary with a black leading edge. Rump and tail white, the tail deeply forked with prolonged outer streamers. Underparts all white with faint rosy bloom. Eye brown. Bill black. Feet dark red-brown. In non-breeding plumage, white mottling extends through black crown.*
IMMATURES: *As non-breeding adults, back mottled brown and upper wings and shoulders shaded dusky.*
DOWNY YOUNG: *White to dark grey or brown, sparsely spotted dusky.*

VOICE
Rasping, high-pitched tsit-tsit-tsit, *and* keh-kreeahk-kreeahk.

NESTING
Breeds October–January, in small colonies. Nest a slight depression in ground amid tussocks, shingle beds or rocks. Eggs: two, occasionally three; slightly glossy stone-coloured, blotched and spotted with umber and grey; oval,

about 46 x 33 mm. Incubation about 25 days, by both sexes.

DISTRIBUTION
Winter migrant to southeast coast, north to about Rockhampton, Qld, west to South Australian gulfs, rarely. Breeds in New Zealand, Chatham and Auckland Islands; small breeding colonies recently self-established on eastern Bass Strait islands. No races.

Common Terns regularly visit Australia between October and March.

Common Tern

Sterna hirundo LINNÉ, 1758

OTHER NAMES
None.

IDENTIFICATION
LENGTH: *320–380 mm.*
ADULTS: *Sexes similar. In non-breeding plumage, forehead and fore-crown white flecked black; hind crown and nape to eye black flecked white. Back and upper wings grey, with broad dusky stripes on outermost primary. Rump and moderately forked tail white, outer webs grey. All underparts white. Eye brown. Bill and feet black. In breeding plumage, crown to bill black, underparts washed grey; bill red with black tip; feet red in western Eurasian race.*
IMMATURES: *As non-breeding adults; wings mottled brownish and toned dusky on bend, tail greyer.*

VOICE
Brisk kik-kik-kik *in contact in flight; grating* keeee-yah *in alarm. Noisy.*

NESTING
Northern Hemisphere, May–August, in colonies on sand dunes and marshes. Eggs: two to four; grey blotched brown; ellipsoidal, about 41 x 30 mm. Incubation about 20 days, by both sexes.

DISTRIBUTION
Non-breeding migrant around eastern and northern Australian coast, vagrant elsewhere. Four subspecies; at least two reaching Australia.

FROM THEIR BREEDING GROUNDS across mid-northern Eurasia, Common Terns migrate south each autumn. Small numbers reach Australia regularly each October–November, mostly from eastern Asia, and filter down the east and along the north coasts. South and west coasts are reached much less often. Everywhere the birds frequent saline or brackish coastal estuaries, inlets and shallow lakes, particularly those with sandy bars, banks and tidal flats. There they remain singly or in small loose groups of up to 10 or so, often on the same local grounds each year, until returning north to nest in April. Flocks of up to 1000 may congregate then on staging grounds on the north coast prior to departure. Some birds, probably immatures, remain behind through the austral winter.

Common Terns forage over shallow inshore waters, lakes and tidal flats in Australia. They beat deliberately along at three-six metres above the surface, the body rising and sinking at each stroke, bill pointing down. Over prey, they hover, dip, and plunge-dive with part-closed wings, often submerging with little splash. Food—mainly insects augmented with some fish—is also picked from the surface from mud or even from nearby cultivated fields.

To rest the birds perch on sand bars and mud flats or often are seen on a stake or jetty post.

On their breeding grounds, a pair performs a 'fish-flight' display, one bird holding a fish in its bill and leading the other in a chase of rapid aerial manoeuvres.

Arctic Terns in breeding plumage. They occasionally visit the Australian coast during migration.

Arctic Tern

Sterna paradisaea
PONTOPPIDAN, 1763

OTHER NAMES
None.

IDENTIFICATION
LENGTH: *320–370 mm.*
ADULTS: *Sexes similar. Non-breeding: forehead white grading into black hind crown and nape. Back and upper wings mid-grey, with narrow dusky stripes on outermost primary. Rump and deeply forked tail white, outer webs grey. Underparts all white with grey bloom. Eye brown. Bill and very short feet black. Breeding: entire crown black to eye; bill and feet deep red.*
IMMATURES: *As non-breeding adults; upper parts and bend of wing dusky.*

VOICE
Grating kee-yaah *in alarm; whistled* kee-kee-kee *in contact.*

NESTING
Breeds on arctic coasts, in colonies. Nest a scrape on bare ground. Eggs: two to three; stone to pale blue, blotched dark brown; ellipsoidal, about 40 x 30 mm. Incubation about 22 days, by both sexes.

DISTRIBUTION
Passage vagrant along southern coast, rarely to eastern Queensland, during migrations. No races.

FROM ITS BREEDING GROUNDS around the Arctic Circle, this tern flies south on two main routes each August–October to its summering quarters along the edge of the Antarctic pack ice. One route passes down the west coast of the Americas; the other converges off mid-western Africa, then spreads out over the southern Atlantic and east into the Southern Ocean. Weaker birds crossing the 'Roaring Forties' may be blown east offcourse, and small numbers of these hit the coast of southwestern and southeastern Aus-

tralia in most years. Most records have been in spring and early summer, towards the end of an exhausting migration.

At breeding and non-breeding quarters the terns feed singly or in small groups in cold waters no higher than 0°C, circling, dipping and diving as Common Terns do, for plankton, fish and crustaceans. Their wide-beating flight is so gracefully fragile that the birds are buffetted by wind and rest often. Remarkably, on migration they fly almost continuously without feeding.

Roseate Tern

Sterna dougallii
MONTAGU, 1813

Roseate Terns can be identified by very long, white outer tail-streamers.

OTHER NAMES
None.

IDENTIFICATION
LENGTH: *350–380 mm.*
ADULTS: *Sexes similar. In breeding plumage, all crown black to bill, eye and over nape. Back and upper wings silver-grey, with broad dusky stripe on both webs of white-tipped outer primaries. Rump and deeply forked tail white, the outer streamers (feathers) of tail prolonged and all white. Underparts all white, with rosy bloom in life. Eye dark brown. Bill grading from all black to all red, beginning from the base. Feet orange-red. In non-breeding plumage, forehead white, flecking crown; bill and feet black.*
IMMATURES: *As non-breeding plumage; back mottled brown, bend of wing shaded dusky; tail squarer, greyer.*
DOWNY YOUNG: *Hairy grey-buff, speckled dusky; white below.*

VOICE
Distinctive harsh, guttural aach *in alarm; soft* tchu-ik *in contact; croaking rattle in nest defence.*

NESTING
Breeds in small to large colonies high on low offshore islands, September–December in eastern Queensland, and then, or March–May, or in both periods in Western Australia, according to island. Nest a scrape in sand, coral or rock, often shrub-sheltered and bolstered with grass, seaweed, shells and pebbles. Eggs: one or two; pale green, spotted and blotched umber, sepia and grey; ellipsoidal, about 38 x 29 mm. Incubation 23–25 days, by both sexes.

DISTRIBUTION
Australian race breeds in Western

Australia from Carnac to Bedout Island, and in Queensland from Bunker Group to Torres Strait. Non-breeding range around west of northern coast to southern New Guinea. Frequents coastal waters and open sea. Three other subspecies in eastern North America south to Caribbean, British Isles, Denmark, North Africa, eastern coast of Africa across Indian Ocean, southeastern China, Philippines to Solomons and New Caledonia.

A FAINT BUT EVANESCENT rosy bloom to the underparts gives the Roseate Tern its name. A tern of tropical and subtropical seas, it occurs patchily, both in Australia and elsewhere around the world. Small fishing parties may be seen off the northern Australian coast at any time of the year, but they gather to nest only on islands along the northeastern coast of Queensland and mid-western coast of Western Australia. Northeastern colonies breed in spring and summer, and those in the west do so again, or instead, in autumn. Winter brings a lull, southernmost groups dispersing north.

Roseate Terns flock in tens to thousands to feed, roost and nest. Fishing by day out at sea or in waters close to the reefs and islands where they breed, they wheel and beat with grace, wings dipping very shallowly, heads down, and now and then plummeting almost vertically on to prey—small fish—from four–eight metres up.

In aerial displays, 'dread' flights are common. Brooding birds suddenly flash silently from their nests as one, hover and swing out over the water, then return to brood. Courtship on the ground is like the Common Tern's, the birds dropping their shoulders, elevating the tail and stretching necks up. In copulation, the male stands for some time on the female's back, and afterwards they preen one another. Birds relieving each other on the nest do so by pushing their mates off or by offering fish. In defence, they head-bob, stretch their necks and neck feathers, and rattle.

Black-naped Tern

Sterna sumatrana RAFFLES, 1822

OTHER NAMES
None.

IDENTIFICATION
LENGTH: *310–330 mm.*
ADULTS: *Sexes similar. Crown white, half-circled by black band from around eyes, broadening over nape. Back and upper wings silver-white, with black line on outer web of outer primary. Rest of body and deeply forked tail white, sometimes tinged rosy; outer tail feathers prolo::ged. Eye brown. Bill and feet black.*
IMMATURES: *Hind crown and nape flecked dusky and white; shoulders mottled brown; tail square and grey.*
DOWNY YOUNG: *Sandy, flecked black.*

VOICE
Sharp yapping chee-chee-chi-chip *in flocks; rattling* chit-chit-chit *in alarm.*

NESTING
Breeds September–January in small colonies. Nest a scrape in sand above highwater mark, usually on coral

islands. Eggs: two; matt stony-grey spotted with brown and dark grey; ellipsoidal, about 39 x 29 mm. Incubation about 25 days, by both sexes.

DISTRIBUTION
Coastal and inshore waters from Northern Territory to the Barrier Reef, Qld. Breeds there and on islands in tropical Indian and western Pacific Oceans, from south of China, through Indonesian arc to New Caledonia. No races.

Black-naped Terns frequent the northeast of Australia throughout the year.

A SMALL TERN OF TROPICAL Indo-Pacific seas, the Black-naped is rather sedentary. Colonies along the Great Barrier Reef tend to leave the area in non-breeding winter months, but for most of the year the birds fish and roost around their nesting islands.

Whether at rest on sand spits or fishing or nesting, the Black-naped Tern gathers in small noisy groups to 10 to 100 or so and associates with other terns: Roseates, Bridleds and noddies. Among them it is easily identified by its elegant, almost all-white

plumage. It is also an inshore fisher, working shallow coral pools, lagoons and reef edges, beating along with short, choppy wing strokes, hovering, then swooping down to snip prey from the surface, or sometimes submerging momentarily after small fish.

Noisy 'dread' flights are a feature of nesting colonies, the entire group rising and swirling through the air with a great clamour. Egg loss—from piratical Silver Gulls, floods and human disturbance—often exceeds 50 per cent in local colonies.

Sooty Tern *Sterna fuscata* LINNÉ, 1766

The Sooty Tern lays its single egg in a small scrape in the ground. Both sexes incubate the egg and care for the chick.

THE WORLD'S VAST TROPICAL OCEANS are the home of the Sooty Tern. It is a pelagic bird, coming to land on small, offshore islands only to breed. At sea it lives in the air, rarely settling on the water and wetting its poorly water-repellant plumage only when dashing through wave crests; it is believed to sleep on the wing. After breeding each year, adults and fledged young disperse out to sea, the young birds travelling farthest. Banded juveniles have been traced from Lord Howe Island to the mid-Pacific and Philippines; others from the Gulf of Mexico to West Africa. Adults may never move far from breeding grounds but in Australia, at least, they visit coastal seas far from the nearest colonies.

On the ocean Sooty Terns keep in flocks to feed. Unlike many other terns, they do not dive for food but instead scoop it up from or just below the surface on the wing, skimming, dipping and wheeling gracefully over the water. Small fish, cephalopods and crustaceans are main prey, many of them species that rise to the surface only after dark. So the terns hunt by night, as well as by day, and particularly at dusk.

After spending three to six years at sea, the young return usually to the colony of their hatching. They may first nest at the age of four years and then continue for at least another 25. Their breeding cycle turns around every 9.6 months, which may partly account for staggered egg-laying and twin spring and autumn peaks of nesting in many Australian colonies.

The return of the Sooties to breed each year is awe-inspiring. Their first visits to their islands are at night, small groups coming at a time. Weeks pass before they are seen by day. Then late one afternoon they pour in over the horizon, the sky filling with a screaming mass of evenly spaced birds, some 100–200 metres up. This continues day after day until small flocks begin to land and lay, two months after the first nightly visits. Ultimately the colony swells to thousands, with nests as little as 50 centimetres apart.

In display, pairs zigzag about in synchronised flight, stretch their wings vertically in a 'V' on the ground, bow, and parade, one bird circling the other, both with shoulders drooped and necks arched to present the nape. Both parents care for the chick which is brooded for about a week, then left to find cover for itself in crèches. About once a day a parent calls it, to feed it by regurgitation. The fledging period is long but flexible—up to 70 days— and chicks can survive for long periods on little food.

OTHER NAMES
Egg-bird, Wide-awake Tern.

IDENTIFICATION
LENGTH: *420–460 mm.*
ADULTS: *Sexes similar. Crown and all upper parts to wings and deeply forked tail black. Forehead white, running back to just over eye. All underparts and underwing coverts white, flight feathers dark grey. Eye brown. Bill and feet black.*
IMMATURES: *Wholly dusky; upper parts spotted buff-white, underwing coverts pale grey, undertail coverts white.*

DOWNY YOUNG: *Sandy, speckled dusky.*

VOICE
High-pitched, nasal ker-wak-wak *('wide-awake') incessantly at colonies; screams in alarm; growls* wruk *and* scra-ar *in threat; quiet* wuk-wuk-wuk *on parade display.*

NESTING
Breeds in vast island colonies, mainly September–December and March–May, but most months except June–August in Australia. Nest a scrape in the ground, often under a bush. Egg: usually one;

off-white often with pink tinge and blotched with purple or brown; long-oval, about 53 x 36 mm. Incubation about 29 days, by both parents. Young fledge in about 70 days.

DISTRIBUTION
Widespread and abundant in tropical seas throughout the world. Breeds in northeastern Australia along islands of northern Great Barrier Reef, and off mid-west coast, from Houtman Albrolhos north to Bedout Island and Ashmore Reef. Five or six races; one in Australia.

Sooty Terns wheeling above their breeding ground. Any human who intrudes into a breeding colony is greeted by screams of alarm from these noisy birds.

Crested Tern

Sterna bergii LICHTENSTEIN, 1823

Crested Terns breed first when two years old. Nests are depressions in the ground, often in areas with plants.

SECOND LARGEST OF AUSTRALIA'S TERNS, the Crested is also one of the most familiar and abundant, frequenting shores and inshore seas around the entire coastline. In ones and twos to flocks of 50 or more, it rests on sand spits, low points and reefs along coastal beaches and inlets and fishes the seas and estuaries nearby; rarely does it range far out from shore into blue water or inland along bodies of fresh water. The terns can swim and float for hours on the water and often bathe there then swim to a beach to dry off and preen. At night they fly to gather in large groups in isolated spits and offshore islands to roost on the ground.

On slender rakish wings, Crested Terns fly gracefully with sweeping leisurely beats. They sometimes play with small shells and pebbles in flight. When fishing they quarter the seas from five–15 metres up, bills pointing down, watching. Sighting prey, they plunge headlong on to it, hitting the water with a splash and submerging momentarily before flying off. Small surface fish five-

eight centimetres long are eaten almost exclusively, grabbed behind the head, although eggs and baby turtles are sometimes taken. Indeed, fishermen have often used flocks of feeding terns to help guide them to shoaling pilchards.

Crested Terns gather in colonies of up to several thousand to breed on offshore islands right around the coast. The colonies are in constant state of flux, varying in their sites, times and numbers from year to year. In display, a bird walks to its mate carrying a fish, crest erect, wings trailing. Its mate parades around it, then both fly up, one behind the other, in a zigzag spiralling flight to often 200 metres before gliding back to earth, twisting and turning. Nests are spaced about one metre apart, just beyond pecking distance. One or other parent broods the young in their first few days until they are old and strong enough to join crèches. After fledging, young disperse far from their parental colonies, some having been recorded travelling half-way round the continent, south to east.

A colony of Crested Terns on Mud Island, Victoria. Nests are spaced about 1 metre apart—beyond pecking distance. Colonies breed on offshore islands.

OTHER NAMES
Greater Crested Tern, Swift Tern.

IDENTIFICATION
LENGTH: *440–480 mm.*
ADULTS: *Sexes similar. In breeding plumage, crown black to eyes, the feathers elongated in erectile crest over nape; forehead broadly white. Upper parts to wings and shallowly forked tail mid-grey. All underparts white. Eye dark brown. Bill mid-yellow, sometimes faintly orange. Feet black. In non-breeding plumage black crown streaked white; bill lemon-yellow.*
IMMATURES: *As non-breeding adults;* upper parts freckled dusky and white in first three months, later washed blotchy dusky and white on shoulders; flight feathers and squarer tail duskier grey; bill dirty lemon.
DOWNY YOUNG: *Sandy, freckled dusky.*

VOICE
Flock call a loud, rasped kirrik; wep-wep *in alarm; cawing in courtship and display; peevish whistles from juveniles.*

NESTING
Breeds in dense island colonies September–December in east and south; March–June *in north; both periods in west. Nest a depression in sand or shingle, often among low plants. Eggs: one, rarely two; slightly glossy stone-grey with sepia, red-brown and black streaks; oval, about 61 x 41 mm. Incubation about 25–26 days, by both sexes.*

DISTRIBUTION
Coasts all around Australia. Breeds on offshore islands. Also occurs throughout Indian Ocean, off southeastern Asia and in western and central Pacific. Up to six-eight races; possibly only one in Australia.

Little Tern *Sterna albifrons* PALLAS, 1764

AUSTRALIA'S SMALLEST TERN, the Little Tern is a gregarious bird of ocean beaches and coral reefs around the north and east of the continent. Its movements are complex and numbers vary seasonally. In the east it may spread south along the coast in small numbers over spring and summer to breed, reaching Tasmania and sometimes the South Australian gulfs. At the same time, Asian summer migrants filter across the north coast. Most of these migrants leave in autumn, and as they do, many of the southern-most breeding groups shift back north up the east coast. There is a winter breeding colony in the Gulf of Carpentaria.

Little Terns gather in smaller flocks than many terns and breed in more dispersed colonies, on quite bare beach sand and shingle just above highwater mark; sites are deserted if they become veg-etated. The nest is a simple scrape, occasionally decorated with wisps of dry seaweed. When flying and fishing, the birds flutter rapidly, then plunge-dive, wings up, on to small surface fish; insects may be taken on the wing. In elaborate courtship behaviour, male and female present fish to each other, parade around one another with drooped wings, chase in spiralling zigzag flights, and glide on upswept wings. Many breeding colonies along the southeast coast are declining through disturbance to nest sites.

The Little Tern nests on sand or shingle beaches, in colonies.

OTHER NAMES
None.

IDENTIFICATION
LENGTH: *210–240 mm.*
ADULTS: *Sexes similar. In breeding plumage crown and nape black; lores black. White forehead extends over eyes in thin line. Back and upper wings grey with black on outer flight feathers; rump and shallowly forked tail pale grey. Underparts white. Eye dark brown. Bill olive- or chrome-yellow, tipped black. Feet and webs orange-yellow. Non-breeders similar, but end* third or half of bill black; lores white; crown pale grey or speckled black and white.
IMMATURES: *As non-breeding adults; crown, back and shoulders flecked brown, washed dusky.*
DOWNY YOUNG: *Sooty or cream, striped sparsely brown.*

VOICE
Sharp, feeble jeep *or* kweek; *urgent* piip-piip-piip *when hovering.*

NESTING
Small colonies on beach, August– *January in southeast and April–July in north. Nest a simple scrape, occasionally decorated with seaweed. Eggs: two, rarely three; stone-coloured with small spots of black and purple-brown; long-oval, about 32 x 24 mm. Incubation about 18–21 days, by both sexes.*

DISTRIBUTION
From Port Hedland, WA, east to Cape York Peninsula and south to Bass Strait, erratically to eastern Tasmania and South Australian gulfs. Up to seven races; one in Australia.

This Fairy Tern's black crown and yellow bill indicate breeding plumage.

Fairy Tern *Sterna nereis* (GOULD, 1843)

OTHER NAMES
None.

IDENTIFICATION
LENGTH: *210–250 mm.*
ADULTS: *Sexes similar. In breeding plumage crown and nape black; fore-lores to bill white; no white line over eye. Back, upper wings and shortly forked tail pearl grey-white. Underparts white. Eye dark brown. Bill orange or orange-yellow, rarely tipped black; legs, feet and webs orange. Non-breeders similar; bill darker, dull yellow centre; crown white streaked black.*
IMMATURES: *Similar to non-breeding adults but wings and wing coverts mottled brown; bill black.*
DOWNY YOUNG: *Light yellow flecked darker; or greyer and striped.*

VOICE
Rather high-pitched chattering note, krik-krikikrik *in alarm; chittering* ket-ket-ket; *loud, low* tchi-wik.

NESTING
Loose colonies on beach sands, August–January in mid-west, September–
March in Tasmania. Nest a bare scrape. Eggs: one–two; stone-grey blotched dark brown; long-oval, about 34 x 25 mm. Incubation about 20 days, by both sexes.

DISTRIBUTION
West and south coasts, breeding from Lacepede Island, WA, to Corner Inlet, Vic., and Tasmania; migrating north to Admiralty Gulf in west and Botany Bay in east. Also southern Great Barrier Reef (New Caledonia race). Three races; two in Australia.

AUSTRALIA'S OTHER TINY TERN, the Fairy Tern, replaces the Little Tern around the southern and western coast. Where their breeding range overlaps on southeastern shores they may nest together and occasionally hybridise. They resemble one another, particularly out of breeding when bills are all dusky and their distinctive face patterns are lost. Fairy Terns nonetheless always have almost white backs and upper wings, right to the tips of their flight feathers.

Throughout its range, the Fairy Tern lives along the coast, rarely out of sight of land or inland; it is rather sedentary. Only in southwestern Australia and Tasmania is it markedly migratory, shifting north at sea to the northwest coast and mainland respect-ively in winter and returning in spring to breed. Fluttering and hovering about on quickly beating wings, the birds hunt in shallow waters close to shore, plunge-diving completely below the surface for small fish and occasional gastropods and crustaceans. Fish are swallowed headfirst, but are carried crosswise in the bill to a mate or chicks.

Fairy Terns nest in small loose colonies of usually less than 100 birds on sandy beaches on islands, shores and lagoons. There they are aggressive and noisy, flying at and defaecating on intruders rather than fighting. In courtship, male and female fly in synchron-ised zigzags, and they present fish when relieving one another at the nest. A male solicits by carrying a fish behind birds in a group. Should a female crouch, he raises his head, tail and wings, turns his head rhythmically from side to side, then mounts. As he dis-mounts, the female seizes the fish and flies off.

Young are brooded in their first few days but later move off to the shelter of seaweed and other cover nearby.

Lesser Crested Tern

Sterna bengalensis LESSON, 1831

OTHER NAMES
None.

IDENTIFICATION
LENGTH: *380–400 mm.*
ADULTS: *Sexes alike. In breeding plumage, crown black to eyes and almost to bill; forehead narrowly white. Upper parts to wings and shallowly forked tail pale grey. All underparts white. Eye brown. Bill rich orange-yellow. Feet black. In non-breeding plumage, whole crown white with streaked black crescent around nape.*
IMMATURES: *As non-breeding adults, but back, upper wings and squarer tail darker grey, mottled brown and dusky.*

VOICE
Similar to Crested Tern.

NESTING
Large colonies on offshore islands, cays and sandbars, September–December in east, March–June in northwest. Nest a scrape on bare sand. Egg: one; white or pale pink, lightly spotted and blotched with sepia, red-brown and purple-grey; oval, about 53 x 37 mm. Incubation about 25 days, by both sexes.

DISTRIBUTION
Breeds in north from Point Cloates, WA, to about Gladstone, Qld. Also along Mediterranean coast, Red Sea to India, Sunda arc and New Guinea. Three races; one in Australia.

This Lesser Crested Tern's white crown indicates non-breeding plumage.

A TERN OF THE TROPICS, the Lesser Crested Tern can be identified from its relative, the Crested Tern, by its smaller, slenderer form and bright orange-yellow bill. It is both gregarious and nomadic, breeding in close-packed colonies of hundreds to thousands, mixing and roosting with other terns, and dispersing from a few local nesting colonies right around the northern Australian coast. Winter influxes may be augmented by nomads from Southeast Asia.

The terns feed over shallow inshore waters and out to sea, beating in wide arcs and plunge-diving for prey, mainly small fish; they often rest on the water and swim freely. There and at breeding colonies they are noisy birds.

To protect their eggs from marauding gulls, they sit tight and lunge. Young are minded by one or other parent until large enough to join crèches, allowing both parents to spend more time fishing.

Lesser Noddy

Anous tenuirostris (TEMMINCK, 1823)

LESSER NODDIES, plumaged like the Common Noddy but smaller, slenderer-billed, and their white caps over the lores, live in two huge but isolated colonies at either end of the Indian Ocean: one from the Seychelles to Madagascar in the west, and the other confined around Houtman Abrolhos off mid-western Australia in the east. Although perhaps dispersing for a few weeks in mid-winter, the birds spend the year around their islands, roosting and nesting in close colonies of tens to thousands on island trees—mangroves in the Albrolhos—and feeding in surrounding open sea. They fly out to fish in regular lines each mid-morning and return in late afternoon, their arrival and departure marked by noisy wheeling. At sea they skim and hover low over the water, taking their prey—fish, plankton, molluscs and jelly fish—from the surface.

In display, male and female chase one another in zigzag flights, and whole brooding groups often flush in alarm to swirl about in 'dreads'. Males attract mates to nest sites of their choosing by feeding them there. In courtship, the male bows and feeds his mate by regurgitation. Both sexes nest-build, the female forming the structure; and both brood the chick, which stays on the nest until it can fly, then moves to a day-time crèche on the beach.

OTHER NAMES
None.

IDENTIFICATION
LENGTH: *310–330 mm.*
ADULTS: *Sexes similar. Entirely sooty brown, except forehead and crown grey-white shading to darker at nape. Small arc of white above eye, larger one below, interrupting black eye-ring. Eye dark brown. Bill and feet black.*
IMMATURES: *Similar to adults.*
DOWNY YOUNG: *Plain grey.*

VOICE
Rattling alarm churs. Purring call. Soliciting females and young squeak.

NESTING
Breeds August–December. Nest a platform of seaweed, placed on low tree branch. Egg: one; matt off-white, sparingly blotched and spotted with rufous-brown and purple-grey;
ellipsoidal, about 45 x 30 mm. Incubation by both sexes.

DISTRIBUTION
Seas around Houtman Abrolhos, WA. Also Seychelles to Chagos and Madagascar, western Indian Ocean. Two races; one in Australia.

The Lesser Noddy builds a tree nest of seaweed cemented with excreta.

Common Noddy *Anous stolidus* (LINNÉ, 1758)

The Common Noddy nests on the ground or on a low shrub. The birds breed on tropical islands and coral cays.

NODDIES ARE DUSKY, white-capped terns of open tropical seas that feed, not by plunge-diving, but by skimming and picking food from the surface; and the pantropic Common Noddy is the most widespread of them. Off Australia it disperses from breeding islands along the west and northeast coast mainly over winter. Flocks of 50 or more move together. Able to swim well and rest on the water for hours without their plumage becoming waterlogged, they nonetheless roost on small islets, reefs, flotsam and even the backs of turtles where they are at hand. They come in from late afternoon into dusk, then move out to feed soon after sunrise, their massing converging flocks resembling smoke on the horizon. At rest, they often lie on the ground with a wing outstretched, resting on the fanned tail—a 'comfort' movement—and they sleep there with heads tucked back into the scapulars.

Fishing parties skim the waves and even dive through the crests as they pick and scoop their food from the surface: mainly fish, but also cephalopods, molluscs and medusae. They dip to drink briefly and will belly-land on the water, wings and tail held aloft.

That breeding birds have homing ability has been demonstrated in the Gulf of Mexico where noddies released 1900 kilometres away were back at their nests in five days. Off Australia, they converge to breed in close-packed colonies of tens of thousands on islets, mainly in spring in the south and autumn in the north, but at any time on some. Courting birds fly over the colony in synchronised zigzags, their wings beating slowly in a 'butterfly' manner. At nest sites, male and female face one another on the ground, parade around with shoulders drooped, then stretch swiftly forward, opening their bills to show their orange mouths. There they fence with their bills, bowing and jerking their heads forward and back. Nesting birds also often rise silently together in sweeping 'dread' flights, only to return moments later with great clamour.

Nest-building is shared by both sexes but later the female guards the nest while the male fishes for them both. He feeds her ceremonially; both birds bow, then the female 'dibbles' her bill against his, causing him to regurgitate to the accompaniment of much cackling. Chicks, brooded by both sexes, take food not only from the bill but also the gullet of their parents. Older chicks beg, cheeping, with head flat to the ground and tail up.

OTHER NAMES
Greater Noddy, Brown Noddy.

IDENTIFICATION
LENGTH: *About 400 mm.*
ADULTS: *Sexes similar. Uniformly sooty black, wing tips and tail darker, except forehead and crown grey-white, sharply demarcated from dusky lores. Tail wedge-shaped with slight central notch. Broken white eye-ring. Eye dark brown. Bill and feet black.*
IMMATURES: *Similar to adults but often lacking a well-defined 'cap'.*
DOWNY YOUNG: *Smoky, sometimes with white blotches on back and wings.*

VOICE
Threat or alarm note when disturbed on nest kraa, kraa, kraa. *Also purring notes in courtship; threatening* kree-aw *or* kuk-kuk-kuk.

NESTING
Breeds in dense colonies, mainly September–November in south and March–June in north. Nest, about 250 mm in diameter, of seaweed or leaves, sometimes interwoven with sticks or coral, slightly hollowed; pressed into shrub or in scrape on bare ground. Egg: one; *matt pale pink, blotched and spotted with rufous and purple-brown; long-oval, about 53 x 36 mm. Incubation about 34 days, by both sexes.*

DISTRIBUTION
Breeds on islands and coral cays along northern coasts of Australia, usually no farther south than Houtman Abrolhos, WA, and Capricorn Group, Qld, Norfolk and Lord Howe Islands. Also breeds in Indian, Pacific and Atlantic Oceans. About five races; one in Australia.

Black Noddy *Anous minutus* BOIE, 1844

BLACK NODDIES APPARENTLY DO NOT migrate or wander much. During the non-breeding season they commonly return to roost on their nesting islands. Individual birds seem to be either involved in breeding or in moult almost all the time; some even nest while still in moult. This is unusual because moulting and breeding each cost so much in energy that birds, as a rule, undergo them separately.

Most of the adult birds leave the roosting and nesting grounds for the open sea to fish in early morning and return just before dark. They snatch up their food—mainly small fish, but also cuttlefish, other molluscs, jellyfish and plankton—from the surface of the water with their bills. In this they are like other noddies, but they work the inshore surf around islands and headlands much more, nipping in and out, under and along curling breakers, with unequalled agility. Plunge-diving for food is rare but it does happen.

Flying young also leave the nesting islands during the day but return in the late afternoon and early evening to be fed by their parents. Their calls at feeding time can be heard from about two kilometres out to sea.

When roosting, the Black Noddy adopts a 'sunbathing' posture, with its tail and one wing spread and its head to one side. It is a tame bird and can be picked up off the nest. It preens frequently; probably, like other seabirds, to remove parasites.

OTHER NAMES
White-capped Noddy, Titerack.

IDENTIFICATION
LENGTH: *360 mm, including 120 mm tail; wingspan 650 mm.*
ADULTS: *Sexes similar. Body plumage, tail and wings sooty black. Forehead and crown silver-white, shading abruptly to grey on back of neck. Lores black, extending to black eye rim, which is broken by thin white arc above and below. Tail forked. Eye brown. Bill black. Legs dark brown. Identified from other noddies by blackish plumage with jet-black lores, intermediate size, longer and more slender bill, and distinctly forked tail.*
IMMATURES: *Similar to adults.*
DOWNY YOUNG: *Grey-white.*

VOICE
Three distinct calls; staccato alarm note loudest and most distinctive. Others are kerr; *and a cackling* krikrikrik *at roosting sites.*

NESTING
Breeds mainly August–January in Australia, in closely packed colonies. Nest a shallow cup of soft leaves interwoven with seaweed, grass and tree roots, cemented with excreta and sticky vegetable matter, about 150 mm in diameter; placed 1–10 m above ground in forks of tree branches. Egg: one; coarse, matt cream, thinly blotched with rufous and purple-grey, particularly at larger end; rounded-oval, 46 x 33 mm. Incubation about 35 days, by both sexes. Young wander from nest, returning in afternoon and evening where they are found and fed by parents.

DISTRIBUTION
Northeastern coast, islands and coral cays from Darnley Island, Torres Strait, south as far as Capricorn Group, Qld; vagrant south to region of Sydney, NSW. Also breeds in tropical Pacific, Indian and Atlantic Oceans, including Norfolk Island. Six or seven races; one in Australian region and another on Christmas Island.

The Black Noddy builds a nest of grass and roots cemented with excreta, which it tramples with its feet.

White-headed Pigeon *Columba leucomela* TEMMINCK, 1821

The White-headed Pigeon is one of the most secretive pigeons in rainforests. It usually builds its nest in bushes or small trees in the understorey.

OF ALL THE RAINFOREST fruit pigeons, the White-headed Pigeon is the most likely to remain abundant in many coastal districts. It did become very rare in the late nineteenth century when most of its rainforest habitat, which extended south to the Illawarra district of New South Wales, was destroyed. However, after the settlers in their early enthusiasm had cleared their properties of every living tree, they were obliged to plant introduced trees such as the camphor laurel and to allow a few rainforest trees to regenerate to provide shade for their cattle. Gullies and rough areas too difficult to maintain in grass reverted to rainforest, refurnishing the White-headed Pigeon with suitable habitat.

As White-headed Pigeons fed increasingly in isolated camphor laurels or maize stubble they increased in numbers, and in some districts—for instance, along the northern rivers of New South Wales—they may be more common than ever before.

The pigeons live in pairs and groups of up to 10–15. They sometimes feed on the ground, but more often in trees, particularly in the lower storeys of the forest. Rarely are they found in the canopy with other pigeons. Fruits of various native laurels are important foods for the birds but the detailed make-up of their diet is not known. To drink they land on the ground near a rainforest pool and walk strongly and swiftly to the water.

White-headed Pigeons are nomads, wandering from place to place according to the ripening of fruit. However, in some districts their numbers seem to remain constant month after month, so the nomadic movements may be only local.

These birds are among the wariest and most secretive of the pigeons living in rainforests. They sit silently in a densely foliaged tree and, if there is any movement on the forest floor, they leave quietly from the opposite side of the tree or remain motionless. Often the first hints of their presence are loud claps of wings and the crash of bodies hurtling through a tree as a flock leaves from a few metres away. In open country they fly at high speed, in a straight path low over the ground, but swerve upwards and away wildly at the sight of an unusual object. At all times, the wings beat continuously and the flight is direct and swift.

In spring the males display themselves prominently, rising above the forest canopy to perform a spectacular, undulating flight up and down their territories. Their bowing display is also distinctive. The male faces the female on a branch. With his body erect and his breast and throat inflated, he depresses his bill towards his upper breast. He inclines his body forward slowly until it is 20–25 degrees from the horizontal; the legs are flexed as the body moves down. At the low point there is a soft deep *coo* and then he returns to an upright position. At the end of several such bows he stretches his neck, holding his head up, and opens and closes his bill several times very rapidly. This bow is very different from the bowing displays of the other members of the genus.

OTHER NAMES
Baldy Pigeon.

IDENTIFICATION
LENGTH: *380–420 mm.*
MALE: *Head and neck milky-white. Back, wings and tail black, with purple-green sheen over back. Lower breast and belly grey; undertail and undersides of wings slate. Eye golden yellow with red-orange outer rings. Bill red with cream tip. Feet red-pink with darker claws.*
FEMALE: *Duller and tinged with grey over head and neck.*
IMMATURES: *Crown of head grey; face white; other parts that are white in adults are mottled grey in immatures; wings and tails grey-brown; eye brown-red.*
DOWNY YOUNG: *Rust-coloured.*

VOICE
Contact call a drawn-out succession of low-pitched coos. *In breeding season a deep, quavering* coo-coo, *sometimes with a third very soft note added. It seems to be an advertising call.*

NESTING
Nests July–March, maximum breeding October–December. Nest about 125 mm in diameter, a small platform of fine twigs and vine tendrils, placed in bushes or small trees 3–20 m above ground in rainforest. Egg: one; cream; ellipsoidal or oval, about 40 x 31 mm. Incubation about 20 days, by both sexes. Young fledge in 21–22 days.

DISTRIBUTION
Ranges from Cooktown, Qld, to Illawarra district, NSW. Lives mostly in coastal strip but inland in places such as Bunya Mountains and Atherton Tableland. In south, most common in lowland rainforest; in north, more abundant in higher rainforests. No races.

Feral Pigeon *Columba livia* GMELIN, 1789

FERAL PIGEONS ARE DESCENDED from the wild rock pigeon of the Northern Hemisphere. They spread through their association with man which began over 5000 years ago when they were first domesticated by the Egyptians. Today in Australia they are found living wild in many towns and there are populations in many rural districts as well. These wild birds retain the cliff-dwelling and ledge-nesting habits of their ancestors and make use of any ledges they can find in their urban environment. There the birds cause trouble and expense by defacing buildings and public places with their droppings. Their nesting material is washed into gutters and downpipes, flooding ceilings and causing damage to buildings. Paradoxically, humans support the pigeons by their own wasteful habits. The birds feed mostly on food scraps in streets and parks and on food which has been put out for poultry and other domestic animals. Otherwise they are grain-eaters.

Perhaps the largest populations outside the major cities are those in the wheat-growing areas of southeastern Australia, where there are vast areas of grain crops and stubble, and many barns and sheds that provide nesting sites. It is sometimes difficult to determine which birds are 'owned' by farmers and which are truly feral, but whatever their source their numbers are great.

There are also colonies of Feral Pigeons nesting in rock holes or cliffs on the southern coast and in holes in river red gums along the banks of inland rivers. Some have reached Norfolk Island.

The mixed stock of the many forms of Feral Pigeons that have been released or escaped in cities has evolved, by cross-breeding and natural selection, into a pigeon of the same general form as its wild ancestor. And they give the same flapping and gliding display flights, with wings held in a high 'V'. The many specialised forms of domestic pigeon that have been bred selectively for ornament or for the table—fantails, mondaines, tumblers and so on—do not survive in the wild. Centuries of cross-breeding has resulted, however, in the development of innumerable colour patterns among feral birds, from mottled whites to blues and red-browns.

OTHER NAMES
Rock Pigeon, Domestic Pigeon.

IDENTIFICATION
LENGTH: *340–360 mm.*
ADULTS: *Sexes similar. Some feral domestic pigeons resemble ancestral rock pigeon, which is blue-grey. Neck has purple and green display sheen. Lower back white; lower rump dark grey. Two conspicuous black bars across closed wing. Broad black band near end of tail. Underwing white. Eye orange. Bill black; cere whitish or grey. Legs and feet red or purple-red. Among other feral domestic pigeons are 'chequers', which have wings profusely blotched with black and all plumage dark grey; 'mealies', cream-grey spotted with brown and white; 'reds', mixed red and brown, with grey and white; 'blacks', dusky black; and 'pieds', blotched white with any other colour.*
IMMATURES: *Resemble female, but with reduced iridescence.*
DOWNY YOUNG: *Usually yellow.*

VOICE
Advertising call a moaning coo; *display call commonly heard is* co-roo-coo-coo.

NESTING
Breeds in all months, but mostly in summer. Nests are placed on any flat surface—including ledges on buildings, cornices, ceilings, understructures of bridges, rock holes and tree hollows. Eggs are laid on bare surface with a few straws loosely arranged around them. Eggs: two; glossy white; oval, about 39 x 28 mm. Incubation 17–19 days, by both sexes; several successive broods. Young fledge in 30–35 days.

DISTRIBUTION
Introduced into Australia where, as a commensal of man, it now extends throughout the southern and eastern halves of the continent. The wild rock pigeon is found in Ireland, Scotland, Faroes and Shetland Islands, eastern Europe, Mediterranean region, Arabia, India and Sri Lanka, Turkestan, Africa north of equator, and western Asia; a closely related form in rest of Asia. Fourteen races; probably one in Australia, with numerous varieties.

The Feral Pigeon has evolved through various domestic forms back towards its ancestor, the rock pigeon of the Northern Hemisphere.

Spotted Turtle-Dove *Streptopelia chinensis* (SCOPOLI, 1786)

A NATIVE OF SOUTHERN ASIA, the Spotted Turtle-Dove was first released in Australia at Melbourne in 1870. Other releases followed in Adelaide (1881), Perth (1898) and Brisbane (1912). Now it is found in all the mainland capitals, in many other cities, in large towns and in agricultural districts between Mossman, northern Queensland, and Melbourne.

Birds of the Chinese and Malayan races, two of the many subspecies of the Spotted Turtle-Dove, were apparently introduced to Australia and today the Australian birds display characteristics of these in all possible combinations.

Overall, they grade from large with deep grey vents and plain shoulders, around Melbourne and Adelaide, to small with whitish vents and black-streaked shoulders, in northeastern Queensland. This suggests that the doves released around Melbourne were of the big, pale Chinese race while those in northeastern Queensland, in the 1940s, were of the small darker Malaysian subspecies or else their traits are selected environmentally.

In agricultural land, scrub along creeks and swamp margins in eastern Australia, the Spotted Turtle-Dove meets the Bar-shouldered Dove, a native bird that is similar in size and in food and habitat needs. Field observations suggest that as the Spotted Turtle-Dove increases in numbers in these places the native dove declines and disappears. On the outskirts of Adelaide, it may have replaced another native, the Peaceful Dove.

Spotted Turtle-Doves in Sydney, Melbourne and Perth eat remarkably similar diets: 44–47 per cent domestic animal feed, 12–23 per cent bread, 32–42 per cent seeds of garden plants. Wheat, presumably fed to poultry, is often the biggest item.

OTHER NAMES
Indian Dove, Spotted Dove, Laceneck Dove.

IDENTIFICATION
LENGTH: *290–320 mm.*
ADULTS: *Sexes similar. Forehead, crown and face grey with pink tinge; nape and back of neck jet-black with conspicuous white spotting; rest of upper parts drab brown with dusky centres to feathers; upper side of tail dark brown, outer feathers black with broad white tips; throat and breast vinaceous-brown; belly and vent greyer or whiter. Primaries dusky with blue edge to shoulder. Eye orange-brown. Bill dark grey-brown. Feet dull red-brown.*
IMMATURES: *All plumage dull brown with no black and white on neck. Eye dull yellow. Bill and cere brown-grey. Feet pink-brown with dusky claws.*
DOWNY YOUNG: *Sand-coloured.*

VOICE
Musical, drowsy coo, coo croo-oo *or* coocoo, croo-croor, *for advertising.*

NESTING
Breeds in all months of the year but mainly spring and summer. Nest a frail platform of sticks and rootlets, 150–200 mm in diameter, usually in tree or shrub. Eggs: two; glossy white; oval, about 29 x 23 mm. Incubation 14–16 days, by both sexes. Young fledge in about 15 days.

DISTRIBUTION
Capital cities and larger towns; also in well-developed agricultural districts. Continuous population between Brisbane and Sydney. Natural range is from India to China and south through Indonesia to Timor. About eight races; two in Australia, integrating.

The Spotted Turtle-Dove, introduced from southern Asia, may compete with some native species that live in the same habitat and eat similar food.

Laughing Turtle-Dove *Streptopelia senegalensis* (LINNÉ, 1766)

OTHER NAMES
Senegal Turtle-Dove, Laughing Dove.

IDENTIFICATION
LENGTH: *250–270 mm.*
MALE: *Head mauve-pink; back brown with rusty tint; lower back and upper tail coverts slate-blue; upper side of tail grey-brown grading to black with broad white tips on outer feathers. Neck and breast mauve-pink toning down to white on lower belly and undertail coverts; a collar of coppery-brown flecks over black. Outer wing coverts slate-blue; flight feathers brown-grey; rest of upper side of wing mottled slate-grey and mauve-pink; underside of wing slate-grey. Eye brown; eye-ring grey with red edge. Bill and cere dark grey-brown. Legs and feet red-purple.*
FEMALE: *As male but duller.*
IMMATURES: *Where adults are mauve-pink, young are dull brown and tawny grey; no collar. Eye light brown. Bill dark grey. Feet pink-red with dark claws.*
DOWNY YOUNG: *Sandy buff to yellow.*

VOICE
Soft and musical cooroocoo-coocoocoo *with a bubbling or laughing quality.*

NESTING
Breeds throughout year; nests found in all months, but mostly September–March. Nest a frail platform of fine sticks and twigs about 150 mm in diameter; placed almost anywhere but usually in trees and bushes. Eggs: two; white; oval, about 29 x 23 mm. Incubation 14–16 days, by both sexes. Young stay in nest for 21 days.

DISTRIBUTION
Found throughout Perth, at many places between Geraldton and Tambellup, and east to Merredin. Isolated colonies at Kalgoorlie and Esperance. Native range includes all of Africa, Arabia, India, Afghanistan and Turkestan and there are local occurrences in Turkey and elsewhere in Middle East. About nine races; one in Australia. From their appearance and size, introduced colonies in Australia came from the nominate race in eastern Africa south of the Sahara.

The introduced Laughing Turtle-Dove spends much of the time on the ground, where it feeds, though it usually roosts in trees or bushes. It walks in a rather hunched posture.

WHEN THE LAUGHING TURTLE-DOVE was first released in Australia, at the Perth Zoological Gardens in 1898, the species was already partly adapted to urban life. It had lived in cities, towns and villages for many centuries in its native Africa and southern Asia. It has now become established in the southwest of Western Australia and has spread more into the bush than the Spotted Turtle-Dove, another introduced bird with a long urban history.

The two turtle-doves closely resemble each other in many ways, including diet, general behaviour and flight. Both feed on the ground—on very similar food—but roost or nest in trees or thick bushes. Both make a display flight, flying up at a steep angle and then gliding down with wings and tail spread wide. Their bowing displays differ from those of native pigeons and doves. The tail remains pointing downwards and the whole body bobs down to horizontal—lower if the bird is on a branch. Between bows the body is raised higher than normal.

When they fly their wings beat continuously and the flight is swift, direct and level—quite unlike that of the native Peaceful Dove or the Diamond Dove, though their posture resembles that of the Bar-shouldered Dove.

Like all these doves, Laughing Turtle-Doves are ground feeders and grain-eaters. Around Perth they thrive on waste, particularly grain and protein pellets put out for domestic and zoo animals, as well as bread and garden seeds.

Brown Cuckoo-Dove *Macropygia amboinensis* (TEMMINCK, 1821)

WIDESPREAD CLEARING OF RAINFOREST and illegal hunting have resulted in a decline of the Brown Cuckoo-Dove. Yet this tree-living bird, which is shot more than any other coastal pigeon, is common wherever its habitat has not been totally destroyed.

It can be found deep in the rainforest, in the understorey and in the canopy, but its preferred habitat is broken vegetation with much shrubbery—along the edge of the forest and along creeks. It is very common, usually in pairs or small groups of up to 10 or so, in clearings where weeds and berry-bearing bushes have grown over the felled timber. Introduced weeds—lantana, wild tobacco, wild raspberry, gooseberry and inkweeds—grow in those places and the Brown Cuckoo-Dove feeds freely on their fruits.

In the lowland rainforests of northern Queensland it spends most of its foraging time in two large trees, the silver and white basswoods; in a vine *Hibbertia,* and in a small shrubby tree, yellow *Evodia.* It also eats the fruits of ivory basswood, buttonwood, native bleeding heart, mistletoes and shrubs of the nightshade fam-

ily. Although feeding agilely in the foliage of these trees and shrubs, it does come to ground at times as well, not so much to drink as to take small stones that help in the digestion of its food.

The Brown Cuckoo-Dove seldom travels far, preferring to move from one clump of bushes or a tree to another nearby. Usually it flies low down, among the tree heads or not far above the lantana and other plants in the open. It appears to be a weak flier because of its long tail and rounded wings, but it can move quickly—and does so with a graceful, languid flapping.

The bowing display of the Brown Cuckoo-Dove is slow and courtly. The male faces the female along a branch and draws himself up to his full height. With bill pressed to his inflated breast, he bows to the horizontal, emits a harsh version of his contact call and slowly raises his body. He neither raises nor spreads his tail. In a display flight the male rises from a clearing, with tail half spread and wings clapping, to about 25 metres. Then he sets his wings downwards, fully spreads his tail and spirals back down.

OTHER NAMES
Brown Pigeon, Pheasant Pigeon, Cuckoo-Dove.

IDENTIFICATION
LENGTH: *300–450 mm, with long tail.*
ADULTS: *Head and all upper parts deep russet-brown with vinous iridescence on neck. Upper breast plain pink-brown; rest of underside buffier-brown. Eye blue-grey with crimson outer ring. Bill and cere brown. Feet dark red.*
FEMALE: *As male but with dusky vermiculations imparting a dirty cast over neck, back and breast.*
IMMATURES: *Crown chestnut; more distinct black barring on neck and upper breast; wings russet-brown*

mottled darker; tail finely barred dusky. Eye dark brown. Bill and cere brown. Feet red-grey.
DOWNY YOUNG: *Yellow to fawn.*

VOICE
Contact call a penetrating whoop-a-whoop—first note low, last higher and longer; similar rasping coo *in bowing display; clucking* coo *in alarm or warning.*

NESTING
Breeding season protracted, peaking September–January in south, earlier in north. Nest a pad of fine sticks and vines, up to 150 mm thick; in fork of low tree, in vine tangles, or on top of tree

ferns; usually within 6 m of ground. Egg: one; smooth, dull creamy white; ellipsoidal, about 35 x 24 mm. Incubation 16–18 days, by both sexes. Young fledge in about 16 days.

DISTRIBUTION
From Mallacoota, Vic., to northern Cape York Peninsula; in coastal lowlands and more humid adjacent highlands, in rainforest. Widely distributed to Sumatra and Philippines. In Australia grades smaller in size south to north; separate race on Cape York Peninsula with greyer-headed males.

The female Brown Cuckoo-Dove (right) broods a single chick in its nest, a pad of fine sticks and vines, on top of a tree fern. Sometimes the bird simply builds a platform in the fork of a low tree or a tangle of rainforest vines. The bird on the left is a male.

Wonga Pigeon   *Leucosarcia melanoleuca* (LATHAM, 1801)

The Wonga Pigeon travels mostly by walking and spends the greater part of its life on the ground. It eats fallen fruit and seeds, and berries on low bushes.

IT IS RARE FOR THE WONGA PIGEON to be seen flying, unless it has been disturbed. It spends nearly all of its time on the ground except when roosting in trees at night, and travels mostly by walking, feeding over the forest floor quietly and nimbly. It is an extremely alert bird and almost impossible to stalk—and it is heard much more often than seen, its monotonously repeated, high-pitched advertising *coos* given from the ground or a low branch. If surprised, a Wonga Pigeon will flush with a very loud wing clap and sail away through the timber, or alight on a branch and sit motionless, back to the intruder, but watching over one shoulder.

Wonga Pigeons inhabit most of the denser east coast and upland forests and scrubs, but are most abundant in tall eucalypt forests with a close under-shrubbery of wattles and rainforest thicket. Such undergrowth is important, because the fruit and seeds that it produces, when falling to the ground, provide staple food for the pigeons. Although they sometimes congregate at sudden food falls, the birds are rather solitary and sedentary, occupying the same territory year in year out.

The male Wonga Pigeon attracts the female with a display quite distinct from that of any other Australian ground pigeon. It stands on a log or the ground, rhythmically raising its wings and tail. As it raises its partly opened wings, it swings its tail up to the horizontal and spreads it fully. As the wings fall the tail drops and closes. In time with the rising and falling of its tail the bird swings its head from side to side and tucks it briefly behind each wing in turn. During this deliberate, rhythmic swinging its white lower breast and belly become very obvious, alternating with a frontal display of its grey breast with its broad white 'V'. A few bouts of this display commonly induce the female to mate, after which the two birds stand side by side, billing and preening one another. There is no male parade. There is also a less conspicuous bowing display, given by the male mainly in threat. It raises its tail and vent from 45 degrees up to the horizontal, spreading its tail slightly but keeping its wings closed. At each swing it trills musically.

Although still abundant in many areas, the Wonga Pigeon has declined overall because of clearing and shooting. It was once much prized as a game bird, for its flesh, unlike that of other Australian pigeons, cooks white.

OTHER NAMES
Wonga Wonga.

IDENTIFICATION
LENGTH: *380–410 mm.*
ADULTS: *Sexes similar. Forehead white; lores dark grey; upper parts uniform slate-grey. Area under bill white; throat pale grey. Breast slate-grey with broad white V-shaped mark; lower breast and belly white spotted with black. Undertail fawn with grey tips to feathers. Eye brown. Bill red with brown tip. Feet pink-red.*
IMMATURES: *Browner over back, greyer on front, with less conspicuous white 'V' on breast.*

VOICE
Advertising call a loud, high-pitched, resonant coo uttered in long sequences with monotonous regularity at half-second intervals. In bowing display male emits a soft, musical, trilling coo.

NESTING
Breeds throughout year, but mostly October–January. Most nests are substantial, others sparse, slightly dish-shaped platforms of sticks, often thicker on outside than in centre, about 300 mm in diameter and 90 mm deep; built in tall, open-headed trees often on edge of scrub, or in vines or tree ferns, 3–20 m above ground. Eggs: two; smooth, lustrous white; long-oval, about 39 x 28 mm.

DISTRIBUTION
From eastern Victoria to the Clarke Range, Qld, throughout coastal forests and moister forests of adjacent ranges and tablelands. In some places range extends inland to drier scrubs—for example, at Springsure and Darling Downs, Qld. No races.

Emerald Ground-Dove *Chalcophaps indica* (LINNE, 1758)

The male Emerald Ground-Dove shares incubation with the female — usually throughout the day. It is quick to drive other ground-doves from its territory.

IN AUSTRALIA, MOST EMERALD GROUND-DOVES are found in eastern coastal rainforests, although the birds also visit wet sclerophyll forests and coastal heaths. In the Northern Territory they live mainly in monsoon forest. Although the ground-dove is primarily a bird of the forest floor, it frequents all types of regrowth, overgrown clearings and lantana-choked country, and often feeds in small isolated patches of scrubs.

Besides feeding on the ground the doves sometimes walk along thick limbs of trees, and take any fruit that is within reach, but they do not cling to the foliage in the way fruit pigeons do. These doves eat seeds and fruit of inkweeds, wild tobacco, wild raspberry and lantana, as well as figs and various falling seeds.

Although Emerald Ground-Doves sometimes gather in small groups in clearings, they are usually solitary birds. Sometimes they are seen walking along jungle tracks or flying across open areas or along scrubby creeks. Their flight is strong, swift and heavy, like a bronzewing. Travelling at high speed from cover to cover they beat their wings continuously and keep close to the ground. In the rainforest they fly between the trees, manoeuvring quickly and easily between the trunks.

As with all pigeons, the males have a display posture that resembles a bow, which they use in sexual or aggressive situations. The Emerald Ground-Dove also performs the bowing display to advertise itself. It flies up to a branch, lowers its head and breast a little and makes its main movement with its tail and lower belly, swinging them up to an angle of 45–60 degrees and then down again, repeating this 15–20 times in perfectly even rhythm. The result is eye-catching, and nearly always a female trots out of the undergrowth and perches beside the male. He then performs a rapid bobbing display and copulation often follows.

Both sexes incubate the eggs, the female during the night and the male during the day, although females have occasionally been found on nests at midday. The birds change over in the morning and late afternoon, but there is no obvious relief ceremony—the incoming partner merely arrives and the other moves off the nest and departs. Although this dove utters its call on the ground, it usually mounts a low branch to do so, and it is on the branch that it performs its display. In the breeding season the males space themselves out through the forest in clearly defined territories. They sit on low, horizontal limbs, or on the nest incubating the eggs, and boom out their territorial call for long periods. They defend an area of only a few metres around the nest and attack any member of the same species that transgresses.

The Emerald Ground-Dove becomes very tame when not disturbed, and visits farm and town gardens. Its needs are modest—some undergrowth in a copse of timber or a scrubby creek as living space—and it should not be difficult to preserve in most districts within its range.

OTHER NAMES
Green-winged Pigeon, Green Dove, Little Green Pigeon, Emerald Dove.

IDENTIFICATION
LENGTH: *260–280 mm.*
MALE: *Head, neck and upper back vinous-brown with grey cast on crown; mid-back crossed by emerald-green band; lower back and upper tail dusky, the former crossed by two light grey bands. Wings and shoulders bright emerald green; edge of shoulders white; flight feathers dusky. Underparts vinous-brown; undertail dusky. Underwings russet-brown. Eye dark brown. Bill bright red. Feet red-brown with dark claws.*
FEMALE: *Vinous tone missing from head and ventral surface; tail and lower back brown with dull bars; shoulder edge small and grey. Bill more orange.*
IMMATURES: *Head and body brown barred and scalloped with dusky; little green on wings. Eye brown. Bill horn. Legs and feet grey-pink.*
DOWNY YOUNG: *Sandy-yellow.*

VOICE
Low-pitched but loud, penetrating coo repeated continuously, as territorial call. Also soft explosive coo in display.

NESTING
Nests found throughout year but mostly in September–December in eastern Australia and January–April in Northern Territory. Nest a well-made platform of interlaced twigs, about 180 mm in diameter, built in a bush, a horizontal fork, a mass of vines or on a fern or tree-fern, 5–10 m above ground. Eggs: two; pale cream; oval, about 28 x 21 mm. Incubation 14–16 days, by both sexes.*

DISTRIBUTION
Two races in Australia; one ranges from southern coast of New South Wales, near Narooma, to tip of Cape York Peninsula. Range is mainly coastal but extends to humid tablelands and inland to Darling Downs. Other race is found in north of Western Australia and Northern Territory usually within 160 km of the coast. It is more brightly marked with more extensive white shoulder edging and brighter rump bars. Species also occurs in New Guinea, Indonesia, southeastern Asia and India.

Flock Bronzewing *Phaps histrionica* (GOULD, 1841)

AS ITS NAME SUGGESTS, the Flock Bronzewing is one of the most gregarious of Australian pigeons. It lives in flocks and breeds in loose groups in small areas. These days the flocks seldom number more than a few hundred birds, although several thousand birds have been seen together after particularly good seasons. In the early days of settlement of the inland plains some of the flocks were enormous, and accounts from that time in New South Wales refer to 'countless multitudes' and to birds breeding in thousands all over the plain. In Western Australia there were at one place 'countless myriads', the roar of their wings sounding 'like heavy surf'.

The coming of sheep to the inland plains finished all that. As the stock destroyed the soft native grasses, and the ground became covered with herbaceous and prickly weeds, the pigeons disappeared from many districts. Their end was hastened by the disastrous droughts of the late nineteenth century, when sheep and rabbits managed to produce near-desert conditions over vast areas. Only in the north where droughts were less severe, and grazing —by cattle—less destructive, did the Flock Bronzewing survive in large numbers, but even there the grazed grasslands no longer support anywhere near the original numbers.

Compounding their appearance and disappearance is their nomadism, for they follow the erratic seasons around the inland. Here their long, pointed wings, longer in proportion than in related bronzewing pigeons, are well-adapted to complete far-ranging flights swiftly. Flock Bronzewings fly in closely packed flocks. Their flight is swift and direct, with continuous wing-beats. Near dusk the birds fly up to several kilometres to drink. Each flock circles the water a few times and then swoops down to land some metres away. The birds run in a dense mass to the water's edge, drink hastily and take off again. When there is a great crush at a small waterhole, some pigeons land on the water like Budgerigars, drink while floating, and take off vertically.

Flock Bronzewings are ground-feeders and eat the seeds of grasses, particularly Mitchell grass, and herbage. On the Barkly Tableland, the birds have learnt that cattle dung provides an easy source of concentrated seed during drought, and they fly to the bore holes in the early afternoon to pick out the undigested seeds. When not travelling to water or feeding, the flocks sit out on the plains, or on the banks of a bore drain in direct and intense sunlight. If disturbed they rise simultaneously, with a roar of wings, and circle the area before leaving or settling again.

When an observer approaches a flock of the pigeons on the ground, each bird keeps quite still, camouflaged by its colours. Only when the observer is very close does the flock rise in a mass.

The postures of courtship display are very similar to those of the Common and Brush Bronzewings.

OTHER NAMES
Flock Pigeon, Harlequin, Bronzewing, Harlequin Pigeon.

IDENTIFICATION
LENGTH: *270–290 mm, with short tail overlapped by wings.*
MALE: *Forehead white; crown black. Upper parts and wing coverts sandy-red; flight feathers slate-grey with white spots at tip; small bronze patch on wing; edge of shoulder slate-grey. Tail tipped broadly white. Face white and black with stripes behind and below eye. Throat black with white collar; breast and belly slate-grey; undertail sandy with grey-tipped feathers. Eye dark brown. Bill black. Feet purple-grey.*
FEMALE: *All head and upper parts sandy-brown; dull grey and white face pattern; breast sandy-brown.*
IMMATURES: *As female but band of wing white and face pattern missing; bill horn.*
DOWNY YOUNG: *Sand-coloured.*

VOICE
Usually silent and no advertising call; a soft coo *during bowing display, and a soft murmuring when feeding in large flocks.*

NESTING
Often colonial. In southern parts of range, most accounts of breeding are in spring or after heavy rain; in northern parts, where there is a monsoonal influence on climate, most nesting apparently soon after wet season when grass has grown; perhaps nesting also influenced by rain. No actual nest— eggs laid in meagrely lined scrape under tussock of grass or low bush; many may be found in same area. Eggs: two; glossy white or cream; oval, about 33 x 25 mm. Incubation 16 days, male alternating with female by day and night. First young leaves nest at seven days.

DISTRIBUTION
A northern inland species that often suddenly appears in an area in large numbers. Its stronghold is Barkly Tableland, NT, but it is usually common from northwestern Queensland across to the northwest of Western Australia. At times it appears in Lake Eyre basin, near northeast coast of Queensland and elsewhere beyond its usual nomadic range. No races.

The male Flock Bronzewing has black and white head markings. The general plumage of both sexes provides camouflage on the ground.

Common Bronzewing *Phaps chalcoptera* (LATHAM, 1790)

A male Common Bronzewing. These ground-feeding birds prefer to walk around when in the scrub; they fly over open areas.

COMMON BRONZEWINGS DO NOT LIVE permanently in treeless places, and avoid dense rainforests, but they are found in all other land habitats. The greatest numbers are in sub-coastal and inland woodlands, particularly those mixed with mulga or other acacias. The species has declined in some places, although the birds have remained common in most of their range, and in the south of Western Australia may even be increasing in numbers.

Much of the Common Bronzewing's range in the south is now a mosaic of wheatfields separated by small patches of scrub. In such areas, waste wheat grain provides about 50 per cent of the bird's food, seeds of weeds such as saffron thistle and Paterson's curse 20 per cent, and pasture plants—mainly legumes—about 12 per cent. The rest of the diet is made up of native plants, eaten mainly in late winter and spring, and includes the seeds of wilga, kurrajong and Acacia and *Cassia* shrubs.

Common Bronzewings occasionally gather in small flocks, but usually live in pairs. They roost and nest in trees and bushes, but spend most of the day on the ground under a bush or in a low tree, where they feed and call mournfully. They forage actively in the early morning and late afternoon, and drink before dawn and immediately after dark, and sometimes during the day.

Common Bronzewings prefer to walk from place to place when in the scrub, but fly—close to the ground with swift, powerful, steady wing-beats—when crossing open areas. These shy, wary birds rise with a loud wing clatter when disturbed.

Although the Common Bronzewing lives in arid regions, rainfall does not affect its breeding much. This may be because in natural habitats it relies on acacia shrubs, which are adapted to producing seeds in all but the very driest of years.

The male Common Bronzewing has a courtship display in which he rapidly bobs his head and breast to the ground and utters a soft *coo*. He then swings up and partly spreads his tail, and holds his wings half open and twisted forward to display their bronze markings. The female then returns his bows; after copulation the male parades around with neck arched and tail sweeping the ground. There is no display flight.

OTHER NAMES
Forest Bronzewing, Bronzewing.

IDENTIFICATION
LENGTH: *320–360 mm.*
MALE: *Forehead russet-cream; lores dusky; centre of crown and sides of nape purple-brown; rest of upper side grey-brown, scalloped with light brown and with a faint olive tinge all over. Tail with black subterminal band Wings as back but have more distinct scalloping and conspicuous bronzing over all wing coverts; flight feathers rufous-brown beneath. Face has black bar from eye to bill; white stripe beneath and behind eye. Throat pale brown; breast pink-brown becoming lighter and greyer towards belly; underside of tail grey. Eye brown. Bill purple-black. Feet purple-pink*
FEMALE: *Duller with grey forehead and greyer breast.*
IMMATURES: *Like female but buff dorsal scalloping and little bronze on wing.*
DOWNY YOUNG: *Sand-coloured.*

VOICE
Soft, deep advertising oom, *with considerable resonance, repeated slowly many times. Also soft abrupt* coo *in display bow.*

NESTING
Some breeding in every month, even in dry period, but peaking in spring and early summer (August–December). Nest a solid (though sometimes frail) saucer, 250 mm in diameter and up to 100 mm thick, of fine sticks and twigs in horizontal fork of thick limb or in a thicket 1–10 m above ground. Eggs: two; smooth, lustrous white; ellipsoidal, about 33 x 25 mm. Incubation 14–16 days, by both sexes.

DISTRIBUTION
Throughout Australia except for most of Cape York Peninsula and some areas of dense forest on east coast and tablelands and treeless areas in deserts. Common over much of its range. No races.

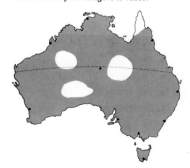

Brush Bronzewing *Phaps elegans* (TEMMINCK, 1810)

IN MANY PLACES THE BRUSH BRONZEWING has declined in numbers as a result of the widespread clearing of its coastal habitat for agriculture and urban development. This may be because the Brush Bronzewing builds its saucer-shaped nest low down or on the ground, where incubating birds or chicks are easy prey to foxes and domestic cats which have gone wild. Today it is common only on the Houtman Abrolhos and south coast of Western Australia.

The Brush Bronzewing lives mainly in dense coastal heathland and tea-tree scrub, but in places its range extends to mallee scrub and undergrowth in coastal forests. In districts where the ranges of the Brush and Common Bronzewings overlap, the latter lives in more open woodland and the former keeps to the adjoining heath and forests with dense undergrowth. The two are similar in appearance, but the Brush Bronzewing is a little smaller, with chestnut shoulders and throat patch, and two bands in the wing.

In solitary behaviour, display and feeding, Brush Bronzewings are also like the Common. They feed on grain on the ground, taking wheat and the seeds of Acacia according to circumstance.

OTHER NAMES
Little Bronze Pigeon.

IDENTIFICATION
LENGTH: *290–310 mm.*
MALE: *Forehead russet, chestnut stripe through eye; crown grey; back of neck and shoulders russet-brown. Back, rump and upper side of tail brown with grey tinge. Tail with black subterminal band. Wings brown and russet with two conspicuous bronze bands rufous beneath. Throat patch russet-brown; breast grey shading to slate on belly and undertail. Eye dark brown. Bill dusky. Feet pink-red.*
FEMALE: *Russet areas reduced to small patch on throat and line behind eye; breast browner.*
IMMATURES: *Like female but without russet marks.*
DOWNY YONG: *Sandy to white.*

VOICE
Low, mournful advertising coo *repeated slowly many times; other calls like Common Bronzewing.*

NESTING
Most often in October–January. Nest is substantial, flat, slightly dish-shaped platform, 180 mm in diameter and 20–30 mm thick, of thin sticks. Placed much closer to ground—usually less than 3 m—than that of Common Bronzewing, in dense bushes or small trees, or sometimes on the ground, sheltered by bush or grass. Eggs: two; smooth, glossy white; oval or ellipsoidal, 33 x 25 mm. Incubation 15–18 days, by both sexes; female broods by day. Young fledge in 17–20 days.

DISTRIBUTION
Occasional records inland, but main distribution is coastal and southern. In Western Australia it is found in a coastal strip from Moora to Esperance and on offshore islands. In eastern Australia has been recorded from South Australian gulfs to Tasmania and Fraser Island, Qld; inland to Brindabella Range, ACT. No races.

Russet patches on the female Brush Bronzewing are duller than on the male and limited to throat and a line behind the eye. The forehead has a tinge.

Partridge Pigeon *Geophaps smithii* (Jardine & Selby, 1830)

The nest of the Partridge Pigeon is a scrape in the ground, sometimes lined with straw. When incubating the eggs, the birds sit tightly and can almost be trodden on before they flush. Outside the breeding season they gather in large flocks that live on the ground.

THE PARTRIDGE PIGEON IS THE REPRESENTATIVE of the Squatter Pigeon in northwestern Australia. Throughout its range it keeps to the same open woodland well grassed with *Sorghum*, but from place to place its numbers vary. The reasons for this are not known, but may be related to types of soil and associated ground cover. The birds are more numerous on light soils and gravel slopes, where grasses are shorter and more delicate than the tall, rank varieties on heavy soils. The largest numbers of these pigeons are found in the woodlands between the East Alligator and South Alligator Rivers in Arnhem Land.

When breeding, pairs of Partridge Pigeons are well dispersed, but at other times they gather in coveys of up to 20 or sometimes even 100 birds. They live on the ground, walking from place to place, often stringing out into a long line of hurrying birds. A moving flock produces a continuous murmur of soft cooing which maintains contact between individuals and cohesion in the flock. In the wet summer season, when the grass is too tall for easy walking, they follow roads and tracks, on which they sometimes roost—although they usually roost in trees. Their favourite feeding places in the dry season are clearings where new growth has begun to shoot after grass fire. There they eat the seeds of herbs and grasses, particularly of legumes.

Partridge Pigeons fly like partridges, in short, swift bursts close to the ground, with rapid wing-beats alternating with gliding on slightly down-curved wings.

They are also shy, but when in need of water will not be deterred by the presence of an observer. They seldom drink in the early morning, but during the heat of the day—from about 11 am until dusk—there is a steady procession of flocks along the ground to creeks and waterholes.

When disturbed on the ground, Partridge Pigeons 'freeze' or squat, remaining inconspicuous because of their colouring. Only when the birds are almost tramped on does the flock suddenly explode vertically into the air, hurtle up through the trees, and disperse. After the danger has passed the scattered pigeons begin calling from all directions and the covey gradually re-forms.

The display of the Partridge Pigeon is similar to that of the Common Bronzewing, except that when bowing, the male Partridge Pigeon fluffs out his feathers to a greater extent, swells his throat and utters a loud, explosive *coo* at the low point of the bow. He holds this bowing posture for some seconds, bobbing his body rapidly up and down several times. The bird apparently does not have the twig-bobbing display of the Squatter Pigeon, nor the aerial display-flight of the Crested Pigeon. After copulation, the male parades around the female, body stiffly erect, bill pressed to breast, making courtly bows every few steps.

OTHER NAMES
Red-eyed Squatter, Bare-eyed Pigeon.

IDENTIFICATION
LENGTH: *250–280 mm.*
ADULTS: *Sexes similar. Upper parts drab brown; tail dusky. Wings drab brown with bronze patch on inner secondaries and coverts; underside of shoulders white. Throat white; breast drab brown with a small central patch of blue-grey scalloped with black; belly and flanks buffy-white, the white of flanks extending up side of breast. Eye white; large area of bare skin through eye scarlet or chrome-yellow, flanked with white feather lines. Bill black. Thick feet red-purple.*
IMMATURES: *Like adults but duller with red-brown flecking and scalloping, and brown eyes.*
DOWNY YOUNG: *Sandy white-cinnamon.*

VOICE
Low long coo *in advertisement; murmuring cooing* oo-poop-poop *in contact; abrupt* coo *in display bow.*

NESTING
Nests are found in most months of year, but are more common in late wet and early dry seasons, February–September, when ground seed abundant. Nest a scrape in the ground, sometimes lined with a few straws, placed close to a clump of grass or a bush. Eggs: two; cream; oval, about 30 x 23 mm.

DISTRIBUTION
Tall, open tropical woodlands, from Kimberleys to McArthur River southwest of Gulf of Carpentaria. Does not range inland more than 300 km. Also on large offshore islands such as Melville Island. Two races: one with scarlet eye-skin in Arnhem Land; the other with yellow in the Kimberleys.

Squatter Pigeon

Geophaps scripta (TEMMINCK, 1821)

FORMERLY SQUATTER PIGEONS ranged frequently south on the inland plains of New South Wales to Dubbo and Cobar. Today they are abundant only in the more tropical woodlands north of the Burdekin–Flinders River catchment in Queensland. There they are most common in areas of open grassfield on sandy soil broken by low gravel ridges, with water nearby. Shooting, introduced predators and the effects of stock on the grasslands have all played their part in the decline of this pigeon. However, the disappearance of the bird from sheep country and its survival in cattle country in the north suggests sheep grazing as the main cause. Sheep are more destructive grazers than cattle.

The Squatter Pigeon is like the Partridge Pigeon in its displays, general behaviour, diet and habitat requirements, but it seems to spend more time in trees. It spends most of its time on the ground, feeding, resting, sunning or dust-bathing. Drinking, too, is a regular daily event. When disturbed, it tends to escape by running or freezing in a squat; hence, perhaps, its name. The male has a peculiar display that has not been seen in any other ground-living pigeon. He flies to a thin branch a couple of metres above the ground and there he bobs his body up and down rapidly. The branch swings up and down at the same time. This display is believed to advertise the male's presence. After copulation, he parades about holding his body erect.

These pigeons can breed at any time of the year when conditions for rearing young are exceptionally favourable. Birds with this ability must be faced with situations in which an opportunity to breed coincides with the moult and may create a physiological clash. Squatter Pigeons have been found moulting in every month, but the main period was September–March, when sexual activity is lowest. It appears that moulting stops if an opportunity to breed arises, as for example in the dry season when, following rain, food becomes abundant.

Squatter Pigeons eat mainly seeds. In northern Queensland the most important sources of grains are grasses and plants of the pea family, above all the introduced stylo or Townsville lucerne *Stylosanthes humilis*. Squatter Pigeons also eat the seeds of sedges, herbs, trees and shrubs. In some months, insects are also an important, although small, part of the birds' diet.

The Squatter Pigeon spends much of its time on the ground in grassland.

OTHER NAMES
Partridge Bronzewing, Partridge Pigeon.

IDENTIFICATION
LENGTH: *260–290 mm.*
ADULTS: *Sexes similar. Upper parts and tail drab brown. Wings drab brown, scalloped and fawn on shoulders, with small bronze patch on inner secondaries and their coverts. Face black with white stripes behind and below eye and white patch on cheek. Throat white; upper breast drab brown; lower breast blue-grey, tapering to a point on belly; belly buff; white on flanks, extending as stripe up side of breast. Eye dark brown; skin around eye red-orange or whitish blue. Bill black. Thick feet dark purple.*
IMMATURES: *Like adults but duller, with fawn-scalloped back and breast, dull facial pattern and buff eye skin.*
DOWNY YOUNG: *Fawn-coloured.*

VOICE
Low, musical coo or poop in contact, often heard as coo-poop-poop; a long-drawn coo in advertisement; and a sharp short coo in bowing display.

NESTING
In every month some males are sexually active; activity peaks in dry season, May–June. Nest a scrape in the ground sheltered by a bush or tussock of grass, thinly lined with a little dry grass. Eggs: two; smooth, lustrous, pale cream; oval, about 30 x 23 mm. Incubation about 17 days, by both sexes.

DISTRIBUTION
Widely distributed in drier parts of southern Cape York Peninsula and eastern Queensland as far inland as Charleville, and now rarer south to Darling catchment in New South Wales. Two races: one with red eye-skin in north ranging south to the lower Burdekin River and Proserpine; the other with pale blue eye-skin in all regions further south.

The northern race of the Squatter Pigeon, with red eye-skin, feeds mainly on grasses and plants of the pea family.

Crested Pigeon *Geophaps lophotes* (TEMMINCK, 1822)

The Crested Pigeon has adapted to living on farms and around homesteads in many parts of inland Australia.

IN MOST PARTS OF THEIR RANGE Crested Pigeons live in dry, lightly wooded grasslands. They avoid all dense forests and in central Australia prefer the moister areas, such as timber-fringed watercourses. This pigeon has benefited from human settlement wherever very large areas that were formerly thick scrub and closed woodland have been cleared for crops and grazing, leaving scattered trees ideal for roosting and nesting. The birds have been able to advance from the inland across the slopes of the Great Dividing Range in the east, even to the coast, and in the south and west they have reached Adelaide and penetrated the Western Australian wheat belt in the past 50 years.

Inland, Crested Pigeons live around country homesteads, nesting in windbreaks along watercourses and feeding on the plains. On the coast they are found on small, intensely worked farms, feeding with pigs and poultry or on the verges of roads. Ground-feeders and seed-eaters, they eat little else than seeds from crops and exotic weeds over much of their rural range. No doubt their ability to adapt to such food has helped their coastwards spread.

Although they are usually seen in groups of five or six, they often gather in large numbers in bushes near a waterhole. They wait until one or two pluck up the courage to fly to the ground and run in, with heads bobbing, to drink. The rest then follow. When flushed, they burst off with a loud wing clatter but seldom go far before alighting together on a bare branch. The flight is swift and direct, with rapid whistling wing-beats interspersed with periods of gliding on downspread wings. On alighting they swing the tail high above the body for a moment. The whistling wing-beats may be caused by a specially narrowed third primary, and their function, perhaps, is a warning signal.

In display, Crested Pigeons are like other bronzewings and even more spectacular in the bow, spreading their patterned tails vertically. They also have a distinctive display flight: clapping up from a perch, the bird rises steeply for about 30 metres and then glides straight down again. This has been thought to put the Crested Pigeon in a separate genus, but its red eye-skin, crest, barred shoulders and gliding flight reveal that it is no more than a derived ground bronzewing, *Geophaps*.

OTHER NAMES
Topknot Pigeon, Crested Bronzewing.

IDENTIFICATION
LENGTH: *300–340 mm.*
ADULTS: *Sexes similar. Crown grey with darker, erect crest. Back and rump grey with olive tinge; upper side of tail dusky with green tinge, white tip. Wings fawn with black barring on shoulders and purple and green iridescent patch edged white below; flight feathers dusky. Throat and breast light grey; belly and underside of tail darker grey. Eye red-orange; skin around eye red. Bill black. Feet pink-red.*
IMMATURES: *Duller in tone and marks.*
DOWNY YOUNG: *Fawn to cream.*

VOICE
Identity call a loud, wavering coo; *in contact a low musical* coo; *males utter sharp* coo *at low point of each bow in their bowing display.*

NESTING
Breeds mostly in spring and early summer, but at any time after rainfall. Nest a frail platform, about 170 mm in diameter, of fine sticks placed seldom more than 5 m above ground on a horizontal fork, usually in a low, thickly foliaged bush. Eggs: two; smooth, glossy white; oval, about 31 x 23 mm. Incubation 18–20 days, by both sexes. Young fledge in 20–25 days. May rear up to seven successive broods, breeding continuously for several months.

DISTRIBUTION
Common throughout most of mainland Australia, except coastal southwest, southeast and far north. Vagrants may wander to all regions. Populations on coast and in districts of intense cultivation inland are sedentary, but in more arid country are locally nomadic. Two races: one in Western Australia north to Pilbara, with vestigial white tail tip; the other with broad white-tipped tail everywhere else.

Spinifex Pigeon *Geophaps plumifera* GOULD, 1842

MANY TYPES OF BIRDS ARE FOUND in the arid spinifex grasslands of central and northern Australia, but few are permanent residents. The Spinifex Pigeons are adapted to living there at all times. Although not confined to spinifex, they are closely associated with it, usually on stony ground, particularly where it is hilly.

It is essential for these pigeons to have access to water. In times of drought they concentrate on the few remaining waterholes, and if the water lasts, they survive. After the rains, when the ground is covered with quick-growing plants, the pigeons breed and their numbers gradually recover. Flocks become widespread then, and not so closely tied to springs and soaks.

There is a regular annual cycle of sexual activity, and some Spinifex Pigeons are capable of breeding in every month of the year—even in drought. Rain has a strong effect on the breeding cycle, bringing the birds into condition, and synchronising the whole population to breed when food is most abundant.

After rain has fallen, grasses, herbs and legumes grow quickly on the bare red ground between the hummocks of spinifex. They produce a heavy seed crop and then die. The food of the Spinifex

Pigeons consists almost entirely of these seeds. Spinifex grass itself flowers erratically, and in some years no seeds are available, but in others they are abundant and very important in the birds' diet.

These pigeons are usually seen in small coveys of up to 15 birds, although they may sometimes form large concentrations. They live on the ground, feeding there, and can walk for long distances, but usually prefer to fly part of the way. Their flight is like that of the partridge—fast, low over the ground, with bursts of rapid wing-beats alternating with gliding on downswept wings. Sustained flight is uncommon and the birds usually land after 30 metres or so.

Spinifex Pigeons, adapted to life in the desert, have a low metabolic rate. This reduces their food requirements and the amount of water needed for cooling through evaporation. Perhaps to conserve energy, they also roost in tight-packed groups, clustering in small depressions or scrapes on the ground.

The bowing display is like that of other bronzewing pigeons, and they use it in bouts of aggression as well. Fighting males lower head and body to the horizontal and attack on the run, circle bill to bill, and buffet one another with their wings.

OTHER NAMES
Plumed Dove, Red Plumed Dove, Ground Dove, Red Plumed Pigeon.

IDENTIFICATION
LENGTH: *190–230 mm.*
ADULTS: *Sexes alike. White-bellied form has forehead blue-grey; crown rust-red with tall pointed crest; back rust-brown with darker brown scalloping; tail rust-brown, with end half black. Wings rust-brown barred with black and some light grey; bronze patch on secondaries. Cheek and throat white and grey with broad black band below; breast rust-red with broad white band edged with black; lower breast white; belly white to light brown on vent. Eye yellow; skin through eye red. Bill black. Thick feet purple-brown. Red-bellied form has no white bar on breast; upper and lower breast and belly rust-red.*
IMMATURES: *Like adults but duller and without black-and-white face pattern.*
DOWNY YOUNG: *Sand-coloured.*

VOICE
Contact and advertising call soft, low-pitched oom *given as single double-note or in repeated phrases; in bowing display long aspirated* coooo; *in alarm, a cluck; growling* coo *in threat.*

NESTING
Breeds throughout year, but affected by rainfall; mostly September–November. Nest a scrape in the ground lined with a few pieces of grass, usually beside a hummock of spinifex or a rock. Eggs: two; cream, rather glossy; ellipsoidal, about 26 x 20 mm. Incubation 16–17 days, by both sexes. Young fledge in about eight days.

DISTRIBUTION
Two races. Range of white-bellied race Geophaps plumifera plumifera *extends throughout arid zones of western Queensland north to Gulf of Carpentaria, northwestern South Australia, Northern Territory and, in Western Australia, from southern Kimberleys to Dampier Land. Range of red-bellied form* Geophaps plumifera ferruginea *extends from Pilbara, WA, north almost to southern Dampier Land.*

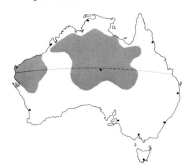

The red-bellied form of the Spinifex Pigeon lives in stony spinifex grassland in the Pilbara, WA. These birds have adapted to life in the desert.

White-quilled Rock-Pigeon *Petrophassa albipennis* GOULD, 1840

THE FORM, HABITS, BEHAVIOUR AND DIET of the White-quilled Rock-Pigeon are much the same as those of the Chestnut-quilled, but the birds are recognised as different species because of subtle but important differences in plumage pattern: not only do White-quilled have a white patch in their flight feathers, but also a black throat spotted with white and plain brown feathering from neck to rump. White-quilled Rock-Pigeons do vary in colour, becoming redder-brown and with less white in their wings eastwards, but do not show any trend towards the Chestnut-quilled. So far as is known, the two birds nowhere come into contact, their habitat cut by the Daly River drainage in the Northern Territory.

Like the Chestnut-quilled Rock-Pigeon, the White-quilled lives among cliffs and hills of broken sandstone and conglomerate, spending all of its time on the rocks in pairs or small loose groups. It sleeps there, nests there, drinks there and feeds there, mainly on the seeds of grasses and legumes which it takes on nimble foraging forays among the tumbled boulders. Even when flushed it rises with a clatter of wings not to a tree but to plane quickly off to the shelter of the rocks. Its usual ruse to avoid detection, however, is to freeze in a squat, the bird blending with its substrate.

Calls and displays are virtually indistinguishable from those of the Chestnut-quilled Rock-Pigeon.

OTHER NAMES
Rock Pigeon.

IDENTIFICATION
LENGTH: *260–290 mm.*
ADULTS: *Sexes alike. Crown brown with lighter scalloping, lores dusky; rest of upper parts brown with russet scalloping. Wing brown; in some areas primaries have a large white patch, which may be smaller or missing in other regions. Throat black, boldly spotted with white; white line under eye; breast as upper parts; belly and undertail dusky. Eye dark brown; skin around eye blue-grey. Bill black. Feet purple-brown. General plumage redder than the Chestnut-quilled.*

IMMATURES: *Duller than adults with indistinct throat spotting.*
DOWNY YOUNG: *Sand-coloured.*

VOICE
Advertising call a two-to-five note coo, coo-car-rook, varied in excitement and alarm; higher-pitched croaking coo also in alarm; display coo loud and hoarse, given at bottom of each bow by male.

NESTING
Few nests reported, all from March–November in dry season. Nest a few loosely arranged spinifex stalks and twigs in an open rock crevice to a substantial pad of sticks, 150 mm in diameter and 25 mm thick, like nest of

the Chestnut-quilled species; placed on ledges or in crevices sometimes sheltered from above, 1–6 m above ground. Eggs: two; smooth, glossy white; ellipsoidal, about 26–30 x 20–22 mm. Incubation about 17 days, by both sexes. Young fledge in about 15 days.

DISTRIBUTION
In sandstone ranges throughout Kimberley region, WA, and Victoria River district, NT. Two races: one almost without white wing patch in Stokes Range, Victoria River district; the other with extensive wing patch everywhere else.

White-quilled Rock-Pigeons drink at sheltered soaks in sandstone outcrops in the Kimberleys. The birds spend all of their time on the rocks.

Chestnut-quilled Rock-Pigeon *Petrophassa rufipennis* COLLETT, 1898

The Chestnut-quilled Rock-Pigeon lives on sandstone rocks and cliff faces in Arnhem Land. In hot weather it shelters in crevices and on narrow shaded ledges and moist soil under rocks, drinking at dusk and also at intervals during the day.

THE ESCARPMENT OF WESTERN ARNHEM LAND rises abruptly from the plain and at its base are tumbled blocks of fallen sandstone. Some are as large as houses. Among the rocks grow pockets of trees and shrubs and, wherever there is soil, spinifex, other grasses and herbs. The Chestnut-quilled Rock-Pigeon lives among these sandstone blocks and on the cliffs above, seldom venturing more than 100 metres out into the plain woodland that spreads from the base of the escarpment.

Chestnut-quilled Rock-Pigeons live in pairs or parties of about six to twenty individuals. They keep strictly to the rocks or cliff faces, never perching in trees. In the extreme heat of the day the birds rest in the shade, in crevices in the cliff face or on narrow ledges, or under sandstone blocks at the base of the cliffs. Some even lie in holes scratched in moist soil far under rocks that rise little more than 200 millimetres above the surface of the ground.

Chestnut-quilled Rock-Pigeons forage actively in the early morning and late afternoon. When feeding they run with considerable agility over, around and under the rocks, or fly out to the flat ground away from the cliff. If disturbed they immediately fly back to cover. They eat the seeds of a variety of grasses and herbs, and of some trees and shrubs. Legumes may be more common in their diet than grasses and they are not known to eat green leaves or insects.

Although Chestnut-quilled Rock-Pigeons walk a great deal, they also fly from place to place when feeding, alternating bursts of rapid wing-beats with gliding on downswept wings. When they descend from a cliff, the descent is often a glide, except for the take-off, which is accompanied by a loud clap of wings. The birds fly almost vertically up a cliff face, but otherwise seldom fly more than three metres above the surface of the rocks, skimming over them and running as they touch down on landing.

The birds drink at dusk and also at intervals during the day. When approaching the water—a soak at the base of a cliff or, sometimes, a pool in a stony creek bed—they usually land on a rock some distance away, or on a cliff ledge high above, and pause before moving to the water's edge. At any disturbance, they tend to freeze and squat before flushing, if at all.

Although rock-pigeons are members of the bronzewing group their bowing display is distinctive. The male lowers his head and inclines his body forward until his breast touches the rock—he can move only slightly because he has very short legs. He spreads but does not lift his tail, splaying the feathers down on to the rock instead. He partly spreads and raises his wings, but does not tilt them forward—there is no shining bronze patch to display. Rather, he displays his plumage by raising the feathers on his back. Such a bow is usually repeated several times, each lasting about one-and-a-half seconds, often while the male is chasing the female. It is a display used both in courtship and aggression. In defence at the nest, the responding bird crouches and raises its wings.

OTHER NAMES
Rock Pigeon.

IDENTIFICATION
LENGTH: *280–310 mm.*
ADULTS: *Sexes similar. Head, face and neck dark brown, marked with large pale grey spots; lores dusky. Rest of upper parts duskier mottled with lighter brown scalloping; upper side of tail dusky. Wing dark brown with a large chestnut patch in primaries. Throat very pale brown; white line under eye; breast as back; belly dusky. Eye dark brown. Bill black. Feet purple-brown.*
IMMATURES: *Duller than adults.*
DOWNY YOUNG: *Sandy to yellow.*

VOICE
Identity call coo-carook, two–five syllabic, on same pitch; soft, conversational coos from birds feeding among the rocks; at low point of bowing display a harsh coo.

NESTING
Main nesting season March–September, during dry season. Nest a thick base of sticks, and on it a pad of spinifex leaves and stems, 25 mm thick and 230 mm in diameter, depressed into a saucer; placed on ground rock in deep-shaded ledges and crevices. Eggs: two; smooth, glossy cream-white; ellipsoidal, 26–27 x 22 mm (measured from 16 eggs of captive birds). Incubation about
16–18 days, by both sexes. Young fledge in about 21 days.

DISTRIBUTION
As far as is known, restricted to western escarpment of Arnhem Land from vicinity of Oenpelli to Katherine Gorge. No races.

Bar-shouldered Dove *Geopelia humeralis* (TEMMINCK, 1821)

The Bar-shouldered Dove has adapted to human settlement on the northern half of the east coast of Australia. This one has built its nest in a pelargonium.

IN THE TROPICAL NORTH of Australia, fringes of pandanus palms often separate river flood-plains from eucalypt uplands. It is in and near these strips that the Bar-shouldered Dove is most numerous, and in the Northern Territory the bird is appropriately known as the Pandanus Pigeon. It favours the scrubby borders of plains, swamps and creeks, and mangroves along estuaries, never moving far from water and fairly dense cover.

Bar-shouldered Doves are usually seen in small groups, but at the end of dry seasons more than 100 birds may gather at concentrations of food. They eat a wide variety of bulbs of sedges and the seeds of grasses, lucernes, *Medicago* and herbs; the food changes from month to month according to availability.

Bar-shouldered Doves feed entirely on the ground—where they walk and run swiftly—but they roost and build their frail nests in trees or pandanus palms. They usually fly low over the ground and when disturbed will move a long way away. Their flight is swift and direct, with regular wing-beats. They go to water at any time of the day but mainly in the late afternoon when their crops are full. The doves usually alight in a nearby tree before dropping down to walk to the water.

Bar-shouldered Doves are sedentary or locally nomadic, moving to food sources within a small area, or dispersing to breed. As a rule, the same birds remain in the same area year after year.

Male Bar-shouldered Doves take off in a display flight, rising for 20–30 metres on clapping wings, then descending on outstretched wings and tail. Their bowing display is similar to that of the Peaceful Dove, but they do not lift their tails so high.

The Bar-shouldered Dove has adapted well to human settlement in the agricultural districts of the east coast, especially where land clearing has opened up dense forests and farms provide waste food. Since the 1930s, however, competition with the introduced Spotted Turtle-Dove seems to have resulted in a decrease in the native bird's numbers in these areas. No such threat exists across northern Australia or in southern New Guinea.

OTHER NAMES
Pandanus Pigeon, Mangrove Dove.

IDENTIFICATION
LENGTH: *280–310 mm.*
ADULTS: *Sexes alike. Crown blue-grey, edges of feathers black; back of neck vinaceous with black-tipped feathers. Rest of upper parts brown, barred with black; upper side of tail dark brown. Throat pale grey; upper breast blue-grey; lower breast and belly white with pink wash. Underside of tail brown with white tips to feathers; underside of wings rufous-brown; flight feathers brown. Eye green-yellow; eye-ring pale blue to red during breeding. Bill and cere blue-grey. Feet pink.*
IMMATURES: *Duller than adult; crown and hind neck brown; throat and breast streaked.*
DOWNY YOUNG: *Fawn.*

VOICE
Identity call a penetrating coo *of three syllables,* kook-a-wook, *or* holly-hock. *In bowing display, bird emits harsh* coo-ah; *also abrupt rallying* cuck-oo, *and jumbled, laughing* cooos.

NESTING
Nests can be found at all times of year; in northern Australia mostly March–July; in south mostly November–January. Nest a frail platform of fine twigs, 100 mm in diameter and 20 mm thick; on a horizontal branch or in a pandanus palm usually within 6 m of ground. Eggs: two; smooth, glossy white; oval, about 28 x 21 mm. Incubation 14–16 days, by both sexes. Young fledge in about 21 days.

DISTRIBUTION
Found in better-watered coastal and near-inland regions from Kimberley region, WA, across north coast and down east coast to Manning River, NSW; semi-isolated population in coastal Pilbara, WA. In south, distribution extends inland to Darling–Lachlan valleys. Lives in scrubby fringes to plains, swamps and creeks and mangrove fringes along estuaries. Also in southern New Guinea. Three races in Australia: one small and pallid brown in the Pilbara; another medium-sized and brown from the Kimberleys to Cape York Peninsula; a third large and grey-brown southwards in eastern Australia.

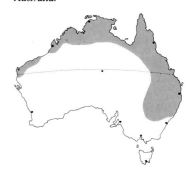

Diamond Dove *Geopelia cuneata* (LATHAM, 1801)

THE SMALLEST MEMBER OF THE pigeon family, the Diamond Dove is widely distributed in Australia but is essentially a bird of the arid zone. It is particularly common in dry, open savanna in mulga areas. It must have access to water and some trees for nesting and roosting, but it feeds and spends much of its time on the ground.

When feeding, the Diamond Dove walks with a slow and regular gait, although it can run quite fast, with a wobble, holding its long tail up and away from the ground. Its flight is swift and direct, but has a swooping character over long distances as the bird alternately beats its wings rapidly and closes them for a moment.

In arid regions Diamond Doves are nomadic and move in large numbers from place to place, seeking out areas where rain has fallen. Usully they live in small groups, but in the early morning hundreds of birds may gather at water. Before dawn at desert waterholes the air is filled with a soft cooing as the birds await sunrise before going to drink. Most drinking, nevertheless, is done in the later afternoon. The doves often arrive in procession then, each bird walking to the water's edge, submerging its bill and sucking to imbibe its fill before flying off to make way for the next. In times of drought in the interior the populations disperse. Many of the small local flocks that live in well-watered districts towards the coast probably have arisen from past invasions and are not necessarily permanent there.

Diamond Doves feed on the ground, almost entirely on very small seeds from a wide variety of drought-evading ephemeral plants, mostly herbs and grasses. In central Australia the most important source of seeds is *Glinus lotoides,* which provides more than a quarter of the birds' total diet. Diamond Doves also eat a little green material and, occasionally, insects—which can be an important addition to their diet in some months.

The sexual displays of the Diamond Dove are similar to those of other members of the genus *Geopelia,* but in the bow it raises its tail vertically, much higher than the other species.

OTHER NAMES
Little Turtle-dove, Red-eyed Dove.

IDENTIFICATION
LENGTH: *190–215 mm.*
MALE: *Head and neck pale blue-grey; back, rump and upper side of slender tail delicate grey-brown; outer tail feathers tipped very extensively white. Throat and breast pale blue-grey; lower breast and underside of tail white. Upper side of wings brown-grey spotted liberally with white spots; under shoulders grey-brown; flight feathers chestnut. Eye, and skin around eye, red. Bill light grey. Feet pink.*
FEMALE: *Similar to male but duller and browner on foreparts.*
IMMATURES: *Upper parts brown with obscure dusky and grey flecking. Throat and breast grey with darker brown scalloping; lower breast and belly light brown. Eye, and skin around eye, fawn. Bill grey. Legs greyish.*
DOWNY YOUNG: *Sand-coloured.*

VOICE
Sad mournful soft coo-oo...coo-oo, *and shorter, louder* corr-coo. *Explosive* coo *in bowing display.*

NESTING
Most males are in a state of sexual readiness throughout year; breeding possibly peaks in September–November, or after heavy rain. Nest a frail platform up to 50 mm diameter; of fine twigs or grass stems, placed in low fork of tree. Eggs: two; smooth, white; ellipsoidal, 20 x 15 mm. Incubation about 13 days, by both sexes. Young fledge in 12–14 days.

DISTRIBUTION
Inland northern and central Australia where nomadic; occurs in arid and semi-arid zones, where rainfall exceeds 300 mm a year. No races.

The Diamond Dove lives in arid country, but it must have water. When a source dries up, flocks search far and wide for places where rain has fallen.

Peaceful Dove

Geopelia placida GOULD, 1844

OTHER NAMES
Zebra Dove, Turtle-Dove.

IDENTIFICATION
LENGTH: *200–220 mm.*
ADULTS: *Sexes similar. Forehead and face blue-grey; crown grey-brown with fine black bars. Upper parts grey-brown boldly barred with broken black lines. Throat blue-grey; upper breast blue-grey barred with wavy black lines; lower breast and belly white with pink tinge. Upper side of tail deep grey; underside dark brown, feathers tipped with white. Underwing rufous-brown; flight feathers dark grey. Eye grey-white; skin around eye blue. Bill blue-grey. Feet dark red-brown.*
IMMATURES: *Duller and browner than adults, with less distinct barring.*
DOWNY YOUNG: *Silver-grey.*

VOICE
Identity call a moderately high-pitched goo-la-goo, doodle-doo or coo-a-luk; also coo-luk and soft, drawn-out ah-coocoo in contact; and repeated short soft coos in alarm.

NESTING
Breeds any month of year. In tropics, peak is end of season, March–April; in south, mostly September–January. Nest a frail platform of sticks up to 70 mm in diameter; placed in a horizontal fork of a thick limb or in a clump of twigs, 1–12 m above ground. Eggs: two; smooth, lustrous white; oval, about 23 x 17 mm. Incubation 13 days, by both sexes. Young fledge in about 16 days.

DISTRIBUTION
In well-grassed eucalypt woodland with water nearby, across northern and eastern Australia. Also in New Guinea. Two races: one, pallid grey, in the Pilbara; the other, darker, elsewhere.

The Peaceful Dove, like other grass seed-eating pigeons and doves, drinks by immersing its bill and sucking up water. Though locally nomadic in drier country, they prefer grassy woodland with water nearby.

THE WAY IN WHICH CLOSELY related species of animals can live together yet be ecologically separated is well demonstrated by the Peaceful Dove and its relatives the Diamond Dove and the Bar-shouldered Dove. Their ranges overlap considerably, they live in the same habitat and their food comes from essentially the same sources, yet they are able to co-exist with one another.

The Diamond Dove avoids direct competition when it is in the same areas as the Peaceful and Bar-shouldered Doves by selecting its food from seeds in a different range of sizes. In addition it is highly nomadic which enables it to move to more arid and unreliable areas than its more sedentary relatives. The Peaceful and Bar-shouldered Doves feed on seeds in the same size range but they remain separated, selecting different places in which to feed.

The Peaceful Dove, which eats seeds of a very wide variety of grasses, herbs and shrubs, shows a preference for feeding at roadsides, in dusty places and in areas that have been burnt. The Bar-shouldered Dove eats a narrower range of seeds and prefers those of plants growing in moister soil. When they are living in the same area, Peaceful Doves feed freely through the woodland but Bar-shouldered Doves feed closer to the edge or along creeks. In the tropics in the wet season, when dense tall grass makes much of the food unavailable, Peaceful Doves move to the more sparsely vegetated gravelly ridges inland, where collecting food is simpler.

The Peaceful Dove finds suitable habitat in any well-grassed woodland, provided water is nearby and it is also found living in farmland, feeding with pigs and poultry, and in town parks and gardens. In a few southern towns, however, it comes into competition with the introduced Spotted Turtle-Dove and, according to some ornithologists, has declined as a result.

Peaceful Doves usually live in pairs or small groups, but large congregations can be found when many such groups converge on a favourite feeding place or at water. They nest and roost in trees and bushes but feed entirely on the ground and drink often. When running they move nimbly with heads bobbing. Flight is rapid, low and undulating, with a dip caused by a closing of the wing that alternates with a series of rapid wing-beats. The birds rise from the ground with whirring wings and seldom fly far before alighting on the branch of a tree or shrub.

The general behaviour and courtship display postures of the male Peaceful Dove are similar to those of the other doves of the genus *Geopelia*. All perform the bowing display towards a female or while walking swiftly behind one, when they pause and bow every few steps. At the bottom of each rapid bow of the head and breast, the bird, with a *coo,* partly opens his wings, raises his tail and fans it fully open.

Peaceful Doves commonly perform such displays on a thick branch or fence rail, more so than other Australian *Geopelia* spp. Like the others, they also have a steep, clapping display flight.

Topknot Pigeon *Lopholaimus antarcticus* (SHAW, 1793)

WHILE CAPTAIN COOK'S SHIP *Endeavour* was laid up in 1770 at the present site of Cooktown, the crew, seeking fresh food, shot some pigeons. The botanist of the expedition, Joseph Banks, described one as 'a Beautiful Bird crested differently from any Pidgeon I have seen'. There is no doubt that the bird was the Topknot Pigeon.

Cook's men set a tradition. In the early years of settlement on the east coast, pioneers found Topknot Pigeons were a handy supply of food. At that time there were immense numbers and flocks of several thousand were common. Today most of the east coast rainforest has gone and Topknot Pigeons have declined with it. They still occupy their original range wherever the rainforest remains, but flocks seldom number more than 200 birds and usually less than 50.

The Topknot Pigeon moves from place to place to concentrate on different fruiting trees and is highly nomadic. It seems that some flocks traverse the full length of the Queensland coast. Individuals have occasionally turned up as far south as Tasmania. On the other hand other flocks seem never to move far. Their flight is direct, swift and seemingly effortless.

The diet of the Topknot Pigeon varies from year to year and season to season according to the fruiting of various forest trees but in different districts the important food trees are much the same. Some, like the bangalow palm, fruit so regularly that the appearance of some flocks gives the impression of regularity. On the south coast of New South Wales there is a fairly regular cycle of food through the fruiting of ironwood, pigeonberry ash, hard aspen,

lilly-pilly, white beech, the small-leafed fig and cabbage palm. In northeastern New South Wales the Topknot Pigeons base their diet on the fruits of several figs, bangalow palm, lilly-pilly, blue quandong, saffron heart, yellow tulipwood and corkwood. They may also leave the forest to feed on the berries of the introduced camphor laurel, grown as a shade tree in paddocks.

In the forest the Topknot Pigeon feeds in the canopy and lower storeys and never comes to the ground. It obtains most of its water by drinking from leaves but in dry weather drinks at streams, perching on rocks or clinging to low hanging branches.

When feeding it hangs upside down on clumps of foliage and clings to very thin branches, flapping its wings loudly and dislodging showers of fruit.

The Topknot Pigeon stands apart from other pigeons in its courtship display as well as in its plumage. When pairing, the male lands on a branch close to the female, immediately half-spreads his wings and tail and holds his body erect. The two birds, their crests fully erect, entwine their necks. In the bowing display, the male, crest erect, presses his bill to his breast. The body is held erect then driven forcibly downwards. At the lowest point there is a squeak and then the body is raised. The bow, which is presented in bouts, resembles that of no other pigeon. There is no obvious relationship between the Topknot Pigeon and other well-defined groups of pigeons, although its bifurcate neck feathers and broken iris are parallelled in the fruit-doves, and its size, tail structure and colour pattern in the imperial-pigeons.

OTHER NAMES
Flock Pigeon.

IDENTIFICATION
LENGTH: *420–450 mm.*
ADULTS: *Sexes similar. Crest on hind crown rust-red; crest on cere and forehead slate-grey. Feathers on back of neck grey and bifurcate, with darker bases, giving streaked effect; back, rump and base of tail slate-grey; rest of tail black with 10 mm wide slate-grey band near tip; flight feathers black. Underparts paler grey than upper parts, with bifurcate feathers over neck and breast. Eye golden yellow with red outer ring. Bill red with brown tip. Feet purple-red; claws grey.*
IMMATURES: *Like adults but crests vestigial, neck feathers not bifurcate, tail band duller. Eye, bill and toes browner.*
DOWNY YOUNG: *Sandy.*

VOICE
Usually silent except for short sharp screech during feeding and low squeak in display. Soft low coo heard infrequently.

NESTING
Breeds June–December but mainly in spring. Some nests substantial platforms of sticks 250 mm in diameter and 50–70 mm deep, but some small and flimsy, and 2–30 m high in outer branches. Egg: one; glossy white; oval, about 43 x 29 mm. Incubation about 23 days, by both sexes. Young fledge in 22–26 days.

DISTRIBUTION
Coastal eastern rainforests from Cape York Peninsula to about Ulladulla, NSW. No races.

The nomadic Topknot Pigeon gets its name from its rust-red crest, which makes it unlike any other pigeon.

Torres Strait Imperial-Pigeon *Ducula bicolor* (G.R. GRAY, 1858)

THE LATE DRY SEASON in New Guinea heralds the breeding season for Torres Strait Imperial-Pigeons, which are widespread in the lowlands of the island. Many remain there to nest, but large numbers leave for offshore islands, where they gather in breeding colonies, and for Australia. Flocks reach Cape York Peninsula in July and Arnhem Land in mid-August. By late August the eastern Australian population has occupied breeding islands as far south as Cairns. There they remain until the end of summer, most birds departing in February to April.

Some of the breeding islands are merely mangrove and coral, and none has enough fruiting trees to feed the birds that colonise it. So the pigeons fly out in large flocks each morning to the mainland, spreading out to feed on fruit and rainforest trees. They return in late afternoon in a continuous stream of small groups flying low to the water. Each returning bird bellows its territorial call and a veritable roar rises from the island.

The male and female of each pair incubate, brood and feed the young on alternate days, the off-duty parent flying to the mainland to feed. On the breeding islands, however, Torres Strait Imperial-Pigeons are forced to nest very close together. The colony may be so densely packed that—as on an island off Port Douglas which contains 25 000 birds in some years—there is a nest to each one-and-a-half square metres in the best nesting trees. Placed on leafy horizontal branches, the nests are substantial platforms constructed of twigs with leaves attached.

In both aggressive and courting situations the Torres Strait Imperial-Pigeon performs vigorous and noisy bowing displays. In the upright position it inclines its body forward with the neck and breast greatly distended. It holds its wings close to its body and does not spread its tail. Its bill is pressed to its breast. The bird bows forcefully and deeply as many as 15 times in rapid succession. During the display each sudden swing of the body below the horizontal is accompanied by a loud bellowing *coo*.

The number of Torres Strait Imperial-Pigeons visiting Queensland has declined greatly this century. In the 1900s the author E. J. Banfield described 60 000–100 000 birds breeding in the Family Islands, off Rockingham Bay; south to Mackay there were other immense colonies. Today there are no large colonies south of Port Douglas, 600 kilometres to the north. The Family Islands support only a few hundred birds and the more southerly populations are only remnants of what they once were.

Much of the decline is doubtless due to the widespread clearing of lowland rainforest and the consequent destruction of the birds' food supply, but this cannot explain the whole decline as there is still extensive forest on the mainland opposite some decimated colonies. Shooting and associated disturbance during the breeding season must contribute as well.

There is a suggestion that Torres Strait Imperial-Pigeons are more numerous in years when fruit is particularly abundant in the mainland forests. The food the pigeons eat varies from season to season, because the trees they feed on have different flowering seasons and many of them fruit irregularly. A two-year study of a colony off Port Douglas showed that the fruits most eaten by the pigeons were from the lawyer vine; from northern laurel and scrub turpentine, large trees of the canopy; and from native olive and northern walnut, smaller trees of the lower storeys. Fruits of the nutmeg were not of great importance, even though the birds are also known in some areas as Nutmeg Pigeons.

The Torres Strait Imperial-Pigeon migrates from New Guinea to breed around the north coast of Australia.

OTHER NAMES
Torresian Imperial Pigeon, Nutmeg Pigeon.

IDENTIFICATION
LENGTH: *350–400 mm.*
ADULTS: *Sexes similar. Pure white, often with grey bloom to head; lower half of tail and flight feathers slate-black. Vent and thighs spotted with black. Eye dark brown; surrounding skin blue-grey. Bill lemon with yellow tip. Feet blue-green.*
IMMATURES: *As adults but black and white parts greyer and ventral spotting absent.*
DOWNY YOUNG: *Yellowish.*

VOICE
Identity call a deep, powerful coo-hoo; *in display a deep* coo *uttered at low point of each bow; in courtship a metallic click.*

NESTING
Breeds September–January. Peak egg-laying is September–November. Nest a platform, often of mangrove twigs with leaves attached, 130–310 mm in diameter and 20–25 mm deep; set on leafy horizontal branches 1–15 m high. Egg: one; smooth, glossy white; oval, about 45 x 31 mm. Incubation about 27 days, by both sexes. Young fledge in about 23 days.

DISTRIBUTION
Coastal northern Australia between northern Kimberleys and Mackay, Qld, on summer migration from southern New Guinea. Other races with milk-white plumage, slaty bills or plain vents in northern New Guinea, Bismarck Archipelago and northwest through Indonesia to India.

Wompoo Fruit-Dove *Ptilinopus magnificus* (TEMMINCK, 1821)

OTHER NAMES
Wompoo Pigeon, Wompoo Fruit Pigeon, Green Pigeon, Magnificent Fruit-Dove, Purple-breasted Pigeon, Bubbly Mary.

IDENTIFICATION
LENGTH: *350–450 mm, including long tail.*
ADULTS: *Sexes similar. Head light grey; upper parts and tail yellowish green; flight feathers green with blue tinge. Neck and throat light grey; breast and lower breast bright purple; vent and undertail coverts dull yellow; underside of tail grey; underside of wing shoulder yellow; underside of flight feathers grey. Eye red-orange. Bill orange-red with yellow tip. Feet yellow-green; claws darker.*
IMMATURES: *As adults but purple breasted blotched irregularly with green; eye brown.*

VOICE
Identity call a loud, baritone-like, far-carrying wallock-a-woo. *Other calls include* bah-roo, *a single, explosive* boo *and a low* pak-pak *when feeding.*

NESTING
Breeds June–January, but mostly August–October. Nest a flimsy platform, about 150 mm in diameter, of slender sticks, built in horizontal fork in clump of leaves near end of long slender branch at 5–20 m high. Egg: one; smooth, lustrous white; ellipsoidal or long-oval, 35–48 x 24–30 mm, largest in southern race.

DISTRIBUTION
In lowland and adjacent highland rainforest, originally from Illawarra of New South Wales to Cape York Peninsula. Today seldom seen south of Bellinger River, NSW, and uncommon in New South Wales generally. Three races: one huge on central east coast north to near Bowen; another large in northeastern Queensland from Seaview Range to Cooktown; and a third medium-sized with reddish tone to breast on Cape York Peninsula. Other small redder-breasted races occur in lowland New Guinea.

The Wompoo Fruit-Dove—named for its growled, far-carrying call—broods its chick on a flimsy platform nest.

THE WOMPOO IS THE LARGEST FRUIT-DOVE and brilliantly hued, but in lowland rainforests where it lives the bird is inconspicuous. It lives entirely in densely foliaged trees and never comes to the ground. When flying, it weaves its way through tall rainforest canopy, but just above the canopy in lower types of rainforest. Its flight is quite heavy.

These fruit-doves live in pairs or small parties, although they sometimes gather in large groups in a favourite feeding tree. They are sedentary, but move around locally to follow the fruiting of different trees in the rainforest. Like others of the genus *Ptilinopus,* they are very agile feeders. They crawl over the foliage, often along very thin twigs, and hang upside down like parrots to reach berries. In dense forest the presence of Wompoo Fruit-Doves is revealed as often by the sound of fruit falling through the undergrowth as by their strange, human-like voice.

The food the birds eat varies from place to place, according to the types of trees in the rainforest, and from year to year, because of the irregular fruiting cycles of many of the trees. In northeastern New South Wales wild figs—particularly the smaller varieties—are their most important food in the summer. In winter, Wompoos concentrate on the fruit of white cedars. They also feed on rose maple, lilly-pilly, native ivy and wild lime. In northeastern Queensland their diet is more varied; they eat the fruit of more than 50 trees and vines—mainly blue quandong, rusty laurel, woolly pine, bollywoods and palms. Nearly all foraging is done in or close to the forest canopy.

Although Wompoo Fruit-Doves are protected, many are still shot in some places. Their loud call and their habit of remaining in one tree as long as it has fruit make them an easy target. The southern race was once abundant but is now rare, the main cause being extensive clearing of rainforests for agriculture and heavy shooting in the remaining pockets. The northern races have not been so badly affected, for much virgin land remains; a continuing of clearing, however, could have serious results.

A male Superb Fruit-Dove on its nest, which is flimsy but is made secure with interlocking forked sticks.

Superb Fruit-Dove *Ptilinopus superbus* (TEMMINCK, 1810)

RAINFOREST EDGE IS THE MAIN habitat of the Superb Fruit-Dove, from which it also forages out into eucalypt or acacia woodland wherever there are some fruit-bearing trees. This patchy growth is widespread in eastern Queensland and southern New Guinea, where the second storey, or shrub layer, of the woodlands is often full of species which grow in rainforests. The birds also nest in open situations, even when rainforest is nearby.

In northern Queensland the laurels are the Superb Fruit-Dove's most important source of food. Apart from these, the birds eat the fruit of more than 50 other trees, figs, palms and vines. They feed among the foliage of fruit trees, where they are camouflaged by their green plumage, and keep more to shrubberies and lower levels than most other fruit-doves.

Nothing is known of the bird's movements except that it is rather nomadic and often travels long distances, at times reaching as far south as New South Wales, and even Tasmania. There are many records of single birds flying into lighted windows and lighthouses, which indicate that the birds travel at night. Whether nomadic or migratory, these large-scale movements involve only part of the population. Some birds never leave the forests near Port Moresby, New Guinea, and many are present in all seasons near Al Arish, northern Queensland, although the greatest numbers are seen between August and October.

The sexual behaviour of the Superb Fruit-Dove is similar to that of other members of the genus *Ptilinopus*. The breeding pair stay near the nest and share incubation duties. The male sits during the day and, if disturbed, lifts its tail so that all that is seen is the undertail; the brilliant head and neck plumage is hidden. If the observer moves to the other side of the nest, the male turns accordingly, so that it shows only the dullest part of its plumage.

OTHER NAMES
Purple-crowned Pigeon, Superb Fruit Pigeon.

IDENTIFICATION
LENGTH: *220–240 mm; short-tailed.*
MALE: *Crown rich purple, back of neck red-brown; rest of upper parts dull green; tail tipped white; wings gold-dark green blotched with black; primaries black. Throat grey with lilac tinge; broad black band on lower breast; flanks green; rest of underparts pale cream. Eye bright yellow. Bill olive. Feet red. Claws dusky.*
FEMALE: *Upper parts as male but crown patch small and deep blue; no red-brown on neck or white tip on tail.*

Throat grey; breast grey-green; lower belly cream, undertail blotched cream and green.
IMMATURES: *Crown and rest of upper parts green with some yellow edging. Throat grey; breast green flecked with yellow; rest of underparts mottled green and yellow. Eye yellow. Bill green-grey. Feet buff-brown.*
DOWNY YOUNG: *Yellowish.*

VOICE
Identity call loud resonant two-syllable coo; *also softer single* coo.

NESTING
Breeds June–February in northern Queensland; most nests begun in November–December. Some birds sexually active in all months. Nest a flimsy platform of fine sticks, most of which are forked, permitting more secure tangling. Placed in forks in trees and shrubs or built on horizontal palm leaves or in vine tangles, usually 1–10 m above ground. Egg: one; smooth, glossy white; oval, about 30 x 21 mm. Incubation 14 days, by both sexes. Young fledge in about seven days.*

DISTRIBUTION
Coastal Queensland from Byfield near Yeppoon to Cape York Peninsula. Lives mainly in lowlands but ranges inland to tablelands. Also in New Guinea, without races; Bismarck Archipelago, Solomons, Moluccas, and Sulawesi.

Banded Fruit-Dove

Ptilinopus cinctus (TEMMINCK, 1810)

IN THE TIMES WHEN RAINFORESTS covered more of northern Australia than they do now, the Banded Fruit-Dove was probably more widely distributed. Today it has a more restricted range than any other Australian pigeon. It lives in scattered shrubberies and in the small patches of rainforest growing among boulders and in gullies on the sandstone escarpments of Arnhem Land, probably never moving more than a couple of kilometres away from the cliffs. This rare bird is in danger of a decline in numbers unless it is actively protected. Although a national park which includes some of the escarpment has been declared, the pigeon's habitat is prone to disturbance by the mining of uranium.

Banded Fruit-Doves are usually seen alone or in pairs, flying along a cliff edge or feeding in trees that grow at the base or on the face of a cliff. Occasionally groups of 20–30 birds may gather with much flapping in a tree bearing ripe fruit. Banded Fruit-Doves dwell mainly in trees but they descend to the ground to drink at soaks where water seeps from the sandstone. They eat wild figs and other fruit, including the berries of rainforest trees.

The Banded Fruit-Dove utters a loud, hooting call to announce its territory. While calling, it holds its body erect with the tail pointing downwards, and presses its head and bill hard against its inflated throat and breast. The courting male stands upright, inflates its neck and breast, then swings its body downwards slowly until it is at an angle of about 20 degrees above the horizontal. It presses its bill against its breast, and hardly moves its tail. Then it utters a low *coo* and returns to its upright stance.

The Banded Fruit-Dove is found only on the escarpments of Arnhem Land.

OTHER NAMES
Black-banded Pigeon, Black-banded Fruit Pigeon, Black-banded Fruit-Dove, Banded Pigeon.

IDENTIFICATION
LENGTH: *320–350 mm; long-tailed.*
ADULTS: *Sexes similar. Head white; back and wings black; rump and upper tail coverts pale grey. Upper breast buff-white; a broad black band on lower breast; belly pale grey. Eye red. Bill grey-green with yellow tip. Legs red.*
IMMATURES: *Parts that are white in adults are pale grey with yellow flecks.*

Those that are dark grey in adults are bronze-green edged with yellow. Eye deep red with blue surround; bill yellow; toes pink-red, claws black.
DOWNY YOUNG: *Pale grey.*

VOICE
Loud, clear coo *or* hoot *repeated at short intervals. Low* coo *during the bowing display.*

NESTING
Breeding recorded April–November. Nest a flimsy platform about 250 mm in diameter, built of thin sticks in horizontal forks near ends of branch 2.5–4 m above ground. Egg: one; matt white; ellipsoidal, about 37 x 26 mm.

DISTRIBUTION
Has been seen only on sandstone escarpments of Arnhem Land between Oenpelli and Katherine. Not known how far east it penetrates Arnhem Land plateau. Rare—probably about two-three pairs to a kilometre along a narrow band at escarpment edge. Other races in Lesser Sunda Islands.

Rose-crowned Fruit-Dove *Ptilinopus regina* SWAINSON, 1825

THIS LITTLE FRUIT-DOVE is often not noticed. Its colours are bright but blend perfectly with the foliage in which it lives so that, unless it moves, it is very hard to see. In the south of its range the bird lives within dense rainforests often with a substantial understorey, although it commonly visits the tops of the tallest trees if these have fruit. In the north it spreads into a wider range of habitats and is commonly found in monsoon forests, deciduous vine thickets, mangroves and paperbark forests, provided there are fruit-bearing trees in the area.

In open country Rose-crowned Fruit-Doves are often seen flying about swiftly, just above the trees, but in rainforests they merely dart from one tree to another, seldom leaving cover. The best way to see the birds is to wait under a tree in which they can be heard feeding. Sometimes they form large feeding flocks, although they usually live in pairs or groups of five or six.

Like all other fruit pigeons, Rose-crowned Fruit-Doves are tree-dwellers. In northern Queensland 88 per cent of their food is the fruits of laurels and basswoods but they also eat the fruits of many other trees, including scaly ash, tropical quandong, bangalow palm, figs and mistletoe. The Rose-crowned Fruit-Dove spends more time in large trees and palms than the Superb Fruit-Dove and feeds less among epiphytes, vines, and small shrubs.

In the forest, Rose-crowned Fruit-Doves are nomadic, moving from place to place as different fruits ripen. They also make long journeys, but it is not yet known how far individual birds travel. In northeastern New South Wales for example, rainforest is suddenly full of birds in September; but in April or May they disappear, though odd ones remain throughout the winter. Further north the reverse is true: some birds are present all the time but the numbers increase markedly in June and decrease again in September.

In their courtship displays and general behaviour, Rose-crowned Fruit-Doves are similar to the other members of the genus *Ptilinopus*, performing courtship bows, advertising coos and a pre-copulatory series of jumps from left to right on a branch.

OTHER NAMES
Red-crowned Pigeon, Pink-cap, Pink-capped Fruit-Dove, Pink-headed Dove, Red-crowned Fruit-Dove, Red-crowned Fruit Pigeon, Rose-crowned Fruit Pigeon, Rose-crowned Pigeon.

IDENTIFICATION
LENGTH: *220–245 mm, short-tailed.*
MALE: *Crown deep to light magenta with yellow fringe. General plumage dull green above; neck grey with green tinge; tip of tail yellow; wing coverts bright green, fringed with yellow; primaries black. Throat and breast grey marked with green; lower breast magenta; belly and undertail orange to yellow; thighs green. Eye orange-yellow. Bill dark green. Feet grey-green; claws darker.*
FEMALE: *Generally duller than male, particularly on underside.*
IMMATURES: *Crown green; upper parts green barred faintly yellow; underparts green scalloped and washed with yellow; wings as in adults. Eye brown.*
DOWNY YOUNG: *White.*

VOICE
Surprisingly loud. Up to 20 deep resonant coos, uttered slowly at first, increasing in speed and decreasing in duration and pitch as call proceeds. Other calls include soft two-syllable coo *and single explosive* coo.

NESTING
Breeds usually November–April through the northern wet season. Nest a flimsy, open platform about 60 mm in diameter and built of a few thin, loosely interwoven sticks—placed on a horizontal *fork in a branch or in a tangle of vines; mostly 3–6 m but sometimes up to 30 m above ground. Most nests of eastern race are in dense rainforest; those of Northern Territory race usually in mangroves or paperbark trees in swamps. Egg: one; smooth, glossy white; ellipsoidal, about 30 x 21 mm. Incubation 17 days, by both sexes. Young fledge in 11-12 days.*

DISTRIBUTION
Small western race with pale pink cap, yellow-green back and yellow-orange belly ranges from Derby to McArthur River area. Large eastern race with magenta cap, deep green back and magenta and orange belly ranges from Bellinger River, NSW, northwards through lowland and some highland districts to west coast of Cape York Peninsula, where distribution is not known in detail. Other races occur in Timor and nearby islands.

The Rose-crowned Fruit-Dove is a tree-dweller and feeds entirely on fruit. It moves from place to place as the fruit ripens on different trees.

Palm Cockatoo *Prosbosciger aterrimus* (GMELIN, 1788)

The Palm Cockatoo is the only 'black' cockatoo in Australia without a coloured band on its tail.

THE MAJESTY OF THE PALM COCKATOO can be appreciated only by watching the bird in the wild. Its great size, black plumage and spectacular crest make it very conspicuous, and it is easy to locate by its piercing call notes. The cockatoos are usually seen singly, in pairs or in small parties, perching at the top of tall trees or flying just above the rainforest canopy.

In Australia, Palm Cockatoos are confined to the tip of Cape York Peninsula. Rainforest is the essential element of their habitat, for they are never found far from it and drop out as soon as it is replaced by extensive tracts of eucalypts. The birds roost singly on the topmost branches of tall trees—nearly always among dead or leafless branches of trees growing at the edge of rainforest. They stir only after sunrise, when they spend some time preening before moving off, dusting their plumage with powder down from feathers at the base of the tail. The powder imparts a slaty cast to their very dark grey or black plumage.

Palm Cockatoos look heavy in flight with their slow, full wing-beats. When coming to alight, they glide straight into a tree and do not spiral down from above, as do many other cockatoos. During flight the bill is pressed to breast at all times but cannot be closed because of the angling of the jaws, itself an adaptation to feeding.

Up to seven birds often congregate in a large tree in the morning and indulge in a variety of elaborate displays before flying to the feeding trees in open woodland or along the rainforest edges. Accompanied by the shrill-whistled contact call, displaying birds on their perches commonly lunge forward, tail up, head down, wings spread and crest erect. After feeding they return to their roost trees in late afternoon.

The diet of Palm Cockatoos is made up of seeds, nuts, leaf buds and fruit including berries. These they take mostly in the crowns of trees, only rarely coming to ground to harvest seeds from fallen fruit. To extract seeds, the cockatoo shifts the fruit from left foot to bill, anchors it in the notches of its upper mandible, then turns it around with its tongue while using its sharply honed lower mandible to peel off or cut through the coat. The huge bill has jaw muscles to match and can exert tremendous force.

The birds nest in a tree hollow, and line the bottom with twigs. These are chewed into short splinters and dropped into the hollow, where they accumulate to form a porous platform. The layer varies from a few centimetres up to a metre or more deep. Only the female incubates the single egg. After leaving the nest, the chick is fed by both parents for a further six or so weeks.

Red-tailed Black-Cockatoo

Calyptorhynchus banksii
(LATHAM, 1790)

OTHER NAMES
*Banksian Cockatoo, Red-tailed
Cockatoo.*

IDENTIFICATION
LENGTH: *500–610 mm, including
long rounded tail.*
MALE: *Body plumage black. Broad
band of bright red near end of tail,
except for two central tail feathers
which are black. Cere naked. Eye dark
brown; naked skin around eye dark
grey. Bill dark grey. Toes dusky grey.*
FEMALE: *General plumage brown-
black with many yellow speckles on
head, neck and shoulders. Feathers on
underparts barred with yellow and
yellow-orange. Undertail coverts
barred with orange-red. Band in tail
light yellow merging to orange towards
edge of tail and barred with black. Bill
bone-coloured.*
IMMATURES: *Resemble adult female. As
immature males get older their bills
darken and they lose progressively
more yellow speckles and tail barring
until in their fourth year they moult
into adult male plumage.*
DOWNY YOUNG: *Densely
yellow-downed.*

VOICE
Loud harsh grating single-note kree *or*
krurr.

NESTING
*Egg-laying takes place from March to
July in Northern Territory; May to
September in Queensland; and in
parts of Western Australia egg-laying
takes place in March and April, and
in July to October. Nest a lining of
wood chips in tree hollow. Eggs: one,
rarely two; white; oval, 51 x 36 mm.
Incubation about four weeks, by
female. Young fledge in 10–12 weeks.*

DISTRIBUTION
*Four races: one large and large-billed
widespread and abundant across
northern Australia from the
Kimberleys to northeastern New South
Wales; another small and large-billed
in the jarrah forests of southwestern
Western Australia; a third small and
small-billed with dully marked
females in the wheat belt of Western
Australia and gum-lined river systems
of inland Australia east to the Darling;
the fourth small, small-billed and
with brilliantly marked females
isolated and rare in the stringybark
forests of southeastern South
Australia–western Victoria.*

A male Red-tailed Black-Cockatoo. The tail band of the female is yellow, graduating to orange.

THE FIRST AUSTRALIAN PARROT to be illustrated
was the Red-tailed Black-Cockatoo. Sydney
Parkinson, Joseph Banks' draughtsman on the
Endeavour, sketched a female in pencil in 1770
when Captain Cook's ship put in at the Endeavour River for repairs.

This spectacular bird, with its brilliant tail
band of vermillion or orange-yellow, is the most
widely distributed of the black-cockatoos and
the only one of its genus found in the drier pastoral districts. It is a particular feature of northern Australia, where flocks of up to 200 are a
common and impressive sight. On the wing they
are even more imposing, flying slowly and
buoyantly with languid wing-beats and calling to
one another in their unusual yelping cries.

In the forested parts of their range, these
cockatoos are found in pairs, family groups or
small parties made up of several families. They
feed high in the trees, coming down to the
ground only to drink. In open woodlands much
larger numbers forage together, and in the wheat
belt of Western Australia flocks of up to 200 are
commonly seen feeding on the ground. Like
many inland birds they are highly nomadic and
may be only seasonally present in some areas.

Like all black-cockatoos, the Red-tailed is a
seed-eater, and its four races are distinguished as
much by their food and feeding as by their size
and plumage. One in the heavy eucalypt forests
of southwestern Australia lives in the crown of
the forest, feeding mainly on the seeds of the
marri, *Eucalyptus calophylla,* which it extracts
by tearing open the bottom of fruiting capsules.
In the Western Australian wheat belt, and river
systems of arid Australia, another race feeds in
proteas, casuarinas and other small trees; it is
primarily a ground-forager and has taken to both
the introduced storksbill *Erodium* and double-
gee *Emex* in pastoral areas. The third, isolated in
the southeast of South Australia and western
Victoria, lives in brown stringybark forests,
Eucalyptus baxteri, taking its seeds. The last
subspecies, ubiquitous across northern Australia, is also ubiquitous in its feeding, eating the
seeds of a wide variety of trees, shrubs and
grasses, and even mangroves.

The cockatoos will nest in any tree that has a
hollow of a suitable size. In the southwest of
their range the hollows are at least 180 mm in
diameter at the entrance, widening considerably
near the floor. The entrances vary from two
metres above the ground in salmon gum country
to well over 30 metres in heavy karri forest. The
birds chew the inside, making a layer of wood
chips on which the single egg is laid. While the
female incubates the egg, she is fed by the male.
She broods the nestling continuously for two or
three weeks, and thereafter only at night. The
nestling is fed in the morning and evening by
both parents which, in the manner of other
black-cockatoos, enter the nest hollow tail first.

Glossy Black-Cockatoo *Calyptorhynchus lathami* (Temminck, 1807)

GLOSSY BLACK-COCKATOOS ARE UNOBTRUSIVE but not rare in the eucalypt forests of eastern Australia. Unlike other black-cockatoos they do not congregate in large flocks or fly noisily over the trees. Instead they spend virtually all day feeding quietly in low shaded trees of casuarina, in groups of twos and threes, rarely more than 10. Often the only sound that they make for hours on end is a soft *clik-clik-clik* as their bills break into casuarina cones.

The birds seem to feed exclusively on casuarina seeds which they win from the cones in an unusual manner. First they bite off a cone from a branchlet, transfer it to the left foot, and bring it up to the lower mandible. The lower mandible in Glossy Black-Cockatoos is remarkably broadened and hollowed at the tip. Instead of cutting the cone, the tip supports it firmly while the tongue rotates it and the upper mandible bites in to break off small seed-bearing chunks. After the chunks have built up on the inside of the upper mandible, the bird discards the cone, and husks the seeds out by working the tongue and right point of the lower man-

dible against the upper. The chaff falls to the ground, leaving tell-tale signs, and as soon as the process is finished, the birds return to cone-chewing once more.

Because of the size of their bills, the cockatoos can only handle the large cones of such species as *C. littoralis* and *C. stricta*. They follow the fruiting of these trees, remaining locally all year round if sufficient fruit keeps ripening and moving on whenever it fails.

The black-cockatoos nest in tree cavities, but how they select the hollow and prepare it for nesting is not fully understood. The female incubates the single egg. She sits all the time and is fed by the male during this period. For the first week or so after hatching she broods the nestling continuously, but thereafter only at night. Both parents feed the chick in the morning and evening.

The Glossy Black-Cockatoo is often confused with the Red-tailed, but it can be distinguished by its soft, drawn-out call and the absence of a distinctive crest. The female is also blackish-billed and has yellow patches on the head and neck.

OTHER NAMES
Casuarine Cockatoo, Leach's Black-Cockatoo.

IDENTIFICATION
LENGTH: *460–500 mm, with long rounded tail about half body length.*
MALE: *Body plumage dusky brown with undertail coverts brown-black. Tail has a broad band of bright red through centre, except for two central feathers. Cere naked. Eye dark brown; naked skin around eye dark grey. Bill dark grey. Feet and toes dusky grey, and small.*
FEMALE: *As male but has yellow patches on head and sides of neck; tail*

band is red with varying amounts of yellow washed through it, and is barred black. Bill dark grey like male.
IMMATURES: *Resemble adult female but young females may have sparse yellow spotting on wings and belly. In young males the tail is plain red barred black.*
DOWNY YOUNG: *Densely, long, yellow-downed.*

VOICE
Soft, drawn-out wheezing, tarr-red, given in contact. Alarm call of guttural notes.

NESTING
Breeds March–August. Nest a fairly

large tree hollow lined with decayed wood, often in dead tree, with entrance usually high up. Egg: one; white; oblong-oval, about 45 x 33 mm. Incubation about 29 days, by female. Young fledge in about nine–ten weeks.

DISTRIBUTION
Found in coastal forest and open inland woodland in eastern Australia north to Mackay and south to Cocoparra and Strathbogie Ranges, wherever casuarinas are common. Also a very small, isolated population on Kangaroo Island, SA, of less than 100 individuals and on the decline. No races.

Glossy Black-Cockatoos feed on the seeds of casuarina trees. The female is distinguished from the male by the splashes of yellow on head and neck.

Yellow-tailed Black-Cockatoo *Calyptorhynchus funereus* (SHAW, 1794)

The female Yellow-tailed Black-Cockatoo has a large, bright yellow cheek pattern; the male's is smaller and duller.

OTHER NAMES
Funereal Cockatoo, Yellow-eared Black-Cockatoo, Wylah.

IDENTIFICATION
LENGTH: *550–650 mm, with long tapered tail about half body length.*
MALE: *Body plumage dusky black; feathers narrowly edged with yellow; feathers on underparts often have wider yellow edges. Small yellow cheek patch. Wings dusky. Broad band near end of tail yellow speckled with dark brown; centre tail feathers all black. Eye dark brown with pink surround. Bill very dark grey. Feet and toes grey-brown; claws dusky.*
FEMALE: *As male but cheek patch larger and brighter yellow; bare skin surrounding eye dark grey. Bill bone-coloured. Feet and toes buff-olive.*
IMMATURES: *Similar to adult female. Young male may have small, dull yellow cheek patch like adult male.*

DOWNY YOUNG: *Long, yellow-downed.*

VOICE
Calls similar to White-tailed Black-Cockatoo; flight call drawn-out whistle whee-la. Also single syllable harsh call in alarm. Fledglings rasp harshly.

NESTING
March–August in north; July–January in south. Nest a hollow in a tree, very high up; at least 180 mm in diameter at entrance, widening to at least twice that size at floor. Eggs: two; white; oval, 45–50 x 37 mm. Incubation four weeks, by female. Young fledge in about three months.

DISTRIBUTION
Coastal eastern Australia and adjacent ranges north to about Emerald, Qld, west to Eyre Peninsula and Kangaroo Island, SA, and south to Tasmania; in eucalypt forests, heaths and pine plantations. Two races.

A FLOCK OF Yellow-tailed Black Cockatoos flying slowly over the trees, its members calling with long-carrying wailing cries, is one of the characteristic sights and sounds of the eucalypt forests and pine plantations of southeastern Australia.

The flocks seem to wander up and down between the coast and adjacent ranges for their food, which varies from the seeds of introduced conifers, banksias and hakeas to wood-boring larvae in eucalypts and acacias. These they take in trees and shrubs. Their bills are narrow and sharp-pointed, and well-fitted for biting into the cones of pines and banksias. The upper mandible pierces and hooks in, while the lower cuts through in a powerful pincer action.

Only one of the two races eats both seeds and insect larvae; it is the larger one occuring in small family parties of up to 10 or 20 on the east coast south to Gippsland. The other in Tasmania, western Victoria and South Australia seems to be exclusively a seed-eater, often congregating in great flocks of up to a hundred or more to feed on plantations of radiata pine.

The birds nest in tree hollows high above the ground. The female starts incubating as soon as the first egg is laid and sits for the four weeks the hatchlings take to emerge. The male provides the food during this period. As with the white-tailed species, only one chick survives. Both parents feed the nestling, which fledges in about three months but does not become independent until just before the next breeding season.

White-tailed Black-Cockatoo *Calyptorhynchus latirostris* CARNABY, 1948

OTHER NAMES
Short-billed Black-Cockatoo.

IDENTIFICATION
LENGTH: *550–600 mm, with long tail about half body length.*
MALE: *Body plumage dusky black; feathers narrowly edged with off-white; on underside pale edges wider, giving lighter look. Wings dusky. Tail with broad usually plain white band near end, except for two all-black central feathers. Small patch on cheek dull white. Eye dark brown, with surrounding bare skin pink. Bill grey-black, shortly rounded, and like that of Yellow-tailed Black-Cockatoo in proportion. Feet and toes dark grey-brown.*
FEMALE: *As male, but cheek patch larger and purer white, bare skin round eye dark grey; bill bone-coloured with grey tip to upper mandible; feet flesh-buff.*
IMMATURES: *Similar to adult female, but young males may have smaller cheek patch, dull white like adult male.*
DOWNY YOUNG: *Long, cream-downed.*

VOICE
Contact call in flight a high-pitched drawn-out whistle whee-laa lasting about three-quarters of a second, the last syllable rather prolonged. Also a single-syllabled harsh call in alarm. Fledged young wheeze harshly and constantly.

NESTING
Egg laying takes place July–November. Nest a hollow in a tree, with entrance from 2 m above ground in some wandoo trees to over 20 m in marri trees; entrance at least 180 mm in diameter, widening to at least 350 mm at floor; depth at least 150 mm. Female selects and prepares hollow, lining floor with wood chips from sides. Eggs: two; white; oval, about 48 x 35 mm. Incubation four weeks, by female. Young fledge in 10-11 weeks.

DISTRIBUTION
Centred in drier, eucalyptus wandoo woodlands and forests of southwestern Australia, from the Perth coastal plain and northern Darling Ranges southeastwards through the wheat belt towards Albany and Hopetoun in mallee and sandplain. Flocks wander to more coastal southwestern areas when not breeding, occasionally reaching Bunbury and the karri Eucalyptus diversicolor *forest belt. No races.*

THIS LARGE, SEEMINGLY slow-flying cockatoo was recognised and described only recently, and today is commonly seen flying over the centre of Perth or foraging in suburban gardens.

When sexually mature, White-tailed Black-Cockatoos pair permanently and return to breed in the same areas year after year, mainly the open *Eucalyptus wandoo* woodlands of the northern Darling Ranges and inner wheat belt. The female selects and prepares a tree hollow—not necessarily the one used the previous year—and lays two eggs at an interval of one to 16 days.

As soon as the first egg is laid the female, fed in the morning and evening by the male, starts incubating. Usually, both eggs hatch but the second nestling dies within 48 hours of birth. Occasionally the second nestling survives for varying periods, and in a few cases both nestlings are fledged. For the first three weeks the female—still fed by the male—broods the nestling all the time; from then on until the chick fledges at the age of 10 or 11 weeks it is brooded only at night and fed by both parents. To feed, they enter the nest tail first. The young bird remains dependent until just before the following nesting season and is not ready to breed until its fourth year.

After the chick has fledged, the family joins others from the same area. Together, they move away towards the coast, where they spend the non-breeding season foraging for food. Groups from other breeding areas also congregate with them and large flocks of several thousand may build up at plentiful food sources.

The short, rounded bill of the White-tailed Black-Cockatoo is well adapted to the bird's preferred food and manner of feeding. Like other cockatoos, the White-tailed is a seed-eater and feeds mainly on the kernels of proteaceous plants such as *Hakea, Grevillea, Dryandra* and *Banksia*. These it extracts by biting and tearing open the thick, woody capsules and cones that enclose the seeds. Most food is taken at the perch in trees and shrubs, but the birds readily go to ground to forage on the wild geraniums *Erodium*. The birds will also come down to feed on fallen marri nuts or pine cones.

As soon as it became clear that the Long-billed and White-tailed Black-Cockatoos were separate species, the idea was raised that the White-tailed was only a race of the equally short-billed Yellow-tailed Black-Cockatoo of eastern Australia, its white plumage marks only resembling those of the Long-billed by chance, through evolutionary convergence. On present evidence, its slender feet with thin attenuate claws and narrower, more tapered wings suggest that the Long-billed is its closest relative.

A female White-tailed Black-Cockatoo perching in mallee, one of the woodland habitats of this species.

Long-billed Black-Cockatoo *Calyptorhynchus baudinii* LEAR, 1832

IT IS A RECENT DISCOVERY that the familiar White-tailed Black-Cockatoos of southwestern Australia actually comprise two distinct species. One uses its short, round bill to bite into and break open the cones of proteaceous shrubs and pines for their seeds. The other—the species described here—reefs seeds from the capsules of the marri *Eucalyptus calophylla* instead.

The only clue to the two species in their outward appearance is in their bills, for both are otherwise identical in black and white plumage pattern, sexual differences, and slender feet with thin, finely curved claws. The 'biter' has a slender but rather short and rounded bill like the Yellow-tailed Black-Cockatoos in eastern Australia, but the 'reefer' has a still slenderer bill with an extraordinarily prolonged tip for levering out its food. This it usually takes arboreally, clipping off a capsule, transferring it to the left foot, and then deftly pulling out the seeds with its attenuated upper mandible without damaging the rim of the capsule. X-rays show that the elongation of the upper mandible is not just an outgrowth of the horny covering on the bill, but is supported by a marked extension of the maxillary (upper jaw) bones.

Although the seeds of the marri are staple diet, Long-billed Black-Cockatoos are not restricted to them or to feeding in trees. They often feed on the bull banksia *Banksia grandis,* extracting the seeds as they do those of the marri, and as well, gouge wood-boring larvae from their holes in timber, win nectar from the blossoms of marri and banksia, and even dig into growing apples and pears for their seeds, discarding the fruit. Like the White-tailed Black-Cockatoo, they also go to ground to feed on wild geraniums *Erodium,* and fallen marri nuts and seeds shed by burnt trees after bush fires.

Long-billed Black-Cockatoos seem to be little different from the other white-tailed in habits, breeding and aspects of their life-history. They pair permanently, are similarly communal, and although rarely gathering in flocks of more than 50 or so, they fly to and from roosting and feeding sites with the same slow, buoyant flapping through and over the tops of forest, giving strange wailing cries. To breed they withdraw to the tall karri *Eucalyptus diversicolor* forests in the extreme southwest. Afterwards, they wander northwards with their young, gathering into larger flocks, and reaching the Darling Range east of Perth and Stirling Ranges north of Albany, wherever there is close forest.

At such times they overlap widely with the White-tailed Black-Cockatoo, but the individual flocks never seem to mingle.

OTHER NAMES
Baudin's Black Cockatoo.

IDENTIFICATION
LENGTH: *550–600 mm, with long tapered tail about half body length.*
MALE: *Body plumage dusky black; feathers narrowly edged with off-white, the pale edges wider on underside giving a scalloped appearance. Wings dusky. Tail with broad usually plain white band towards end, except for two all-black central feathers. Small patch on cheek dull greyish white. Eye dark brown, with surrounding bare skin pink. Bill grey-black, very slender with prolonged tapered tip to maxilla. Feet and toes dark grey-brown; claws dusky.*
FEMALE: *As male, but cheek patch larger and purer white; bare skin round eye dark grey; bill bone-coloured with dark tip to upper mandible; feet flesh-buff.*
IMMATURES: *Similar to adult female, but young males may have smaller, duller cheek patch approaching adult male.*
DOWNY YOUNG: *Long, cream-downed, pale-billed.*

VOICE
Contact call in flight (and sometimes when perched) a high-pitched, drawn-out, wailing whistle, whee-la, lasting about half a second, the last syllable rather short and not much longer than the first. Also a single-syllabled harsh screech in alarm. Recently fledged young wheeze or rasp harshly and rather constantly.

NESTING
Egg-laying takes place August–January. Nest a large hollow in tree, usually very high up in a karri or jarrah at 20–30 m or more; entrance about 180–200 mm in diameter, widening to at least 350 mm at floor; depth at least 150 mm. Female selects and prepares hollow, lining floor with wood chips from sides, and entering hole tail first to do so. Eggs: two; white; oval, about 48 x 35 mm. Incubation unknown but probably by female for about four weeks. Usually only one young survives to fledge.

DISTRIBUTION
Centred in tall, heavily timbered hills and ranges of jarrah Eucalyptus marginata and karri E. diversicolor of extreme southwestern Australia, breeding there, and foraging more widely north to the Darling Ranges and east to the Stirling Ranges when not nesting.

Only by studying their feeding behaviour was it realised that Long-billed Black-Cockatoos are a separate species from White-tailed Black-Cockatoos. Not known to have been photographed in the wild, these birds live in tall, heavily timbered ranges in the extreme southwest and are rarely seen.

Cockatiel *Leptolophus hollandicus* (KERR, 1792)

OTHER NAMES
Quarrion, Cockatoo-Parrot, Weero.

IDENTIFICATION
LENGTH: *About 320 mm, including slender tapered tail.*
MALE: *General plumage deep grey, underparts paler and sometimes washed with brown. Forehead, cheeks and throat yellow fringed white; slender erectile crest grey, fringed yellow; ear coverts orange; white patch extends across wing coverts to inner flight feathers. Rump, upper tail coverts and central tail feathers paler grey; outer feathers and underside of tail dark grey. Eye dark brown. Bill and cere dark grey. Feet and claws dark grey.*
FEMALE: *Crown, crest and cheeks dull grey tinged with yellow; ear coverts dull orange; rump, lower underparts and central tail feathers pale grey lightly vermiculated with pale yellow; outermost tail feathers yellow irregularly barred with dark grey. Underside of flight feathers sparsely barred pale yellow.*
IMMATURES: *Similar to adult female; young males usually have brighter yellow on face; crest and tail shortly rounded; bill, cere and feet buffy-flesh. Young males gain full adult plumage at second annual moult.*
DOWNY YOUNG: *Wispy yellow-downed.*

VOICE
Contact call, frequent during flight, a prolonged, warbling queel-queel ending with an upward inflection repeated three or four times, then followed by a brief pause, and repeated yet again. Silent while feeding or at rest.

NESTING
Breeds August–December in south, April to July or August in north. Nest a hollow in a tree in or near water, at 1–8 m above ground; bed for eggs of wood dust. Eggs: two to eight, usually five; white; oval, 25–26 x 18–20 mm. Incubation 18–20 days, by both sexes. Chicks remain in nest for four or five weeks and are fed by both parents.

DISTRIBUTION
Common throughout Australia in open or lightly timbered country, particularly in mid-north where bird is nomadic. Absent from extreme north (northern Kimberleys to Cape York Peninsula) and from Tasmania. Migratory in south, arriving in Victoria, much of New South Wales and southern South Australia and Western Australia in spring and leaving in late summer and autumn. No races.

Cockatiels nest in the hollow limbs of trees in or near water. In this pair, the upper bird is a male.

IS THE COCKATIEL a parrot or a cockatoo? This much debated question has only now been resolved, and the answer has come from recent research into the bird's behaviour, anatomy, and the identity of its liver isozymes. The Cockatiel is certainly a cockatoo, perhaps acquiring its tapered parrot-like wings and tail in adaptation to long, nomadic flights.

Anatomical clues are weighty. Cockatiels not only have a crest but also a gall bladder and powder downs on the lower back; and, like cockatoos, they lack the structural pigment that gives the green colours to other parrots. The short, round-tipped tongue is cockatoo-like, as is the structure of the palate and honing plate of the maxilla. As well, females have bars on the wings and rump as do female Gang-gang Cockatoos, and yellow and black mottled tails like those in female black-cockatoos.

Clues from daily routines are unhelpful because Cockatiels are so like both parrots and cockatoos in general habits. They congregate in groups of about five to several hundred and roost communally. They are seed-eaters and forage by gleaning mainly on the ground for the seeds of grasses, herbs and trees, particularly of *Acacia*. They drink daily if possible, scooping up water with the lower mandible. They roost and rest quietly in trees and on telegraph lines. If disturbed they fly to dead trees and perch lengthwise on the limbs, their grey tones blending with the timber. Only their flight, graceful and buoyant on steadily beating wings, is distinct.

Rituals of breeding show more clearly that the Cockatiel is a cockatoo. In display and copulation, males click their bills quietly, and when excited both sexes will raise their wings above their heads. Both sexes incubate and brood, entering the nest hole tail first like black-cockatoos. Young beg for food with an insistent pulsing wheeze, followed by a shrill piping as they are fed by regurgitation.

Gang-gang Cockatoo

Callocephalon fimbriatum
(GRANT, 1803)

OTHER NAMES
*Red-crowned Cockatoo, Helmeted
Cockatoo.*

IDENTIFICATION
LENGTH: *About 350 mm, including
short, square tail.*
MALE: *General plumage grey including
wings and tail; feathers edged with pale
grey or white. Crest and head bright
red. Wing coverts on outer webs strongly
washed with dull green. Feathers of
lower belly and undertail coverts edged
with faint orange-yellow. Eye dark
brown. Bill horn. Feet and toes grey.*
FEMALE: *Crest and head grey; wings
and tail coarsely marked with pale grey
or white bars; feathers of underparts
broadly edged with orange and green-
yellow, imparting a distinct cast.*
IMMATURES: *Resemble adult female.
Underside of tail heavily barred with
grey or white. Young males have crest
tipped with red, and red markings on
forehead and crown by end of first year;
bill dark grey.*
DOWNY YOUNG: *Long, yellow-downed.*

VOICE
*Contact call in flight or from top of
forest tree—a prolonged jarring
croak—a little like sound of a cork
being pulled from a bottle. When
feeding the bird 'growls' softly.*

NESTING
*Breeds October–January. Nest a hole in
trunk or dead branch of a eucalypt, at
great height, chosen by female. The
birds enlarge the hollow by chewing at
the sides and scraping out the chips.
Eggs: two, rarely three; white; oval, 36 x
28 mm. Incubation about 30 days, by
both sexes. Chicks leave nest about
seven weeks after hatching and are fed
for four–six more weeks.*

DISTRIBUTION
*From seaboard to high inland
mountain ranges of southeastern
Australia, through heavily timbered
and wooded areas; ranges northeast to
Hunter Valley, NSW, and southwest to
Portland district, Vic., and sometimes
southeast of South Australia;
introduced on Kangaroo Island, SA.
Rare at extremities of its range,
including King Island, where extinct,
and Tasmania where it is a vagrant.
No races.*

The Gang-gang Cockatoo feeds on seeds and berries in trees. Only the adult male's crest and head are red.

THE GANG-GANG COCKATOO lives in the mountain eucalypt forests and heavily wooded areas of southeastern Australia. It has become well known for its remarkable tameness when feeding among branches and may almost be touched.

Gang-gangs will return each day to the same tree or bush until the food there is exhausted. They feed mainly on the seeds of native shrubs and trees, including eucalypts, acacias and cypress pine, but have taken to the seeds of introduced species such as hawthorn *Crataegus* and *Cupressus* and other conifers. There is a continual noise as they crack seed capsules open with their strong bills, and the ground beneath the trees becomes littered with debris. They also bite off clusters of berries or seeds, and hold them in one foot to eat. Usually these cockatoos remain in the trees, and visit the ground only to drink or examine fallen nuts and pine cones.

During the breeding season Gang-gang Cockatoos stay in pairs or family parties, but at other times of the year they gather in small flocks. Larger flocks may form where there is a bountiful food supply, and up to 100 birds have been seen feeding in clumps of berry-laden hawthorn bushes. A feeding flock may suddenly leave a tree or bush for no apparent reason, fly in wide circles overhead, screeching noisily, then return to the same tree and continue feeding. While rain or snow is falling, Gang-gangs may fly in circles above the forest canopy, periodically swooping down through the tree-tops. Their flight is heavy and sways from side to side, with deep sweeping wing-beats. During the hottest part of the day they either sit for hours among the branches of a eucalypt, almost without moving, or sidle up to each other for mutual preening.

The cockatoos breed in the mountain forests, then come down to the lower valleys and coastal regions for the winter, frequenting gardens and parklands, and entering Canberra and outer suburbs of Melbourne. Some birds stay in the mountains during the winter, especially if the weather is mild, and small parties of non-breeding birds, generally the young of the previous year, may stay in the lowlands throughout the summer months. Like other short-tailed cockatoos, Gang-gangs enter their nests head first.

Pink Cockatoo
Cacatua leadbeateri (VIGORS, 1831)

THE BEAUTIFUL PINK COCKATOO, its delicate pink tones suffusing its plumage, particularly under the wings in flight, is often called Major Mitchell, after the famous explorer Sir Thomas Mitchell (1772–1855), who wrote about it in glowing terms on his journey to the interior of New South Wales in 1835.

It is usually found in pairs or small groups, sometimes in the company of Galahs or Little Corellas. Large flocks of more than 100 are rare, even where Pink Cockatoos are common, as in the Wyperfeld National Park in northwestern Victoria. Normally these birds will not allow observers to come close—although, if disturbed, they seldom move far and often land on the ground a short distance from where they were first seen.

Pink Cockatoos spend most of the day feeding on the ground or among the branches of trees and shrubs. They eat seeds, nuts, fruits and roots, particularly the seeds of cypress pine *Callitris* and acacias which they find in the trees or on the ground beneath. In the late afternoon and early morning they go to waterholes to drink, sometimes arriving before sunrise. During very hot, dry weather they return to water throughout the day.

When courting, the male bird struts along a branch towards a female and, with crest raised, bobs its head up and down and swishes it from side to side in a figure-eight movement. The male utters soft chattering notes; then the pair preen each other. Couples nest in hollow limbs of trees, entering head first, and line the bottom of the nest with wood dust and bark strips which are removed from the entrance to their nest hole. Both parents incubate the eggs—the male during the day, the female at night—and feed the young. After leaving the nest the young remain with the parents to form a family group.

The flight of Pink Cockatoos is rather staccato, of flapping wing-beats alternating with gliding for brief periods like that of the Sulphur-crested Cockatoo. They rarely fly high, and even where travelling long distances usually move by a succession of low, short flights. After alighting they raise their forward-curving crests.

Unlike the Galah which lives in the same environment, the Pink Cockatoo has not prospered under the rural development of inland Australia. Loss of its native food plants is probably the main cause for decline in most regions, but the trend has undoubtedly been exacerbated by trapping for the illicit bird trade. Unfortunately, Pink Cockatoos cannot recover their numbers as easily as other parrots, for they are aggressively territorial when breeding, not tolerating others within several kilometres of the nest site.

OTHER NAMES
Major Mitchell, Leadbeater's Cockatoo, Wee Juggler.

IDENTIFICATION
LENGTH: *About 360 mm, including short, square-cut tail.*
MALE: *Crown white suffused with salmon-pink. Narrow, forward-curving crest scarlet, with central band of yellow and tipped with white. Forehead scarlet, sides of head, nape, breast, upper belly and underwing coverts salmon-pink. Lower belly, undertail coverts and upper parts, including tail, white. Undersides of flight and tail feathers strongly washed with deep salmon-pink. Eye dark brown. Bill bone-coloured. Feet and toes mid-grey; claws darker.*
FEMALE: *Similar to male but has pale red eye. Central band of yellow in crest broader than in male in eastern race.*
IMMATURES: *Similar to adults. Eye dull brown.*
DOWNY YOUNG: *Fine, yellow-downed.*

VOICE
Usual contact call, given frequently in flight, a two-syllable quavering screech, similar to Little Corella. Alarm call three or four harsh screeches. Fledglings wheeze constantly.

NESTING
Breeds May–December, earlier in north than south. Nest a hollow limb or hole in a tree, lined at bottom with decayed wood dust and with strips of bark. Eggs: two to four, usually three; white; oval, about 39 x 30 mm. Incubation 26–30 days, by both sexes. Young fledge in about six weeks.

DISTRIBUTION
Sporadically distributed throughout arid and semi-arid interior of Australia, with a major gap through the Flinders Ranges to the Simpson Desert. Lives in sparsely timbered grasslands, scrublands, stands of cypress pines growing along sand ridges, casuarinas covering rocky outcrops, mallee, and trees surrounding cereal fields or bordering watercourses. Locally common in favoured districts, but generally scarce. Sedentary near good supplies of water, otherwise nomadic. Two races: one in Murray-Darling basin, with broad yellow band through scarlet crest; the other in Western Australia east to central Australia and Eyre Peninsula, with only faint traces of yellow band in crest.

The Pink Cockatoo raises its crest for a moment after alighting. It feeds on the ground and among tree branches.

Sulphur-crested Cockatoo *Cacatua galerita* (LATHAM, 1790)

FEW AUSTRALIAN BIRDS are as well known as the Sulphur-crested Cockatoo. In eastern and northern Australia its discordant call is a familiar sound in the forests and open farmlands. In other countries it can be found in most zoos and well-stocked aviaries. It is also popular as a pet. In northern Australia pairs or small parties are the normal social units irrespective of the time of year, but in the south, outside the breeding season, the birds congregate in large flocks. Wherever they inhabit open country, they have a well-established 'sentinel warning system'. While the main flock is feeding on the ground, a few birds perch watchfully in trees and screech loudly at the approach of an intruder. The entire flock immediately rises into the air.

Each flock has its own roosting site, which is rarely deserted even if the cockatoos have to fly long distances to feeding grounds. As evening falls the noise in the roosting trees is deafening as the birds jostle for positions and squabble with one another, and it is long after sunset before the screeching subsides. Soon after sunrise the noise starts again when the birds fly off to feed. Going to or coming from the roosting site they fly at a considerable height, with characteristically staccato flap-flap-glide action.

Until mid-morning the cockatoos usually feed on seeds on the ground, then during the hottest part of the day they sit in trees near the feeding area, stripping the leaves and bark. In the afternoon they feed again, then fly back to the roosting trees for the night. Each day they return to feed in the same area until the food supply is exhausted. They eat the seeds of grasses and herbaceous plants, grain, bulbous roots, berries, nuts and leaf buds, often causing considerable damage to crops, particularly oats and maize. To some extent, they compensate for this destruction by eating the seeds of weeds. They also eat insects and their larvae.

OTHER NAMES
White Cockatoo.

IDENTIFICATION
LENGTH: *450–500 mm, including broad, square tail.*
ADULTS: *Sexes alike. General plumage white. Narrow, forward-curving crest yellow; ear coverts and bases of cheek and throat feathers yellow; undersides of flight and tail feathers strongly washed with yellow. Naked eye-ring white or tinged with blue. Eye dark brown. Bill grey-black. Feet and toes dark grey; claws darker.*
IMMATURES: *Similar to adults. Very young have faint tinges of grey on crown, back and wings; eye paler brown.*
DOWNY YOUNG: *Fine, yellow-downed.*

VOICE
Contact call in flight very loud, harsh, raucous screech ending with a slight upward inflection. Alarm call a succession of abrupt guttural screeches. Feeding and preening are accompanied by an occasional squawk or shrill two-syllable whistle.

NESTING
Breeds August–January in south; May–September in north. Nest a hollow limb or hole in tree, usually high up in a eucalypt near water; along lower Murray River nests also in cliff holes. Eggs: two, rarely three; white; ellipsoidal, 45–47 x 32–34 mm. Incubation about 30 days, by both sexes. Chicks remain in nest about six weeks. Adults enter nest head first.

DISTRIBUTION
Widely distributed and common in most types of open timbered country throughout northern, eastern and southeastern mainland, Tasmania and some offshore islands, including Kangaroo Island. Also in New Guinea, New Britain and Aru Islands, Indonesia. Introduced to Perth area, WA, and some islands in southwestern Pacific. One race in Australia; grading from smaller with heavier bill and shorter crest in north, to larger with smaller bill and longer crest in east and smaller again in extreme south in South Australia.

In flight, the undersides of the feathers of the Sulphur-crested Cockatoo are strongly washed with yellow. The bird is a popular pet worldwide.

Little Corella *Cacatua pastinator* (GOULD, 1841)

The widely distributed Little Corella has no coloured crest, but it does erect the short, straight feathers on top of its head.

SEVERAL THOUSAND LITTLE CORELLAS may flock together at roosting time—midday and night—and gather in trees along watercourses. Seen from afar, they appear to transform their roosting trees into capes of white, an appearance enhanced by their habit of stripping the leaves from the trees as well. They are noisy and gregarious, particularly when not nesting.

While the birds breed, they are silent and secretive in their nesting areas, with well-established pair-bonding and nest-maintenance rituals. Pairs may be permanent and use the same nests in successive years. They nest almost exclusively in tree hollows. In the eastern Kimberleys their favourite nest tree is the baobab *Adansonia,* and elsewhere the river red gum *Eucalyptus camaldulensis.* The birds prepare fresh litter every year by chewing the inside of the hollow, which often results in its destruction after several years. A pair may prepare other hollows as well as the one in which they are nesting.

Like other Australian white cockatoos, Little Corellas feed on the ground and eat the seeds of grasses and legumes. In southwestern Australia, local corellas have long bills which help them to dig up corms and bulbs. This has led to their becoming confused with the Long-billed Corella of southeastern Australia. Western long-bills, nonetheless, have the straight erectile crests, more rounded wings, longer tails and fully feathered throats of Little Corellas, revealing their true affinities. They occur alongside Little Corellas in southwestern wheat lands, apparently without interbreeding. This suggests that they represent a third species, the Bare-eyed Corella.

Long-billed Corella

Cacatua tenuirostris (KUHL, 1820)

DURING THE BREEDING season Long-billed Corellas are usually seen in pairs or family parties, but at other times they gather in flocks of up to 50 or more birds. In southwestern Victoria, the centre of their distribution, a concentrated food supply may attract large flocks of several hundred. These may give the false impression that the birds are plentiful when in fact they are not common except in areas where large gum trees offer suitable nesting sites.

These noisy birds often attract attention with their yodelled cries. Very early, often well before sunrise, they leave the roosting trees and, after coming down to drink, move out into the neighbouring open country where they spend most of the day feeding on the ground. Their underparts become smeared with dirt and vegetable stains as they scratch about for seeds and dig up roots and bulbs. Towards dusk they drink again, then indulge in pre-roosting acrobatics, flying through the trees and screeching loudly.

Long-billed Corellas have a 'sentinel' warning system like that of the Sulphur-crested Cockatoo. While the main flock is feeding on the ground, a few birds remain in the trees above, on the lookout for danger.

Both male and female Long-billed Corellas share in the incubation of the eggs—the male sits during the day and the female at night, for 24 days. The chicks remain in the nest for about seven weeks after hatching and are fed by both parents. After leaving the nest they are fed for a further three weeks, particularly by the male.

The noisy Long-billed Corella uses its bill to dig up roots and bulbs. It nests in a tree hollow.

Galah *Cacatua roseicapilla* VIEILLOT, 1817

Galahs at their evening drink. Afterwards, as they fly in flocks to communal roosts, they perform aerial acrobatics which are interpreted as play.

GALAHS ARE SUCH A COMMON SIGHT in Australia that their beauty is often taken for granted. They are usually seen in flocks of 30 to 1000 birds, foraging together or flying over the plains—now pink, now grey as they change direction. In the breeding season they separate into pairs that may be permanent.

Each pair defends a nest tree which contains a nesting hollow, and returns to the same site year after year. Often several nests occur quite close together in a clump of trees, and neighbours are tolerant of each other and of visitors as long as they do not come within about three metres of the nest.

As spring approaches, the birds spend more time around the nest tree, and both sexes prepare the nest hole, entering head first and lining it with eucalypt leaves. A courting male then often approaches his mate with crest raised and head waving from side to side, uttering a soft chattering. Most nest trees have a conspicuous area from which the birds, particularly the male, have removed the bark. Throughout the nesting season both male and female visit this bare patch and spend much time wiping their bills and faces over it. This may be a form of advertising ownership of the site.

As soon as a young Galah leaves the nest it can fly almost as efficiently as its parents—its first flight may be up to two kilometres. Landing seems to pose more problems—they seem to crash land. New fledglings gather together in special patches of woodland and form crèches of up to 100 birds. The parents forage in the surrounding countryside and, as they fly back to the crèche, the fledglings recognise their call and gather in the same tree to be fed. This continues for six to eight weeks, after which the young birds have to fend for themselves while the parents withdraw to the nesting area and complete their annual moult.

Many young Galahs die in the early summer while they are learning to live on their own. Only 10 out of every 100 fledglings survive to breed, but once the birds reach adulthood they generally live for many years. Young Galahs do not breed until they are three or four years old. They spend their first two or three years in flocks of immature birds, which may wander 50 kilometres or more from their birthplace, especially during winter.

Adult pairs seldom move this far, but because Galahs are such strong, fast fliers—they have been timed at more than 50 km/h—they often travel as far as 15 kilometres to look for food, returning to the nest area to roost at night. Their flight is a continuous deep flapping, swaying from side to side.

Galahs, like most parrots, are seed-eaters. They gather nearly all their food from the ground after the seed has fallen. Because ripe seeds are not uniformly distributed, but occur patchily, galahs are generally found in flocks at abundant food sources.

OTHER NAMES
Goulie, Roseate Cockatoo, Rose-breasted Cockatoo, Willie-Willock.

IDENTIFICATION
LENGTH: *350–360 mm, including tail.*
MALE: *Head, nape and underparts pink, grading from whitish on crown to deep ventrally. Back, wings and tail light grey. Skin around eye red in eastern birds but crusty white and powdery in western ones. Eye brown. Bill horn-coloured. Legs and feet grey.*
FEMALE: *Like male but eye light red.*
IMMATURES: *In their first year pink-grey over breast and crown. Eye brown.*
DOWNY YOUNG: *Fine, pinkish-downed.*

VOICE
Single-note screeches in contact; harsh screeching territorial calls. Nestlings and fledglings beg with a heavy-breathed, wheezing whine.

NESTING
Mostly August–November, earlier in north. Nest a hollow limb or hole in a tree, 2–20 m above ground, lined with green leafy twigs. Eggs: two to six; white; oval, about 35 x 26 mm.

Incubation about 30 days, by both sexes. Nestling period six–eight weeks.

DISTRIBUTION
Throughout savanna woodlands and open grasslands. Two races; one throughout eastern, central and northern Australia west to the Kimberleys, with warty red eye-skin and whitish crown; the other through Western Australia north to the Pilbara with grey crusty eye-skin and pinker crown.

Double-eyed Fig-Parrot   *Cyclopsitta diophthalma* (HOMBRON & JACQUINOT, 1841)

THE DOUBLE-EYED FIG-PARROT was given its curious name because of a spot close to the eye in some races, giving the impression of a second eye. The joke is completed in its generic name, *Cyclopsitta,* meaning Cyclops parrot.

These small, green, stumpy-tailed birds resemble lorikeets in much of their appearance and behaviour. They are wholly arboreal, living and feeding high in rainforest trees, running hunched along branchlets with ease, and flying between roost and food trees with swift directness over the top of the forest canopy; although they draw their wings to the body after a series of beats in flight, this movement is so quick that no undulation results. There the similarities to lorikeets end. Fig-parrots are seed-eaters and have broad, sharp-edged bills which they use to cut into figs and other fruit to work out the kernels. Fruits are never pulled off whole but are broken into on the stem. Nectar is sometimes taken, too, as well as the fruits of other rainforest trees, insect larvae, and perhaps fungi from bark.

Fig-parrots roost together at communal camps when not breeding, and disperse in small groups through the day to feed sporadically from early morning till near dusk. In flight they call constantly in contact but when feeding are almost silent, the only signs of their presence being the movement of foliage and a stream of chewed debris falling to the ground. They are difficult to find and see in the canopy of forest and so have often been thought rarer than they really are. Only the population straddling the Queensland–New South Wales border is really rare and possibly on the verge of extinction; it has been seen no more than once or twice in the past 20 years. Destruction of its habitat—lowland rainforest rich in figs—is the likely cause.

When breeding, fig-parrots spread out in pairs to hold small territories centred on food trees. Both sexes prepare the nest hole, but the female does most of the excavation, lining it with wood debris, roosting in it, and spending much of the day there. The male feeds her frequently during courtship, and copulates with a shrill chattering.

Eggs are laid at 48-hour intervals and incubation—by the female—begins with the laying of the first. While on the nest the female is fed by the male each morning and afternoon, and she in turn feeds the nestlings—by regurgitation—until they are about half-way fledged. From then on both parents feed the noisy young, although the female continues to roost in the nest until fledging. Young males attain adult plumage at the second annual moult, about 14 months after leaving the nest.

OTHER NAMES
Lorilet, Marshall's Fig-Parrot, Red-browed Fig-Parrot, Blue-faced Fig-Parrot, Coxen's Fig-Parrot.

IDENTIFICATION
LENGTH: *130–140 mm, including short, round tail.*
MALE: *General plumage bright grass-green, light on belly, darker on back. Outer flight feathers deep blue, innermost with red spot; underwing coverts mid-green edged yellow and a broad yellow band through dusky underside of flight feathers. Yellow stripe down sides of breast to flanks. Marked with red and blue on face according to race.* Cape York Peninsula race: *all forehead, lores and cheeks bright scarlet, giving red-faced appearance, the red grading to green through yellow-orange on the crown and through an edge of pale cobalt on the lower cheeks; a small deep turquoise spot in front of eye.* North Queensland (Cairns) race: *facial red limited to wide dull scarlet spot on forehead and broad sash through cheeks underlined by elongate cobalt spot; turquoise spot in front of eye expanded over lores, splitting red on forehead and cheeks.* Central east coast race: *facial red reduced to yellowish scarlet wash over hind cheeks underlined by moderate cobalt wash; area in front of eye dull green, grading to turquoise wash in centre of forehead. Eye dark brown. Bill leaden, becoming darker at tip; cere dark grey. Feet and toes olive-grey; claws darker.*
FEMALE: *As male but differing in face marks according to race.* Cape York Pensinsula race: *entire forehead pale cobalt, lores and cheeks salmon-buff underlined by a dull cobalt edge.* North Queensland race: *as male but cheeks dull brownish green.* Central east coast race: *similar to male in all marks or with slightly less scarlet-yellow wash on hind cheeks.*
IMMATURES: *Resemble adult female.*
DOWNY YOUNG: *Sparsely white-downed on back.*

VOICE
Contact call a shrill, penetrating tseet *repeated two or three times in flight. Alarm call a high-pitched, rolling screech.*

NESTING
Probably breeds August–October. Nest a small hollow excavated in a rotting branch of a tree. Eggs: two; white; rounded, 22 x 19 mm. Incubation about 18 days, by female. Young fledge in seven–eight weeks.

DISTRIBUTION
Restricted to lower altitude rainforests and their edges, and isolated in three racially distinct populations down the eastern seaboard. One on Cape York Peninsula south to the McIlwraith Range; another in northeastern Queensland from Cooktown to just north of Townsville; and a third, larger than the other two, on the central east coast between Gympie, Qld, and the Macleay River, NSW. Other races occur in New Guinea and offshore islands.

There are three distinct races of Double-eyed Fig-Parrot in Australia, geographically isolated along the east coast of the mainland. This is a male of the red-browed race in northern Queensland, eating wild figs.

Rainbow Lorikeet *Trichoglossus haematodus* (LINNÉ, 1771)

Brilliantly plumaged Rainbow Lorikeets are commonly seen feeding in suburban gardens.

OTHER NAMES
Coconut Lory, Red-collared Lorikeet, Blue-bellied Lorikeet, Blue Mountain Lorikeet.

IDENTIFICATION
LENGTH: *300–320 mm, including long tapering tail.*
ADULTS: *Sexes similar. Head violet-blue with lighter feather shafts. Yellow-green or coral-red collar on nape; rest of upper parts, including wings and tail, mid-green; mantle of red-collared race marked with dark blue. Breast and sides of belly bright yellow-orange, with or without faint dark blue barring; large patch of deep violet-blue or green-black on centre of belly. Thighs, lower flanks and undertail coverts green strongly marked with yellow. Underwing coverts orange washed with yellow; broad yellow band on underside of flight feathers. Eye orange-red. Bill coral; cere reddish grey. Feet and toes brown-grey.*
IMMATURES: *Duller than adults, with shorter tail. Eye brown. Bill brown with yellow markings towards tip.*
DOWNY YOUNG: *Whitish-downed, dark-billed.*

VOICE
Contact call a metallic, rolling, continuous screech in flight. Shrill chatter when feeding. While resting during heat of day, a soft twitter.

NESTING
Breeds August–January, but varies in north, where nesting has been recorded in most months. Nest a hollow limb or hole in a tree near water. Eggs: two, rarely three; white; oval, 27–28 x 22–23 mm. Laid on wood dust at bottom of hollow. Incubation 25–26 days, by female. Young, fed by both parents, fledge in about eight weeks.

DISTRIBUTION
Widespread in most forests and closer woods of northern and eastern Australia from Kimberley Division to Cape York Peninsula, Tasmania and Eyre Peninsula, SA. Introduced into Perth area, WA. Abundant and locally nomadic; vagrant in Tasmania. Prefers lowlands where there are flowering trees. Occurs also in Lesser Sundas, southern Moluccas, New Guinea and adjacent islands, through Bismarck Archipelago and Solomon Islands to Vanuatu and New Caledonia. Four races in Australia: one in the northwest east to Gulf of Carpentaria, with red collar, blackish belly and very broad yellow wing bar; one on Cape York Peninsula, small, with very bright blue head, green collar, bright blue belly and rather stumpy tail; one throughout the east from Cairns area to eastern Victoria, large, with green collar, blue belly, narrower wing bar, and medium tail; one from western Victoria to the South Australian gulfs, like eastern race but with much attenuated tail and small bill.

THE RAINBOW LORIKEET was the first Australian parrot to be illustrated in colour — in Peter Brown's *New Illustrations of Zoology,* published in 1774. Since then, this gaudy parrot has been found to be the most widespread of lorikeets and to exemplify much of their habits and behaviour. It is a blossom-feeder, harvesting nectar and pollen — as well as associated insects and fruit on occasion—from any nectar-bearing plant that it finds, from eucalypts, paperbarks and banksias to rainforest trees, palms and grass-trees *Xanthorrhoea.* Like other lorikeets it has a tongue covered with brush-like papillae for mopping its food from flowers, and a prolonged thin-walled stomach for ready digestion. The nectar provides carbohydrate and the pollen, it is thought, protein. The lorikeet needs to harvest them for only two to three hours a day to satisfy its nutritional needs.

Like all lorikeets, the Rainbow is arboreal and gregarious, flocking in groups of two to fifty by day to several hundred when clumping to roost. Early each morning, even as day breaks, they fly out from their roosts and disperse to feed, sometimes travelling 50 kilometres or more. Their flights to and from feeding areas are at times low through tree tops and at times high above, the birds moving like arrows in compact groups on pointed, whirring wings, screeching regularly. There is no gliding. At food trees they clamber agilely about the outer foliage, often hanging upside-down and rifling blossoms. During the heat of midday there is usually a lull in activity as the birds sit about, preening one another, idly stripping leaves, or feeding briefly.

Then, after another bout of intense feeding in late afternoon, the lorikeets return to set roosts, on the coast or on hills and sometimes even in mangroves. The sight of hundreds of these brilliant birds converging on their camps is spectacular. They flush in low through the trees, screeching and chattering loudly, clump together on branches preening one another, and then dash around to repeat the performance several times before settling down.

Pairing is probably permanent. In courtship, male and female bow, bob and squirm close together and sometimes roll over and over, playing at biting. Although the female appears to incubate alone, the male spends much time with her in the hollow, feeding her by regurgitation and roosting with her at night. For several days after fledging, young return to sleep in the nest.

The red-collared race of the Rainbow Lorikeet.

Scaly-breasted Lorikeet *Trichoglossus chlorolepidotus* (KUHL, 1820)

'SCALY-BREASTED' APTLY DESCRIBES this bird, which has yellow breast feathers broadly edged with green that look like scales. Its habits are similar to those of the Rainbow Lorikeet, and mixed flocks of the two species are often seen; in such flocks one species usually outnumbers the other.

The presence of the birds in their food trees is revealed by a non-stop chattering and screeching and by movement of leaves as the lorikeets climb among the outer branchlets to get at blossoms, often hanging upside-down to feed. Their plumage blends so well with the foliage that they are otherwise difficult to see.

When disturbed, Scaly-breasteds fly off, screeching loudly like other lorikeets. Flight is swift and direct, on rapidly beating pointed wings without any gliding; it exposes a broad sash of red on the underwing which contrasts with the green body.

Scaly-breasted Lorikeets feed on nectar, pollen, blossoms, berries, other fruit and seeds. They feed frequently on cultivated fruits and often cause damage in orchards; they also raid sorghum and maize crops to feed on unripe milky grain.

OTHER NAMES
Green Lorikeet, Green and Gold Lorikeet, Green Keet.

IDENTIFICATION
LENGTH: *About 230 mm, including short, pointed tail.*
ADULTS: *Sexes similar. General plumage green. Crown and sides of head emerald-green slightly tinged with blue. Feathers of back of neck, throat and breast yellow, broadly edged with green, giving scaly appearance. Lower back and wings green. Tail green with base of outer tail feathers marked with orange-red. Lower flanks, thighs and undertail coverts green strongly marked with yellow. Underwing coverts orange-red. Eye orange-red. Bill coral; cere flesh-grey. Feet and toes mid-grey; claws dusky.*
IMMATURES: *Similar to adults, but tail shorter. Eye pale brown. Bill brown with some yellow markings.*
DOWNY YOUNG: *Whitish downed, dark-billed.*

VOICE
Various calls like those of Rainbow Lorikeet but higher in pitch.

NESTING
Breeds in all months except March and April; in south usually August–January. Nest a tree hollow, usually high above ground, with layer of wood dust at bottom. Both sexes prepare nesting cavity, chewing away and scratching out decayed wood and sometimes taking six weeks to do so. Eggs: two, rarely three or one; white; rounded, about 26 x 20 mm. Incubation about 25 days, by female. Young, fed by both parents, leave nest six–eight weeks after hatching. Fledglings return to nest to roost in first few nights after leaving.

DISTRIBUTION
Common in most timbered areas of coastal eastern Australia from Cape York Peninsula south to Illawarra district, NSW; also on some offshore islands. Generally confined to coastal plains and adjacent tablelands; occasionally found along watercourses west of the Great Dividing Range; introduced about Melbourne. Abundant and mostly sedentary in north; less numerous and more nomadic in south. Favours open, lightly timbered woods. No races.

The Scaly-breasted Lorikeet's plumage provides effective camouflage. In flight, a broad sash of red on the underwing aids identification.

A Varied Lorikeet searching for nectar in a blossoming grevillea.

Varied Lorikeet
Psitteuteles versicolor (LEAR, 1831)

OTHER NAMES
Red-capped Lorikeet.

IDENTIFICATION
LENGTH: *About 190 mm, including short, acute tail.*
MALE: *Forehead and crown dark red; ear coverts bright green-yellow. Upper parts, including wings and tail, rich green. Throat and around nape dull green-blue with yellow shafts. Upper breast dull mauve-pink with yellow feather shafts. Rest of underparts yellow-green. Underwing black. Naked eye-ring white; eye yellow. Bill coral; cere grey-white. Feet and toes deep grey; claws darker.*
FEMALE: *Like male but duller and slightly paler in all parts, particularly the greens.*
IMMATURES: *Like adult female. Before post-fledging moult, only forehead band red; crown dull green with scattered red markings. Eye brown. Bill brown with yellow marks.*

VOICE
Thin, cricket-like contact screech in flight; shrill chatter while bird is feeding; soft twitter while bird is resting during day: all higher in pitch than those of Rainbow Lorikeet.

NESTING
Breeds at all times of year, but mostly April–August. Nest a hollow limb in tree near water, prepared by both sexes and lined with wood chips and sometimes chewed leaves. Eggs: two to four; white; round, about 24 x 20 mm. Incubation about 22 days, by female. Young, fed by both parents, fledge in five–six weeks.

DISTRIBUTION
Denser woodlands of northern Australia east to Great Dividing Range. Nomadic. No races.

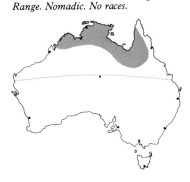

ALTHOUGH NOWHERE ABUNDANT, Varied Lorikeets range nomadically across the northern Australian woodlands in search of nectar flows from blossoming trees. These they converge upon in small groups to large flocks, scrambling about the foliage and clinging in all possible positions to the flowering sprays. Sometimes they chase one another from the preferred tree, bowing and hissing in threat. Favoured nectar sources are eucalypts, paperbarks and grevilleas, but the lorikeets also feed on pollen, fruits, seeds and itinerant insects associated with blossom.

Like other lorikeets they pair permanently and preen and groom one another at roost sites daily. They also water- and foliage-bathe, sometimes dashing headlong into surface water.

Musk Lorikeet *Glossopsitta concinna* (SHAW, 1791)

OTHER NAMES
Green Keet, Green Leek.

IDENTIFICATION
LENGTH: *About 220 mm, including short, acute tail.*
ADULTS: *Sexes alike or female duller. Generally mid-green; paler on underparts. Forehead, lores and band from eyes to side of neck red; crown dull turquoise; nape and mantle bronze-brown tinted with green. Yellow patches on sides of breast; underwing coverts green; tail green with outer feathers washed with orange-red. Eye orange.*

Bill black with coral tip; cere black. Feet olive; claws darker.
IMMATURES: *Duller than adults. Eye brown. Bill black-brown.*
DOWNY YOUNG: *White-downed, dull-billed.*

VOICE
Contact call, uttered in flight, a shrill metallic screech. Feeding accompanied by continuous chattering and intermittent screeching.

NESTING
Breeds August–January. Nest in a high hollow limb of tree. Eggs: two; white; rounded, about 24 x 20 mm. Incubation 21–25 days, by female. Young fledge in six–seven weeks.

DISTRIBUTION
Plentiful in open forest, farmlands, trees along watercourses, orchards, parks and gardens of southeastern Australia, inland to Riverina and Murray Mallee, south to Tasmania and west to Eyre Peninsula and Kangaroo Island. Nomadic. No races.

FLOCKS OF MUSK LORIKEETS are generally seen flying high overhead on their way to and from feeding areas or among branches of flowering eucalypts, feeding on pollen and nectar. They remain in food trees throughout the day, circling out and back in ones and twos at intervals. Only the continuous chattering and shuffling of leaves and blossoms betray their presence, for their green plumage hides them among foliage.

Feeding is most active in early morning and late afternoon. Towards dusk the small feeding flocks return to converge at main camps. It is there that pairs sidle up to one another to preen and face-lick each other.

Rarely nesting more than once a year, both male and female prepare the nest hollow high in a tree, making a bed of fine wood dust for the eggs. Only the female incubates, but the male roosts with her in the nest at night and apparently feeds her by regurgitation. Both share feeding of the two young.

Like all other lorikeets, the Musk is primarily a nectar- and pollen-feeder, the pollen being thought to provide much of the protein in its diet. For the ready digestion of this liquid food with its tiny particles, the birds have a simple alimentary tract without a crop and quite a small unmuscled stomach.

The Musk Lorikeet is so called because, according to some people, it emits a musky odour.

Purple-crowned Lorikeet

Glossopsitta porphyrocephala
(DIETRICHSEN, 1837)

OTHER NAMES
Porphyry-crowned Lorikeet, Blue-crowned Lorikeet, Zit Parrot.

IDENTIFICATION
LENGTH: *About 160 mm, including short acute tail.*
ADULTS: *Sexes alike. Forehead yellow-orange, becoming red on lores and in front of eyes. Crown deep purple. Ear coverts pale orange washed yellow; rest of head green. Nape and upper parts and wings green. Tail green with outer feathers washed with orange-red. Throat, breast and belly pale blue with yellow patches at sides. Underwing coverts crimson; bend of wing blue. Flanks, thighs and undertail coverts yellow-green. Eye brown. Bill and cere black. Feet and toes mid-grey, with dark claws.*
IMMATURES: *Duller than adults. Purple crown patch absent or only slight.*
DOWNY YOUNG: *White-downed, dull-billed.*

VOICE
Contact call, given almost continuously in flight, a rapid shrill trilled tsi-i-it; lacks tone of Little Lorikeet and is longer. Feeding accompanied by shrill twittering.

NESTING
Breeds August–December. Nest a hollow limb or hole in a tree, usually a eucalypt. Colonial nesting has been recorded. Eggs: three or four; white; round, about 20 x 17 mm. Incubation probably by female. Young leave nest four weeks after hatching and within a further two or three weeks are independent of their parents.

DISTRIBUTION
Ranges across southern Australia, ranging north to mulga–eucalypt line in Western Australia and South Australia, covering most of Victoria, just reaching southwestern New South Wales, and wandering as a vagrant to southern Queensland. Lives in a wide variety of habitats and is the only lorikeet native to southwestern Australia. Plentiful in mallee, open woodlands and dry sclerophyll forest, but also fairly common near coast, especially where inland vegetation reaches seaboard. Nomadic, following flowering eucalypts, and numbers fluctuate unpredictably. No races.

A Purple-crowned Lorikeet on a banksia flower. It feeds on nectar and pollen mopped up by its brush tongue.

IN SPITE OF THE ARRAY of colour on the Purple-crowned Lorikeet, it blends remarkably well with the foliage in which it feeds and roosts.

These birds usually move in small groups, but large flocks, sometimes of hundreds of birds, congregate where there is a profusion of flowering eucalypts. They feed on pollen, nectar, blossoms, fruits, including berries, and insects and their larvae. Although they prefer the pollen and nectar from eucalypts, they feed often on cultivated fruits, particularly apples and pears, and can cause considerable damage in orchards. They utter sharp screeching notes on the wing and constantly when feeding, when they also allow observers to come close.

Purple-crowned Lorikeets nest in hollow limbs or holes in trees, usually eucalypts standing near water. Frequently the lorikeets nest in flocks, and the nesting area is full of activity as the birds flit to and from the feeding areas. Together each breeding pair cleans out and prepares its nesting hollow, usually in a eucalypt at three to forty metres above the ground. The female then lays her eggs on the decayed wood dust lining the bottom of the hollow. Both birds spend each night in the nest. The female may leave the nest for an hour or so in the morning and evening to feed on her own. At other times, the male may feed her by regurgitation, particularly in courtship.

The Purple-crowned Lorikeet, with its pointed wings, has a direct, swift flight with rapid wing-beats. It does not seem to fly as fast as the Little Lorikeet, probably because it is heavier and has a stockier build. It also has a crimson patch under its wing, distinguishing it from the Little Lorikeet in flight. Like other lorikeets, they clump to roost at set camps and often fly long distances in search of food trees.

Little Lorikeet *Glossopsitta pusilla* (SHAW, 1790)

A BIRD OF THE TREETOPS, like other species of lorikeets, the Little Lorikeet—one of the smallest parrots—moves about among the leaves with remarkable agility. It is a most difficult bird to see in its natural surroundings because of its small size and its predominantly green colour. Little Lorikeets usually keep in small groups, often in the company of other species of lorikeets, but sometimes large flocks may gather, attracted by a profuse flowering of eucalypts. They eat pollen, nectar, blossoms, native and cultivated fruits and seeds, mopping up nectar and pollen with their brush-tipped tongues. The birds will visit orchards to feed on fruit, but they do not seem as troublesome as the larger lorikeets.

Little Lorikeets camp together at set roosts but in smaller numbers than other lorikeets. By day they also disperse widely in search of blossom—but on finding it, they keep much more to the tops of flowering tree crowns. They will also bathe in the leaves there after rain.

Their flight is swift and direct, with rapid wing-beats that produce a whirring sound. Over long distances the birds fly high, in a straight path, but when flushed from a feeding tree they generally weave their way through the treetops or pass between the trees along a river. In flight they display yellow-green under their wings that distinguishes them from Purple-crowned Lorikeets.

Little Lorikeets appear to mate permanently, each individual preening itself and its mate at their roost camps after a day's feeding. Nests are usually excavated by both sexes in small hollows of eucalypts five–fifteen metres above the ground. Only the female incubates, not beginning until the last of the clutch is laid. The male feeds her in the nest by regurgitation.

OTHER NAMES
Little Keet, Jerryang.

IDENTIFICATION
LENGTH: *150–160 mm, including short acute tail.*
ADULTS: *Sexes alike. General plumage and wings grass-green, lighter on underparts. Forehead and face red. Nape and upper mantle bronze-brown tinted with green. Tail green; outer tail feathers washed with orange-red. Underwing coverts yellow-green. Eye orange-yellow. Bill and cere black. Feet and toes green-grey; claws darker.*
IMMATURES: *Face duller red than in adults; eye brown; bill dark olive-brown.*
DOWNY YOUNG: *White-downed, dull-billed.*

VOICE
Contact call, given constantly in flight, is a high-pitched, short wheezing screech. While feeding the birds chatter constantly.

NESTING
Breeds July–January, but has been recorded in north as early as May. Nest a hollow, preferably in a living eucalypt near water. Both birds prepare hollow for laying. Eggs: three to five; white; rounded, about 20 x 17 mm. Laid in layer of wood dust at bottom of nest. Incubation about 22 days, by female. Young leave nest at about five–six weeks and are independent within the next two.

DISTRIBUTION
Sporadically distributed in eastern and southeastern Australia, north to Atherton Tableland and west to inland fringes of Great Dividing Range and southeast of South Australia; vagrant to South Australian gulfs and Tasmania. Nomadic. Prefers open forest and timber along watercourses in the lowlands but occurs also in mountain eucalypt forests. No races.

Little Lorikeets feed on pollen, nectar, blossoms, fruits and seeds in the treetops in open forests. They are among the smallest parrots.

A pair of Eclectus Parrots look like different species. The male is green.

Eclectus Parrot

Eclectus roratus (P.L.S. MÜLLER, 1776)

OTHER NAMES
Red-sided Parrot, Rocky River Parrot.

IDENTIFICATION
LENGTH: *About 430–450 mm, including short square tail.*
MALE: *General plumage emerald green. Bend of wing blue; primaries deep blue; underwing coverts and sides of belly rich scarlet. Central tail feathers green tipped with blue; outer tail feathers blue tipped with white. Underside of tail dusky tipped with dull yellow. Eye orange. Upper mandible coral, lower black. Feet and toes mid-grey; claws black.*
FEMALE: *General plumage vivid red, darker and duller on back and wings. Fine blue line around eye. Blue collar across mantle. Bend of wing and underwing coverts brilliant blue; primaries deep blue. Broad violet-blue band across belly. Tail red tipped with orange. Eye pale yellow with dark outer ring. Bill black. Feet and toes as male.*
IMMATURES: *Resemble adults. In both sexes bill is dark brown-grey becoming dusky yellow towards tip.*
DOWNY YOUNG: *Sooty-grey.*

VOICE
Contact call in flight a harsh, screeching krraach-krraak *repeated several times. While feeding, the birds infrequently utter a two-syllable wailing cry, or a mellow, horn-like* chu-wee chu-wee; *latter also occasionally given in flight. Also variety of chuckling and bell-like sounds.*

NESTING
July–January. Nest a big, 50 cm to 6 m deep hole in trunk of a tall tree at edge of or in a clearing in forest. Eggs: two; white; rounded, 41–42 x 33 mm. Laid on lining of chips and decayed wood dust. Incubation about 26 days, by female. Chicks leave nest about 11–12 weeks after hatching.

DISTRIBUTION
Rainforests of eastern Cape York Peninsula, from Pascoe River south to Massey Creek and inland to McIlwraith Range. Also widely distributed from Solomon Islands west through New Guinea to Moluccas. One endemic race in Australia, distinguished by large size and dull emerald tone of males.

IT WAS NOT UNTIL 1913 that the Eclectus Parrot was discovered in Australia, in the rainforests of Cape York Peninsula. The parrot was familiar from other parts of its wide range to the north of Australia, and had been known for more than a century. Indeed, its remarkable sexual dimorphism had caused endless confusion.

Eclectus Parrots are birds of the forest canopy and spend much of the day in the trees, feeding on berries and other fruit, nuts, seeds, and blossoms. They are noisy, conspicuous birds, and their loud, raucous cries seem to echo through rainforest.

In the early morning, pairs and small parties leave the roosting trees and move out into the surrounding forest to feed. They are wary and when disturbed fly off or circle high overhead, screeching loudly. The return flights to the roosting trees begin towards dusk; as each group comes in it joins in the screeching and squawking, which goes on until after nightfall. The parrots are strong fliers, and on long flights—such as to and from the roosting trees—they fly high above the treetops. Their flight is direct, with measured, bat-like wing-beats never rising above the horizontal.

Eclectus Parrots indulge in mutual preening and in display the male slowly bobs and dips his head. He also feeds the female then and regularly later when she is incubating. Both parents care for the chicks, and seem to be helped in the task: reports state that up to eight birds of both sexes appear to attend the nests.

Red-cheeked Parrot

Geoffroyus geoffroyi (BECHSTEIN, 1811)

INVESTIGATING REPORTS OF strange parrots near the Pascoe River on Cape York Peninsula, a naturalist, William McLennan, discovered the first Australian Red-cheeked Parrots in 1913.

Red-cheeked Parrots are usually seen singly, in pairs or in small groups, wheeling high above the forest canopy, continually emitting their strident call-notes. They fly swiftly and directly, beating their wings rapidly all the time. They are strictly arboreal and feed on seeds, nuts, berries and other fruit.

A group observed at Iron Range showed a regular daily pattern. In the early morning they left their tall roosting trees and flew to the feeding area. On the way they alighted on a cluster of tall deciduous trees and called loudly for two or three minutes, vibrating their wings—possibly a contact signal. They fed from 10 am until late afternoon, then returned to the roosting area. Before settling for the night, they made brief pre-roosting flights.

The male Red-cheeked Parrot has red cheeks; the female's head is brown.

OTHER NAMES
Geoffroy's Parrot, Pink-cheeked Parrot.

IDENTIFICATION
LENGTH: *About 220 mm, including narrowly rounded tail.*
MALE: *General plumage grass green, paler and yellower on underparts and tail. Forehead, lores, cheeks, ear coverts and throat bright rose-red. Crown and upper nape mid blue-violet. Yellow-red spot on upper scapulars; underwing coverts sky blue. Eye pale yellow with dark grey outer ring. Upper mandible dark coral, lower brown-grey; cere mid-grey. Feet and toes green-grey with darker claws.*
FEMALE: *As male, but cheeks and throat olive-brown; rest of head chestnut-brown. Bill brown-grey.*
IMMATURES: *Head green; cheeks tinged with brown; bill brown-grey. Young males probably acquire adult plumage in second year.*

VOICE
Contact call, uttered continuously in flight, a loud, metallic aank *repeated rapidly 10 or more times, or* aank-aank, *ending with upward inflection. When excited, birds emit peculiar guttural chatter or high-pitched screeches.*

NESTING
Breeding season probably protracted, from August to November or December. Nest 80–120 mm diameter tree hollow excavated by the birds, usually high above ground, lined with chewed wood. Eggs: two to four, usually three; white; rounded, about 29 x 25 mm (New Guinea data). Incubation by female; she is fed outside nest by male.

DISTRIBUTION
Rainforest of eastern Cape York Peninsula from Pascoe River south to Rocky River and inland to western slope of McIlwraith Range. Common along watercourses, and in gallery forest, occasionally wandering into adjacent open woodland. Also throughout New Guinea region west to Moluccas and Lesser Sunda Islands. One endemic race in Australia, with sky-blue underwing and deep chestnut tone to brown head of female.

The male Australian King Parrot is about two and a half years old before it attains this magnificent full adult plumage at the end of a long slow moult.

Australian King Parrot *Alisterus scapularis* (LICHTENSTEIN, 1816)

OTHER NAMES
Southern King Parrot, King Lory.

IDENTIFICATION
LENGTH: *410–430 mm, including long, thick tail.*
MALE: *Head and underparts scarlet. Back and wings dark green; light green stripe on wing coverts. Narrow band on nape, and lower back to upper tail coverts deep blue. Tail black. Undertail coverts green-black broadly edged scarlet. Eye yellow; outer ring grey. Upper mandible red tipped black, lower mandible black. Feet grey; claws darker.*
FEMALE: *Head, wings and back deep green, with light green stripe on wing coverts. Rump and lower back blue tinged with green; upper tail coverts green; undertail coverts green broadly edged with scarlet. Central tail feathers dark green; outer tail feathers blue-green, tipped pink. Throat and chest dull green with red tinge on upper throat. Belly and lower breast scarlet. Eye pale yellow. Bill dark brown washed red. Feet as male.*
IMMATURES: *Like adult female. Older birds develop pale wing covert stripe. Males acquire adult plumage through a slow moult beginning at 16 months and continuing for 14 or 15 months; they have been found breeding in immature plumage.*
DOWNY YOUNG: *Whitish-downed.*

VOICE
Contact call in flight a shrill crassak-crassak, repeated frequently. While perched the bird utters piping whistle, also apparently in contact.

NESTING
Breeds September–January. Nest a layer of decayed wood dust in large deep hollow in trunk of a tall tree; bottom of hollow may be near ground and entrance more than 10 m above. Eggs: three, sometimes four or five; white; rounded, 31–34 x 25–28 mm. Incubation about 20 days, by female. Young, fed first by female then by both parents after half-grown, leave nest about five weeks after hatching.

DISTRIBUTION
Common in heavily timbered mountain ranges and rainforests from Atherton Tableland south to eastern and southern Victoria. Two races: one small on tableland rainforests north of Townsville; the other large, from ranges inland of Rockhampton south to Victoria. The identity of an isolated population in ranges inland from Mackay, Qld, is uncertain.

AUSTRALIAN KING PARROTS are usually seen in pairs or small parties feeding among the outermost branches of forest trees, especially eucalypts and acacias. They eat seeds, berries, other fruits, nuts, nectar, blossoms and leaf buds, but they also come to the ground to pick up fallen seeds, walking with an awkward waddle. Like other parrots they have the habit of holding large fruit in the left foot when tearing it to bits with the bill to get at the kernels. Unfortunately these beautiful parrots raid orchards and maize crops, sometimes causing significant damage.

King Parrots are rather wary and often more difficult to approach than rosellas. When disturbed they take flight, calling loudly. They fly in a heavy, laboured manner with deliberate, rhythmic wing-beats, but are deceptively swift, weaving their way through trees with remarkable dexterity. When travelling to and from their communal roost camps an hour or so after sunrise and before sunset each day, they fly higher over the top of forest.

If King Parrots mate permanently, it is not clear from the way mature males associate with other uncoloured birds when not breeding. The sexes do not preen one another either. Courtship takes place on a perch, the male puffing up his head feathers, drawing up the body, flicking his wings to display the scapular stripe, contracting his pupils to blaze the coloured iris, and giving the harsh contact call. His mate responds in the same way and solicits food by continually bobbing her head. Such feeding begins weeks in advance of egg laying. She alone incubates, but her mate attends her, feeding her at intervals during the day and roosting near the nest.

Red-winged Parrot

Aprosmictus erythropterus (GMELIN, 1788)

CLOSELY RELATED TO AUSTRALIAN KING PARROTS and feeding similarly on seeds, fruits, buds and blossom in the foliage of trees and shrubs, Red-winged Parrots nonetheless differ. They are not so communal, usually living in pairs or small family groups, and rarely gather in feeding flocks. To scratch their heads they push the foot forward under, not over the wing, and their flight is more erratic with deep irregular wing-beats and swooping undulations. Red-winged Parrots usually come to ground only to drink.

When courting, the male Red-winged Parrot chatters softly while taking short flights around the female. He alights on the same or a nearby branch and droops his wings, exposing the blue on his lower back. He then draws his body plumage in tightly and, with his iris blazing, takes two or three slow steps towards the female.

OTHER NAMES
Crimson-winged Parrot.

IDENTIFICATION
LENGTH: *About 320 mm, including long, round tail.*
MALE: *General plumage bright green. Back of head slightly tinged blue. Scapulars and upper back black; lower back blue, paler on rump. Wing coverts rich red; underwing coverts, bend of wing pale green. Tail green tipped with yellow. Eye orange-red. Bill and cere orange-coral. Feet and toes mid-grey; claws darker.*
FEMALE: *General plumage dull green with yellow wash on underparts. Red on outer wing coverts. Lower back and rump pale blue. Eye pale brown. Bill and feet as male.*
IMMATURES: *As adult female. Males don adult colours at third year moult.*
DOWNY YOUNG: *White-downed.*

VOICE
Contact call a sharp, metallic crillik-crillik. Alarm call a harsh screech.

NESTING
Breeds August–February; in north as early as May. Nest of wood dust in a hole in a tree, often near water, with egg chamber near ground. Eggs: five, occasionally six; white; rounded, 30–32 x 25–26 mm. incubation about 20 days, by female; leaves nest to be fed by male. Young, fed by both parents, fledge in about five weeks.

DISTRIBUTION
Common in eucalypt woods along and near streams across north, east to much of Queensland coast and south to inland deserts, and Lake Eyre and Darling River drainages. Sedentary, with irregular movements along fringes of range. Also occurs in southern New Guinea. No races.

Only the male Red-winged Parrot has extensive red on its wings.

Regent Parrot *Polytelis anthopeplus* (LEAR, 1831)

WHEN NOT BREEDING THIS gleaming gold bird gathers in flocks of 10 to 100 or more at communal roosts in the taller gums along streams or around farm dams. Daybreak sees them first on the topmost branches, preening and chattering. Then they go down to drink and from there out to feed, often travelling many kilometres. Most of the day is spent on the ground, or sometimes in trees and shrubs, feeding on seeds and fruit, and even blossom and shoots; grain and cultivated fruit are also exploited at times. The approach of dusk finds them flying back to their roost, pausing only to drink.

Flight is swift, graceful and direct, on steadily beating wings.

This routine alters during breeding when males alone band together in small feeding groups, leaving females to incubate and brood. Males nonetheless attend their mates closely then, roosting near the nest, rarely travelling far for food, and returning to feed the female by regurgitation each morning and afternoon. Courtship, including courtship feeding by the male, begin weeks before laying, but the pair do not preen each other. Display resembles that of the Superb Parrot but is less elaborate.

OTHER NAMES
Smoker, Rock Pebbler, Marlock Parrot.

IDENTIFICATION
LENGTH: *About 400–450 mm, including long tapering tail.*
MALE: *Head, underparts bright yellow. In Western Australia males are much duller yellow and olive-toned on crown and nape. Mantle and back dark olive-green, rump yellower. Broad band of red along inner wing coverts and secondaries; outer wing coverts blue-black; shoulder bright yellow. Outer webs of primaries and secondaries dark blue. Underwing coverts rich yellow. Tail plain blue-black. Eye orange-brown. Bill and cere orange-coral. Feet and toes mid-grey.*
FEMALE: *Head and breast dull olive-yellow; rest of back dull green. Wings as male but duller; median wing coverts bright yellow. Undertail coverts dull olive-green. Tail dark blue-green, outer tail feathers edged and tipped on undersides with rose-pink.*
IMMATURES: *Similar to adult female. On leaving nest, males usually have yellower tinge on head. Full adult plumage acquired at about 14 months.*
DOWNY YOUNG: *White-downed, dull-billed.*

VOICE
Contact call, given in flight, similar to but harsher than call of the Superb Parrot. After alighting the bird twitters softly.

NESTING
Breeds August–January. Most nests are bed of wood dust in large hollows down main trunks of trees. Eggs: four, sometimes five or six; white; rounded, 30–32 x 23–25 mm. Incubation 21 days, by female. Young fledge in about six weeks.

DISTRIBUTION
Two isolated races: one through mallee wheat belt of southwestern Australia; the other along central Murray River between Robinvale and Morgan in southeast. Nomadic; eastern race contracts to river gums on Murray system to breed and wanders widely through surrounding mallee at other times.

The Superb Parrot roams woodlands in search of seed crops. This is a male; the female has a bluish-green face and pink tipped tail feathers.

Superb Parrot
Polytelis swainsonii (DESMAREST, 1826)

SUPERB PARROTS CONGREGATE IN small groups throughout the year, foraging for seeds on the ground or feeding on eucalypt blossoms. They also eat fruits and leaf buds, and sometimes visit farmlands to feed on wheat and oats. After drinking early, the parrots spend much of the morning feeding, and then rest quietly in the crowns of nearby trees. After more feeding in late afternoon they fly back to a set roost. Non-breeding parties include immatures but these break up at the onset of nesting when adult males often band together to forage for their brooding mates.

The courtship display of the male Superb Parrot is lively. He sometimes makes short flights around the female, bowing as he alights. He puffs out his head feathers, tightly draws in the rest of his feathers, partly spreads his wings, and, with irises blazing, rushes to and fro on his perch, chattering continually. The female crouches low, puffs her head feathers, partly spreads her wings and utters soft begging calls. The male then feeds her. The male also feeds his mate while she is incubating, and for the first week or so after the young hatch. Thereafter he helps to feed the young.

OTHER NAMES
Barraband Parakeet, Green Leek.

IDENTIFICATION
LENGTH: *About 400 mm, including long tapering tail.*
MALE: *General plumage brilliant green. Fore-crown, throat and cheek patches rich yellow; wide crescent of scarlet across throat. Underwing coverts green; bend of wing and outer webs of primaries dull blue, black beneath. Tail green above, black below. Eye yellow-orange. Bill and cere coral. Feet dark grey.*
FEMALE: *Head and body dull green. Face pale blue-green; throat pinkish-green; thighs orange-red. Edges and undersides of outer tail feathers rose-pink. Eye yellow. Bill and feet as male.*
IMMATURES: *As adult female. Eye brown. Males acquire adult plumage gradually over next six–nine months.*
DOWNY YOUNG: *White-downed, dull-billed.*

VOICE
Contact call a long, abruptly ending warble; emitted frequently in flight. Also a soft twittering when resting.

NESTING
Breeds September–December. Nest a hollow limb or hole in a tree, at great height. Eggs: four to six; white; rounded, 28–30 x 23–24 mm. Incubation about 20 days, by female. Young fledge in five–six weeks.

DISTRIBUTION
Woodlands of western watershed of Great Dividing Range, NSW, west to eastern edge of Hay Plains, south to Murray–Murrumbidgee Rivers, east to Canberra and Gunnedah and north to Barwon catchment. Nomadic and partly migratory, ranging north to Barwon catchment in autumn–winter and south to Murrumbidgee–Lachlan system to breed. No races.

Regent Parrots occur in mallee and river red gums. Here the more brightly coloured male with its rich yellow plumage rests on the upper branch.

Alexandra's Parrot *Polytelis alexandrae* GOULD, 1863

LITTLE IS KNOWN ABOUT THE HABITS of the Alexandra's Parrot, a rare inhabitant of the arid interior. At irregular intervals, perhaps more than 20 years, a pair or a small flock will appear on a tree-lined watercourse, stay to breed, and then disappear as abruptly as it arrived. The flock usually numbers no more than 15 to 20 birds, but larger groups have been reported.

Several pairs of Alexandra's Parrots may come together to form a small breeding colony. As many as ten nests have been found in one tree. Fed by the male, the female incubates the eggs and broods the chicks. About five to six weeks after hatching, the young leave the nest and accompany their parents on an almost immediate exodus from the nesting area. Young males acquire adult plumage in their second year.

The parrots spend most of the day on or near the ground searching for seeds of grasses and herbaceous plants, especially spinifex *Triodia*. They also feed on acacia blossoms and the berries of mistletoe *Loranthus*.

When disturbed, Alexandra's Parrots will fly to a nearby tree, where they often perch lengthwise along a stout limb. This posture presumably helps them to avoid detection. Flight is similar to that of the Superb Parrot and as swift. The wing-beats are irregular, so that the bird undulates slightly while flying. Before landing, it seems to pause momentarily in midair, then drops to the ground fluttering its wings. It flies high when travelling long distances but stays close to the ground on short flights.

Males have a spatulate tip to the third and longest primary flight feather, but its purpose is not known.

Courtship display is also similar to that of the Superb Parrot. The male erects a few feathers on his forehead into a tiny crest, bobs his head animatedly, and utters excited shrieks.

OTHER NAMES
Princess Parrot, Rose-throated Parakeet.

IDENTIFICATION
LENGTH: *About 400–450 mm, including very long tapered tail.*
MALE: *Crown and nape light blue; forehead and sides of head pale blue-grey; chin, throat and foreneck rose-pink. Mantle, back and wings pale olive-green; shoulder wing coverts bright yellow-green; underwing coverts blue-violet. Rump and upper tail coverts violet-blue. Central tail feathers olive-green washed with blue towards tips, outer tail feathers blue-grey edged with rose-pink. Breast and belly blue-grey tinged with green and yellow; thighs and lower flanks rose-pink; rest washed with blue; crissum olive-yellow. Eye orange. Bill and cere coral. Feet and toes mid-grey; claws darker.*
FEMALE: *Like male, but crown grey-mauve; rump and upper tail coverts grey-blue; wing coverts duller and greener; central tail feathers shorter.*
IMMATURES: *Like adult female; males acquire adult plumage gradually at second annual moult.*
DOWNY YOUNG: *White-downed, dull-billed.*

VOICE
Normal contact call in flight of strident rattling notes, more like that of a kingfisher than a parrot. Also cackling notes, and when flushed into trees or bushes, a soft twittering.

NESTING
Breeds mainly September–January. Nest a hollow limb or hole in a tree, generally a riverine eucalypt but sometimes a casuarina away from water. Eggs: four to six; highly glossy white; round, 26–28 x 21–23 mm. Laid in wood dust at bottom of hollow. Incubation about 20 days, by female. Young fledge in five–six weeks.

DISTRIBUTION
From Fitzroy River and Coolgardie, WA, eastwards to southern Northern Territory, northern South Australia and lower Diamantina River, southwestern Queensland. Frequents sandy, spinifex deserts, dry acacia scrublands and eucalypts bordering watercourses. Rare and highly nomadic. No races.

Alexandra's Parrot was named in honour of Queen Alexandra when she was still Princess of Wales. The male, shown above, can erect a few feathers on its forehead in a tiny crest during courtship.

Budgerigars are gregarious birds. Several pairs may nest in holes in the same tree.

Budgerigar
Melopsittacus undulatus
(SHAW, 1805)

OTHER NAMES
Budgerygah, Shell Parrot, Shell Parakeet.

IDENTIFICATION
LENGTH: *175–185 mm.*
ADULTS: *Sexes similar but cere darker blue in males. Back of crown, sides of neck, upper back and shoulders barred black and yellow, narrowly on head and mantle, coarsely on wings. Lower back, rump, upper tail coverts and underparts plain bright green. Forehead, lores, throat and forepart of cheeks yellow. Feathers of cheeks tipped violet-blue; a series of black spots across throat. Flight feathers dusky green, with broken yellow stripe above and below; primary coverts dusky green; underwing coverts bright green. Central tail feathers green-blue, outer feathers green with a broad oblique yellow band across centre. Eye white. Bill olive-grey; cere blue. Feet and toes leaden; claws darker.*
IMMATURES: *Duller than adults. Black spots on throat ill-defined or absent. Forehead barred. Eye brown. They acquire adult plumage at three or four months, at the first post-fledging moult.*
DOWNY YOUNG: *White-downed, cream-billed.*

VOICE
Most common is the warbled chrp *call which is given singly or in quick repetition when flocks are flying, feeding, drinking or perching; pre-flight* zit *and lower-pitched alarm* zit; *warbling composed of several elements given by breeding pairs, usually by male, and often during courtship; food-begging call by young and female before being fed by male.*

NESTING
Breeds mainly August–January in south and June–September in north. Each pair may have several broods in succession. Nest is a hollow or hole in a tree, log or fence post. Communal nesting is common—several nests have been seen in the same tree branch. Eggs: four to six, occasionally up to eight; white; round, about 19 x 14 mm. Laid on alternate days on layer of wood dust in hollow. Incubation 18–20 days, by female, who is fed by male at regular intervals. Young leave nest about five weeks after hatching and are independent within a few days.

DISTRIBUTION
Ranging throughout most of Australia, chiefly the interior. Nomadic, but moving south in spring, north in autumn. Inhabits trees bordering watercourses, sparsely timbered grasslands, mallee, mulga and spinifex desert. No races.

BUDGERIGARS ARE HIGHLY NOMADIC and their movements and breeding appear to follow flushes of seeding grasses throughout the arid zone. In the south—which has reliable winter rains—the birds arrive in spring, breed and depart, whereas in the north they are abundant during the wet season and breed early in the dry (autumn and winter). In the centre and north, Budgerigars may remain for extended periods if seasons remain favourable.

Most activities are performed as a flock which is usually less than 100 birds. Larger groups may also form, and are well co-ordinated in take-off, midair changes in direction, and landing. Birds in the front lead; with a change in direction a new group leads.

Their diet consists of the seeds of grasses, chenopods and other herbs. There appears to be no special dietary requirements for breeding birds or young. When feeding, the birds move across the ground in a front, climbing up and down tussocks of grass, searching independently yet staying together as a flock.

Budgerigars perch mostly in green trees. They roost in trees selected most often along watercourses, and usually change their roost site each night. Before sunrise the birds preen, call softly and move about, and then leave for their feeding areas at about sunrise. Feeding occurs throughout the day but peaks in the early morning and later in the afternoon. They are efficient at water retention and only need to drink when it is very hot and then do so mainly through the middle of the day. They can descend on a waterhole in droves, immersing their heads in the water and ladling it down with a rapid gulping before flying quickly off. Towards sunset flocks rise in spectacular display flights, calling loudly, and turning and swirling at high speed over the trees; at its end they fly to the roost site and drop into the foliage.

During courtship there is much chasing; then, after they alight on a limb the male begins to feed the female by regurgitation. While mating, the male places a wing around the shoulder of the female, changing wings alternately. After this, the male continues to feed the female, then they rest side by side on a perch before flying off to feed together. The female not only broods unaided but also prepares and cleans out the nest, which she defends.

The Budgerigar is extremely popular as a cage bird and societies devoted to the raising and caring for various strains of domesticated Budgerigars have been formed in most countries.

Ground Parrot *Pezoporus wallicus* (KERR, 1792)

The Ground Parrot's long legs enable it to run quickly through heath.

ONE OF THE WORLD'S THREE ground-living parrots, the Ground Parrot is sparsely distributed, rare and difficult to find in swampy heaths and pastures around the southern coast of Australia. It roosts by day in squats beneath tussocky vegetation, flushing reluctantly with an audible flutter to fly 50 metres or more before diving back to cover. The parrot lacks a furcula or wishbone attaching to the pectoral flight muscles and this is thought to assist vertical takeoff.

Contrary to popular belief, Ground Parrots are strong fliers and capable of flying long distances. Nonetheless they seem to be fairly sedentary and solitary; certainly they usually roost singly. Flight is swift in a zigzag pattern low over the heaths: deep sweeping wing-beats are succeeded by a brief glide on downswept wings, to be followed by another series of beats in a different direction.

Ground Parrots are largely nocturnal. Towards nightfall they become active and start calling, fluttering over the heath to do so. Whether calling advertises a territory or identifies the caller or serves both purposes is not clear. It continues for 30–40 minutes and is repeated again at sunrise, but during the day the parrots are usually silent. The birds apparently forage mainly at night—and they feed their young then. With rather long slender legs and claws they are able to run and clamber quickly and nimbly through dense vegetation and to climb up on seeding stalks; the waddling gait characteristic of other parrots is missing.

Ground Parrots have suffered greatly from the destruction of their habitat by too-frequent burning and clearing along the coast.

Night Parrot *Pezoporus occidentalis* (GOULD, 1861)

THE NIGHT PARROT IS AUSTRALIA'S most famous 'extinct' bird. There has been no hard evidence of its survival since the turn of the century, sporadic sight records notwithstanding. It is nocturnal, secretive, nomadic and lives in remote parts of inland Australia: searching for it is like looking for a needle in a haystack. Yet it probably still survives in small numbers in spinifex *Triodia* breakaways and the samphire-covered margins of salt lakes.

The Night Parrot is closely related to the Ground Parrot, which it resembles in habits and appearance. Both birds are ground-dwellers and night-active. The Night Parrot, nonetheless, has a number of distinctive features, all of which seem to reflect its life in an arid environment. The claws on its slender feet are short and rounded, suitable for running and walking on bare ground. Its nostrils are reduced to slits and ringed with fine hairs. The wings are very long and its tail short and pointed, possibly in adaptation to long nomadic flight.

That Night Parrots are nomadic and have to travel far for food and water is not surprising considering their environment. According to the meagre information available—all recorded 50 years ago and more—they first fly from their roosts soon after dusk to group and drink at waterholes and then go on to feed. The seeds of spinifex have been quoted as staple diet but, judged by the behaviour of a single bird in the London Zoo in 1868, shoots and vegetable matter are also eaten.

By dawn the parrots have returned to their roosts. Their flight has been described as quail-like, but it may well be little different from that of the Ground Parrot. Night Parrots sleep singly in small squats excavated beneath bushes, reaching them by open tunnels.

Red-capped Parrot *Purpureicephalus spurius* (KUHL, 1820)

RED-CAPPED PARROTS AND THE MARRI TREE *Eucalyptus calophylla* go together. The bird not only favours the hollows in marri for nesting but also depends on its seeds for food. It is even possible that the parrot's very long and slender bill has become adapted to extract the seeds out of large marri fruit capsules.

Most feeding is done through much of the day high in the tree crowns where the birds are hard to see. The parrots also come to ground from time to time to feed on fallen marri and other fruits and seeds, particularly those of grasses along roadsides in the early mornings of spring and summer. Additional foods eaten are the seeds of other eucalypts, grevilleas, hakea and casuarinas, orchard fruits and occasional lerps and other leaf insects.

Adults and immatures commonly forage in different situations, the young birds banding into wandering flocks of 20 or so. Adults, apparently permanently mated, tend to keep to isolated pairs in the same patch of nesting timber year round. Their flight between trees is a rapid fluttering broken by very shallowly undulating glides.

In display there is no mutual preening. With a harsh rattling, the male alights on the perch by the female, erects his red cap, droops the wing to expose his yellowish rump, and slowly raises his fanned tail. He also feeds the female in courtship and while she is incubating and brooding young.

OTHER NAMES
King Parrot, Western King Parrot, Pileated Parakeet, Hookbill.

IDENTIFICATION
LENGTH: *360–370 mm, including long tapered tail.*
MALE: *Forehead, crown and nape dark red; back and wings deep green, grading to deep blue on flight feathers. Cheeks, rump and upper tail coverts bright yellow-green; breast and upper belly deep blue-violet. Lower belly and crissum red mixed with some bright green. Underwing coverts blue; underside of flight feathers black. Central tail feathers deep green, outer tail feathers blue tipped with white. Eye dark-brown. Bill whitish grey; cere leaden. Feet and toes deep olive-grey.*
FEMALE: *Duller than male. More green on flanks and undertail coverts. Some birds have green feathers on crown and a dull grey-mauve breast.*
IMMATURES: *Crown and nape green; frontal band rust-coloured. Blue on wings and tail and yellow-green on cheeks noticeably reduced in both extent and intensity. Distinct white stripe in wings. Underparts dull red-brown, washed with violet-blue lower down; lower belly and crissum red strongly suffused with pale green. Young males have acquired much of the adult plumage by first complete moult, at 12–15 months, but young females may not acquire adult plumage until second moult.*
DOWNY YOUNG: *White-downed, yellow-billed.*

VOICE
Grating kurr-ak *repeated several times, uttered regularly during flight. Sharp shrieks in alarm. No chattering when feeding.*

NESTING
Breeds August–December. Nest a hollow limb or hole usually high in a tree, generally a marri. Eggs: four to seven, usually five; white; rounded, 26–27 x 22–23 mm. Laid on wood dust. Incubation about 20 days, by female. Young, fed by regurgitation by female for first two weeks and then by both sexes, leave nest about five weeks after hatching.

DISTRIBUTION
Restricted to southwestern Australia, from just north of Perth to south coast west of Esperance. Eastern boundary coincides roughly with Great South Railway. Inhabits eucalypt forest and open timbered lands, extending to parks and gardens. Sedentary, but local movement according to availability of food. No races.

Because it spends a lot of its time in the treetops, the Red-capped Parrot is difficult to observe. This is an adult male; most birds seen are immatures.

Ringneck _Barnardius zonarius_ (SHAW, 1805)

This is one of the western races of the Ringneck, known as the Port Lincoln Parrot. It is much more widely distributed than its name suggests.

RINGNECKS FLYING ACROSS AND ALONG the road, their plumage flashing now green now yellow in the sunlight, add sparkle to the dry landscape of inland Australia. They frequent belts of timber lining roads, pockets of taller mallee and river gums _Eucalyptus camaldulensis_ along creek beds. In southwestern Australia they enter the denser forests of jarrah and karri _E. marginata, E. diversicolor_ as well, occupying the niche that the Blue-cheeked Rosella fills in eastern Australia.

Whether feeding in the outer foliage of eucalypts and other trees or on the ground, Ringnecks blend extremely well with their surroundings, their green, blue, black and yellow patterned plumage camouflaging rather than exposing them. They eat the seeds of grasses and herbs, eucalypts, cypress pines and acacias, fruit, blossoms, leaf buds and, irregularly, insects and their larvae. Their bills are heavier than those of rosellas and well fitted for tearing open hard fruits which the birds often clasp or tether in the left foot. Like rosellas, Ringnecks often chatter quietly when they are foraging and clambering about foliage, remaining quite silent on the ground.

Ringnecks seem to pair permanently, keeping to ones or twos throughout the year or to small family groups of about five to eight when not breeding. The groups are probably made up of the adult pair and their young of the year. Soon after sunrise they leave their roosts in tree crowns and, after pausing to drink, move out to feed until midmorning. During the hottest part of the day they shelter in trees or forage in shade for seeds and fallen fruits. Towards dusk

they again become active, and feed and drink before settling to roost for the night.

Sedentary birds, Ringnecks may never move very far from their birth-grounds: banded birds have been retrapped at the banding place several times over a decade. They are nevertheless strong fliers, their vigorous flapping low among trees being interspersed with swooping glides on folded wings resembling the flight of Crimson Rosellas. They land swooping up to a branch with tail fanned. Group landing is often accompanied by much chattering and tail wagging. Then and in alarm their calling attracts other Ringnecks, the disturbance sometimes bringing together a dozen or more clinking and chattering birds. In this respect, the western Port Lincoln race seems to be noisier and more inquisitive than others.

Mating habits are similar to those of rosellas. The displaying male stands up before the female, squares his wings to expose the coloured shoulders, and fans and moves his tail quickly from side to side. While doing so he chatters constantly, occasionally bobbing his head up and down. He also feeds her in courtship and later when she is brooding, but there is no mutual preening. After choosing a nesting hollow, the pair spend much time preparing it, lining it with a bed of decayed wood dust for the eggs and defending it against other parrots.

During incubation and the first week or so of brooding young, the female leaves the nest briefly in early morning or late afternoon to feed or be fed by the male. She alone passes food on to the young then, but later both parents feed them independently.

OTHER NAMES
Mallee Ringneck, Port Lincoln Parrot or Ringneck, Twenty-eight Parrot, Cloncurry Parrot, Buln-Buln.

IDENTIFICATION
LENGTH: *340–380 mm, including a long, attenuately rounded tail.*
MALE: *General plumage green. Head black or pale green wreathed olive-grey around hind crown, with or without scarlet frontal band; cheeks extensively mid-blue or green fringed pale blue. Broad yellow or narrow yellow-green collar around hind neck. Back, scapulars and rump uniformly mid-green, or the back and scapulars blue-green contrasting with a paler green rump. Shoulders of wing mid-green or deep blue, grading through yellowish green to pale bluish green on primary coverts; flight feathers dusky, washed deep blue, grading to green on inner secondaries; underwing coverts turquoise. Throat and breast deep green or pale green, with or without broad yellow or narrow orange-yellow band across lower back and upper belly; belly, thighs and crissum pale green. Central pair of tail feathers uniformly blue-green; all outer dusky blue with broad pale blue tips. Eye dark brown. Bill greyish bone-white; cere dark grey. Feet, toes and claws dark grey.*
FEMALE: *Barely duller and smaller than males in black-headed races; smaller, duller grey-green on hind crown and back, and with rather persistent white underwing bar in green-headed races.*
IMMATURES: *Duller than female; head washed brownish; broad off-white underwing stripe on flight feathers, disappearing early in juvenile males of black-headed races. Young of northwestern Queensland race fledge with a russet frontal band which disappears in several months. Full adult plumage gained with a complete moult when birds 12–15 months old.*
DOWNY YOUNG: *White-downed, buff-billed.*

VOICE
Contact call, often given in flight, is a sharply whistled kwink-kwink *or* kwink-kwink-kwink. *In alarm, a rapid harsh, clattering* chuk, chuk, chuk, *also uttered in flight and from a perch. Black-headed western races are more guttural in their utterances; the large southwestern birds give a strident tri-syllable variant of the contact call sounding like* twenty-eight, *the last note at higher pitch, hence their local name— Twenty-eight Parrot. Feeding and displaying Ringnecks chatter with varying degrees of animation.*

NESTING
Breeds July–February through central and southern Australia, but February to June in northwestern Queensland, coinciding with seeding after wet seasons. Sometimes two broods a year. Nest a hollow or hole on a tree trunk or limb, usually a eucalypt, at 1–15 m above ground. Eggs: two to six, usually four to five; white; rounded, 27–33 x 22–26 mm. Laid on bed of decayed wood dust. Incubation 19–20 days, by female. Young fledge in about five weeks.

DISTRIBUTION
Eucalypt woodlands, forest, mallee and eucalypt-lined streams in deserts through southern Western Australia to central Australia, and the mallee lands and drier eucalypt woodlands of South Australia east to the mallee of Victoria, New South Wales and southwestern Queensland, with an outlier in the wooded uplands of northwestern Queensland. Four races. One, the Twenty-eight Parrot, occurs in the forests and woodlands of southwestern Australia north and east to the wheat belt where it intergrades with the inland black-headed race; large, with black head, red frontal band, mid-blue cheeks, mid-green back and rump and deep green breast grading to light green belly without an intervening yellow band. Another, the Port Lincoln Parrot, ranges throughout Western Australia north and east of wheat belt to Pilbara and central Australia as far as Eyre Peninsula and Georgina drainage in east; medium-sized, with plain black head, mid-blue cheeks, mid-green back and rump and deep green breast separated from pale green belly by broad yellow band; intergrades with eastern Mallee Ringneck through Flinders Ranges. A third throughout the mallee and stream-side eucalypts of the Murray–Darling basin in South Australia, Victoria and New South Wales north to channel country and fringing ranges in southwestern Queensland, reaching Forsythe Range; small, with green head wreathed olive-grey, scarlet frontal band, green cheeks fringed pale blue, blue-green back contrasting with pale green rump, and pale green breast and belly separated by narrow orange-yellow band. The last, known as the Cloncurry Parrot, is almost completely isolated in the uplands of northwestern Queensland between the Gregory and McKinlay Rivers. Apart from its pale tones, this race blends the plumage patterns of Port Lincoln and Mallee Ringnecks, having the broad neck band, plain front, and broad yellow belly band of the first, and the crown markings, green cheeks, pale green breast, contrasting rump, and small size of the second.

The eastern mallee race of the Ringneck has a patterned crown and blue back.

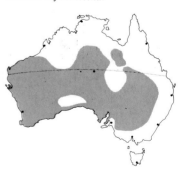

Crimson Rosella *Platycercus elegans* (GMELIN, 1788)

THAT THE CRIMSON ROSELLA of the Great Dividing Range and Yellow Rosella of the Murray basin are one species may surprise many. Yet they hybridise or intergrade wherever they meet, whether in the Mt Lofty Ranges or along the upper Murray, Murrumbidgee and Tumut Rivers. Colour tone—either red, orange or yellow—is in fact the only marked difference between them and it is probably controlled by very few genes. Otherwise, in colour pattern, habits, calls and even liver enzymes, these rosellas are alike. Reduced to tone, the slight differences between them are those usually associated with races or subspecies.

Crimson Rosellas live in and along the edges of tall-timbered eucalypt forests and woodlands, from river red gums along the Murray–Darling Rivers to rainforests on the Atherton Tableland. Only the population in the Mt Lofty Ranges has spread extensively into cleared lands and rural areas, reaching the western belts of the Murray mallee. They are gregarious birds, immatures commonly banding with occasional adults in wandering feeding groups of up to 30 and more out of the breeding season. Adults are less communal and seem more sedentary; although often gathering in groups of five or six, they tend to stay in pairs around their breeding grounds throughout the year. The bands of immatures frequently break up at the beginning of breeding as the birds begin to don adult plumage and find mates. There is no feeding territory, and breeding territory—if it exists—probably does not extend beyond the actual nest site.

Essentially seed- and fruit-eaters, Crimson Rosellas forage adeptly both on the ground and in the outer foliage of trees. They pick up seed freely or break into fruit, holding it firmly in the left foot if it can be held. Early morning sees them flying out to drink and feed, clambering among the outer branches of trees and shrubs, progressing slowly on the ground and, at times, taking dew by pulling sodden leaves through their mandibles. When on the ground in sunlight, they keep to patches of shade. The seeds of eucalypts are staple diet, but the birds are catholic in their taste, taking a wide range of grains from weeds, grasses, and shrubs as well, harvesting lerps from leaves, sometimes becoming a local pest in orchards, and even rifling eucalypt blossom for its nectar.

Through the middle hours of the day the rosellas rest quietly in the crowns of trees, occasionally nibbling or stripping leaves, or socialising in small, softly chattering groups. After another bout of feeding in the late afternoon they fly up to their roosts. Flight is undulating: a series of heavy flaps interspersed with swooping glides in which the wings are held onto the sides of the body. When excited, males can move into a stiff-winged slow erratic flapping, accompanied by harsh, alarm-type screeching.

Pairing seems to be permanent even though adults group in small social gatherings both in and out of breeding, to the accompaniment of much chattering and tail wagging. In display, on a fairly horizontal branch, the male straightens up, squares his shoulders and droops the wings, fluffs body feathers and shakes his spread tail from side to side while bowing up and down, chattering musically all the while. The female responds similarly but with less intensity. Male and female do not preen one another, but he does feed her in courtship and while she is incubating and brooding young. As a rule she is called to be fed on a branch outside the nest morning and afternoon. After young are about two weeks old, both parents feed them, ceasing two or three weeks after fledging and abandoning them a month or so later to flocks of juveniles. No more than one brood is usually raised each year.

Adult Crimson Rosellas are usually seen in pairs or in parties of four or five; immatures commonly gather in flocks.

OTHER NAMES
Yellow Rosella, Adelaide Rosella, Mountain Lowry.

IDENTIFICATION
LENGTH: *320–360 mm, including long, attenuately rounded tail.*
ADULTS: *Sexes alike; male a little larger, with broader head and heavier bill; female of yellow-plumaged races, including orange Mt Lofty Ranges population, often redder than male, with flushes of red on throat, face and crissum, and with duller greener tone to scalloping on back. Head, entire rump and entire ventral surface crimson or mid-yellow or of intermediate shades in hybrid populations. Brow red in yellow-plumaged forms. Cheeks cobalt-blue. Mantle, upper back and scapulars black, broadly edged or scalloped with colour of body plumage. Inner wing coverts black, outer and underwing coverts bright blue; flight feathers dusky, grading to a cobalt wash on secondaries. Tail blue-green, all feathers except central pair broadly tipped with pale blue. Eye dark brown. Bill bone-coloured; cere dark grey. Feet and toes dark grey.*
IMMATURES: *Dull olive-green, uniformly so on upper surface, blotched with red on throat and crissum in red-plumaged races, and washed uniformly yellowish on undersurface in yellow-plumaged races. Brow or forecrown dull red. Cheeks dull blue. Flight feathers dusky blue with a broken bar of off-white on undersurface visible only in flight. Tail dusky blue, tipped pale blue in all feathers except central pair. Adult plumage begins to appear extensively when young are about a year old and is complete at about 15 months. Race on Atherton Tableland apparently fledges in virtually all red adult plumage.*
DOWNY YOUNG: *White-downed, buff-billed.*

VOICE
Four main calls: (1) harsh, shrill sharp two or severally repeated screeches, usually given in flight in alarm or excitement: regional variations in pitch are dialectical; (2) a high-pitched, usually two- or three-note bell-like whistle that, given from a perch, carries far and appears to be a contact call; (3) a lower-pitched, softer call of five or so whistled or piping notes used also as a contact call between birds in loose feeding or resting groups; (4) a rich musical chatter given by birds flocking and displaying in trees.

NESTING
Breeds September–January. Nest a hollow, usually in a tall living or dead eucalypt 5–20 m above ground. Eggs: four to eight, usually five; cream-white; rounded, 27–30 x 22–34 mm; laid on a bed of wood dust. Incubation 19–21 days, by female. Young fledge in about five weeks, but remain with parents for another month or so before disbanding.

DISTRIBUTION
Red races: one small and dark, almost blackish-red in rainforests of northern Queensland between Cooktown and Townsville; one medium-sized to large and deep to mid-crimson through the hill and mountain eucalypt forests of southeastern Australia, north to Clarke Range, Qld, and west to southeast of South Australia; one large with reduced crimson scalloping on back in sclerophyll forests of western Kangaroo Island.
Yellow races: Medium-sized with bright yellow rump and broad yellow scalloping on back throughout the river red gum woodlands of Murray–Murrumbidgee–Lachlan–lower Darling systems, ranges east to about Hume Highway on Murray–Murrumbidgee system and hybridising there with crimson race and west to about Mannum or Murray River, hybridising along Marne River with Mt Lofty Ranges race.
Orange races: one rather uniformly orange-red in sclerophyll forests and woodlands of Fleurieu Peninsula, Mt Lofty Ranges; one rather uniformly orange-yellow in creekside woodlands of southern Flinders Ranges. Populations between throughout the bulk of the Mt Lofty Ranges and around Adelaide north to the Bundaleer hills are intergrades. The southeastern crimson race has been introduced to and established on Norfolk Island.

The Adelaide form of the Crimson Rosella lives in the sclerophyll forests and savanna woodlands of the Mount Lofty and Flinders Ranges. It has adapted to cleared habitats.

The yellow form of the Crimson Rosella keeps to the red gums of the Murray River system.

Green Rosella *Platycercus caledonicus* (GMELIN, 1788)

OTHER NAMES
Tasmanian Rosella, Mountain Rosella.

IDENTIFICATION
LENGTH: *320–360 mm, including long, attenuately rounded tail.*
ADULTS: *Sexes alike; male usually a little larger, with broader head and heavier bill. Head and neck lemon-yellow with scarlet brow and cobalt cheeks. Back green-black with individual feathers narrowly and indistinctly edged with dark green. Rump copper-yellow. Wings dusky black, washed rich blue on inner flight feathers; under and outer coverts bright blue; inner coverts jet black. Tail green-blue, all feathers except central pair have broad pale blue edges. Entire underside rich yellow, sometimes washed with orange-red on breast, particularly in female. Eye mid-brown. Bill pale grey, with slate-grey cere. Feet and claws dirty or dark slate-grey.*
IMMATURES: *Dull green on upper surface and dull green-yellow on undersurface. Brow scarlet; cheeks blue; flight feathers dusky blue with concealed white bar. All tail feathers except central pair with broad pale blue tips.*
DOWNY YOUNG: *White-downed, buff-billed.*

VOICE
Calls are of four kinds: a series of high-pitched, Ringneck-like clinking notes in alarm, often given in flight; a high-pitched, usually two- or three-note, bell-like whistle that carries for a considerable distance and appears to be a contact call; a lower-pitched, softer call of five to ten quickly repeated whistled notes used also as a contact call; a rich, musical chatter given by birds flocking in trees.

NESTING
Breeds September–January. Nest a hollow, usually in tall eucalypt, the egg bed of rough wood chips and debris. Eggs: four or five, sometimes six; cream; rounded, 30 x 24 mm. Incubation 20–22 days, by female.

DISTRIBUTION
Abundant in all wooded habitats in Tasmania, particularly eucalypt forests, at all altitudes from sea level to 1500 m, and on islands in Bass Strait.

The Green Rosella is found only in Tasmania.

THESE LARGE ROSELLAS ARE often regarded as pests in Tasmania, where they are occasionally seen quietly eating fruit from orchards; however, they mostly eat the fruit and seeds of native trees and shrubs, and sometimes nectar from eucalypt blossoms. They usually feed between early and mid-morning and in the late afternoon.

Green Rosellas are often seen in parks and vacant areas on the fringes of towns, sometimes in noisy flocks—but when feeding they are quiet and unobtrusive.

Adult Green Rosellas appear to mate for life, yet they often join together in small flocks of up to three or four pairs when feeding or 'socialising' in trees. This association may even continue throughout the breeding season.

There is no feeding territory, and territory for breeding, if it exists, probably does not extend beyond the actual nest site. The birds display to their mates in trees, and often to other birds in the social groups. Males straighten up, droop their wings, fluff their body feathers and shake their tails, then bow slightly, chattering musically all the while.

Usually one brood is raised each year, incubated by the female. The young leave the nest about five weeks after hatching, but remain with their parents for another month or so before disbanding to form flocks. They stay in flocks for about 15 months before attaining adult plumage and mating.

Green Rosellas have a rather strong, direct flight interspersed with long glides on folded wings. Their tails are fanned when they alight. They live in coastal and mountain eucalypt forests, woodlands and scrubs, temperate rainforests and forest edges from sea level to 1500 metres, avoiding open fields.

The female of the eastern race of the White-cheeked Rosella has duller head and breast feathers than the male.

White-cheeked Rosella

Platycercus eximius (SHAW, 1792)

THIS IS THE ORIGINAL 'ROSELLA'. The name was coined by early settlers who, on their journeys between Sydney and Parramatta, regularly saw White-cheeked Rosellas at Rose Hill. They called the birds 'Rose Hillers', which was pleasantly corrupted to rosella.

White cheeks apart, the three main races of White-cheeked Rosellas are so different in appearance that they are often regarded as separate species. One, the familiar eastern rosella of southeastern Australia, has a bright scarlet head and yellow-green body; another, the pale-headed rosella of eastern Queensland, has a white, unpigmented head and blue body; the third, the northern rosella of northwestern Australia, has a black head and cream body. Only the red-headed and pale-headed races actually meet, in the more open woodlands of the Great Dividing Range around the New South Wales–Queensland border. There they interbreed and intergrade freely on both eastern and western scarps of the range. Indeed, a minor form of the red-headed race down the north coast of New South Wales to the Hunter Valley owes its distinctive traits — golden-fringed mantle and bluish-grey rump and belly—to introgression from the pale-headed.

The black-headed race, however, does not contact any of the others today, so interfertility cannot be tested. Instead, the population of pale-headeds closest to it, on Cape York Peninsula, gives the clues to its relationships. Unlike pale-headeds further south, the Cape York rosellas have cream breasts and rumps like the black-headed; blue is restricted to the belly. Cape York juveniles are even cream over the entire ventral and dorsal surface and occasionally have a spattering of black-centred feathers on the head. Thus they are intermediate between black-headed and pale-headed rosellas, and cannot be identified surely with either.

Faced with such a dilemma, the ornithologist has little alternative but to treat all these forms as distinctive races of a single polymorphic species. If more supportive proof were needed, recent molecular research indicates that the red-headed forms on the mainland are more closely related to the pale-headed and the black-

OTHER NAMES
Eastern Rosella, Pale-headed Rosella, Mealy Rosella, Northern Rosella, Smutty Rosella, Brown's Rosella, Golden-mantled Rosella.

IDENTIFICATION
LENGTH: *280–320 mm, including long, attenuately rounded tail.*
ADULTS: *Sexes similar; female duller, often flecked with red on head in pale-headed and black-headed races, and smaller; off-white underwing stripe persists in younger females to greater or lesser extent. Head plain scarlet, white or black to lores and nape; cheeks white-edged with pale blue to a greater or lesser extent, according to race. Mantle and scapulars black, the feathers broadly edged with golden yellow, lemon or cream; mid-back to upper tail coverts lettuce green, pale blue or cream, according to race. Shoulders of wing black, grading to mid-blue on bend of wing and primary coverts, then to dusky washed deep blue on flight feathers; underwing coverts deep blue. Ventral surface varies according to race: throat and upper breast scarlet and lower breast and belly yellow-green in red-headed race, throat to belly pale blue or cream-white on throat and breast in pale-headed race, and throat to belly cream with fine black feather fringes in black-headed race; crissum scarlet in all races. Tail with central pair of feathers uniformly dusky blue-green and all outer feathers dusky blue with extensive pale or whitish blue tips. Eye dark brown. Bill bone-coloured; cere dark grey. Feet, toes and claws dark grey.*
IMMATURES: *Like female but still duller and with broad off-white underwing stripe through flight feathers; belly as well as breast cream in pale-headed race on Cape York Peninsula and head sometimes speckled black. Young moult gradually into adult plumage, finishing early in their second year.*

DOWNY YOUNG: *White-downed, buff-billed.*

VOICE
Loud, harsh, staccato chut-chit, chut-chit...chut-chit *as contact call in flight and in alarm. Perched birds give tri-syllabic whistle or metallic, piping whistle, possibly to signal position. Tree-feeding and displaying or socialising birds chatter musically. All calls resemble equivalent vocalisations in Crimson Rosella but are higher pitched.*

NESTING
Breeds June to February, earlier in northern Australia where seeding after wet season peaks from March to May. Nest a deep hole or hollow in tree at 2–15 m above ground, usually in eucalypt; sometimes a stump or fallen log. Eggs: three to nine, usually four to six; white; round, 26–29 x 21–23 mm. Laid on bed of decayed wood dust in bottom of hollow. Incubation 19–20 days, by female. Young fledge in five-six weeks.

DISTRIBUTION
Eucalypt woodlands, open forests and their edges throughout eastern and northern Australia inland to fringes of inland plains. Seven races. One in Kimberleys, WA, east to Victoria River district, with black head, cream body finely flecked with black ventrally and on mantle, and white cheeks suffused with blue. Another in Arnhem Land between Victoria River district and head of Gulf of Carpentaria — like Kimberley race but coarse black flecking ventrally and on mantle and cheeks white with blue edges. A third on Cape York Peninsula south to Cooktown, Lynd and lower Mitchell Rivers — head white, mantle and rump cream, throat and breast cream grading to pale blue belly, and white cheeks suffused with blue. The fourth in eastern Queensland south of Cape York Peninsula to New

A pale-headed form of the White-cheeked Rosella.

South Wales border — head and cheeks white, mantle golden yellow, rump pale blue, throat to belly pale blue. A fifth, the familiar eastern rosella, throughout eastern New South Wales (west of spine of Great Dividing Range north of Hunter River) to Victoria (except mallee), southeast of South Australia, and Mt Lofty Ranges—head scarlet, mantle edged lemon-yellow, rump lettuce green, throat and upper breast scarlet, lower breast and belly yellow to greenish. A sixth in northeastern New South Wales north of the Hunter River and east of the spine of the Great Dividing Range—like red-headed eastern rosella but mantle edged golden yellow, and rump and lower belly bluish green. The seventh in Tasmania—like

red-headed eastern rosella but slightly large, white cheeks larger, nape broadly yellow-collared.

headed races than to their red-headed counterparts in Tasmania.

White-cheeked Rosellas are commonly found in eucalypt woodlands and open forests and their fringes. They avoid tall forests — except in northern coastal New South Wales—and seldom range above 1000 metres altitude in mountains. Although sedentary and rarely travelling many kilometres from their birthgrounds, the rosellas are moderately gregarious, banding together in small family groups of five to eight or so, or occasional flocks of 20 to 30 when not breeding. These groups wander locally on their foraging sorties.

Usually drinking early in the morning, the rosellas then move out to feed. Most feeding is done on the ground where, keeping to the shade of the bushes and trees in sunny weather, they search silently and unobtrusively for fallen seeds of all kinds.

Often they gather at concentrations of windblown seed and spills of grain on roadsides where they are sometimes killed by passing vehicles. They forage less frequently but with more chattering in the foliage of trees and bushes as well, clambering around for seeds, fruit, blossom, nectar and occasional insect larvae; their visits to fruiting orchards then cause problems. When cutting into fruits for pulp or seeds with their bills, the birds often anchor the fruit in one foot, usually the left.

White-cheeked Rosellas usually rest in the tops of trees through the hotter middle hours of the day, occasionally stripping leaves or chattering. Later afternoon sees them out feeding once more and, often after a final drink, flying to roost. Their flight, usually low among trees or occasionally high above when covering long distances, is undulating: quick-fire, staccato flapping is interspersed with swooping glides on folded wings. To land, the birds glide upward on to a branch, fanning their tails as they alight.

As breeding approaches, the feeding groups break up as mated pairs disengage to establish nest and territory. The rosellas become rather noisy then, chattering much and fluttering and wagging their tails among the branches of trees. Male and female display in much the same manner as Crimson Rosellas, squaring their shoulders, wagging spread tails, and chattering to the occasional bob of the head. Courtship feeding may precede or follow.

Only the female incubates and broods, and she leaves the nest briefly two or three times a day to feed or be fed by the male. She alone passes on food to the nestlings in their first 10–12 days, but from then on both parents feed the young. Young become independent within a month of fledging but may remain with their parents into the next breeding season. Usually one, but sometimes two broods may be raised each year.

The northern or black-headed race of the White-cheeked Rosella, if disturbed feeding on the ground, will fly to the upper foliage of a tree.

Western Rosella *Platycercus icterotis* (KUHL, 1820)

IN CONTRAST TO MOST OTHER ROSELLAS, the Western is a quiet, unobtrusive bird, and often overlooked as it shelters from the heat of the sun amid the leaves of a tree, or moves about on shaded ground searching for seeds. It is also much smaller than other rosellas and the females are distinctly duller than males, with mottled green and red head and underparts. During the non-breeding season it seldom congregates in flocks, but family groups may come together to take advantage of a good source of food, such as a heavily laden fruit tree or a spilled bag of wheat. After crops have been harvested, pairs or family parties of Western Rosellas move over the stubble, picking up fallen grain. On the ground they walk quickly and easily. They also feed in the tree tops, but less often than other rosellas. Their diet is varied and includes the seeds of grasses and other plants, berries, nuts, blossoms, nectar, and insects and their larvae.

Western Rosellas have a buoyant, fluttering flight, unlike the heavy, undulating flight of other rosellas. They usually fly short distances, from one tree to another, rather than over open expanses of land. Like other rosellas they rest and roost in trees and display there, squaring their shoulders, shaking their spread tails, and whistling softly. Pairing is permanent.

The male feeds his mate several times in the morning and again in the afternoon while she is brooding, and both feed one another from time to time when not breeding.

OTHER NAMES
Stanley Rosella, Yellow-cheeked Rosella.

IDENTIFICATION
LENGTH: *260 mm, including long, attenuately rounded tail.*
MALE: *Head and entire underparts red. Yellow cheeks. Feathers of back and shoulders black, broadly edged with dark green or a mixture of dark green and red. Rump and upper tail coverts green or grey-olive, sometimes edged with red. Flight feathers and underwing coverts dusky blue. Central tail feathers bronze-green washed with blue, outer tail feathers blue edged with white. Eye brown. Bill pale grey; cere dark grey. Feet and toes dark grey.*
FEMALE: *Head and upper breast green with faint yellow and red markings. Frontal band red; dull yellow cheeks. Dull black centres to back and wing feathers. Off-white underwing stripe persistent. Lower breast, belly and vent dull red strongly suffused with green.*
IMMATURES: *Like adults, but lack most of red on underparts and yellow cheeks. Head is green with red frontal band. Off-white underwing stripe present. Young gain adult plumage rapidly at about 14 months.*
DOWNY YOUNG: *White-downed.*

VOICE
Contact call in flight is soft and musical—a series of two-note whistles in quick succession.

NESTING
Breeds August–December. Nest a hole or hollow in a eucalypt. Eggs: three to seven, usually five; white; rounded, 26–27 x 21–22 mm. Laid on wood dust. Incubation 19–20 days, by female. Young fledge in about five weeks.

DISTRIBUTION
Common in most types of timbered country in southwestern Australia, north to Moora and east to Dundas. Sedentary. No races.

A male Western Rosella brings food to its offspring. The female is much duller, more so than in other rosellas.

Blue Bonnet

Northiella haematogaster
(GOULD, 1838)

OTHER NAMES
Bulloke Parrot, Red-bellied Blue Bonnet, Naretha Parrot, Little Blue Bonnet, Red-vented Blue Bonnet.

IDENTIFICATION
LENGTH: *280–320 mm, including long tapered tail.*
MALE: *Upper surface from crown to scapulars, back, rump and two central tail feathers mid to pale fawn-brown. Face and brow rich blue or grading to turquoise on brow; hind cheeks washed cream-white. Throat and breast mid to pale fawn-brown, with or without cream mottling. Lower breast to flanks and crissum mid-yellow, with large blood-red patch on belly only (central races), on crissum only (western Naretha race), or from belly to crissum (eastern race). Wings grading from golden green (or blood-red, eastern race) on shoulders to deep blue on primary coverts and bend of wing (bend of wing turquoise in eastern race); flight feathers dusky, the outer washed blue above, the inner fawn; underwing coverts yellow-green. Outer tail feathers deep blue broadly tipped bluish white. Eye pale grey. Bill pale bone-grey; cere slate-grey. Feet, toes and claws dark grey.*
FEMALE: *As male but narrower in the head, and less blue on face, less red, or yellow (Naretha race) on belly. Vestiges of white wing bar persist.*
IMMATURES: *Like adults but duller with less red on belly. Buff-white bar along base of underside of flight feathers disappears early. Eye, bill and feet as in adults; bill yellow in fledglings. Adult plumage attained at first post-fledging moult when young are three–four months old.*
DOWNY YOUNG: *White-downed, buff-billed.*

VOICE
Two-syllable or rapidly repeated harsh chattering notes kluk-kluk *in alarm and often in flight; resembles staccato flight call of White-cheeked Rosella. Also softer penetrating whistle, sometimes repeated, as contact call from a perch, similar to that of Crimson Rosella.*

NESTING
Usually breeds July–December, after good rains. Nest a deep hollow or hole in a tree, rarely more than 7 m above ground. Eggs: four to seven, usually five: white; rounded, 23–24 x 18–20 mm. Incubation about 20 days, by female. Young fledge in four–five weeks.

These Blue Bonnets are of the red-bellied race. The female, right, has less blue on its face and is duller.

DISTRIBUTION
Semi-arid southern inland Australia, in open casuarina, cypress pine, Myoporum *and acacia woodlands. Four races. One isolated in myall woodlands around western fringes of Nullarbor Plain; slightly smaller than others, with blue face grading to turquoise on brow, yellow belly and red crissum; this is the Naretha Parrot or Little Blue Bonnet. Another ranges from Eyre Peninsula and near Adelaide to the Victorian mallee and southwestern New South Wales east to the Riverina where it begins to intergrade with the Red-vented Blue Bonnet; this, the Red-bellied Blue*

Bonnet, has an all-blue face, red belly and yellow crissum. The third race is restricted to the eastern Lake Eyre Basin in South Australia, east to the Paroo–Darling Rivers in far western New South Wales and Queensland where it intergrades with Red-bellied and Red-vented Blue Bonnets; it resembles the red-bellied race but for its much paler fawn body. The last, along the Lachlan-Barwon drainages in central northern New South Wales and adjacent parts of Queensland, is the Red-vented Blue Bonnet; it has a red crissum, a red wash over the shoulder of the wings and, in males, a turquoise band on wing.

IT IS THE FACE OF THE Blue Bonnet that is blue, and not the head as the name implies. Blue Bonnets are often seen on the ground, feeding on seeds in the shade of a tree, where they scuttle about in an erect posture. During the heat of the day they perch in the foliage of trees and shrubs and remain extremely quiet, and then may be difficult to find. Early in the morning and late in the afternoon, however, they come out to feed and drink, interspersing foraging with rests on exposed bare branches or telegraph lines.

Blue Bonnets are gregarious. Adults appear to form permanent pairs but often associate in small social or feeding flocks of up to 30 individuals. Their staple diet is the seeds of various native plants—particularly of acacias and chenopods, *Atriplex* and *Maireana*—which they pick off the ground or from low shrubs.

At the start of the breeding season, males display for their mates. They stand erect, raise and vibrate their wings, fan and shake their tail from side to side, rapidly head-bob, and raise the fore-crown feathers into a crest. A paired male and female do not preen one another but the male does feed his mate, both during courtship and while she is incubating and brooding young; at this stage the female alone passes food on to young, by regurgitation. During that time the male calls her out of the nest to be fed, morning and afternoon.

As brooding of young ceases, when they are about two weeks old, the male begins to assist feeding them directly and continues to do so through the first week or two of fledging.

Blue Bonnets are closely related to Grass Parrots which they resemble in their size, pale eyes, some aspects of display and liver enzymes; some ornithologists recognise this by including them all in one genus, *Psephotus*. Yet Blue Bonnets also have many attributes of rosellas, *Platycercus:* coloured cheeks, calls, staccato flight reminiscent of White-cheeked Rosellas and an erratic, slow-beating display flight from seemingly excited males. Even their unusual brown plumage, which blends so well with their dry woodland environment, is parallelled in its pattern in immature Crimson Rosellas.

As well as that, Blue Bonnets have their own distinctive traits. Fawn-brown plumage is one. A vestigial crest is another. This they may raise, like a cockatoo, while thrusting their shoulders forward and bobbing the head jerkily. Unusually pointed flight feathers are also unique to them. How these affect flight is not clear but Blue Bonnets do flutter agitatedly, with little undulation, low between trees and shrubs, alighting without much tail fanning; their rapid wing-beats are broken regularly by short glides on folded wings.

Golden-shouldered Parrot *Psephotus chrysopterygius* GOULD, 1858

THE RARITY AND ELEGANCE OF THE Golden-shouldered Parrot have made it so much sought after by collectors willing to pay high prices for birds smuggled out of Australia that the future of the species is threatened. If this illegal trafficking continues, the Golden-shouldered Parrot may become extinct.

Although augmented with berries and vegetable matter, diet is almost entirely of small grass seeds. These the parrots pick up from the ground or strip deftly from seeding heads. The birds spend much of the morning and late afternoon out feeding and drinking, often mixing both activities. They prefer to drink at small and shallow holes that they can walk into. Around midday they fly up to rest in the shady foliage of trees.

Golden-shouldered Parrots rarely occur other than in pairs or parties of three–eight which seem to be the family group of the year. They disperse from breeding grounds after nesting, not returning until the end of the wet season. Flight is swift and direct, with slight undulations on folded wings.

Breeding begins at the end of the wet season, in April, when grasses are seeding and the ant hills in which the parrots burrow to nest are still damp and easily dug out. The same anthill or burrow may be used for several years.

In courtship the male makes short flights around his perched mate, and then with frontal feathers raised in a short crest, and breast puffed out, he lands and struts towards her. Females incubate alone, but leave the nest each day to feed with and be fed by their mates, and may cease brooding young within a week.

OTHER NAMES
Golden-winged Parakeet, Antbed Parrot, Anthill Parrot.

IDENTIFICATION
LENGTH: *240–260 mm, including slender tapered tail.*
MALE: *Forehead, lores and area below eyes pale lemon-yellow; crown and nape black; back and shoulders grey-brown; rump and upper tail coverts turquoise-blue. Median wing coverts golden yellow; underwing coverts, bend of wing and outer webs of flight feathers blue. Chin and throat grey; cheeks, neck, breast and belly turquoise-blue. Lower belly, vent, thighs and crissum red with white bases and tips to feathers. Central tail feathers blue with bronze wash and black tips; outer tail feathers green-blue with white tips. Eye dark brown. Bill pale grey; cere dark grey. Feet,*
toes and claws brownish grey.
FEMALE: *Crown and nape bronze-brown; back of neck, back, wings, upper breast and sides of neck dull yellow-green. Vague dull yellow frontal band; throat and sides of face grey tinged bronze-green. Lower breast, upper belly and flanks green grading to white; crissum pale turquoise-blue. Off-white stripe on underside of flight feathers. Underwing coverts, bend of wing and outer webs of flight feathers pale blue.*
IMMATURES: *Resemble adult female, but male undertail coverts and face much darker and brighter. Young males do not gain full adult plumage until 15–16 months after fledging.*
DOWNY YOUNG: *White-downed, yellow-billed.*

VOICE
Normal contact call in flight a whistle-like fweep-fweep *repeated several times and sometimes drawn out. While perched the parrots repeat an abrupt* weet *or* fee-oo. *Alarm or distress call a* cluk-cluk.

NESTING
Breeds April–August; two broods may be reared in a season. Nest a chamber in a termite mound, entered by 40–50 cm long tunnel. Eggs: four to six; white; rounded, 20–21 x 17–18 mm. Incubation about 20 days, by female. Young fledge in about five weeks.

DISTRIBUTION
Centred in strip of dry, well grassed savanna woodland, about 130 x 240 km, around Musgrave, Cape York Peninsula. Sporadically distributed in interior and along west coast of range. After breeding, birds probably move towards west coast, returning to central and eastern districts at start of next breeding season. No races.

Hooded Parrot
Psephotus dissimilis COLLETT, 1898

OTHER NAMES
Black-hooded Parakeet, Anthill Parrot.

IDENTIFICATION
LENGTH: *260–280 mm, including slender tapered tail.*
MALE: *Forehead, lores, crown and nape black; mantle and back mid-brown; rump and upper tail coverts turquoise-green. Shoulder golden-yellow; underwing coverts, bend of wing bluish green; outer webs of flight feathers dusky. Throat, breast and belly turquoise-green. Crissum pale red. Central tail feathers bronze-green; outer feathers blue-green, tipped white. Eye dark brown. Bill pale grey; cere dark grey. Feet, toes and claws mid-brown.*
FEMALE: *General plumage olive-green; pale blue tinge on cheeks, lower breast, belly and rump; undertail coverts salmon-pink. Off-white stripe on underside of flight feathers.*
IMMATURES: *Similar to adult female; young males generally have brighter green cheeks and gain full adult plumage at second annual moult.*
DOWNY YOUNG: *White-downed, yellow-billed.*

VOICE
Contact call a whistled chu-weet, chu-weet *repeated several times; alarm call a harsher* chissik-chissik.

NESTING
Breeds usually April–July. Nest a burrow in a termite mound. Eggs: two to six; white; rounded, 21 x 18 mm. Incubation 19–20 days, by female. Young fledge in five weeks.

DISTRIBUTION
Southern and eastern Arnhem Land. Uncommon; in dry open eucalypt forest and grassland. No races.

THAT THE HOODED PARROT is closely related to the Golden-shouldered Parrot is obvious not only from their appearance but also their feeding and breeding habits. Hooded Parrots may flock more in groups of 20 and 30 and have a more screeching alarm call, but otherwise the two are alike in every way.

Some ornithologists regard the two parrots as distinctive races of the same species. Yet there are significant differences between them in appearance. The Hooded is markedly larger; its males have an all-black face, complete golden shoulders and ventral red restricted to the crissum; its females have a blue-green belly and red crissum. Added up, these differences are substantial, and certainly equivalent to those indicating separate species in other sympatric Australian grass parrots.

A male Hooded Parrot perches on a termite mound in Arnhem Land.

The male Golden-shouldered Parrot is one of Australia's most beautiful birds but illegal trapping threatens the future of the species.

Paradise Parrot *Psephotus pulcherrimus* (GOULD, 1845)

This photograph of a Paradise Parrot was taken in 1921, the year before the last authenticated sighting. The bird is a male.

JOHN GILBERT, ASSISTANT TO THE eminent ornithologist John Gould, discovered the Paradise Parrot on the Darling Downs of Queensland in 1844. Charmed by the bird's colours and grace, he requested that it be named after him. Instead, because Gould disliked the use of proper names for new species, it was termed *pulcherrimus* —very beautiful. Gilbert did not live to learn this, for he was killed by Aborigines in 1845, while on an expedition led by the explorer Ludwig Leichhardt. During the expedition, Gilbert encountered the bird —'my new green parrot of the Darling Downs'—in several parts of eastern Queensland, but he wrote only of its beauty and agreeable voice, without discovering its distinctive nest, a tunnel and chamber burrowed in a termite mound.

Later the Paradise Parrot became fairly well known to settlers in Queensland and certain adjacent parts of New South Wales; they called it various names, one being Soldier Parrot because of its upright bearing. In habits and habitat it resembled the closely allied Golden-shouldered and Hooded Parrots, and its flight was evidently similar, with swift undulations.

Trappers, taking advantage of the parrot's readily accessible nest site, captured many birds. The species also seems to have been affected by competition from grazing sheep and cattle and, more drastically, by recurrent droughts, so that by early in the present century its numbers had fallen seriously.

During several years after 1917 the naturalist Alec Chisholm, disturbed by the absence of news of the parrot, enlisted the aid of several Queensland newspapers, both in city and country areas. Nothing positive was heard until in 1921 C.H. Jerrard, a cattleman in the Burnett River region, some 300 kilometres north of Brisbane, reported having found an occupied nest of the 'lost' parrot. To prove his claim, he sent photographs of both the male and female at their nest in a termite mound. Today, these photographs remain the only ones of the living birds ever taken.

The next year Alec Chisholm joined Jerrard in the same area, and there, after a trying search, the men came upon a single pair of Paradise Parrots; Jerrard continued to see the birds there until 1927. Since then, many searches for the beautiful bird have been conducted, but no substantiated discovery has been recorded; the last, in 1980–81 supported by the World Wildlife Fund, drew the customary blank. Nor is there any confirmed specimen in captivity, and fears have arisen that the Paradise Parrot is now extinct. Fragmentary reports from bushmen over the past few years, however,

indicate that scattered pairs may still be living in the north.

During the public inquiry regarding this bird in Queensland about 1920, a few old settlers reported that it had been known to nest in burrows in termite mounds and, on occasions, in cavities excavated in the banks of creeks. Nesting in termite mounds is also the practice of the Golden-shouldered and Hooded Parrots.

OTHER NAMES
Beautiful Parrot, Scarlet-shouldered Parrot, Anthill Parrot, Soldier Parrot.

IDENTIFICATION
LENGTH: *270–280 mm, including long tapered tail.*
MALE: *Crown black with red frontal band, grading to mid-brown on mantle and scapulars; lower back to upper tail coverts turquoise. Shoulders of wing scarlet; flight feather coverts and inner flight feathers dark brown grading to dusky blue on outer flight feathers. Face and throat turquoise-green, grading to yellow around eye and turquoise-blue on breast and flanks. Belly and crissum scarlet. Central tail feathers brown-green, dusky at tip; all outer feathers greenish blue, tipped broadly bluish white. Eye dark brown. Bill leaden; cere dark grey. Feet and claws brownish grey.*
FEMALE: *Like male but much duller; frontal band, face, throat and breast buff-yellow. Lower breast, belly and crissum dull turquoise with small patch of red in centre belly. Shoulder of wing red, but reduced; off-white underwing stripe on flight feathers.*
IMMATURES: *Resemble adult female; young males have emerald-green feathering in face and breast, richer black crown and red shoulders.*

VOICE
Only contact note recorded is a sweet plaintive tit-sweet; *short, sharp musical* queek *in alarm.*

NESTING
Nest a 20–30 cm long tunnel and 40 cm wide chamber usually burrowed into a terrestrial termite mound. Breeds summer and early autumn. Eggs: usually five; white; rounded, 20–22 x 17–18 mm. Incubation and brooding by female.

DISTRIBUTION
Open woodlands with termitaria from northern central New South Wales (Casino–Moree) to central eastern Queensland (Suttor–Belyando drainage). No races. Possibly survives in northern sectors of range, but may be extinct.

A mounted male.

Mulga Parrot *Psephotus varius* CLARK, 1910

QUIETER AND LESS OBTRUSIVE, Mulga Parrots replace their close relative, the Red-rumped Parrot, in the drier mallee and mulga woods of the western and southern inland. As well as their more varied colouring and red-shouldered females, they also appear more slender because of their longer tails. They rarely flock, but pairs or family parties of up to eight often gather to feed where food is plentiful—at a railway siding where grain has been spilled, for example. Most feeding is done on the ground, where they search for the seeds of grasses, herbaceous plants and shrubs, and berries.

Like other parrots of arid regions, Mulga Parrots forage early in the morning and late in the afternoon, and usually drink then. During the hottest part of the day they sit quietly among the branches of a tree, their plumage blending well with the foliage. The birds fly swiftly, close to the ground, with a buoyant, slightly undulating flight, gliding regularly on folded wings. On alighting they fan their tails.

They may wander more widely than Red-rumped Parrots in search of food, and their numbers fluctuate wildly in some areas. In recent years they seem to have declined in southern regions, probably because of clearing of mallee for wheat farming.

Display and courtship feeding match those of the Red-rumped Parrot, and the sexes preen one another as well. The male, however, stays close to the nest—foraging nearby—while his mate is brooding, not joining other males in feeding groups, and calling loudly at any approaching threat.

OTHER NAMES
Many-coloured Parrot.

IDENTIFICATION
LENGTH: *270–280 mm, including long tapered tail.*
MALE: *General plumage bright bluish green. Forehead yellow; red patch on nape. Shoulder patch yellow; underwing coverts, bend of wing, primary coverts, and outer webs of flight feathers rich blue. Rump and upper tail coverts green; red patch near base of tail, a vague yellow-green band above it and then a dark blue-green band on top towards the back. Throat and breast rich bluish green: belly and thighs yellow strongly washed with red. Vent and undertail coverts green-yellow. Central tail feathers dark green washed with blue; all outer tail feathers blue broadly tipped with white. Eye brown. Bill leaden; cere dark grey. Feet and claws dark grey.*
FEMALE: *Forehead dull orange-yellow; dull red patch on crown. Head, neck, back and upper breast brown-green; rest of underparts pale green: rump pale green with red patch at base. Wings dull green grading to blue flight feathers; dull red shoulder patch; off-white underwing bar rather persistent. Tail as male but duller. Eye, bill and feet as male.*
IMMATURES: *Resemble adults. In young males the red of belly and thighs is reduced or absent and there are red tinges on shoulder patches. Off-white underwing bar variably persistent. Young gain adult plumage at first complete moult two–three months after fledging. White underwing bar remains in males for another year.*
DOWNY YOUNG: *White-downed, buff-billed.*

VOICE
Contact call a mellow flute-like whistle repeated quickly three or four times, often in flight. Occasional soft chattering in display and when feeding. Commonly silent.

NESTING
Breeds July–December, but in north and west of range at any time after good rains. Nest is a hollow high in a tree or as low as 2–3 m above ground. Eggs: four to six, usually five; white; rounded, 24–25 x 18–19 mm. Laid on bed of wood dust. Incubation 19 days, by female. Young fledge in about four weeks.

DISTRIBUTION
Widespread in lightly timbered country in western and southern inland Australia. South and east to limits of mallee in Western Australia, South Australia, Victoria and New South Wales, and north to main limits of mulga in Pilbara, central Australia and western Queensland. Sedentary except in arid areas, where birds may congregate and breed after rain. No races.

A male Mulga Parrot at the entrance to its nest hole. The female alone incubates the eggs.

Red-rumped Parrot *Psephotus haematonotus* (GOULD, 1838)

MUCH OF THE RED-RUMPED PARROT'S time is spent on the ground searching for grass seeds. The birds scurry here and there, or flutter from the shade of one tree to that of another, often congregating around haystacks or in stubble paddocks to feed on fallen grain. They also eat unripe seeds, especially the seeds of crowsfoot *Erodium botrys*. Besides seeds they eat shoots, leaves and flowers.

Red-rumped Parrots are sedentary and seem to pair permanently. Although banding together with their young of the year into loose foraging flocks that sometimes reach 100 or more, they do so only when not breeding and rarely wander far. During the early part of the breeding season, males will gather together in small feeding parties which later disband when they leave to participate in feeding young directly.

Soon after sunrise, the birds fly out to drink at watering points — which they visit several times a day in hot weather—and then move off to feeding areas. There they remain till dusk, resting only during the hot hours of the middle of the day in the shaded inner branches of trees and shrubs. Mated birds often sidle up and preen one another then. The flights of flocks back to roosting trees is conspicuous, the birds often flying high, whistling continuously. Flight itself is swift and direct, with only slight undulation as the birds intersperse flapping with brief glides on folded wings like rosellas.

Courtship is rosella-like. The male stretches up on a branch, thrusts out his shoulders to expose the yellow and blue, droops his wings, fans and wags his tail from side to side, and bobs his head up and down. This display precedes courtship feeding and is given by both sexes when feeding chicks. Nest trees and nest holes are defended by both sexes too, but only the female incubates and broods the young in their first weeks. The male then feeds her, calling her out to feed or be fed at almost hourly intervals throughout the day. Afterwards, both sexes feed the young.

OTHER NAMES
Red-backed Parrot, Grass Parrot.

IDENTIFICATION
LENGTH: *260–270 mm, including long tapered tail.*
MALE: *Forehead and cheeks blue-green; rest of head and neck bright green. Back dull blue-green; rump scarlet. Throat and breast bright green; belly yellow; vent and undertail coverts white with a few tinges of green. Shoulder patch yellow; underwing coverts, bend of wing and flight feathers blue, the latter grading to dusky. Upper tail coverts green; central tail feathers green slightly tinged with blue; outer feathers blue-green broadly tipped with white. Eye brown. Bill and cere black. Feet, toes and claws deep grey.*
FEMALE: *Head, neck, back and shoulders of wing dull olive-green; rump and upper tail coverts bright green. Bend of wing pale blue, grading to dusky blue on flight feathers and underwing coverts; broad off-white underwing bar in flight feathers. Throat and breast dull olive-grey, grading through yellow wash on lower breast to bluish white belly and crissum. Tail as male. Eye greyish cream. Bill leaden-grey.*
IMMATURES: *Similar to but duller than adults. Females have pale bills and eyes. Young don adult plumage at their first complete annual moult two–three months after fledging but young males retain the white underwing stripe and dull rump for another year.*
DOWNY YOUNG: *White-downed, buff-billed.*

VOICE
Contact call, often in flight, a high-pitched two-syllable whistle with an upward inflection; also a warbling call, almost a song, when perched. When squabbling or defending nest site the birds chatter harshly.

NESTING
Breeds August to December or January, or after rain in north. Nest a hollow limb or hole in a tree, preferably near water, 2–12 m above ground; sometimes a crevice in buildings. The bottom of the hollow is lined with wood dust. Eggs: two to seven, usually four or five; white; rounded, 22–24 x 19 mm. Incubation about 20 days, by female. Young fledge in four–five weeks.

DISTRIBUTION
Widely distributed in southeast, though infrequent in southern Victoria. Common in sparsely timbered grasslands, open plains, mallee and cultivated farmlands below 1000 m. Two races: one from coasts to Darling–Paroo drainages, Qld, in north and Yorke Peninsula–Flinders Ranges, SA, in west; males bright green with extensive yellow bellies and deep scarlet rumps, females mid olive-grey with small bluish white belly. The other race is more or less isolated in the gum-lined drainages of the lower Cooper–Strzelecki Creek systems in the eastern Lake Eyre basin; males pale bluish green with small yellow bellies and pale scarlet rumps, females pale grey with extensive pure white belly.

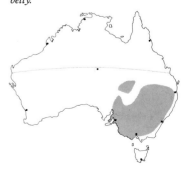

During the day the male Red-rumped Parrot regularly feeds its mate which sits tightly on its tree-hole nest.

Blue-winged Parrot

Neophema chrysostoma
(KUHL, 1820)

OTHER NAMES
Blue-banded Grass Parakeet.

IDENTIFICATION
LENGTH: *About 210 mm, including narrow tapered tail.*
MALE: *Crown dull golden-olive; frontal band ultramarine-blue with pale green-blue edging on upper side; lores yellow. Nape and rest of upper parts dull olive-green. Cheeks, throat and breast pale green; lower underparts and underside of tail yellow. Wings and underwing coverts uniformly deep royal blue. Central tail feathers blue-grey; outer tail feathers pale blue broadly tipped with yellow. Eye brown with yellow surround. Bill and cere blackish-grey. Feet and toes grey-brown.*
FEMALE: *As male but crown dull olive-green; wings duller and suffused with green. Yellow underwing stripe faint or absent.*
IMMATURES: *Duller than adult female; no blue frontal band; dull slate-blue wings. Yellow underwing stripe present in females and most males.*
DOWNY YOUNG: *White-downed, yellow-billed.*

VOICE
Contact call, usually in flight, a soft, melodic tinkling. Sharp, high-pitched two-syllable note in alarm, tseet-tseet. *Feeding sometimes accompanied by a soft twitter; similar twittering sound made by male when calling female from the nest and in display.*

NESTING
Breeds October–January. Nest an upright hollow limb or hole in a tree, stump, fence post or log. Eggs: four to six; white; rounded, about 22 x 19 mm. Laid on wood dust. Incubation 19–20 days, by female. Young fledge in four–five weeks.

The Blue-winged Parrot nests in upright tree hollows. It may use the same nest in successive years.

DISTRIBUTION
Tasmania, islands in Bass Strait and southeastern mainland Australia westwards to Eyre Peninsula and northwards to Lake Eyre basin and Darling–Barwon drainage. No races.

THE MIGRATIONS OF THE BLUE-WINGED PARROT are still not well understood. It breeds in the southeast of South Australia, southern Victoria, Tasmania and Bass Strait islands. From there it disperses north in autumn, reaching Eyre Peninsula, the Lake Eyre basin and Darling River plains, and returns in spring. But not all birds leave the breeding grounds—indeed, sometimes none seem to—and those that do often appear to travel north by one route and to return by another in a 'loop' migration. There is always a moderately large population in southern Victoria and the southeast of South Australia. Whether they are resident and leap-frogged by Tasmanian birds on northwards migration or themselves move north in winter, to be replaced by Tasmanian birds, is a question still unanswered.

On their travels, Blue-winged Parrots exploit a variety of habitats, from forested valleys and sparsely timbered grasslands in Tasmania and Victoria to sand dune heath, mallee, acacia shrublands and saltbush plains inland. There the birds are generally seen in pairs or small flocks, depending on the season and locality. They are very social, and even during the breeding season groups of up to 20 birds can be seen. They are sometimes found together with Elegant Parrots and Orange-bellied Parrots. Blue-winged Parrots can be identified by their extensive plain dark blue shoulders, their almost uniformly dark frontal band which does not extend above the eyes, and by their olive-green body tone.

Blue-winged Parrots spend the morning and most of the afternoon on the ground feeding on the seeds of grasses and herbs. Their plumage blends so well with their surroundings that they are almost impossible to see foraging among the blades of grass. They can be approached closely, but when disturbed the whole flock rises simultaneously and flies to nearby trees to wait the passing of danger before returning to the ground in twos and threes. During the middle of the day the birds perch quietly in trees or on fences and telegraph wires. They fly high when travelling long distances, moving swiftly, directly and with little undulation, interspersing rapid flaps with brief glides on half-spread wings. Flying from tree to tree they move buoyantly and erratically, spreading their tails as they alight.

Pairing seems to be permanent. A courting male draws himself up erect, fans his tail, droops his wings half-open to display the blue shoulders and bobs his head as he courtship-feeds his mate, giving his soft, twittering contact call at the same time. Nest hollows, sometimes several to a tree, are selected, cleaned and guarded by the female alone; she may return to the same nest in successive years. She also broods unaided; the male stays close by, calling her out several times a day to feed, drink and be fed, by regurgitation. She alone passes the food on to the young in their first several weeks, but as brooding ceases, both parents feed the young independently. They stay with adults for some months.

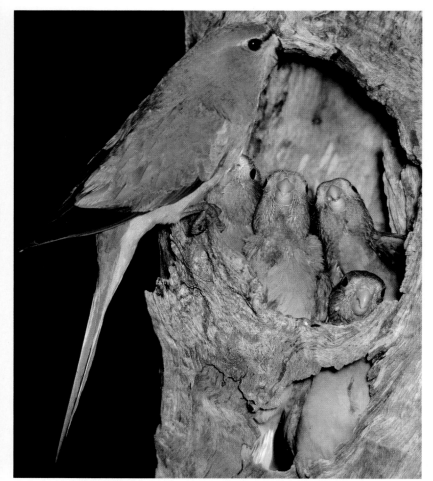

The Elegant Parrot raises four or five young in a nest in a tree hole.

Elegant Parrot
Neophema elegans (GOULD, 1837)

OTHER NAMES
None.

IDENTIFICATION
LENGTH: *About 220 mm, including narrow tapered tail.*
ADULTS: *Sexes similar; female rather duller with variable yellowish underwing bar. Upper parts, including crown and nape, rich golden olive; duller in female. Frontal band deep blue, bordered above by pale blue line extending over and beyond eyes. Lores, throat and forepart of cheeks bright yellow. Breast dull yellow-green. Rest of underparts, including underside of tail, bright yellow. Outer wing coverts and flight feathers deep blue; shoulder patch pale green-blue. Central tail feathers dull blue washed with olive; outer tail feathers blue broadly tipped with yellow. Eye brown. Bill and cere black. Feet and toes mid grey-brown.*
IMMATURES: *Like adults but frontal band vague or absent; yellow underwing bar present. Full adult plumage comes at only three or four months old.*
DOWNY YOUNG: *White-downed, yellow-billed.*

VOICE
Contact or position call a sharp, reedy tsit-tsit-tsit ... tsit-tsit-tsit in flight. Occasional plaintive though penetrating twittering heard during feeding.

NESTING
Breeds August–November. Nest in a hollow limb or hole in a tree. Eggs: four or five; white; rounded, 21–22 x 18 mm. Laid on decayed wood dust lining bottom of hole. Incubation about 18 days, by female. Young fledge in about four–five weeks; maintain loose association with parents within flock.

DISTRIBUTION
Open country, including coastal sand dunes, lightly timbered grasslands and cultivated paddocks, mallee, acacia scrublands and arid saltbush plains. Also lives in fringe zone between pasture and high forest. Partly nomadic. Uncommon to rare only in extreme east of range. No races, notwithstanding two isolated populations in southeast and southwest.

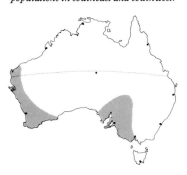

IN SOUTHWESTERN AUSTRALIA the Elegant Parrot is extending its range and increasing its numbers by colonising the scattered clearings. The birds congregate in flocks of 20 to 100 or more, except in the breeding season when they are usually seen in pairs or small parties. They are sometimes found in the company of Blue-winged Parrots, which they closely resemble in habits and appearance. In lightly timbered open country the bird's plumage blends well with the grass in which the bird spends much of the day searching for seeds. It particularly likes the seeds of grasses and clover, but eats other vegetable matter, including berries and fruits.

When alarmed, Elegant Parrots often sit motionless and are not flushed until the last moment, when they fly to a nearby tree or land behind a bush or tussock. Their flight is high, swift and direct, its delicate fluttering interspersed with brief glides on half-spread wings, except over short distances, when it can be low and erratic. When alighting they spread the tail.

In courtship the male raises his wings and spreads his tail before bobbing and feeding the female, by regurgitation.

Bourke's Parrot *Neophema bourkii* (GOULD, 1841)

OTHER NAMES
None.

IDENTIFICATION
LENGTH: *About 190 mm, including slender tail.*
MALE: *Forehead and line above eyes blue; face and eye-ring flecked white. Crown and back greyish brown. Rump and upper tail coverts brown intermixed with mid-blue. Shoulders and wing coverts brown edged with cream. Underwing coverts, bend of wing and outer webs of dusky flight feathers mid-blue. Throat and breast brown, the feathers edged with pink; belly rose-pink; vent, undertail coverts, thighs, flanks and sides of upper tail coverts pale blue. Central tail feathers brown tinged with blue; outer tail feathers blue tipped with white. Eye brown. Bill and cere blackish. Feet and toes mid-dark grey.*
FEMALE: *As male; duller; no blue brow.*
IMMATURES: *As adults, but less pink on belly; off-white underwing stripe in females, sometimes males. Adult plumage at four or five months.*
DOWNY YOUNG: *White-downed, yellow-billed.*

VOICE
Contact call, usually in flight, a mellow, repeated chu-wee. Occasionally a plaintive, rolling whistle, almost a soft warble while perching. Shrill, metallic two-syllable note in alarm, kik-kik.

NESTING
Breeds August–December. Nest a small hollow, usually in an acacia or a casuarina tree, 1–3 m above ground. Eggs: three to six; white; rounded, 20–21 x 17–18 mm. Incubation about 18 days, by female. Young fledge in about four weeks; fed by both parents for another week or so.

DISTRIBUTION
Widely distributed from Ashburton River and about Morawa, WA, east to southwestern Queensland, Ivanhoe and Lightning Ridge, NSW. No races.

Bourke's Parrot lives in the mulga.

CONTRARY TO EARLY REPORTS, Bourke's Parrot is moderately abundant throughout the mulga woods of the interior and may have increased with the establishment of stock watering points since the 1950s. They are nomadic, with irregular movements.

Bourke's Parrots usually keep to pairs or small family parties, although sometimes gathering in flocks of 100 or more at waterholes in droughts. They come to water before dawn and after dusk regularly, sometimes not settling to roost until 9–10 pm. They drink occasionally during the day as well, but spend most of the time feeding on the ground on seeds—often of legumes—or resting in bushes and low trees. Flight is swift and direct, of quick shallow wing-beats interspersed with brief glides on partly spread, downswept wings.

Because of its colour pattern, Bourke's Parrot has often been distinguished in a genus of its own. But its tail shape, with second and third innermost pairs of feathers almost as long as the central pair, is characteristic of the *Neophema* parrots. Its display—males standing erect, tails spread and wings open—is the same.

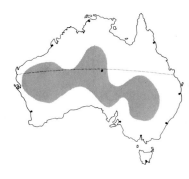

Orange-bellied Parrot

Neophema chrysogaster (LATHAM, 1790)

An adult (right) and two immature Orange-bellied Parrots feeding.

VERGING ON EXTINCTION, the Orange-bellied Parrot is restricted today to breeding only in Tasmania where perhaps no more than 500 survive. It only migrates to winter as far as the south coast of mainland Australia between Port Phillip Bay and the Coorong.

Although breeding and feeding in the fens of western Tasmania, they keep close to coasts throughout the year, foraging on tidal flats, sedge-swamps and grassfields. At their wintering quarters the parrots congregate in small flocks, dispersing to breed in pairs.

Orange-bellied Parrots spend most of the day on the ground, either searching for seeds or quietly sitting under a tussock or small bush. Seeds of grasses, shrubs and salt-adapted plants and fruit are their food, though they have been seen eating decaying kelp.

In the field, Orange-bellied Parrots are identified by their bright grass-green plumage and distinctive buzzing alarm call, given as they are flushed to rise high in the air before dropping again. Flight is like that of the Rock Parrot, and display and nesting habits are like other *Neophema* parrots.

OTHER NAMES
None.

IDENTIFICATION
LENGTH: *About 210 mm, including slender tail.*
MALE: *Upper parts, including crown, bright grass-green. Frontal band blue. Sides of head, throat, breast and flanks mid-green. Belly yellow grading to bright orange in centre. Undertail coverts and underside of tail bright yellow. Underwing coverts, greater coverts and outer webs of dusky flight feathers deep blue. Central tail feathers green washed with blue. Outer tail feathers blue broadly tipped with yellow. Eye brown. Bill and cere grey-black. Feet and toes buff-grey.*
FEMALE: *As male, but upper parts duller with vague black frontal band.*
IMMATURES: *Duller than adult female. Well-marked but smaller orange belly patch. Yellow underwing stripe present.*
DOWNY YOUNG: *White-downed, yellow-billed.*

VOICE
Contact call, generally in flight, of soft 'tinkling' notes, like call of Blue-winged Parrot. Alarm call is a buzzing chitter-chitter.

NESTING
Breeds November–December. Nest a bed of rotten wood chips in hollows in living eucalypts. Eggs: four to six; white; rounded, about 22 x 18 mm. Incubation 20–21 days, by female. Young, fed by both parents after 10 days, fledge in four–five weeks.

DISTRIBUTION
Tasmania, rarely more than 60 km from coast, and coastal southern mainland. Frequents open grassland and light scrub, sand dunes, tidal flats, cultivated paddocks and swamplands. Migratory. No races.

Rock Parrot

Neophema petrophila (GOULD, 1841)

STOCKY BIRDS, Rock Parrots live in treeless shrublands on the coast and offshore islands of southern Australia, rarely ranging more than 10 kilometres inland. They are generally in small parties, but sometimes up to 100 birds congregate to feed or to nest on an island.

Rock Parrots feed on seeds and fruits of plants adapted to salty conditions, and are particularly fond of the seeds of pigface *Carpobrotus*. They are inconspicuous as they forage and feed early in the morning and towards late afternoon. The rest of the day they spend sitting quietly in a bush or sheltering under a rock. Flight is swift and erratic with jerky side movements, and rapid wing-beats are interspersed with brief glides on downswept wings.

In courtship, the male stands erect, spreads wings and tail, then bobs his head to feed his mate, begging with *tsit-tsit* cries. He also calls her out from the nest to be fed in the same way while she is brooding.

Rock Parrots frequent coastal sand dunes, and feed on plants adapted to salty conditions.

OTHER NAMES
None.

IDENTIFICATION
LENGTH: *About 220 mm, including slender tail.*
ADULTS: *Sexes similar. Upper parts including crown dull olive. Frontal band deep blue with pale blue edges; lores, eye-surround and foreparts of cheeks pale blue-green. Throat, breast and sides of head dull grey-olive. Belly and lower underparts, including underside of tail, bright yellow. Underwing coverts, bend of wing and outer webs of dusky primaries deep blue; primary coverts paler blue. Tail feathers blue-green, tipped and edged with yellow. Eye dark brown. Bill and cere black. Feet grey.*
IMMATURES: *Duller than adults. Foreparts of cheeks grey-olive. Underwing stripe present. Adult plumage at three or four months.*
DOWNY YOUNG: *White-downed, yellow-billed.*

VOICE
Contact call, always in flight, is plaintive, penetrating tsit-tseet, repeated rapidly and often. Occasional subdued titter-titter during feeding.

NESTING
Breeds August–December on offshore islands. Eggs: four or five; white; ellipsoidal, about 24 x 20 mm. Laid in depression under slab of rock or in crevice behind overhanging plants. Incubation about 18 days, by female. Young fledge in about 30 days; maintain loose association with parents within flock.

DISTRIBUTION
Coastal sand dunes, samphire flats and heathy offshore islands in south and southwest; absent from Head of Great Australian Bight. Plentiful and sedentary, or moving to offshore islands to breed and back to mainland after. Two races: one brighter citrine-olive in Western Australia east to Israelite Bay; the other browner olive and darker yellow ventrally around South Australian gulfs between Fowlers Bay and Robe.

Turquoise Parrot *Neophema pulchella* (SHAW, 1792)

THE TURQUOISE PARROT WAS ONCE more widespread than it is today, but now occurs only in scattered areas. Though it is uncommon, it is not endangered as long as there are areas in which it can live—the zone between woodland and grassland. The birds have responded well to the preservation of their habitat in the Warrumbungles National Park, in northern New South Wales.

Turquoise Parrots are usually seen in pairs or small parties, but flocks of up to 30 are occasionally seen. They spend most of the day on the ground, searching for the seeds of grasses and herbaceous plants, or browsing on vegetable matter. They prefer to feed in the shade of a tree. Drinking is regular and daily, the birds usually flying in to drink at first light. They move through the air with swift, erratic fluttering, gliding sporadically on downswept wings, and alighting and taking off with a flash of yellow tail feathers.

Courtship is simple. The male sits bolt upright in front of his mate, fanning his tail and opening his wings to highlight the blue shoulders, while chirruping excitedly. Courtship feeding often follows. The male also calls the female out to feed or be fed each morning and afternoon while she is brooding. This usually happens in a nearby tree; she goes to drink before returning to the nest.

A male Turquoise Parrot. The female has a paler face and lacks the red patch on the wings. Turquoise Parrots are usually seen in pairs or small parties, browsing around on the ground.

OTHER NAMES
Turquoisine Parrot, Beautiful Grass Parakeet, Red-shouldered Parakeet.

IDENTIFICATION
LENGTH: *About 200 mm, including slender tail.*
MALE: *Upper parts, including crown, bright green. Face shining blue. Inner wing coverts chestnut-red; lesser and median wing coverts turquoise; underwing coverts, bend of wing, primary coverts and outer webs of dusky flight feathers dark blue. Cream underwing stripe often persistent in flight feathers. Throat to crissum bright yellow. Central tail feathers green; outer tail feathers dull blue broadly tipped with yellow. Eye pale brown. Bill and cere black-grey. Feet and toes grey-brown.*
FEMALE: *As male but forehead and face paler blue; lores pale yellow; front of neck and breast green. No chestnut-red on shoulders. Off-white underwing stripe present.*
IMMATURES: *Duller than adult female. Males have darker blue on face and faint chestnut-red patch on inner wing coverts. Underwing stripe present. Adult plumage gained at about 14 months.*
DOWNY YOUNG: *White-downed, yellow-billed.*

VOICE
Contact call, usually in flight, is soft but penetrating two-syllable whistle; similar to but more subdued than call of Blue-winged Parrot. Weak high-pitched twittering while feeding.

NESTING
Breeds August–December; sometimes two broods a season. Nest a hollow low in often dead tree, log or post; on decayed wood dust; occasional green leaves in nest probably carried in by female in rump feathers. Eggs: two to five or six; white; rounded, 20–22 x 17–18 mm. Incubation about 18 days, by female. Young fledge in about four weeks; remain with parents for some months afterwards.

DISTRIBUTION
Eastern and western scarps of Great Dividing Range, north to Maryborough and Taroom, Qld, west to Griffith, NSW, and south to Nowra, NSW, and Benalla, Vic. Open forest and timbered grasslands on mountain slopes, on ridges and along watercourses. Partly nomadic. Uncommon. No races.

Scarlet-chested Parrot *Neophema splendida* (Gould, 1841)

OTHER NAMES
Scarlet-breasted Parrot, Splendid Parrot.

IDENTIFICATION
LENGTH: *About 200 mm, including slender tail.*
MALE: *Upper parts bright green. Face brilliant blue, deepening on throat and cheeks. Flanks and sides of breast and neck green. Front of neck and middle of breast scarlet. Rest of underparts rich yellow. Underwing coverts and bend of wing dark blue; wing coverts pale blue; outer webs of dusky flight feathers green-blue. Central tail feathers blue-green; outer tail feathers blue broadly tipped with yellow. Eye dark brown. Bill and cere dark grey-black. Feet and toes grey-brown.*
FEMALE: *As male but face paler and colour more restricted in area; entire breast green. No underwing stripe.*
IMMATURES: *Similar to adult female but duller. Blue of face slightly darker in males. Vague cream underwing stripe. Fully adult plumage gained at second annual moult, 15–16 months after fledging.*
DOWNY YOUNG: *White-downed, yellow-billed.*

VOICE
Call is soft twittering, lacking in penetrations of other Neophemas.

NESTING
Breeds mostly August–January, depending on rain and food supply. Nest a hole or hollow in tree, generally a vertical spout in an acacia or small eucalypt. Eggs: three to five, rarely six; white; rounded, about 23 x 19 mm. Laid on wood dust. Incubation about 18 days, by female. Young fledge in about four weeks; remain with parents in family group for some months after.

DISTRIBUTION
Southern inland Australia, from southeastern Western Australia, through all central and northern South Australia south to middle of Eyre Peninsula and Murray River, east to extreme southwestern Queensland and Darling River, NSW. Sporadically distributed in mallee, acacia scrublands, clumps of trees or shrubs along stony ridges and open saltbush or spinifex sandplains. Extremely nomadic. Few records. No races.

Only the male Scarlet-chested Parrot has a scarlet breast; the female's breast is green. These parrots feed on or near the ground, on the seeds of herbaceous plants and grasses, often holding down a stem with one foot.

SPECTACULAR IRRUPTIONS OF hundreds, even a thousand Scarlet-chested Parrots and their sudden vanishing for long periods has left ornithologists nonplussed about their status. The birds seem to be geared to the boom-and-bust cycles in the Australian arid zone, breeding up in good seasons, crashing in bad, and wandering nomadically far and wide for feeding grounds. There may even be some regularity in the movements—parrots in the Murray mallee consistently shifting south in summer, north in winter. When not breeding the birds band into quite large flocks, but to nest they disperse in pairs or small groups. Some occupied hollows are no more than four metres apart.

Scarlet-chested Parrots are very unobtrusive birds that spend most of their time on the ground or in low shrubs, searching for seeds of grasses and herbaceous plants. They are extremely quiet in their movements and, unless flushed, they may easily go unnoticed. They are usually seen in isolated pairs or small parties of rarely more than 10. They have frequently been found far from water and this gives credence to the claim that they obtain sufficient moisture by drinking dew or chewing water-storing plants, such as *Calandrinia,* which grow profusely in sandy mulga country.

The flight of the Scarlet-chested Parrot resembles that of the Turquoise Parrot.

When courting, the male hops excitedly round the female and makes short, fluttering flights, in addition to sequences of wing and tail spreading. He also feeds her then and later, while she is brooding, on a branch outside the nest. In captivity female Scarlet-chested Parrots have been seen placing aromatic green leaves under their rump feathers and carrying them into the nesting hollow. The female of the Turquoise Parrot has been seen doing this too, using the leaves of the tea-tree *Leptospernum stellatum.* The effect of the leaves may be to provide humidity or to deodorise the nesting chamber; the leaves are not used for nest-building.

Swift Parrot

Lathamus discolor

(SHAW, 1790)

The Swift Parrot often hangs upside down to reach eucalypt blossoms. Its main food is pollen and nectar.

OTHER NAMES
Swift Lorikeet, Red-shouldered Parakeet.

IDENTIFICATION
LENGTH: *About 250 mm, including slender pointed tail.*
ADULTS: *Sexes alike. General plumage mid-green, paler below. Crown dark blue; face red; lores and borders of face yellow; ear coverts suffused with turquoise. Flanks and crissum red with green markings. Flight feathers blue-black edged with pale yellow; inner webs of tertiaries scarlet; underwing coverts, bend of wing and shoulders deep red. Central tail feathers dull brown-red tipped with blue; outer tail feathers dull blue edged with brown-red. Eye pale yellow. Bill and cere horn. Feet and toes pale brown.*
IMMATURES: *Duller than adults. Less red on throat and undertail coverts. Eye brown.*

VOICE
Contact call, usually in flight, a metallic clink-clink, *repeated quickly four or five times to produce a chirruping sound. Feeding accompanied by subdued rosella-like chattering. All call-notes have bell-like tone, unlike screech of lorikeets.*

NESTING
Breeds late September to early January. Nest in a hollow limb or hole often high in a tree, usually a eucalypt. Eggs: three to five, usually four; white; rounded, 24–27 x 19–22 mm. Laid on wood dust. Incubation about 20 days, by female. Young fledge in about six weeks.

DISTRIBUTION
Most types of timbered country where there are flowering trees. Breeds in Tasmania and migrates to mainland for autumn and winter, reaching the Mt Lofty Ranges, SA, and following the east coast and Great Dividing Range north to Fitzroy River drainage, Qld. No races.

SWIFT PARROTS ARE tree-living birds and are usually seen in small parties feeding on blossom among the topmost branches of eucalypts or flying high overhead. Visits to the ground are infrequent and only for drinking and for examining fallen seeds and flowers. The parrots inhabit most types of timbered country and follow the flowering of its trees; they are regular visitors to gardens and parks and are often seen in trees lining the streets of towns and cities. Noisy birds, they appear to be always on the move, darting from one tree to the next, clambering about in the foliage or hanging upside down to get at blossoms, chattering all the while. Their main food is pollen and nectar, particularly from eucalypt trees, and they follow the blossoming of various species. They also feed extensively on lerps, insects and their larvae, as well as seeds, fruit including berries, and some vegetable matter.

Swift Parrots breed in Tasmania and on some of the Bass Strait islands, migrate to the mainland between March and May, and return to Tasmania in August and September. Much of the movement seems to be at night. Some birds winter in Tasmania, but none has been recorded on the mainland in the summer. During the non-breeding season the birds appear to concentrate mainly in southern and central Victoria; their appearance elsewhere is a result of dispersal.

During the breeding season Swift Parrots may share a nesting tree with other breeding pairs.

The details of their breeding cycle are not well known; most of what is known comes from studies of captive birds. In display, the male first bows then draws himself up to feed the female. She alone broods, leaving the nest briefly in the morning and again in the afternoon to be fed by the male. In courtship he first bows to her, then draws himself up to feed her, by regurgitation. The nesting period is long and only one brood is reared a season. Fledglings undergo a partial moult into brighter plumage at a few months of age, but do not acquire adult plumage until the following autumn.

Swift Parrots live up to their name, for their flight is extremely fast and direct on pointed, quick-beating wings. A flock moves with remarkable precision; as the birds pass overhead their rapid wing-beats produce a whirring noise. The birds often mix with lorikeets and may then be difficult to identify. They can be best recognised by their distinctive calls and, in flight, by the red under their wings and their fine, pointed red-brown tail.

Their similarities to lorikeets in appearance and feeding seem nonetheless coincidental. Evidence that Swift Parrots have really arisen from rosella-like parrots comes from their single left carotid artery, submissive nape spot, variable underwing stripe, ladle-drinking, and clinking contact calls. Their tongues do have brush tips for mopping up nectar like a lorikeet, but the papillae are short and localised.

Pallid Cuckoo *Cuculus pallidus* (LATHAM, 1801)

AT LEAST 80 OTHER SPECIES of birds play unwitting host to the egg and young of the Pallid Cuckoo. The most commonly parasitised are honeyeaters of the genus *Lichenostomus* —Yellow-faced, White-plumed and Singing. Others include miners and *Melithreptus* honeyeaters, woodswallows and, less often, thornbills, robins, whistlers and flycatchers. As with other cuckoos, the nestling ejects the eggs or young of its adoptive parents from the nest. After it has left the nest, its loud squawks for food sometimes induce birds other than its foster parents to feed it.

Hairy caterpillars, grasshoppers and beetles make up the diet of the Pallid Cuckoo, and the hairs from the caterpillars can line its stomach like fur. It feeds by sallying, perching still on a vantage point—often a dead branch—then diving to ground to pick up its prey in its bill. Its flight is gracefully undulating, on pointed wings, and it raises its tail erect as it lands.

Pallid Cuckoos are solitary birds, frequenting mostly open woodland, and are nomadic, even migrating across southern Australia. There they appear in spring, the males heralding breeding with their loud rising piping to advertise themselves. Pairing is brief, males courting females by offering food and peeping softly.

OTHER NAMES
Brainfever-bird, Grasshopper Hawk, Harbinger of Spring, Mosquito Hawk, Rain-bird, Scale-bird, Semitone-bird.

IDENTIFICATION
LENGTH: *280–330 mm.*
MALE: *Upper parts rich mid-grey when fresh, becoming brownish with wear. White spot on nape. Face with dusky line through eye. Underparts uniformly pale grey. Wing and shoulders mid-grey with white patch on leading edge near shoulder; inner webs of primaries have white tooth-like spots, forming bars. Upper side of tail dusky black, becoming brown with wear, with white or buff tooth marks on outer webs and broad white tooth marks on inner webs. Eye dark brown, with yellow eye-ring. Upper bill dark brown, lower dark olive-brown. Feet pale olive-brown; claws duskier.*
FEMALE: *Similar to male; browner and faintly mottled on upper parts.*
IMMATURES: *Juveniles strongly streaked dark brown and white, with white edges and tips to wing feathers. Immatures have upper parts heavily mottled with chestnut and dark brown; underparts pale grey; breast buff with dark brown bars, later replaced by uniform grey, with a few dark brown and chestnut feathers on side.*

VOICE
About eight loud melancholy whistling notes by male rising up the scale in chromatic sequence, the second note often lower than first. Also hysterical crookyer, crookyer in pursuit of female; staccato pip-pip-pip-pip. Female has harsh single call. Male often calls at night, like other cuckoos.

NESTING
Breeds September–January. Egg: one; flesh-pink to salmon-buff, sometimes with a few small scattered dark specks; long-oval, about 25 x 18 mm. Laid in open cup nest of another species; probably several nests parasitised by same female each year.

DISTRIBUTION
Throughout Australia in all types of open vegetation, least often in rainforest. Partial migrant moving north and inland in winter; present all year round north of 26° S. Mainly juveniles remain over summer in far south. Some birds reach the Moluccas, New Guinea and Timor on non-breeding migration. No races.

A Pallid Cuckoo calling. During breeding, the male often calls at night, emitting loud, rising whistling notes.

Barred underparts distinguish the Oriental Cuckoo from the Pallid Cuckoo. In its winter quarters in Australia it is dispersed and rather solitary.

Oriental Cuckoo *Cuculus saturatus* BLYTH, 1843

OTHER NAMES
Himalayan Cuckoo, Blyth's Cuckoo, Saturated Cuckoo, Hawk-cuckoo.

IDENTIFICATION
LENGTH: *280–340 mm.*
ADULTS: *Sexes similar; male slightly larger. Upper parts dove-grey with light bronze gloss; lighter on head. Tail dark grey to black, spotted and tipped white, especially below. Flight feathers dove-grey with pale bars. Chin, throat and upper breast pale dove-grey; rest of underparts white, sometimes washed cinnamon, strongly barred with brown-black. Underwing coverts white, barred with grey-brown. Eye brown with cream or yellow outer ring; naked skin around eye cream to yellow. Bill brown-black, lower mandible olive-brown. Feet cream-yellow.*
IMMATURES: *Upper parts mid to dark rufous-brown with black bars. Flight feathers grey-brown above with rufous bars; lighter below. Tail black above, with white tip and rufous bars; grey-brown below with white tip and cinnamon-to-white bars. Underparts white with rufous wash, strongly barred in chocolate-brown from throat to crissum, tending to mottled grey-brown towards chin. Eye paler than in adult; skin around eye green-cream. Bill brown, becoming green-tinged towards base of lower mandible. Feet yellow.*

VOICE
In Australia, two to six rather rapid whistled notes similar to those of Australian Kestrel—a piercing pi-pi-pi-pi identical in tone, volume and spacing, but at an even pitch and not rising in scale. Other calls gaak-gaak-gak-ak-ak and

kuk-kuk-kuk, often when feeding. Commonly silent.

NESTING
Breeds northern spring and summer in Eurasia. Parasitic. Egg: one; white or pale brown with very small black or purple spots; long-oval, about 21 x 14 mm. Laid in nest of another species.

DISTRIBUTION
Non-breeding migrant from Asia (northeastern Europe to China, Burma and Taiwan) wintering across northern Australia from Kimberley Region, WA, to Brisbane, occasionally south to Narooma, NSW. Inhabits monsoon forests, wet sclerophyll forests, paperbark swamps, denser open forests, scrubby gullies and mangroves. Also winters in New Guinea, Philippines, Celebes, Moluccas, Solomons and southern India. Two races often recognised, differing in size, but possibly only one; Australian migrants are commonly intermediate.

MIGRATING LIKE THE EUROPEAN CUCKOO, the Oriental Cuckoo travels from its breeding grounds right across Eurasia each autumn to non-breeding winter quarters in southeastern Asia, Indonesia, New Guinea and Australia; stragglers sometimes even reach New Zealand. It arrives along the northern Australian coast in November–December in ones and twos, trickles down the eastern seaboard, and then leaves again during April; some, probably younger non-breeders, may stay all year. Departure can be marked by loose congregations at staging points along the northern Australian coast, but during most of their stay Oriental Cuckoos are dispersed and rather solitary, only gathering in small flocks at swarms of food.

Oriental Cuckoos feed on larger insects, mainly caterpillars, stick insects, ants and beetles. These they take from the foliage of trees and bushes or from the ground by sallying. Perching on an open branch from which they can look about, the cuckoos swoop on to prey, grasp it in the bill, and fly back to a perch to batter and eat it. At all times they are quiet, shy and elusive, slipping off and weaving swiftly away through the trees whenever approached. Flight, whether fast or slow, is graceful and slightly undulating on pointed wings; in form and movement it can resemble an Australian Hobby.

Eating much the same food as the Pallid Cuckoo and foraging in the same way, the Oriental Cuckoo is a potential competitor. Actual competition between them, however, rarely eventuates—for two reasons. First, Oriental Cuckoos arrive in northern Australia over summer when most Pallid Cuckoos have shifted south to breed; secondly, Oriental Cuckoos commonly occupy denser forest than the open woodlands frequented by the Pallid. They inhabit vine and gallery monsoon forest, wet sclerophyll, paperbark swamps, scrubby gullies and even mangroves, keeping mainly to the shelter of higher branches.

Oriental Cuckoos arrive in Australia in a variety of plumages, ranging from birds in full adult grey plumage and varying degrees of immature plumage to mottled brown young of the year. This explains the two phases—grey and brown—that the species has been thought to have had in Australia.

Brush Cuckoo *Cacomantis variolosus* <small>(Vigors & Horsfield, 1827)</small>

OTHER NAMES
Square-tailed Cuckoo.

IDENTIFICATION
LENGTH: *220–240 mm.*
MALE: *Upper parts olive-brown with greenish sheen; head, mantle, chin and throat leaden grey; underparts grey-brown to rufous fawn; wings browner, faintly mottled and barred brown; underwing with broad cream-white stripe; tail slaty brown with purple tinge, the webs notched white, most strongly on inner edge. Eye chestnut-dark brown; eye-ring paler. Bill black-brown; lower mandible olive or dull yellow with darker tip; mouth deep orange. Feet orange-yellow to olive; claws darker.*
FEMALE: *As male but duller; underparts sometimes faintly mottled. Eye brown-olive. Mouth yellow-light orange. Feet greenish-grey.*
IMMATURES: *Juveniles mottled dark brown and deep buff on upper parts, and dark brown and pale buff on*
underparts. *Moults into immature plumage of brown and buff barred upper parts and white and brown barred underparts. Later, upper parts, wing and tail become similar to adult, but head remains dark brown with buff markings; underside becoming replaced by leaden grey breast, washed russet.*

VOICE
Far-carrying, descending chromatic sequence of six–eight mournful whistled notes. Also shrill repeated rising phrases by displaying males—'where's the tea'— *becoming hysterical towards end.*

NESTING
Breeds October–February in south; for greater part of year in north. Parasitic. Lays different egg types (with intermediates) similar to host's: Leaden Flycatcher type—creamy-white to white and speckled, spotted or blotched olive-brown with underlying tones of lavender forming a zonal ring at the
larger end; *rounded to rounded-oval(most regions). Grey Fantail type— pale cream to cream buff, spotted and speckled with darker shades of brown, olive-brown and lavender to form a zonal ring at the larger end (in south and east); rounded to rounded-oval. Brown-backed Honeyeater type—white, sparingly spotted or speckled at the larger end with black-brown and underlying tones of dark mauve-lavender (in northeast); oval to elongate-oval. Rhipidura type—similar to Grey Fantail type but tinged grey-green (in northwest). 16–20 x 17 x 12–16 mm. Two to four eggs may be laid by one female in one season, each in different nests. Incubation 12–14 days. Young fledge in 15–17 days.*

DISTRIBUTION
Coastal and subcoastal Kimberleys and Arnhem Land to Cape York Peninsula, and coastal eastern regions inland to Great Dividing Range and south to Dandenong Ranges, Vic. Also Malay Peninsula through Indonesia to Solomons. About 18 races; two in Australia: one small, pale and sedentary across the north; the other larger, dark and migratory along the central and southeast coast.

Brush Cuckoos sit on bare perches.

WIDESPREAD FROM SOUTHEAST ASIA to Australasia, the Brush Cuckoo is a rather sedentary bird through most of its range. Across northern Australia it is present year round, although more vocal and noticeable during summer breeding. In the southeast, however, the endemic race there is migratory, arriving in August–September and leaving in April–May to winter as far north as the New Guinea region. Everywhere, it lives within tangled forest edges— rainforest fringe, galleries of monsoon scrub and thickets lining streams— feeding on insects and caterpillars among branches by perch-and-pounce sallying; only during the wet season in the north does it venture out much into open woodland.

Although it has been recorded as parasitising about 50 species, the Brush Cuckoo lays mainly in the open, cup-shaped nests of flycatchers, fantails and red-breasted robins in the southeast, and in the deeper domes of Brown-backed and Bar-breasted Honeyeaters across the north. Its eggs commonly resemble those of its chosen host.

Brush Cuckoos are commonly solitary, only gathering in brief noisy communal displays of up to eight birds at times when breeding. Males advertise themselves and their loosely held territories with long and sometimes excited calling, carrying on into the night. In courtship and display, males feed females and chase with their darting but graceful pointed-wing flight.

Chestnut-breasted Cuckoo

Cacomantis castaneiventris <small>(Gould, 1867)</small>

The Chestnut-breasted Cuckoo lives in rainforest on Cape York Peninsula.

LITTLE IS KNOWN about the Chestnut-breasted Cuckoo because of its remote and inaccessible habitat and secretive habits. Spending most of its time in the shrubbery and understorey of tropical rainforest, it flies to the ground to pick up its food by perch-and-pounce: caterpillars, ticks, beetles and grasshoppers. Sedentary, it moves about singly and in pairs. It is possibly more abundant in Australia than recorded but is common in New Guinea.

Parasitic on scrubwrens, the Chestnut-breasted Cuckoo lays its eggs mainly in the nests of Tropical Scrubwrens on Cape York Peninsula and in those of Large-billed Scrubwrens to the south. Like the Fan-tailed Cuckoo, it selects hosts that build domed nests and lays eggs superficially similar to those of scrubwrens.

OTHER NAMES
None.

IDENTIFICATION
LENGTH: *230–250 mm.*
ADULTS: *Sexes similar; female duller ventrally. Upper parts, including head, side of face and chin dark steel-grey with metallic tinge. Wings brown-black, with broad cream-white stripe on underside. Tail metallic purple-black tipped white, the white triangular notching on the inner tail feathers becoming bars on outermost feathers. Underparts a rich cinnamon- to chestnut-rufous. Eye mid- to red-brown; eye-ring lemon to yellow. Bill black to grey-black with basal portion of lower mandible buff to brownish yellow; mouth orange to orange-buff. Feet dull orange to yellow; claws dusky.*
IMMATURES: *Duller than adults. Upper parts rust-brown, rufous on back and rump. Underparts pale cinnamon.*

VOICE
A richly trilled falling whistle, similar to the Fan-tailed Cuckoo. Another call, perhaps by female, is a mournful three-note song, the first and third notes leisurely and up-slurred, the second shorter.

NESTING
Breeds October–December. Parasitic on species that build domed nests. Egg: one; faint pinkish-white, marked all over with spots of mid-brown and fainter pale grey; oval, about 21 x 15 mm.

DISTRIBUTION
Confined to rainforest tracts and wet gullies of eastern Cape York Peninsula, from Torres Strait south to Endeavour and Bloomfield Rivers and Daintree region. Also New Guinea and Aru Islands. Three races; one in Australia.

Fan-tailed Cuckoo _Cacomantis flabelliformis_ (LATHAM, 1801)

OTHER NAMES
Ash-tailed Cuckoo.

IDENTIFICATION
LENGTH: _245–270 mm._
MALE: _Upper parts mid to dark slate-grey; underparts light to medium cinnamon-rufous becoming paler on the abdomen and vent; throat and chin greyish. Wings brownish grey, with broad cream-white stripe on underwing and white mark on front of shoulder. Tail dark blue-black, notched white on the inner tail feathers, developing into bars on outermost. Iris chestnut brown to dark brown; eye-ring yellow. Bill black or black-brown; lower mandible browner with yellowish or flesh tone to base; mouth orange. Feet yellowish to olive-yellow; claws dusky._
FEMALE: _Duller, especially on ventral surface that tends to greyish with obscure barring towards the abdomen and vent._
IMMATURES: _Upper parts generally dark brown, barred with alternating dull, finely patterned red-brown and darker grey-brown. Ventrally, throat and breast dully mottled grey-brown and white and washed with russet on occasions; belly lighter or greyer. Wings plain dark grey-brown; tail black, barred russet. Iris grey-brown; eye-ring greenish yellow. Bill brownish black with a buff base to lower mandible. Feet dark pink to bright yellow. Birds can be found in varying stages of plumage between immaturity and adulthood. Female appears to retain subadult plumage states for longer, perhaps permanently._

VOICE
Slow or rapid descending plaintive trill repeated several times by male in advertisement, especially August to March; also by male, a high-pitched single whistle pree-ee or too-brreeet with a downward slur ending with an upward inflexion during courtship. A plaintive chiree by female only.

NESTING
Breeds August–January. Parasitic; lays its eggs mainly in domed nests. Egg: one; slightly lustrous, white to mauve, finely speckled, flecked and spotted all over, especially towards larger end, with varying shades of chestnut, purple-brown and lavender; oval, 18–25 x 14–18 mm. Incubation 14–15 days. Young fledge in 16–17 days.

DISTRIBUTION
Cape York Peninsula subcoastally to southern Victoria and Tasmania, and west to Eyre Peninsula and southwestern mainland. Also New Guinea to Fiji, New Caledonia, occasionally reaching New Zealand as a vagrant. About six races; one in Australia.

A pale eye-ring, darker toning and trilled calling distinguish the Fan-tailed Cuckoo from the Brush Cuckoo.

THE FAN-TAILED CUCKOO SIGHTS its prey of caterpillars, moths, beetles or other insects from a perch, flies out to make a capture and often returns to the same perch to eat. Sitting silently on a vantage stump, fence-post or bare branch, it adopts an upright posture with the tail pointed downwards. It frequents the lower and middle storeys of rainforest, wet and dry sclerophyll forest through to woodland, coastal heath or treed areas of cities and towns. There it flies out to pick insects off foliage or hops along the ground to pounce. It undulates gracefully in flight on pointed wings, and elevates the tail temporarily when alighting. Less secretive than females, males are usually solitary, rarely gathering in groups of two to four.

The male probably defends a territory when breeding, advertising it and himself with much calling—a repeated plaintive trill—from a van-tage perch, and will feed a female in courtship.

These cuckoos parasitise about 50 species of other birds, dominant among which are dome-nesting thornbills, scrubwrens and fairywrens —particularly the Brown Thornbill. The White-browed Scrubwren is also commonly parasitised, as well as the Large-billed and Yellow-throated, the Scrub-tit, Redthroat, hylacolas, Origma and Pilotbird.

While Fan-tailed Cuckoos in southwestern Australia do not move over very great distances from one season to the next, many southeastern birds—particularly immatures—migrate considerable distances northwards during the non-breeding winter months. Most of the Tasmanian birds migrate to the mainland and although the distances cuckoos move is not established, at least some cross Torres Strait to New Guinea and the Aru Islands, returning south in spring.

Black-eared Cuckoo

Chrysococcyx osculans (GOULD, 1847)

The Black-eared Cuckoo, an elusive migrant, is found in dry woodlands.

OTHER NAMES
None.

IDENTIFICATION
LENGTH: *190–210 mm.*
ADULTS: *Sexes similar. Upper parts dull grey-brown with slight purple-copper sheen on back, wings and tail; rump paler fawn; wings with concealed broad cream-white bar on underside; tail tipped white with concealed white barring. White line from base of bill extends over eye to form patch behind eye; narrow black line extends through base of eye and forms black patch over ear coverts and down side of neck. Underparts salmon pink to pale fawn, becoming cream with wear. Eye brown. Bill and legs black.*
IMMATURES: *Upper parts grey-brown; chin, throat and breast pale grey; tail darker with slight sheen. Line over eye and patch behind eye pale buff; patch through eye over ear coverts dark brown.*

VOICE
A quiet descending whistle, drawn out until it fades away; by male from vantage perch. Also livelier pee-o-weet-pee-o-weer in display.

NESTING
Breeds August–January in south; March in centre. Parasitic, laying mainly in domed nests. Egg: one; dark chocolate, but readily rubbed off; long-oval, about 22 x 14 mm.

DISTRIBUTION
Southern inland Australia, from west coast to western slopes of Great Dividing Range and north to Tropic of Capricorn. Migrates through northern Australia to winter from Moluccas to New Guinea. No races.

A QUIET, DRAWN-OUT WHISTLE that fades away identifies the Black-eared Cuckoo. With the onset of breeding, however, courting males give chase to females—uttering noisy lively calls and spreading their tails as they dash about. Flight is typically swift and slightly undulating, on pointed wings.

Females lay their eggs singly in domed nests, particularly those of the Redthroat and Speckled Warbler. Their hosts lay chocolate eggs which the eggs of the cuckoo mimic closely.

Black-eared Cuckoos are solitary, quiet and elusive, particularly out of breeding. They are migratory, arriving across southern inland Australia in September–October and leaving in March–April. Records in northern Australia are probably all of passage migrants en route to and from winter quarters around the Arafura and Banda Seas. The main path of migration seems to flow through Arnhem Land and the Kimberleys.

On their breeding grounds, the cuckoos live in the shrubberies of open mallee and bulloke woodlands, feeding by perch-pouncing on insects and larvae; at winter quarters they may enter rainforest.

Horsfield's Bronze-Cuckoo *Chrysococcyx basalis* (HORSFIELD, 1821)

A MOURNFUL DESCENDING WHISTLE, often repeated, and uttered from an exposed perch such as a high, bare branch, announces the arrival of Horsfield's Bronze-Cuckoos to breed in spring. It is given by males to advertise themselves and their territory to mates. Noisy but brief courtship displays of fast chasing flights in and around bushes and back to a perch, usually start in late winter.

Dullest of the bronze-cuckoos, Horsfield's is an insect- and caterpillar-eater and hunts for its prey by perch-and-pounce through various habitats from open woodlands to shrub-steppe, avoiding only dense forest and thicket.

Dome-nesting species are its main hosts, particularly those fairy-wrens, thornbills and gerygones which lay white, red-spotted eggs mimicked by the cuckoo's. Eggs laid in the nests of robins, flycatchers, chats and honeyeaters are less successful. On occasions the bronze-cuckoo damages the nest while laying and this can lead to the nest being deserted.

Like most Australian cuckoos, Horsfield's is solitary and migratory, rarely gathering in small feeding groups, and shifting south to breed in spring, and north in winter, when most but not all reach New Guinea and the Sunda arcs. Some birds stay south year round.

Horsfield's Bronze-Cuckoo calls from exposed perches in woodlands throughout Australia.

OTHER NAMES
Rufous-tailed Bronze-Cuckoo, Narrow-billed Bronze-Cuckoo.

IDENTIFICATION
LENGTH: *150–170 mm.*
MALE: *Head brown with purple-bronze tinge; back dull green with metallic copper-bronze sheen. Wing coverts with buff edges; underwing with concealed broad cream-white bar. Tail green with metallic sheen; inner webs with concealed dusky and white barring and deep rufous patch on each side of central feathers. White line over eye and down sides of neck; dusky brown stripe through eye. Underparts white with* dusky brown bars across sides of breast and belly, rarely meeting in centre. Eye red. Bill black. Feet grey.
FEMALE: *Similar to male in plumage; eye grey.*
IMMATURES: *Juveniles dull brown with green sheen over back; undersurface dull grey with no bars; belly white. Immatures similar to adults but duller, with broader buff edges to wing coverts and duller brown ventral barring. Male eye pink; female eye grey.*

VOICE
Rather mournful whistle, descending the scale and often repeated; by male in advertisement.

NESTING
Breeds July–December. Lays one egg, usually in the domed nest of foster-parent. Egg: one; pale pink with small red dots; oval, 18 x 12 mm.

DISTRIBUTION
Throughout woodlands and steppes of all Australia but avoiding thick forest. Disperses inland and northwards during winter as far as New Guinea, Moluccas and Sunda arcs. Greatest concentrations across southern Australia. No races.

Shining Bronze-Cuckoo *Chrysococcyx lucidus* (GMELIN, 1788)

The Shining Bronze-Cuckoo parasitises mostly thornbills and gerygones, though its egg does not mimic them.

OTHER NAMES
Golden Bronze-Cuckoo, Greenback, Broad-billed Bronze-Cuckoo.

IDENTIFICATION
LENGTH: *170–180 mm.*
MALE: *Crown to mantle dull copper-bronze in Australian race, contrasting with bright bronze-green back and wings; broad concealed white bar through underwing. Outer tail feathers banded black and white; rest dark bronze-green with dark band near tip. Indistinct white line over eye. Underparts white with close, complete copper-bronze bars. Eye brown, grey or pale pink; eye-ring pale grey. Bill black; 4–5 mm wide in front of nostril in Australian race, wider in New Zealand race. Feet dark olive-grey.*
FEMALE: *Similar to male but change between mantle and back not so clean cut. Eye brown, becoming grey.*
IMMATURES: *In juveniles, crown to mantle dull brown-green tinged with purple-copper. Back, wings and tail shiny bronze-green with bronze edges to feathers. No white line over eye. Chin, throat and breast grey-white with faint bars; belly white, barred brown on flanks.*

VOICE
Short series of high-pitched, upslurred whistles by advertising male, like a person whistling a dog; often ends in long descending note. Also staccato notes by displaying males.

NESTING
Breeds August–January. Parasitic, usually choosing domed nests of thornbills, gerygones and fairy-wrens. Egg: one; pale olive-green to bronze-brown, the colour readily rubbed off; long-oval, about 18 x 12 mm. Incubation 14–17 days. Young fledge in about 19 days.

DISTRIBUTION
Common in forests from Cape York Peninsula to Victoria and Tasmania; Eyre Peninsula, SA, and southwest of Western Australia where isolated. Breeding migrant to southern Australia, and migrates north in autumn to New Guinea, Lesser Sunda Islands and Bismarck Archipelago to Solomons. Four races; two in Australia: one a breeding migrant in all areas; the other a straggler on migration from breeding grounds in New Zealand.

THE SHINING BRONZE-CUCKOO lays its eggs in the nests of at least 65 other species of birds. It usually chooses the domed nests of thornbills, gerygones, fairy-wrens and scrubwrens but sometimes lays in the cup-shaped nests of Weebills, flycatchers, chats, silvereyes, sitellas and honeyeaters. A female may lay as many as 16 eggs in a season, depositing them singly in a host's nest usually after the commencement of incubation. Paradoxically, it is the newly hatched young of the Shining Bronze-Cuckoo, not its eggs, that mimic those of the host, perhaps because the cuckoo usually lays after the host has begun incubating and so, sometimes, nestlings of the two species share the nest briefly. As with other cuckoos, fledglings are fed by their foster parents and sometimes other birds, even Shining Bronze-Cuckoos themselves, for several weeks after leaving the nest. Rates of parasitism vary from year to year. Up to 30 per cent of local populations of Yellow-rumped Thornbills, a favoured host, may be parasitised in one season and only five per cent the next.

Caterpillars, spiny-haired moth larvae and beetles form the bulk of the diet of the Shining Bronze-Cuckoo which also takes dipterans such as craneflies, plecopterans and ants. These it captures by perch-and-pounce sallying, sitting watchfully on bare vantage branches just under the forest canopy, then flying out to pick its prey from foliage, branches or the ground, and returning to a perch to eat it. The spines from larvae become embedded in the lining of the gizzard and it is likely that they are disposed of by regurgitating the peeled-off lining. Bronze-cuckoos eat a number of insects that are generally considered unpalatable to most birds.

Shining Bronze-Cuckoos live in the mid and upper strata of rainforest and the denser eucalypt woodlands and forests receiving over 380 mm of rain a year. There they are commonly solitary and silent, males calling to advertise themselves and their territory only when breeding. Strong on wing but feeble of foot, they fly swiftly and gracefully, in long undulations on finely pointed wings, from set perch to set perch.

Although occasional birds stay south year round, Shining Bronze-Cuckoos are also migratory. The southwestern population travels to winter in the Sunda arc each autumn, returning in July–August, and the eastern Australian population shifts to New Guinea then, returning later, in August–September, to breed.

At times of migration, occasional stragglers of the broad-billed, green-crowned New Zealand race, which winters mainly from the Bismarck Archipelago to the Solomons, also move up and down the east coast.

Little Bronze-Cuckoo *Chrysococcyx minutillus* (GOULD, 1859)

THE LITTLE BRONZE-CUCKOO has the parasitic habits of most other Australian cuckoos. In the north it usually lays its egg in the nest of the Large-billed Gerygone, and on the central east coast in those of the White-throated Gerygone, although at least another eight species serve as foster-parents to its young.

The egg of the cuckoo often hatches before the eggs of the host and the young cuckoo ejects the host's eggs from the nest, manipulating them up to the edge by cupping the egg in the hollow of its back and gripping the wall of the nest with its strong claws. If the host's chicks have already hatched, it ejects them in much the same manner. Gerygones build dome-shaped nests in which the opening is often concealed by an overhang. The inside is dark and this may help the cuckoo's contrastingly coloured egg from being detected by the host; here there is no mimicry.

There is, nevertheless, a striking similarity between the nestlings of the versatile Little Bronze-Cuckoo and those of its hosts. Nestlings parasitising Large-billed Gerygones are black-skinned with four white tufts on the back of the crown, hardly different from those of its host's except for lacking additional wisps on the hind crown and white down on the back. Those in nests of the White-throated Gerygone, by contrast, are pinkish and adorned with yellow plumules, again like the nestlings of the host.

The northwestern race of the Little Bronze-Cuckoo *Chrysococcyx malayanus minutillus* intergrades with the rufous-breasted race *C.m. russatus* in northern and northeastern Queensland south to Bowen–Mackay. Both these populations are sedentary but the darker, more pronouncedly marked southern-most race *C.m. barnardi* migrates northwards from the central east coast during the winter to New Guinea and Cape York, there becoming interspersed with the rufous-breasted form in a confusing array of plumages.

Like other bronze-cuckoos, the Little is rather solitary and quiet, a graceful flier and, living in the mid stages of rainforest and broadleaf scrub, feeds on insects and caterpillars by perch-and-pounce sallying. Congregations of three to six courting birds are rare and brief during breeding.

A male Little Bronze-Cuckoo, showing red eye-ring.

OTHER NAMES
Gould's Bronze-Cuckoo, Rufous-breasted Bronze-Cuckoo.

IDENTIFICATION
LENGTH: *140–160 mm.*
MALE: *Crown and back of head dark bronze-green; mantle, shoulders, back and rump light to mid bronze-brown to green, usually contrasting with head. Side of face white, speckled black, ear coverts forming a small dark spot behind eye. Flight feathers mid-brown with slight bronze tinge to outer webs, and broad concealed light cream-russet bar through underwing, showing in flight. Upper surface of central two tail feathers as back, remainder becoming increasingly barred black and white towards outer. Underparts white with numerous narrow dark bronze-green bars. In resident northeastern Queensland race a variable russet tinge to upper surface and inner webs of flight feathers; underparts cream to white, washed variously rufous on throat, breast and bars; tail feathers rufous on inner and outer webs. Eye pinkish-red to scarlet; eye-ring orange-red to scarlet. Bill slate to black, with greenish to grey* base of lower mandible. Feet and claws slate.
FEMALE: *As male but eye-ring pale cream-green to cream; eye orange-brown to grey-brown.*
IMMATURES: *Upper parts dull bronze-brown; face, lores and line over eye pale grey; tail similar to adults but much paler; neck and throat greyish or washed russet, belly and abdomen white, bars becoming more evident with age. Eye grey to grey-brown; eye-ring not pronounced. Bill grey-brown to slate with paler base to lower mandible. Feet dull slate-grey.*

VOICE
Prolonged, high-pitched rippling whistle by advertising male, like a deep inhalation followed by a gradual exhalation producing the trilling; may be repeated in quick succession similar to that of a grasshopper. Also soft piping call, and four-note call.

NESTING
Breeds September–January. Parasitic; main hosts Large-billed and White-throated Gerygones and their relatives. Egg: one; slightly lustrous, brown-bronze to buff-olive, peppered all over but particularly at larger end with tiny darker specks; long-oval, about 19 x 13 mm.

DISTRIBUTION
In mangroves, monsoon and rainforests, wattle thickets, stringybark forests, Melaleuca woodland, and gardens across northern coastal Australia and south along the east coast to about Clarence-Macleay Rivers; migrating north in winter, some individuals reaching New Guinea. Perhaps 10 or more races; three in Australia.

The Little Bronze-Cuckoo occurs in mangroves and rainforests across northern coastal Australia.

Common Koel *Eudynamys scolopacea* (LINNÉ, 1758)

AN UNUSUAL CRISSCROSS MIGRATION seems to be undertaken by Common Koels in Australia. The smaller race that breeds across northern Australia each summer migrates northeast each year to winter in New Guinea. Crossing it, the larger form that nests down the eastern seaboard moves to and fro in the other direction to winter through Indonesia to perhaps the Philippines. Both races are present and nesting in Australia at the same time, arriving in September–October, and live in riverside scrubs, monsoon thicket, rainforest and dense pockets of eucalypts.

Koels keep to the seclusion of leafy trees and shrubs, and are often hard to observe. The females are silent and retiring, but the males are less secretive and easier to see, particularly when there is a female nearby or when they are in more open habitats around towns. Their shrill *coo-ee* calls can be heard mainly in the mornings and evenings and often at night.

Koels are usually found singly, in pairs, or in small courting groups, generally of one female and two or three males. At times they can be seen in fairly large groups, feeding in fruiting trees in association with flocks of other species.

The Common Koel does not build a nest but lays its egg in the nests of other species, including Blue-faced Honeyeaters, Red Wattlebirds, friarbirds, figbirds, orioles and magpie-larks. Female koels lay one egg in each nest, appear to choose foster parents whose eggs have a similar size, shape and colouring to their own, and time egg-laying to occur just after the host bird's. A pair of Magpie-larks have been recorded raising three successive koels in one breeding season; a pair of breeding koels may occupy a territory covering those of up to five pairs of Magpie-larks.

Koel chicks hatch after about 13 or 14 days, and they are able to monopolise the food brought by the foster parents. The other nestlings starve or are even ejected from the nest by the young koel. Although adult koels are mainly fruit-eaters, the nestlings accept insects and other food from their foster parents.

OTHER NAMES
Cooee-bird, Rainbird, Indian Koel.

IDENTIFICATION
LENGTH: *390–460 mm.*
MALE: *All dark glossy black with blue-green tinge. Eye dark red to vermilion. Bill blue-grey to cream-grey with a lighter tip, or at times greenish. Feet mid to dark grey or grey-brown.*
FEMALE: *Head glossy black with blue-green tinge. Rest of upper parts brown tinged with bronze-green, feathers indistinctly barred and tipped white; upper tail coverts, tail and flight feathers crossed with white bars. Chin and sides of face dull black; pale buff line from base of bill to throat. Centre of throat and neck washed cinnamon to buff and often mottled black. Rest of underparts and underwing coverts off-white to pale buff barred dusky brown. Eye red. Bill cream-grey. Feet grey-brown.*
IMMATURES: *Accounts differ on whether young birds resemble adults sex for sex, or whether they resemble female only. Eye dark olive-brown; bill deep buff; feet and claws blue-grey.*

VOICE
Long-drawn, upslurred whistled coo-ee *repeated monotonously in advertisement by male. In courtship or excitement, a whirling whistled crescendo by male, often introduced antiphonally by female with about four loud shrieking whistles. Also gurgles, chuckles and croaks; these are given especially by female when pursued by courting males.*

NESTING
Breeds mainly September–March, depending on rain and breeding of hosts. Parasitic. Egg: one; smooth, pink or buff, usually with slight sheen, sprinkled with spots, dots and sometimes short wavy streaks of dull purple-red, with underlying markings of purple-grey; oval, about 34 x 24 mm.

DISTRIBUTION
Breeding summer migrant across coastal and subcoastal northern and eastern Australia, occasionally straggling to northeastern Victoria and even New Zealand. Mainly in monsoon forests, rainforests and denser vegetation of river courses; also open forests, denser woodlands, paperbark swamps and mangroves. Elsewhere India and southeastern Asia to Solomons. About 15 or more races; two in Australia.

The fig-favouring Channel-billed Cuckoo has a massive, curved bill.

Channel-billed Cuckoo
Scythrops novaehollandiae LATHAM, 1790

A MASSIVE, CURVED, STRAW-COLOURED BILL together with a long barred tail identify this migratory cuckoo as it arrives from Papuasia in August–October and moves south to breed. It parasitises at least eight species, notably the Collared Sparrowhawk, White-winged Chough, Australian Magpie-lark, Australian Magpie, Pied Currawong, Australian Raven, Little Crow and Torresian Crow. When the young cuckoos hatch they do not, like other cuckoos, kick out the host's eggs or young and yet rarely do these survive. It is likely that the faster-growing cuckoo nestlings out-compete the young of the host which decline, die and are removed by the parents. Only the late nests of the hosts to the south are parasitised, however, because the Channel-billed Cuckoos arrive after Pied Currawongs have begun nesting.

The Channel-billed Cuckoo is unusual not only for its bulk but also because it is a fruit-eater favouring ripe figs. They also select other fruit and berries, occasionally eggs and young of other birds, as well as large insects; wings and tail are spread as the cuckoo reaches out to pluck an insect, such as a stick insect, from foliage. While breeding they are solitary or in territorial pairs, but later may gather in small foraging flocks.

A courtship display precedes copulation: in response to the female's quiet reedy trumpetings from a high branch, the male offers an insect; as he approaches, she squats low on the branch and spreads her wings; then he mounts and she takes the food.

OTHER NAMES
Storm Bird, Fig Hawk, Flood Bird.

IDENTIFICATION
LENGTH: *580–650 mm.*
ADULTS: *Sexes similar; male slightly larger. Head, nape, throat and breast light to mid smoky grey; belly, abdomen and vent inclining towards white with indistinct barring on lower abdomen, darker blackish-brown on flanks. Wings, back, rump and tail darker grey; all feathers broadly margined with black-brown, more so on the flight feathers; central two tail feathers tipped white with a broad subterminal blackish brown bar; outer tail feathers exhibit more extensive white tipping and are marked with alternate cream-white toothing and black-brown bars on inner webs. Underwing and tail similar but lighter than above. Eye bright scarlet-red-brown; facial skin deep pink-scarlet to maroon. Bill large and toucan-like— 55–70 mm from nostril to tip—pale to mid greyish brown with whitish tip and notched edges; inside mouth deep pink to pinkish white. Feet plumbeous grey to deep pink-scarlet.*
IMMATURES: *Head, mantle, nape, throat and breast mid to deep buff verging on golden. Rest of undersurface light cinnamon to creamy white barred with narrow blackish brown bars. Wings, back and rump mid grey-brown, tipped with light to mid russet-brown and indistinct darker brown subterminal bars; flight feathers darker grey (greenish sheen) broadly tipped with light brown passing into white. Less distinctly barred tail. Eye olive to chestnut-brown; facial skin greyish brown. Bill 45–60 mm, light bluish grey to greyish horn tipped white. Feet mid-grey to pale greyish green.*

VOICE
Loud raucous deliberately spaced shout: awk, wark *or* kawk-awk-awk-awk *—the first syllable loud and pronounced, the remainder quickening and lower in pitch or rising. Uttered from perch or in flight, both day and night.*

NESTING
Breeds August–December. Parasitic. Eggs: usually one–two; slightly glossy, dull white to yellowish or reddish brown, spotted and blotched with light to mid-brown and lavender; rounded-oval, about 43 x 29 mm.

DISTRIBUTION
Coastal and subcoastal northern and eastern Australia, from Kimberleys to Bega, NSW, and inland irregularly to Lake Eyre drainage. Migratory, arriving through August–October and departing January–March to winter from New Guinea to Flores and Sulawesi. Frequents tall timber areas, especially along watercourses and rainforest streams, particularly where fig trees abound. No races.

A glossy black male Common Koel. Fruit-eaters, they have been seen feeding in association with Channel-billed Cuckoos, figbirds and various pigeons.

Pheasant Coucal *Centropus phasianinus* (LATHAM, 1801)

OTHER NAMES
Swamp Pheasant, Coucal.

IDENTIFICATION
LENGTH: *Male 500–600 mm; female 600–700 mm.*
ADULTS: *Sexes alike. In breeding plumage head to back sooty black with shiny black feather shafts. Back dull black with faint buff bars. Shoulders and wings barred and mottled with russet-brown, black and buff, with a* paler straw colour on shoulders. Tail brown with black mottling and buff bars; outer tail feathers sooty black, with sandy buff tips. Throat and upper breast sooty black with shiny black feather shafts; rest of underparts dull black. In eclipse plumage, head to mantle straw-chestnut, with feather shafts glossy straw. Back sooty black with faint buff bars. Tail dark brown, mottled and barred with rufous to buff. Throat and breast pale straw,* shading to patchy buff and black on belly and undertail coverts. Eye red. Bill light horn or black when breeding. Feet grey.*
IMMATURES: *Mottled with black and tan all over, with rufous on primaries.*
DOWNY YOUNG: *Shiny black-skinned, covered in coarse white threads, the sheaths of the developing feathers. Eyes dull black; inside of mouth orange, tongue orange-scarlet with a shiny black tip. Pin-feather sheaths* drop off after about six–seven days as fledglings become covered with mottled black and brown feathers.*

VOICE
Many times repeated hollow oop, *falling, then rising slightly and accelerating in series of up to 12 notes; a short, sharp, dog-like yelp;* nah-oo, nah-oo *in alarm; harsh scolding in threat. Female's voice deeper than male's. Young trill* pssch *and click.*

NESTING
Breeds mostly October–March. Nest built on platform in tussock 100–600 mm above ground, of twigs and green leaves with surrounding plants pulled down to form canopy. Built in thick grass, reeds, rank growth, a small leafy bush or a clump of pandanus palms. Eggs: two–five; slightly lustrous, chalky texture; dirty white; rounded to long-oval, about 38 x 29 mm. Incubation about 15 days, by both sexes. Young fledge in 12–15 days.

DISTRIBUTION
Wetter coastal and subcoastal areas of northern and eastern Australia, from the Pilbara (Ashburton–Fortescue Rivers) to Cape York Peninsula, ranging inland to Mataranka and MacArthur River, then south along the Great Divide to Jervis Bay, ACT. The Pilbara population is isolated from the Kimberley population by the Great Sandy Desert. Sedentary in deeply grassed woodlands and open forest. Also in New Guinea, D'Entrecasteaux Archipelago and Timor. Six races; two in Australia.

UNLIKE OTHER CUCKOOS the Pheasant Coucal, a long-tailed bird which lives mainly on the ground, builds its own nest and rears its young. After rain, heavy dew or hunting in wet undergrowth, it commonly perches on a low bush or a post, spreading its long loose plumage to dry—to restore its limited powers of flight. Then the coucal climbs in a series of leaps to the top of a tree and planes from one tree to another in long glides, fluttering and flopping sporadically on shortly rounded wings, long tail trailing.

A Pheasant Coucal in breeding plumage.

To collect nesting material, male and female climb trees, break off small leafy branchlets and let them drop to the ground. They then drag the branchlets through the undergrowth to the nest site. To return to the source of the branchlets, the birds fly from one bush to another, gradually gaining height until they reach the leaves.

At the nest site the birds tramp down the centre of a clump of plants and form a platform. On this they form the nest by piling leafy green twigs up to about 100 mm high. More twigs are added as incubation proceeds, then the parents pull down the tops of surrounding plants to form a roof over the nest, leaving two side entrances. On a sparsely vegetated site the birds may not make a dome, relying instead on adjacent grasses and herbs for protection. Both parents incubate, the head and tail of the sitting bird protruding through the opening of the nest.

Coucals may breed twice a season in close succession, building another nest, laying and incubating a second clutch while the first brood is still being fed nearby. The young of the first brood are driven from the area before the second brood is very old.

Pheasant Coucals eat small reptiles, frogs, house mice, young water rats and bandicoots, large insects, eggs, young birds and even crabs that are snatched from among the mangroves at low tide. These the bird takes by searching, running and threading along in an almost reptile-like manner. Much of its hunting is done under cover of a sward of rank grass field, wherein it holds territories while breeding and about which it wanders locally afterwards.

The Powerful Owl preys on possums and other small mammals.

Powerful Owl *Ninox strenua* (Gould, 1838)

OTHER NAMES
None.

IDENTIFICATION
LENGTH: *600–650 mm.*
ADULTS: *Sexes similar; male larger. Upper parts dark grey-brown barred with white and pale brown, the barring finer on crown and coarser on wings and tail. Face mask incomplete, dark grey-brown with white streaks. Throat and underparts cream or pale buff barred with grey-brown chevron-shaped markings. Eye orange-yellow. Bill bone-grey grading to black at tip; cere bone-grey. Toes creamy yellow; claws dark grey.*
IMMATURES: *Similar to adults.*
DOWNY YOUNG: *White-downed.*

VOICE
Territorial call, by both sexes, a mournful, loud, slow woo-hoo *on the same pitch or slightly rising, with about 10 seconds between each hoot, given through closed bill. Male's call lower pitched and slower than that of female. Courting male and female rumble, rasp, and males give pulsating* poorp-poorp-poorp. *Nestlings beg with shrill trill.*

NESTING
Breeds May–October, laying May–early June; one brood a year. Nest a 50–180 cm deep hollow 12–40 m above ground in trunk of towering eucalypt, lined with wood debris and prepared by male. Eggs: two, laid four nights apart; pure white; rounded, 50–50 x about 45 mm. Incubation 35–38 days, by female, beginning with laying of first egg. Young fledge in eight–nine weeks. Female given food outside nest by male and passed by her alone to young during brooding.

DISTRIBUTION
Southeastern South Australia, to Dawson River, near Rockhampton, Qld, mostly in wet sclerophyll forest along coast hills and Great Dividing Range. No races.

SHY BIRDS, POWERFUL OWLS live in pairs and keep to large permanent territories of 800–1000 hectares. They roost by day, heads erect, in tall forest trees which give them a commanding view of their surroundings. Each pair has a number of roosting trees and the birds roost on different trees on different days, not always together, but always within calling distance. The mournful *woo-hoo* of the Powerful Owl may be heard at any time of the year, but the birds are more vocal during the breeding season, particularly just after dusk and just before dawn. They sometimes begin calling before sunset.

At night, the Powerful Owl preys on birds and mammals. Its diet consists mainly of small to medium-sized tree-living mammals, especially the Great Glider *Petauroides volans* and the Common Ringtail Possum *Pseudocheirus peregrinus*. These it snatches from foliage and branches in banking swoops through the forest midstage. It also eats Sugar Gliders *Petaurus breviceps* and, less often, young Common Brushtail Possums *Trichosurus vulpecula*. Rats, birds, and young rabbits are also taken. It tears its prey apart and eats it by the piece, usually beginning with the head which it often swallows whole. Sometimes it will take the rear end of the animal back to its roost, carefully place it on the branch and hold it all day in its talons, then eat it before leaving the roost in the evening. The owls need to eat the equivalent of a large possum every two–three days to survive.

Rufous Owl *Ninox rufa* (Gould, 1846)

OTHER NAMES
None.

IDENTIFICATION
LENGTH: *450–550 mm.*
ADULTS: *Sexes similar; male slightly larger. Upper parts dark brown with fine pale cream bars; barring much coarser on wings and tail. Underparts pale buff with fine rufous-brown bars. Sides of face dark; dusky mask around eye. Eye lemon. Bill and cere bluish white. Toes yellow; claws slate-black.*
IMMATURES: *Similar to adults.*
DOWNY YOUNG: *White-downed, with flesh-white feet.*

VOICE
Territorial call a mournful woo-hoo, *similar to Powerful Owl's call but softer and slightly falling, given mainly in months opening nesting. Both sexes hum, twitter and chirrup in courtship. Nestlings beg with coarse trilled whistles.*

NESTING
Breeds June–September, one brood a year. Nest a vertical or steeply sloping deep hollow in trunk of tall eucalypt or paperbark, 8–40 m high; access gained from side; lined with wood debris and dead leaves, cleaned out and prepared by both sexes; same nest used repeatedly. *Eggs: two (or one), laid at two–three night intervals; creamy white; rounded, 50–55 x 45–50 mm. Incubation 36–38 days, by female; she is fed outside nest by male. Young fledge in six–eight weeks.*

DISTRIBUTION
Three races: one in coastal northeastern Queensland north to Cooktown (dark and small); another in coastal Cape York Peninsula (pale and small); a third in coastal Arnhem Land and the Kimberleys (large and pale). Also in New Guinea.

THE CHIEF FOOD OF THE rarely seen Rufous Owl is birds and arboreal mammals, such as the Sugar Glider *Petaurus breviceps* and flying-fox *Pteropus* which it snatches from the foliage and branches of trees with its talons. Its silent, quick-flapping flight is

The Rufous Owl is a forest-dweller about which little is known.

interspersed with long glides and well-suited to planing onto prey. It also seizes and eats large beetles and stick insects.

It seem to hold large and permanent territories in rainforest and similar dense forests, and hunts by night out into adjacent eucalypt forest and woodland. During the day it roosts, singly or in pairs, in leafy trees that command a view of its surroundings. At the roost it often holds the remains of a kill. Each pair appears to have a number of roosts. The Rufous Owl is a secretive bird and usually slips away from its daytime roost when an intruder approaches, but during the breeding season it defends its nest vigorously.

Southern Boobook *Ninox boobook* (LATHAM, 1801)

The Southern Boobook, the smallest and most common Australian owl, is also the most widespread, reaching New Guinea and Indonesia.

THE SOUTHERN BOOBOOK — often called a 'mopoke' after its call—is the smallest and most abundant of the Australian owls. It can live in all types of country from dense forest to desert, and it is found in towns and suburbs with abundant trees. It is not often seen, however, and the chief evidence of its presence is its characteristic call.

Boobooks are rather nomadic and have daytime roosts, generally in the dense foliage of a tree, but sometimes in a cave where trees are not plentiful. They live in pairs, but usually only single birds are seen roosting. Each bird or pair has a number of roosts while it is feeding locally, usually in a territory of up to 10 hectares.

The Southern Boobook does not often fly off when people walk past. At the approach of an intruder the bird will sit bolt upright with its feathers pressed tight against its body. Then it turns side-on, and appears very long and slender. The position of a roosting boobook is often betrayed by the persistent mobbing calls of birds that discover it.

Boobooks eat birds up to the size of a House Sparrow, and small mammals, especially the House Mouse *Mus musculus*. They also eat more invertebrates than other Australian owls, and night-flying beetles and moths are important in their diet. They have even been seen catching large moths flying around street lights. Most feeding is done in the first hour or two after dusk and the hours before sunrise, when they also bathe. As breeding approaches, pairs of boobooks establish their nesting territory with much territorial hooting, particularly after dusk and before dawn. Like other *Ninox* owls, each mated pair courts side by side on a perch, bubbling, purring, nibbling and preening one another. Whether they pair permanently has not yet been established.

Southern Boobooks are often thought to belong to the same species as New Zealand Boobooks *Ninox novaeseelandiae* which are found also on Lord Howe and Norfolk Islands. Southern Boobooks do resemble the New Zealand owls in their cryptically toned plumage— perhaps convergingly — but are quite different in shape: their tails are much stubbier and their wings more tapered.

OTHER NAMES
Spotted Owl, Boobook Owl, Mopoke.

IDENTIFICATION
LENGTH: *250–350 mm.*
ADULTS: *Sexes similar; female slightly larger, with richer brown on back, more streaked ventrally and sometimes more spotted white on head. Upper parts pale to dark brown, depending on geographical race; shoulders and back usually with white spots. Flight feathers and tail dull-barred light and dark brown. Underparts dull white mottled and streaked pale to dark brown. Facial disc indistinct, usually much duskier than body colour, with distinct white frons. Eye orange-yellow to pale green-yellow. Bill and cere blue-grey, tipped black. Toes pale leaden to white or yellow in Tasmania; claws black.*
IMMATURES: *Similar to adults, but paler and more streaked and spotted.*
DOWNY YOUNG: *White-downed, with powder blue eyes.*

VOICE
Two-syllable territorial hoot boo-book, mo-poke, *or* more-pork, *the second note pitched lower than the first, given by both sexes through closed bill from set perch, carries a kilometre or more. Also low trilling calls for contact and screams in aggression. Immatures beg with whistling cricket-like trill.*

NESTING
Breeds August–January; one brood per season. Nest a 50–250 cm deep hollow in living or dead tree 3–25 m above ground; cleaned and prepared with bed of wood chips, leaves and twigs by male, attended by female. Eggs: two–three or four, each laid at two–three nightly intervals; plain white; rounded, 40–45 x about 35 mm. Incubation 26–33 days, by female, beginning with laying of first egg. Female fed with food brought by male outside nest. Young fledge in five–six weeks; fed by both parents then and, perhaps, by additional 'helper' adults.

DISTRIBUTION
Australia-wide, including Tasmania, in all wooded habitats; also in New Guinea and islands in Timor–Banda Sea. Introduced unsuccessfully on Lord Howe Island. Four Australian races: one large and rather deep brown in eucalypt forests and woods of east coast north to foot of Cape York Peninsula, and west to far fringes of Great Dividing Range, Mt Lofty–Flinders Ranges, and Kangaroo Island, SA; one small and paler rufous to sandy-brown throughout remainder of mainland and north coast islands; one small, moderately dark and extensively spotted white over head and back in Tasmania and Bass Strait islands; the last small and very dark chocolate with plain back and dull spotting, not streaks, ventrally, in and on the edges of rainforest in northeastern Queensland. Tasmanian race has migrated to mainland in past winters.

Barking Owl *Ninox connivens* (Latham, 1801)

THE BARKING OF THIS NOISY OWL is one of the pleasant night sounds of the Australian bush all year round. But occasionally, usually in autumn, it produces a rather terrifyingly loud, high-pitched, tremulous scream that has earned it the name 'screaming-woman' bird. The familiar barking signals territory, which mated male and female commonly advertise with quick-fire call-and-answer duets just as they rise each evening and again before going to roost at daybreak.

The Barking Owl may be found around houses in the country. It is the least nocturnal and most hawk-like of Australian owls, sometimes calling during daytime and on duller winter days sometimes beginning to hunt before sunset. Prey is seized on the ground, from trees and in the air.

The Barking Owl is found in forest and woodland and is most common in savanna woodland. It sometimes roosts in rainforest, but it needs the more open country for hunting and hollow eucalypts for breeding. It is quite common, particularly in northern Australia.

Although hunting widely, Barking Owls are usually found in pairs which occupy 30–200-hectare territories all year round. Each pair has a number of sites where they roost by day — usually in a leafy tree in a copse, but not always well hidden. When three or four Barking Owls are seen roosting together, the extra birds are the young of that year.

Mammals and birds are the chief prey of the Barking Owl, and it also feeds on insects and other invertebrates, capturing all with its talons. In southern Australia it feeds particularly on rabbits. It also takes young hares, rats, mice, occasional small bats and some marsupials, including possums. Birds up to the size of magpies and Tawny Frogmouths are killed as well. Any prey too big to be swallowed whole is torn up and eaten piece by piece, beginning with the head. The rear parts of the victims are sometimes found with cast pellets beneath roost trees.

OTHER NAMES
Winking Owl, Screaming Woman.

IDENTIFICATION
LENGTH: *350–450 mm.*
ADULTS: *Sexes similar; male slightly larger. Upper parts mid to dark grey or grey-brown, some white blotches on wing coverts and scapulars. Tail and flight feathers grey-brown with grey-white bars and tip. Underparts white, boldly shaft-streaked dark grey-brown to (in north) russet-brown. Face mask obscure, grey like crown, with small white frons. Eye yellow. Bill and cere olive-yellow to grey with dark tip. Toes dull yellow; claws grey-black.*
IMMATURES: *Similar to adults, but ventral streaking lighter and fine mottling on nape.*
DOWNY YOUNG: *Cream-white downed, with greenish eyes and whitish toes.*

VOICE
Repetitive rapid two-note bark, wook-wook, the second note lower pitched, and the first prefaced with a barely audible growl; given from a perch through closed bill. Male's call lower and slower than female's. Chorus of barking may be interspersed with growling sounds. Occasionally a loud high-pitched tremulous scream. A growl if intruders approach nest. Young and brooding females beg food with a continuous grating trill. Soft rabbit-like squeaking during copulation.

NESTING
Breeds July–November, earlier in north; one brood per season. Nest an open hollow 20–250 cm deep in trunk or spout of tree at 3–30 m above ground; selected and excavated by male, preparing a flat bed of wood debris for eggs. Eggs: two–three, laid two–three nights apart; pure white; rounded, 45–50 x 35–40 mm. Incubation 34–38 days, by female; she is fed outside nest each evening by male. Young fledge in about seven weeks.

DISTRIBUTION
Well-forested hills and flats, eucalypt savanna, and riverine woodland in coastal and subcoastal eastern, northern and southwestern mainland Australia. Two races: one large and dark in southwestern and eastern Australia north to foot of Cape York Peninsula, the other smaller, paler and more russet across northern Australia east to Cape York Peninsula and southwest to the Pilbara, WA.

The Barking Owl spends the day roosting in a leafy tree. It is the least nocturnal of Australian owls, and sometimes begins to hunt before sunset.

Sooty Owl _Tyto tenebricosa_ (GOULD, 1845)

THE RARELY SEEN SOOTY OWL has the largest eyes and roundest wings of all the masked-owls, attributes that are well-fitted for its life in the dimly lit gully rainforests of southeastern Australia. Like the Masked Owl, it seems to pair permanently and to hold the same

The Sooty Owl has the largest eyes of all the masked-owls.

OTHER NAMES
None.

IDENTIFICATION
LENGTH: _Male 370–430 mm; female 450–500 mm, with much larger talons._
ADULTS: _Sexes similar. Upper parts sooty black finely speckled with white spots. Flight feathers unbarred, the third and fourth outermost longest. Tail dusky with six–seven obscure bars. Facial disc pale grey or brown; edge of disc complete and black. Underparts sooty black with white spots and small irregular grey bars. Feathers on feet dense and furry. Eye dusky. Bill grey; cere flesh. Toes and claws grey._
IMMATURES: _Similar to adults or paler ventrally._
DOWNY YOUNG: _First short, white-downed; later long and sooty grey._

VOICE
Loud, descending whistling screech, apparently a territorial call. Also variety of whistles, churs, twitters and rasps in courtship. Young beg with prolonged rasps.

NESTING
Breeds erratically, at any time, but only one brood a year. Nest a roomy, 40–500

territory—about 200 to 800 hectares—year in, year out. The pair roost apart by day, on one of a number of set perches through their territory: a deep hollow, the interlacing stems of a giant fig, or a crevice under a bank or cliff.

Soon after dusk, the owls are abroad hunting, flitting through the forest and along its edge, picking off possums and gliders from branches, and rats, bandicoots and other mammals from the ground; birds are sometimes taken too. Like other masked-owls, they bolt their food, ripping off and swallowing the head first.

As breeding approaches, male and female call to one another on rising and often join in a tree for a prolonged duet of whistling, chattering, churring and rasping, interspersed with their amazing territorial call: a siren-like descending whistle, sounding like a falling bomb. If cornered, they crouch, spread their wings, sway from side to side, and hiss and snap.

cm deep hollow, usually in a tall eucalypt in or on edge of rainforest; prepared by both sexes and used repeatedly. Eggs: one, usually two, laid at four-night intervals on bed of rotten wood debris, pellets and fur; pure white; ellipsoidal, 45–50 x 35–40 mm. Incubation about six weeks, by female; male brings food to nest each night, ceasing territorial calling. Young fledge in about 12 weeks.

DISTRIBUTION
Rainforests, particularly rainforest gullies overtopped by eucalypts, along eastern scarp of Great Dividing Range, north to Conondale–Blackall Ranges, Qld, and south to Dandenong Ranges, Vic. Odd records from Grampians, Vic, and Furneaux group, Bass Strait. One

race in Australia and another, smaller, in montane New Guinea.

Lesser Sooty Owl

Tyto multipunctata MATHEWS, 1912

OTHER NAMES
None.

IDENTIFICATION
LENGTH: _Male 310–350 mm; female 350–380 mm, with marginally larger talons._
ADULTS: _Sexes similar. Upper parts cold grey-black, coarsely spotted with white. Flight feathers flecked grey-white and barred plain grey-black, the third and fourth outermost longest. Tail flecked grey-white, with six–seven clear blackish bars. Facial disc greyish white grading to dark grey around eyes; edge of disc complete and black spotted with white. Underparts grey-white, closely marked with grey-black chevrons. Feathering on feet dense and furry. Eye dusky. Bill bone-grey; cere pale flesh. Toes flesh-grey; claws darker grey._
IMMATURES: _Similar to adults, or whiter-bellied._
DOWNY YOUNG: _First short white-downed, later long and grey._

VOICE
Territorial call a piercing, descending whistle, as from a falling bomb; given through open bill by both sexes from a perch. Insistent duets of twitterings, rasps, churs during courtship, initiated by male.

NESTING
Probably little different from Sooty Owl; apparently breeds July–September, usually moulting October–November. Nest a vertical 200–300 cm deep hollow 10–30 m above ground, usually in rainforest trees and figs, rarely a eucalypt, in or on the edge of rainforest. Eggs: one, usually two; white; more rounded than in other masked-owls, 41–42 x 36–39 mm.

DISTRIBUTION
Rainforests of northeastern Queensland, mainly above 300 m altitude, north to Mt Finnegan, south to Paluma Range, and inland to Windsor and Atherton Tablelands. No races.

The Lesser Sooty Owl of northeastern Queensland rainforests.

THE LESSER SOOTY OWL REPLACES the Sooty Owl in northeastern Queensland, living in much the same habitat—big stands of rainforest—and having much the same habits. They mate permanently and hold territory—a hundred or so hectares—throughout the year. Except when breeding, however, a male and female may stay apart, roosting and hunting in different sectors of their territory. Both have three or four set roosts, usually underneath an overhanging bank or the chimneys and passages in the interlacing trunks of figs. These they use in rotation, judged by the cast pellets and excreta found under them.

Lesser Sooty Owls are versatile hunters, taking a wide range of terrestrial rodents, bandicoots, arboreal possums and gliders from all strata of the forest. Even frogs, geckos and birds figure in their diet, but rarely insects. Their manner of hunting is simple but effective: the owls sit watching on exposed branches at the edges of clearings or openings in the forest, then fly out to pounce on prey on the ground, trunks or branches. Except for occasional bouts of territorial screaming from set perches they are rather silent. The approach of breeding, however, is heralded by a build-up of noisy duets from May through July. Upon rising after dusk and again before going to roost towards dawn, male and female call to one another and join in a high forest tree to chirrup, rasp, twitter and scream for an hour or more.

That the Lesser Sooty Owl is a species distinct from the Sooty will always be debated. Yet it is not only smaller, with little difference between the sexes, but also differently marked: the back is much more heavily spotted with white, the flight feathers are clearly barred, and the underparts are white chevroned with clear dark grey, not sooty and spotted with white as in the Sooty Owl.

Barn Owl *Tyto alba* (SCOPOLI, 1769)

THE ALMOST COSMOPOLITAN BARN OWL is not often seen in Australia except when car headlights reveal it as a ghostly white form flashing across country roads at night. Nor is it often heard, because it calls infrequently, but it is common in many places.

Open wooded country and grass plains rather than forest are the habitats where Barn Owls are most abundant. They are nomadic birds, their numbers rising and falling dramatically with variations in their food supply. A plague of house mice or a few species of native rodents will lead Barn Owls to concentrate in the infested area and to breed in every available hollow. No territory is held and up to four or five nests have been found in a single tree. After the plague collapses, many dead bodies of emaciated Barn Owls tell their own story. Dead Barn Owls are also found during hard winters in the colder parts of Australia.

In southern Australia the House Mouse *Mus musculus* has become the chief prey of the Barn Owl. Hunting birds usually quarter open country close to the ground, flying with a steady but silent flapping; or they listen from a low perch. From there they glide or drop on to the prey and usually swallow it whole. Their diet also includes other rodents, some marsupials, small birds, lizards and night-flying insects, particularly beetles and moths.

Many regurgitated pellets of the indigestible parts of prey are found beneath daytime roosts and in the nests of Barn Owls. These pellets and uneaten food make the nest a stinking affair.

Barn Owls live alone or in pairs. They roost quietly by day, heads erect, in places such as tree hollows, thickly foliaged trees, caves and rock crevices, buildings and even wells. Their reaction to the approach of an intruder is to stand bolt upright with partly closed eyes and look very slender. If cornered, they react by crouching, fluffing up their feathers and spreading their wings, swaying from side to side, snapping their bills and hissing.

OTHER NAMES
Delicate Owl, Screech Owl, White Owl.

IDENTIFICATION
LENGTH: *300–400 mm.*
ADULTS: *Sexes similar; female slightly more spotted black ventrally. Upper parts pearl-grey washed gold with numerous fine black spots tipped white. Flight feathers dull-barred dark grey, the three outermost longest. Tail feathers pale buff with four dark grey bars and fine flecks. Facial disc white with chestnut mark around eye; buff and black border to facial disc. Underparts white with dusky flecks at tips of some feathers. Feathers on lower parts of feet usually reduced to few sparse bristles. Eye dusky. Small bill bone-white; cere flesh. Toes pale yellow-brown to flesh; claws dusky.*
IMMATURES: *Similar to adults, but more dusky-spotted ventrally.*
DOWNY YOUNG: *First short white-downed; later dense, long, cream-downed.*

VOICE
Contact call an infrequent loud, drawn-out rasping screech, uttered in flight through open bill. Male and female chitter, squeak and snore in courtship. Young beg with soft rasps.

NESTING
Breeds mainly autumn–spring, but in any month depending on food supply. Mating temporary, for duration of

single nesting. *Usually nests in a deep tree hollow, but also in caves, poorly lined with wood debris, leaves and old pellets. Eggs: three to seven, laid on alternate nights; white; ellipsoidal, about 43 x 32 mm. Incubation 33–35 days, by female. Young, fed first by female and later by male as well, fledge in nine–ten weeks.*

DISTRIBUTION
In all parts of Australia, particularly open wooded country. Single grey Australian race straggles to New Zealand and other islands in southwestern Pacific. Other races occur in New Guinea, Indonesia, Eurasia, Africa and North and South America.

Grass Owls live in remote heaths and grasslands; they are not often seen.

Grass Owl *Tyto capensis* (SMITH, 1834)

OTHER NAMES
Eastern Grass Owl.

IDENTIFICATION
LENGTH: *320–380 mm.*
ADULTS: *Sexes similar; female rather larger. Upper parts patchy chocolate-brown and tawny, with fine white tips to feathers. Flight feathers barred tawny and dark brown, the three outermost longest. Tail whitish, with four, rarely five dark bars. Facial disc white to pale tawny, with patch of chestnut around front of eyes; facial disc bordered by often incomplete ring of chestnut-brown. Underparts cream-white or pale buff, with some brown spots. Eye dusky, small. Bill bone; cere flesh. Feet grey-brown; feathers on lower half reduced to few bristles; claws dark.*
IMMATURES: *Similar to adults.*
DOWNY YOUNG: *First short white-downed; later long tawny-gold-downed.*

VOICE
Usually silent. A harsh, rasping screech in contact. Twittering and chirruping in courtship. Young beg with soft rasp. Also hiss and bill-snap in Masked Owl-like defence.

NESTING
Breeds any time, but mainly March–June after monsoonal rains; sometimes nests in loose community. Mating apparently temporary. Nest a scrape or platform of plant stems under tussock, entered by up to 10 m long tunnel under vegetation. Eggs: three–eight, laid on alternate nights; dull white; ellipsoidal, 40–45 x 30–33 mm. Incubation by female; male roosts with her by day and brings food by night. Young, fed by both parents after four–five weeks, are able to fly at two months and roost in tunnels outside nest in preceding weeks.

DISTRIBUTION
Grasslands and heaths of coastal eastern Queensland south to Manning River, NSW; and grass banks and reed beds of Barkly Tableland and channel country, western Queensland. Disperses south to Victoria and northwest to coastal Arnhem Land and Kimberleys. No races; Australian race also through Indonesia to southeastern Asia. Other races in Africa and montane New Guinea.

LIKE THE BARN OWL, the Grass Owl is a nomadic wanderer and preys on small nocturnal ground mammals. However, it is much more limited in its range and habitat, living only in coastal heath and flood-plain grasslands across northern Australia. There seem to be two main populations, one throughout coastal eastern Queensland into northeastern New South Wales, the other on the Barkly Tableland and channel country of western Queensland and the Northern Territory. Wandering parties occasionally reach the Murray–Darling plains and Port Phillip or settle on the flood-plains of western Arnhem Land but do not often remain long. No wonder Grass Owls are rarely seen.

The coastal population seems moderately stable and permanent, preying mainly on the Canefield Rat *Rattus sordidus,* and other rodents. The owls roost alone by day in squats on the ground entered by runways beneath undergrowth. At dusk they rise to spend much of the night quartering their hunting fields silently on steadily beating wings, at about five–25 metres above the ground. Locating prey by sight or sound, they plummet onto it talons first, and bolt it down on the spot, cutting out the entrails, then nipping off and swallowing the head, and finally breaking and consuming the body.

The inland population, however, fluctuates with the remarkable rises and falls of its primary prey, the Long-haired Rat *Rattus villosissimus.* In plague years the owls breed up on the rats in lignum- and reed-beds where they roost. When the plagues crash, so do the Grass Owls, either perishing or dispersing as far afield as Darwin or Melbourne.

It is often thought that Grass Owls can be identified from Barn Owls by the dangling of their long legs on flushing and landing; but Barn Owls also do this. Much more reliable is the tone of the back: patchy tawny-brown in the Grass Owl and freckled pearl-grey in the Barn Owl.

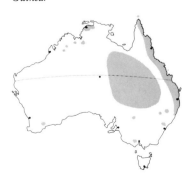

Three Barn Owl fledglings peer out from their nest in a tree hole. Barn Owls are found in all parts of Australia, particularly in open wooded country.

Masked Owl _Tyto novaehollandiae_ (STEPHENS, 1826)

This is a female of the Tasmanian race of Masked Owl. It is over 550 mm long—the largest of all Masked Owls.

OTHER NAMES
Cave Owl, Chestnut-faced Owl.

IDENTIFICATION
LENGTH: _Male about 350–400 mm,
with much smaller talons; female 400-
500 mm; over 550 mm in Tasmania._
ADULTS: _Sexes similar; male paler.
Upper parts light dusky washed
ochreish and finely speckled with white
to grey-white boldly flecked with dusky
grey. Flight feathers dull-barred dusky
grey, the second and third outermost
longest. Tail feathers with six to seven
dark grey bars and mottlings. Facial
disc tawny to white, with patch of dark
chestnut around front of eyes; complete
chestnut and black border ring to facial
disc. Underparts tawny-ochre with
extensive dusky spots and chevrons or
white with sparse dusky grey spots.
Feathers on lower parts of feet dense and
furry, sparse only in far northern
Australia. Three basic phases in
plumage: (1) dark tawny, with dusky
back toned tawny and faintly spotted
white, rich ochreish face and ventral
surface; (2) intermediate, with dusky
back toned pale tawny and coarsely
spotted white, whitish face and ventral
surface; (3) white, with grey-white
back coarsely speckled grey-and-white,
white face and ventral surface. Eye
dusky. Bill bone-white; cere flesh-white.
Toes pale to mid grey-brown; claws
darker._
IMMATURES: _Similar to adults._
DOWNY YOUNG: _First short white-
downed; later long, cream-downed._

VOICE
_Drawn-out, rasping screech similar to
call of Barn Owl, often in flight; also
chattering, ticking and rattling._

NESTING
_Breeds erratically, at any time. Nest a
40–500 cm deep, vertical hollow in tall
eucalypt, or ledges in caves, prepared by
male and used in successive years.
Eggs: usually two–three, laid on
alternate nights; off-white; ellipsoidal,
43–50 x 35–38 mm. Incubation about
35 days, by female; she is fed in nest by
male each night. Young, brooded by
female for first two–three weeks and
then fed by both adults, fledge in
10–12 weeks._

DISTRIBUTION
_All coastal and subcoastal Australia
except Eighty-mile Beach and
Kangaroo Island, in eucalypt forests
and denser woodlands. Five races: one
large and dark-phased, with some
males medium-phased in Tasmania
and Bass Strait islands; one medium-
sized, dark- and paler-phased in
females, and about equally
intermediate- and white-phased in
males throughout southern Australia
north to the Pilbara and foot of Cape
York Peninsula; one medium-sized with
sparsely feathered feet and only
intermediate- and white-phased in the
Kimberleys and Arnhem Land east to
the Gulf of Carpentaria; one like
Kimberley-Arnhem Land race but
smaller on Cape York Peninsula; one
small but in dark- and intermediate
phases on Melville Island._

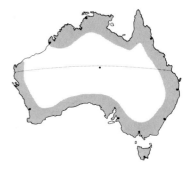

SUPERFICIALLY, THE MASKED OWL looks like a big, heavy Barn Owl. It roosts in the same places: big hollows in trees, crevices in cliffs and even caves, but rarely heavy foliage like the _Ninox_ owls. It reacts in the same way if cornered, crouching, spreading its wings, swaying from side to side, and hissing, snapping and rasping. And it hunts in the same way, quartering forest country and clearings low on the wing or listening from low perches, sometimes even standing motionless on the ground.

The Masked Owl also takes similar, but larger prey: mainly small terrestrial mammals up to the size of a rabbit, varied with occasional possums and medium-sized birds such as magpies and kookaburras. If too heavy to lift, large prey is eaten on the spot, but otherwise it is carried off in the bill or feet to a perch or the roost. Small kills are bolted whole but larger ones are usually torn into manageable strips, beginning with the

head. Rabbits have become the main prey of the very large race in Tasmania.

There the similarities to Barn Owls end. Masked Owls usually keep to heavier forested eucalypt country, never more than 300 kilometres inland from the coast. They also seem to mate permanently and hold to the same territory all year round. When rising each evening, male and female join each other from separate roosts, purring, chattering and chuckling in greeting in the way that Sooty Owls do. The great difference in size between them, particularly the feet, may help them take prey of different size.

The approach of breeding is signalled by much twittering from both birds around the nest hollow, led by the male; before mating they go through elaborate head-bobbing and wing-waving. To enter the nest hollow they slide down tail-first: a characteristic of the whole masked-owl group, Barn and Sooty Owls included.

Papuan Frogmouth *Podargus papuensis* QUOY & GAIMARD, 1830

BIGGEST OF THE FROGMOUTHS, with a huge wide bill, the Papuan Frogmouth also handles a larger range of prey, from large nocturnal beetles and grasshoppers—its main food—to spiders, myriapods, caterpillars, lizards, frogs, rodents and even small birds. These it catches at night in methodical sorties through its foraging territory—only about 20–30 hectares—by perch-and-pounce sallying. It flies from low perch to low perch looking for movement and, seeing it, planes down on to the kill on the ground or tree trunk, snaps it up in the bill, and returns to a perch to bash, crush and eat it.

Throughout their range around the fringes of Cape York Peninsula, Papuan Frogmouths hunt along the edges of rainforest and out in adjacent woodland. There they slot into a feeding niche between the Marbled Frogmouth within

rainforest and Tawny Frogmouth which lives only in eucalypts and mulga scrubs inland.

By day Papuan Frogmouths roost in deeper cover within rainforest galleries and even mangroves, either propped against a vertical trunk or perched lengthwise along a horizontal fork or branch some 10–30 metres above the ground. At the approach of potential danger the birds freeze in a broken stick pose, their dappled russet plumage compacted and blending into the broken background vegetation.

Contrary to popular belief, Papuan Frogmouths are sedentary birds and keep to the same territory year round, using the same favoured roosts for long periods. They also pair permanently, and male, female and sometimes the young of the year will roost together side by side in the same or adjacent trees.

OTHER NAMES
None.

IDENTIFICATION
LENGTH: *500–600 mm, including long pointed tail.*
MALE: *Slightly larger, with light to dark russet-grey-fawn upper parts, mottled white and marked black, particularly the scapulars. Shoulders of wing mottled russet, with white blotches on primary coverts; flight feathers dusky brown ocellated and barred with russet-flecked cream. Face russet flecked cream, with cream brow and dusky white-flecked bristles spreading towards tip of bill. Underparts fawn to rufous-grey, speckled and mottled with white from chin to crissum, and sparingly streaked with black, mostly on sides of breast. Tail barred greyish and russet. Eye orange-red. Bill dull lemon to grey-brown. Feet grey to olive-brown; claws darker.*
FEMALE: *As male, but much more finely speckled and marked, with plain russet scapulars, so appearing more uniformly reddish; true rufous phases are rare and invariably female.*
IMMATURES: *Fledglings downy, dull brown, sparingly barred dusky brown and broadly tipped white on upper parts, faintly barred and streaked dusky on underparts. Adult plumage gained at post-fledging moult, in several months.*
DOWNY YOUNG: *Short, white-downed; bill and feet flesh.*

VOICE
Territorial and contact call a pulsating, monotonously repeated uum-uum-uum *by both sexes, often alternately for long periods, mainly through breeding and from nest site. Also a bubbling series of descending ho-ho-hos, ending in bill snapping by male (?), perhaps in aggression, an open-mouth croaking scream where disturbed and mournful more-pork, the first note rising, the second falling.*

NESTING
Breeds August–January, peaking October–November, one brood per season. Nest a rough 15–30 cm diameter platform of crisscrossed twigs on horizontal fork 6–20 m above ground; built by both sexes, one breaking off and bringing twigs, the other working them into the nest. Eggs: one, rarely two; pure white; ellipsoidal, 45–55 x 30–35 mm. Incubation probably by both sexes, one feeding and attending the other constantly by night. Young fed by both adults.

DISTRIBUTION
Cape York Peninsula, on edges of rainforest, in gallery and paperbark forests along streams, and mangroves. Two races: one large and pale around coastal Cape York Peninsula south to area of Cooktown; the other smaller and very dark in coastal northeastern Queensland between Cooktown, and Paluma Range. Another race widespread in New Guinea.

During the day the Papuan Frogmouth perches in a tree, looking like the stump of a dead branch.

Marbled Frogmouth *Podargus ocellatus* QUOY & GAIMARD, 1830

RESTRICTED TO RAINFOREST, the nocturnal Marbled Frogmouth is found only in two tracts in Australia: the tropical coastal vine forests on Cape York Peninsula and lower altitude subtropical rainforests on the central east coast. Why it should be missing from the lush forests between Townsville and Cooktown poses a thorny question, but no Marbled Frogmouths have ever been confirmed from there.

The population on the central east coast is now in dangerously low numbers due to clearing of its habitat for farming.

Marbled Frogmouths are sedentary birds, pairing permanently and holding to the same territory—perhaps little more than a few hectares—all year round. By day they sleep alone perched lengthwise along low branches or among leafy vegetation, most commonly on projections against the erect trunks of small trees where, with head sloping up and tail depressed in camouflage, they resemble an American potoo. By night they call and feed methodically through the forest in the hours just after dusk and just before dawn. They eat mostly large, hard-shelled insects such as beetles—and occasional grasshoppers and even frogs—which they pick up from the ground or tree trunks in shallow, diving glides from vantage perches. Their hunting method is to perch, look about, and pounce, seizing prey in their much-strengthened bills. If difficult to manage, prey is battered and softened up before swallowing.

Nesting duties, typically, are shared by male and female: both build the nest and both probably share incubation and the feeding of young. While one is brooding, the other brings food frequently within each hour, and both drum continuously from and by the nest for long periods.

IDENTIFICATION
LENGTH: *370–410 mm (Cape York Peninsula race); 440–480 mm (central east coast race), including very long tail (Australian races only).*
MALE: *Slightly larger, with chestnut-russet upper parts washed greyish, speckled with black and marbled with cream-white, particularly the scapulars. Shoulders of wing plain russet, with cream-white tips to primary coverts; flight feathers dusky brown ocellated and barred with cream-buff and russet. Face plain chestnut with cream brow and long cream-and-brown-barred bristles spreading beyond tip of bill. Underparts rufous-fawn, mottled with cream-white from chin to crissum, and sparingly streaked with black, mostly on sides of breast. Tail flecked russet and barred black. Eye dark yellow to orange. Bill dull lemon or light brown. Feet light flesh-buff.*
FEMALE: *As male, but much plainer russet-fawn, without grey cast dorsally or cream mottlings and black streakings generally, and so appearing more uniformly rufous.*
IMMATURES: *Fledglings are downy rufous-brown faintly barred white and tipped dusky on head and underparts, and faintly barred dusky on back and shoulders. Adult plumage gained at post-fledging moult, in several months.*
DOWNY YOUNG: *Short, white-downed.*

VOICE
Territorial call, by both sexes, a pulsating, monotonously repeated two-note boom or drumming koo-loo, koo-loo, koo-loo, *the second note rising slightly. Also an explosive high-pitched gobbling, a high-pitched trilled* brrr, *and short barking* chuck, *all of unknown function. Male and female feeding one another at nest squeak and hiss softly.*

NESTING
Breeds August–December. Nest a small, unlined cup of interwoven vine tendrils, twigs and moss on horizontal forks or crowns of epiphytes 3–15 m above ground. Egg: one, rarely two; dull white; ellipsoidal, 35–39 x 26–30 mm (Cape York Peninsula race). Incubation by both sexes.

DISTRIBUTION
Rainforests of eastern coast. Two races: one small on east coast of Cape York Peninsula south to McIlwraith Range; the other large on central east coast north to Gympie and south to Manning River. Other races in New Guinea and Solomon Islands.

A plain-plumaged female Marbled Frogmouth on Cape York Peninsula. These birds are rarely seen.

Tawny Frogmouths of the deep grey western race feigning camouflage at their daytime roost. Only when threatened do they react with bill-snapping.

Tawny Frogmouth *Podargus strigoides* (LATHAM, 1801)

THE DAYTIME CAMOUFLAGE of the Tawny Frogmouth is extraordinary. Male and female pair permanently and during the day roost near one another—often side by side or with their young just after breeding—on bare but sheltered branches, stumps, and even shaded ground. At the hint of threat or disturbance they freeze, compacting their plumage and closing eyes to slits and looking just like a broken branch. Only if pushed do they flush or react with a frightening snapping of their yellow-mouthed bills.

Tawny Frogmouths are sedentary birds, apparently living in the same 20–80 hectares of woodland year after year, and often using the same roosts. Like other frogmouths they are night-active, mainly in the several hours just after dusk and before dawn, and

they hunt for similar prey in the same way. Large nocturnal insects, spiders and myriapods are prime prey and these the birds snatch from the ground or low branches in gliding dives from a vantage perch. They flit from perch to perch with flap-glide goshawk-like flight, and sit and watch for the movement of prey.

Nesting duties are shared evenly by the sexes: building, incubating, brooding and feeding one another on the nest, as well as young. Each may spend up to 12 hours in incubation, the male often by day. The onset of breeding is advertised by both partners drumming nightly from the nest site. This the birds often select by placing a green sprig across it; then they leave it for a few days, finally building the nest to completion in several nights.

OTHER NAMES
Podargus.

IDENTIFICATION
LENGTH: *350–530 mm; much larger in southeastern Australia than north.* ADULTS: *Sexes similar; female slightly smaller, less heavily mottled and streaked; sometimes in russet phase in northern and inland Australia. Upper parts silver to dark grey, streaked black; coarsely mottled and tipped white with russet flecks and wash on scapulars and shoulders of wing; flight feathers dusky, spotted and barred white and rufous. Face plain grey or washed russet, with white brow and dusky, white-tipped bristles spreading towards tip of bill. Underparts pale to mid-grey, with sparse black streaks becoming coarsely flecked with white on belly and crissum. Tail mid to deep grey, barred black. Eye lemon to orange-yellow. Bill olive to black-grey.*

Feet olive-brown to sepia; claws darker. IMMATURES: *Like adults from first post-fledging moult at one month.* DOWNY YOUNG: *First short, white-downed; later long, grey-downed with white flecking and barring.*

VOICE
Territorial and contact call a soft pulsating ooom, ooom, ooom repeated quickly 10–50 times in successive bursts; may be varied to did-did-do, or koo-loo and given antiphonally. Also a motorcycle-like rattling, a sharp too-took, too-took, in alarm, and growling, hissing and snapping in threat or defence.

NESTING
Breeds August–December; apparently one brood per season. Nest a flimsy, 10–30 cm diameter platform of crisscrossed twigs on horizontal fork of

tree 3–15 m above ground, or sometimes stumps and derelict nests; same site used repeatedly. Eggs: one-three, usually two, laid at one–three-night intervals; pure white; ellipsoidal, 40–50 x 30–35 mm in southeast to 35–45 x 25–33 mm in north. Incubation 28–32 days, by both sexes. Young fledge in 25–35 days.

DISTRIBUTION
Open forests and woodlands of eucalypts and acacias throughout Australia, and offshore islands except Kangaroo Island. Three races: one large, dark grey and strongly marked and mottled in southeastern Australia north to region of Cairns–Cooktown and west to inland fringes of Great Dividing Range and southeastern South Australia; one medium-sized and uniformly rich grey in Western Australia north to Great Sandy Desert, northeast to Channel Country,

Qld, and southeast to Murray mallee, Vic; the last small and pale throughout northern Australia, south to Great Sandy Desert, Barkly Tableland and southern plains of Gulf of Carpentaria, Qld.

Australian Owlet-nightjar *Aegotheles cristatus* (SHAW, 1790)

OTHER NAMES
Owlet-nightjar, Crested Owlet-nightjar.

IDENTIFICATION
LENGTH: *210–250 mm, including long round tail.*
ADULTS: *Sexes similar; female slightly larger and often more reddish-toned; all red phase birds apparently female. Plumage rather variable, from usually grey to somewhat reddish-toned. Upper parts soft deep grey, finely speckled and barred with white and sometimes rufous. Head with central black stripe and two lateral black stripes—one over each eye—meeting on nape and subtended by grey-white to rufous collar; cheeks plain grey-white, often washed rufous; a series of ciliate vibrissae curving up in front of head and over bill from each lore. Flight feathers dusky-grey, spotted or toothed with ochre or rufous. Underparts white, sparsely to densely speckled and barred with grey, particularly on throat and breast, or washed pale rufous. Tail dusky-grey, lightly to brightly barred with pale to rufous-grey. Eye deep brown. Bill sepia to dusky; base of mandible flesh and palate pink-white. Feet cream to pale grey-pink; claws dusky.*
IMMATURES: *Like adults but head pattern blurred and facial bristles and tails shorter.*
DOWNY YOUNG: *First long, white-downed, with black bill and feet; later possibly grey-downed, with fading bill and feet.*

VOICE
Loud, two or three note rattling churring—chir-churr—on much the same pitch, by both sexes throughout year; probably a territorial call. Also sharp, high-pitched chirk-chirk-chirk or yuk. Young beg with soft, low trilling and adults respond with same call.

NESTING
Breeds August–December throughout range; usually one brood per season. Nest a rough, concave bed of fresh leaves of eucalypts and acacias in bottom of small hollow or cliff-crevice 1–5 m above ground. Eggs: two–five, usually three, laid one–two nights apart; pure white; ellipsoidal, 27–32 x 21–23 mm. Incubation, beginning with laying of first egg, about 25–27 days, by both sexes. Young fledge in 20–30 days; remain with adults for several months after.

DISTRIBUTION
Eucalypt and acacia forests and woodlands throughout mainland Australia, Tasmania and offshore islands except Kangaroo Island; also southern New Guinea. Two races: one pale to deep grey, large and long-tailed throughout mainland to New Guinea; the other dusky grey, small and short-tailed in Tasmania.

BIG BROWN EYES and black-striped crown give the Australian Owlet-nightjar the engaging appearance of a small possum. Despite being one of the most widespread of Australia's nocturnal birds, it is one of the most rarely seen. By day it hides to roost in tree and stump hollows at two–eight metres above the ground, and sometimes in cliff crevices and roofs of derelict homesteads. Resting crouched with head erect and feet tucked up under its breast, it sometimes churrs loudly from the hollow and even suns at its entrance on warm winter days—but only those familiar with its churring call will recognise its presence.

Tapping or scraping the roost tree often flushes an Owlet-nightjar. It breaks out without warning, dashing with direct undulating flight to another tree, usually diving into another hollow there. The ease with which it finds such refuge suggests that it knows every potential roost and nest site in its territory of about 50–100 hectares. It is a sedentary bird, keeping to the same patch of woodland year in, year out; and it mates permanently, even though male and female roost apart and alone by day.

Owlet-nightjars are abroad hunting mainly in the first hours after dusk and the last hours before dawn. They are insect-eaters, taking a wide variety of small beetles, ants, grasshoppers and spiders in several ways. At times the bird hawks on the wing low among trees like a nightjar; at others it perch-pounces like a frogmouth, sitting crosswise on a low vantage perch, looking about, and then planing down on to prey on the ground or base of a tree, snapping it up in the bill. It may even sit and walk on the ground pecking food.

Both sexes share the duties of nest-building and feeding of young from the time brooding ceases altogether at about 10 days. Both probably also share incubation. Nestlings, helpless at hatching, are brooded night and day until their eyes open at four–five days, and then by day for almost another week.

Australian Owlet-nightjars roost inside a hollow tree or a hole in a cliff face. This is the rufous colour phase.

The White-throated Nightjar spends the day on the ground, amid leaves and debris, where its beautifully marked plumage makes it almost invisible.

White-throated Nightjar *Caprimulgus mystacalis* (TEMMINCK, 1826)

LIKE MOST OTHER AUSTRALIAN nocturnal birds, the White-throated Nightjar is rarely seen; it is nonetheless widespread in the coastal ranges of eastern Australia, from far northern Queensland to Melbourne. White-throated Nightjars are north–south migrants in the southern half of their range, moving house each winter after breeding and often reaching New Guinea then. Migrating birds travel in groups of up to 20–30 and are silent.

White-throated Nightjars favour the tops of ridges in the coastal ranges, where the eucalypt forests are dry with dense leaf litter and few plants growing close to the ground. This affords the birds near-perfect camouflage; their beautifully marked plumage becomes almost invisible where they roost in the ground against a background of fallen leaves and debris. They rarely flush until almost trodden upon and then fly, weaving away low among the trees for up to 100 metres before dropping suddenly to ground. Less often they land on a low branch, their bodies aligned with the branch to avoid detection.

At dusk, the White-throated Nightjar takes off to hunt on the wing for nocturnal insects, which it catches in its wide mouth. Moths and flying beetles are its main prey, but it takes a few other insects as well. Its flight is swift on pointed, hawk-shaped wings—hence its popular name, Night-hawk—but it also jerks about with deep, erratic, stiff-winged beats as it plunges, props, twists and glides after prey over and around the tops of trees and through open glades. Most hunting is done in the dim light of dusk and dawn. Later at night the nightjars rest and use other ploys, either making short sallies out from temporary perches in trees or sitting in open ground to flutter up after occasional insects.

White-throated Nightjars are very local birds, returning to breed in the same few hectares year after year, probably as the same, permanently mated pair. It is then that their strange laughing flight call is heard most often. Courting birds flutter and switch about on the ground, crooning and chopping. They (perhaps only the males) also display aerially, beating and diving over their territories with wind ripping through their wings. If disturbed, brooding adults stumble and flap about, barking and bill-clacking, or crouch on the ground in defence, hissing with wings spread and mouths gaping to show their startling colours.

Both sexes brood, taking turns day by day. Young, their eyes opening within hours of hatching, are rather precocial and soon totter off from the nest site, shifting up to 100 metres away in nightly wanderings in the first week. By day they crouch motionless on the forest floor, camouflaged by their down.

OTHER NAMES
Laughing Owl, Moth-hawk, Night-hawk.

IDENTIFICATION
LENGTH: *320–370 mm.*
ADULTS: *Sexes similar; female much bulkier. Upper parts dusky grey, speckled white and marked black. Crown with black stripe of pointed feathers down centre; narrow broken rufous collar; scapulars mid-grey; shoulder of wings plain black, the greater coverts ocellated grey-white and ochreish. Flight feathers dusky, marked with rows of small ochreish spots, the end spot on second–fourth outermost feathers slightly larger and whiter. Face and cheeks dusky black. Throat black, tipped with ochre, with two oblate patches of white forming a broad bar; breast dusky, ocellated with small ovals of mid-grey; belly and crissum tawny, barred with black. Tail dark grey, speckled paler, and narrowly barred black. Eye deep brown. Bill dusky black, finely feathered to nostrils; palate pink. Feet sepia to dusky; claws darker.*
IMMATURES: *Duller than adults with deep russet over all upper and underparts; even white throat patch. Adult plumage gained two–three months after fledging.*
DOWNY YOUNG: *Thick, rusty to gold-brown-downed.*

VOICE
Territorial and contact call a rising, deliberate series of nine–12 low mellow notes — wow-wow-wow-wow-ho-ho-ho-o-o — resembling a laugh; given by both sexes through closed bill, in flight or from a perch. Crooning and chopping notes — tok-tok-tok — in display; hissing and barking notes in threat; may croon when brooding.

NESTING
Breeds September–February, earlier in north than south. No nest; egg laid and incubated on ground among leaf litter. Egg: one; cream to buff, boldly spotted and blotched with black and sepia towards larger end; ellipsoidal, 37–42 x 27–30 mm. Incubation 22–28 days, by both sexes. Young fly in about three weeks.

DISTRIBUTION
Drier forested ridges of coastal ranges of eastern Australia from Cape York to Otway Range, Vic. Also occurs in New Guinea and Solomon Islands. No Australian races.

Spotted Nightjar *Caprimulgus argus* HARTERT, 1892

OTHER NAMES
None.

IDENTIFICATION
LENGTH: *290–310 mm.*
ADULTS: *Sexes alike. Upper parts mid-grey speckled white and marked tawny and black, with complete tawny collar. Flight feathers dusky, spotted ochreish; enlarged white spots at end of wing form conspicuous bar in flight. Throat and breast flecked and barred tawny and black, with two large white* patches forming broad bar on throat; belly and crissum plain tawny. Tail grey, finely barred black. Eye deep brown. Bill and feet sepia to dusky.
IMMATURES: *Pervadingly cinnamon-russet on upper parts and duller than adults below. Adult plumage gained at post-fledging moult, early in first year.*
DOWNY YOUNG: *Red-brown to chestnut-downed.*

VOICE
Territorial and contact call a deliberate series of two–three rising mellow caws, followed by a quick run of eight–15 clinking double-notes or gobbles on same pitch; given erratically by both sexes during breeding. Also occasional grunts, chopping notes and hisses; otherwise silent. Downy young cheep-beep, beep, beep continuously at night.

NESTING
Breeds September–January, earliest in north; one brood per season. No nest; egg laid and incubated among ground litter. Egg: one; greenish cream, sparingly but boldly spotted and blotched purple-brown and blackish mauve; broad-ellipsoidal, 32–37 x 23–26 mm. Incubation 20 days, by both sexes. Young, nidifugous and brooded and fed by both adults, fly by four weeks.*

DISTRIBUTION
Sparsely wooded stony and sandy rises of all mainland west of Great Dividing Range and offshore islands; not recorded Kangaroo Island or Tasmania. Reaches islands just north of Australia on migration. No races.

PROBABLY THE MOST often seen of all Australian nightjars, the Spotted Nightjar is common along many inland roads. Car headlights often reveal its bright ruby-red eye reflections and conspicuous white wing patches as it flies off in the darkness. West of the Great Dividing Range it replaces the White-throated Nightjar, whose habits it largely shares. Like that species, the Spotted Nightjar roosts by day on bare ground on low, sparingly shrubbed and wooded ridges— both sandy and stony; it hunts on the wing in the first and last hours of the night for nocturnal flying insects—mainly beetles and moths—with the same erratic and jerky stiff-winged flight.

Southern Spotted Nightjars also seem to move north after breeding, even reaching islands in the Banda and Bismarck Seas. At their breeding and wintering grounds they are solitary or disperse in pairs to nest, but when shifting about they often move in loose groups of 10–15.

Living in such exposed habitats, Spotted Nightjars have special physiological facilities for lowering their body temperature and cooling by gular flutter. They also rotate on their roosts by day, keeping their backs to the sun. Other aspects of behaviour, particularly threat and distraction displays at the nest, are very like those of the White-throated Nightjar.

The Spotted Nightjar's speckled plumage camouflages it so well on its bare roosting sites that the bird is overlooked by predators.

The Large-tailed Nightjar rears its young on the forest floor among leaf litter. Pairing permanently, they maintain a small territory year round.

Large-tailed Nightjar *Caprimulgus macrurus* HORSFIELD, 1821

THIS BIRD IS SOMETIMES CALLED the White-tailed Nightjar to emphasise its main distinguishing feature—the white tips on its outer tail feathers. Its territorial call is also distinctive, a loud, monotonously repeated *chop-chop-chop* which has been likened to the distant chopping of wood.

Large-tailed Nightjars are tropical birds and in northern Australia live along the edges of rainforest and in rainforest galleries through woods. Pairing permanently and keeping to the same small territory all year, they roost alone by day on leaf litter on the ground inside the shelter of forest. Then at dusk and towards dawn they come out to feed in more open woodland nearby. Like other nightjars, they hunt aerially for flying insects—beetles, moths and

others—which they catch, open-mouthed, in erratic fluttering, gliding and twisting circles on stiff wings. Through the middle hours of the night they sit on open ground or rest on a low branch; particular perches are used repeatedly and males call territorially from them.

Courtship may sometimes involve two or three pairs of birds on the ground together crooning, bill touching and swaying. Males also give brief floating display flights on raised wings and spread tails, but do not wing-clap.

Young are precocial and totter off the nest site within hours of feeding. If they are threatened, the female will thrash around, with flapping wings and gaping mouth, in distraction.

OTHER NAMES
White-tailed Nightjar.

IDENTIFICATION
LENGTH: *270–290 mm.*
ADULTS: *Sexes similar; white bars and tips to wings and tails respectively smaller and tinged brownish in female. Upper parts rich grey-brown, speckled with cream-white and mottled and streaked with black, forming a stripe down crown. Wings with coverts mottled cream and flight feathers dusky with a broad white bar on four outermost. Face rufous-brown with white malar stripe and broad two-part bar of white across throat; breast grey-brown flecked white; belly to crissum buff barred dusky. Tail*

flecked brown and barred black, the outer feathers with broad pure- or brownish-white tips. Eye blackish brown. Bill dark sepia, flanked by a series of long, thick, white-based maxillary bristles. Feet sepia.
IMMATURES: *Like adults, but slightly duller.*
DOWNY YOUNG: *Short, pink-buff-downed.*

VOICE
Loud, endlessly repeated t-chop, t-chop, t-chop *on same pitch, to advertise territory; given mainly by male and always from a perch. Also loud frog-like croaks, hisses in defence and crooning or growling in courtship. Chicks peep at night.*

NESTING
Breeds August–January; usually one brood per season. No nest; eggs laid and incubated on ground among litter and moved if disturbed. Eggs: two; glossy pinkish buff, marbled with cloudy marks of sepia and light grey; ellipsoidal, 26–33 x 20–33 mm. Incubation 21–22 days, mainly by female. Young, nidifugous and fed by both parents, fly in about three–four weeks.

DISTRIBUTION
Coastal brushes between Staaten River and Maryborough, Qld, and Port Keats and Roper River, NT. One race extending to New Guinea region. Other races through Indonesian

archipelagos to southeastern Asia and India.

White-throated Needletail *Hirundapus caudacutus* (LATHAM, 1801)

ONE OF THE FASTEST-FLYING swifts in the world, the White-throated Needletail feeds and cruises at 50–130 km/h, alternating long glides with short bursts of flapping. The needletails sometimes glide in groups. They can turn sharply, or circle slowly, rising in a thermal, their tails widely fanned.

They feed and drink only while they are flying and are claimed even to mate on the wing. Feeding on insects, they sometimes brush past the leaves of a tree to stir the insects into flight. They feed from a few centimetres above the ground to about 100 metres or higher in the mornings and evenings. They can fly long after dark and have excellent twilight vision. A ridge of feathers in front of their eyes, and a nictitating membrane, or transparent 'third eye-lid', protect and clean their eyes. To drink, they skim over the surface of the water.

During the middle of the day they rest circling or feeding at high altitudes. At night they roost in trees in forested country, clinging upright to foliage; it is also possible that they sleep on the wing in communal rafts, particularly at sea on migration. It is thought that the spines in the tail act as a prop when the bird clings to vertical surfaces. Despite reports that their feet are useless, White-throated Needletails grip with strength sufficient to draw blood.

The birds feed chiefly ahead of weather changes, and prefer warm, humid, rising air, where there is maximum movement of insects — they are often seen before summer thunderstorms. They are attracted to bushfires and feed around smoke clouds.

White-throated Needletails, among the largest of the swifts, breed in northern Asia, south of the tundra. They are among the few swifts that do not use cementing saliva in their nests, and they lack well-developed salivary glands. They migrate to Australia, arriving in October, and make their way slowly down the eastern mountain chain, appearing in numbers in Victoria and southeastern New South Wales by December. Their departure northwards starts in mid-March and continues until the end of April. Their exact migration route to and from Australia is still being studied. The needletails moult while in Australia.

Once they have reached their 'winter' quarters, the birds become nomadic, responding to local weather changes. Sometimes White-throated Needletails associate with Fork-tailed Swifts, where these move eastwards with major weather shifts. On migration they also associate with Wood Swallows, Martins, Rainbow Bee-eaters, Dollarbirds and other species.

At their breeding grounds in the Northern Hemisphere, groups of the birds often stage aerial courtship displays, and similar displays have been recorded throughout the summer in Australia. Groups of a flock suddenly stop to chase one another through the air or dive vertically down for 30 metres or so before swooping back up to the main flock.

To reach their nests at the bottom of deep hollows they also dive in vertically. There is usually only one nest to a tree.

OTHER NAMES
Storm-bird, Needle-tailed Swift, Spine-tailed Swift.

IDENTIFICATION
LENGTH: *200–220 mm; wingspan 500 mm.*

ADULTS: *Sexes similar. Sooty brown above, pale whitish brown on centre of back; glossed green-black over head and rump. White frontal band above bill. Wings dark glossy purple-green above with flash of white on innermost secondaries, dark below; wings project 50–80 mm beyond tail tip when bird is at rest. Throat and crissum white; breast and belly sooty-brown. Tail dark glossy purple-green above; 4 mm long spine projects from centre of each tail feather. Eye black. Bill black, broad and slightly down-curved, with wide gape when feeding. Feet dusky grey, with hind toe.*
IMMATURES: *Similar to adults, but have a dusky frontal band; dull brown head, mottled nape, and fine brown lines at extreme tips of some outer undertail coverts.*

VOICE
Shrill twittering or chattering, continuous or intermittent; considered to be contact call in flight.

NESTING
Breeds May–August in Northern Hemisphere. Nest an unmade bed of wood debris at hollow bottom of tall broken-off trunks of trees (larches, oaks). Eggs: usually five–seven; porcelain white; ellipsoidal, about 28–32 x 18–22 mm. Incubation begins with laying of first egg.

DISTRIBUTION
A summer migrant to eastern Australia, essentially eastern highlands, coastal plains, offshore islands and immediate hinterland on fringe of arid inland. Stragglers visit Tasmania, Northern Territory, Western Australia and the South Australian gulfs. Vagrant on other islands in far southwestern Pacific to Macquarie Island. Breeds in Northern Hemisphere across forests of northern Asia and Japan, south of tundra; odd birds may winter on Cape York Peninsula. One race in Australia; light-toned and with complete white forehead band in adults.

A needle-tipped tail props the White-throated Needletail when it clings to vertical surfaces with its claws.

White-rumped Swiftlet *Aerodramus spodiopygius* (PEALE, 1848)

OTHER NAMES
Grey Swiftlet, Grey-rumped Swiftlet, Moth-bird.

IDENTIFICATION
LENGTH: *110–115 mm; folded wings extend 20–25 mm beyond tail tip.*
ADULTS: *Sexes similar. Uniformly black-brown above; upper wings slightly glossy black. Narrow pale grey band on rump appears dirty white in flight. Tail has a moderate fork. Underparts uniformly grey-brown. Eye black-brown. Bill black, flattened and slightly down-curved. Feet black, feathered, with hind toe.*
IMMATURES: *Duller and paler.*

VOICE
Soft cheeping and squealing notes in flight. Sharp clicking notes to echo-locate in caves.

NESTING
Breeds July–February; probably several broods per season. Nests tiny, deep, bracket-shaped cups of mosses, grass, feathers and other fine particles of plant matter bound and reinforced with congealed saliva; fixed in groups to overhanging or vertical portions of cave walls or rock caverns. Egg: one; white; long-oval, about 18 x 13 mm. Incubation about 22 days, by both sexes. Young, fed by both adults, fledge in 40–50 days.

DISTRIBUTION
Coastal eastern ranges from south of Mackay to Cape York Peninsula, Qld, and Great Barrier Reef islands. Occasionally south to Clarence Valley, NSW. Two races: one medium-sized, dark with dull rump along coast; the other small, paler with bright white rump in Chillagoe district.

White-rumped Swiftlets build nests of moss, grass and feathers, reinforced with saliva, in caves.

RECENTLY RECOGNISED as an echo-locating species, the White-rumped Swiftlet emits a series of sharp clicks inside its dark breeding caves and, like a bat, uses the echoes received from the walls to orientate itself accurately. It has not been recorded making this sound outside the breeding caves. In flight, it normally utters shrill cheeping and squealing notes.

White-rumped Swiftlets roost and nest in colonies of up to several hundred or more in caves and deep overhangs of rock that receive little or no light. So far, breeding holes are known only from the tropical eastern Queensland coast and offshore islands north to Cairns, south to Mackay and inland to Chillagoe, but there are almost certainly others on Cape York Peninsula and perhaps further south.

The birds have an unsynchronised breeding season, nests between September and January being anything from new to holding fledged chicks. Space may be so limiting in the caves that nests are joined to one another, bound with hardened saliva which the birds produce from specially enlarged salivary glands. Despite their sturdy structure, however, the nests crumble and fall soon after nesting.

To roost, the swiftlets cling with their tiny feet to bare vertical or overhanging walls of rock, or use empty nests during breeding. Although they dive back to their caves during the day to feed, incubate or rest while breeding, they spend all other daylight hours on the wing, catching small flying insects—mainly flies and bugs—in their wide mouths. Like all swifts they have deep-set eyes protected by a ridge of feathers and a nicti-tating membrane which can cover the eye-balls as insects are taken. When feeding young or perhaps to last them through the night, they bind the insects into wads with saliva and carry them in the mouth back to roost.

Their flight, which carries them up and down the Queensland coast, is nowhere near as swift and direct as in the bigger swifts; it is an easy gliding on downswept wings, interspersed with a brief burst of flapping to gain height or maintain speed as the birds circle, bank, twist and dive just above the rainforest canopy, down through glades, and over cleared land nearby.

Fork-tailed Swift *Apus pacificus* (LATHAM, 1801)

ENORMOUS LOOSE FLOCKS of migratory Fork-tailed Swifts fly across southeastern Australia several times a year, following the eastward drifting low-pressure systems in the atmosphere. Near Melbourne they turn and move northwards along the western flanks of the Great Dividing Range, keeping within regions where rainfall is between 130 and 225 millimetres a year. They arrive in western Australia about mid-October from their breeding areas in northeastern Asia, and leave again by the end of April; some birds may winter in the north. They probably fly across the Timor Sea to the Malay Peninsula and up the Asian coast.

Except at their breeding grounds, Fork-tailed Swifts spend all day and most, if not all, nights on the wing, hunting, resting, and even sleeping. At night, rafts of sleeping birds circle at great height. When hawking for food—flying insects such as termites, ants, flies and bugs—they fly fast in circling sweeps, picking up food in their wide-gaped mouths. They also drink from inland lakes and rain-water puddles, skimming over the surface. Their flight is lighter and more erratic than that of the other large Australian swift, the White-throated Needletail, from which they can be identified most easily by their smaller, bow-like silhouette and long slender tail: the fork is rarely obvious in flight. The birds have excellent twilight vision and probably good night vision. They are attracted to scrub fires, feeding around smoke columns, and make extensive use of thermal currents for gliding and feeding.

OTHER NAMES
White-rumped Swift, Pacific Swift.

IDENTIFICATION
LENGTH: *160–180 mm; wingspan 380–430 mm.*
ADULTS: *Sexes similar. General plumage warm black. Upper wings blacker; slender and sickle-shaped in flight. Rump almost white. Tail dark, conspicuously forked. Chin and throat almost white. Breast to crissum warm-black flecked white. Eye black, protected in front by ridge of feathers and a nictitating membrane. Bill slightly down-curved, broad and black, gape very large. Feet small and black, all four toes forward.*
IMMATURES: *Similar to adults but dorsal feathers edged white.*

VOICE
Shrill excited twittering on wing, similar to that of lorikeets. Also long, subdued buzzing scream.

NESTING
Breeds June–August in Northern Hemisphere, in clusters on sides of rocks, cliffs or buildings. Nest of grass, rootlets and feathers, cemented with saliva. Eggs: usually two or three; white; long-oval, 26 x 17 mm. Incubation by both sexes; copulation in midair.

DISTRIBUTION
A summer migrant to the west of Australia, spreading irregularly across the east and south to Tasmania. One large, white-rumped, dull brown-black race reaching Australia, breeding in northeastern Asia south to Mongolia, central China and Japan.

The Laughing Kookaburra usually nests in a large tree hole. The nest chamber opens directly to the entrance, through which the young excrete.

Laughing Kookaburra _Dacelo novaeguineae_ (HERMANN, 1783)

ACCORDING TO AN ABORIGINAL legend, the kookaburra's famous chorus of laughter every morning is a signal for the sky people to light the great fire that illuminates and warms the earth by day. The legend captures the imagination, but the true function of the familiar cacophony is to advertise the territory of this bold bird. The Laughing Kookaburra is the largest member of the kingfisher family but, unlike most of its relatives, it is sedentary and occupies the same territory the year round. Before the spring breeding season, when family groups adjust their boundaries, an observer can actually locate the territories by listening to the noisy choruses at dusk as each group calls in turn and awaits the replies of neighbouring groups. Calling birds are unmistakeable, squatting on their haunches close to one another, tails raised and heads thrown up as they churr and chortle.

Laughing Kookaburras live in woodlands and open forests. They do not need free water to exist and occur in almost any part of eastern Australia with trees big enough to contain their nests and open patches sufficient to provide hunting grounds. Kookaburras are not particularly selective feeders—their diet of snakes, lizards, rodents and the odd small bird is probably best known, but they live mainly on various insects and other invertebrates.

Their method of hunting, by perch-and-pounce, is typical of kingfishers. The bulky birds settle motionless on a vantage point—a stump or branch rarely more than 10 metres high—staring fixedly at the ground below. Sighting prey, they flutter down on to it, seize it in the bill, and fly back to a perch to eat it. Between trees their flight is buoyant, of deliberate floating wing-beats.

In favourable conditions, kookaburras may live for 20 years or more. Their birth rate is low to keep pace with their low death rate, and the population turnover is very slow. Kookaburras form permanent pairs and take so long to rear their young to independence that more than one clutch a season is unlikely. After a short courtship in early spring, the pair raise two or three young that are fed by their parents for a further eight to 13 weeks after fledging. Instead of being forced out of the territory on reaching maturity, most young stay to help their parents defend the boundaries and rear and protect further offspring. The young birds may remain in this auxiliary role for four years or so; on average they form one-third of the adult population and inhabit as much territory as do the breeders. Through their mere presence, by occupying areas that would otherwise be taken over by potential breeders, they reduce the birth rate by about one-third.

Although the breeding pairs must expend some energy to maintain their dominance they also benefit by having to devote less time to the strenuous job of rearing the young. Auxiliaries contribute 32 per cent of the time spent on incubating the eggs and brooding the young, and provide up to 60 per cent of the food for the nestlings. They also look after the needs of the fledglings.

Although reducing breeding potential, the kookaburras' social system actually improves the chances of survival for all members of the family. The young are better cared for, the parents under less strain, and the auxiliaries gain experience which in turn may enhance their chances of survival once they rise to become dominant and breed themselves.

OTHER NAMES
Kookaburra, Great Brown Kingfisher, Laughing Jackass, Bushman's Clock.

IDENTIFICATION
LENGTH: _400–450 mm, including 50–60 mm bill._
ADULTS: _Sexes similar; male flecked extensively blue-white over lower back and rump. Head off-white, marked with dark brown stripe through each eye and over centre of crown. Mantle and wings dark brown, flecked light blue over shoulders (coverts) and a large white band through base of outer flight feathers. Lower back and rump barred russet brown and black. Tail russet-brown barred black, with pale tips. Underparts entirely off-white, faintly barred dark grey-brown down flanks. Eye deep brown. Bill with maxilla dusky and mandible cream-bone. Feet pale olive-cream; claws dusky._
IMMATURES: _As adults but short, dark billed, more strongly barred grey-brown ventrally, edged white on brown mantle and wings, and rump brown marked black in both sexes._

VOICE
Six different short calls varying from chuckles to a pronounced kooaa. _Rollicking laugh,_ koo-hoo-hoo-hoo-hoo-hoo-haa-haa-haa-haa, _usually sung in chorus to advertise territory._

NESTING
Breeds September–January. Nest a large cavity in almost any object big enough to contain an adult—usually a hole in a tree trunk or branch, or a termite mound. Flat-floored chamber, about 500 mm across, opens directly to entrance hole, through which chicks excrete. No nesting material used. Eggs: one to four, usually two; white; rounded, about 46 x 36 mm. Incubation, beginning with laying of first egg, about 24 days, by female and helpers. Young, fed by all members of group, fledge in five weeks.

DISTRIBUTION
Eucalypt woodlands and open forest of eastern Australia, north to Cape York Peninsula, inland to western fringes of Great Dividing Range and southwest to Eyre Peninsula. Introduced and established in Tasmania and southwestern Australia. Two races: one small on Cape York Peninsula; the other large and everywhere else.

The male Laughing Kookaburra adopts this posture, with head and tail up, when sounding its familiar call.

Blue-winged Kookaburra *Dacelo leachii* VIGORS & HORSFIELD, 1827

THE CLOSEST RELATIVE OF the Laughing Kookaburra, the Blue-winged Kookaburra lives in the northern and northeastern coastal fringes of Australia as well as in New Guinea. It prefers a wetter habitat than the Laughing Kookaburra, and is usually found in gallery forests along creeks or in swampy coastal paperbark. However, on the Queensland coast from Brisbane to Cape York Peninsula there are also vast areas where the two species live together. Their ranges overlap especially in places where cane fields—in which they hunt—grow amid forests, and where wet woodlands give way to drier ones.

There it is not unusual to see two or three Blue-winged Kookaburras and several Laughing Kookaburras perched in a row on a telephone wire, watching motionlessly for movement of prey in the cane fields below. In a shared habitat the two species actually interact in their territorial behaviour: each bird excludes the other from its territory, almost as if it were a member of the same species. This phenomenon—fairly common between closely related species—suggests that when the two kookaburras diverged as separate species while living apart in the past, differences evolved in their form rather than in their feeding and nesting requirements, which are still much the same.

The method of each species' territorial defence against the other does not appear to be the same as when territories are defended against members of the same species. The Blue-winged Kookaburra has a less ritualistic defence display—the families circle and chase an intruder in a loose and raucous fashion—whereas the Laughing Kookaburra gives a neat performance in which the birds fly to and fro, passing each other in midair like trapeze artists, with relays of laughter reverberating between the disputing groups. To maintain mutually exclusive land rights, the morning and evening choruses with which both species announce their territories are normally sufficient; in these the Blue-winged Kookaburra's high-pitched trilling howl sometimes mingles with the Laughing Kookaburra's less frantic song.

Both species have similar feeding, mating and nesting habits, and are aided in breeding by auxiliary helpers. This form of social behaviour seems to have the same effect on the biology and population of each. The only difference is that the families of Blue-winged Kookaburras are often larger, up to 12 members.

OTHER NAMES
Leach's Kookaburra, Howling Jackass.

IDENTIFICATION
LENGTH: *380–400 mm, including 60–70 mm bill.*
MALE: *Head off-white, lightly to strongly streaked dirty brown. Mantle and scapulars mid-brown; lower back and rump glistening sky-blue. Shoulders (coverts) entirely sky-blue, the tone washing down as strong mid-blue suffusion over flight feathers; large white band through base of flight feathers. Tail mid-blue tipped white. Throat plain white. Breast to crissum off-white to cream-buff, variably scalloped with thin bars of grey-brown. Eye cream-white. Bill with maxilla dusky and mandible cream-bone. Feet pale olive-cream to flesh-grey; claws dusky.*
FEMALE: *As male but slightly larger, with tail feathers russet barred with blue-black.*
IMMATURES: *As female but paler ventrally; scalloping varies with wear.*

VOICE
Six or seven short calls varying from sharp ow *to pronounced trill. Cacophony of rapid, high-pitched coughing cackles, usually sung in chorus. Starts with a coarse* huff-huff-huff ... *developing into a sharp bark of* ow-ow-ow *and a series of trills; ends abruptly.*

NESTING
Breeds September–January. Nest a hollow tree cavity like that of Laughing Kookaburra, but with greater preference for termite mounds and baobab trees Adansonia. *Eggs: one to four, usually two; white; rounded, about 45 x 35 mm. Incubation about 23–24 days, by members of group. Young, fed by group, fledge in five weeks.*

DISTRIBUTION
Eucalypt and gallery woodlands of coastal and subcoastal northern Australia; also eucalypt woodlands of southern New Guinea. Two Australian races: one large and white-headed in Pilbara, WA; the other smaller and dark streak-headed from Kimberleys, WA to Toowoomba, upper Brisbane River, Qld.

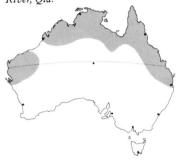

The Blue-winged Kookaburra emits a high-pitched trilling howl—a harsher call than that of its closest relative, the Laughing Kookaburra.

Yellow-billed Kingfisher

Syma torotoro LESSON, 1827

OTHER NAMES
Lesser Yellow-billed Kingfisher, Saw-billed Kingfisher, Lowland Yellow-billed Kingfisher.

IDENTIFICATION
LENGTH: *180–210 mm.*
MALE: *Head and neck orange with thin black line around front of eyes and black spots on either side of back of neck. Mantle and shoulders dusky grading into mid green-grey; lower back and rump mid turquoise-green. Tail dull cobalt blue above, dull grey below. Wings rich olive-grey; flight feathers dusky black; underwing coverts ochre-cream. Chin and throat cream grading into richer cinnamon-buff on breast and paler cream on belly, flanks and crissum. Eye dark brown. Bill yellow to orange-yellow; dusky line on tip of culmen. Feet cream to orange-yellow.*
FEMALE: *Like male but top of crown black; sides of head paler orange; black spots on sides of neck larger, sometimes almost meeting at back of neck. Back and breast duller.*
IMMATURES: *Pale and at least the females black-headed like adult female; black in front of eye extends behind eye into a stripe. Cheeks, sides of neck and breast flecked with black; upper bill extensively dusky black.*

VOICE
Loud, clear, usually descending trill of whistled notes, very like that of Fan-tailed Cuckoo but often more prolonged and sometimes rising and fading away at end. Calling becomes animated and persistent throughout the day during breeding, but birds rather silent at other times of year.

NESTING
Breeds November–January, probably longer. Nest a burrow drilled into arboreal termite mound or hollow limb in tree, 3–18 m above ground. Burrows are 100–300 mm long, enlarged at the end into egg chamber. Eggs: three or four; smooth, glossy, pearly white; rounded, about 26 x 23 mm; laid on wood dust or termite rubble in egg chamber.

DISTRIBUTION
Restricted to edges of rainforests and fringing tropical woodland, monsoon forest and landward edges of mangroves on Cape York Peninsula south to Watson River and Princess Charlotte Bay. One endemic race, with very washed out blue-green back and persistent dusky wash on culmen. Other races widespread in lowlands of New Guinea and on offshore islands.

The Yellow-billed Kingfisher lives on Cape York Peninsula, New Guinea and offshore islands. This is a male.

THE TROPICAL HAUNTS of this least known of Australian kingfishers are so remote that few ornithologists have penetrated them for long enough to learn much of its behaviour. What is known suggests that in its habits it resembles other small land kingfishers such as the Sacred Kingfisher. Its habitat, however, is very different: the shady lower stages of rainforest and galleries of monsoon forest, particularly their drier edges abutting on eucalypt woodland. The bird is quiet and retiring—and usually solitary. Only during and immediately after breeding does it form loosely knit pairs and small family parties. Wherever it is found it is probably numerous.

Its diet includes dragonflies, beetles and other insects, and small lizards and earthworms. It hunts by perching motionless on a low, bare branch; when prey appears, it dives on it.

Although the bird has been thought to be a sedentary breeder on Cape York Peninsula, its numbers appear to fluctuate with the time of year. This suggests local wandering rather than migration to New Guinea, judged by the fact that Australian Yellow-billed Kingfishers, which have distinctively pale grey-green backs, have never been found in New Guinea.

Almost nothing has been recorded of the bird's breeding habits and behaviour, but it is known that neither sex defends the nest at all aggressively and may even desert it if disturbed.

The female Yellow-billed Kingfisher can be distinguished from the male by the black on the top of its crown.

Sacred Kingfisher *Todiramphus sanctus* (VIGORS & HORSFIELD, 1827)

THE SACRED KINGFISHER, the most familiar of the smaller Australian kingfishers, is encountered so widely—in all types of open, wooded country, along streams, near dams, and even in mangroves—that it is often confused with the Azure Kingfisher and the Collared Kingfisher. The Azure, however, is recognisable by its deep royal blue back and short cut-off tail, and the Collared by its larger size and pure white breast.

The breast colour of the Sacred Kingfisher can vary perplexingly, from rich ochre-buff to a dull white, caused by wear or fading; in winter and early spring the birds are always much more richly coloured than in late summer, before the post-breeding moult.

The Sacred Kingfisher—which is a land kingfisher—is usually solitary, pairing only for breeding. Afterwards the birds form family groups for a short period before dispersing in the autumn. Many of them reach islands north of Australia then, migrating to winter there from March to October. Not all of them may be migratory, however; seasonal movements are clear-cut only in southern Australia, where the birds arrive to breed from late August to October, announcing their presence by the staccato calls and concommitant tail raising each pair exchanges while establishing a territory.

Both sexes excavate the nesting burrow; both incubate the eggs in turn and rear the young; and both defend the nest with tenacity. The birds make the initial impression for a burrow by flying at the site like guided missiles. They dig by using the bill as a pick and clawing out debris with the feet. In display both sexes engage in courtship feeding but do not wing-wave.

Their diet consists mainly of small reptiles, crickets, grasshoppers, beetles and their larvae, and—when the birds are near water—fish and both freshwater and saltwater crustaceans. Sacred Kingfishers feed in the manner of the Forest Kingfisher and the Red-backed Kingfisher, spending much of their time perched on a small, bare, fairly low branch; they sit very still, occasionally bobbing the head as they watch for prey, then plunging down on to it, grasping it in the bill and flying back up to a perch to eat.

OTHER NAMES
None.

IDENTIFICATION
LENGTH: *190–230 mm.*
MALE: *Head dusky turquoise-green, with ochre-buff spot in front of each eye; broad black band from base of bill through eyes and ear coverts and around nape, bordered below by ochre to cream collar. Mantle and shoulders dusky turquoise-green grading to bright turquoise-blue on lower back and rump. Tail turquoise-blue above, dull grey below. Wings rich turquoise-blue with some black on flight feathers. Chin and throat cream or white, grading to rich ochre-cinnamon on breast, belly and crissum. Eye dark brown. Bill black with flesh-coloured base to mandible. Feet dark grey-brown to black.*
FEMALE: *Similar to male, but crown, back, wings and tail duller and greyer; underparts usually lighter.*
IMMATURES: *Like female. Birds up to one year extensively flecked and scalloped with dark brown on collar, sides of face, breast and belly, with cinnamon-cream edging on forehead, shoulders and wing coverts; bill and feet paler.*

VOICE
Loud, measured, three–four-syllable, staccato ek-ek-ek-ek, *repeated monotonously or same pitch throughout the day at beginning and during breeding. Modified and strained* kee-kee-ee-ee *sometimes in excitement, rising trills and harsh churring notes in alarm. Usually silent when not breeding.*

NESTING
Breeds September–March; mostly September–December in southern Australia. Usually two broods a season. Nest a burrow, 1–20 m above ground, in arboreal termite mound, hollow limb, sometimes earth bank and even fence post. Eggs: three to six; smooth, rather glossy white; broadly oval, about 26 x 22 mm. Incubation about 16–17 days, by both sexes. Young fledge in four weeks.

DISTRIBUTION
Widespread in tall, open eucalypt forest and woodland, paperbark forest, mangroves and sometimes along wooded rivers throughout coastal and subcoastal Australia. One Australian race—averaging whiter breasted in west—wintering on islands north of Australia from Timor to Solomons. Other resident races on islands from New Zealand to Loyalties in southwestern Pacific.

The Sacred Kingfisher eats small lizards, crickets, grasshoppers, fish and other invertebrates. This is a male.

Red-backed Kingfisher

Todiramphus pyrrhopygius (GOULD, 1840)

OTHER NAMES
None.

IDENTIFICATION
LENGTH: *200–240 mm.*
MALE: *Head streaked dull blue-green
and white merging into dull white spot
in front of each eye, bordered by broader
black band running through eyes to ear
coverts and back of neck. Collar white,
often rufous-tinted. Mantle dull
turquoise-blue, sometimes rufous-
tinted. Rump and upper tail coverts
rufous. Tail dull turquoise-blue above,
paler and grey-tinted below. Wings light
turquoise-blue to almost caerulean-blue
on shoulders. Most flight feathers edged
with turquoise on outer web, grading to
dusky on inner web. Entire
undersurface white, often dirty. Eye
very dark brown. Bill black with flesh-
coloured base to mandible. Feet dark
olive-grey to dusky.*
FEMALE: *As male, but crown, mantle,
wings and tail duller and greyer.
Usually no rufous tint on collar.*
IMMATURES: *Similar to female on upper
surface; sides of undersurface and white
collar lightly scalloped or marked with
dusky grey; shoulders lightly flecked
with white.*

VOICE
*Single, drawn-out, rather mournful
whistle during breeding, possibly
uttered by male only as territorial or
self-advertising call from vantage
perch in tree or post. Also harsh,
chattered alarm notes when nest is
threatened. Usually silent when not
breeding.*

NESTING
*Breeds August–February, mainly
October–November. Nest a burrow,
300–600 mm long and 80–120 mm in
diameter, usually dug in soft bank of a
creek, less often in termite hills or
mounds in trees. At end of upward
running burrow an unlined nest
chamber, 200–250 mm in diameter and
150 mm high. Eggs: three to five;
smooth, rather dull pure white; broadly
oval or almost spherical, about 27 x 23
mm. Eggs laid on powdered earth or
termite mound rubble on nest chamber
floor. Incubation about 20 days, by both
sexes, beginning with laying of first egg.
Young fledge in just over three weeks.*

DISTRIBUTION
*Open mulga, mallee, dry stream-beds,
low tropical woodlands and savannas
throughout most of inland Australia
and the coast, except southeast,
southwest and Tasmania, unless as
stragglers. No races.*

A male Red-backed Kingfisher. This nomadic kingfisher is able to live far from water.

RED-BACKED KINGFISHERS are better adapted to
Australia's desert lands than any of their relatives. They can live far from water, possibly
because they obtain sufficient moisture from
their food, and are found in open mulga, mallee,
dry coolabah-lined river beds, and low tropical
woodlands and savanna. They are nomadic over
much of their range, a characteristic which contributes to their success in arid habitats.

Across southern Australia, Red-backed Kingfishers are mostly migratory. They usually arrive
in the south in early spring to breed, announcing
their advent with mournful whistles that sound
incessantly through the arid woodlands. They
depart again towards the end of summer. In
northern Australia the southern immigrants
mingle with resident birds during winter
months. Red-backed Kingfishers usually live in
loose groups of four or five or in dispersed pairs
when breeding, and are often solitary when not.

They are mostly carnivorous, taking grasshoppers, beetles and other insects, frogs, small
reptiles and even young birds. They capture
their prey through the same strategy as the Forest
and other land kingfishers: perched on bare
branches, ant hills or telegraph wires, they sit
staring down motionless except for perhaps an
occasional bob of the head and a lift of the tail.
When they sight prey they dive and seize it on
the ground. Flight, as in other kingfishers, is
swift and direct.

Both sexes appear to take part in nest-drilling,
which they carry out in the manner of the Forest
Kingfisher. Both share in incubating the eggs—
certainly the female does by day—and both rear
the young. Neither sex is as vigorous in defending the nest as the Forest Kingfisher, and often
takes no action at all to protect it from an
intruder. Young hatch naked and do not begin to
gain pin feathers until about a week old.

A male Collared Kingfisher at its nest. The Australian subspecies is confined to northern coastal mangroves.

Collared Kingfisher

Todiramphus chloris
(BODDAERT, 1783)

OTHER NAMES
Mangrove Kingfisher, Sordid Kingfisher, White-collared Kingfisher.

IDENTIFICATION
LENGTH: *250–280 mm.*
MALE: *Head blue to brown-olive. White spot in front of eye; broad black band from base of bill through eyes and ear coverts and around nape, bordered by a white collar below. Back, shoulders, rump and upper tail coverts blue- to brown-olive. Tail deep turquoise-blue above, dull dark grey below. Wings deep turquoise-blue, with flight feathers dusky on inner webs, grading to deep turquoise-blue on outer. Underparts pure white with lower thighs dusky olive. Eye dark brown. Bill black except for pale flesh base to mandible. Feet dark flesh-grey.*
FEMALE: *As male, but duller; browner wash to crown and back; rump, wings and tail duller green-blue.*
IMMATURES: *Dull like female, but with collar, cheeks, breast and flanks flecked or finely barred with black. These flecks may be retained until second year.*

VOICE
Double-note kik-kik or ke-kik, repeated three or four times in fairly rapid succession; heard for several hundred metres and given by birds perched on high vantage points in mangroves, perhaps to signal territory.

NESTING
Breeds September to probably March. Normally two broods a year. Nest a burrow, 100–150 mm or more long and 50–60 mm in diameter, excavated in arboreal termite mound, tree hollow or sometimes an earth bank, 4–15 m above ground; usually in mangroves or adjacent tall trees. End of burrow is widened into a chamber 150 mm in diameter and 100 mm high. Eggs: two or three; smooth, rather glossy white; broadly oval to almost spherical, 32 x 26 mm. Laid on rubble on chamber floor.

DISTRIBUTION
Confined to mangroves patchily around northern coast of Australia and offshore islands south to Shark Bay, WA, and northern New South Wales in the east. Two subspecies: one large and moderately rich bluish green dorsally from Kimberleys, WA around north coast to mouth of Richmond–Clarence Rivers, NSW; the other small and quite dull brown-green on coast of Pilbara, WA. Over 40 other races widespread from Red Sea to northern Polynesia.

WHY THIS KINGFISHER is restricted to mangroves in Australia has never been satisfactorily explained. Elsewhere, throughout much of its wide range, it lives in a variety of wooded habitats, from open woodlands and gardens to mangroves and rainforest. Its plumage also varies in colour from region to region. In India and Indonesia, the birds have a turquoise-blue head and back, whereas on some of the smaller island groups east of New Guinea they are buff-breasted with white and cinnamon heads, and show marked differences between the sexes. The Australian races are the dullest and greenest.

In Australia, Collared Kingfishers live mainly along the seaward fringe of mangroves and bigger tidal creeks, spaced out singly or in loose pairs in territories of several hundred metres or more of waterfront. They do not dive into water to feed, but pick up their food—crustaceans, small fish, worms, insects, reptiles and other small tidal animals—from the surface of muds and shallow pools exposed by low tide. Their method is conventional perch-and-pounce. Sitting motionless out on bare branches, staring intently down for any sign of movement, they suddenly plummet down on to the victim, grasping it in the bill, and carry it back to a perch to eat, head first.

In southeastern regions, the kingfishers appear to be nomadic or migratory; most birds arrive in September to breed in the mangroves of southern Queensland and northern New South Wales and leave in March for Torres Strait and southern New Guinea. In other northern regions they are more sedentary.

To drill their nest burrow into the side of a termite mound, both the male and female work in turn. They gouge out the entrance with their bill, which points straight ahead as the birds fly swiftly at the mound and pierce it. After this initial opening-up operation the birds cling to the sides of the entrance and work with the bill and then the feet to dig the burrow—a task which takes about two weeks. They may then leave the burrow vacant for a week or more, presumably so that the termites can seal off exposed sections of their chambers and withdraw.

During courtship, males chase females—and perhaps vice versa—in vigorous, darting flights accompanied by harsh twittering.

Forest Kingfisher

Todiramphus macleayii
(JARDINE & SELBY, 1830)

OTHER NAMES
Macleay's Kingfisher, Blue Kingfisher,
Bush Kingfisher.

IDENTIFICATION
LENGTH: *190–220 mm.*
MALE: *Head dark royal blue with*
white spot on each side of forehead;
broad black stripe from base of bill
through eyes to ear coverts. A white
collar at back of neck. Back royal blue,
tinted deep turquoise-blue to
turquoise-green. Tail royal blue above,
black to dusky grey below. Wings royal
blue, flight feathers duskier with
broad white band on inner webs;
underwing coverts white. Underparts
white, usually washed with buff on
thighs. Eye deep brown. Bill black,
with pale flesh base to mandible. Feet
slate-grey to black.
FEMALE: *As male but back of neck blue.*
IMMATURES: *Like adults but slightly*
duller, with forehead and shoulders
scalloped faintly white, and breast
scalloped faintly black. Immature
males have an indistinct, blue-mottled
white collar.

VOICE
Harsh trilling chatter of repeated
notes, t'reek t'reek... Also similar
high-pitched repeated whistle. Usually
silent except when breeding.

NESTING
Breeds late August–December. Usually
two broods a season. Nest a burrow in
a termite nest 2–15 m above ground in
a tree; sometimes in hollow limb or in
earth between roots of fallen tree.
Burrow ends in small egg chamber.
Eggs: four to six; smooth, slightly
glossy white; oval to almost spherical,
about 25 x 21 mm. Incubation by both
sexes.

DISTRIBUTION
Open forests, woodlands and their
edges in Arnhem Land and
northeastern Australia from Cape York
Peninsula south to Hunter Valley,
vagrants reach Victoria. Two races.

A female Forest Kingfisher of the eastern form at its nest in a termite mound. Both sexes excavate the burrow.

THE DRY PLAINS AND DOWNS at the head of the Gulf of Carpentaria appear to separate two populations of Forest Kingfishers which differ slightly in appearance and habits. The birds in Arnhem Land east to the McArthur River are resident there; they have a deep blue back and a large patch of white in the wings, very like that of a small, isolated breeding population in southeastern New Guinea. The birds in eastern Australia have a more turquoise back and smaller white wing bar, and tend to be migratory: most birds of the more southern populations fly north to winter in northern Queensland and New Guinea and return to breed in spring and summer.

Forest Kingfishers are moderately abundant. They often occur in the same forests and woodlands as the Sacred Kingfisher and the Yellow-billed Kingfisher but are easy to identify by their deeper blue upper parts, gleaming white underparts, and the white 'dollars' on their wings in rapid, direct flight.

Alone, in pairs, or in loose family groups after breeding, the Forest Kingfisher is usually seen sitting motionless on a telegraph wire or bare branch, staring down intently for prey. It feeds over land, rarely water, on invertebrates such as beetles, bugs, spiders and grasshoppers, and on small reptiles, frogs, and worms. It plunges down, grasps prey in its bill and then returns to the perch to swallow it. Indigestible parts are cast as small pellets.

When breeding, the males advertise their territory by calling and tail-raising in concert, and by a display involving much fanning of the tail. Both sexes excavate the nest burrow. The birds select a site such as a termite nest in a tree—and open up a hole in it by flying at it head on, with such force that on rare occasions they die from the impact. They use their bills as picks to dig out the burrow, which may be only a few centimetres long.

Nest sanitation is aided by the fact that the floor of the nesting chamber at the end of the burrow is only a little below the entrance level; the nestlings eject their droppings—which they do with great force—through the burrow into the open. Both sexes incubate and feed the young, and defend the nest aggressively.

Buff-breasted Paradise-Kingfisher

Tanysiptera sylvia GOULD, 1850

BUFF-BREASTED PARADISE-KINGFISHERS arrive in northern Queensland from central New Guinea in early November each year to breed. Their appearance is remarkably sudden—one afternoon there will be none, and the next morning the forest will echo with the clattering of birds establishing their territories. At this time they are also at their most attractive: their plumage is neither stained nor worn from the nesting chamber, and they look like so many large blue-and-buff butterflies flying and fluttering around in the rainforests.

Having established territories and paired off, the birds start nesting in small termite mounds. They make an entrance in the side of a mound that is about 350–500 mm high, and spend three or four weeks tunnelling out a nesting chamber which is left unlined. Then, after about a week's delay, the eggs are laid. Both parents incubate and feed the young.

Most chicks hatch between the last week in December and the second week in January. They grow quickly and have a covering of down at four to six days old. The bill is short and thick at this age, and the chick will peck with it in defence if molested. The first pin feathers appear after about two weeks and by 20 days the bill is almost fully grown. By this stage the chicks, their feathers encased in persistent sheaths that give them a scaly, reptile-like look, are fighting among themselves almost constantly and will attack anything that comes near them. From soon after hatching the chicks keep up a continuous squeaking while awake, and the racket intensifies if an adult kingfisher approaches the nest entrance.

The young stay in the nest about 24 days, and by the time they are ready to leave they have shed the sheaths of the pin feathers. When fledging, young plop unceremoniously on to the ground and quickly flutter to a bush and, as they become stronger, work their way higher and higher into the forest canopy.

The adults eat insects, snails, frogs and lizards, which they pick up from the ground or on low branches in pounces from set perches within the rainforest midstage. It is typical kingfisher hunting. The same items of food are fed to the young, but during the squabble for them, much is dropped to the floor of the nesting chamber, which soon becomes a carpet of half-decayed prey, in which scores of maggots of flesh flies (family Tachinidae) writhe and crawl.

When perched on their horizontal branches, adults raise and lower the tail—which is often abraded during nesting—slowly backwards and forwards, or faster and in time with the call if the bird is calling. They start leaving northern Queensland in late March to early April, the young departing a little later; all have gone by the end of April.

OTHER NAMES
White-tailed Kingfisher, Racquet-tailed Kingfisher.

IDENTIFICATION
LENGTH: *290–320 mm, including attenuately pointed 130 mm tail.*
ADULTS: *Sexes alike. Crown royal blue. Broad black band from forehead through eye around nape. Back and rump white edged with black. Tail royal blue with white shafts and two long white central streamers. Wings royal blue; tips of flight feathers dusky. Underparts uniformly rich buff-ochre. Eye dark brown. Bill bright orange. Feet bright coral-red; claws dark grey.*
IMMATURES: *Crown and wings matt dull blue; tail short, black. Back and rump dirty grey; breast dull buff. Bill and legs dull black.*

VOICE
Territorial call an ascending chuga-chuga-chuga *repeated four–five times from a perch, through closed bill; soft descending trill between male and female, in contact; also screeches when chasing intruders.*

NESTING
Breeds November–February. Nest a burrow in a 350–500 mm high termite mound on rainforest floor, usually on rich, red, basaltic soils. The bird makes a tunnel about 150 mm long in the side of the mound, leading to a chamber 150 mm across by 130 mm high. Nesting chamber is unlined but often stained with a dark, glossy substance. Eggs: three or four; white; round, about 26 x 23 mm. Incubation by both sexes. Young fledge in four–five weeks.

DISTRIBUTION
Breeding migrant in northeastern Queensland from Cape York Peninsula to Townsville; stragglers may reach Mackay; restricted to lowland rainforest below 600 m. Winters in central New Guinea. One endemic race in Australia. Other distinctive races in southeastern New Guinea and New Britain.

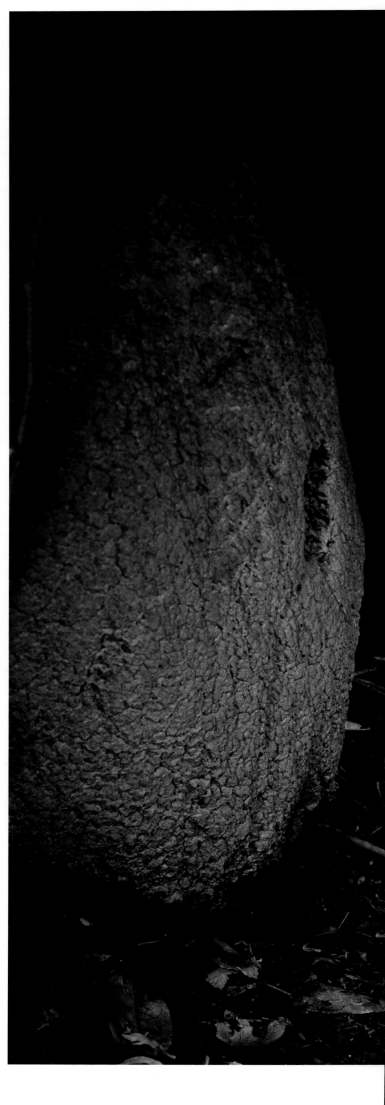

The Buff-breasted Paradise-Kingfisher tunnels an entrance in the side of a termite mound, then hollows a nesting chamber where the eggs are hatched.

The Azure Kingfisher swallows its prey head first. It eats crustaceans, fish and water insects, which it catches by plunging from a perch above water.

Azure Kingfisher *Alcedo azurea* LATHAM, 1801

ALONE OR SOMETIMES in dispersed pairs, the Azure Kingfisher spends much of its day staring down from its perch on a low bare branch, rarely more than a metre above the water. Quiet, intent, the bird will sit for an hour or more looking into the water, its bent head occasionally bobbing if it becomes uneasy or excited. When a suitable fish appears, the bird dives down in a flash of blue, seizes it, carries it back in its bill to the perch, and proceeds to eat it head first. Afterwards the bird reverts to its watching position, waiting for more fish, or for crustaceans or water insects, its staple diet.

At times it moves systematically from perch to perch up and down a stream, zigzagging with a rapid beating of stiff wings interspersed with long, meteor-like glides. The Azure Kingfisher is the Australian counterpart of the European river kingfisher, although it has two instead of three front toes. It resembles the European species in its feeding habits and in living along small streams and waterways overhung by trees, where an adult pair usually keeps a permanent territory of about 200–500 metres of waterfront.

In display, male Azure Kingfishers have been seen chasing females in flashing zigzag flights up and down streams, often far from the nest site. Two or three birds have also been seen perched close, facing one another, waving their wings and whistling shrilly. The nest is a tunnel which both sexes—using the bill as a digging tool—excavate in the bank of a stream. The tunnel is about one metre long and is enlarged at the end into a small chamber.

In Australia there are three forms of the Azure Kingfisher. One form *azurea ruficollaris*, living in northern Australia from the Kimberleys in the west to Cape York Peninsula in the east, is rather small, with a deeply rufous-brown belly and extensively blue and lilac flanks. Another form *A. a. azurea* is paler, of medium size, and has a more cinnamon-brown belly and less blue and lilac on the flanks; it lives in eastern Australia from the foot of Cape York Peninsula to southern Victoria and the Mount Lofty Ranges where it is now extinct. The third form, *A. a. diemenensis* of Tasmania, resembles the second in colour but is larger.

OTHER NAMES
Blue Kingfisher, Purple Kingfisher.

IDENTIFICATION
LENGTH: *170–190 mm, including 40–50 mm bill.*
ADULTS: *Sexes alike. Head and back uniformly rich deep blue with large buff-white to rufous-buff spot on each side of forehead and neck. Wings deep blue with dusky black flight feathers; tail very short, deep dusky blue above, dusky black below. Throat white to buff, merging gradually into deep cinnamon-brown to rufous-brown on the central breast, belly and undertail coverts. Sides of neck, breast and flanks rich deep violet-blue with lilac suffusion on flanks. Eye deep brown. Bill black, usually with fine white tip. Two front toes, feet orange-red; claws black.*
IMMATURES: *Like adults but crown faintly scalloped mid-blue on deeper blue; lower back and rump mid-blue; breast and belly paler, more cinnamon-brown; sides of neck, breast and flanks black without lilac suffusion. Immatures appear to moult into adult plumage at the end of first year.*

VOICE
A shrill peeee peeee, *usually given in flight, particularly when disturbed; uttered by both sexes.*

NESTING
Breeds September–January in southeastern and eastern Australia; probably October–April in north during wet season. Usually two broods a year, at least in southern regions. Nest a tunnel drilled into the stream bank, enlarged into small chamber at end, and loosely lined with fish bones, scales, remains of crustaceans. Eggs: four to seven; lustrous white; rounded, about 23 x 19 mm. Incubation 20–22 days, by both sexes. Young fledge in three–four weeks.

DISTRIBUTION
Along forested coastal streams and mangrove-lined waterways of northern and eastern Australia, ranging southwest to Mount Lofty Ranges and south to Tasmania. Also in lowland New Guinea, its offshore islands and Moluccas. Three races in Australia.

Little Kingfisher *Alcedo pusilla* (TEMMINCK & LAUGIER, 1836)

THIS MIDGET, GEM-LIKE kingfisher is Australia's smallest. Usually solitary, unobtrusive and sedentary in remote habitats, it is rarely seen. Like the Azure species, it is confined to streamside vegetation, and spends much time perched on low branches over the water. It looks down fixedly, occasionally bobbing its head as it waits for its prey—tiny fish, crustaceans and aquatic insects. It dives to seize prey and returns to the perch to eat it there.

The Little Kingfisher flies fast, like the Azure, darting low over water and through forest.

Both sexes appear to collaborate in making a nest. With their bills, they drill and excavate a tunnel some 150 millimetres or more long in a mound of mud, the bank of a stream, or the base of a rotting stump or low termite mound. The end of the tunnel is enlarged to form a small nesting chamber which becomes littered with cast fish skeletons and scales.

Presumably the Little Kingfisher's breeding habits resemble those of other fishing kingfishers such as the Azure.

OTHER NAMES
None.

IDENTIFICATION
LENGTH: *120–130 mm, including 30 mm bill.*
ADULTS: *Sexes similar. Head and upper surface shining royal-blue, sometimes tinged turquoise on front of crown, with a white spot on each side of forehead and neck. Wings like back but flight feathers tinged dusky black. Tail very short, dull royal-blue above, dusky below. Underparts pure white with sides of breast and flanks varying shades of rich royal-blue. Eye dark brown. Bill black. Two front toes, feet dark brown.*
IMMATURES: *Like adults but upper parts dusky turquoise-grey to dark grey-blue, with crown scalloped in lighter and darker blue. Forehead and neck spots tinged orange. Underparts scalloped with black on breast. Sides of neck, breast and flanks turquoise-grey to black.*

VOICE
Shrill, sharp, high-pitched whistle, sometimes rapidly repeated, like that of the Azure Kingfisher but pitched higher; usually given in flight or when disturbed, by both sexes.

NESTING
Breeds October–March, during wet months in northern Australia. Probably one brood a season. Nest a tunnel in bank, between protruding roots of streamside tree, or mangroves, or low termite mound near ground. Eggs: five or six; smooth, glossy, pearly white; almost spherical, about 17 x 14 mm. Incubation by both sexes.

DISTRIBUTION
Coastal Northern Territory from Joseph Bonaparte Gulf to Roper River, and Cape York Peninsula south to near Normanton on west coast and Townsville–Mackay on east. Lives along densely mangrove-lined estuaries, ranging inland along small rainforested creeks to nearby tablelands in eastern part of range. Also New Guinea. Two races in Australia: one bright turquoise-blue and small in Arnhem Land and west coast of Cape York Peninsula; the other rich royal blue and larger in coastal east Queensland south of Cape York Peninsula. Populations on east coast of Cape York Peninsula intergrade.

The Little Kingfisher, Australia's smallest, perches on branches over water.

Rainbow Bee-eater *Merops ornatus* <small>LATHAM, 1801</small>

RAINBOW BEE-EATERS ARE COMMUNAL BIRDS, whether at their breeding grounds across southern and central Australia, or in their winter quarters in far northern Australia and islands beyond, or on migration between. Groups of 20 and 30 fly in loose parties when migrating, calling constantly to one another and travelling by night as well as day over seas. They also roost together at night, cramming into the same, often small shrubby tree.

By day, Rainbow Bee-eaters spend their time perched out on bare, exposed horizontal branches or less often on the ground, making convoluted aerial sallies after insects. They are elegant fliers with broad but pointed wings on which they flutter, glide, twist, wheel and swoop with ease. All food is captured on the wing, mainly venomous Hymenoptera—wasps and bees—and dragonflies, damsel flies, beetles and other flying insects of similar size. Snapping up prey in the bill, the bee-eaters fly back to a perch to batter it and squeeze out any sting before eating. Several hundred wasps and bees may be taken in a day, and their indigestible parts are cast as pellets. At perches, bee-eaters are as immobile as they are free on the wing, their weak, partly fused toes allowing them to clasp a branch or sit and little else.

Sociality peaks during breeding. Rainbow Bee-eaters nest in communes of up to 30 and 40 birds; sometimes more. They not only help one another dig their nesting burrows but also share the duties of incubation, brooding and feeding of young; up to eight birds have been seen assisting at a single nest. Much of the help comes from unmated males, usually younger birds, which outnumber females by about three to two. Burrows are dug with the bill and scraped out rapidly with the feet.

OTHER NAMES
Australian Bee-eater, Rainbow-bird.

IDENTIFICATION
LENGTH: *210–240 mm, including two central tail feathers, which extend 20–40 mm beyond rest of tail.*
ADULTS: *Sexes similar; female slightly duller, with tail shorter and thicker. Crown golden green grading to light rufous on nape. Back and wing coverts golden-green, rump sky-blue. Flight feathers russet-green tipped black, the innermost secondaries plain blue-green; underwing rufous-buff. Face with broad black stripe through eye, edged turquoise-blue above and below. Chin mid-yellow grading to rufous-yellow on upper throat, subtended below by thick black bar with or without blue wash on lower edge. Breast golden-green grading to pale blue-green on belly; crissum sky-blue.*
Tail bluish black, duller below. Eye crimson. Bill black. Feet dark grey; claws black.
IMMATURES: *As adults, but head and back dull greyish green, throat buff-yellow without black band; breast, belly and vent grey-green; no extended central tail feathers; eye brown. Young gain adult plumage—without tail streamers—at winter quarters in first year; may not breed until second year.*

VOICE
Constant, high-pitched chirruping trrrrp, trrrrp, mainly in flight, given by all birds probably as contact call.

NESTING
Breeds November–January in south; just before and after extended wet season in north, usually September–October and May–July. Nest a tunnel up to 1 m or more long, with the circumference just larger than that of the bird's body, dug into a sandy bank or into bare, flat ground, opening into a wider unlined egg chamber 250 mm from the end. Eggs: three to seven, usually four or five, laid every second day; glossy, translucent white; rounded, about 24 x 18 mm. Incubation 21–25 days, by parental pair and helpers; begins with first egg. Young, brooded and fed by parents and helpers, fledge in about four weeks; naked at hatching, pin feathers in about a week.

DISTRIBUTION
Mainly north to south breeding migrant, throughout drier Australian woodlands; moves south to breed in spring south of Kimberleys and Gulf of Carpentaria, and north to winter across far northern Australia (Arnhem Land, Cape York Peninsula) in March–April, reaching Lesser Sundas, New Guinea and Bismarck Archipelago regularly. Some birds present year round in mid-far northern Australia, at least some of which breed there in autumn after wet season. No races.

Rainbow Bee-eaters, which can eat hundreds of bees daily, have two extended central tail feathers. These are shorter in the female (right).

In the spring, the breeding season, the Dollarbird migrates to Australia from New Guinea. It usually nests in shallow hollows in tall trees.

Dollarbird *Eurystomus orientalis* (LINNÉ, 1766)

THE ONLY SPECIES OF THE roller family to reach Australia is the Dollarbird, or Broad-billed Roller. Essentially a tropical bird, the Australian race winters in northern New Guinea and on some adjacent islands and migrates to northern and eastern Australia in the spring and summer to breed. On migration, it travels by night as well as day, reaching heights of 2500 metres. Stragglers sometimes reach the Mt Lofty–Flinders Ranges in South Australia.

Usually solitary, in pairs or in family parties just after breeding, Dollarbirds commonly perch conspicuously on the topmost bare branches of tall trees beside clearings. They do not walk or hop, but simply sit motionless, their toes partly fused for grasping, not perambulation. Their silhouette is characteristic—broad-headed, short-necked and stumpy-tailed. High, bare perches serve as springboards for the Dollarbird's sorties after insects and in display over clearings and above tree tops. The birds are buoyant fliers, making broad sweeps and glides on long, deeply and erratically beating wings after prey or diving and swooping in acrobatic evolutions in display. All food—flying beetles, bugs, moths, mantids, cicadas—is taken on the wing by the heavy bill and eaten there, if manageable, or taken back to a perch and battered or softened before swallowing. Much of the hunting is done in the early morning and twilight of dusk.

Breeding Dollarbirds are noisy, both sexes chattering harshly to one another during the day, but at winter quarters they are rather silent. Their name comes from a large round dollar-like patch of blue-white exposed in each wing in flight.

OTHER NAMES
Broad-billed Roller.

IDENTIFICATION
LENGTH: *260–300 mm.*
ADULTS: *Sexes similar; female duller. Head and upper back dark grey-brown, grading to dull grey-green-blue over lower back and wing coverts. Flight feathers dark bluish black, with large bluish white band—dollar—through outer six–seven; underwing coverts dull turquoise. Throat streaked and washed deep cobalt. Breast dull grey-brown, acquiring turquoise tone over belly and crissum. Tail dark bluish black. Eye dark brown. Bill deep orange; hook black. Feet deep orange; claws black.*
IMMATURES: *More brown-grey than adults; lack blue throat. Area around eye pale; bill and feet yellow-brown.*

VOICE
Advertising or territorial call a harsh, rattling kak-kak-kak, the notes repeated quickly four–ten times in each bout; given by both sexes.

NESTING
Breeds in spring and summer in Australia, usually October–January.

Nest a shallow, unlined cavity in a tall tree. Eggs: three to five, usually four; glossy, translucent white; oval, about 37 x 29 mm. Laid on wood dust at bottom of cavity. Incubation probably by both sexes; young fed by both sexes.

DISTRIBUTION
Arrives in Australia in mid-October to breed; leaves late February to March for New Guinea, wintering mainly in northern lowlands. Lives on edges of tall tropical forest and open woodland. Race in Australia is dull, short-tailed Eurystomus orientalis pacificus. Other, more richly coloured races from southern Asia to Solomons.

Noisy Pitta

Pitta versicolor SWAINSON, 1825

OTHER NAMES
Anvil-bird, Buff-breasted Pitta, Dragoon-bird.

IDENTIFICATION
LENGTH: *170–200 mm.*
ADULTS: *Sexes similar. Head and throat black, with a broad stripe of chestnut over each eye meeting behind crown. Back and wings glistening mid-green; shoulder stripe and rump iridescent turquoise-blue; outer flight feathers black with concealed white centre bar. Breast and flanks tan-buff. Centre of upper belly black; centre of lower belly and crissum scarlet. Tail black, narrowly tipped green. Eye dark brown. Bill black. Feet pink or pink-bown.*
IMMATURES: *Generally duller than adults, with upper markings less pronounced and black and red of belly absent or slight.*

VOICE
Territorial call a loud, chirped melodious whistle, resembling walk-to-work *or* want-a-watch, *with first note low and last questioning, higher in pitch and a little drawn out. Usually repeated twice and followed by pause, as if in wait for an answer. Also a single, liquid, mournful* keow, *often at night and perhaps for contact.*

NESTING
Breeds October–January, sometimes August–March. Large, loosely constructed domed nest, 300 x 300 x 200 mm, with rounded side entrance, 90 mm high, and a stage-like approach of animal dung, 150 mm long. Nest of sticks, leaves, fronds, bark strips, roots and moss, lined with decayed wood pieces and other debris and sometimes secured with mud; on or near ground, between buttressed roots, in tree-trunk clefts or on tops of stumps. Eggs: three or four, rarely five; glossy; pearly white with varying amounts of dark brown, chestnut and purple-grey spots or blotches; rounded-oval, about 32 x 25 mm. Incubation by both sexes. Incubation period of Australian pittas unrecorded; 17 days has been recorded for an Asiatic species.

DISTRIBUTION
Fairly common in east coast rainforests south to Hunter Valley, NSW. Regular south to Illawarra before extensive clearing from turn of the century; occasionally still south to Sydney area. Some local movement within Australia and perhaps to southern New Guinea. Indications are that much of the population is regionally resident. Two races: one from north coast, NSW, to Cairns-Cooktown area, Qld, grading from large to medium in size northwards and frequently with black streaks in green back; the other, restricted to the east coast of Cape York Peninsula and Torres Strait islands south to McIlwraith Range, is small without black dorsal streaks.

A shy rainforest-dweller, the colourful Noisy Pitta is rarely seen but a loud whistling call signals its presence. The birds live on the ground and hop about foraging for insects, worms and snails on the forest floor.

PITTAS, OR 'JEWEL-THRUSHES' as they are sometimes called, include some of the most brightly coloured birds in the world. There are about 26 species, three of which live in Australia.

The Noisy Pitta is one of the biggest, and is typically dumpy in shape, with short tail, rounded wings and long legs. These are all attributes fitted for a life on the ground.

Noisy Pittas spend most of their time alone or in dispersed pairs on the floor of rainforests. Secretive and silent except when nesting, they are seldom seen. Sometimes they appear for a tantalising moment on a forest trail or edge of a clearing before disappearing back into the undergrowth. At other times they make their presence heard with loud territorial whistling, particularly during breeding.

These advertising calls are commonly given from a vantage perch in a tree up to 10 metres above the ground, where the birds also roost. Bouts of continuous calling are considered to be an omen of rain in some areas, probably because the breeding season also coincides with the start of monsoonal rains.

The contrast between noisy calling during nesting and out-of-breeding silence gives the impression that the birds may leave an area altogether after rearing young, and migrate. That there is some seasonal movement and local dispersal seems clear from regular altitudinal shifts on the Atherton Tableland, and the stray appearance of pittas on Barrier Reef islands. Nevertheless a consistent north-to-south increase in the body size of pittas is tangible evidence that local populations are fairly sedentary. They may be present—but not being heard, are not seen.

The Noisy Pitta has an upright posture, and characteristically flicks its tail and bobs its head as it forages alone or in pairs on the forest floor. It hops about, turning over leaves and twigs in search of insects, wood-lice, worms, snails and other small animals. It also eats small berries and fruit. Snails are particularly favoured as food, and the birds choose special sites for the task of separating the snails from their shells. The pitta holds a snail in its bill and repeatedly strikes the shell against an 'anvil'—a stone or a piece of wood—until it cracks open and the soft parts can be extracted and eaten. Little heaps of broken shells can be found lying around convenient anvils, which are sometimes worn smooth with constant use.

The Noisy Pitta's display behaviour is not well understood. A form of display a captive bird was seen to perform is known as a 'passive threat', and may be associated with courtship. When approached, the bird would turn its back to the danger and crouch slightly. Peering back over its shoulder, it then cocked its tail and spread its wings, showing their white 'windows', which contrasted with the bird's bright colours. This position would be held for four to 20 seconds.

The Noisy Pitta, like some other pittas, makes a peculiar addition to its bulky nest in the form of a 'doormat' of moist mammal dung. It also carries the dung into its nest on its feet, staining the eggs. Both parents incubate the eggs in turn, and are not easily discouraged from doing so. One pair is known to have tolerated the felling of a tree at whose base they were nesting.

Rainbow Pitta

Pitta iris GOULD, 1842

ENDEMIC TO northwestern Australia, the Rainbow Pitta replaces its close relative, the Noisy Pitta, in pockets of monsoon vine forest there. It is sedentary and rather solitary, and single birds or pairs seem to occupy the same patch of forest thicket year round, even if it is no larger than several hectares.

In habits, Rainbow Pittas have much in common with the Noisy Pittas. They forage unobtrusively in the leaf litter of the forest floor, hopping along, pausing to poke with the bill and to snatch and break open hard-shelled prey. Land snails, worms, and ground-living insects are staple diet.

Rather silent for much of the year, the pittas become noisy at the onset of breeding, just before the arrival of the summer monsoon. Males often climb trees then to chirp out their three–four note territorial whistle from a vantage perch, mostly in the early morning and late afternoon. Rainbow Pittas also roost in trees.

The Rainbow Pitta, a rare and little-known bird, is found only in Australia.

OTHER NAMES
Black-breasted Pitta.

IDENTIFICATION
LENGTH: *160–180 mm.*
ADULTS: *Sexes similar. Head velvety black; thick red-brown stripe over each eye. Back, rump and wings glistening mid-green; shoulder iridescent sky-blue grading to cobalt at edge; outer flight feathers black with concealed white centre bar. Throat to upper belly velvety black; lower belly and crissum scarlet with tan-buff fringes. Tail black, broadly tipped green. Eye dark brown. Bill black. Feet grey-brown to dark grey.*
IMMATURES: *Like adults but duller;*

throat dusky, speckled off-white; blue shoulder patch small; red-brown head stripes vestigial. Adult plumage gained within three–five months of fledging.

VOICE
Loud, clear two-note whistle, want-a-whip, *similar to that of Noisy Pitta.*

NESTING
Breeds November–March. Large domed nest, similar to that of Noisy Pitta, varying to shallower, partly open nest, 110 mm in diameter and 40 mm deep; of sticks, leaves, grasses, pieces of dead bamboo; lined with pieces of decayed

wood and grass; in mangroves, bamboo clumps, around trees, on the ground or up to 3 m above. Eggs: three or four; glossy; cream with sepia blotches and underlying markings of dull purple-grey; round, about 30 x 24 mm.

DISTRIBUTION
Pockets of vine forest in coastal Arnhem Land, NT, and northwestern Kimberleys, WA; also Melville Island and Groote Eylandt. No races.

Red-bellied Pitta *Pitta erythrogaster* TEMMINCK, 1823

OTHER NAMES
Blue-breasted Pitta, Macklot's Pitta.

IDENTIFICATION
LENGTH: *160–180 mm.*
ADULTS: *Sexes similar, or female slightly duller about the face. Crown dusky; back of head and nape brick-red. Back and shoulders dull blue-green, grading to dull mid-blue rump, tail and inner flight feathers; outer flight feathers dusky with concealed small central white bar; white shoulder spot conspicuous. Cheeks and chin grey-brown grading to large black throat. Upper breast light shining blue, subtended by narrow black breast band; lower breast to crissum scarlet. Eye dark brown. Bill black. Feet slate to bluish grey.*
IMMATURES: *Upper parts dull olive-brown, grading to dull blue on rump and tail. Face, throat and breast mid-brown, shaft-blotched brownish white; white patch in centre throat. Belly and crissum pale red. Mandible ochreish.*

Young gain adult plumage slowly in first year, losing white throat patch last.

VOICE
*Territorial call a mournful whistle of four notes, sometimes with rasping quality—*quor-eye, quor-or; *last doublet drawn out.*

NESTING
Breeds October to December or January. Nest of twigs and leaves, dome-shaped with side entrance, lined with fibres; on the ground up to about 3 m, in tangles of vines, on a stump or at base of tree. Eggs: two to four; glossy; cream with purple-brown and blue-grey markings; round, about 28 x 23 mm.

DISTRIBUTION
Breeding summer migrant in tropical rainforests of Cape York Peninsula south to McIlwraith Range. Species polytypic, with about 26 races, ranging

from Philippines to Bismarck Archipelago and Cape York Peninsula. Australian race distinct, characterised by pale upper parts, large white shoulder spots, and small size.

An adult Red-bellied Pitta.

THE BRIGHTLY COLOURED Red-bellied Pitta breeds from October to December or January in the rainforests of Cape York Peninsula, then migrates to southern New Guinea for the dry season, from March or April. Although perhaps flocking on migration, it disperses singly or in pairs at its breeding quarters, keeping there to the floor of tropical rainforest and overlapping the more sedentary Noisy Pitta. Apart from marked differences in colour pattern, the Red-bellied Pitta has a distinctive territorial call: a long-drawn, mournful whistle, the first one or two notes rising, the second one or two falling away. This the bird usually gives from a vantage perch in a tree, as much as 25 metres above the ground. It roosts in trees at night and often calls then.

When feeding, the Red-bellied Pitta hops about on the forest floor and pauses after every few hops to peck at items in the leaf litter. It then moves its short, downward-pointing, often flicked tail slowly up and down a few times. During the pauses, it may also raise its head slightly, then quickly thrust it towards the ground. This behaviour may flush small animals from the litter, which the bird then snaps up.

Like the Noisy Pitta, the Red-bellied Pitta smashes snail shells on an 'anvil' and probably has a similar diet. It follows an erratic course when feeding, and sometimes makes short, undulating flights—up to about five metres—between foraging areas. When flying it usually keeps close to the ground, but may rise a few metres higher when it passes through more open sections of the forest understorey.

Superb Lyrebird *Menura novaehollandiae* LATHAM, 1801

NO AUSTRALIAN BIRD has such charisma as the Superb Lyrebird. Its size is imposing—it is the largest of passerine song birds; the male's filmy train, shimmered overhead in display, is breathtaking; and its voice, which resounds powerfully through the damp, tree-ferned gullies where it lives, is unmatched in vocal repertoire and mimicry. Its syrinx or voice box is worked by three instead of the usual four intrinsic muscles, giving flexibility.

Displaying males scratch up a number of earthen display mounds on elevated ground, through their territories of two–three hectares. These they visit daily in the months of courtship, from autumn through winter. On the mounds the birds break into song, stiffen, spread the tail up and forward over the head, vibrating, then prance and stamp this way and that, pouring forth a medley of cadences and mimicry, punctuated by resonant territorial chords, buzzing and clicking.

Although the birds are capable of imitating almost any sound—from a mill whistle to a cross-cut saw—they usually restrict their mimicry to loud clear sounds made by other birds and mammals. The essential function of the song seems to be to advertise. Young learn their sequences from local elders, as the songs and mimicry of individual birds in any group are very similar in form.

Females occupy separate foraging territories overlapping those of males. Attracted by displaying males, they mate with them itinerantly on or near the mound without forming any pair bond. Before copulation, the males stop singing and shimmering to make a soft clicking sound. A male may mate with more than one female but takes no other part in nesting duties.

After breeding, males, females and young gather in small locally foraging groups of four or five. Powerful in leg, with long toes and claws, they walk along the ground, raking over the litter of the forest floor for insects, worms and other invertebrates. With each step, one foot then the other makes sideways sweeps to right and left. They are wary birds, escaping by running and dodging rapidly through the undergrowth; they do not hop and rarely perch up into the middle of trees except to roost. Nor do they fly much, using their short, round, weakly muscled wings for little more than planing low between feeding and roosting points.

OTHER NAMES
None.

IDENTIFICATION
LENGTH: *800–1000 mm, including 500–600 mm tail; female smaller.*
MALE: *Upper parts plain chocolate-brown. Underparts paler, greyer brown; throat rufous in younger birds. Tail dark brown above, silver-grey below, of two long central wire-like plumes, 12 filamentary rays, and two outer, broad, lyre-shaped feathers toothed rufous in southern race, and less curved and tawnier in northern race. Eye brown. Bill and feet black.*
FEMALE: *As male; throat rufous. Tail shorter; all feathers broadly webbed.*
IMMATURES: *As female; male tail not gained until 3–4 years.*
DOWNY YOUNG: *Dense, black with crown tuft in first days, later grey.*

VOICE
CALL: *Loud high-pitched shriek or chuck in alarm; male clicks during copulation; territorial call a resounding chonk-chonk in southern race, rippling descending trill in northern.*
SONG: *Protracted, non-stop medley of rich cadences, rasps, clicks, and mimicked calls.*

NESTING
Breeds May–October, mainly June–July. Nest a bulky dome of sticks, ferns and moss, lined with moss, feathers and rootlets; secreted in banks and tree-ferns, among rocks or on tree stumps, to 3 m above ground. Egg: one; pale purple-brown, streaked and blotched black; oblong-oval, about 64 x 45 mm. Incubation about six weeks, by female. Young fledge in six weeks.

DISTRIBUTION
Wet eucalypt and rainforests of coastal eastern Australia and Great Dividing Range, south to Dandenong Range, Vic., and north to Ballandean, Qld; introduced in Tasmania. Two races: one in northern New England, NSW–Qld; the other everywhere else.

The female Superb Lyrebird builds a nest and tends the young alone. Here she is removing the chick's droppings; she drops them in water, or buries them.

A male Superb Lyrebird spreads its tail feathers into a fan and breaks into song. To attract a mate, it builds a mound and stages an elaborate display.

Albert's Lyrebird *Menura alberti* BONAPARTE, 1850

SMALLER AND MORE RUSSET than the Superb Lyrebird, Albert's Lyrebird also has a much more limited distribution, being restricted to the rainforests around the old volcanic craters straddling the New South Wales–Queensland border. Its adaptations for display seem to be less specialised too. Lyrates and filmy plumes are poorly developed in the shorter tail, and males do not scratch up earth mounds for their performances. Rather, each bird clears a few small circular, vine-crossed patches of ground in its territory, or displays from platforms of vines and fallen branches or even a rock or log.

OTHER NAMES
None.

IDENTIFICATION
LENGTH: *Male about 850 mm, including 450 mm tail; female 750 mm.*
MALE: *Upper parts plain deep chestnut. Throat rufous; rest of underparts grey-buff, deepening to russet under tail. Tail dusky, the two central feathers ribbon-like and curving in to cross one another, the 10 flanking it tipped filamentous, silvery on underside, and the two outermost (lyrates) rather straight, short and broadly rounded.*
FEMALE: *As male; shorter tail lacks filamentary feathers.*
IMMATURES: *Similar to female.*

VOICE
CALL: *Loud, high-pitched shriek in alarm; loud, frog-like* bronk-bronk *in territorial advertisement.*
SONG: *Long, loud rich medley; also mimics other species; often many curious rattling noises.*

NESTING
Breeds June–July. Nest a large dome of sticks, roots and moss, on rocks or cliff faces, in tree ferns, on stumps or on the ground. Egg: one; pale purple-brown blotched and streaked with black; oblong-oval, about 67 x 43 mm. Incubation six weeks, by female.

DISTRIBUTION
Subtropical rainforest from Mistake Range, Qld, to Nightcap Range, NSW. No races.

Males sing for up to four hours a day during the peak of breeding —in mid-winter—each stanza continuing unbroken for up to an hour. As with the Superb Lyrebird, some song is given without tail fanning. In full performance, however, the tail is erected up and forward over the back, then spread and lowered until the bird is almost cocooned, its silvery fan contrasting with russet undertail coverts. Singing and mimicking, the bird begins to prance, lifting each foot in turn, and turning this way and that to 'beam' its voice to rival territorial males. It probably copulates with any female attracted at or near the mound. No pair bond is formed.

Males and females appear to have separate but overlapping territories, and females build the nest, incubate and rear young unaided. Like the Superb Lyrebird, they feed in the litter of the forest floor, scratching over debris for insects, worms and land snails, and run to escape danger, rarely flying except up into the forest subcanopy to roost at night. After breeding, territories break down, as birds group in twos and threes and wander locally.

In its distribution, Albert's Lyrebird is restricted to a small area of subtropical rainforest, and they feed in the litter of the forest floor.

Rufous Scrub-bird

Atrichornis rufescens
(RAMSAY, 1867)

OTHER NAMES
None.

IDENTIFICATION
LENGTH: *Male about 180 mm; female about 165 mm.*
MALE: *Upper parts uniformly dark rufous-brown, finely barred black. Throat white-grey. Breast heavily mottled black, running in broad band down either side; centre lower breast and belly buff, deepening under tail. Wings short, rounded; tail tapered and round-tipped. Eye deep brown. Bill brown. Feet red-brown.*
FEMALE: *As male but pattern on underparts duller, buffier.*
IMMATURES: *Plain reddish, browner above.*
DOWNY YOUNG: *Densely tufted grey-white.*

VOICE
CALL: *Sharp squeaks and feeble* zit *calls by both sexes in alarm.*
SONG: *High, loud* cheep, cheep, cheep *by male, falling and accelerating, to advertise territory; ringing notes and churrs, accompanied by mimicry.*

NESTING
Breeds September–December. Domed nest with short tunnel leading to small side entrance; of interlaced rushes and grass with some leaves. Nest chamber completely lined with hard cardboard-like substance made from decayed rush and wood. Built close to ground in rushes or thick shrub. Eggs: two; pink-buff with blotches of red-brown mostly at larger end; oblong-oval, about 23 x 18 mm.

DISTRIBUTION
Scattered from Mistake Range, Qld, to Barrington Tops, NSW, along coast ranges; confined mainly to national parks. Occurs in subtropical and temperate rainforest and wet temperate forest where a dense understorey has developed. Beech Nothofagus *appears to be primary habitat. No races.*

A male Rufous Scrub-bird, with head thrown back, sings its penetrating territorial song in the breeding season.

SCRUB-BIRDS ARE A SMALL, very distinctive group of birds that, found only in Australia, live their entire lives under the cover of dense vegetation. They creep, run and hide beneath every nook and cranny of their territories without almost ever taking to wing. That they can hardly fly is reflected in their furcula—or wish-bone—which is cartilaginous. This, their reticulately scaled feet and unusual syrinx or voice-box worked by only three intrinsic muscles suggests that they are related to lyrebirds. Like lyrebirds, they have loud, penetrating voices which males use to protect their territories during breeding; and they mimic well.

The Rufous Scrub-bird, confined today to ranges along the mid-east coast, lives in pockets of dense undergrowth and shrubbery in rainforest and along its edges into very wet eucalypts. A close cover to at least a metre high, an ever-moist microclimate at ground level and abundant leaf litter are essential. There they poke about, feeding on insects, worms, other invertebrates and seeds, sometimes working some distance completely under the litter.

Males occupy widely dispersed territories of about one or two hectares, at an average density of four territories per square kilo-metre in prime habitat; often they are out of earshot of one another. It is only when breeding that males sing much, unlike the Noisy Scrub-bird. They do so with wings drooped, breasts flared, and tails raised from various vantage points through their territories. Females also occupy their own territories, of about the same size which only partly overlap male ground. Although their pair-bond may often be closer than lyrebirds', the female probably builds the nest, incubates, and rears the young alone.

Because of clearing, the world's population of Rufous Scrub-birds is now limited largely to fragmented pockets of suitable habi-tat in national parks and state forests; and the total population may number little more than 1000. Habitat is the bottle-neck, for although 200 plus pairs produce 100 plus young a year, the surplus has no place to go. Here selective logging in rainforest, to increase the density of undergrowth, may be of benefit.

Noisy Scrub-bird *Atrichornis clamosus* (GOULD, 1844)

A TERRESTRIAL BIRD, the Noisy Scrub-bird spends most of its time on or close to the ground in the dense heathy understorey and thickets of thickly vegetated drainage lines and swamp edges where the microclimate is permanently moist and deep leaf litter covers the ground. It is a fast and agile runner but a poor flier, using flight mainly to move from shrub to shrub or from shrub to the ground. Because of this persistent habit of keeping under cover and its subdued plumage it is rarely seen.

The Noisy Scrub-bird was first discovered in Australia by John Gilbert, at Drakesbrook in the Darling Range, WA, in 1842, isolated on the other side of Australia from the Rufous Scrub-bird. It was subsequently found elsewhere in the southwest—at Margaret River, Augusta, Torbay, and in the Albany area. But after 1899 it was not recorded again, and was believed to be extinct—until 1961 when it was rediscovered at Two Peoples Bay. To protect the bird, a planned townsite was cancelled and a nature reserve established. There the population, judged by the number of singing males, has increased from 45 in 1970 to 137 in 1983. In 1983, ten males and six females were translocated to Mt Manypeaks, 15 kilometres to the northeast of Two Peoples Bay.

Each male Noisy Scrub-bird occupies a territory which it defends throughout the year with a loud song that carries for over a kilometre. The males' singing increases at the start of the breeding season and remains at a high but variable level until breeding is finished. The males also have a 'short song' that incorporates modified songs of other species and is used when interacting with other males or females. Females only give the two alarm calls.

Territories are well dispersed and average six hectares with a core area of one to two in which the male spends up to 80 per cent of his time. At the start of the breeding season, presumed young males may establish small (one–two hectare) feeding territories in sub-optimal habitat where they may sing for up to 12 weeks. Although males may be polygamous, only one breeding female has ever been found in each of their territories. Some females may breed well outside a territory; these seem to be either young females or older females breeding in unoccupied territories.

The female builds the nest, incubates and feeds the chick unaided. She may build another nest and re-lay if the first egg is lost, but not if the chick dies. Nest building takes her about three weeks. For the first week after hatching, the female broods the chick at night and after every feed. The chick is fed a wide variety of invertebrates, including spiders, grasshoppers, cockroaches and various larvae and the occasional small frog or gecko. After it fledges, it stays with its mother for a month or more, possibly until its post-fledging moult when three months old. Females breed in their first year but males probably not until three years old.

Noisy Scrub-birds feed on a variety of invertebrates—insects, spiders, worms and larvae—taken mainly on the ground, flushing insects from the litter or turning leaves over with a quick flick of the head. Occasionally they also search up into thick shrubbery under trees.

OTHER NAMES
Western Scrub-Bird.

IDENTIFICATION
LENGTH: *Male about 230 mm; female about 200 mm.*
MALE: *Upper parts brown with fine cross bars of dark brown. White throat forms inverted V above black upper breast; lower breast dull white; belly and flanks buff-brown to rufous. Wings short and rounded, tail long. Eye dark brown. Upper mandible red-brown, lower pink-white. Feet pink-brown.*
FEMALE: *Similar; no black on breast.*
IMMATURES: *Head to upper back plain cinnamon-brown; lower back to tail grey; throat and breast cinnamon, grading to grey on flanks and belly.*
DOWNY YOUNG: *Dense, tufted, grey.*

VOICE
CALL: *Two alarm notes, loud and harsh* squeak *and softer* zit. *Three-note call* zip da dee.
SONG: *Two variable songs. Territorial song, sharp loud penetrating whistles of 10–15 notes in accelerating descending crescendo, often ending with sharp crack. Short song, more tuneful but softer than territorial song. Does not mimic other birds.*

NESTING
Egg-laying late May to October. Domed nest 200 mm long, 180 mm high and 150 mm wide, of rushes with a few leaves and twigs. Short platform leads to small side entrance. Bottom of nest chamber lined with cardboard-like substance. Nest usually in rushes or tangled shrub about 200 mm above ground. Egg: one; pale buff blotched with orange-brown, especially at larger end; long-oval, 29 x 20 mm. Incubation 36–38 days, by female. Young fledge in three to four weeks.

DISTRIBUTION
Formerly in pockets around extreme southwest coast; now known only from Two Peoples Bay, east of Albany, WA. Sedentary in dense moist copse and thicket in coastal heath and low eucalypt forest. No races.

The Noisy Scrub-bird was thought to be extinct until it was rediscovered at Two Peoples Bay east of Albany, Western Australia, in 1961.

Singing Bushlark *Mirafra javanica* HORSFIELD, 1821

The Singing Bushlark lives in open grasslands where it favours areas with cropped grasses. It nests on the ground, and feeds on seeds and insects.

IN TONE RATHER THAN PATTERN, Singing Bushlarks vary much around Australia, no less than 10 races having been recognised at one time or another. They change from rich rufous in the Pilbara to deep russet-brown on the back across northern Australia, to pale rufous in the central eastern inland, and to blackish above and grey-white below in the southeast of South Australia. Many of the changes match the colour of regional soils, rufous populations occurring often on red soils, dark-brown-plumaged ones on black soils and greyer plumaged ones on grey soils. Such apparent adaptation may aid camouflage in these ground-living birds and therefore survival. But it does not explain all variation, for many local populations vary greatly in colour within themselves.

Singing Bushlarks are rather communal birds, nesting in loose groups and wandering locally in parties of one or two to several hundred after breeding. Regional influxes can be quite dramatic—and erratic—in the Murray–Darling basin. Inhabiting dense to open short grasslands and crops, the larks forage on the ground for fallen seeds and insects, walking nimbly on bent feet, without stopping and bobbing as pipits do. If surprised, they may freeze; and if flushed they rise to flick-flutter low over the grass, tail down and wings beating fast in spasms, before dropping to cover. Spasms of wing beating are interspersed with short, diving glides on downswept wings, giving flight a characteristic jerkiness.

During breeding—spring to early summer—males perform typically lark-like song flights, hovering high and singing richly by night as well as day. When dropping to earth after the display, they do so in stages unlike the Skylark which dives directly, and may sing in low undulating flights. They will also perch on wires and fence posts and sing from there as well.

OTHER NAMES
Cinnamon Bushlark, Horsfield's Bushlark.

IDENTIFICATION
LENGTH: *130 mm.*
ADULTS: *Sexes similar. Colour varies considerably within Australia but basic pattern of plumage is constant. Upper parts brown with darker central streaks to feathers; feather edgings can vary from buff or rufous to grey and streaks from brown to black. Rufous patch at base of main flight feathers. Outer tail feathers white. Distinct buff eyebrow. Underparts paler than back, varying from off-white to light brown with dark spots on throat and breast. Eye grey-brown to red-brown. Sparrow-like, short and blunt bill, brown above, paler below. Feet pale flesh-brown to grey-brown.*
IMMATURES: *Similar to adults but generally paler with lighter edges to primaries and light tips to crown feathers forming crescents.*

VOICE
CALL: *Single, slurred* chirrup *call when on the ground or alerted.*
SONG: *Rich, varied, tinkling song, including mimicry of other species.*

NESTING
Breeds September–January in south and following extensive rains inland; in north breeding probably related to start of wet season. Nest small, usually fully or partly domed, of dried grasses and fine roots, thickly lined with soft dry grasses; placed on the ground under edge of tussock or in cereal crops. Eggs: two to four; dull white, freckled with dark grey to grey-brown; oval to oblong-oval, about 15 x 13 mm.

DISTRIBUTION
Open grasslands from open plains of interior to short cropped pastures of settled areas. Ranges from Nigeria to Arabia, India, Indonesian Archipelago and New Guinea. About 10 races.

Skylark *Alauda arvensis* LINNÉ, 1758

ONE OF EUROPE'S MOST MELODIOUS SONGSTERS, the Skylark was introduced to Australia in the mid- to late 1800s. The earliest introductions, at Geelong in 1850 or 1854, and at Melbourne, Adelaide, Sydney and in Tasmania between 1855 and 1866 proved successful. Those in Queensland in 1869 and in southwestern Australia in 1912 failed, partly because of unsuitable habitat. Skylarks are birds of temperate, moist pastures and short-grassed fields, and have followed the spread of these man-made habitats throughout most of southeastern Australia.

Skylarks forage, roost and nest on the ground. Singly, in pairs, or loose groups of 10–30 or more after breeding, they walk through the grass or over the ground on flexed legs, picking up seeds, shoots, insects and other invertebrates. If disturbed they may freeze in a crouch or flush, either to flutter on quivering wings before dropping to cover or more usually covering longer distances with strong undulating flight. A pale trailing edge to the wing is a useful field guide. Occasionally they land to sing on stumps and fence-posts when they may raise a short crest.

Skylarks breed in dispersed pairs. Males have a song-flight for which they are justly famous. Rising on quivering wings, they ascend almost vertically for up to 100 metres, singing a continuous medley of rippling trills, and stay aloft for many minutes before sinking and then dropping silently to ground, wings closed. On the ground, the male displays to his mate, wings drooped and tail and crest raised; she responds with quivering wings and spread tail. Young are incubated by the female, fed by both sexes, and two to three broods may be raised in a season.

Skylarks, like other larks, are distinguished structurally from similar-looking pipits by their rudimentary outermost primaries, reticulate scaling along the sides of the tarsus, no pessulus in the syrinx or voice box, and remarkably long, spurred hind claw.

OTHER NAMES
Common Skylark, English Skylark.

IDENTIFICATION
LENGTH: *170–190 mm.*
ADULTS: *Sexes similar; male larger. Upper parts pale brown with strong black shaft streaks to feathers, giving a mottled look. Small erectile crest on head. Thin buff line over eye outlines brown ear coverts. Two outer tail feathers on each side edged white. Throat, lower breast and belly cream; upper breast and flanks dull brown with black streaks. Eye brown. Bill and feet horn-buff.*
IMMATURES: *Similar to adults but paler with more white behind and below eye; light edges to feathers of upper parts, forming scallops on crown; breast streaking reduced.*

VOICE
CALL: *Clear, slow* chirr-r-up.
SONG: *High-pitched, musical warbling, often continuing during 'song flight'; also sung from the ground or a perch.*

NESTING
Breeds September–January. Cup-shaped nest of dried grasses, built on the ground in grass. Eggs: three to five; dull white, thickly speckled with brown; tapered-oval, about 24 x 17 mm. Incubation 11–13 days, by female. Young fledge in about 10 days.

DISTRIBUTION
Introduced to southeastern Australia, including Tasmania; locally nomadic. Also temperate regions of Europe and Asia, where extensively migratory. About 20 races; probably one—from northwestern Europe—in Australia.

The Skylark, introduced from Europe, is found in moist grasslands, including golf courses, throughout the southeast of Australia.

White-backed Swallow *Cheramoeca leucosternum* (GOULD, 1841)

The White-backed Swallow rarely lands on the ground.

WHITE-BACKED SWALLOWS—Australia's only endemic species— are communal birds. Although they disperse to hawk and feed on the wing along inland watercourses and out over lakes by day, they return to burrows in sand banks, creek banks, roadside cuttings and gravel pits to roost at night. Up to 80 birds may form a colony, 20–30 of which will roost in a single burrow. Each colony digs out a number of burrows about four–five centimetres in diameter and 50–80 centimetres deep; these are used for both roosting and nesting. Only one pair of nesting birds occupies a burrow, and they usually leave the area after breeding.

OTHER NAMES
None.

IDENTIFICATION
LENGTH: *140–150 mm.*
ADULTS: *Sexes similar. Forehead, upper back, throat and upper breast white; crown mottled with pale brown. Lores, back of neck, lower back, wings, deeply forked tail, belly and vent black. Underwing coverts white. Eye dark brown. Bill black. Feet dusky grey.*
IMMATURES: *As adults but duller; crown grey; black areas dusky; feet pink-grey; tail squarer.*

VOICE
CALL: *Dry* jk, jk *in flight.*
SONG: *Attractive twittering song.*

NESTING
Breeds August–December. Nest a chamber at end of tunnel about 50 mm in diameter and one metre long, dug into bank of creek or cutting, lined with fine grasses, small leaves and rootlets. Eggs:

four to six, usually five; glossy, pure white; oval, about 17 x 11 mm. Incubation about two weeks, probably by both sexes.

DISTRIBUTION
Open fields and lightly timbered country inland, usually near water, though generally avoids wetter areas. Sedentary or nomadic. No races.

In their burrows roosting birds cluster together in a chamber at the end, often going into a state of torpor for several days or more at a time during bad weather in winter. This practice rather than migration may be their strategy for surviving winters.

White-backed Swallows feed on small flying insects, taking them in their broad mouths in graceful aerial manoeuvres with much martin-like barking, swooping and fluttering. To drink they skim down low along the surface of water in flight. They occasionally rest in small groups on power lines and bare high branchlets and never come to ground except to burrow, nest and sleep.

Barn Swallow

Hirundo rustica LINNÉ, 1758

ONE OF THE BEST-KNOWN BREEDING migrants in the Northern Hemisphere, the Barn Swallow reaches the northern coast of Australia in small numbers each monsoonal summer. Australia is the end of the line for the race that breeds in eastern Asia and 'winters' in vast numbers through tropical Malaysia and Indonesia, from October–November to April. Although the birds may trickle into Australia all along the northern coastline, most seem to arrive in the northwest, from Derby to Cobourg Peninsula, where flocks of up to several hundred sometimes gather.

Both in its breeding range and at wintering quarters, the Barn Swallow forages low over all types of country, particularly surface water, avoiding only thick forests. In habits it resembles the Welcome Swallow, commonly roosting communally on wires, buildings and bare tree twigs, and spending much of its time on the wing, from dawn till dusk, in pursuit of its food: small flying insects, particularly flies, midges and mosquitoes. Its flight is graceful and wayward, blending swoops, glides, turns and dives. It also picks insects from the surface of water, plants or the ground in flight and drinks by sipping as it skims along.

Both sexes build the nest and feed the young, but the female does most of the incubating which takes 14–15 days. Young fledge at 17–24 days, allowing more than one brood a season.

Both sexes of Barn Swallows share in the feeding of their offspring.

OTHER NAMES
Chimney Swallow, European Swallow.

IDENTIFICATION
LENGTH: *140–160 mm; tail streamers longer in male.*
ADULTS: *Sexes similar. Upper parts metallic blue-black. Forehead and throat chestnut-red or -yellow; blue-black band below throat. Rest of underparts buff to white. Underwing coverts white. Deeply forked dusky tail with white bar on underside. Eye dark brown. Bill and feet black.*
IMMATURES: *As adults but lack sheen; short tail-streamers.*

VOICE
CALL: *High pitched, often repeated* tswit

or tswee; *rapid* twitter *when excited.*
SONG: *Weak, a mixture of rapid twittering and warbling, chiefly on wing.*

NESTING
Breeds March–June in Eurasia; often several broods in a season. Nest a bulky cup of pellets of mud and plant fibre, lined with feathers; often placed against building or occasionally in cave entrances. Eggs: four to six; glossy white, spotted with various shades of brown, lavender, grey or dusky; oval, about 20 x 14 mm. Incubation 14–15 days, mostly by female. Young fledge in 17–24 days.

DISTRIBUTION
May occur anywhere across northern

Australia—map indicates regular sitings; vagrants recorded Mt Lofty Ranges, SA, and McGrath's Hill, NSW. Breeding range throughout North America, Europe and temperate Asia; populations in extreme south of breeding range apparently sedentary. Wintering grounds in tropical South America, Africa and southern and southeastern Asia through Indonesia to New Guinea and northern Australia. Six races; one, small and white-bellied, reaching Australia from eastern Asia.

Welcome Swallow *Hirundo neoxena* GOULD, 1842

THE WELCOME SWALLOW IS AUSTRALIA'S representative of the holarctic Barn Swallow and the similar but broader-billed and squarer-tailed Pacific Swallow of Indonesia and Melanesia. It builds the same cup-shaped mud nest under eaves, in open sheds, beneath culverts and bridges, and inside mine shafts and hollow trees. It has the same twittering song, the same russet forehead and throat and plain back. It flocks after breeding and roosts gregariously in groups of up to 100 or more at night. And it forages in the same way, winging out and about from vantage perches, to skim, swoop, circle, bank and dive gracefully after small flying insects—moths, flies and midges—often over water.

The Welcome Swallow is partially migratory. Avoiding the deserts, it breeds over spring and summer around the better-watered regions of southern Australia north to about Shark Bay in the west and Cairns in the east. Man-made clearings and structures have enabled it to spread, the clearings providing foraging space and the buildings and other structures nest sites.

After breeding, many but not all swallows shift a little northwards. While there is little obvious movement in the west, most Tasmanian birds flock to the mainland; those on the southeastern mainland move towards central Australia; and those breeding farther north may move to Torres Strait for the winter.

As spring comes, many birds return to the same nest of previous years, or a site nearby, often with the same partner. Both sexes build, settling beside earth pools to pick up mud. They walk awkwardly, shuffling along with the help of their wings.

Young Welcome Swallows are dependent on their parents for about three weeks after fledging.

OTHER NAMES
Australian Swallow, House Swallow.

IDENTIFICATION
LENGTH: *About 150 mm; outer tail streamers longer, more attenuated in male.*
ADULTS: *Sexes similar. Upper parts metallic blue-black; flight feathers duskier. Forehead and throat russet, separated by black lores. Rest of underparts whitish fawn, edged white on undertail coverts. Underwing coverts dusky. Deeply forked tail dusky, with white subterminal bar on underside, broader and more complete in male than female. Eye dark brown. Bill black. Feet dark flesh-grey.*
IMMATURES: *As adults but lack body sheen; tail more square-cut with vestigial outer streamers; russet paler.*

VOICE
CALL: *Sharp chep in contact, usually in flight; high-pitched, whistled seet in alarm, often repeated.*
SONG: *Warbling and twittering notes strung together and usually sung from a perch for up to 15 or more seconds.*

NESTING
Breeds August–December; often two or more broods per season. Nest a cup of pellets of mud and vegetation, usually plastered to vertical surface of culvert, wall of a building, side of a bridge, mine shaft, tree hollow or cave wall; thickly lined with grass, animal hair and feathers. Eggs: four to six, usually four or five; white, freckled and spotted red-brown, usually at larger end; oval, about 19 x 13 mm.

DISTRIBUTION
Throughout open areas of eastern and southern Australia, including Tasmania; vagrant in northwestern Australia. Nomadic and partially migratory after breeding, reaching Torres Strait, northwestern Australia and southern New Guinea. Self-introduced to New Zealand; also on Lord Howe and Norfolk Islands. No races.

Tree Martin *Hirundo nigricans* VEILLOT, 1817

The Tree Martin lives in eucalypt woodland, where it gathers in loose colonies. A single tree may contain several nests—holes lined with leaves or grass.

OF THE FEW SWALLOW-LIKE birds in Australia, the Tree Martin is probably the most common and widespread. Largely a bird of the bigger eucalypts—which offer roosting and nesting holes—it spends most of the day on the wing feeding above the treetops. It also feeds on the swarms of tiny insects that gather over water, and it will even dive down to pick up insects floating on the surface. In this situation the Tree Martin often mixes with the Fairy Martin and the Welcome Swallow. It can be identified from the former, however, by its blue-black head and from the latter by its square tail and off-white rump.

Like them, the Tree Martin has a short but very broad bill for catching insects on the wing, as well as long and pointed wings with only nine obvious primaries to power graceful, effortless flight, and glossed downy plumage that reduces friction in the air; swiftlets have similar plumage. Like all swallows, Tree Martins are fitted for life as aerial foragers, going to trees only to rest, roost and nest, and almost never landing on the ground except to sun or to pick up mud for nest-building. Its feet are weak and tiny, able to grasp perches and little else. When landing to rest, they flutter gently up to a twig or wire to gain direct purchase with their feet, or plunge into hollow roosting or nesting spouts in full flight; apart from inept shuffling they can barely move on their legs.

Tree Martins are regularly migratory in Australia. In spring they spread out across all wooded parts of the continent south of the Tropic of Capricorn and to Tasmania to breed, frequenting large spreading trees near water. In autumn most—but not all—shift north. Large flocks gather then in more open areas, sometimes perching in long lines on telegraph wires and fence lines. Many of these spread through far northern Australia and others fly beyond to islands in the east Sunda arc.

Tree Martins nest in small holes and ledges inside trees, often colonially in several neighbouring trees; sometimes a single entrance leads to several nest chambers. If the entrance is too large or nesting ledges inside a hollow trunk too flat, the birds will shove and shape them with mud. The same nests are used year after year.

Communal roosting is spectacular. At dusk Tree Martins circle slowly around the treetops, their numbers swelling; then, as light fails, they dive vertically down, one by one, to disappear straight into a tree hole. This course is usual during nesting. At other times they may prefer dense rushes in swamps and then flocks of hundreds may dive to roost simultaneously.

OTHER NAMES
Australian Tree-martin, Tree Swallow.

IDENTIFICATION
LENGTH: *120–130 mm.*
ADULTS: *Sexes similar. Crown to mid-back glossed blue-black; flight feathers and shallowly forked tail duskier. Rump off-white. Forehead buff. All underparts dull off-white, finely streaked grey on throat. Eye brown. Bill black. Feet flesh-grey.*
IMMATURES: *As adults but lack dorsal glossing; forehead duller.*

VOICE
CALL: *A dry* drrrt; *clear* tweeet.
SONG: *Animated twittering, in flight and at perch.*

NESTING
Breeds July–January; loosely colonial. Nest usually a tree hole, but cliff holes, caves and holes in city buildings used. Base usually lined with small dried leaves, sometimes feathers and grass. Eggs: three to five; dull white, speckled with brown and mauve; oval, about 18 x 13 mm. Incubation about 15–16 days, by both sexes.

DISTRIBUTION
Throughout Australia, in wooded habits. Migratory, ranging north to New Guinea, east to Solomons and west to Timor and Moluccas in winter; straggles to New Zealand. Two races; one, large, in Australia.

Fairy Martin *Hirundo ariel* (GOULD, 1842)

FAIRY MARTINS ARE THE MOST COMMUNAL of Australian swallows. Whether nesting or foraging on migration after breeding, they keep to tight flocks of a dozen or so to some hundreds. They feed weaving about, fluttering lightly and gliding, banking and circling effortlessly, hawking for small flying insects through open woodland glades, and over paddocks and particularly open swamps, rivers and streams. During low skimming flight over water they often hesitate momentarily and dip their bills in the water, apparently to drink or take insects. They roost in their nests or on ledges under banks, bridges, and overhangs, often clasping vertical surfaces; they rest there and on small twigs in the open.

Fairy Martins are partly migratory. In the west the birds seem to be local rather than seasonal nomads. But in the east they shift regularly north in autumn, reaching Arnhem Land and Cape York Peninsula, and return south to breed in spring; few groups are left in the southeast south of Sydney in winter. Breeding colonies range north to the southern Kimberleys and southern Arnhem Land.

In breeding colonies, the birds build rows of close-packed, retort-shaped nests of mud that may run to hundreds under overhangs of any kind; this position allows the birds to fly straight into their nest entrances to land and to take off by simply falling into the air. By day there is almost continual movement at the colony: birds come and go as pairs feed their young and relieve one another in incubation and brooding. A high-pitched twittering begins before dawn—and continues through the day—as one bird, then another and another joins in, the sound increasing until the first birds leave to feed at daybreak. Several birds may combine to construct or repair one nest, working persistently until it is built, when disputes over occupancy often arise; sparrows, pardalotes and Zebra Finches also usurp the nests.

Few Fairy Martins seem to rear more than one brood a season. Although breeding may proceed over several months, it seems that first nesters vacate their nests if successful, leaving them for others to take over. Membership of colonies may be in permanent flux. The core of each colony nonetheless returns to the same site to breed each year, at least in eastern Australia.

OTHER NAMES
Bottle Swallow, Cliff Swallow.

IDENTIFICATION
LENGTH: *115–120 mm.*
ADULTS: *Sexes similar. Head rust-coloured. Back and scapulars glossed blue-black; rump white. Wings and square tail dusky. Underparts white streaked grey on throat and washed russet on sides. Eye dark brown. Bill and feet black.*
IMMATURES: *As adults, without dorsal gloss.*

VOICE
Sweet high-pitched churrs and twitters.

NESTING
Breeds spring and early summer, August–January, or, in far north, May–March. Nest in massed colonies, roughly bottle- or pear-shaped, with entrance tunnel, 250 mm long, usually sloping downwards from nesting chamber, 150–200 mm in diameter; built of mud pellets and lined with fine grasses and feathers; on various sites such as caves, rock overhangs, cliffs, culverts, bridges, creek banks, and old buildings often near or above water. Nests in colonies. Eggs: four or five; dull white, often faintly speckled with rust-brown or rufous, generally at larger end; oval, about 17 x 12 mm. Incubation about 15 days, by both sexes.

DISTRIBUTION
Throughout mainland Australia, mainly in open areas; vagrants to Tasmania and New Guinea. Nomadic and partly migratory, breeding north to 14°S. No races.

The Fairy Martin nests in colonies, building rows of bottle-shaped nests of mud pellets. This bird clasps the entrance neck.

Richard's Pipit is a ground-dweller in open fields, shores and steppe. It is found in all parts of Australia except densely forested regions.

Richard's Pipit *Anthus novaeseelandiae* (GMELIN, 1789)

IN OUTWARD APPEARANCE, Richard's Pipit resembles a lark, the result of converging adaptation to similar ecological niches. Both are dull brown streaked with camouflaging black over the back and have white flashes down either side of their tails; and both live on the ground in open country where the pipit occupies a particularly wide range of habitats, from wet heaths and pastures to arid shrub steppes, samphire, beach and grassed clearings in woodland. Much bare ground interspersed with spare patches of cover is preferred. That the similarities between pipits and larks are superficial is revealed by deeper-seated differences in their structure. Pipits are trimmer birds and longer in leg, and have a conventional syrinx or voice box and conventionally scaled tarsi, for a passerine; their juveniles, too, are simply dully marked on the upper parts, not 'scaled' as young larks are.

Richard's Pipit, the most wide-ranging of all pipits—from Africa and Eurasia to Australia and New Zealand—also differs from larks in its habits. Although it runs along the ground to feed, it darts here and there to pick its food—small grasshoppers, ants, caterpillars, beetles and other insects and occasional seeds—from off leaves, plant clumps, rock crevices and the ground. Its gait in doing so is jerky, broken by frequent stops to perch on low stones or vantage projections, teetering the tail up and down as wagtails do. If alarmed it flies to the top of a bush, bare branch or fence post. Flight is low and swift with long undulations, and at the bottom of each undulation the tail is often fanned, flashing its white sides.

Richard's Pipit eats, sleeps and nests on the ground. Wherever its habitat occurs across Australia, there it will be found whatever the climate, from Tasmania to Arnhem Land, sea-level to the summit of Mt Kosciusko. It colonises newly cleared ground quickly. Despite this, it is not migratory nor markedly nomadic. Many—but not all—Tasmanian birds evidently shift to the mainland for winter, and populations in the Snowy Mountains descend to lower altitudes then, but most birds do little else than band together in loose groups of up to 100 to wander locally.

To breed they break up into pairs with often close territories. Like larks, males display and advertise with a song flight—but its form differs. Rising from a low vantage perch, they fly high in quivering dives on spread wings, swooping and rising, each dip accompanied by a sweet but quavering trill which reaches peak volume at the bottom of the dip. The flight ends with an abrupt dive to the ground. Males also trill from vantage perches on rocks, stumps and bushes. The female mainly incubates while the male stands guard nearby; both feed the young.

Despite the range of climates in which they live, Richard's Pipits vary little in their plumage tones across Australia. Only those on the coastal plains of the northwest differ, being smaller and darker with heavier black spotting on the back and breast; they resemble populations in New Guinea.

OTHER NAMES
Australian Pipit, Groundlark.

IDENTIFICATION
LENGTH: *160–180 mm.*
ADULTS: *Sexes similar. Upper parts mottled brown, with dusky-centred, cream-edged feathers. Cream-white eyebrow and malar stripe flank white, dusky-lined cheeks. Flight feathers and tail dark brown, the outermost tail feathers white. Underparts cream-white, spot-streaked dusky across breast. Eye brown. Bill and feet horn-flesh.*
IMMATURES: *As adults or duller.*

VOICE
CALL: *Thin* tswee *or sparrow-like* chirrup.
SONG: *Repeated trilled* peer *in flight.*

NESTING
Breeds August–January. Nest a depression in the ground, built into shallow cup with grass, other plant materials and sometimes hair. Often sheltered by tussock, shrub, stone or piece of wood. Eggs: two to four; off-white to light brown, spotted and clouded with dark grey and brown; tapered-oval, about 23 x 17 mm. Incubation about 13–14 days, by female. Nestling period about 13–14 days.

DISTRIBUTION
In open country throughout Australia. Widespread across much of Africa and Asia to New Guinea and New Zealand. About 25 races; two in Australia.

Yellow Wagtail *Motacilla flava* LINNÉ, 1758

UNTIL A DECADE OR SO AGO, the Yellow Wagtail was only known in Australia from several records of apparent vagrants, the first at Duaringa on the Dawson River in eastern Queensland in 1905. Since then, more consistent observation along the northwest coast has shown it to be a regular, if uncommon and patchy migrant there, trickling in small numbers each summer—from November to April—from its breeding grounds in temperate and subarctic Eurasia and northern America. From there occasional birds stray further south.

Yellow Wagtails are gregarious birds on migration and at winter quarters, but groups larger than 50 are rarely seen in Australia; often they are solitary. Australia seems to receive only the overflow from main summering grounds in Indonesia. The birds arriving are a polyglot of two or possibly three races that breed from southwestern Russia to Alaska.

Wagtails, pipit-like but trimmer and longer in wing and tail and more brightly coloured, take their name from their gait. They are terrestrial birds, walking briskly with long steps, head nodding forward and back and tail teetering constantly up and down. Food—various insects, larvae, spiders and occasional molluscs and worms—is picked up as they go, often in short dashes or flutters into the air. When not feeding the birds spend much time preening, either on the ground or perching on a bare tree or stump. Their flight is graceful and undulating, in long curves with wings closed; if flushed they commonly chirrup when taking to wing. At night they roost on the ground, often in flocks at non-breeding quarters, among grass and herbage or in reedbeds.

In Australia, Yellow Wagtails frequent open wetlands, foraging along the bare shores of freshwater swamps, crops and bare bore drains, as well as over short-grassed fields and even rocky coasts. On their Eurasian breeding grounds they keep to similarly damp areas near water, from sea-level to 1000 metres or more altitude. Males fluff their plumage, draw in their heads, sing and shiver their wings in display, whether around the female on the ground or hovering over her in midair, with tail fanned down. She undertakes most of the nest-building and incubation, but both parents feed and care for the young and often rear two broods in a season.

OTHER NAMES
Barnard's Wagtail.

IDENTIFICATION
LENGTH: *160–190 mm.*
ADULTS: *Sexes similar; male larger; female browner-headed and duller creamier-yellow ventrally in all plumages. Breeding male citrine-green over upper parts; wings dusky with yellow-white feather edging. Tail dusky with outermost feathers white. Head citrine to grey with yellow to white eyebrow and malar stripe according to race. Underparts from throat to undertail rich yellow. Eye dark brown. Bill and feet grey-black. Non-breeding male duller browner citrine or greyer over head and back; eyebrow duller and yellower; underparts paler, becoming whitish.*
IMMATURES: *As adults but upper parts brown; underparts white washed buff; brown lines down sides of chin.*

VOICE
Shrill, slurred tsweep. *Brief trilling,* tsip-tsip-tsipsi.

NESTING
Breeds in Eurasia June–July. Nest a cup of plant fibres, mammal hair and sometimes moss, in depression in ground, often in thick vegetation. Eggs: usually five or six; ochre, sometimes mottled or with thin dark streaks; oval, about 19 x 14 mm. Incubation about 14–15 days, mostly by female. Young fledge in 11–13 days.

DISTRIBUTION
Breeds in Northern Hemisphere June–July and migrates south. About 18 races; two, possibly three reaching Australia.

The Yellow Wagtail is a rare visitor. It breeds in Eurasia, and migrates south for the northern winter. Only a few reach northern Australia each year.

Black-faced Cuckoo-shrike *Coracina novaehollandiae* (GMELIN, 1789)

CUCKOO-SHRIKES—SO NAMED BECAUSE of their cuckoo-like form and flight and shrike-like bills—are distinctive, medium-sized songbirds that paradoxically hardly sing. Most of their notes are metallic grinds, churrs and hisses, and even their most animated territorial singer during breeding—the White-winged Triller—does little else than chatter loudly.

Just as characteristic are their meagre cobweb-bound nests and dense and usually grey plumage which, sleek on the outside, is matted and downy inside and furnished with powder downs along the sides of the body under the wings. Woodswallows are the only other songbirds to have such downs. Feathering on the rump is densest of all and somewhat spiny and may be raised in a hump in display and defence by brooding birds.

The Black-faced is the most widespread of cuckoo-shrikes. In Australia it frequents all more open forests and woodlands and is partly nomadic, partly migratory. After breeding in late summer and autumn, pairs and family parties often group in loose flocks of half-a-dozen to a hundred or more and roam widely. Movements are generally northerly. Most—but not all—birds leave Tasmania and the southern tablelands of southeastern Australia in winter—hence one of their names, Summerbird—and it is then that large numbers appear on Cape York Peninsula and across southern New Guinea. Many are juveniles.

Each spring, flocks disperse and adults appear to return to the same breeding territory year after year, probably remating with the same partner. In display, they flutter-fly in circles among the trees of their territory, uttering long sequences of grinding metallic trills. Male and female share nest-building, seeking positions on open horizontal forks, usually near the end of a branch and always shaded from above. Many forks are tested for suitability, the birds squatting in one, then another, simulating brooding position, until one is finally chosen. Both sexes incubate and feed the young, and defend them by diving steeply and clapping their bills at intruders. The nest is so small that growing nestlings end up sitting on it rather than in it; many are blown out in windy weather.

Like most cuckoo-shrikes, the Black-faced are tree-living birds and forage on a variety of large insects and occasional fruits and perhaps even nestlings of other birds taken among branches and foliage. Weak in foot but strong in wing they capture prey not by clambering about but by pounce-diving on to it from an open vantage perch. Their technique is to fly from tree to tree, pausing briefly on each to look about before moving on. In this way they cover large areas, and few breeding territories are less than five hectares. Occasionally the birds also drop to the ground for food and will hover over it.

Their flight is of long graceful undulations and when landing they characteristically refold their wings several times—hence another name, Shufflewing.

OTHER NAMES
Blue Jay, Shufflewing, Summerbird.

IDENTIFICATION
LENGTH: *320–340 mm.*
ADULTS: *Sexes alike. Upper parts plain light grey; flight feathers black, the inner becoming edged broadly grey. Tail darker, the outer feathers black and tipped broadly white. Forehead, face and throat black. Breast light grey; grading to white on belly and undertail. Eye dark brown. Bill and feet black.*
IMMATURES: *As adults but face grey with broad black line from bill through eye; breast faintly barred grey-and-white; outer flight feathers edged narrowly white in juveniles.*
DOWNY YOUNG: *Flecked darker and lighter grey over body.*

VOICE
Rolling metallic churrriink in contact by both sexes, often in flight; also higher-pitched metallic trilling chereer-chereer-chereer in display and excitement; harsh scolding skair.

NESTING
Breeds August–February. Nest a small, shallow saucer, of small sticks and bark, heavily bound with cobweb; usually near end of branch 8–20 m or more above ground. Eggs: two or three; green to olive, almost plain, or softly blotched with brown and grey; oblong-oval, about 34 x 24mm. Young fledge in about 25 days.

DISTRIBUTION
Woodlands and open forests throughout Australia. Nomadic and partial migrant to southern New Guinea, Bismarck Archipelago and Solomons; accidental in New Zealand. Also through Indonesian archipelagos to southeastern China and India. About 19 races; three in Australia: one silver-grey in Pilbara; one short-billed in Tasmania; the other everywhere else.

The Black-faced Cuckoo-shrike builds its nest on a flat fork, towards the end of a branch high above the ground.

Yellow-eyed Cuckoo-shrike

Coracina lineata (SWAINSON, 1825)

DISTINCTIVELY BARRED ON BREAST and belly, Yellow-eyed Cuckoo-shrikes are fruit-eaters that live in the canopy of rainforests and their margins. Although they do eat insects, up to 90 per cent of their diet is fresh-plucked fruit and seeds. When feeding, they forage vigorously, working rapidly through one tree before moving quickly to the next. Because they swallow fruit whole, they take only those of the right size.

In search of their food, Yellow-eyed Cuckoo-shrikes wander nomadically in flocks of up to 50 or more. In southern limits they tend to shift north in winter and south in summer, but are present year round in northeastern Queensland. Groups travel long distances, flying from tree to tree just over the rainforest canopy, calling continuously in contact, and interspersing their fluttering flight with rising, falling and circling glides on characteristically downswept wings. At night they roost communally, one or more flocks congregating in the crown of a single tree.

Breeding birds disperse to nest in pairs, and flocks—which are smaller then—probably comprise mainly non-breeders which nesting birds join temporarily and leave.

The Yellow-eyed Cuckoo-shrike swallows fruit and seeds whole.

OTHER NAMES
Barred Cuckoo-shrike, Swainson's Cuckoo-shrike.

IDENTIFICATION
LENGTH: *240–260 mm.*
ADULTS: *Sexes similar. Upper parts deep grey, paler on rump. Flight feathers black edged dark grey; tail feathers black, washed grey at base. Base of forehead, lores and front of eye black; rest of face, chin, throat and upper breast deep grey. Rest of underparts closely barred black and white. Eye yellow; bill and feet black.*

IMMATURES: *Juveniles plain white below, sometimes vaguely scalloped darker. Immatures less barred than adults; may have white flecks over ears.*

VOICE
Short, somewhat nasal, whaaan, *singly or repeated. Also trilling chatter* aw-loo-ack, aw-lak *in flight.*

NESTING
Breeds October–January. Nest a small, flat saucer of fine twigs, bark, and sometimes casuarina needles, bound with spiderweb. Placed in a horizontal fork of a tree, 15–25 m up. Eggs: two; dull white to green-grey, dotted with grey, olive and brown, often forming a zone at larger end; oblong-oval, about 31 x 22 mm.

DISTRIBUTION
Cape York Peninsula to Manning River district, NSW, erratically farther south. In rainforest and sometimes neighbouring eucalypt forest. Also in New Guinea, Bismarck Archipelago and Solomon Islands. Up to 10 races; one in Australia, barred in both sexes.

A female White-bellied Cuckoo-shrike of the northwestern form.

WHITE-BELLIED CUCKOO-SHRIKES resemble Black-faced Cuckoo-shrikes in their feeding, flight and preferred habitat; and they probably co-exist with them by taking smaller items of prey, a reflection of their smaller size. White-bellied Cuckoo-shrikes are also more solitary, gathering in family groups of three to five, and seem to be less nomadic. Pairs nest in well-dispersed territories, and both sexes appear to nest-build, incubate and feed the young.

White-bellied Cuckoo-shrikes occur in open eucalypt forests and woodlands around the north and east of Australia, avoiding only the colder mountain areas. They forage in both canopy and shrubbery, flying from vantage perches through the forest midstage, and diving on to food—both insects and fruitlets—in foliage and bark crevices. Their flight is undulating, brief bursts of flapping alternating with long curving glides; when they land, the birds settle

White-bellied Cuckoo-shrike

Coracina papuensis (GMELIN, 1788)

OTHER NAMES
Papuan Cuckoo-shrike, White-breasted Cuckoo-shrike, Little Cuckoo-shrike.

IDENTIFICATION
LENGTH: *260–280 mm.*
ADULTS: *Sexes similar; male jet black-lored, female grey-black-lored. Upper parts pale grey; flight feathers dusky, edged grey on inner secondaries. Tail dusky, outer feathers tipped white. Broad stripe from bill to eye black. Underparts almost pure white in northwest to pale grey in northeast and mid-grey in southeast. Eye brown. Bill and feet black.*
IMMATURES: *As adult female; flight feathers edged white; breast faintly barred in eastern races.*

VOICE
Shrill kiseek *in contact by both sexes, often in flight; other churring notes.*

NESTING
Breeds August–March. Nest a shallow saucer of fine twigs and bark bound with spiderweb; moulded into horizontal fork of tree, high above ground. Eggs: two or three; green with brown and grey markings; oblong-oval, about 30 x 22 mm. Incubation about 20 days, by both sexes.

DISTRIBUTION
Eucalypt woodlands and open forests, from Kimberleys to mid-western Victoria and southeast of South Australia. Also Moluccas; New Guinea, Bismarck archipelago and Solomons. About 14 races; three in Australia.

their wings by flicking one, then the other, into place. Members of groups call frequently to one another in contact.

There are three races of White-bellied Cuckoo-shrikes in Australia. One in the northwest to the eastern Gulf of Carpentaria is white-breasted, with immaculate immatures; another from Torres Strait and Cape York Peninsula south to about the Burdekin River, Queensland, is greyer white-breasted, with finely bar-breasted juveniles; the third, southeast from the Burdekin, is larger, deep grey breasted, extensively white-tipped on the tail and has frequent black-faced morphs marked with black to the belly.

The male and female Cicadabirds differ in colouring. This is a female. The male is wholly dark grey and a little larger.

Cicadabird *Coracina tenuirostris* (JARDINE, 1831)

DRY RASPING CICADA-LIKE CALLS give the Cicadabird its name. They are uttered in sporadic bursts throughout the day only during breeding by males advertising or signalling their territory. Cicadabirds are birds of the tree tops, feeding quietly in foliage there, in ones and twos, on a variety of adult and larval insects — beetles, wood crickets and stick insects—and fruit and seeds taken from leaves and under bark. In the canopy of tall forest trees they are elusive birds and easily flushed, flying in swift undulations through and just over the tree tops to perches often several hundred metres distant. This, their solitariness and their silence out of breeding make them difficult to observe.

There are two distinct populations of Cicadabirds in Australia, each with different seasonal behaviour. One, ranging patchily across the north from the Kimberleys to northern Cape York Peninsula, is sedentary or locally nomadic and has a rather low-pitched and slow territorial call. It retreats into pockets of rainforest during the dry season, May–October, and spreads out into adjacent denser eucalypt- and paperbark-forests and mangroves to breed in the monsoonal wet, November–April.

The other population, with rapidly buzzing territorial notes, is migratory along the eastern Australian coast. Each year it travels north in February–April to spend non-breeding winter months from Cape York Peninsula to New Guinea. From August–October it returns to breed, spreading out through tall eucalypt forests from the Atherton tablelands southwards to near Melbourne. Individual birds or pairs may return to the same well-spaced territories year after year, which males defend aggressively.

It seems that the male bears the brunt of building the meagre nest. If the pair are disturbed, he may dismantle the structure and rebuild again nearby—an operation taking nine to eleven days. The single large egg, laid at sunrise, is incubated only by the female. She may be fed on the nest by the male but just as often leaves to forage by herself. Both members of the pair feed the nestling, often in bursts of up to six visits an hour, interspersed with gaps of several hours. Feeding is quick, adults rarely remaining for more than a minute at the nest unless the female settles to brood.

OTHER NAMES
Caterpillar-catcher, Jardine Caterpillar-eater, Jardine Triller.

IDENTIFICATION
LENGTH: *240–270 mm; male larger.*
MALE: *Upper and underparts grey-blue. Indistinct broad black line through eye. Wing coverts and flight feathers black, edged with slate-grey; underwing coverts grey-blue. Two central tail feathers blue-grey with black tips; rest black with light blue-grey tips. Eye dark brown. Bill and feet black.*
FEMALE: *Upper parts brown-grey. Black streak from bill through eye to buff-streaked ear coverts; eyebrow off-white. Wing coverts and flight feathers dark brown, edged buff to cream. Two central tail feathers grey-brown with buff edging; rest black edged buff. Throat white; rest of underparts cream-buff, lightly barred black. Underwing coverts cinnamon.*
IMMATURES: *Similar to adult females but lightly scalloped with black and white above; barring below more conspicuous. Eye mud-brown. Bill and feet light brown.*

VOICE
Usually silent, but in breeding months males emit loud, high-pitched, slow buzzing notes repeated about 12 times: kree-kee-kree or kee-kee-kee. Alarm calls by both sexes are sharp, whistling tcheep; parrot-like tweet-tweet-tweet, wheet-wheet-wheet. Contact call, a rolling clewk-clewk or tchuit-tchuit, often by female approaching nest.

NESTING
October–March but mainly November–January. Nest a small shallow cup of fine twigs and pieces of bark interwoven with cobweb and stuck together with saliva, decorated with lichen and moss, and lined with finer material; usually placed on bare horizontal fork 3–28 m above ground. Egg: one; slightly glossy; pale blue to green-grey, spotted and blotched with red-brown and grey, with slate-grey underlying spots and blotches at times in irregular zone at larger end; oval, about 32 x 22 mm. Incubation 22 days, by female. Young fledges in 27–28 days.

DISTRIBUTION
Moderately common from Broome, WA, around coasts to near Melbourne. In northwest of range it inhabits mangroves, monsoon forests and paperbark swamps; to east it inhabits tall coastal and mountain eucalypt forests, rainforests, and mangroves. Also occurs from Celebes to Solomon Islands. Up to 33 subspecies; two in Australia: one smaller in northwest to Cape York Peninsula, the other larger, on east coast.

Ground Cuckoo-shrike *Coracina maxima* (RÜPPELL, 1839)

OTHER NAMES
Ground Jay, Long-tailed Jay.

IDENTIFICATION
LENGTH: *330–360 mm, including 200 mm tail.*
ADULTS: *Sexes similar. Crown to upper back, scapulars and breast light grey; face duskier. Lower breast, belly and rump white, finely barred with black. Wings black; long, forked tail black with white tip. Eye pale yellow; bill and feet black.*
IMMATURES: *Back of neck, mantle and throat faintly barred instead of plain grey. Wing quills finely edged with white.*

VOICE
Carrying, high, tinkling ti-yew, ti-yew by both sexes, usually in flight. Also various other, almost metallic notes; one resembles galink galink.

NESTING
Breeds August–December but in desert at any time after good rain. Nest of fine twigs, grasses, plant stems, loosely lined with wool, plant down, feathers and cobweb; well bound with cobweb into soft, fairly loose shallow bowl. Built into horizontal fork of shrubby tree such as mulga, she-oak or pine 3–23 m, but usually about 8 m, above ground. Eggs: two or three; dull green either unmarked or with indistinct brown markings; oval, tapered, about 34 x 24 mm. More than one clutch has been recorded in a nest; incubation by occupant male and female at least.

DISTRIBUTION
Savannas and shrub steppes of all interior, reaching coast sporadically except in Gulf of Carpentaria and central eastern Queensland. Nomadic and widely dispersed in small numbers. No races.

The Ground Cuckoo-shrike of the inland feeds in small groups and almost exclusively on the ground.

TRUE TO NAME, THE GROUND CUCKOO-SHRIKE walks and feeds on the ground, and is the only member of its family to do so. For this it has long legs which enable it to run well. Its usual gait, however, is a brisk walk, its head nodding backwards and forwards like a pigeon's as it wends its way between tussocks and shrubs, picking here and there for its food: grasshoppers, beetles and other insects. Occasionally it leaps into the air to catch a flying insect.

Perhaps linked to its ground-foraging is the contrasting plumage pattern on its back: startling white, barred rump, light grey head and back and black wings and tail. The reverse of ventrally contrasting patterns in other cuckoo-shrikes, it is obvious in birds taking off low from the ground and may be used as a signal in alarm or for keeping contact. Such a reversal is found also between Australian magpies and butcherbirds, the ground-living magpies also having contrasting white on the back instead of the breast.

Ground Cuckoo-shrikes are birds of open spaces, living on well- but short-grassed plains and shrub steppes throughout the drier parts of Australia, usually where there are small scattered copses of small trees for roosting and nesting. There they are nomadic, occasionally wandering out to coastal regions; they have established themselves along the central coast of Queensland since 1950.

Ground Cuckoo-shrikes are also communal birds. Although sometimes in ones and twos, they usually flock in small groups of three to seven. These probably comprise mostly family parties of parents and young of previous years. They feed and roost together, sleeping in trees and resting both on bare branches and fence posts. Flying from point to point, they flutter-and-glide more directly than other cuckoo-shrikes, on somewhat downswept wings, and utter their high-pitched tinkling contact notes continuously. On landing they settle their wings in characteristic cuckoo-shrike fashion, flicking one, then the other into place.

Nesting is also communal. Birds other than the parental pair help at the nest and contribute to the feeding, and sometimes more than one female lays in the same nest.

White-winged Triller *Lalage tricolor* (SWAINSON, 1824)

ONE OF THE MOST CONSPICUOUSLY migratory songbirds in Australia is the White-winged Triller. It arrives across southern Australia to breed each spring, the numbers settling in any one area varying from year to year according to seasonal conditions. Most nesting is south of the Tropic of Capricorn. Then in March–April they shift to the tropical north but without leaving the continent in any numbers; some birds remain there year round—in the Kimberleys and Arnhem Land—to breed. Throughout, they occur in open eucalypt and acacia woodlands and scrub.

On migration and at winter quarters the trillers usually travel in flocks of two or three to 50 or more. These groups forage widely across the countryside, taking a range of insects — beetles, grasshoppers, phasmids, larvae—and spiders, fruits and seeds. Prey may be picked off in flight, or gleaned from branches and foliage—particularly among flowering bushes—but often the birds hunt on the ground, hopping along and poking into tussocks, fallen logs and rocks, then flying on. Flight is swift and graceful, with long loping undulations.

Their movements are made obvious at all times by the showy males which, although they moult out of pied nuptial plumage into a brown-and-grey feminine dress when not breeding, retain black-and-white marked wings and tail. Indeed, the older the bird, the more nuptial colours are retained. Male White-winged Trillers share with malurine wrens the unique trait among Australian songbirds of moulting into and out of breeding dress twice a year. This, their pointed wings and lack of a white brow are reasons why they have been separated as a species from the closely related *Lalage sueurii* of Timor.

Breeding trillers are also often colonial. Several pairs may nest within a few metres of each other in the same group of trees yet defend separate foraging territories for up to a kilometre out from them; each pair may require up to 15 hectares of feeding space. Males, in contrast to the quiet females, advertise their ground with noisy chattering from high perches and in showy circling display flights, fluttering around slowly or climbing high then gliding down on spread wings and tail; they even sing from the nest.

Both sexes participate in selecting the nest site (two–four days) and building (two–five days). Both also share incubation, in spells of about 30 minutes, during which one will feed the other, and both feed and brood the young, the female doing most.

OTHER NAMES
White-shouldered Caterpillar-eater.

IDENTIFICATION
LENGTH: *160–180 mm.*
MALE: *In breeding plumage, crown to upper back plain glossy black; rump pale grey. Wings black, with bold white flash from wing coverts down edges of secondaries. Tail black, tipped white on outer feathers. Eye dark brown. Bill and feet black. In non-breeding plumage, crown to upper back mid-brown; white edging to wing coverts buffier; off-white eyebrow.*
FEMALE: *Resembles non-breeding male. Crown to upper back mid-brown; eyebrow cream-buff; rump grey-brown. Wings and tail dusky brown, the coverts and secondaries edged pale buff. White underparts washed brown over breast. Bill dark brown, paler at base. Feet dusky brown.*
IMMATURES: *As female; breast streaked.*

VOICE
Territorial song by male a loud, incessant musical chatter—chiff chiff chiff chukka chukka chukka — often ending in canary-like trill, given in display flight or from vantage perch or nest. Otherwise silent.

NESTING
Breeds mainly September–March.

Nest a small, shallow saucer 80 mm in diameter, of fine rootlets and grass, small pieces of bark and lichen on outside, bound with spiderweb to a thin fork on a horizontal or sloping branch 1–12 m or more above ground, usually protected by foliage above. Eggs: two or three; blue or green-tinged, blotched and streaked with red-brown; oblong-oval, about 21 x 15 mm. Incubation about 14 days, by both sexes. Young fledge in 12–14 days.

DISTRIBUTION
Throughout mainland Australia in all open forests, woodlands and scrubs; vagrant in Tasmania. Migratory-nomadic, south in spring, north in autumn. Also southeastern New Guinea (isolate?). No races, or one in New Guinea.

In the breeding season the male White-winged Triller's dull, brown plumage, shown here, changes — crown, nape and back turn black, and rump grey.

Varied Triller

Lalage leucomela
(VIGORS & HORSFIELD, 1827)

OTHER NAMES
White-browed Triller, White-browed Caterpillar-eater.

IDENTIFICATION
LENGTH: *180–200 mm.*
MALE: *Upper parts glossy black; rump grading from dusky tipped white (races* yorki, rufiventris, macrura) *to plainer grey (race* leucomela). *Wings black with broad white edging on wing coverts and inner secondaries. Tail black, tipped white on outer feathers. Eyebrow white. Underparts plain white except for pale cinnamon-rufous crissum (race* yorki); *or grey-white and faintly barred with deep cinnamon-rufous crissum (race* leucomela); *or rather uniformly pale buff with clear dusky barring (races* rufiventris, macrura). *Eye brown. Bill and feet black.*
FEMALE: *As male with slightly stronger ventral barring (race* leucomela); *as male but with strong ventral barring (race* yorki); *or as male but brownish backed (races* rufiventris, macrura).
IMMATURES: *As female of relevant race but greyer, often flecked white on upper parts; rump rusty, barred black; underparts buffier and streaked as well as barred.*

VOICE
Churring trill, drr-eea drr-eea, *repeated in short bursts between both sexes, in contact; a reflective* kar-r-r-r. *Also gives high notes at intervals and a trilling song.*

NESTING
Breeds August–April, but mainly September–December. Nest a small, shallow saucer, 70 x 30 mm, of fine twigs and vine tendrils bound with spiderweb and ornamented with pieces of bark; lined with fine rootlets and lichen with egg chamber 10 mm deep; usually placed in horizontal fork. Egg: one; slightly glossy pale green, speckled, streaked or blotched with red-chestnut to purple-brown and grey, sometimes concentrated at larger end to form a zone; oval, about 26 x 17 mm.

DISTRIBUTION
Pockets of rainforest and denser fringing scrubs around coastal northern and eastern Australia, in Kimberleys (race macrura), *Arnhem Land (race* rufiventris), *Cape York Peninsula south to about Cairns–Townsville, Qld (race* yorki), *and thence south on east coast to about Manning River, NSW (race* leucomela). *Sedentary; dispersed in moderate numbers. About 15 races; four in Australia.*

The Varied Triller builds a small nest, usually in a tree fork. The female, shown here, lays one large egg.

VARIED TRILLERS ARE AS unobtrusive as White-winged Trillers are conspicuous. They live within the canopy of dense forest, are fairly sedentary, stay in pairs or at most a family party of three year round, and males give no showy song-flight when breeding. Individual pairs seem to hold or keep to the same loose territory all year yet may never defend it very actively even when breeding—being permanently established it may be well-enough known.

Living in the tall thickets that fringe rainforests and range out along creeks into adjacent eucalypt and paperbark forests and even mangroves, Varied Trillers are as much fruit- as insect-eaters. Their feeding zone extends from the crown of trees down to the lower shrub layer. In rainforest Varied Trillers usually stay in the upper and middle layers of the canopy, but in more open country, such as riverine thickets and open forest, they may forage low down, sometimes even on the ground.

When feeding, they move slowly through the foliage, searching carefully for insects and their larvae on and under leaves, twigs and branches. They eat small fruits which they swallow whole. Occasionally they hawk to catch flying insects. Any fruit that they take is small and eaten whole; figs are favoured. Their progress is marked at all times by their churring contact calls, which both sexes utter repeatedly while foraging. At such times they sometimes associate with other rainforest birds in mixed feeding flocks.

Both sexes apparently build the nest, incubate and rear the single young. Their meagre nest is proportionally the smallest of any Australian cuckoo-shrike and their single egg the largest; young are moderately advanced upon hatching.

The four races of Varied Trillers in Australia are easily identified from White-winged Trillers by their bar-breasted females, rufous-vented males and white brows in both sexes. The two northwestern races are more female-plumaged than those in the east, such that their adult males match eastern females and their females are still duller brown-backed and more clearly barred on a uniformly pale ochre-buff undersurface.

Red-whiskered Bulbul *Pycnonotus jocosus* (LINNÉ, 1758)

BULBULS ARE ACTIVE, INQUISITIVE, sociable birds of the palaeotropics. They live in trees and shrubbery where they eat both insects and fruit and where their short rounded wings and long, balancing tails aid their movements through dense growth. Most have distinctively long upper tail coverts, many have hair-like feathers on the nape, and some, like the Red-whiskered Bulbul, are crested. Noisy chatterers, they are southern Asia's ecological equivalents of Australia's honeyeaters.

Red-whiskered Bulbuls were introduced to suburban Sydney in 1880 by the then Zoological and Acclimatisation Society. Success was limited and early in the present century others were brought in from China and released; some escaped from aviaries and others—sold by dealers as 'Persian Nightingales'—were perhaps liberated intentionally by owners who found their song too noisy and monotonous. Today they are well-established throughout urban Sydney, with thriving outlying colonies south to Nowra and north at Coffs Harbour. There is also a colony in the Melbourne Botanic Gardens and occasional reports come in from Geelong, following releases in the mid-1900s, but attempts to establish them in Adelaide have failed so far.

Everywhere in Australia Red-whiskered Bulbuls are commensals of man, keeping like sparrows close to human habitation without entering far into native habitats. They frequent thickets of shrubbery and undergrowth in parks and along creeks, where they forage for insects, flower buds and fruit, including the berries of lantana. Gregarious birds, they commonly group restlessly in twos and threes to 50 or more, chattering persistently, and fly jerkily with stiff erratic wing-beats from thicket to thicket, never far. They are more often heard rather than seen—and their red 'whisker' or ear-patch is noticeable only at close quarters.

OTHER NAMES
Red-eared Bulbul, Black-crested Bulbul.

IDENTIFICATION
LENGTH: *200–220 mm.*
ADULTS: *Sexes similar. Conspicuous black upright crest about 25 mm high. Crown and nape black. Rest of upper parts and wings dull brown. Tail dusky, outer feathers tipped white. Red ear patch; cheeks white, separated from white throat by thin black line; broad black band from nape down sides of neck. Breast and belly pale fawn; undertail coverts red. Eye, bill and feet black.*
IMMATURES: *Duller than adults, with black crown greyer.*

VOICE
When perched, a staccato trilling whistle resembling kink-a-jou, *in contact and advertisement. Continual animated chattering and musical, scolding notes.*

NESTING
Breeds August–March. Nest an open cup of bark strips, rootlets, leaves and often pieces of paper, lined with fine tendrils and soft fibres; placed 2–3 m from ground in fork of a low tree, vine or shrub. Eggs: two to four; slightly glossy; pale pink with numerous speckles, spots and streaks of varying shades of red, especially at larger end; oval, about 22 x 17 mm. Two to three broods per season. Incubation and feeding of young by both sexes.

DISTRIBUTION
Introduced to Sydney (successfully), spreading to Shoalhaven River and Coffs Harbour, NSW, and to Melbourne area and Adelaide (unsuccessfully) in Australia. Also introduced to Hawaiian islands, parts of USA, and western Indonesian archipelago. Natural range is India, Himalayan region, Burma, all Indo-China to northern Malay Peninsula, southern and eastern China, Andaman Islands. About nine races; one, jocosus, introduced to Australia.

The Red-whiskered Bulbul was named for its ear patch, but its erect black crest is a more obvious field mark.

White's Thrush is well camouflaged by its plumage, which blends in with the litter on the forest floor. It feeds on invertebrates and fallen fruit.

White's Thrush *Zoothera dauma* (LATHAM, 1790)

WHITE'S THRUSH IS AUSTRALIA'S ONLY native member of the true old world thrushes, to which the Blackbird and European Song Thrush belong. It is a species that disperses widely, ranging from most of Asia to New Guinea and outlying islands in the Bismarck Archipelago and Solomons, and it has evidently reached Australia fairly recently, breaking up into four or five races. Even within Australia it will wander widely particularly out of breeding, individual birds having been found as far away from nesting grounds in the cool wet forests of the Great Dividing Range as Mildura in the middle Murray River area.

White's Thrush is a quiet and unobtrusive ground forager on the floor of cool, damp forests, both under rainforest and tall eucalypt forest, wherever leaf litter is dense and moist. It hops silently along, stop-start, pausing here and there to watch and bill-probe the leaf litter for prey. Earthworms, insects, molluscs and fallen fruit form

its diet. If alerted, it often freezes, its mottled plumage blending with its background; and if flushed, it flies off quickly and silently through the undergrowth.

Out of breeding, White's Thrush sometimes gathers in loose foraging groups of 10 to 20 or more. When nesting, pairs are strictly territorial, males singing at dawn and dusk in advertisement.

At times the several distinctive populations of White's Thrush in Australia have been treated as species. The weight of evidence, however, indicates that they intergrade where their breeding ranges abut, at middle altitudes along the eastern scarp of the Great Dividing Range between the Hunter River, NSW, and Bunya Mountains, Qld. If separate species are to be recognised, it may be more realistic to segregate all Australasian forms in one; these differing in common from their Asian relations in their more pointed wings, only 12 tail feathers and more deeply white-tipped tails.

OTHER NAMES
Scaly Thrush, Ground Thrush, Mountain Thrush.

IDENTIFICATION
LENGTH: *250–290 mm, according to race.*
ADULTS: *Sexes alike; female slightly smaller. Face and upper parts mid olive-grey to coppery brown, the feathers edged black in scaly crescents. Lores and eye-ring white. Flight feathers brown, broad buff-white mid-bar in flight. Tail brown, the outermost pair of feathers tipped variously white. Underparts white, often washed russet across breast, edged with black scallops from throat to lower breast and flanks. Eye dark brown; bill horn-brown, the mandible paler; feet pale flesh.*
IMMATURES: *As adults, but centres of*

crown and back feathers spotted buff.

VOICE
Mostly silent; thin seep *in contact and from nest; high-pitched staccato* chi-lit *in alarm, often with wing flicking. Song by males, either two prolonged, descending whistles* wheeer-dooo *(central east coast races), or these notes broken up and extended into a series of carrying whistled trills, often upslurred (southeastern and northeastern races).*

NESTING
Breeds July–December, varying with races. Nest a rounded cup, built of bark strips, leaves and grasses, decorated on the outside with green moss and lined with rootlets. Placed in the fork of a tree, often between tree-trunks or between the bark and trunk, or on a

stump, up to 15 m. Eggs: two or three; variously pale green, fleckled and blotched with red-brown; oblong-oval, about 34 x 23 mm. Young, fed by both adults, fledge in about 14 days.

DISTRIBUTION
Wet, cool forests of coastal eastern Australia and Great Dividing Range, in several isolated populations: montane rainforests of Cairns–Atherton region, Qld (race cuneata*); upland forests of Mackay region, Qld (race* mackaiensis*); central east coast rainforests from about Gympie, Qld, south to near Gosford, NSW (race* heinei*); cool mountain forests atop Great Dividing Range from Bunya Mountains, Qld, to southeast of South Australia and Tasmania (race* lunulata*); Mt Lofty Ranges and*

Kangaroo Island, SA (race halmaturina*). Also from western Asia to islands in southwestern Pacific. About 18 races; five in Australia.*

The female Blackbird is brown. The bird takes its name from the male.

Blackbird *Turdus merula* LINNÉ, 1758

RENOWNED FOR ITS SERENE SINGING when breeding, the Blackbird was introduced and established in Australia first at Melbourne in the late 1850s and 1860s, and then around Adelaide over 1878–1882. Releases at Sydney in 1872 failed, present populations there probably spreading from stocks let go in 1940. They were breeding in Tasmania by 1919 and at Albury, NSW, by 1926.

They have since spread over almost the whole of southeastern Australia, penetrating the densest mountain forests and following wooded rivers and irrigated orchards inland. They reached Canberra in 1949, Kangaroo Island in 1947, the central Murray–Murrumbidgee orchards in the mid-late 1960s, and Broken Hill, Cobar and Armidale to the north in the mid-1970s. Although it is still expanding, further spread northwards by this temperate-adapted bird may be slowed by physiological limitations. Already there are signs that local populations in southeastern mountains are differentiating from parental stocks.

Blackbirds are ground foragers among damp litter, feeding on a variety of insects and fruit. They work noisily, hopping along, scattering litter, and flicking their wings and tails up and down. Females nest-build and incubate unaided, but males, which sing from high vantage perches early during breeding, do help with the feeding of young.

OTHER NAMES
European Blackbird, Merle.

IDENTIFICATION
LENGTH: *250–260 mm.*
MALE: *Entirely dull black. Eye brown with orange-yellow eye-ring; bill orange-yellow; feet brown-black.*
FEMALE: *Upper parts and wings dark grey-brown; tail dusky. Throat grey-white, streaked dusky; rest of underparts mid grey-brown, mottled darker over breast and belly. Bill dull yellowish brown.*
IMMATURES: *As female, but underparts paler, more russet-toned; crown and back with pale shaft streaks.*

VOICE
CALL: *A thin, high* tsiii *in contact; harsh, erratically repeated clucks in agitation, with wings and tail flicked; screeching alarm chatter in flight.*
SONG: *Loud sustained melodious flutings and trills in measured phrases, by male from vantage perch, morning and late afternoon.*

NESTING
Breeds September–January. Nest a cup of dried grasses and other plant matter, bound together with mud and lined with fine grasses; placed in any thick clump of shrubbery or low dense tree. Eggs: three to five, usually four; green-blue, liberally freckled and marked with red-brown and grey; oval, about 30 x 22 mm. Incubation 13–14 days, by female. Young fledge in 13–14 days.*

DISTRIBUTION
From Eyre Peninsula, SA, throughout southeast to central-eastern New South Wales and reaching well inland to Flinders Ranges. Also Lord Howe and Norfolk Islands, and New Zealand. Introduced from Europe, and also occurs in North Africa and through southern Asia to China. About 16 races; one in Australia, introduced from northwestern Europe.

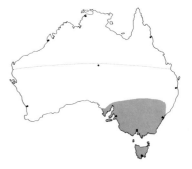

Yellow bill and eye-ring are the only touches of colour on the otherwise all-black male. The Blackbird, a fine singer, is heard in spring and summer.

Song Thrush *Turdus philomelos* BREHM, 1831

The Song Thrush is established only in the Melbourne region. Males sing in the mornings and evenings during courtship and nesting.

AS FAMOUS IN EUROPE for its melodious song as the Blackbird, the Song Thrush was also introduced to various centres in Australia from the late 1850s to 1880s. It succeeded only around Melbourne and Geelong. Other attempted introductions—Brisbane in 1869, Sydney in 1872 and Adelaide in 1879–80—all failed and so did another at Canberra in 1935. The reason may be its physiological susceptibility to heat, for even in Melbourne it keeps very much to shaded undergrowth during summer.

Song Thrushes are ground-feeding birds of parks and gardens. In ones and twos, they run, pause and peer, head cocked on one side, or hop along rapidly. Earthworms, spiders, centipedes and a variety of insects and their larvae are picked from the leaf litter. Snails are habitually smashed on stones or rocks. Flight is low and direct, with almost continuous wing-beating and little undulation.

Males sing persistently during breeding, mostly at dawn and dusk from high vantage perches in trees. In display they posture with breast puffed out and run before their mates, head back, bill open and tail spread and pressed to the ground. Females nest-build and incubate unaided, but both sexes feed the young. Two or three broods may be raised each season.

OTHER NAMES
European Thrush, Throstle, Mavis.

IDENTIFICATION
LENGTH: *About 230 mm.*
ADULTS: *Upper parts, wings and tail plain warm brown, upper wing coverts and flight feathers duskier, edged buff; underwing coverts yellow-buff. Faint cream eyebrow. Underparts from chin to undertail white, washed buff over breast, and freckled with small dusky triangular spots around throat and over breast and flanks, sparser on belly. Eye dark brown. Upper mandible dusky, the lower yellow-brown. Feet pale flesh.*

IMMATURES: *As adults but feathers of upper parts with buff shaft streaks and edges to wing coverts.*

VOICE
CALL: *Thin* sipp *in contact, often in flight when flushed. Clucking* tchook, tchook *in alarm, developing into tinny chatter.*
SONG: *Clear, spirited sequence of phrases, each phrase repeated two–four times between pauses. Also mimics.*

NESTING
Breeds September–January. Nest a cup of grasses, small twigs and leaves, strengthened with earth and lined with debris cemented with saliva; built into bushes, hedges or thick, low vegetation. Eggs: four or five; pale green-blue, spotted with black, especially at larger end; oval, about 29 x 21 mm. Incubation about 13–14 days. Young fledge in 13–14 days.

DISTRIBUTION
Introduced and established only at Melbourne and Geelong. Also established on Norfolk and Lord Howe Islands and New Zealand. Native to Europe and central western Asia. About four races; one in Australia, from western and southern Europe (England).

Rose Robin *Petroica rosea* GOULD, 1839

Only the male Rose Robin has the rose-coloured breast; the female's underside is grey-white, though sometimes flushed with pink. Both sexes feed the young but the female alone incubates.

DELICATE IN FORM AND TONING, the Rose Robin lives in the denser eastern Australian forests, both rainforest and gullies in wet sclerophyll forests filled with treeferns and blackwood *Acacia melanoxylon*. In the northern part of its breeding range it keeps mainly to the higher altitude rainforests but in the south it spreads out into heavy forest almost to sea level.

An unobtrusive bird, it is the most arboreal of Australian robins, foraging high in the middle and upper storeys of forest, and rarely coming to ground except occasionally in winter. It is also more like a flycatcher in its feeding. It flits about foliage, picking insects off leaves, and often darts into the air in tumbling pursuit, tail fanned. Food includes spiders and adult and larval stages of insects such as bugs, leaf-eating beetles, flies, small moths, ants and wasps. Large prey is taken to a perch to dispatch. At a perch, Rose Robins characteristically droop and flick their wings and raise and lower their comparatively long tails.

Rose Robins are migratory. Each autumn they shift out of breeding territories, both to warmer lower altitudes, and northwards. Some reach rainforest ranges in central eastern Queensland and the Mt Lofty Ranges, and nearly all leave Victoria. Birds of passage are silent and often spread out through lighter woodlands and even urban gardens. Whether at breeding or winter quarters, or en route between, the birds are solitary or in pairs. Members of established pairs may return to the same breeding territory year after year.

Male Rose Robins may breed in immature plumage. While the female does most of the nest building and incubates the eggs, the male feeds her on or near the nest; both feed the nestlings. The nest-building takes 14 days but as few as seven for a later brood; up to three broods a season may be raised, each being disbanded quickly after fledging. Rose Robins are among the chief fosterers of the Brush Cuckoo in southeastern Australia.

OTHER NAMES
Rose-breasted Robin.

IDENTIFICATION
LENGTH: *115–125 mm.*
MALE: *Upper parts slate-grey. Small white forehead spot. Wings and tail plain grey tinged brown; outer tail feathers edged and tipped white. Throat slate-grey; breast with small rose-red patch; belly and undertail white. Eye dark brown. Bill and feet dusky; soles yellow to orange.*
FEMALE: *Upper parts brownish grey. Forehead spot buff-white. Wings tinged browner with two broken buff-white bars through flight feathers; tail dark brown with whitish outershafts. Underside pale grey, breast sometimes flushed rose-pink, belly and undertail whiter. Eye, bill and feet as male.*
IMMATURES: *Resemble adult female but wing bars often buffier. Juveniles mottled finely buff-white on brown.*

VOICE
CALL: *Series of low, weak, piping notes, or dry ticking like the snapping of a small twig, by both sexes; chirring in alarm.*
SONG: *Low, reedy series of trills on same pitch, reee-areee-areee, by male.*

NESTING
Breeds September–October to January–February. Nest a cup of green moss and fibre bound with cobweb and decorated with camouflaging lichen; 40 x 31 mm inside, lined with fur and plant down; built on mossy, lichen-spotted fork or horizontal limb 1–2 m from ground in leafy cover. Eggs: two or three; pale green-grey or blue-grey with brown markings often concentrated in zone at larger end; rounded-oval, about 17 x 14 mm. Incubation about 13 days, by female.

DISTRIBUTION
Breeds in wet mountain and coastal forests of southeastern Australia, north to Macpherson Range, Qld, and south to southwestern Victoria. Out-of-breeding migration to Clarke Range, Qld, and Mt Lofty-Flinders Ranges, SA. No races.

Pink Robin *Petroica rodinogaster* (DRAPIEZ, 1819)

SHADY UNDERGROWTH AND fern-filled gullies in the recesses of temperate rainforest and wet sclerophyll forest are the habitat of Pink Robins. Antarctic beech *Nothofagus* and southern sassafras *Atherosperma* are often dominant trees. Established pairs may keep to the same territory or its environs year round, but others shift seasonally, particularly the young of the year, which tend to disperse northwards through more open country in winter months. Some travel as far as the central New South Wales coast, and birds pass regularly, if quietly and unobtrusively, through Canberra each autumn and spring. Evidence that Tasmanian robins cross Bass Strait is still circumstantial.

Just as solitary and quiet as the closely related Rose Robin, the Pink nonetheless forages strictly within the forest substage. Its manner of feeding is characteristic. The birds, singly or in dispersed pairs, flit silently from low vantage perches on branches within undergrowth, some 50–200 centimetres or more above the ground. From each perch they watch intently, body hunched and wings and tail drooped and then flicked upwards erratically, waiting for varying periods before moving on. Flight is low, dashing and erratically undulating. Most prey is taken on the ground, by diving on to it from the perch, but the birds will also hawk out low to catch insects on the wing or to pick them off foliage. Beetles, bugs and spiders are main dietary items.

Breeding territories are advertised and held by males which sing from vantage perches up to 15 metres high; their song, although sounding far off, is often heard to carry no more than a few metres. Females do most or all of the nest building and incubate unaided, but both adults feed the young, rearing one or two broods a season. Young males do not appear to gain adult plumage until their second or third annual moult, their last immature plumage showing more pink on the breast. They may breed in this plumage.

OTHER NAMES
Pink-breasted Robin.

IDENTIFICATION
LENGTH: *120–130 mm.*
MALE: *Upper parts sooty; wings and tail uniformly black tinged brown, with hint of buff bar in wing; small white spot on forehead. Throat sooty, breast and belly magenta or deep pink; undertail white. Eye dark brown. Bill black. Feet black-brown; soles orange to lemon.*
FEMALE: *Upper parts rich brown to greyish brown. Wings and tail dark brown, with two incomplete conspicuous buff bars in flight feathers. Small buff to white forehead mark. Underside pale brown grading to whitish on belly and undertail. Eye, bill and feet as male.*
IMMATURES: *Resemble adult female; wing bars often less pronounced; pink wash developing on breast. Juveniles mottled finely buff-white on brown.*

VOICE
CALL: *Low, sharp, monotonous ticking like snapping of small twig or clicking of grasshopper, by both sexes; varies to short, rasping twitter in agitation.*
SONG: *An upslurred whistle, followed by a tinkling chatter of about six–seven notes repeated over and over, by male from vantage perch.*

NESTING
Breeds September–January. Nest a deep cup of green moss bound with cobweb and adorned with camouflaging lichen; 47 x 32 mm inside and lined with fur and plant down; placed in upright or oblique fork 300 mm to 6 m above the ground in deep undergrowth. Eggs: three or four; white tinged green, with very small brown and purple-grey freckles concentrated towards larger end in distinct belt; rounded-oval, about 18 x 14 mm. Incubation about 13 days, by female.

DISTRIBUTION
Breeds in Tasmania and uplands of eastern Victoria, from Otway Ranges to Snowy Mountains, NSW. Disperses in autumn and winter to warmer, low-altitude scrubs and northwards, occasionally reaching central east coast of New South Wales and Mt Lofty Ranges, SA. Two races.

Only the mature male Pink Robin has an extensively pink breast — the female is brown. The nest is a compact cup, built of moss, bound with spiderweb and covered with lichen, and placed in a small tree or bush.

Flame Robin *Petroica phoenicea* GOULD, 1837

AS MIGRATORY AS THE Rose and Pink Robins, the Flame nonetheless inhabits much more open country. In spring it withdraws to the highlands and far south coasts of southeastern Australia, from Tasmania to the New England tablelands, to breed in alpine and subalpine woodlands and scrubby forest. Snow gum *Eucalyptus pauciflora* and associated woodland is favoured on the mainland.

Groups form territory-holding pairs, the male singing to advertise territory and the female building the nest—in about 14 days—and incubating unaided. She may use the nest for successive broods—sometimes two a season—or re-build. The male feeds his mate while she is incubating; both feed the young.

After breeding, the robins gather in loose family groups of five to 20–30 or more, first in late summer in the woods around the breeding grounds, and then spread out into open lower country and pasture in autumn and winter. Some move north as far as southeastern Queensland and west to Yorke Peninsula, SA. Main quarters are the rolling downs along the southwestern slopes of the Great Dividing Range. The groups, in which brown immatures and females invariably outnumber adult flame-breasted males, work along fence-lines in open fields, dropping to the ground or hawking from low perches for prey.

Returning to the same site each winter, individual birds may share their field with a partner, diving to ground alternately for food: small insects and their larvae. Posts, bare low branches and rocks are favoured perches. At night, the flocks roost communally in dense foliage in trees.

When perched, the Flame Robin flicks its wings and tail; flight is short, swift and undulating. They appear to play-chase by flying low, swooping to the ground or a fence, then darting off again.

OTHER NAMES
Robin Redbreast, Flame-breasted Robin.

IDENTIFICATION
LENGTH: *125–135 mm.*
MALE: *Upper parts, wings and tail smoky grey; small white spot on forehead; irregular double white bar in flight feathers and wing coverts and white webs in outer tail feathers. Chin smoky grey; throat, breast and upper belly brilliant orange-red; undertail white. Eye, bill and feet black-brown.*
FEMALE: *Upper parts russet-brown with darker wings and tail. Small buff forehead spot; wing and tail markings as male but buffier. Underside light brown, grading to whitish. Old females have breast washed with orange.*
IMMATURES: *Resemble adult female; buffier forehead, wing and tail markings; juvenile finely flecked brown and buff-white. Immature males, washed orange on breast, may not reach adult plumage until second or third annual moult.*

VOICE
CALL: *Faint, thin, repeated piping or subdued ticking, by both sexes.*
SONG: *Sweet, lilting up-and-down cadence of about nine whistled notes, in triplets, by male.*

NESTING
Breeds August–September to January–February; males will breed in immature plumage. Nest cup-shaped, 47 x 38 mm; of fine strips of bark, grass and fibre, coated with cobweb or dry moss; built between piece of bark and tree trunk, hollow tree, rock crevice, cleft in creek bank, or rafters of building to 19 m above ground. Eggs: three or four; pale blue to pale green, spotted and blotched with brown and purple-grey; rounded-oval, about 18 x 14 mm. Incubation 14 days, by female. Young fledge in 14 days.

DISTRIBUTION
Breeding in southeast, dispersing mainly on western slopes of Great Dividing Range to winter north to southeastern Queensland and west to the South Australian gulfs; much of Tasmanian population remains. No races.

A male Flame Robin. When perching, Flame Robins often flick their wings and jerk their tails as they watch the ground for food. The female is brown with a buffier forehead mark.

Scarlet Robin *Petroica multicolor* (GMELIN, 1789)

OTHER NAMES
Scarlet-breasted Robin, White-capped Robin.

IDENTIFICATION
LENGTH: *120–130 mm.*
MALE: *Upper parts black; conspicuous white patch on forehead. Wings and tail black, with broad white stripe on wing coverts running into two irregular white bars in flight feathers; webs of outer tail feathers edged and tipped white. Throat black, breast scarlet, belly and undertail white. Eye dark brown. Bill and feet black.*
FEMALE: *Upper parts grey-brown, with large buff-white forehead spot. Wings and tail grey-brown, with irregular double off-white wing stripe; webs of outer tail feathers white. Throat grey-brown; breast dull red; belly and undertail dull white.*
IMMATURES: *Resemble adult female but duller, with little red. Males moult into red and black plumage in their first autumn. Juveniles finely streaked or mottled brown and buff-white.*

VOICE
CALL: *Faint, thin dry tick, by both sexes occasionally.*
SONG: *Sweet, short, rippling cadence of whistled notes, wee-cheedalee-dalee, by male.*

NESTING
Breeds July–August to December–January. Nest a cup of fine bark strips, moss and grass, matted with cobweb and often ornamented with camouflaging pieces of rough bark, charred wood or lichen; about 45 x 40 mm inside, lined with fine bark, fur, feathers, fern down or hair; 0.5–20 m high in tree fork or hollow stump. Eggs: usually three; pale blue, green or grey thickly marked and freckled with purple-grey or brown, often forming a zone at larger end; swollen-oval, about 18 x 14 mm. Incubation about 15–17 days, by female. Young fledge in 15–17 days.

DISTRIBUTION
Scrubby eucalypt forest and woodland of southeastern Australia north on Great Dividing Range to granite belt, southeastern Queensland, and west to Eyre Peninsula, SA, and southwestern Australia inland to wheat belt. Sedentary; young of year wander but established adult pairs stay near territory year round. Up to 10 races; two in Australia: one east, one west.

Although not participating in nest-building and incubation, the male Scarlet Robin helps the female feed the chicks. The female also has a red breast but she is paler than her mate, and has a grey-brown back.

AS WITH OTHER RED OR PINK ROBINS, it is the female Scarlet Robin that builds the neat, cobweb-bound nest. The male may bring building material but otherwise spends his time singing in defence of territory, feeding the female while she is incubating the eggs, or perching nearby. In the first days after the chicks have hatched he passes food to her for the nestlings and for herself; later both birds feed the young. Some pairs may raise up to three broods a season. Several species of cuckoos, including Horsfield's Bronze-Cuckoo, parasitise the nests of Scarlet Robins.

The birds breed in scrubby eucalypt forests and woodlands but forage out into more open habitat in autumn and winter. They feed by perch-and-pounce, sitting waiting on high branches in summer, lower in winter, then dropping to the ground or hawking out into the air to snatch insects. In the spring and summer many insects are picked from the leaves and bark in the canopy.

Scarlet Robins are solitary or remain in pairs all year, and established pairs hold permanent territories. A male courts a female by feeding her, then alternately extends each wing downwards displaying the white wing patch. She often quivers her wing before and during such feeding.

Scarlet Robins are identified among other red robins by the white cap on the male and the bright red breast of the female. Male Scarlets can also be distinguished from Flame Robins by their black throats and deeper, more limited scarlet breasts. Where their foraging areas overlap during breeding, they occupy mutually exclusive territories, the Scarlet keeping to drier habitat.

A male Red-capped Robin at its well-camouflaged nest. He shares the load of feeding the nestlings with the female, and helps tend the fledglings.

Red-capped Robin *Petroica goodenovii* VIGORS & HORSFIELD, 1827

REPRESENTING THE RED ROBINS in the arid mallee, mulga and bulloke scrubs across inland Australia, the Red-capped Robin is also the smallest of them and the most brightly coloured. Its feeding habit, however, is little different. Keeping to the open, lower stages of the scrub, usually within a metre of the ground, it forages by perch-and-pounce on a range of insects: grasshoppers, bugs, beetles, flies, moths, wasps, ants and small mantids; a high proportion of caterpillars are fed to nestlings.

Feeding birds flit from perch to perch—a bare branch, stump or post—in short, low, undulating flights. Landed, they sit hunched, silent and motionless except for an occasional upflicking of wings and tail, watching and waiting for varying periods. Sighting prey, they dive on to it, usually on the ground, then fly back to a perch to eat. At times the birds also hawk out briefly after flying insects, and hop and shuffle about in debris on the ground, presumably to flush insects. They are sedentary or only locally nomadic over much of their range, although in winter northern populations apparently wander more widely. Established pairs may remain together, but otherwise the robins are largely solitary.

A male advertises territory by singing from low vantage perches and courts a female by offering her food, occasionally beginning with a fast, chasing flight. It ends when the female lands and quivers her wings as the male approaches with food. He continues to bring food during nest-building—which takes eight–ten days— feeding her at the nest-site or close by. As the nest nears completion the female will snuggle down into it, sometimes dropping her wings over the edge, after positioning the material she has carried in. She alternately pokes at the nest and nestles down, for up to half a minute each visit, finally raising her tail and leaving with a dropping, curved flight. There may be a delay of several days between completion of the nest and laying of the first egg, particularly early in the season or following inclement weather. The nest is the smallest of the robins' and built entirely by the female; it may be used again in the same season if there is a second clutch.

Both parents feed the nestlings about equally, although when the female is busy brooding or shading the young, the male compensates by feeding more. Following a feed, a nestling may wriggle around, present its rear and excrete a faecal sac which the parent carries away or occasionally eats. Approaches to, and departures from, the nest are always silent. Parents continue to feed young for about three weeks after they have fledged. If there are only two, each parent tends a particular one.

OTHER NAMES
Redhead.

IDENTIFICATION
LENGTH: *110–115 mm.*
MALE: *Upper parts dull black, with conspicuous bright red forecrown. Wings and tail black, with broad white stripe on wing coverts running into two irregular white bars in flight feathers, and webs of outer tail feathers white. Throat dull black, sometimes with wash of red; breast bright red; rest of underside white. Eye dark brown. Bill and feet black. May breed in immature plumage.*
FEMALE: *Upper parts russet-brown with rust-red forecrown. Wings and tail grey-brown with irregular double buff-white wing stripe; webs of outer tail feathers white. Underparts cream-white, washed brown on breast.*
IMMATURES: *Resemble adult female but lack red-brown forehead. Young males have some red wash on breast. Juveniles finely streaked or mottled brown and buff-white.*

VOICE
CALL: *Soft, dry* tick, *repeated slowly, by both sexes.*
SONG: *Low, insect-like rattling trill,* dtit-dtit-dtrrr-it, *repeated at intervals, by male.*

NESTING
Breeds July–August to December–January. Nest a compact cup of bark strips and grass bound with cobweb and adorned with lichen and spiders' egg sacs; about 38 x 31 mm inside, lined with vegetable fibre, fur and feathers; 0.5–10 m above ground on branch or trunk crevice. Eggs: two or three; pale blue-green to grey-white dotted with grey, brown and lavender to form zone at large end; rounded-oval, about 15 x 13 mm. Incubation about 14 days, by female. Young fledge in about 14 days.

DISTRIBUTION
Well-dispersed in light timber, mallee, mulga and grassland areas of the interior; moves locally towards coast to winter in west. Absent north of 20° C. No races.

Dusky Robin

Melanodryas vittata (QUOY & GAIMARD, 1830)

OTHER NAMES
Stump Robin, Wood Robin, Dozey Robin, Native Sparrow, Sad Bird.

IDENTIFICATION
LENGTH: *160–170 mm.*
ADULTS: *Sexes similar. Upper parts dark grey-brown. Wings and tail dusky, with off-white band in base of flight feathers and outer tail tipped white. Throat off-white; rest of underparts light brown, with centre of belly white. Eye brown. Bill and feet black.*
IMMATURES: *Uniformly brown; juveniles coarsely streaked above and mottled below with brown and white.*

VOICE
CALL: *Low, far-carrying double whistle, monotonously repeated, by both sexes.*
SONG: *Lively and sweetly plaintive choo-wee, choo-we-er.*

NESTING
Breeds July to December–January. Compact to loose cup-shaped nest, of bark strips and rootlets bound with cobweb; *63 x 40 mm inside; lined with grass and fine vegetable matter; 1–6 m from ground in hollows of stumps or fallen trees, and limbs of bushes. Eggs: usually three; pale green-blue to brown-olive with obscure darker shadings; oval, about 22 x 16 mm. Incubation about 14–15 days. Two, perhaps three, broods a season.*

DISTRIBUTION
Confined to Tasmania and Bass Strait islands. Sedentary or locally nomadic depending on food. Two races: one, rustier, endemic to King Island.

The Dusky Robin often nests in holes in fire-blackened trees.

A BULKY, SEDENTARY ROBIN, the Dusky frequents a wide range of wooded habitats, from the edges of rainforest to open woodland with shrubby undergrowth; everywhere it needs open ground to forage. Feeding by perch-and-pounce, it sits silent and motionless on the top of bare twigs or stumps, tail occasionally flicking, waiting to dive onto prey on the ground, less often on trunks or in the air. Diet includes beetles, flies, spiders, worms and snails. In winter family groups may forage widely but in spring adult pairs return to established territories in denser forest to breed.

Hooded Robin *Melanodryas cucullata* (LATHAM, 1801)

OTHER NAMES
Pied Robin, Black Robin.

IDENTIFICATION
LENGTH: *140–170 mm.*
MALE: *Upper parts, wings and tail black; white sash on shoulders; white bar from base of primaries down leading edge of secondary flight feathers; tip and basal half to two-thirds of outer tail feathers white. Throat and upper breast black; rest of underside white washed grey. Eye dark brown. Bill and feet black.*
FEMALE: *Upper parts fawn to dark grey; wings and tail brown, white markings as male. Underparts pure to off-white, washed greyer over breast.*
IMMATURES: *Resemble adult female; white wing and tail markings less definite. Young breeding males may be darker grey or blackish above and mottled dusky and white on upper breast. Juveniles coarsely mottled brown-grey and white; belly whiter streaked with light grey.*

VOICE
CALL: *Soft piping or churring.*
SONG: *Penetrating piping whistling and higher chattering notes, by male.*

NESTING
Breeds mainly July–December. Nest a strong cup of bark strips, grass and fibre bound with cobweb; 53 x 35 mm inside, lined with fine fibre and down; in tree fork, crevice or hollow, 0.5–4 m above ground. Eggs: two; olive- to blue-green, clouded red-brown to olive at larger end; oval, about 21 x 16 mm. Incubation about 14 days, by female.

DISTRIBUTION
Lightly timbered country. Widespread, solitary or in pairs. No races.

A male Hooded Robin at its nest, a cup-shaped structure in a tree-fork. Both parents and helpers defend the nest.

MOST WIDESPREAD OF Australian robins, the Hooded is a rather sedentary bird in lightly wooded country throughout the continent except Tasmania and Cape York Peninsula. Established pairs keep to the environs of their territory— 10–20 hectares—year round, do not flock, and band in family groups only briefly after breeding; solitary wanderers in winter are mostly dispersed young of the year.

The Hooded Robin is usually quiet and shy. It spends much time on the ground looking for insects, but more often perches on low, dead stumps, sitting hunched and still for a long time, hunting by perch-and-pounce. It frequents places with standing dead trees and fallen timber. Its flight is short and swiftly undulating.

Mostly silent by day, males sing regularly in the pre-dawn chorus during breeding, advertising territory. Both sexes defend the nest with tumbling displays of injury-feigning.

White-breasted Robin *Eopsaltria georgiana* (QUOY & GAIMARD, 1830)

CLOSE THICKETS, WHETHER along streams under tall forest or out in coastal heaths, are the habitat of White-breasted Robins. According to conventional theory, this robin is an early evolutionary offshoot of the yellow robins that lost its yellow tones after it became isolated from eastern stocks during a past cold dry glacial period. Eastern stocks later reinvaded the west to budd off the Western Yellow Robin.

Characteristically the White-breasted Robin perches motionless, except for flicking its tail upwards—frequently to an angle of 45 degrees—and pressing the tips of the closed wings downwards. Sometimes it clings sideways, low down on a tree trunk—as low as 100 mm—watching the ground for insects. To capture them it sallies out and down in swift dives, often to ground. Food includes small beetles, wasps, ants, bugs, flies and various insect larvae.

When courting, the male feeds the female. She begs, quivering her wings and uttering a soft, warbling call. The male faces her, cocks his tail, fluffs out his body feathers and bows to her, uttering a loud, excited *wee-oh* or *chirr-up*. When the male postures aggressively, he holds his body erect, puffs out his feathers, and utters a harsh, churring call. Breeding birds will perform a distraction display, running along the ground and trailing their wings.

White-breasted Robins commonly breed in groups with one-three helpers, and exceptionally as a pair. The same nesting area is used in successive years. Only the nest environs are defended and there is no aggression between neighbours. The breeding female alone builds the nest, incubates the eggs, and broods and guards the young, never going more than 25 metres from the nest. She solicits food and is fed by her mate and helpers, both on and off the nest, passing a proportion of food on to the nestlings. Her mate and helpers also feed the young directly, both in the nest and when fledged. A pair with a helper can raise up to three broods in the one season; a pair alone cannot. Males outnumber females, and helpers are usually progeny of the breeding pair from previous years. Breeders dominate helpers of their own sex.

At the end of the breeding season adult males disperse, leaving females and juveniles in their nesting areas. Outside the breeding season, or away from the nest when breeding, adult robins are not seen in groups; they move and forage singly.

OTHER NAMES
White-bellied Robin.

IDENTIFICATION
LENGTH: *145–155 mm.*
ADULTS: *Sexes alike. Upper parts plain dark smoky grey, lores dusky black. Wings and tail dusky, with single concealed white bar through base of flight feathers that shows in flight; bend of wing white; outer tail feathers tipped white. Underparts white, washed grey over breast and throat. Eye dark brown. Bill black. Feet black-brown.*
IMMATURES: *Resemble adults, but may be spotted brown. Juveniles brown, coarsely spotted and mottled white.*

VOICE
CALL: *Often calls* twick-twick; *when defending territory* zick-ker-r-r; *at dusk loud* z-ick.
SONG: *Animated chirruping song by male. In early morning, and during night-flying, a liquid call* che-op, *ending abruptly like a whip crack; sometimes varied to* e-che-op *with* e *soft and drawn out like a dog whining.*

NESTING
Breeds July to December–January. Nest a loosely built cup of grass and rootlets, perhaps bound with cobweb, with pieces of lichen or bark strips attached, usually in upright fork of small tree or shrub in dense scrub near water, up to 6 m above ground. Eggs: usually two; light brown, olive or pale green, faintly marked or clouded with dull brown-red; oval, about 21 x 16 mm. Incubation 14–15 days, by female. Young fledge in 11–14 days.

DISTRIBUTION
Two populations in southwestern Australia. Northern population is moderately common in dense coastal thickets from just north of Geraldton south to Lancelin. Southern population occurs from Busselton through forest and woodland of southwestern corner, along streams and swamps, ranging in reduced numbers to Esperance and Bald Island; occurs in Darling Range to 250 m. Some nomadism or seasonal movement. Apparently no races.

The White-breasted Robin lives in dense thickets in far southwestern Western Australia, where it may perch clinging sideways low down on a tree trunk, watching for insects. It feeds on beetles, wasps, flies and insect larvae.

Western Yellow Robin

Eopsaltria griseogularis
GOULD, 1838

OTHER NAMES
Grey-breasted Robin.

IDENTIFICATION
LENGTH: *145–155 mm.*
ADULTS: *Sexes alike. Upper parts plain mid-grey, dull citrine to bright yellow on rump. Wings and tail darker browner grey, with concealed white wing bar through base of flight feathers and narrow white tip to tail. Face mid-grey; lores dusky. Throat white; upper breast broadly grey; lower breast to undertail bright yellow. Eye dark brown. Bill black. Feet dusky.*
IMMATURES: *As adults but duller, moulting from juvenile plumage in first autumn. Juveniles brown above coarsely mottled and streaked cream-white; white below coarsely mottled brown on throat and breast, with pale mouth streak.*

VOICE
CALL: *Soft, repeated piping notes on same pitch, by both sexes.*
SONG: *Explosive* chip-chip *or* k'chilp *by male, in alarm or territorial advertisement. Series of trilled whistles at dawn.*

NESTING
Breeds July–December, rarely January. Nest a beautiful cup of bark and coarse grass, sometimes dry leaves, bound with cobweb. Bark strips are attached to the outside by cobweb and hang down to about 110 mm from the rim; 63 x 31 mm inside, lined with finer fibre; built in fork of tree, particularly in younger tree with bark strips hanging from the forks; up to 8 m from ground. Eggs: usually two; apple-green to pale yellow-green, marked with browns especially at larger end; oval, about 20 x 15 mm. Incubation about 15–16 days, by female.

DISTRIBUTION
Ranges north to Peron Peninsula, WA, and in patches east to Eyre Peninsula, SA. Common to fairly common singly, in pairs or family parties in forest and woodland with scrub cover. Some movement to more open areas, lowlands or coast in winter and some local movement dictated by food supply. Two races; one in extreme southwest of Western Australia; the other, duller-backed, through Western Australian wheat-belt to Eyre Peninsula, SA.

A white throat and broad grey breast band distinguish the Western Yellow Robin from its eastern relative.

AS ITS NAME suggests, the Western Yellow Robin represents the Eastern Yellow Robin in Western Australia. It has similar habits and occupies much the same niche, although frequently more open woodland and mallee; some ornithologists treat the two as races of one another. This question is difficult to resolve satisfactorily because the two species are geographically isolated and cannot be shown to be inter-fertile or not under natural conditions. The Western differs mainly in its white throat and broad grey breast band which may have evolved when its ancestors became separated from eastern stocks during cold dry epochs in the past.

Western Yellow Robins move about in the scrubby covers of forests and woodlands. They remain still or drop to the ground to pick up an insect, sometimes eating it there, and then rising again to a vantage point. Their diet consists mainly of ground insects, especially ants and spiders; other insect food includes moth larvae, beetles, small cockroaches and wasps.

When the Western Yellow Robin perches— either by clinging sideways low down on a tree trunk, or in the more conventional way on a branch—it often jerks its tail up and down and droops or flicks its wings. Its flight—which is short, even when the bird has been disturbed— is rapid and undulating and includes short glides to a perch.

The Western Yellow Robin usually builds its nest in a fork of either a standing or a fallen tree, particularly a young tree with strips of bark hanging from the branches. Using cobwebs, the bird attaches similar bark strips, about 110 mm long, to the rim; the result is a masterpiece of camouflage.

The female does the incubating and brooding, and the male feeds her. Both birds feed the young in the nest and for a while afterwards. A pair may raise more than one brood a season. This species sometimes breeds co-operatively; other individuals have been recorded helping the parents to feed the chicks. A parent bird often feigns a broken wing when an intruder approaches its nestlings. It ruffles up its feathers and appears to make painful progress along the ground, with one wing trailing.

In the non-breeding season Western Yellow Robins are sometimes seen in the mixed feeding flocks of small insect-eating perching or song birds. Destruction of large tracts of their habitat for agriculture has probably brought a decline in their numbers over the past 40 years.

Eastern Yellow Robin *Eopsaltria australis* (SHAW, 1790)

The Eastern Yellow Robin is completely yellow on the underside. It ranges from Queensland to South Australia, and favours coastal mountain forests.

PERCHING SIDEWAYS ON LOW vertical branches and saplings is characteristic of yellow robins; the Eastern, yellowest of them all, is no exception. At the more open centre of the shrubberies in which the birds forage, it gives them a less obstructive view in their hunting. The robins flit quietly from perch to perch, sitting and waiting with tail occasionally rising and wings flicking, then flying on or darting quickly to ground to pick up prey. They will also capture food in foliage and, rarely, while flying. They seem to start feeding earlier in the day and to continue later than most birds, moving about until dark. Diet includes ants, bugs, spiders, moths, grasshoppers, wasps and flies.

In winter the robins often join mixed foraging flocks of small insectivorous birds. It is then that they may move locally out from the closely shrubbed forests where they breed into more open woodland. Common to all their habitats is an understorey of shrubs five–eight metres high with little ground cover.

Breeding pairs hold a small restricted territory but may have one or two additional helpers at the nest, probably previous young, to help feed the nestlings. Up to three broods may be raised in a season. The female takes about a week to build the nest; eggs are laid at about 27-hour intervals, and while she broods, the male feeds her on the nest and later assists in feeding young. Adults often feign injury to protect the brood. And during the non-breeding season, parents and offspring may forage as a family unit.

OTHER NAMES
Bark Robin, Creek Robin, Yellow Bob.

IDENTIFICATION
LENGTH: *145–155 mm.*
ADULTS: *Sexes similar. Upper parts plain mid-grey with olive wash on back grading from citrine to bright yellow on rump. Wings and tail darker brown-grey, with concealed white bar through base of flight feathers that shows in flight, and narrow white tip to tail. Chin white; rest of underparts yellow with faint to absent grey wash on breast. Eye brown. Bill black. Feet dusky.*
IMMATURES: *Resemble adults but duller, moulting from juvenile plumage in first autumn. Juveniles brown above, coarsely mottled and streaked cream-*white; white below coarsely mottled brown on throat and breast, with pale mouth streak.

VOICE
CALL: *Succession of soft piping notes on same pitch, by both sexes.*
SONG: *Explosive chip-chip or k'chilp by male, in alarm or advertisement. Series of trilled whistles at dawn.*

NESTING
Breeds July–January. Nest a cup of bark strips, fine twigs, moss, skeleton leaves and grass bound with cobweb, and often adorned with hanging strips of camouflaging grey bark; lined with fibres or grass, 50–70 mm x 30–40 mm deep inside; usually in slender fork or low crotch in tree, mostly below 7 m but sometimes up to 25 m. Eggs: usually two, sometimes three; grey-green to pale blue, with red-brown and purple-brown spotting, sometimes evenly distributed, at other times concentrated in cap at larger end; oval, about 22 x 16 mm. Incubation 15–16 days, by female. Young fledge in 10–14 days.

DISTRIBUTION
Coast and ranges of eastern Australia, from Cooktown, Qld, to southeastern South Australia. Distribution patchy; mainly coastal mountain forests, but ranges through woodland with scrubby cover on inland slopes. Often sedentary, but some partial migration from highlands to lowlands in winter, at least in southeastern Australia. Two races: one north of Hunter River, NSW; the other south.

White-faced Robin *Tregellasia leucops* (Salvadori, 1875)

OTHER NAMES
White-throated Robin.

IDENTIFICATION
LENGTH: *120–130 mm.*
ADULTS: *Sexes similar. Face, around eye to chin white, circled broadly black from below cheeks, behind eye to forehead. Crown dusky olive; rest of upper parts deep olive. Wings and tail duskier, the feathers edged olive. Underparts rich yellow, washed olive on sides of breast. Eye black-brown. Bill black, with pale buff base to lower mandible. Feet rich greyish yellow.*
IMMATURES: *As adults but duller. Juveniles plain rich cinnamon-brown above and over breast, paler below; juvenile plumage moults out within a month or so of fledging.*

VOICE
Similar to Pale-yellow Robin.

NESTING
Breeding period not established, probably August–January. Nest a deep cup of bark and plant fibre, bound with cobweb, and decorated outside with camouflaging pieces of lichen, bark and moss; lined with finer fibre; placed low in vertical fork or rattan Calamus *to*

2–3 m high. Eggs: usually two; pale blue-green, freckled with dull red, chestnut and grey, concentrated at larger end; oval, about 19 x 14 mm.

DISTRIBUTION
Tropical rainforests of coastal Cape York Peninsula south to McIlwraith Range. Also Trans-Fly and hill rainforests of New Guinea. About nine races; one endemic to Australia.

The White-faced Robin at its nest in rainforests of Cape York Peninsula.

LIKE THE PALE-YELLOW ROBIN, the White-faced is confined to rainforest and forages within its mid and lower stages. It is a sedentary bird, established pairs keeping to much the same territory year round although often gathering with their young of the year and perhaps neighbours in loose feeding groups of four or five. They hunt by perch-and-pounce, sitting motionless and often sideways on vertical saplings and branches and then diving to the ground, low foliage and trunks to pick off insects of various kinds.

Mangrove Robin *Eopsaltria pulverulenta* SALVADORI, 1878

MANGROVE ROBINS ARE CONFINED to mangroves along the coast and estuaries of northern Australia, keeping within the denser, low, mallee-like brakes of *Avicennia* and *Ceriops* rather than the taller forests of *Rhizophora* and *Brugiera*. There they are sedentary, pairs and family groups of up to six or eight staying in the same small territory year round.

In their foraging they work from the midstage of the mangroves, at about half–two metres above mud level. Flitting quietly from perch to perch—bare horizontal and vertical branches—they pause to watch and wait, wings or tail sometimes flicking, then dive down on to prey among stilt roots and on the surface of the mud.

More rounded wings and tails than those of other robins aid their manoeuvrability in flight in the confines of close mangrove thickets. Often they hop along the surface of the mud, picking and probing with their rather long bills; at other times they cling to the trunks of mangroves, probing bark. Food includes small crustaceans, and insects such as beetles, ants and wasps.

During breeding, members of local groups display communally, chasing one another, drooping and fluttering their wings, singing, and fanning their tails, displaying their concealed white side bars. Both sexes, and probably helpers, feed the young, but the female nest-builds and incubates unaided.

The Mangrove Robin often picks its food from mangrove mud.

OTHER NAMES
Ashy Robin, Mangrove Shrike-robin, White-tailed Robin.

IDENTIFICATION
LENGTH: *145–160 mm.*
ADULTS: *Sexes similar; male slightly larger. Upper parts mid to dark slate-grey; lores and rump black. Wings dark ash-brown, with concealed dull white bar through base of flight feathers showing in flight. Tail black, with basal half white, except two central feathers. Underwing coverts black. Underparts white with breast washed smoky grey. Eye dark brown. Bill and feet black, dark grey or sepia.*
IMMATURES: *As adults but duller, moulting from juvenile plumage in one–two months of fledging. Juveniles mid-brown above, coarsely mottled and streaked cream, buff-white below, coarsely mottled with brown over breast, with pale mouth streak. Feet flesh-grey.*

VOICE
CALL: *Soft, plaintive, drawn-out one- or two-note whistle on one pitch, by both sexes for contact.*
SONG: *Harsh, repeated* chuck *by male in alarm or territorial advertisement. Also a varied whistled song by male.*

NESTING
Breeds August–May, mainly September–March. Nest small, shallow cup of thin bark strips interwoven with cobweb, decorated with green lichen; lined with wiry fibres and rootlets; usually in mangrove fork, often against trunk, 1–4 m above mud. Eggs: normally two or three; lustrous, pale olive-brown, green or yellow-green, marked with blotches and spots of various reds and browns, with underlying slate-grey, usually forming zone towards larger end; rounded-oval, about 19 x 15 mm. Incubation probably 14–16 days, by female.

DISTRIBUTION
From about Point Cloates, WA, along northern coast to Proserpine, Qld. Locally common but patchy and absent from Eighty Mile Beach. Also in Aru Islands, and New Guinea. Two or three races; at least two in Australia.

Pale-yellow Robin _Tregellasia capito_ (GOULD, 1854)

THE RECESSES OF UPLAND subtropical rainforests along the central and northeast coasts of Australia are the habitat of the Pale-yellow Robin. It forages in the mid and lower stages of the rainforest by perch-and-pounce. Sitting still and silent on a low bare branch within six or seven metres of the ground—and often sideways on vertical trunks or saplings—it watches down and about, without any of the tail and wing flicking of other yellow robins. Sighting prey, it drops or dives down on to it, on the ground, fallen logs, trunks and low foliage. At times the robins also flutter out on their rounded wings to snap up insects in midair, for which their flattened flycatcher-like bills are well suited. Ants, flies and beetles form a major part of their diet.

Pale-yellow Robins are sedentary. Established pairs appear to keep to the same small territory of a few hectares year round and, although often seen to be solitary, may tolerate additional members, perhaps their young of earlier seasons. These birds may assist the dominant pair in feeding the young, but it seems likely that only the female nest-builds and incubates; she is fed on the nest by the male.

The Pale-yellow Robin and its close relative, the White-faced, may resemble other yellow robins in their colouring and habit of sitting sideways on vertical stems, but they differ in significant ways. Their flycatcher-like bills are rather flat; their fledglings are plainer reddish brown—like those of some whistlers; their nests are adorned with flakes of lichen rather than strips of bark; and they do not raise their tail at rest.

Pale-yellow Robins are confined to the rainforests of eastern Australia. Their beautifully decorated nests are adorned with flakes of lichen and wisps of moss, possibly for camouflage.

A Grey-headed Robin brings food to its chick in its moss and lichen-covered nest; the birds eat insects, grubs, snails.

Grey-headed Robin

Poecilodryas albispecularis (SALVADORI, 1875)

OTHER NAMES
Ashy-fronted Robin, Black-eared Robin.

IDENTIFICATION
LENGTH: *160–180 mm.*
ADULTS: *Sexes alike. Crown and nape dark grey. Back and shoulders olive-brown; rump tawny, shading into chestnut on base of tail. Rest of tail dull grey-brown. Two white wing bars; rest of wing olive-brown edged black. Lores and chin dusky; cheeks grey-brown darkening to black under eye. Throat white, running back to line under eye. Rest of underparts white, washed grey over breast and tawny on flanks and undertail. Eye brown-black. Bill black with bone-white tip. Feet creamy flesh.*
IMMATURES: *As adults. Juveniles rusty brown, blotched white on face and underparts; wing bars present.*

VOICE
CALL: *Soft, repeated, short piping whistles, on same pitch, by both sexes in contact. Chattering and chirping in alarm.*
SONG: *Loud thin whistle followed by two or three shorter notes at lower pitch and repeated, advertising territory all months.*

NESTING
Breeds August–January. Nest a coarse cup of thin twigs, rootlets, leaf skeletons and fibre, covered with moss and lichen; lined with fine fibre; placed in crotch or fork, often rattan, up to 2–3 m above ground. Eggs: one or two; cream-buff to pale green marked with brown, particularly in zone at larger end; rounded-oval, about 26 x 19 mm.

DISTRIBUTION
Mountain rainforests above 500 m on tablelands between Helenvale and Mt Spec, northeastern coastal Queensland, to sea level near Cape Tribulation. Also montane New Guinea. Five or six races; one endemic in Australia.

LONG PALE 'LEGS' reflect the Grey-headed Robin's ground-foraging habits. A sedentary bird, it occurs singly or in territorial pairs or small family groups or three or four in the substage of montane rainforest in northeastern Queensland. There it spends much time feeding in the shelter of the forest floor, hopping quietly along for several metres, pausing, picking up prey, and then moving on. Insects, spiders, grubs and snails make up its diet.

Like other related yellow robins, the Grey-headed hunts by perch-and-pounce from low branches in the forest substage, often working the edge of a track or clearing, on to which it will dart to pick up food, then flutter back to its perch in cover. At times it even snatches slow-flying insects, such as termites, on the wing. At most of its perches, it will sit upright and motionless for long periods between sallies for food. Hunting commonly continues until after dusk, for which the bird's very large eyes may be accustomed. It often clings to the sides of vertical trunks on its sorties, most of which are within a metre or so of the ground.

White-browed Robin

Poecilodryas superciliosa (GOULD, 1847)

OTHER NAMES
Buff-sided Robin, Buff-sided Shrike Robin, White-browed Shrike Robin, Buff-sided Flycatcher.

IDENTIFICATION
LENGTH: *140–180 mm.*
ADULTS: *Sexes alike. Crown, cheeks and upper parts warm dusky brown, darker on crown and face. Broad white brow over eye and small white crescent under eye. Wings and tail dusky, with broad white band through base of flight feathers and edge of greater coverts, a second narrow white band in middle of primaries, and inner secondaries edged white; tail with broad white tip except central pair of feathers. Underparts from chin and sides of neck to undertail white, washed lightly or heavily grey across breast and without or with rusty flanks and undertail respectively, according to race. Eye black-brown. Bill black. Feet dark grey-brown to black.*
IMMATURES: *As adults but duller.*

VOICE
CALL: *Series of soft, piping whistles, repeated three or four times, by both sexes in contact.*
SONG: *Three or four sharp churring notes, slurred together, by male or sometimes both sexes in territorial advertisement. Also series of sweetly trilled whistles.*

NESTING
Breeds July–March. Nest a loosely woven cup of plant stems, tendrils, rootlets, twigs and cobweb, decorated with strips of bark and sometimes moss and lichen; lined with finer grass stems, plant fibre and tendrils; placed in fork or upright crotch of tree usually 1–3 m above ground. Eggs: two; smooth; usually matt pale yellow-green, green-grey, blue-green or buff-green, spotted and blotched with browns all over, or in indistinct zone at larger end; oval to long-oval, 20 x 15 mm.

DISTRIBUTION
Gallery forests on river systems of coastal northern Australia, from Derby, WA, to Broad Sound, Qld. Two races: one in east; the other in west.

The buff-sided race of the White-browed Robin in northwestern Australia.

GALLERIES OF VINE SCRUB along streams and pockets of monsoonal rainforest in open eucalypt woodland across tropical northern Australia are the habitat of the White-browed Robin. In the northwest and Gulf of Carpentaria it also occurs locally in mangroves. Like other robins it is sedentary, pairs or local groups of three or four holding to the same territory year round and living on the shrubbery of the middle and lower forest strata.

When it feeds, its movements are jerky and rapid, with much drooping of wings, tail-cocking and flicking of wings and tail. Its most common feeding behaviour is to fly to the ground for a few minutes of foraging and then flit up into the trees again. It also chases insects in the manner of Jacky Winter and—like treecreepers *Climacteris*—searches for prey on tree trunks. It strongly resembles the Mangrove Robin in the way it clings to a trunk while extracting insects from crevices in the bark, and the way it hops over the ground. It eats mainly insects, small beetles, green tree ants, caterpillars and grasshoppers. In mangroves, small crabs and molluscs are also picked up from the surface of the mud.

There are two races. *Poecilodryas superciliosa cerviniventris* is found from around Derby, WA, east to the Gregory River system south of Burketown, Qld; *P.s. superciliosa* occurs sparingly from the Mitchell and Coleman Rivers on the west of Cape York Peninsula, south along the east coast to Broad Sound, Qld. It is the smaller of the two White-breasteds and lacks the rusty flanks and undertail coverts of the northwestern race.

Northern Scrub-robin *Drymodes superciliaris* GOULD, 1850

The little-known Northern Scrub-robin shares many habits with its relative, the Southern Scrub-robin, suggesting a common widespread ancestor.

INHABITING VINE-HUNG RAINFOREST on Cape York Peninsula and in the hills of New Guinea, the Northern Scrub-robin is isolated from its only close relative, the Southern Scrub-robin, by most of the Australian continent. This suggests that their common ancestral stock was once widespread across Australia, perhaps before the now-arid centre turned to desert. On the Roper River in Arnhem Land, two or three specimens of a paler rufous population were purportedly obtained about 70 years ago. No records have come to light since, suggesting that the report was a hoax, or that the bird is now lost through indiscriminate burning.

On Cape York Peninsula these elusive birds live in the forest floor, wherever the litter is deep, the substage open, and the canopy above dense. They are sedentary, may pair permanently, and keep to a moderate-sized foraging territory year round. Feeding mainly in the early morning and late afternoon into dusk, they hop and run methodically, picking up insects and small land snails and leaving trails of broken snail shells in their wake. They crouch-and-run as they go, or bounce hurriedly from one feeding point to another. Commonly their long tails are raised, twitched and fanned, both when they pause on the ground and on low to mid-height perches from which they sing. Feeding birds forage in dispersed pairs and keep in contact with penetrating lisping whistles.

Females apparently nest-build and incubate unaided, but both sexes share the feeding of young.

OTHER NAMES
Papuan Scrub-Robin.

IDENTIFICATION
LENGTH: *210–220 mm.*
ADULTS: *Sexes similar; female smaller. Upper parts cinnamon-brown, with crown browner and rump rufous. Tail dark brown with outer feathers rufous and broadly tipped white. Wings black with white-tipped wing coverts in two bars and some white-edged feathers forming third stripe. Face white with broad black vertical bar through eye from crown to cheek. Underparts white with rufous-buff suffusion on breast and flanks. Eye brown. Bill black. Legs pale pink-flesh.*

IMMATURES: *As adults but duller. Juveniles pale brown above with white and black feather edges from crown to mantle; tail russet with dull white edges; underparts cream-buff, flecking brown on throat and breast; vertical black eye-stripe dull.*

VOICE
Both call and song are little known. Some notes resemble those given by Southern Scrub-robin. Thin, carrying whistle in contact. Also scolding sharp hiss, believed to be threat call.

NESTING
Breeds October–January. Nest a saucer-shaped depression in the ground, usually at foot of a tree or shrub; small sticks added and dead leaves strewn around; lined with vine tendrils, bark shreds and plant fibres. Eggs: one or two; white or pale grey, spotted and blotched with blue-grey and red-brown; oval, about 22 x 18 mm. Incubation by female.

DISTRIBUTION
Coastal and hill rainforests of Cape York Peninsula south to McIlwraith Range and Rocky River; maybe Roper River, NT. Also New Guinea. Four or five races; one or two endemic in Australia.

Southern Scrub-robin *Drymodes brunneopygia* GOULD, 1840

A GROUND BIRD OF HEATHIER MALLEE, the Southern Scrub-robin is thrush-like in form and behaviour. Indeed, some recent classifications align it with the old world thrushes, Turdinae. It forages unobtrusively on the ground beneath shrubberies, hopping bouncily and cock-tailed along or running in short dashes with tail lowered, stopping to pick up food and pausing to watch, tail rising and falling and wings flicking sporadically. Breeding males also hop up into trees to beam out their far-carrying territorial whistles from bare vantage perches towards the tree canopy, again raising their tails. These mannerisms are also those of the endemic Australian robins and it is to this group that recent biochemical evidence suggests the scrub-robins are closely related.

Scrub-robins are sedentary, established pairs or loose communal groups of three or four occupying a hectare or so of mallee under optimal conditions. Clearing of habitat for wheat has decimated their numbers, and this once-common bird is scarce in many areas. The birds usually forage alone, keeping contact with one another with peevish, long-drawn whistles. Beetles and other ground- and litter-living invertebrates form a major part of their diet.

Males sing much only when breeding and then intermittently throughout the day, even during the hot middle hours. Females may nest-build and incubate unaided—laying only one egg which is unusual for Australian songbirds in temperate latitudes—but both sexes share the duties of feeding the young.

OTHER NAMES
Mallee Scrub Robin, Pale Scrub Robin.

IDENTIFICATION
LENGTH: *210–230 mm, including 100 mm tail.*
ADULTS: *Sexes similar; female slightly smaller. Upper parts uniformly dark grey-brown; rump rufous; tail dusky brown tipped narrowly white on outer feathers. Wings dusky brown with two faint white bars on shoulders; some white edging on primaries. Face grey with white toning on lores and eye-ring and dusky vertical smudge through eye. Throat and breast pale grey, grading to white on belly and cinnamon on flanks and undertail. Eye dark brown. Bill and feet dusky black.*
IMMATURES: *As adults. Juveniles: upper parts and wings sandy-brown with black flecks and white streaks; underparts white with dark feather tips on throat and breast; tail with buff tip.*

VOICE
CALL: *Long, thin, high-pitched slightly rising whistle, in contact by both sexes; also a harsh dry rattling scold.*
SONG: *Loud, repeated carrying series of whistled notes — chip-pip-er-eee, chip-pip-ee or chip-per-a-peet, the last syllable rising—by male, usually from vantage perch.*

NESTING
Breeds July–January. Nest a shallow cup of twigs and bark strips, lined with fine rootlets and grass stems; usually on ground well-strewn with bark and twigs, close to or beneath trunk of bush or within buttress of mallee. Egg: one; cream or pale green, spotted and blotched with shades of brown to form cap at larger end; oval, about 25 x 19 mm.

DISTRIBUTION
Mallee lands north to Shark Bay and east to Lake Dundas and Israelite Bay, WA; Eyre Peninsula, SA, east to the mallee limits of New South Wales and Victoria, with pockets around Great

Australian Bight and in Flinders Ranges, SA. No races.

When the Southern Scrub-robin alights it often flicks its wings and raises or fans its long brown tail. Its tail is almost as long as its body.

Lemon-bellied Flycatcher *Microeca flavigaster* GOULD, 1843

OTHER NAMES
Lemon-breasted Flycatcher, Brown-tailed Flycatcher, Kimberley Flycatcher.

IDENTIFICATION
LENGTH: *120–140 mm.*
ADULTS: *Sexes similar. Upper parts mid citrine-brown, slightly greyer over head in Arnhem Land and eastern Queensland, or uniformly browner with olive wash on back in Kimberleys. Wings and tail browner, the outer webs of feathers tinged citrine and tail feathers narrowly tipped off-white. Throat and brow-line off-white, washed yellow on Cape York Peninsula. Rest of underparts lemon-yellow tinged olive on breast or, in Kimberleys, white :tinged greyer over breast. Eye dark brown. Upper mandible dusky, lower greyish brown with flesh-coloured base. Feet dusky.*
IMMATURES: *Duller than adults, moulting out white-tipped primary coverts of juveniles last, at second annual moult. Juveniles olive-brown above, coarsely spotted cream, giving streaked appearance, white below, mottled brown on throat and breast. Bill and feet buffier-brown.*

VOICE
CALL: *Clear, bouncy* chauncey-chauncey *or* chickup, *possibly in contact or alarm, by maybe both sexes.*
SONG: *Sweet clear series of rising and falling whistled notes* chew-chew-swee-so-wee-chew, *repeated with frequent variations.*

NESTING
Breeds August–January, rarely much later. Nest a tiny shallow cup of fibre and bark strips, bound with cobweb, covered patchily with camouflaging bark scales and pieces of dried leaves; lined with fine strips of bark fibre and grass; bound to small, bare horizontal branch, usually at a fork, at 1.5–10 m above the ground, often over water. Egg: one; off-white tinged blue-grey, spotted and blotched all over with chestnut to olive-brown and underlying lavender, often forming irregular zone at larger end; long-oval, about 19 x 14 mm. Incubation probably by both sexes.

DISTRIBUTION
Wetter woodlands, open forests and mangroves of coastal and subscoastal northern Australia, from Broome, WA, to Broad Sound, Qld. Restricted to mangroves in Kimberleys, absent from mangroves and dry head of Gulf of Carpentaria, Qld, and rarely in rainforest anywhere. Also wooded grasslands in New Guinea. Five races; four in Australia.

The Lemon-bellied Flycatcher feeding its single young at its tiny, well-camouflaged nest.

THE MID-STAGES OF THE moister paperbark *Melaleuca,* eucalypt and mangrove woodlands and forests across tropical northern Australia are the habitat of the Lemon-bellied Flycatcher. Alone or in dispersed pairs, it hawks quietly and leisurely out to catch insects—flying beetles, ants, flies and grasshoppers—among foliage or on the wing from a set bare horizontal perch, often returning to the same perch to eat. Unlike the Jacky Winter, it does not wave its tail at rest. Flight is buoyant and fluttering, on rounded wings, with frequent hovering.

In the Kimberleys, where it is confined to dense stands of mangroves subject to regular tidal flooding, the flycatcher also forages regularly on the ground. Its technique there is to perch and pounce and to snatch prey—small crabs and other marine animals as well as insects—while fluttering low over the mud. Most perches for its sorties are from one–eight metres above the ground, and the bird rarely covers more than 20–30 metres on each feeding sally.

Lemon-bellied Flycatchers are apparently sedentary birds, established pairs rarely seeming to wander far from their breeding territories throughout the year. Displaying birds have a conspicuous song-flight, circling up among and sometimes over the tops of the tree canopy before dropping back to cover. It is likely that both sexes incubate and nest-build, constructing a nest that is so small and well camouflaged that it appears as little more than an obscure hump on the bare horizontal branch to which it is bound; sitting birds may hide it entirely by fluffing out their feathers. The birds sing often from perches in the forest midstage, both in and out of breeding, with daily peaks early morning and late afternoon.

By convention, the Lemon-bellied Flycatcher is represented by three yellow-green races in Australia: one small with a whitish throat and brow in Arnhem Land and western Gulf of Carpentaria; another larger with the same colouring in eastern coastal Queensland north to the foot of Cape York Peninsula; a third with yellowish throat and brow on Cape York Peninsula itself (and southern New Guinea). To them recent research has added a fourth: a browner-backed, white-bellied population in the Kimberley mangroves. The Kimberley population was formerly treated as a separate species—the Brown-tailed or Kimberley Flycatcher — but it intergrades with the green-backed, lemon-bellied race from Arnhem Land in mangroves around Cambridge Gulf, at Wyndham, with a full range of intermediates.

The white-bellied race of the Lemon-bellied Flycatcher in the Kimberleys.

Jacky Winter

Microeca leucophaea
(Latham, 1801)

OTHER NAMES
Brown Flycatcher, Peter-Peter, Post-sitter, Stump-bird, Spinks.

IDENTIFICATION
LENGTH: *120–140 mm.*
ADULTS: *Sexes similar. Upper parts mid to deep grey-brown; brow over lores and eyes white. Wing brown, inner flight feathers edged white; tail black-brown, outer two or three pairs of feathers wholly or broadly edged and tipped white. Underparts white, washed pale grey-brown over breast. Eye brown. Bill and feet dusky.*
IMMATURES: *Resemble adults, with small white tips to primary wing coverts. Juveniles brown above with cream spots and arrow-shaped markings; underparts white, spotted with brown, concentrated over breast.*

VOICE
CALL: *Occasionally high whistling notes, by both sexes.*
SONG: *Jingling, far-carrying paired double syllable,* peter-peter; *repeated quickly several times, by both sexes; sweeter, more musical and varied in spring and summer.*

NESTING
Breeds July–August to January–February; in north affected by rainfall. Nest a tiny frail saucer of fine grass, rootlets, sometimes hair or fine bark, bound with cobweb, decorated with lichen or bark; lined with finer fibre, sometimes fur or a few feathers; placed on large, bare branch or horizontal fork, 0.5–22 m above ground. Eggs: usually two, rarely three; pale grey- or green-blue, marked with browns and lavender-grey all over, often forming a cap or band at larger end; long-oval, about 20 x 15 mm. Incubation 17–18 days, by both sexes. Young fledge in about 18 days.

DISTRIBUTION
Dry eucalypt forest, woodland, mallee, cultivated and grazing areas throughout Australia. Fairly common in east and south but less plentiful across north; absent from northern Cape York Peninsula and higher Australian alps. Also in southeastern New Guinea. Three races; two in Australia: one, grey-brown-backed and with two outer pairs of tail feathers completely white, throughout woodlands of east and north, including Mt Lofty Ranges; the other dark brown-backed with only outermost pair of tail feathers almost all white, through southwest and central Australia east to Murray mallee. These two races could represent separate species, but the evidence is equivocal—there are intermediates from areas of contact. Populations of the eastern race grade paler and smaller northwards.

The Jacky Winter builds a small and frail nest on a bare, exposed branch in its woodland habitat. Both sexes take part in nest-building, incubating the eggs and caring for the young.

WIDESPREAD THROUGHOUT Australia's open eucalypt woodlands, the Jacky Winter is a familiar bird in most rural areas. It occupies much the same feeding niche and habitat as the Lemon-bellied Flycatcher, but keeps to more open drier woodland where the birds overlap in the north. The edge of forest or lines of woodland through open fields are favoured, wherever there are bare branches and stumps at one–five metres above the ground and the undergrowth is clear enough to allow free hawking.

Like most flycatchers, Jacky Winters feed by sallying out from set perches—a bare, exposed branch, stump, post or wire. They flutter out in leisurely sorties, picking insects out of the air, from foliage, and even from tree trunks and the ground before returning to a perch or another. Feeding flights may cover up to 30–50 metres; on them the birds take a wide range of invertebrates: small grasshoppers and crickets, termites, bugs, weevils, gnats, butterflies, ants, bees, spiders and adult and larval beetles, flies and moths. Most feeding is done at morning and dusk, and at other times the birds associate with mixed feeding flocks of other species.

Feeding actions are deft and graceful, aerial manoeuvrability at slow speeds being assisted by rounded wings and tails. The birds hover much, low over the ground, or close to tree trunks and foliage when searching for food, and dive, twist and back-turn easily. Back at their perches, they may sit quietly for extended periods, twitching their tails from side to side and displaying the white shafts; this signalling may serve to maintain contact between individuals.

Jacky Winters are rather sedentary, established pairs keeping to much the same territory of 10–15 hectares year round; birds in marginal areas and young of the year may disperse more widely through winter when southernmost populations often shift a little north. Except for family groups at the end of breeding, the birds are solitary or in pairs.

Quiet for much of the year, Jack Winters sing incessantly through the day when breeding, either in circling song-flight around tree tops or more often from a vantage perch. At other times, song features in the dawn chorus. Both sexes build the nest—a tiny cup—taking about eight days to do so, and both share incubation, brooding and the feeding of young. Sitting birds are fed at the nest by their mates.

Yellow-legged Flycatcher

Microeca griseoceps DE VIS, 1894

A MORE SLENDER FORM AND rich yellow 'legs' distinguish the Yellow-legged Flycatcher from the similar-looking Lemon-bellied Flycatcher. It also keeps to rainforests and vine scrubs, and is much more active.

For most of the time it wanders locally without holding to a particular territory, at least when not breeding. Working the upper branches and forest edge, it forages by gleaning, hawking and picking flushed insects off foliage and branchlets and catching them in midair on fluttering flights out and back to set perches. Sitting birds often raise and wave their tails.

The female may nest-build and brood unaided, only foraging for brief periods with the male during incubation. This, however, needs confirmation, because in other *Microeca* flycatchers, both sexes brood. Young are dispersed soon after fledging, adults staying in pairs or becoming solitary for the rest of the year.

The Yellow-legged Flycatcher lives in the crowns of rainforest trees.

OTHER NAMES
Little Yellow Robin, Little Yellow Flycatcher, Yellow-footed Flycatcher.

IDENTIFICATION
LENGTH: *About 120 mm.*
ADULTS: *Sexes similar. Head and nape mid-grey. Back and scapulars dull green. Wings and tail grey-brown edged with olive, tail feathers tipped faintly white. Face and ear coverts brown-grey; off-white over lores. Throat and upper breast off-white, grading to pale lemon on lower breast, belly and undertail, washed grey on flanks. Eye dark brown. Upper mandible black, lower flesh-yellow. Feet rich orange-yellow.*
IMMATURES: *Duller than adults; upper wing coverts—the last immature feathers to be moulted—retain small white tips. Juveniles brown, spotted heavily white on upper parts.*

VOICE
CALL: *Repeated zzt-zzt-zzt erratically while feeding and in contact.*
SONG: *Trills and piping whistled notes, probably by male only.*

NESTING
Breeds probably October–February. Nest a very small neat cup about 40 mm in diameter, of rootlets bound with cobweb, decorated on the outside with paperbark and lichen; 10–15 m above ground on horizontal branch or fork. Eggs: usually two; pale blue speckled and blotched dark brown and grey; long-oval, about 15 x 12 mm.

DISTRIBUTION
Rainforest and its edges, including fringing paperbark and eucalypt woodland, on Cape York Peninsula west to Weipa and south to Silver Plains. Records from Atherton–Cooktown bloc unconfirmed. Also New Guinea. About four races; one endemic to Australia.

Crested Shrike-tit *Falcunculus frontatus* (LATHAM, 1801)

THE POWERFUL BILL of the Crested Shrike-tit is used in diverse ways when foraging for spiders, larvae, beetles and other insects. It can prise peeling bark and decaying wood from tree-trunks and branches, cut into hard galls on live twigs, and rip apart the 'nests' of leaf-tying caterpillars. Yet these birds also hang upside-down in the outer foliage gleaning insects from the leaves. Large prey are carried to a suitable perch, pinned down with one foot, and dismembered with the bill.

Shrike-tits forage unobtrusively in ones, pairs or family groups in the upper branches of tall forest eucalypts. They work methodically through one tree, then fly through and over the canopy for 50 or more metres to another. Foraging territories for these sedentary birds are large and can cover over 50 hectares.

The female constructs the bulk of the nest. Both sexes incubate and feed the young, which may be tended for five months or more. Often there is co-operative breeding, parents being helped by a third bird in feeding young; the third bird is probably one of the offspring of the previous season.

OTHER NAMES
Crested Tit, Bark Tit, Eastern Shrike-tit, Western Shrike-tit, Northern Shrike-tit.

IDENTIFICATION
LENGTH: *160–190 mm.*
MALE: *In eastern race, head, chin and throat black, with broad white band across cheek, and another from over eye to nape; white lore spot; crown feathers erectile in crest. Back and rump green-olive, contrasting with mid-grey edging on dusky wing coverts, wings and tail. Outer tail feathers edge-tipped white. Breast to undertail plain lemon-yellow. Eye red-brown. Bill massive, hooked, black. Feet leaden-grey. In western race, centre belly broadly white; back and rump bright citrine, washing over edges of dusky wing coverts, wings and tail. Northern race blends upper parts of western race with ventral pattern of eastern, and is smaller.*
FEMALE: *As male of respective race but throat mid olive-grey; chin grey.*
IMMATURES: *As adults. Juveniles pale russet-brown over back, head striped as adults, pale yellow below with cream-white throat; bill dusky with pale cutting edge.*

VOICE
CALL: *Drawn-out, high-pitched down-slurred whistle, by both sexes in contact. Also subdued chuckle or stutter of two-five syllables.*
SONG: *Closely repeated contact whistles, finishing in louder lower-pitched upslurred note.*

NESTING
Breeds mainly September–January. Nest a deep goblet of fibrous strips of bark matted compactly with cobweb into smooth outer surface; lined with soft grass and finely shredded bark; placed in prolonged vertical branches in topmost foliage of tree, to 30 m above ground. Eggs: two–three; white, freckled with dark brown, slate and lavender; oval, about 24 x 15 mm. Incubation at least 15 days, mainly by female. Young fledge in about 15 days.

A Crested Shrike-tit of the eastern race begging food from its male parent.

DISTRIBUTION
Eucalypt woodlands and forest of southwestern Australia, avoiding jarrah belt; northwestern Australia— where rare—east to McArthur River, NT, and eastern Australia from Atherton Tablelands to Mt Lofty Ranges and inland along River Red Gum-lined rivers, avoiding box. Three endemic races: one each in southwest, northwest and east.

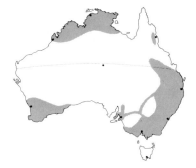

The Grey Whistler forages for insects within tropical lowland rainforest.

Grey Whistler

Pachycephala simplex GOULD, 1843

OTHER NAMES
Grey-headed Whistler, Brown Whistler.

IDENTIFICATION
LENGTH: *140–150 mm.*
ADULTS: *Sexes similar. Cape York Peninsula race: Crown grey; rest of upper parts olive-green, greyer on flight feathers and tail. Underwing creamy yellow. Throat white grading to dull lemon on rest of underparts, faintly streaked and washed grey-brown on breast and flanks respectively. Arnhem Land race: Upper parts mid-brown; underwing white; underparts white with faint brown wash on breast and flanks. Off-white eyebrow meeting across brow in both races, and lores darker grey-brown. Eye deep red-brown or ruby. Bill black. Feet dark grey.*
IMMATURES: *As adults; eyes browner. Juveniles washed plain rufous-brown on upper parts, more faintly so over breast, moulting into adult dress within a month or two of fledging.*

VOICE
CALL: *Clear, complex whistle, without whipcrack quality of other whistlers; two notes, second note lower than first; given perhaps in contact, by both sexes.*
SONG: *Call, followed by three or more notes—one longer and higher, next two shorter and lower—often leading into long song by territorial male.*

NESTING
Breeds September–March. Nest a cup of dead leaves interwoven with rootlets and tendrils and sparingly bound with cobweb; lined with fine dry grass and tendrils; placed in fork, or vine tangle, usually high in forest canopy. Eggs: two; glossy white, with umber and purple-grey spots, mostly at larger end; oval, about 21 x 16 mm.

DISTRIBUTION
In Queensland common in lowland rainforest and its edges, from Cape York Peninsula to Townsville. In Northern Territory, along coast and islands from about Port Keats to Rose River and Groote Eylandt in mangroves and monsoon forests. Also New Guinea and intervening islands. About seven races; two in Australia.

A VOCAL BIRD, the Grey Whistler calls incessantly through the day for much of the year. Its optimal habitat is tropical lowland rainforest, although it does range up to 500 metres altitude in northeastern Queensland and into tall *Rhizophora* mangroves in Arnhem Land. Singly or in pairs, it forages through the mid and upper forest strata, hopping methodically from branchlet to branchlet, gleaning for insects. At times it sits motionless within cover for hours, singing sporadically. At others, it searches vigorously, scratching at disturbed insects and fluttering in the outer leaves like a flycatcher. In northeastern Queensland, Grey Whistlers associate with mixed feeding flocks of other birds, but in Arnhem Land they forage alone.

The two races of Grey Whistler in Australia are so different in appearance that they have often been regarded as separate species. Their plumage patterns are nonetheless connected by a range of intermediates through the Kai Islands and southern New Guinea.

Rufous Whistler

Pachycephala rufiventris (LATHAM, 1801)

OTHER NAMES
Rufous-breasted Whistler, Rufous-breasted Thickhead, Echong, Mock Whipbird, Thunderbird.

IDENTIFICATION
LENGTH: *160–170 mm.*
ADULTS: *Upper parts mid-grey. Wings and tail duskier, with pale grey feather edges. Black through eye and, in south, through lores to encircle white throat. Breast rufous, grading greyer on upper flanks and paler on belly. Eye ruby. Bill black. Feet slate-grey.*
FEMALE: *Upper parts browner grey; faint streaking on head. Lores whitish. Throat white, grading to pale rufous breast, belly and undertail; fine dusky streaks on throat and upper breast.*
IMMATURES: *Upper parts cinnamon-grey with paler feather edges; green tinge on back and wings in males. Throat to belly white with dusky streaks. Eye brown; bill pale grey. Juveniles heavily streaked, with pointed tail feathers.*

VOICE
CALL: *Succession of musical chattering notes.*
SONG: *Breeding song loud and tuneful, resembling* pee-pee-pee, joey-joey-joey *and ending with* eeee-chong *with*

explosive last syllable, often given repeatedly all day, mainly by male.

NESTING
Breeds September–February. Nest a flimsy cup of fine twigs and grasses, lined with fine grass and rootlets; placed in tree-fork or low bush, up to 10 m above ground but mostly lower. Eggs: two or three; dull olive blotched dark brown; oval, about 23 x 17 mm. Incubation 12–15 days, by both sexes. Young fledge in 10–15 days.

DISTRIBUTION
All types of open forest and woodland throughout mainland Australia. Also New Caledonia. Two races; one in Australia.

The Rufous Whistler takes its name from the male; the female is greyer.

DURING THE BREEDING SEASON pairs of Rufous Whistlers establish territories. Boundary disputes take the form of a song, initially, with rival males drawing closer, to perch sometimes within half a metre of each other. They cock fanned tails, raise their crown feathers, rock, bow, bob and sometimes erupt into chasing flights. A resident female will assist in territorial defence. Both sexes are equally adept vocalists. There is much displaying and bowing between the male and female of a pair, with birds calling often in chorus. The female is usually quieter during nesting.

During courtship feeding either bird will emit begging noises while, crouched with wings spread, it hops along behind the other. The male inspects potential nest sites but the female appears to make the choice, and she builds the nest. Only the female incubates at night but both sexes brood and feed the young.

Throughout the day the birds can be seen gleaning from, or hovering among foliage, occasionally dropping to the ground to forage. They hop quietly and methodically from branch to branch, taking insects, including larvae; berries and fruits are taken infrequently. There is a high overlap between Rufous and Golden Whistlers in diet and feeding behaviour through the mid and upper strata of trees; the two species do not co-exist often.

The Rufous is common throughout much of its range, and there is scarcely a tract of open forest anywhere in Australia without it.

Rufous Whistlers occur mostly alone or in pairs because early in the breeding season young of the previous year are expelled from territories, but when autumn migration takes southeastern birds north, small parties often congregate en route. Migratory birds return south to their territories during late August. Elsewhere, however, the species is only a partial migrant and locally breeding birds are commonly sedentary or, at most, nomadic.

Olive Whistler
Pachycephala olivacea VIGORS & HORSFIELD, 1827

A WHISTLER OF THE undergrowth, the Olive replaces the Red-lored and Gilbert's Whistlers in the cool, moist upland shrubberies of the southeast. North of the Hunter River, it is confined to temperate rainforests of Antarctic beech *Nothofagus* along the summit ridges of the Great Dividing Range just into Queensland. To the south it spreads out into sclerophyll glades and descends to coastal heaths in Victoria, Tasmania and far southeastern South Australia. Apart from dispersing young of the year, it is a sedentary bird except in the Australian alps, from which there is a winter exodus to lower ground, reaching urban Melbourne and Canberra.

Under cover, Olive Whistlers glean for insects mainly on the ground, hopping along and up on to lower branches to pick up their food: various insects, particularly beetles and weevils. They feed solitarily and are quiet out of breeding.

Males sing sporadically throughout the day when breeding. No other Australian bird varies so much in its dialects. Populations north of the Hunter Valley vary on the theme of a double-note long-drawn whistle; others in the Australian alps utter resonant up- and down-slurred whistles, reminiscent of those of a Gilbert's Whistler; still others on the south coast and in Tasmania give explosive whistles. There is only partial concordance between these variations and the geographical races of Olive Whistlers.

Photo caption: Olive Whistler in the undergrowth.

OTHER NAMES
Olivaceous Whistler, Olive Thickhead.

IDENTIFICATION
LENGTH: *200–210 mm.*
MALE: *Crown and hind neck deep grey; rest of upper parts olive-brown, slight rufous wash on rump; wing and tail feathers edged dull citrine. Throat dull white, flecked grey; mid-grey band across upper breast; rest of underparts ochreish buff, undertail coverts edged yellow. Eye ruby. Bill black. Feet black-brown.*
FEMALE: *As male; slightly smaller and duller in mainland races. Like immatures but greyer headed with red eye and black bill in Tasmania.*

IMMATURES: *Upper parts including crown uniformly dark olive-brown; underparts as adults but duller and without grey breast band. Eye and bill dull brown. Juveniles washed rufous on wing coverts; tail feathers pointed.*

VOICE
CALL: *Low plaintive whistles.*
SONG: *Two main long-drawn whistles in northeast, the second often much lower in pitch,* peeee-pooo; *resonant series of rising and falling whistles in alps,* weee-e-tchow; *slow, rising* cheer-ritty *with whipcrack effect in Tasmania. Also monotonous, repeated, swelling* jiff, jiff, jiff *as territorial call.*

NESTING
Breeds September–January. Nest a loosely built cup of fine twigs and grass-stems, lined with finer similar material; placed in low fork of tree-branch, in shrubs or dense grass-clumps. Eggs: two or three; pale buff spotted with brown and grey; oval, about 28 x 19 mm.

DISTRIBUTION
Upland forest shrubberies of southeast, north to Mistake and McPherson Ranges, Qld, south to Tasmania, and southwest on coast to Robe–Kingston, SA. Nowhere common. Three races: one in southeastern mainland; one north of Hunter River, NSW; one in Tasmania and Bass Strait islands.

Gilbert's Whistler

Pachycephala inornata GOULD, 1840

ALTHOUGH A MALLEE BIRD, Gilbert's Whistler occurs patchily in small pockets of mixed shrubbery—mainly *Melaleuca*—wherever they form stands dense enough to provide cover. There established pairs appear to occupy permanent territory year round.

Gilbert's Whistlers feed under the cover of shrubbery within a metre or two of the ground. They hop methodically about among the branches, gleaning for insects—beetles, weevils and particularly caterpillars—and often drop to the ground to poke about in litter. Flight is low and undulating, from shrub to shrub.

Gilbert's Whistlers are quiet and retiring. Males sing very sporadically during the year, to advertise territory, but more actively when breeding. Song is delivered from a vantage perch, but usually close to the ground well under cover. Both sexes nest-build and feed the young, but the female shoulders most of the incubation. Males may breed in immature plumage.

In its name, Gilbert's Whistler commemorates John Gilbert, one of Australia's pioneering ornithologists and collector for John Gould.

This male Gilbert's Whistler has brought a caterpillar for its nestlings. Both parents feed young.

OTHER NAMES
Black-lored Whistler, Red-throated Whistler, Gilbert's Thickhead.

IDENTIFICATION
LENGTH: *190–200 mm.*
MALE: *Upper parts dark grey with brown suffusion, slightly darker on head; lores and area around eyes black. Throat rich rufous. Breast and flanks pale grey, faintly dark streaked, grading to white or ochreish buff on belly and undertail. Eye ruby. Bill black. Feet dark grey.*
FEMALE: *As male, but lores mid-grey as face; throat greyish white. Bill grey-brown.*
IMMATURES: *As female, but ventral*

streaking stronger; eyes browner. Juveniles washed russet over head, back and breast, moulting out within a month or so of fledging. Tail feathers pointed.

VOICE
CALL: *Low, indrawn, plaintive whistle.*
SONG: *Rich, resonant, and far-carrying. Deliberately repeated swelling whistle* pew-pew-pew-pew-pew, *breaking into explosive* er-whit er-whit, *or* e-chop; *also explosive* jok-jok-jok-jok, *repeated in sequence of 10–15, by male.*

NESTING
Breeds September–December. Nest a

cup of bark strips, grasses and twigs, loosely bound with cobweb, wool and vine tendrils; lined with fine bark strips and rootlets; about 13 cm in diameter and 10 cm high; placed in dense upright fork of shrub or low tree, up to 2 m above ground. Eggs: two to four; cream-buff spotted with brown-black and lavender, often in zone at larger end; oval, about 23 x 17 mm. Incubation mainly by female.

DISTRIBUTION
Mallee and associated woodland across south, from inland southwestern Australia, narrowly around Nullarbor Plain east to heathy upper reaches of Lachlan River, NSW. No races.

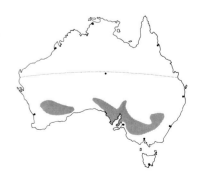

Red-lored Whistler *Pachycephala rufogularis* GOULD, 1840

A male Red-lored Whistler at its nest in the Pulletop Nature Reserve, NSW, in 1962. Red-lored Whistlers have not been found in the reserve—which may be too small to support a viable population—for the past decade.

THE RED-LORED WHISTLER is one of a group of three large whistlers that, endemic to Australia, live in shrubby undergrowth, have stubby bills and bowed outermost flight feathers, and utter deliberate song-notes of extraordinary richness and resonance. The other two are the Olive and Gilbert's Whistlers.

Of the three, the Red-lored is much the least known; indeed, the full extent of its distribution and habitat requirements have not become clear until the past decade or so. Whereas mallee-broombush *Melaleuca uncinata* communities were previously thought to be core habitat, now it is known that the bird is centred in still wetter heath, of *Banksia* and stringybark *Eucalyptus baxteri*, in the Ninety Mile and Big Deserts across the South Australian–Victorian border. Throughout its range, the Red-lored abuts on Gilbert's Whistler. The two seem to occupy mutually exclusive territories, which suggests that they compete; as a rule, Gilbert's occupies the drier, more open habitat.

Apart from dispersing young of the year, Red-lored Whistlers are sedentary birds, established pairs holding territories in pockets of shrubby heath and broombush in wet mallee. There they feed mainly on the ground, hopping methodically along under cover and into low branches, gleaning for food: large insects, larvae and occasionally berries and seeds. They fly little and only in swift, low undulations between bushes.

Out of breeding, the whistlers are silent, secretive and solitary in their feeding. In spring, however, males hop and fly up to bare vantage perches in the mallee midstage to sing sporadically through the day. Singing males throw up their head as they call. Both members of the pair construct the nest, working the material in alternately and giving a faint chuckle before flying off for more. Unlike Gilbert's Whistler, which uses only dead material, the Red-lored incorporates some greenery into the walls and lining. Both sexes incubate and brood and feed the young.

OTHER NAMES
Red-throated Whistler, Rufous-throated Thickhead, Buff-breasted Whistler.

IDENTIFICATION
LENGTH: *200–210 mm.*
MALE: *Upper parts dark grey. Wings and tail duskier, edged with pale grey. Lores and throat cinnamon-rufous, with mid-grey band across upper breast. Lower breast to undertail cinnamon-rufous, flanks greyer. Eye ruby. Bill black. Feet black-brown.*
FEMALE: *As male; paler grey upper parts and paler cinnamon-rufous on lores, throat and underparts.*
IMMATURES: *Upper parts as female; underparts streaked dusky; lores white; eye and bill deep brown. Juveniles washed plain russet-brown over upper parts and flanks; underparts white streaked dusky; tail feathers pointed. Juvenile plumage moults out within a month or so of fledging.*

VOICE
CALL: *Low, indrawn plaintive whistle.*
SONG: *Resonant and far-carrying, by male. Swelling, repeated whistles seeee-saw-saw-saw, the first note longer and upslurred, concluding two or three shorter and progressively dropping in pitch. Also explosive, repeated chop-chop-chop, in long series on same pitch.*

NESTING
Breeds September–December. Nest a substantial cup, mainly of coarse bark and mallee leaves, neatly woven around rim; lined with fine bark shreds, rootlets, grass, tips of bushes or green twining plants; placed within 0.5 m of ground, in forked branch of mallee, in clump of porcupine grass Triodia, *or in stout shrubs, such as broombush. Eggs: two or three; pale buff to white, sparingly marked with umber-brown, with blurred lavender streaks; oval, about 24 x 17 mm. Incubation about 15 days, by both sexes.*

DISTRIBUTION
Heathy mallee tracts of southeastern South Australia, northwestern Victoria and southwestern New South Wales, with isolated outlier in mallee in midwestern New South Wales between Pulletop and Round Hill Nature Reserves. No races, but identity of midwestern New South Wales population not established.

Mangrove Golden Whistler *Pachycephala melanura* GOULD, 1843

OTHER NAMES
Black-tailed Whistler, Robust Whistler.

IDENTIFICATION
LENGTH: *150–160 mm.*
MALE: *Crown, sides of head and band across upper breast black; broad golden-yellow collar; rest of upper parts golden-olive. Tail all black or grading golden-olive to base. Edges of wing quills grey. Throat white; rest of underparts deep yellow. Eye ruby. Bill and feet black.*
FEMALE: *Head grey; rest of upper parts dull olive; tail dusky (northern race) to olive-grey (western race). Throat white flecked brown, rest of underparts yellow (northern race); or all underparts creamy white with yellow undertail (western race).*
IMMATURES: *In first year upper parts washed russet; tail olive, with black shafts; throat white with dark fringes, rest of underparts buff; undertail coverts bright yellow; eye brown; bill dull brown. In second year resemble female.*

VOICE
Call and song resemble those of Golden Whistler.

NESTING
Breeds October–December. Nest a loose cup of grasses and rootlets, lightly bound with cobweb; lined with finer rootlets and tendrils; placed in upright leafy fork of mangrove or other tree among adjacent coastal vegetation. Eggs: two or three; buff or stone-coloured, spotted with dark red-brown and grey, often in zone at larger end; oval, about 21 x 16 mm.

DISTRIBUTION
Mangroves and neighbouring scrub of coastal northern Australia, from Carnarvon, WA, to Repulse Bay, Qld. Also eastern New Guinea and Bismarck Archipelago. Probably four or five races; two in Australia.

The male Mangrove Golden Whistler resembles the male Golden Whistler, but is longer-billed and richer in tone.

AS ITS NAME IMPLIES, the Mangrove Golden Whistler inhabits mangroves. It is virtually restricted to them across northern Australia—wherever there are extensive stands of taller *Rhizophora–Bruguiera* forest—and only occasionally forages out into fringing monsoon scrubs. Like the Golden Whistler, it forages solitarily or in dispersed pairs through the middle strata of the vegetation, at one–five metres above the ground. It hops methodically and alertly among branchlets and foliage beneath the forest canopy, gleaning for insects and occasionally diving to trunks or mangrove mud and tidal debris to pick up small crabs. Flight, from tree to tree within the forest, is undulating.

Mangrove Golden Whistlers appear to be sedentary and established pairs may hold to the same territory year round. Males sing sporadically throughout the year, more when breeding.

The Australian distribution of the Mangrove Golden Whistler is broken at the Eighty Mile Beach, but this does not coincide with the limits of the two races there. The paler western race is found on both sides of the break; only further north, around Port Warrender in the northern Kimberleys, does it meet and intergrade with the more richly coloured northern form. Both races have longer bills than the related Golden Whistler, and these may enable the birds to feed more effectively on their main prey in the mangroves: grubs, ants, shield bugs, and leaf and lace beetles.

This is an immature or a female Mangrove Golden Whistler, western race.

Golden Whistler

Pachycephala pectoralis (LATHAM, 1801)

ADULT MALE GOLDEN WHISTLERS are much more showy than the plain-plumaged females. They do not seem to don this brilliant dress, however, until at least their second and mostly third years. They are widespread in the taller, wetter, coastal forests of southern and eastern Australia, but also range into mallee, eucalypt woodland and heaths.

Golden Whistlers forage singly or in pairs through the forest and mallee midstage at one–20 metres above the ground. Their movements are slow, deliberate, and usually quiet. Hopping methodically from branch to branch they watch constantly for insects and their larvae, picking and gleaning them and occasionally berries from leaves and branches. At times they sally out briefly on the wing to snap up prey from foliage or in midair; at other times they drop to the ground to forage in litter, hopping along. Flight from tree to tree is graceful and swooping, the wings opening and closing in steep undulations without beating.

Breeding Golden Whistlers sing persistently through the day from bare vantage perches; females may contribute, as well as males. Like Rufous Whistlers, they will break into a crescendo at any loud noise. Both sexes incubate and brood and feed the young, each sinking so low in the nest that even the male becomes inconspicuous. Males may breed before attaining adult plumage.

Seasonal movements are complex. Many populations, such as those in the east coast rainforests and Tasmania, are largely sedentary. Other populations in the southwest across to the southeast may wander rather more widely in winter. Only those breeding in the southeastern corner of the mainland are consistently migratory, shifting down from the high mountains in winter and moving north and inland, reaching southeastern Queensland and occasionally the Mt Lofty–Flinders Ranges, SA.

A female Golden Whistler. The plumage colour varies around Australia.

OTHER NAMES
Golden-breasted Whistler, White-throated Whistler, Golden-breasted Thickhead, Thunder-bird, Cut-throat, Ring-coachman.

IDENTIFICATION
LENGTH: *160–175 mm.*
MALE: *Head and face black, with broad yellow collar. Back, shoulders and rump green-olive. Wings dusky, with coverts and inner flight feathers edged citrine; tail all black to all grey. Throat white; black band from side of face around upper breast. Rest of underparts rich to pale yellow. Eye ruby. Bill and feet black.*
FEMALE: *Upper and underparts plain mid-grey, washed olive over back and buff on breast and belly in different regions; throat whiter flecked grey; undertail white, yellow or buff.*
IMMATURES: *First-year juveniles grey with russet edging on wings; bill pale grey-brown; eye brown. Second-year birds resemble female, but bill duller and males with brighter yellow undertail.*

VOICE
CALL: *In winter calls limited and resemble a weak version of parts of breeding song. Single rising, whistled seeep, in contact.*
SONG: *Rather melodious, loud, persistent and clear whistling notes* chee-chee-chee-chee-tu-whit, *with upslurred whip-cracking ending.*

NESTING
Breeds September–January. Nest a rough cup up to 10 cm in diameter, of rootlets, plant stems, grass and slender leaves, loosely bound with cobweb; lined neatly with finer fibre; placed in upright fork or tall shrub up to 5 m above ground. Eggs: usually two; pale salmon or stone-coloured, with spots of dark red-brown and grey; oval, about 23 x 17 mm. Incubation 14–17 days, by both sexes. Young fledge in 10–13 days.

DISTRIBUTION
Forests, mallee and denser woodlands of coastal and subcoastal southern and eastern Australia, from Shark Bay, WA, to rainforest tablelands, northeastern Queensland. Also archipelagos of southwestern Pacific. About 40 races; four in Australia.

This male Golden Whistler has just fed its nestling. Golden Whistlers are common in denser coastal forests.

White-breasted Whistler *Pachycephala lanioides* GOULD, 1840

FOR SUCH AN imposing whistler—it is one of the largest and most strikingly patterned of its genus—the White-breasted frequents a limited and unprepossessing habitat. Not only is it confined to mangroves along the northeastern Australian coast, but it keeps to the more stunted brakes along inlets and estuaries, where the stems are dense and the canopy only three–five metres high. There it is apparently sedentary, established pairs holding near-permanent territories of 50 to several hundred metres.

White-breasted Whistlers feed quietly and solitarily in mangrove undergrowth. They work slowly and methodically, hopping and pausing among the branchlets and sheltered foliage to glean for insects, and making short undulating flights under cover from shrub to shrub as they go. At low tide they drop to the mud to hop about for crustaceans—tiny crabs—which appear to form a major part of their diet in drier months. Their sturdy bills—which are particularly well-fitted for this mode of feeding—and tails and feet often become muddied.

White-breasted Whistlers sing sporadically through the year to defend their territory. Their song is like that of the Rufous Whistler but, surprisingly for such a large bird, lacks the same verve and volume. Males usually sing from a low vantage perch within the cover of mangrove shrubbery and can rarely be heard for more than 50 metres. The birds breed in drier months of the year, perhaps because staple food—crustaceans—is more plentiful then when unaffected by freshwater run-off during the summer monsoon. Females may carry out most of the nest-building and feeding of young while the male patrols territory.

There are three races of this endemic species: one small, with fawn females on the coast of the Pilbara; one large with fawn-grey females in the Kimberleys; the last smaller with grey females around Arnhem Land.

The large sturdy bill of the White-breasted Whistler helps it to feed on the tiny crabs gleaned from mangrove mud. This is a female.

OTHER NAMES
White-bellied Whistler, White-bellied Thickhead.

IDENTIFICATION
LENGTH: *180–200 mm.*
MALE: *Head and side of face black; indistinct chestnut collar around nape. Back and rump mid-grey, rarely mottled black; upper tail coverts black. Wings with coverts and flight feathers black edged mid-grey. Tail black above with grey tip, grey below. Throat white; broad black band from side of face around breast, edged chestnut below; rest of undersurface white merging to pale grey on flanks; thighs black. Eye ruby. Bill black. Feet black or brown-grey.*
FEMALE: *Upper parts and face uniformly mid-grey to fawn. Wing coverts and flight feathers dusky grey with paler edges. Tail grey to black, edged with grey. Throat off-white and breast washed grey to fawn, all moderately streaked with black-brown extending over flanks; belly light buff to white; vent white; thighs grey or grey-brown. Eye, bill and feet as male.*
IMMATURES: *Similar to female but back lighter, with streaking more conspicuous, particularly on pale cinnamon-tinged underparts; flight feathers and coverts edged cinnamon to light rufous. Eye dull brown; bill light brown with yellow gape.*

VOICE
CALL: *Contact call is whistled notes of two or three syllables, rising in inflection; harsh alarm whistle per-weet, with the second syllable louder, also whistled twit.*
SONG: *Male gives sequence of four–six clear whistled notes, more subdued than those of Rufous Whistler; female's song still less animated.*

NESTING
Breeds March–November; possibly sporadically throughout year. Nest a scanty cup, of interwoven rootlets and twigs, lined with finer rootlets; usually in fork in dense mangroves 1–3 m above the mud. Eggs: one or two; smooth, glossy buff-olive, spotted with umber and olive-brown, usually darker in zone at larger end; oval, about 26 x 19 mm. Incubation probably by female.

DISTRIBUTION
Locally common along coast in low dense mangroves usually on the seaward side, rarely in adjacent monsoon scrub; from Shark Bay, WA, east to Karumba, Qld. Three races.

The male White-breasted Whistler is identified by its black collar.

Little Shrike-thrush

Colluricincla megarhyncha
<small>(QUOY & GAIMARD, 1830)</small>

OTHER NAMES
Rufous Shrike-thrush.

IDENTIFICATION
LENGTH: *170–190 mm.*
ADULTS: *Sexes similar. In eastern races upper parts russet-brown with variable grey bloom; wing and tail quills darker, edged lighter brown or rufous in Ingham–Cooktown population. Face paler than upper parts, with vague buff lores and eyebrow. Throat whitish, grading to cinnamon-brown or pale rufous from breast to undertail and streaked variably dusky over breast. Eye red-brown. Bill pink-grey, washed darker on culmen. Feet pale grey. In northwestern race, upper parts uniformly flat brown. Face pale grey-brown, with bright white lores and eyebrow. Throat and upper breast white, grading to pale grey-fawn flanks and undertail; belly white; breast and throat extensively streaked dusky. Bill black.*
IMMATURES: *As adults but wing quills and upper wing coverts edged russet, tail quills tipped tawny-buff below and pointed; eye brown.*

VOICE
CALL: *Abbreviated song in contact; chirps and wheezes in alarm.*
SONG: *Series of four–five clear whistles, the first rising, the rest shorter and rapid on same pitch, by both sexes. Singing more subdued than in Grey Shrike-thrush.*

NESTING
Breeds September–February. Nest a rough, deep cup of dead skeleton and green leaves, bark strips, twigs and (in eastern birds) sometimes moss, bound with tendrils, coated with cobweb and cocoons; lined with rootlets and thin plant stems; well camouflaged in vertical foliage fork, shrub, vine tangle, lawyer cane Calamus, *pandanus or mangrove, but sometimes in open sites, 0.3–10 m above ground. Eggs: two or three; glossy, pearly white to pale pink-brown, freckled with varying amounts of olive, slate or red-brown, particularly at larger end; elongate to round-oval, variable in size, about 25 x 19 mm.*

DISTRIBUTION
Coastal and hill rainforests, vine scrubs and mangroves around northern Australia, west to mid-northwestern coast of Kimberleys, WA, and south in east to Barrington Tops, NSW. Most common in lowlands. Also in New Guinea, nearby islands and Sangi Islands, near Celebes. About 30 races; five in Australia.

The Little Shrike-thrush lives beneath the canopy of rainforest and mangroves. It builds a rough, cup-shaped nest.

LITTLE SHRIKE-THRUSHES are sedentary birds of the interior of closed-canopied vine forests: rainforest up to 1000 metres in northeastern Queensland, monsoon jungles in northwestern Australia, and mangroves along most of the northern Australian coastline. Although joining mixed feeding flocks of other birds, they forage as much alone, or in pairs, working methodically through all strata of the forest, from just under the canopy to shrubbery close to and on the ground. The bird hops and flits deliberately from branch to branch, working out into foliage and vine tangles and on trunks, picking and gleaning—and even tearing away bark to expose prey. Spiders, beetles and other large insects are taken and, in mangroves, crabs. It also tears open the nests of other birds for their young.

Established pairs may occupy permanent territories of up to several hectares, which they defend by sporadic singing, particularly in the early morning. Song battles heighten during breeding when neighbours of both sexes may gather in border areas, hopping excitedly around, tails cocked high, singing in a non-stop medley and duetting.

The Little Shrike-thrush belongs to a group of small, rainforest-inhabiting shrike-thrushes in the southwestern Pacific which includes Bower's Shrike-thrush and the Sooty 'Whistler' *Colluricincla umbrina* of New Guinea. In all of them, males and females are alike.

The Little Shrike-thrush is much the most variable, and breaks up into five races around northern Australia. There are four in the east, between northern coastal New South Wales and Cape York Peninsula. All are generally rufous and pale billed; they differ in minor nuances of size, tone and breast streaking. To the west around the coast of Arnhem Land and the Kimberleys is the fifth race—black-billed, brown-backed, and whitish breasted. Despite its appearance it is linked to the eastern races by a range of intermediate populations around the western head of the Gulf of Carpentaria.

Bower's Shrike-thrush

Colluricincla boweri (RAMSAY, 1885)

THE SONG OF BOWER'S SHRIKE-THRUSH is a characteristic summer sound in tropical mountain rainforest where the bird rarely occurs lower than 400 metres in altitude. An often-heard item in its repertoire sounds like *da-dee-da-dee, pon-pon-pon*. The first four notes are quick and quiet, and the latter rich, plunking whistles carrying far through the forest.

The birds live singly or in pairs in the middle and lower forest strata. They forage for large insects and larvae, often perching to wait and pounce on prey. Occasionally they hop deliberately up to the tops of the trees, or down to pick an insect off the ground.

The Bower's Shrike-thrush flies in short swoops from one tree to another in the rainforest. In its movements it is quiet and unobtrusive—particularly in winter, when it also ceases to call and when it descends locally to low altitudes, even sea level.

Bower's Shrike-thrush, distinctively grey-backed and heavy billed, is closely allied to the Little Shrike-thrush and replaces it at many higher altitudes above 800 metres in the mountain rainforests betweeen Ingham and Cooktown, Qld.

A Bower's Shrike-thrush carrying a nymph of the family *Gryllidae*.

OTHER NAMES
Bower Thrush, Stripe-breasted Shrike-thrush, Stripe-breasted Thrush.

IDENTIFICATION
LENGTH: *190–200 mm.*
ADULTS: *Sexes similar. Upper parts dark grey; wing and tail quills grey-brown edged mid-brown. Face dark grey, lores grey-white. Underparts rich tawny-ochre, whiter on chin, finely streaked dark grey over throat and upper breast. Eye red-brown. Bill large and black. Feet leaden-grey. Some birds* have pale ring of feathers around eye.
IMMATURES: *As adults; back browner, duller, and breast more heavily streaked; eye brown.*

VOICE
CALL: *Loud* chuck, *clicking chirps, and harsh gratings in alarm.*
SONG: *Deep, rich series of whistles:* da-dee-da-dee, pon-pon-pon.

NESTING
Breeds October–January. Nest a coarse open cup of dry leaves and bark strips; lined with finer fibre and rootlets; placed in vine tangle or leafy fork of small tree, 1–10 m above ground. Eggs: two; smooth, lustrous, pearly off-white, freckled with pale brown, red-brown and grey, often forming zone at larger end; swollen-oval or long-oval, about 25 x 19 mm.

DISTRIBUTION
Mountain rainforest above about 400 m, from Cooktown to Ingham, Qld. Occasionally moves to lower altitudes locally in winter. No races.

Sandstone Shrike-thrush *Colluricincla woodwardi* HARTERT, 1905

A Sandstone Shrike-thrush perched in a dead tree. More often they are to be seen on sandstone boulders and cliff tops.

OTHER NAMES
Brown-breasted Shrike-thrush, Woodward's Shrike-thrush, Sandstone Thrush, Rock Thrush.

IDENTIFICATION
LENGTH: *About 250 mm.*
ADULTS: *Sexes similar; more slender and longer-tailed than Grey Shrike-thrush. Crown deep grey-brown, grading to sepia-brown back, wings and tail. Face, lores and throat buff-white; rest of underparts, including underwing, dull rufous, with faint brown streaks on throat and breast. Eye ruby. Bill black in male, mid grey-brown in female. Feet dark brown.*
IMMATURES: *Similar to adults; wing darker and breast colour more subdued with stronger streaking; eye browner.*

VOICE
CALL: *Clear, rather strident, metallic* pwink.
SONG: *Two quickly repeated strong clear whistles, usually followed by a varied series of rich, flute-like whistles that resound through sandstone gorges.*

NESTING
Breeds November–January. Nest an untidy cup, mainly of red-brown roots of spinifex Triodia *and bark strips; usually placed in cracks or holes of* sandstone cliffs, or underneath overhanging rocks. Eggs: two or three; pearly white with well-defined brown-black, brown and slate-grey spots, mostly large and sparingly distributed, mainly at larger end; oval, about 30 x 21 mm. Incubation about 16 days.

DISTRIBUTION
Sandstone gorges and escarpments, in Kimberley area, WA, from Fitzroy River to south of Kununurra; the lower Victoria River, NT; Arnhem Land, from King River to South Alligator and Mary Rivers, NT; and southeast on subcoastal outcrops around western Gulf of Carpentaria to Nicholson River area on Queensland-Northern Territory border. No races.

SANDSTONE CLIFFS, GORGES, boulder-strewn ridges and crevices are the habitat of the Sandstone Shrike-thrush, discovered in 1902 by John Thomas Tunney in the Arnhem Land escarpment.

In an otherwise tree-living group of birds, the Sandstone Shrike-thrush has exploited its niche thoroughly. It forages among the rocks, dives to hide within their caverns when disturbed, sings from vantage points on projecting cliff tops and pinnacles, and nests on sheltered rock ledges. The birds do fly up to perch in trees occasionally, when disturbed or to sing, but their stay is brief.

Sandstone Shrike-thrushes are sedentary, established pairs seeming to hold to much the same large territory year round. Pair members forage alone or in tandem, one bird then the other moving ahead, each maintaining contact with single ringing whistles. They hop deliberately along the tops and sides of rock faces, poking into crannies and under ledges, then flying in shallow, swooping glides to the next feeding point close by. Food includes a range of insects, particularly grasshoppers, and spiders.

The birds breed in dispersed territories. Their songs, given sporadically in the early morning throughout the year, are prolonged during breeding. Richer and more elaborate than those of other shrike-thrushes, the liquid bell-like quality is echoed and accentuated by their rocky environment.

Grey Shrike-thrush *Colluricincla harmonica* (LATHAM, 1801)

OTHER NAMES
Grey Thrush, Western Shrike-thrush, Brown Shrike-thrush, Buff-bellied Shrike-thrush, Harmonious Shrike-thrush, Whistling Shrike-thrush, Whistling Dick.

IDENTIFICATION
LENGTH: *220–240 mm.*
MALE: *Upper parts vary from deep grey overall to mid-brown overall or mid-grey on crown and rump with mantle olive-brown. Lores white; eye-ring dark. Underparts light grey-white, washed darker on breast, or with cream-buff suffusion, and in one race, grading to rufous-buff on belly and undertail. Eye ruby. Bill black. Feet dark grey.*
FEMALE: *As male but eye-ring white; lores grey; throat and breast lightly streaked grey; bill grey-brown.*
IMMATURES: *Wing primary coverts washed rufous; pronounced streaking on underparts, young males less streaked and dusky billed; eye brown. Adult plumage in second or third year.*

VOICE
CALL: *Single, strident, whistled* yorrik *or* ching, *sharply by both sexes in contact. Also short, harsh descending cackle of two–three notes.*
SONG: *Clear, melodious sequence of whistled notes—*purr-purr-he -whew-it *and* pip-pip-pip-pip-ho-eeee—*the last syllable usually rising high. Often given by both sexes in call-and-answer duets.*

NESTING
Breeds mainly July–February. Nest bowl-shaped and built of bark strips, plant fibres and coarse grass, lined with fine rootlets; placed in stump-hollows, log hollows, on broken-off branches, in upright tree forks, crevices in buildings, eroded creek-banks, rock ledges, thick shrubs or even on ground. Eggs: three, occasionally four; white or cream, sparsely but clearly blotched or spotted with dark olive-brown and grey; oval, about 28 x 20 mm. Incubation 16–18 days, by both sexes.

DISTRIBUTION
Woodlands and open forest throughout Australia. Also in eastern New Guinea. Five races; all in Australia.

Grey Shrike-thrushes build their nests in a variety of sites, from hollow stumps to on the ground, as this female has. Male Grey Shrike-thrushes have a black bill and eye-ring, and white lores.

THE GREY SHRIKE-THRUSH is well named *harmonica*. Its clear melodious notes, powerful, pure and rhythmic, can sometimes carry for more than half a kilometre. The birds sing sporadically through much of the year—particularly during the early morning—but when breeding, males sing constantly at intervals through the day from open vantage perches beneath the tree canopy.

Grey Shrike-thrushes are as widespread as their habitat: open forest and woodlands of all types throughout Australia; only rainforests and treeless deserts are avoided. They are common and familiar birds in most regions but, except in southeastern Australia, have retreated into undisturbed bushland.

Feeding with purpose, Grey Shrike-thrushes forage through all strata of their habitat. They hop along upper branches and among foliage, poking in crevices and under leaves, work over the trunks of trees, pulling off bark to expose prey, and bound over the ground, gleaning among litter and logs. They are quite carnivorous, taking a wide range of insects and spiders, lizards and small mammals, nestlings of other birds and even carrion. Flight, usually through the woodland midstage, is a series of swooping undulations, the wings opening and closing with little flapping.

Grey Shrike-thrushes are sedentary. Established pairs hold to year-round territories of about two–ten hectares, or may wander a little farther afield in winter. Unattached birds travelling more widely are mostly young of the year, expelled from parental territories. Usually only one brood is reared in a year, both sexes building the nest, incubating, and rearing the young.

Several of the five races in Australia have been treated as separate species, but all intergrade, except the Tasmanian race with its thin, dagger-like bill. Western and central populations are grey-backed and russet-vented; those on Cape York Peninsula—and in New Guinea—are greyer with a prominent white eyebrow; those in the east are olive-brown-backed and white-vented.

Crested Bellbird *Oreoica gutturalis* (VIGORS & HORSFIELD, 1827)

OTHER NAMES
Bellbird.

IDENTIFICATION
LENGTH: *200–220 mm.*
MALE: *Face and throat white, separated from belly and crown by a black band on breast that passes up through eyes to join a black erectile crest along centre of crown. Rest of upper parts flat brown, cinnamon on rump. Wings and tail dusky, feathers edged grey-brown. Belly white, grading to ochreish on flanks and undertail. Eye yellow-orange. Bill*
black. Feet dull grey.
FEMALE: *Forehead, lores and sides of head grey; rest of upper parts as male. Small stripe of black on crown, but crest vestigial. Underparts cinnamon-brown, grading to white on chin and belly. Eye red-brown. Bill dark grey to black.*
IMMATURES: *Similar to female.*

VOICE
CALL: *Guttural* chuck *or* chuck-a-chuck-chuck, *uttered when feeding.*
SONG: *Distinctive series of five–six far-*
carrying mellow, liquid notes of ventriloquial quality, pan-pan-pallella, *last three or four syllables slurred up-and-down together.*

NESTING
Breeds August to December or January in peripheral regions; triggered at any time by heavy rain in arid central zone. Nest a deep cup solidly composed of strips of bark, twigs and leaves, adorned with live caterpillars; compactly lined with finer material, grass, bark and leaves; placed in a hollow stump, in a
thick vertical fork or in hanging bark of a tree, 1–3 m above ground. Eggs: three or four; white, spotted and blotched sparingly with grey, black and dark-brown; long-oval, about 27 x 20 mm.

DISTRIBUTION
Arid and subcoastal mulga and eucalypt scrubs and woodland of all inland Australia, north to the fringe of the Kimberleys and Arnhem Land, east to the western slopes of the Great Dividing Range and south and west to most coasts; formerly locally east to coast in central eastern Queensland. No races.

ONE ABORIGINAL NAME for the Crested Bellbird was 'panpanpalala', in alliterative imitation of its song. This the male gives with crest raised, from a high bare vantage perch often at the top of a tree, beaming it in all directions to signal his territory. As he swivels on his perch and varies volume, the song can sound ventriloquial.

Crested Bellbirds are widespread throughout Australia's arid zone, living in a range of lightly wooded habitat from mallee woodland to belar *Casuarina* and mulga scrub. There they are sedentary and rather solitary. Established pairs appear to hold to a rather large territory; occupant males will sing throughout the year,

although less frequently when not breeding.

Crested Bellbirds rise to trees and bushes to roost, sing and nest—but even as they finish singing, males dive back in swooping undulations to the ground. The birds forage there, hopping quickly but methodically along beneath shrubbery, plump bodies upright, picking for both insects and seeds. Caterpillars are prominent items and the birds keep a larder of them around the nests.

Their habit of ornamenting their nest with hairy caterpillars is unique. They squeeze each caterpillar in the middle, immobilising it, and then attach it to the rim of the nest.

The Yellow-breasted Boatbill is named for its remarkably flattened broad bill adapted for snapping up insects.

ACTIVE FEEDERS, Yellow-breasted Boatbills work the middle and upper strata of lower altitude rainforests in northeastern Queensland. They forage alone or in pairs, hawking out from perches to snap up fast-moving insects in midair and returning to eat, or picking them off the surface of leaves. At times the boatbills will join mixed feeding flocks of other species.

As they move through the forest in a crouch, boatbills call constantly in their soft, wheezy trills; at rest on twigs the birds sit more upright and quiver their tails sporadically. In excitement or display, the birds cock their tails like wrens. Group interactions may involve several males flying back and forth on a line of about 30 metres, calling constantly.

Most of the nest-building is done by the male and the nest is usually complete within a week. Both sexes share the incubation, changing over at irregular intervals. As the relieving bird approaches, it calls, but only when it has hopped to within a few centimetres of the nest does the sitting bird vacate.

Yellow-breasted Boatbill

Machaerirhynchus flaviventer GOULD, 1851

OTHER NAMES
Boat-billed Flycatcher, Yellow-breasted Flatbill, Yellow-breasted Flycatcher.

IDENTIFICATION
LENGTH: *110–120 mm.*
MALE: *Upper parts olive-green to almost black. Crown and tail black; three outer tail feathers tipped white. Upper wing coverts green to black, tipped white; flight feathers black, inner secondaries edged pale yellow. Lores, face and ear coverts black; eyebrow bright yellow. Chin and throat white; breast to undertail rich yellow. Eye dark brown. Bill black, tipped bone. Feet leaden.*
FEMALE: *Upper parts generally dull olive; eyebrow cream-yellow; yellow breast flecked dusky.*
IMMATURES: *As female; breast and belly paler, strongly flecked dusky.*

VOICE
CALL: *Short, repeated chips.*
SONG: *Series of three or four short, soft, sweet whistles, last changing in inflection and continuing into a soft trill* wit-wit-zee-ee-ee-wit *by male. Stanzas last about two seconds and are joined into series by a short chip between each.*

NESTING
Breeds September–March. Nest a shallow saucer of vine tendrils and plant stems bound with cobweb, lined with finer tendrils; usually suspended in leafy horizontal fork 2–25 m high. Eggs: two; slightly lustrous, white, dotted and spotted with shades of red and purple, concentrated at larger end; oval, about 17 x 13 mm. Incubation by both sexes.

DISTRIBUTION
Lowland and hill rainforest from Cape York Peninsula to Ingham, Qld. Also in New Guinea and nearby islands. Six races; two in Australia.

A white face and throat ringed with black distinguish the male Crested Bellbird from the female. The male can raise his crown feathers into a crest. Bellbirds usually nest in a vertical tree-fork and often place several incapacitated hairy caterpillars around the rim. Nestlings do not appear to eat them.

Black-faced Monarch *Monarcha melanopsis* (VEILLOT, 1818)

The Black-faced Monarch nests in a shaded gully or stand of rainforest. The Black-winged Monarch resembles it but has black flight feathers.

ONE OF THE LESS ACTIVE of the Australian flycatchers, the Black-faced Monarch only sporadically hawks out to capture its prey on the wing. It finds most of its prey—insects and spiders—on branches and leaves, particularly in the middle layers of rainforest and wet eucalypt forest, and spends most of its time there. It commonly feeds in forest over understorey tangles, moving along a branch, poking into crevices and cracks, and after a short distance hopping to a higher branch. In this way it works progressively upwards to about eight metres and then descends rapidly, stopping once or twice on the way, to repeat the procedure.

Black-faced Monarchs are migrants, but much remains to be learned of their movements. In southern Australia the birds arrive in September—at least on the south coast of New South Wales—breed over the summer months and leave about mid-March. On the Atherton Tableland they are most abundant and breed during summer, after which their numbers too decline markedly through winter. At Iron Range, Qld, the birds appear for only short periods around September and March, apparently on migration. In the lowlands of southern and eastern New Guinea the birds are present only during winter (March–October) and have never been found breeding there. It would seem that most if not all of the breeding population on the east coast of Australia shifts to New Guinea to winter. Evidence from lighthouses in Torres Strait indicates that it migrates by night as well as by day.

The Black-faced Monarch is solitary or in pairs during breeding and at its winter quarters, but may gather in small groups on migration. Its nest is usually secreted in shrubbery in a sheltered gully or stand of rainforest. While the female incubates the eggs the male perches nearby, calling frequently to advertise the territory. Normally during incubation the black face of the bird is conspicuous against the nest; if approached, however, the bird points its bill straight up in the air, averting its face.

OTHER NAMES
Black-faced Flycatcher, Carinated Flycatcher, Pearly-winged Flycatcher.

IDENTIFICATION
LENGTH: *160–180 mm.*
ADULTS: *Sexes similar; female slightly duller. Head and upper parts plain mid blue-grey; tail slightly darker. Ear coverts paler to dirty white. Wing coverts blue-grey; wing quills dusky, broadly edged blue-grey. Forehead and throat black. Upper breast and sides of neck pale blue-grey; rest of underparts rich rufous. Eye dark brown with thin black eye-ring. Bill steel-blue with pale tip. Feet leaden-grey.*
IMMATURES: *Similar to adults but duller, with all-grey face.*

VOICE
CALL: *Flycatcher-like creaks and downslurred chatterings.*
SONG: *Loud, whistling call with churring quality, introduced by one or two short notes, second lower than first, followed by long, ascending, whip-like note and finishing with shorter swirling drop, why-you-wichye-ou, by territorial male. Sequence of notes varies with individual birds.*

NESTING
Breeds October–January. Nest a deep cup or goblet of thick green moss on a foundation of more robust plant material such as she-oak needles; sometimes lined with rootlets; placed in a vertical shady fork of a small tree or shrub, *1–12 m above ground. Eggs: two, sometimes three; smooth, matt white to pale pink dotted with shades of red and red-brown and underlying purple–grey, uniformly or in zone at larger end; oval, about 24 x 17 mm. Incubation by female.*

DISTRIBUTION
From Cape York Peninsula to Dandenong Ranges, Vic., but only breeding between Cooktown, Qld, and MacAlister River in Gippsland. In rainforest, wet sclerophyll and denser eucalypt forests, damp gullies and mangroves. Migrant to southeastern New Guinea and associated islands. No races.

Black-winged Monarch *Monarcha frater* SCLATER, 1874

THE BLACK-WINGED MONARCH is a rare breeding summer migrant to the tropical rainforests of Cape York Peninsula. It arrives in small numbers through October and leaves again in March, presumably to winter in the Trans-Fly and southern New Guinea.

On their breeding grounds, the birds space themselves out solitarily or in territorial pairs and often forage alone. Like the Black-faced Monarch, they work through the forest mid- and lower stages. Hopping rather leisurely through the branchlets and foliage of trees and shrubs, they glean for insects more than hawking out to snap them up on the wing. Feeding occasionally takes them outside rainforest into fringing eucalypt woods.

Black-winged Monarchs resemble Black-faced Monarchs, and have been grouped as one species. Their plumage differences—black wings and tail and reversed proportions of facial black in the Black-winged—are nonetheless constant; their breeding ranges, judged by their overlapping migration, are mutually exclusive.

OTHER NAMES
Pearly Flycatcher, Black-winged Flycatcher.

IDENTIFICATION
LENGTH: *170–180 mm.*
MALE: *In Australian race, upper parts, median wing coverts and shoulders pale whitish or pearly grey. Forehead, front of lores, chin and most throat metallic blue-black. Wing to lesser coverts and tail black. Breast pale pearly grey; rest of underparts rich rufous. Eye dark brown. Bill pale blue-grey. Feet leaden-grey.*
FEMALE: *In Australian race, as male but dorsal grey darker, ventral rufous paler, wing coverts more extensively grey, and black face smaller, with almost white lores.*
IMMATURES: *Similar to adults but black around face much reduced; wing quills duller, edged brown-buff.*

VOICE
Similar to Black-faced Monarch.

NESTING
Breeds October–March. Nest neat goblet-shaped, of strips of paperbark bound with cobweb, thickly coated with green moss; lined with vegetable fibre, blackish vine tendrils, fern fibre and horsehair fungus; placed in upright usually three-pronged fork among foliage near top of a sapling up to 10 m above ground. Eggs: three; smooth, slightly lustrous, cream, dotted with red-brown and underlying purple, forming zone at larger end; blunt-oval, about 23 x 17 mm.

DISTRIBUTION
Migrates in October from southern New Guinea to Cape York Peninsula, as far south as McIlwraith Range; leaves again in March. Four races; one breeding in Australia.

Spectacled Monarch *Monarcha trivirgatus* (TEMMINCK, 1826)

OTHER NAMES
Black-fronted Flycatcher.

IDENTIFICATION
LENGTH: *150–160 mm.*
ADULTS: *Sexes similar; female slightly duller. Upper parts dark blue-grey. Forehead to ear coverts black. Tail dark slate; three outer feathers tipped broadly white. Wing coverts dark blue-grey, wing quills brown-grey edged with grey-blue. Chin and upper throat black; lower throat, sides of neck, and breast orange-rufous, cut off from or washing over white belly, flanks and undertail, according to race. Eye dark brown. Bill pale blue-grey. Feet dark steel-grey.*
IMMATURES: *Underparts duller than in adults; black face pattern grey; buff-white mark in front of and below eye over lores. White tips to feathers of throat and forehead.*

VOICE
CALL: *Harsh, buzzing gzzhhh repeated several times; also upslurring nasal rattle, zweee-zweee-zweee.*
SONG: *Soft, short squeaky warble.*

NESTING
Breeds October–February. Nest deeply cup-shaped to conical, of tightly interlaced bark strips and rootlets, covered with green moss, cobweb and spiders' egg-cases; lined with finer rootlets; placed in upright fork of tree or a vine tangle, 1–7 m above ground. Eggs: two; dull or glossy cream to pale pink, freckled with red-brown and underlying dull purple, particularly at larger end; long-oval, about 21 x 16 mm.

DISTRIBUTION
Coastal eastern Australia, from Cape York Peninsula to northeastern New South Wales, rarely farther south to south coast, NSW. In rainforests, mangroves, and their fringes. Also Timor, Moluccas, New Guinea and adjacent islands. About seven races; two in Australia.

Large black eye-patches earn the Spectacled Monarch its name. The bird nests in an upright fork or vine tangle.

SPECTACLED MONARCHS LIVE singly and in pairs in the middle and lower layers of rainforest, beneath its sheltering canopy. They forage mostly within five metres of the ground, occasionally reaching the tops of trees, and rarely the ground itself. Frequently a bird will perch sideways on a trunk to pick under loose pieces of bark, then flit to a horizontal vine where it pauses to snatch an insect before returning to a tree trunk. They seldom catch insects on the wing.

As they feed their rapid movements often develop into a jerky fluttering and tumbling among foliage; in the fan palms *Licuala* of northern Queensland, they sometimes tumble and skate over the leaves, presumably disturbing insects, such as flies and moths, which are snapped up as they go. Despite this, they seldom hawk out to capture insects on the wing. Their diet also includes ants, cockroaches, flying termites, spiders and snails, taken mainly from leaves and lower vine tangles. When mixed foraging flocks of birds pass through the rainforest, Spectacled Monarchs are nearly always with them.

There are two Australian races and they differ in status. One, with pure white lower breast, flanks and belly, is endemic to Cape York Peninsula south to the McIlwraith Range and quite sedentary. The other, in which the russet of the breast washes down over the flanks and belly, breeds from Cooktown south to New South Wales and is partly or wholly migratory. Populations south of Maryborough, Qld, all move out in winter, at a time when southern migrants appear on Cape York Peninsula and southern New Guinea. Migration across Torres Strait may be largely by night.

White-eared Monarch *Monarcha leucotis* GOULD, 1850

MORE THAN 70 YEARS elapsed from the discovery of the White-eared Monarch to the finding of its nest, in 1923. Where they are most common, in northeastern Queensland, the birds nest very high in the topmost branches of rainforest trees, while in southern Queensland where they nest lower, the bird is rarer. Although some may be partial migrants, arriving to breed in late winter, spring and summer, most are sedentary. Established pairs hold territory when breeding and wander locally through the rest of the year without ranging far. During breeding both male and female share nest-building, incubation and the feeding of young.

Birds of coastal northeastern rainforests, White-eared Monarchs forage actively day-long among the canopy at their edges, often sallying out into fringing eucalypt scrubs and mangroves. They flutter in and out of the outer foliage, catching the insects that they flush or plucking them from leaves, and often hawking after prey in the manner of fantails, *Rhipidura*. Feeding in sunlight more than other monarchs, and working from tall tree crowns down to shrubbery, they almost hover outside the leaves, darting in to snatch insects, then pausing to perch on branchlets just inside the canopy. Often they sit on leaves, fluttering to keep balance. They rarely join the mixed foraging flocks so characteristic of tropical rainforests, feeding instead alone or in dispersed pairs.

Surprisingly, the nearest allies of the White-eared Monarch occur not in adjacent Pacific islands, but in the Indonesian archipelagos.

The small White-eared Monarch.

OTHER NAMES
White-eared Flycatcher.

IDENTIFICATION
LENGTH: *130–140 mm.*
ADULTS: *Sexes similar. Head, back, wings and tail black; tail coverts, edges of secondaries and tips of outer tail feathers white, and white sash across edge of wing coverts. Small white patches on head in front of eye and above eye forming an eyebrow; large white patch on ear coverts and on throat enclosed by black ring; chin black. Underparts pale grey, darker on breast and flanks, whiter on undertail. Eye brown-black. Bill black, paler at base.*
Feet leaden-slate.
IMMATURES: *Black areas dark brownish grey; underparts washed brown; fore-crown hoary and facial pattern indistinct. Base of bill off-white.*

VOICE
CALL: *Thin, rising and falling, repeated long-drawn whistle, eee-oooo, probably in contact. Also chattering and harsh zit-zit-zit, incessant near nest.*
SONG: *Infrequent animated whistling.*

NESTING
Breeds August–January. Cup-shaped nest, about 70 mm in diameter and 100 mm deep outside, and 50 x 45 mm inside; of bark strips, grass, leaves and moss, bound with cobweb and cocoons; lined with fine plant material such as fern roots; usually placed high, at 10–30 m or more, in outer foliage of rainforest or rarely lower down in a fork. Eggs: two; smooth, white, spotted with shades of red-brown evenly over shell or at larger end; blunt-oval, about 19 x 13 mm. Incubation about 14 days, by both sexes. Young fledge in about 14 days.

DISTRIBUTION
Coastal rainforests and fringes from Cape York Peninsula to Tweed River, NSW, and offshore islands. No races.

The Frilled Monarch resembles the Pied Monarch in appearance and habits but lacks a black breast band.

Frilled Monarch

Arses lorealis DE VIS, 1895

OTHER NAMES
Frill-necked Flycatcher, White-lored Flycatcher.

IDENTIFICATION
LENGTH: *140–160 mm.*
MALE: *Head glossy black, surrounded by pure white erectile ruff. Back, wings and tail glossy black, with broad white band across lower back to scapulars and wing coverts. Large black chin spot; rest of underparts white. Eye dark brown; naked skin round eye cobalt-blue. Bill blue-grey with dark tip. Feet slaty.*
FEMALE: *As male but lores and chin white; ruff reduced.*
IMMATURES: *As adults but much duller: black areas dark grey tinged with brown, chin and lores white, ruff heavily flecked grey, underparts grey-white. Juveniles washed russet on mantle and wings.*

VOICE
CALL: *Frog-like squank when feeding. Also constant buzzing and creaks.*
SONG: *Sequence of short, high trilled whistles.*

IN ITS HABITS, CALLS and feeding, the Frilled Monarch resembles the Pied Monarch which it replaces in the rainforest galleries of Cape York Peninsula. Like the Pied it spirals up, down and around the trunks and branches of trees, from near the ground into the canopy, gleaning insects; but it often works into outer foliage to pick prey off leaves as well, and sallies out, in mixed feeding flocks of other birds, to snap up flying termites. When singing it makes short whirring flights from twig to twig.

Both sexes of Frilled and Pied Monarchs in Australia are pied—differing only in subtle patterns on the head—and they forage in the same way. Females of related frilled flycatchers in New Guinea are brown and russet-breasted, and, unlike pied males there, feed strictly among foliage in the forest canopy.

NESTING
Breeds September–January, perhaps longer. Nest a small loosely woven basket of plant stems and rootlets, bound with cobweb; lined with fibre and decorated with lichen, slung hanging between vines 2–10 m above ground. Eggs: two; slightly glossy, pale pink, freckled with red-brown, chestnut, and fainter purple-grey particularly at larger end; oval, about 19 x 14 mm.

DISTRIBUTION
Gallery rainforests and their edges on Cape York Peninsula south to Endeavour River, Qld. No races.

Pied Monarch *Arses kaupi* GOULD, 1851

A male Pied Monarch on its decorated hammock-like nest in the lowland rainforests of northeastern Queensland.

THE STRIKING BLACK-AND-WHITE plumage of the Pied Monarch makes it conspicuous in its habitat, the interior of coastal and lower altitude rainforests in northeastern Queensland. A sedentary bird, it feeds constantly through the day, usually in pairs but occasionally singly or in small groups, spiralling up and down and around tree trunks and branches in the middle and upper forest strata, searching for food. Many flycatchers, especially monarchs and fantails *Rhipidura,* work over tree trunks, but the Pied, like the Frilled Monarch, is a true specialist in this behaviour.

Superficially, its feeding movements resemble those of a treecreeeper, *Climacteris.* But whereas a treecreeper probes crevices for hidden ants, the Pied Monarch flits rapidly over the trunk, flushing a range of insects—moths, flies and beetles—from the bark and capturing them. As it hops up and down the trunk, it often holds its wings half open and jerks the tail repeatedly downwards. If an insect escapes, the monarch flies out in pursuit and attempts to take it in midair. It fans its tail in flight like a fantail, but moves more directly with less fluttering.

Pied Monarchs, particularly the males, have a neck frill which they raise occasionally during their daily activities and much more often in group and sexual displays. In group display, four, five or even six birds flit about up under the forest canopy, raising their frills and fluffing their feathers while chattering loudly. It may involve dispute over territorial boundaries, for the members of the group usually stay in one area, flying back and forth and chasing one another in a ragged stream. Such displays sometimes last 20 minutes or more, after which the birds quietly disperse. During courtship, the male dances around the female among branchlets, raising and lowering his ruff and buzzing incessantly. Both sexes incubate and brood and feed the young.

Pied and Frilled Monarchs are so alike in appearance and habits that they might be treated as races of one species. Despite a hint of intergradation towards Cooktown, they may also meet there without interbreeding. Evidence either way is equivocal.

OTHER NAMES
Pied Flycatcher, Kaup's Flycatcher.

IDENTIFICATION
LENGTH: *140–160 mm.*
MALE: *Head glossy black, surrounded by white erectile ruff that joins white throat and is flecked faintly black. Back, wings and tail dull glossy black, with broad greyish white band across lower back to scapulars and wing coverts. Very small black chin spot; rest of underparts white with broad black band across breast. Eye brown; naked skin round eye cobalt-blue. Bill blue-grey. Feet slaty.*
FEMALE: *Similar to male but duller black-and-white, the wings tinged*
brown; white collar heavily flecked black and separated from throat by a black line down sides of neck.
IMMATURES: *As adults, but black and white areas dirty grey-brown and grey-white respectively; ruff heavily freckled grey-black; white lower back band obsolete; breast band ill-defined grey-brown, washing on to throat.*

VOICE
CALL: *Quacks and creaks when feeding. Also continuous buzzing.*
SONG: *Ten or more short, soft, high whistled notes, in close sequence.*

NESTING
Breeds October–January. Nest a small
loosely woven basket, 60 x 45 mm outside and 40 x 45 mm inside, of fine tendrils and twigs bound with cobweb, decorated—especially close to the rim— with grey-green lichen; lined with shredded fibre and rootlets; slung like a hammock between two vines well clear of any foliage 2–10 m above ground. Eggs: two; slightly glossy, pale pink freckled with red-browns and fainter purple-grey, particularly at larger end; oval, about 19 x 14 mm. Incubation by both sexes.

DISTRIBUTION
Lowland rainforest up to 700 m and occasionally its edges, from Cooktown to Ingham, Qld. No races.

Restless Flycatcher

Myiagra inquieta
(LATHAM, 1801)

OTHER NAMES
Scissors Grinder, Dishlick, Grinder.

IDENTIFICATION
LENGTH: *190–210 mm (southern inquieta); 160–170 mm (northern nana); both with short erectile crest.*
MALE: Inquieta: *Crown glossy black, grading to dusky slate over rest of upper parts (back, wings, tail). Lores matt black. Entire underparts (throat to undertail) white. Eye dark brown. Bill slaty grey with dark tip; slender, with vestigial rictal bristles. Feet black.*
Nana: *As inquieta but back glossy black, bill broadened with long rictal bristles.*
FEMALE: *As male, but lores dull grey; back of nana slaty black.*
IMMATURES: *As adults but throat washed buff. Juveniles greyer-black above, with dull off-white line through scapulars–wing coverts.*

VOICE
CALL: *Rasping bzzzzp, repeated at intervals or rapidly, in contact; sustained churring grinding often when hovering.*
SONG: *Loud, clear whistle too-whee too-whee, with rising inflection, in short repeated series.*

NESTING
Breeds late July or August to January in south (inquieta); usually August–March in north (nana). Nest a neat shallow broad-based cup of fine strips of bark or fine grass, usually camouflaged with lichen and small grey pieces of bark, bound closely with cobweb; lined with fine grasses, rootlets, hair or fur; placed in exposed position on dead part of horizontal limb, often near and sometimes over water, 1–20 m above ground. Eggs: three or four; dull to greyish white with small markings of grey-brown and lavender usually in central belt or at larger end; oval, about 21 x 16 mm. Incubation about 14 days, by both sexes. Young fledge in about 14 days.

DISTRIBUTION
Southern inquieta: Southwestern to eastern Australia north to about Julia Creek and Mt Isa, Qld, in mallee and open woodland. Northern nana: Northwestern Australia (Arnhem Land, Kimberleys) east to foot of Cape York Peninsula as far as Cooktown–Townsville, Qld, in open and paperbark woodland; also southern New Guinea.

A male Restless Flycatcher of the southern race at its nest. It is identified by its matt black lores.

THIS BLACK-AND-WHITE flycatcher ranges around much of Australia in the same open eucalypt woodlands and patchy scrub where the similar-looking Willie Wagtail occurs, often near water. The Restless Flycatcher can be identified, nonetheless, by its whitish throat, squarer tail and distinctive mannerisms at rest and when feeding. Alone or in well-dispersed pairs, it works with leisurely restlessness through the mid-strata of woodland, one–ten metres above the ground, hawking out for its food without coming much to ground, and never settling long on any perch.

Sallying flights, gracefully buoyant in undulating zigzags on broadly rounded wings, take the flycatcher for 50 metres or more to the outer foliage of trees, rough-barked trunks and low shrubbery and tussocks to snap up prey: beetles, plant bugs, spiders, weevils, ants, wasps, flies, moths, caterpillars, and even centipedes and worms. The bird hovers much to pick insects off the surface of leaves, branches and herbage. With wings beating slowly, it hangs almost vertically in the air, body arched, and head and spread tail pointing downwards. While hovering it often utters a strange rolling grinding, giving the bird its name, Scissors Grinder.

Restless Flycatchers travel from perch to perch, usually a bare horizontal twig, stump or post top one–three metres high. Even when sitting they are rarely still, waving their closed tails from side to side, buzzing and whistling, and raising their short crests in the manner of all *Myiagra* flycatchers.

Up to three broods may be reared in a season. Male and female share nest-building, incubation, brooding and feeding. A sitting bird often calls from the nest. Nests after the first may be built in four to seven days, but the first takes longer. Eggs are laid on successive days. After breeding, both young and paired adults disperse —some wandering locally, others more widely. Southeastern populations shift northwards in winter, some birds reaching mid-Queensland.

Paperbark Flycatcher *Myiagra nana* (GOULD, 1870)

THIS SMALL 'RACE' of the Restless Flycatcher in northwestern Australia has a broader bill with long rictal bristles, may forage for prey a little differently, and possibly represents a distinct species. It lives in tropical woodland, particularly paperbark trees along streams, and otherwise resembles the Restless Flycatcher in its form and habitats. The two do not seem to intergrade where they approach one another in central eastern Queensland.

Broad-billed Flycatcher

Myiagra ruficollis (VIEILLOT, 1818)

OTHER NAMES
None.

IDENTIFICATION
LENGTH: *150–160 mm.*
MALE: *Upper parts blue-grey, extending on to wings; darker and glossier on head. Light eye-ring. Primaries and tail feathers dusky brown edged leaden-grey; outer tail feathers narrowly edged white. Throat and upper breast orange-rufous; rest of underparts white. Eye brown. Bill blue-black. Feet blackish.*
FEMALE: *Similar to male, but duller and paler; lores off-white.*
IMMATURES: *Resemble adults; paler and duller. Juveniles have pale buff wing-edging; white brows, grey feet.*

VOICE
CALL: *Rather silent. Occasional soft, hard* churr.
SONG: *Repeated whistling* too-whee *or* twee-tweet.

DISTRIBUTION
Thinly spread in or near mangroves along north coast and on offshore islands from Broome, WA to eastern Cape York Peninsula; vagrant to coastal southeastern Queensland. Also Timor, New Guinea and adjacent islands. Two races; one in Australia.

NESTING
Breeds October–February. Nest a cup of bark strips and flakes, or plant strips and tendrils, bound and coated with cobweb; decorated with pale green lichen and bark flakes; lined with plant fibres or tendrils; often placed in tree overhanging a channel; usually attached by cobweb to dead twig or fork from about 0.6 m above high-water, or in paperbark to 7 m. Eggs: usually two; white, marked with browns and underlying purple-grey, mostly in ring at larger end; 24 x 16 mm.

The Broad-billed Flycatcher has an orange-rufous throat and upper breast.

EXCEPT FOR local wanderers, Broad-billed Flycatchers are confined to northern coastal mangroves. Established pairs appear to be sedentary in the interior of mid-height *Rhizophora–Bruguiera–Avicennia* mangroves with a moderately clear middle strata. The birds forage alone by hawking and sallying through this level. They flit from perch to perch, usually a bare horizontal twig, snapping up insects in midair or off foliage. On perches they sit upright, continually quivering their tails, and calling sporadically, brief crest raised.

Both sexes build the nest; they also share incubation and the rearing of young. Although Broad-billed Flycatchers may be generally sedentary, young of the year seem to disperse widely, perhaps accounting for records on Torres Strait, southeastern coastal Queensland, and in bamboo thickets and paperbark forests upstream on rivers in the Northern Territory.

As their name suggests, Broad-billed Flycatchers have much broader, flatter bills than other *Myiagra* flycatchers; the bills are flanked by long, protective, vital bristles.

Leaden Flycatcher *Myiagra rubecula* (LATHAM, 1801)

OTHER NAMES
Blue Flycatcher, Frog-bird.

IDENTIFICATION
LENGTH: *150–160 mm; both sexes have a small erectile sub-crest.*
MALE: *Head, upper parts, wings, tail and throat uniformly deep leaden-grey; lores often black. Rest of underparts white. Eye brown-black. Bill leaden-blue tipped black. Feet slaty black.*
FEMALE: *Head and nape leaden grey. Back, wings and tail mid grey-brown. Throat and upper breast orange-rufous; rest of underparts white.*
IMMATURES: *Resemble female. Young males in transition are mottled slaty over upper surface. Juveniles brown with white brows and fine white feathers below.*

VOICE
CALL: *Harsh, guttural* zrrrp, *singly or repeated.*
SONG: *Loud repeated whistling* too-whit, *varied to repeated whistling* too-whee, *lower and sweeter, by both sexes. Also short twittering.*

NESTING
Breeds late September–October to January–February in southeast, August–February in north. Nest a neat shallow, broad-based cup, mainly of fine bark strips and fine grasses, matted together with cobweb, and decorated with bark scales and lichen; lined sparingly with fine rootlets or fine grass, 40 x 28 mm inside; placed on horizontal limb or fork in open, well away from trunk and clear of foliage but immediately below a larger branch, 3–25 m above ground. Eggs: usually three; white or tinged pale blue, spotted with grey-browns with underlying lavender marks, mainly around the centre or at the larger end; rounded-oval, about 17 x 14 mm. Incubation 14–15 days, by both sexes. Young fledge in 12–15 days.

DISTRIBUTION
Widespread in coastal and subcoastal eucalypt and paperbark woodland and open forest around northern and eastern Australia, from Kimberleys, WA, to eastern Victoria; vagrant in Tasmania and, on migration, to Mt Lofty Ranges, SA. Birds breeding in southeastern Australia migrate to northeastern Australia and southern New Guinea in winter. Also resident populations in eastern New Guinea and nearby islands. Four races; two in Australia: one small and black-lored with black chin spot (males) in Arnhem Land–Kimberleys to Gulf of Carpentaria; the other larger and grey-lored throughout east to Cape York Peninsula.

The male Leaden Flycatcher. The female has a rufous throat and breast.

ACTIVE BIRDS, Leaden Flycatchers feed in the mid and upper strata of eucalypt and paperbark forests and woodlands around eastern and northern Australia, keeping to drier, scrubbier habitat than the Satin Flycatcher. They dart from tree to tree, in swooping, undulating flight, working alone or in dispersed pairs. At each perch—usually a bare exposed twig—they call, fan their short crests, and vibrate their tails constantly; stance is upright. The birds capture their food in flight, picking insects off foliage or out of the air in short circling dashes from a perch. Diet includes small dragonflies, termites, cicadas, frog hoppers, beetles, weevils, flies, native bees and wasps.

Leaden Flycatchers across northern Australia are sedentary or locally nomadic, but those in the southeast are migratory. They shift north in March–April for the winter, reaching northern Queensland and New Guinea, and return to breed in September. Individual birds return to the same grounds each year.

Pairs hold breeding territories that may be widely dispersed or clumped. Both sexes build the nest, taking seven to 12 days to do so at a site that may be chosen by the male. They also share incubation and the feeding of young. Unlike most species, both adults will at times call from the nest.

Satin Flycatcher

Myiagra cyanoleuca (VEILLOT, 1818)

The female Satin Flycatcher; she shares nest duties with the male.

OTHER NAMES
Satin 'sparrow', Shining Flycatcher.

IDENTIFICATION
LENGTH: *170–180 mm; both sexes
with erectile subcrest.*
MALE: *Head, all upper parts to wings
and tail, throat and upper breast
glossy blue-black. Lower breast to
undertail pure white. Eye black-
brown. Bill deep blue-grey, tipped
black. Feet black.*
FEMALE: *Head and nape dusky blue-
grey glossed faintly black, with pale
eye-ring; rest of upper parts, wings
and tail duller dusky blue-grey, flight
feathers edged browner. Throat to
upper breast deep ochreish; rest of
underparts to undertail pure white.*
IMMATURES: *As female, but duller and
browner over back; adult male
plumage gained by patchy moulting,
causing mottling. Juveniles still
duller, flecked grey over ventral
surface; bill browner.*

VOICE
CALL: *Single, guttural strident rasp,*
zurrrp *or* bzzurtt, *by both sexes,
repeated often, at intervals.*
SONG: *Loud, clear, two-syllable whistle*
tchoo-eee, tchoo-eee, *the second
syllable rising; usually repeated
quickly several times.*

NESTING
*Breeds September, or usually October–
November to January–February. Nest
a broadly based cup of finely shredded
bark fibre and grass, tightly coated
with cobweb and occasionally decorated
with lichen; inside about 50 x 31 mm,*
lined with rootlets, hair and shredded
fibre; usually placed on horizontal fork
of dead or near-dead bare branch—
with which it blends—well out from
trunk under overhanging foliaged
branch at 3–25 m above ground. Eggs:
usually three; white to pale bluish
green, spotted and freckled with grey-
browns and underlying purple-grey, in
zone towards large end; oval, about
20 x 16 mm. Incubation about
17 days, by both sexes. Young fledge in
about 18 days.

DISTRIBUTION
*Tall wet eucalypt forests in gullies,
plains and tablelands of coastal eastern
Australia and nearby ranges. Breeds
from Blackdown Tableland, Qld, south
to Tasmania and western Victoria.
Migrates to Cape York Peninsula and
southeastern New Guinea and
surrounding islands; vagrant to
Western Australia and New Zealand.
No races.*

SATIN FLYCATCHERS, darker, larger and longer-tailed than the similar-looking Leaden Flycatcher, breed and forage in the taller, wetter eucalypt forests of coastal southeastern Australia, both on rolling plains and in steep mountain gullies. Rainforest is avoided. Feeding singly or in dispersed pairs through the upper strata of the forest, they are incessantly on the move. Food—grasshoppers, beetles, blowflies, crane-flies, moths and long-tailed wasps—is captured on the wing, either in midair or among upper foliage as the birds make short dashing sallies out from a perch, usually a small horizontal twig beneath the forest canopy. Back at a perch their stays are brief and never still as they quiver the tail up and down constantly, raise their stubby crests, and call. Tails are swayed from side to side on landing.

Satin Flycatchers commonly nest in loose colonies of two to five pairs nesting 20–50 metres apart. Both sexes build the nest, incubate, and feed the young; they sometimes feign injury and rodent-run, fluttering along the ground, to divert attention from the nest. Usually only one brood is raised in a season. After fledging, parents and young shift in loose parties to forage in drier, more open forest not used for breeding. Nests are parasitised by the Brush Cuckoo, and occasionally Pallid, and Horsfield's and Golden Bronze-Cuckoos.

Breeding from about the Calliope Range, Queensland, southwards to Tasmania, Satin Flycatchers are strict migrants, travelling to northeastern Queensland and crossing Torres Strait to winter as far as southern and eastern New Guinea and adjacent islands. They move north in March–April and return in September–October, travelling in ones and twos through tree tops, perhaps at night.

The male Satin Flycatcher resembles the male Leaden Flycatcher, but is darker. Where their ranges overlap, the Satin occupies wetter, denser forests.

Shining Flycatcher *Myiagra alecto* (Temminck & Laugier, 1827)

OTHER NAMES
Glossy Flycatcher, Satin Bird.

IDENTIFICATION
LENGTH: *170–180 mm; both sexes have erectile sub-crest.*
MALE: *Completely black with blue or green gloss. Eye very dark brown. Bill blue-grey with black tip; inside mouth brilliant orange. Legs black.*
FEMALE: *Head and nape glossy black tinged with blue or green. Rest of upper parts, wings and tail bright rufous to chestnut. Underparts entirely white, or cinnamon on undertail in eastern Queensland. Eye, bill and legs as male.*
IMMATURES: *Resemble female, but duller, the crown dull dusky grey.*

VOICE
CALL: *Varied. Harsh grating rasp,* tsaaap, *repeated erratically; low frog-like croaks; loud whistles.*
SONG: *Clear piping double-syllabled whistle,* tuu-wheee, tuu-wheee, *the last syllable rising; repeated in bursts.*

NESTING
Breeds August–September to March. Nest a compact cup of bark strips or vines and moss, sparingly bound with cobweb, decorated with camouflaging bark pieces or lichen; neat, thick lining of bark fibre, fine rootlets and grass; often built in upright forks of mangroves or paperbarks in water, or on horizontal limbs in thick vegetation along watercourses, usually 0.6–3 m high. Eggs: two or three; bluish white to pale blue-green, dotted with black and grey-browns, with underlying lavender or grey, predominantly in belt at larger end or centre; oval, about 20 x 15 mm. Incubation by both sexes.

DISTRIBUTION
Mangroves, rainforest along watercourses and densely treed paperbark swamps, along northern Australia and offshore islands, from Roebourne, WA, to Cape York Peninsula, Qld (possibly with gaps around Gulf of Carpentaria) and southwards to Noosa River, Qld. Also Moluccas to New Guinea, Bismarck Archipelago and Admiralty Islands. About 10 races; two endemic to Australia, intergrading on Cape York Peninsula.

The male Shining Flycatcher is glossy black all over—the only entirely black flycatcher in Australia.

The female Shining Flycatcher. The colour of its back and tail varies from rufous to chestnut throughout its range.

THE BRILLIANT COLOURS of male and female Shining Flycatchers, one all glossy black, the other black-headed and patterned in russet and white, contrast strikingly in their habitat: the lower strata and shrubberies of tropical lowland vine forest down to networks of roots and trunks in mangroves around the north coast of Australia. There the birds are sedentary and forage actively alone or in dispersed pairs.

In rainforests they sally out from perch to perch, picking up insects on the wing and from leaves and trunks, in the usual manner of *Myiagra* flycatchers. Returning to a perch, they swing the tail from side to side, and flick it up and down—but more erratically—and call and raise their short crests in excitement.

In mangroves the birds commonly drop down among the maze of interlacing trunks and roots close to the mud. There they creep and flit along, both over the mud and around the stems, picking up food. Their frog-like calling seems to be linked with this manner of feeding. Often they hunt by sitting motionless for a time, then suddenly darting on to prey. At other times, particularly low among mangroves, they move along with wings and tails part-spread, perhaps in a ploy to flush their food. Mangrove mud provides them with minute shellfish and crabs and the lower stages of rainforest with various insects, including beetles and ants.

In courtship, the male twists about on a low horizontal twig, calls and raises his brief crest, and bows to raise and fan his tail. With each dove-like bow he calls. Several males sometimes gather at one site on successive days to display before a female. Both sexes share nest-building, incubation, brooding and feeding the young, both in the nest and after.

The nest—a cup of bark strips or vines and moss, bound with cobwebs—is usually placed in upright forks or horizontal limbs in mangroves or paperbarks in water or along watercourses. Brush Cuckoos are their most common parasite.

A young Rufous Fantail cranes from the edge of its nest as a parent approaches with food. This is the eastern Australian race.

Rufous Fantail *Rhipidura rufifrons* (LATHAM, 1801)

THE SLIGHT FORM AND slow, fluttering flight of the Rufous Fantail, so well fitted for hawking in the confines of close shrubbery, are deceptively weak—for the bird ranges widely among islands in the southwestern Pacific, and in southeastern Australia migrates north to winter in northeastern Queensland and southern New Guinea in March–April and back again to breed in September–October. Migrating birds travel alone, flitting low from shrub to shrub, and picking up food; much travelling is done in twilight hours.

There are two distinct races of the Rufous Fantail in Australia that may well be good species. One in the mangroves and fringing vine scrubs around the north coast has a long, grey broadly white-tipped tail and little rufous on the rump; it is sedentary. The other in the rainforests and wet sclerophyll forests along the east coast and adjacent ranges has a shorter, duskier, pale grey-tipped tail and a broadly rufous back; its movements are more complex. It breeds north almost to Cooktown but only those populations south of 25°S seem strictly migratory; breeding populations further north may be little more than local nomads, only shifting from mountains to warmer coasts in winter.

Wherever they occur, Rufous Fantails forage similarly, in the shrubby substage of forest within a metre or two of the ground. They launch out continuously in short sallying flights from one perch after another, raising their constantly fanned tails vertically for takeoff and tumbling, diving, twisting up and looping among close foliage. The birds glean little from foliage, nor catch much out in open spaces. Rather, they flit and flutter close to foliage and branches to dislodge or flush a range of sedentary insects—beetles, bugs, weevils, mites—and spiders by their twisting and fanning. Flying to perch, they choose, like all fantails, a branchlet thick enough to enable them to sit steady and focus on prey.

Rufous Fantails nest in deep shrubby glades. Both sexes build the nest, incubate and feed young. Brush Cuckoos parasitise them.

OTHER NAMES
Wood Fantail, Rufous Flycatcher, Rufous-fronted Fantail.

IDENTIFICATION
LENGTH: *150–165 mm.*
ADULTS: *Sexes similar. Upper parts and wings brown becoming orange- to dark rufous on lower back and base of tail. Terminal half of tail dusky or mid-grey, tipped grey- or broadly pure white. Face brown with broad rufous brows and light under eye-ring. Throat white; band on lower throat black, grading into upper breast where dappled with white feather edges; belly white, grading to buff on flanks and undertail. Eye, bill and feet blackish-brown; lower mandible paler.*
IMMATURES: *Similar to adults but duller orange-rufous all over upper parts; face pattern dull; upper breast band dull grey-brown; rest of underparts dirty rufous-buff. Adult plumage moulted within several months of fledging.*

VOICE
CALL: *Single high-pitched squeaking chip, at rest or in flight, sometimes doubled in flight.*
SONG: *Thin, tinny short see-saw sequence of notes, similar in quality to Grey Fantail's, but descending and less rhythmically defined.*

NESTING
Breeds late October–February. Nest a neat, tailed cup 50 mm across x 40 mm deep, with a 70 mm long tail, generally of fine grasses and small roots, tightly and smoothly bound with cobweb; lined with soft plant fibre; usually placed on thin sheltered, horizontal fork of shrub or tree, 1–10 m above ground. Eggs: two, occasionally three; pale stone to buff, with minute brown and lavender-grey spots, usually in zone on larger end; long-oval, 16 x 13 mm. Incubation 14–15 days, by both sexes. Young fledge in about 10 days.

DISTRIBUTION
Coastal northern and eastern Australia and adjacent ranges, from Kimberleys, WA, to southwestern Victoria, in wet forests and mangroves. Also many islands in southwestern Pacific. About 20–30 races; two in Australia.

Grey Fantail

Rhipidura fuliginosa (SPARRMAN, 1787)

OTHER NAMES
White-shafted Fantail, Cranky Fan, Fanny, Mad Fan.

IDENTIFICATION
LENGTH: *150–160 mm.*
ADULTS: *Sexes similar. Upper parts plain deep to blackish grey. Wings and long tail duskier grey, wing coverts tipped white in two bars and inner secondaries edged white; tail feathers tapered, the outer five pairs broadly edged and tipped white. Face dark grey with narrow white brow and short white stripe behind eye. Throat dull white; lower throat with plain dusky black bar. Rest of underparts cream-buff, grading to white under tail and grey on flanks. Eye black. Bill black. Feet brown-black.*
IMMATURES: *Duller than adults, washed brown on back; markings on head and wings buff; throat bar obscure grey.*

VOICE
CALL: *Sharp single or double* chip *in all seasons, by both sexes in contact.*
SONG: *High-pitched, squeaky upward-climbing series of eight–ten short notes with twangy whistled quality, usually from a perch.*

NESTING
Breeds August–January. Nest a tiny 150 mm tailed cup of plant fibres smoothly bound with cobweb; lined with fine fibre; placed on thin horizontal fork of tree 1–6 m above ground. Eggs: two, sometimes three or four; dull white to cream, minutely freckled or blotched with brown in zone; long-oval, about 16 x 13 mm. Incubation 13–14 days.

DISTRIBUTION
Taller woodlands and open forest throughout Australia; rainforest in northeastern Queensland. Also islands in southwestern Pacific. About 10 races; five in Australia.

These young Grey Fantails, about two weeks old, are almost fledged.

FORAGING THROUGH THE OPEN mid-strata of forests and woodlands of all types, Grey Fantails fly twisting and turning this way and that, so much so that they are known colloquially as 'Mad Fans' and 'Cranky Fans'. Their tortuous flights are feeding flights out from set perches, carrying the birds for up to 50 or more metres before they land again. Grey Fantails are more constantly active and more aerial in their feeding than other Australian fantails, picking up a range of flying insects in midair. Small prey are consumed as they are caught, but larger items are taken back to a perch, shaken and wiped before being swallowed.

Protracted bouts of hawking are interspersed with less frequent flutter- and hop-gleaning in the open foliage of tall shrubbery. With wings drooped and tail fanned and angled up, the birds spiral up and down tree trunks and zigzag out along branches, never still, picking up small insects as they go. Sometimes they hover over foliage, but almost never do they go to ground. Their vertical foraging range in forest strata overlaps that of the Rufous Fantail, but the Grey Fantail, working alone or in loose pairs or groups, spreads more evenly over a wider range, 20 metres or more high.

The five Australian races of Grey Fantails all feed actively in much the same way, yet differ much in their seasonal movements. The very dark form in the Atherton and Eungella rainforest tablelands, Queensland, is sedentary; so is the moderately dark race in Tasmania, only a few of which shift to the southeastern mainland in winter. The white-tailed race of the central arid zone is more erratically nomadic, while the tiny-billed southwestern race moves consistently north and east in winter but rarely more than about 500 kilometres. Only the intermediate race across the southeast disperses far after nesting, some birds travelling as far as Cape York Peninsula, Arnhem Land and the Kimberleys in winter.

Mangrove Fantail

Rhipidura phasiana DE VIS, 1884

REPLACING THE GREY FANTAIL in the mangroves of northwestern Australia, the Mangrove Fantail resembles the Grey in appearance but its throat bar is little more than a grey smudge and its bill is larger and tail shorter with round-tipped feathers.

It also resembles the Grey Fantail in its habits. Foraging alone or in dispersed pairs, it hawks for insects on sallying flights through the mid and upper strata of mangrove forest, from one–seven metres above tidal mud. Much time is spent gleaning among branchlets and leaves, the birds spiralling this way and that up and down trunks, and out along branches and fluttering into upper foliage. Wings are drooped and tail angled up, spread, and flirted with twists of the body as they go. As a rule, Mangrove Fantails forage in strata above those occupied by the mangrove race of the Rufous Fantail in shrubbery below.

Movements are not well understood. Although breeding adults are probably rather sedentary, there seems to be local wandering, particularly around Arnhem Land and the Gulf of Carpentaria where the fantail is much scarcer than further west.

The Mangrove Fantail gives its high-pitched tinkling song from a perch.

OTHER NAMES
None.

IDENTIFICATION
LENGTH: *145–150 mm.*
ADULTS: *Sexes similar. Upper parts plain mid-grey. Wings and medium-long tail duskier grey, wing coverts tipped narrowly in two thin broken bars, inner secondaries narrowly edged white; tail feathers broadly rounded, the outer five pairs broadly edged and tipped white. Face deep grey with narrow white brow and obsolete white stripe behind eye. Throat dull white; lower throat with dull mid-grey bar.*
Rest of underparts sandy-buff, whiter under tail and greyer on flanks. Eye black. Bill black; lower mandible mostly cream. Feet blackish.
IMMATURES: *Duller than adults with obsolete markings.*

VOICE
CALL: *Sharp, thin,* chip, *by both sexes in contact.*
SONG: *High-pitched, squeaky downward series of six–eight notes with tinkling quality, given from perch.*

NESTING
Breeds July–December. Nest a tiny
100 mm tailed cup of plant fibre smoothly bound with cobweb; lined with fine fibre; placed on thin horizontal fork on mangrove shrubbery 1–4 m above, mud. Eggs: two, sometimes three; pale buffy cream, minutely flecked and blotched with various browns, in zone; long-oval, about 15 x 12 mm.

DISTRIBUTION
Close seaward and estuarine mangroves, from about Carnarvon, WA, to eastern head of Gulf of Carpentaria, Qld. Also locally in southern New Guinea. No races.

Northern Fantail *Rhipidura rufiventris* (VIEILLOT, 1818)

THE VIVACEOUS ACTIVITY and tail fanning of other fantails are missing from the Northern. In its shady galleries of monsoon scrub, mixed woodland glade, rainforest edge and mangroves across northern Australia, it feeds quietly and unobtrusively in ones and twos in the upper strata, at three–20 metres above the ground. Its technique is not to chase insects actively through the forest, but rather to hawk out repeatedly from the same perch.

It may not travel far but it does work persistently, fluttering out and back in flights of 10–30 metres, snapping up small flying insects—especially flies and dragonflies—in midair. Back at a perch, usually a thin horizontal twig five–20 metres up, the fantails sit for a while before launching out again, body rather still and upright and tail closed, only occasionally waving a little. They call and sing insistently there, and often continue on into dusk and early evening, as the Willie Wagtail does when breeding.

Often Northern Fantails join mixed feeding flocks of other birds and then become more animated, quickly moving on with the group instead of returning to vantage perches after capturing food. They feed right through the day.

Although essentially sedentary, Northern Fantails may wander locally after breeding, often shifting out of pockets of vine thickets into more open eucalypt woodland then.

OTHER NAMES
Red-vented Fantail, Banded Fantail.

IDENTIFICATION
LENGTH: *170–180 mm.*
ADULTS: *Sexes similar. Upper parts to wings and tail uniformly dark grey; edge of wing coverts tipped obscurely buff in a single faint line; three outer pairs of tail feathers tipped broadly white. Face dark grey with short white brow, sometimes hidden. Throat white. Broad grey band on breast sometimes faintly spotted white; rest of underparts pale buff to white undertail. Eye dark brown. Bill and feet black.*
IMMATURES: *As adults but duller and washed browner over back; throat and tail tips buff; breast band ill-defined.*

VOICE
CALL: *Short, metallic single or double* chip *or* chunk, *repeated monotonously in contact or rapidly in agitation, by both sexes.*
SONG: *Sweet, short, tinkling descending cadence, resembling that of White-throated Gerygone, but abbreviated.*

NESTING
Breeds August–January. Nest a small dainty cup, wine glass-shaped, about 60 mm across, of thin strips of bark and fibre closely bound with felt-like cobweb, with tail 70 mm long; lined with finer fibre; placed on bare horizontal or hanging twig under sheltering foliage about 2–20 m above ground. Eggs: two, sometimes three; cream with zone of dull brown spots and underlying grey towards large end; long-oval, about 18 x 14 mm.

DISTRIBUTION
From Broome, WA, around coastal and subcoastal northern Australia to about Proserpine, Qld, and following river systems as far inland as Warlock Ponds, NT, and Riversleigh Station, Qld. In pockets of vine forest, open mixed forest with Tristania, tall acacias, melaleucas and eucalypts, edges of rainforest and mangroves. Also in Lesser Sundas, Moluccas, New Guinea and intervening islands, Bismarck Archipelago and Solomon Islands. Up to 15 or more races; one endemic to Australia.

At its high perch, the Northern Fantail sits and watches for flying insects, its body still and upright.

Willie Wagtail *Rhipidura leucophrys* (LATHAM, 1801)

Willie Wagtail usually builds its nest on a horizontal tree fork. It is about 70 mm across, and seems hardly large enough for the three or four chicks.

EXPLOITING CLEARINGS, and familiar in urban areas, Willie Wagtails forage conspicuously in open places and are the only fantails to feed constantly from the ground. Through this capacity they have spread throughout Australia, avoiding only dense forests and treeless—perchless—plains. Clearings with a few exposed stumps, posts or open low trees for vantage perching are optimum habitat. There the birds are sedentary.

Hunting wagtails—usually in ones or twos—cover the ground in series of hops and low zigzagging flights. They peck at insects on the ground but also make long direct flights to hawk before returning to a perch. Before takeoff and after landing, wings are flashed and tails fanned. At rest, too, the bird constantly sways its body and wags its tail from side to side, in the characteristic manner that has given it its name. Like the Grey Fantail, it will hawk for insects over creeks, launching into steep flight from a projecting boulder. In cleared fields the backs of livestock replace rocks as vantage perches, the birds sallying out to snap up insects flushed by the grazing animals. Willie Wagtails feed more sporadically than other fantails but take larger prey.

Willie Wagtails are aggressive when breeding. Here their white brows come into play. In territorial disputes, rivals expose and expand their eyebrows. Submissive or subordinate behaviour is signalled by withdrawing the brows completely, and marks the end of dispute often before any physical contact. Both male and female build the nest and feed the young, sometimes on the same tree as other species. Several broods may be reared in a season, and nests are often reused or dismantled and rebuilt elsewhere.

Eggs are laid at 24-hour intervals, usually before 9 am, and both sexes incubate, often singing from the nest on calm nights. Clutches are larger in cooler areas but only about two-thirds produce nestlings, due to natural predators and feral cats. Later clutches are more successful than earlier ones.

OTHER NAMES
Shepherd's Companion, Black and White Fantail, Australian Nightingale.

IDENTIFICATION
LENGTH: *190–210 mm.*
ADULTS: *Sexes similar. Upper parts and throat black; conspicuous white eyebrow and faint white flecking at sides of mouth. Rest of underparts white; thighs black. Eye, bill and feet black.*
IMMATURES: *As adults; buff tipping on back and wings. Juveniles with grey, buff-tipped upper parts.*

VOICE
CALL: *Short series of hissing, metallic, two-syllable rattles.*
SONG: *Musical chatter of quick notes, alliterated* sweet pretty little creature *or* sweet pretty creature. *Given in all seasons and often heard at night.*

NESTING
Breeds August–January. Nest a small, neat untailed cup about 70 mm across and 40 mm deep, of fine grasses, tightly bound with cobweb; lined with fine fibre; placed on sheltered horizontal branch 1–20 m above ground. Eggs: two to four, usually three; cream-brown to sandy, with spots of brown-grey and grey-black at larger end, sometimes forming a zone; long-oval, about 20 x 15 mm. Incubation about 14 days, by both sexes. Young fledge in about 14 days.

DISTRIBUTION
Lightly timbered country throughout Australia. Accidental to Tasmania. Ranges to New Guinea, Moluccas and Solomon Islands. Sedentary or locally nomadic. Two races; one endemic to Australia.

Logrunner *Orthonyx temminckii* Ranzani, 1822

The Logrunner feeds on the ground, raking through the forest litter for insects and grubs. This is a female, with cinnamon-russet throat.

Unlike other songbirds, Logrunners and Chowchillas possess a tail of 10, not 12 feathers in which the central shafts project in spine-like tips. These the birds press against the ground as a prop as they scratch for food on the forest floor. Birds of upland subtropical rainforests, they are sedentary and communal, established pairs holding permanent territories of as little as two hectares and sometimes breeding in small family parties.

They keep to fern-covered banks and log-strewn areas deep within the forest, but extend into bushy cover and along watercourses in agricultural areas where introduced lantana and blackberry tangles abound. The birds seldom fly and spend most of their time on the forest floor, their colouring blending well with its gloomy browns. Usually the first sign of their presence is the burst of voluble *weet weet weet* calling as they are disturbed.

Feeding Logrunners leave characteristic cleared patches about 150 mm in diameter among the debris on the forest floor; the patches are formed as the birds rake strongly through the litter kicking first with one foot, then with the other, or with a series of kicks with each foot. Smaller items are sifted with front to back scratches. They do this to unearth their food: insects, especially their larvae, as well as crustaceans, snails and slugs.

Logrunners share the habit of another ground-feeder, the Superb Lyrebird, of nesting in winter. The female alone builds the nest, incubates the eggs and broods the young. To construct the nest, a thick stick platform is laid down, then sticks are built up around the sides and back, and finally curved over at the top. A thick moss and leaf roof is added, sloping down to form a hood over the entrance and partly concealing it. Right on top are placed a few short dry twigs, sticks and leaves.

OTHER NAMES
Spine-tailed Log-runner, Scrub-quail, Southern Log-runner, Spine-tailed Chowchilla.

IDENTIFICATION
LENGTH: *180–200 mm.*
MALE: *Crown plain rufous-brown; face mid-grey. Rest of upper parts mottled russet-olive and black, plainer on rump. Wings dusky grey, with two broad black bars. Tail plain dusky. Throat and breast white edged with black line on each side; belly white; flanks grey-russet. Eye dark brown. Bill and feet black.*
FEMALE: *As male but throat and upper breast cinnamon-russet.*
IMMATURES: *Mottled brown.*

VOICE
CALL: *Piercing* weet *repeated in excited manner.*
SONG: *Loud, staccato, resonant be-kweek-kweek-kweek-kweek, repeated quickly, but erratically; varied; several birds may call simultaneously.*

NESTING
Breeds mainly April–August, sometimes later. Nest dome-shaped, about 220 mm in diameter with side entrance, placed on or near ground, often in shelter of ferns or other overhanging foliage, built of twigs, lined with fibrous plant material and hooded with green moss at entrance where platform of sticks forms the approach. Eggs: two; pure white; oval, about 28 x 20 mm. Incubation by female.

DISTRIBUTION
Upland rainforests from Bunya Mountains, Qld, to Illawarra District and Cannbewarra Mountains, NSW. Also montane west and far-eastern New Guinea. Four races; one endemic to Australia.

Chowchilla *Orthonyx spaldingii* RAMSAY, 1868

A female Chowchilla at her nest. The male has a white throat.

OTHER NAMES
Auctioneer Bird, Northern Chowchilla, Northern Log-runner.

IDENTIFICATION
LENGTH: *Male 270–300 mm; female 260–290 mm.*
MALE: *Head black; rest of upper parts dusky olive. All underparts white. Fibrous tail with bare-tipped shafts. Eye brown with blue-white eye-ring. Bill and feet black.*
FEMALE: *As male but throat and upper breast cinnamon-brown.*
IMMATURES: *Dark brown flecked with cinnamon-brown over head, back and underparts.*

VOICE
CALL: *Contact calls: low, throaty* grrrr-grrrr-grrrr *and ringing* chuck *repeated several times.*
SONG: *Resonant, chattering, repeated* chow-chilla-chow-chow-chowry-chook-chook.

NESTING
Breeds most months except wettest ones.

Nest a coarse, bulky dome of over 1000 sticks, some large; placed at base of tree or in vine or fern clump just above the ground. Egg: one; white; oval, about 37 x 26 mm. Incubation and nest building by female.

DISTRIBUTION
Floor beneath upland and valley rainforests between Mt Halifax near Townsville, Qld, and Mt Cook near Cooktown, Qld. Two similar endemic races.

THE DISTINCTIVE CLANGING chattering of the Chowchilla is given at dawn, dusk and periodically through the day in the mountain and valley rainforests of northeastern Queensland. Members of a group often sing sequentially, the female most. The bird, common in these forests, is a ground-dweller, feeding among the leaf litter and only going to trees to roost at night. Flight is weak and whirring with no manoeuvrability but the birds run powerfully.

Chowchillas live in a communal group, comprising an adult pair and their young but sometimes with additional adults. Groups hold foraging territories year round; when one member finds a cache of food—insects, including beetles and their larvae, and occasionally seeds—it calls the others in and they all scratch and rummage for it together with strong, alternate sideways kicks. The birds probably breed only once each year but at any time.

Western Whipbird *Psophodes nigrogularis* GOULD, 1844

The Western Whipbird is a shy and elusive bird of mallee heath.

FAR FROM A WHIPCRACK, the song of the Western Whipbird is a repetitive rising tinkling. Males begin the bouts of singing, often turning the phrases over several times before the female joins in; then the pair may continue to sing antiphonally for several minutes from the cover of the dense mallee heath shrubbery that they inhabit. Song is uttered much more regularly in winter than in other seasons; in summer it may only be given before sunrise as pair after pair call to reaffirm themselves and their territories.

Established pairs hold permanent territories of about 10 hectares, with a core or two or three. The pair work their territory together, bounding low through shrubbery, feeding close to the ground and digging in litter, rarely more than 100 metres apart. Their diet includes a wide range of invertebrates, some seeds and occasionally lizards. Adjacent territories may overlap, but boundary disputes are rare.

One brood is raised a year. Nest building, by both sexes, takes one to two weeks and eggs are laid up to 10 days later. The same location is used year after year unless a mate changes. Incubation is shared but one bird, possibly the female, does more and always sits at night. Both parents feed the chicks and take over caring for one each when it leaves the nest, still unable to fly. Young probably stay with their parents until the beginning of the next breeding season.

Western Whipbirds were formerly much more widespread in the mallee heaths of southern Western Australia and South Australia than they are today. Wild fires and clearing have now reduced them to a few isolated pockets in both states.

OTHER NAMES
Black-throated Whipbird, Mallee Whipbird.

IDENTIFICATION
LENGTH: *220–250 mm.*
ADULTS: *Sexes similar; male larger. Head, crest, back, wings and tail olive-grey; tail feathers, except central two, broadly tipped white. Throat black, flanked by white lines; rest of underparts dull grey or centre of belly patchy white. Eye red. Bill black. Legs dark brown to slate-black.*
IMMATURES: *Olive-brown with rufous-brown throat.*

VOICE
CALL: *A single note,* chur, *which may vary from loud and harsh when repeated to soft when single.*
SONG: *Two variable songs, both rising grating series of whistles,* it for teachers pet *probably by male, and* ti tickerr-te-ar *probably by female, given in call-and-answer.*

NESTING
Breeds July–October. Nest a solid cup of fine twigs, strips of bark and dry grass; lined with fine grass; usually in a dense round bush less than 1 m above ground. Eggs: two; pale blue, sparingly spotted with black; oval, about 27 x 19 mm. Incubation about 21 days, by both sexes. Young fledge in 10–14 days.

DISTRIBUTION
Five main populations—tip of Eyre Peninsula, SA; tip of Yorke Peninsula, SA; on Kangaroo Island, SA; mallee heath on South Australian–Victorian border. In Western Australia several isolated groups in region bounded by Two Peoples Bay, Hopetoun, Pingrup and the Sterling Ranges. Two races: one in east; the other in west, with thin black line above white mouth stripe.

Eastern Whipbird *Psophodes olivaceus* (LATHAM, 1801)

The female Eastern Whipbird incubates the eggs alone, but the male feeds her while she is on the nest. Their whipcrack calls are often heard in wet forests.

THE RESOUNDING WHIPCRACK CALL of the Eastern Whipbird, a common year-round sound in the wet gully forests of coastal eastern Australia, seems to have two functions: to signal territory and to identify the caller's position. Thus both male and female usually combine to produce the call antiphonally, in call-and-answer sequence: the male contributes the long whistled whipcrack, and the female the two or three concluding chirrups. In this way they keep in touch as they forage up to 30 metres apart through dense forest underbrush. The male's call does not vary, but the female's response alters from district to district.

Established pairs hold permanent territories of about five–ten hectares in which they, with their young of the year, feed actively in the litter of the forest floor. They fly little, tail fanned, and forage mostly on foot throughout the day, turning over leaf litter with their powerful feet to unearth a wide range of insects and their larvae. They also search within shrubberies and fallen logs, their noisy rustling interspersed with repeated *chuck chuck* calls.

Unlike the Western Whipbird, the Eastern male does not share incubation and brooding but does feed the female on the nest. Both sexes feed the chicks, which are initially covered in fine black down. Young leave the nest before they can fly, and hide—perched still in the undergrowth—for a week or so until they can. During this stage their otherwise shy and elusive parents become fearless in their defence. Apart from the endemic wedgebills, the Australian whipbirds have no obviously close relatives among song birds except, perhaps, a 'green babbler' *Androphobus viridis* in the montane rainforests of western New Guinea. It nonetheless lacks one of the distinctive features of whipbirds, an un-notched tip to the upper mandible.

OTHER NAMES
Coachwhip Bird, Stockwhip Bird, Whipbird.

IDENTIFICATION
LENGTH: *250–300 mm.*
ADULTS: *Sexes similar. Head and crest black; back, wings and tail olive-green, all tail feathers tipped white except central one–two pairs. Cheeks broadly white, extending on to throat. Centre throat and breast black, grading to mottled white on belly and dusky olive on flanks and undertail. Eye red-brown. Bill black. Feet red-brown to dusky. Race in northeastern Queensland (Cooktown-Ingham) only smaller with disproportionately short tail.*
IMMATURES: *Duller and greyer-breasted and bellied, without white cheeks, until second year.*

VOICE
CALL: *Repeated* chuck, *in contact. Harsh scolds.*
SONG: *Antiphonal, in call-and-answer sequence by male and (usually) female. From male a series of low whistles swelling into a long-drawn crescendo on same pitch, ending with swirling upsweep, the 'whipcrack'. Female responds at once with several sharp chirrups* choo-choo *or* choo-ee.

NESTING
Breeds July–January. Nest a shallow, bulky cup, of long, loosely interwoven twigs; lined with rootlets and fibre; placed in thick foliage of dense shrub or vine in undergrowth, 0.5–4 m above ground. Eggs: two; pale blue with spots and irregular marks of black and underlying lilac; oval, about 28 x 20 mm. Incubation 17–18 days, by female, often laying in afternoon. Young fledge in 10–11 days.

DISTRIBUTION
Thickets in rainforest and wet sclerophyll and brushes of coastal eastern Australia; also in dense wet heaths and moist gullies. Sedentary. Two races.

Chirruping Wedgebill

Psophodes cristatus (GOULD, 1838)

OTHER NAMES
None.

IDENTIFICATION
LENGTH: *190–200 mm.*
ADULTS: *Sexes similar; male larger. Head and upper parts uniformly fawn-brown with faint dusky dappling and prominent dusky crest. Wings and tail duskier brown with white-shafted outer wing quills and broad white tip on all but central pair of tail feathers. Underparts uniformly grey-white with light dusky streaking over breast; flanks greyer. Eye dark brown. Bill black. Feet greyish black.*
IMMATURES: *As adults but softer-plumaged. Bill pale pink-brown; feet brown. Juveniles washed cinnamon on wings; crest feathery.*

VOICE
SONG: *Cycling rolling chirrup,* wu-cheeeer, *repeated over and over; all given by one bird or antiphonally, one bird giving the first soft note and another the succeeding loud descending trill.*

NESTING
Breeds March–May and August–November, or after rains. Nest a shallow loose cup of twigs, grass and bark; lined with finer material; close to ground less than 3 m high in stout upright fork inside dense shrub or tree. Eggs: two–three; greenish blue with sparse black spots of black and purple-grey at large end; tapered-oval, about 24 x 17 mm.*

DISTRIBUTION
Open, dry shrub steppe, with low Acacia, nitrebush and boxthorn shrubberies, in basins of arid central southeastern Australia west to Lake Eyre and Lake Torrens, SA. No races.

The Chirruping Wedgebill lives in arid shrub steppes in eastern Australia.

WEDGEBILLS, NAMED BECAUSE of their shortly tapered, finch-like bills, are the most communal of the whipbirds. Adults establish small, sedentary colonies of up to 20 or so birds in pockets of taller but still broken shrubbery in the rolling shrub steppes of the arid Darling and southeastern Lake Eyre basins. Thickets of spiny *Acacia victoriae,* nitre bush *Nitraria,* and boxthorn *Lycium,* sometimes of only a hectare or so, are favoured.

Keeping to cover, the birds run over the ground and hop up into low branchlets foraging for food, picking a range of small insects and seeds. Flight from bush to bush is low, of flutters and short glides with part-spread tail. After breeding, brown-billed immatures band together in loose foraging flocks of up to several hundred that wander widely across the countryside.

Territorial birds sing sporadically through the day all year, but insistently at dawn, usually perched on top of a bush to beam out the signal. Song is a sparrow-like chirrup and although usually given by one bird, may be antiphonal: one bird gives the opening note and the other, perhaps its mate, the concluding chirrup.

Chiming Wedgebill *Psophodes occidentalis* (MATHEWS, 1912)

The Chiming Wedgebill's nest is loosely constructed of sticks and grass.

THE SONG OF the Chiming Wedgebill—a sweetly whistled, falling chime of four to six notes, often repeated over and over—is given equally by both sexes without any antiphonal participation. This is only one of its differences from the similar-looking Chirruping Wedgebill, of which it was considered a race until the past decade. Chiming Wedgebills are also more uniformly grey, with little hint of breast streaking, and have distinctly longer tails.

The Chiming replaces the Chirruping in arid eastern and central Australia, living in more open shrubberies intermingled with taller mulga *Acacia aneura* woodland. Where the two meet, around the northern and western fringes of the Simpson Desert and western Lake Eyre basin, there is no evidence of intergradation. They probably arose and diverged within the past several million years, where their common ancestral population across inland Australia was split through the centre by increasingly arid climates and possibly seawater barriers in the inland lakes there.

Like the Chirruping Wedgebill, the Chiming is communal, groups of up to 20 or more occupying small territories in pockets of shrubbery year round. They feed on the ground and low branchlets under sheltering shrubbery, picking up seeds and insects, and their low dashing flight is of flutters and glides with part-spread tail flashing its white tip. They are shyer and more elusive than the Chirruping. Singing birds call sporadically through the day, but most frequently at dawn and late dusk, particularly when breeding, beaming the song out from tops of bushes. After breeding, inland birds may gather in larger wandering flocks.

OTHER NAMES
Crested Wedgebill, Chimes-bird, Daylight Bird, Kitty-lintol.

IDENTIFICATION
LENGTH: *200–220 mm.*
ADULTS: *Sexes similar; male larger. Head and upper parts uniformly mid grey-brown, with prominent dusky crest. Wings and tail duskier, with white-shafted outer wing quills and broad white tip on all but central pair of tail feathers. Underparts plain pale grey. Eye dark brown. Bill black. Feet greyish black.*

IMMATURES: *As adults; softer-plumaged. Bill pale pink-brown; feet brown. Juveniles washed cinnamon on wings; crest feathery.*

VOICE
SONG: *Both sexes utter sweet, descending chime of four to six notes,* did-you-get-drunk, *with emphasis on last note; monotonously repeated.*

NESTING
Breeds February–May and August–November. Nest a flattened cup, loosely constructed of small sticks and grass; lined with finer grass and rootlets; placed in dense prickly wattles or clumps of mistletoe 1–3 m above ground. Eggs: two or three; blue to blue-green with black and grey-purple spots, especially at larger end; tapered-oval, about 24 x 17 mm. Incubation 17 days.*

DISTRIBUTION
Arid acacia and melaleuca scrublands with pockets of shrubbery, in midwestern and central Australia, west to coast, east to Simpson Desert and Lake Eyre. No races.

Spotted Quail-thrush *Cinclosoma punctatum* (SHAW, 1795)

THIS, THE LARGEST AND PLUMPEST of the quail-thrushes, is the only one of its group to live in temperate sclerophyll forests. It keeps to the drier sclerophyll forests with a rather clear understorey but heavily debris-littered ground in southeastern Australia, particularly in hilly country and ridges running off high plateaux. It is widespread in small numbers there, but an outlying population in the Mt Lofty Ranges, SA, has become very rare since European settlement and now verges on extinction.

The birds feed, alone or in dispersed pairs, on the forest floor. As they travel, members of pairs or family groups stay in touch with brief bursts of thin, very high-pitched whistles. With body crouched they run along in an erratic path, meandering here and there, picking up food—insects, seeds and small lizards— as they go. Large caterpillars and beetles are pinned to the ground with one foot and pulled apart; grasshoppers are also dismembered.

Quail-thrushes are wary and elusive and, aided by a camouflaging colour pattern, have the uncanny ability of melting into the landscape. If flushed, they rise with a quail-like whirring of wing, and dash off low through the forest in rocketing undulations that nonetheless rarely carry them further than 50 metres. Tails are part-fanned in each undulation, showing their white tips.

Spotted Quail-thrushes are ground-nesters. Pairs hold a breeding territory which the male defends by singing from low bare vantage perches in trees up to 10 metres above the ground; his series of double whistles is unique among quail-thrushes. In courtship and threat the birds fan the tail, flare their body feathers and lift their wings, only spreading the wings right out when defending young. The female alone builds the nest, incubates and broods the sooty-downed nestlings, though she sometimes leaves the eggs for long periods. On returning to sit, she is often accompanied by her mate. Once young hatch, the male shares in the duties of feeding them, on a variety of insects, small lizards and seeds.

OTHER NAMES
Spotted Babbling-thrush, Spotted Ground-bird.

IDENTIFICATION
LENGTH: *260–280 mm.*
MALE: *Crown and back brown-grey liberally arrowed with black. Eyebrow white. Wing coverts black tipped with small white spots; wing quills grey, the innermost quills chestnut and black. Tail feathers dusky grey and, except central two, broadly tipped white. Throat and lores black; broad white patch on sides of throat. Sides of face, neck and breast mid-grey with narrow black band on lower breast; belly white. Flanks buff, spotted black; undertail coverts buff-white, with black spots. Eye blue-grey to lilac. Bill black. Legs pale pink.*
FEMALE: *As male but duller with no black areas except for spotting. Brow buff-white; patches on throat pale orange; throat off-white tinged buff; lores grey. Wing coverts grey-brown with off-white tips. Tasmanian females have black band on lower breast.*
IMMATURES: *Upper parts brown flecked black; eyebrow slightly buff; throat pale buff with dusky fringes to feathers; breast and flanks tinged buff, heavily speckled black; belly white; eye and bill brown. Immatures resemble female; in first winter male resembles adult male.*

VOICE
CALL: *Repeated, long-drawn, very high-pitched whistle, both in contact and alarm; also harsh guttural call.*

SONG: *About 10–12 soft, repeated penetrating double whistles, second higher than first. Loudness varies; ventriloquial effect produced by bird moving head from side to side.*

NESTING
Breeds July–February, mainly August–December. Nest a depression in the ground, loosely lined with grass, leaves and bark to form a cup; placed near base of tree, stump, boulder or grass tuft. Eggs: two, occasionally three; white, spotted and blotched with dusky brown and deep purple; long-oval, about 32 x 24 mm. Incubation by female. Young fledge in about 19 days.

DISTRIBUTION
Dry, and sometimes wet, sclerophyll forest. Three isolated populations: Mt Lofty Ranges, SA; southeastern mainland; Tasmania. Two races, in Tasmania and mainland.

The Spotted Quail-thrush—the largest of the quail-thrushes— lives in dry sclerophyll forest. This is a female. The male has a black throat.

Chestnut Quail-thrush *Cinclosoma castanotum* GOULD, 1840

The female Chestnut Quail-thrush nests in a depression in the ground lined with fine bark strips and dead leaves. She usually lays two eggs.

THE CHESTNUT QUAIL-THRUSH inhabits the mallee and sclerophyll woodlands of the semi-arid parts of southern Australia, and the desert scrubs of Western Australia's Great Victoria Desert and central highlands region. Southern birds have only a patch of chestnut on the lower back, but ranging north the amount of chestnut becomes more extensive, covering the back from the mantle to the rump and encroaching on the shoulders and wings. Western desert birds are quite chestnut on the back, and blend in well with the red sands.

Everywhere the bird occurs on soils that are sandy, feeding on the ground often among spinifex *Triodia,* in dispersed pairs or small family groups of three or four. It meanders along, walking or running around and about, changing direction continually, picking up insects and seeds as it goes.

To keep in touch, the birds call frequently to one another in thin almost inaudible high-pitched whistles. When flushed, they explode from the ground with a whirring of wings and rocket in jerky undulations low through the vegetation, white tail-tip flash-ing, for 10–100 metres before landing and running off.

In the south the quail-thrushes are rather sedentary but in the central deserts they appear to be partly nomadic. Breeding pairs hold to a small territory, which the male defends by alighting on top of a bush or bare branch and giving his song of piping whistles. Sometimes the notes are repeated so rapidly that they run into a pleasant trill, lower-pitched than those of the Cinnamon and Chestnut-breasted Quail-thrush and without their melancholy quality. In display, the male raises and fans his tail, puffs out his body feathers and lifts his wings so that the patterns of black-and-white on his tail and shoulders show out boldly.

The sequence of moult in this bird is unusual. The young male moults from a speckled juvenile plumage into a plumage like that of the female before moulting into the adult garb. Sometimes there is an overlap in the acquisition of the sub-adult and full adult male plumages. In the Cinnamon Quail-thrush and the Nullabor Quail-thrush the juvenile males moult directly into adult plumage with black on the throat.

OTHER NAMES
Chestnut-backed Quail-thrush,
Chestnut Ground-bird.

IDENTIFICATION
LENGTH: *Male 230–260 mm; female 225–250 mm.*
MALE: *Head, upper back and upper tail grey-brown; lower back and rump red-chestnut. Tail appears grey-brown when closed but when fanned is black with conspicuous white tip. Shoulders black with white spots; outer wing quills grey-brown slightly edged buff; inner quills black, chestnut and rufous. Eyebrow white with buff tinge behind eye. Lores, throat and breast glossy black. Sides of throat have broad white lines, edged with black on face extending to base of bill; sides of breast grey. Belly white with black spots fringing sides. Flanks grey, buff, or chestnut tinged grey. Undertail boldly spotted black and white. Eye red to red-brown. Bill black. Legs grey.*
FEMALE: *Throat, breast and flanks grey. Head greyer and back has less chestnut than male. Shoulders brown or black-brown with off-white spots. Undertail boldly spotted white and brown.*
IMMATURES: *Similar to adult female. In juveniles back brown-chestnut or grey-brown speckled black, especially on crown. Breast, flanks and throat speckled grey and black, tinged buff on flanks. Belly white; sides of throat pale buff or off-white with light grey flecking. Eye brown to red; bill dark grey.*

VOICE
CALL: *Contact and warning whistles, sibilant, high-pitched, insect-like, often inaudible to people because of pitch; uttered when feeding or in danger.*
SONG: *Repetitive monotonal calls, like a trill, uttered by male when perched.*

NESTING
Breeds August–December. In desert areas depends on rainfall. Nest a depression in the ground, usually under a bush or tuft of grass, like spinifex, or close to fallen branch; lined with fine bark strips, dead leaves and grass, sometimes with small bib attached on one side. Eggs: usually two; white, spotted with shades of brown and lavender; oval to oblong-oval, 30 x 21 mm.

DISTRIBUTION
Mallee, sclerophyll woodland, open heaths, desert scrubs and mulga woodland, all on sandy soils, often with spinifex Triodia, *across arid southern Australia from west coast to central Australia and Riverina mallee, NSW. No races.*

A female Cinnamon Quail-thrush. The females in the Nullarbor look similar but males have a black throat and breast.

Cinnamon Quail-thrush

Cinclosoma cinnamomeum GOULD, 1846

OTHER NAMES
Nullarbor Quail-thrush, Cinnamon Ground-bird.

IDENTIFICATION
LENGTH: *180–210 mm; male slightly larger.*
MALE: *Head rufous-brown (Nullarbor) to grey-brown (Lake Eyre), grading to mid rufous-brown over all upper parts. Wing coverts black, broadly tipped white; outer flight feathers dusky, edged pale rufous. Tail feathers except central rufous pair black, the outer four pairs tipped broadly white. White-cream eyebrow; broad white stripe over cheeks to sides of neck. Lores, throat and all breast black (Nullarbor), or divided by broad white-cinnamon band on upper breast (Lake Eyre). Belly to undertail white, flecked black at sides; flanks cinnamon.*
FEMALE: *As male but wing coverts duskier, face greyer, cheek stripes cream-buff, extending over grey throat, breast pale grey-fawn (Lake Eyre), darker (Nullarbor). Belly to undertail white; flanks pale rufous. Eye brown; bill black; feet mid-deep grey.*
IMMATURES: *As female; dusky speckling on upper parts, buff cast over breast and sparse dusky flecking from centre of throat to all breast and flanks. Adult plumage gained at first annual moult.*

VOICE
CALL: *Several, thin, very high-pitched upslurred whistles, in contact and alarm.*

SONG: *Series of short, soft but far-carrying monotone whistles on same pitch.*

NESTING
Breeds regularly July–September; also other times depending on rain. Nest a shallow scrape, under bush or against tussock or boulder, formed of bark strips, grass and debris into cup. Eggs: two–three; pale cream-grey spotted with browns and greys; oblong-oval, about 28 x 20 mm. Incubation by female.

DISTRIBUTION
Saltbush-bluebush steppe on Nullarbor Plain and central Lake Eyre basin, southwest to Gawler Ranges, SA, east to lower Cooper-Diamantina drainage, Qld. Two races; one in each region.

SALTBUSH AND BLUEBUSH shrub steppe on stony ground, whether hard pan, gibber plain or low rolling ridges, is the habitat of the Cinnamon Quail-thrush on the Nullarbor Plain and central Lake Eyre basin. Smallest of the quail-thrushes, and plumper with a disproportionately shorter tail than that of the closely related Chestnut-breasted Quail-thrush, it lives almost its entire life on the ground, under conditions of extreme temperature and exposure.

Out of breeding, the quail-thrushes wander locally, singly, in pairs or small loose groups of up to six foraging across the plains. Feeding birds walk slowly, body hunched, lifting their feet deliberately and meandering in diverse directions, circling and back-tracking, picking food—insects and seeds—as they go. Contact is kept with sporadic, thin, high whistles. To find food, they will dig the bill into the ground and shift it from side to side or overturn stones. Large prey is grasped and pinned to the ground by one foot while being dismembered with the bill.

If alerted, the bird stands up craning, flicking and fanning its tail, then lowers its head as if ready to take flight. If flushed, it whirrs up and dashes away in rocketting undulating bursts, its part-fanned white-tipped tail flashing. Often they hide beneath bushes.

Breeding pairs maintain a local territory. Early in the season, males sing much—the Nullarbor birds less—during the day, stationed on top of a small shrub; later they sing less as their territories firm. The female nest-builds, incubates and broods, but when returning after a break she may be accompanied by her mate to within 10 metres of the nest. He helps feed the young.

Chestnut-breasted Quail-thrush *Cinclosoma castaneothorax* GOULD, 1849

OTHER NAMES
Western Quail-thrush.

IDENTIFICATION
LENGTH: *215–240 mm; male slightly larger.*
MALE: *Head russet-brown grading to dark rufous over all upper parts, browner in east. Wing coverts black, broadly tipped white; all flight feathers dusky, edged rufous. Tail feathers except central dark rufous pair black, the outer four pairs tipped broadly white. Cream eyebrow; broad white stripe over cheeks to side of neck. Lores and throat black. Upper breast and flanks mid (west) or dark (east) rufous, bordered on lower edge by broad (west)* or narrow (east) black line; belly white; undertail marked black-and-white. Eye dark red-brown. Bill black. Feet grey.
FEMALE: *As male; wing coverts duskier, face greyer, lower cheeks and throat buff, breast washed grey (west) or russet-brown (east), white belly without black border and ill-(west) or well-(east) defined, undertail mottled rufous-brown and white.*
IMMATURES: *As female; duller and flecked dusky over head to back and from throat to breast and flanks.*

VOICE
CALL: *Several, thin, very high-pitched, upslurred whistles, in contact or alarm.*
SONG: *Series of short, soft but far-carrying slightly down-slurred whistles on same pitch.*

NESTING
Breeds regularly July–September; also other times depending on rain. Nest a shallow scrape under bush formed of bark strips, grass, twigs and leaves into cup. Eggs: two or three; pale- to buff-grey, peppered with brown and underlying blue-grey spots; oblong-oval, about 29 x 20 mm. Incubation by female.

DISTRIBUTION
Open acacia or mallee scrub on hard pan or stony ground, in central western Australia from Pilbara, through Gibson Desert to central Australia; and in Diamantina–Cooper–Bulloo–Darling drainages. Two races; one in each region.

PATCHY MULGA AND MALLEE woodland on hard or stony ground is the habitat of this slender quail-thrush, which occurs in two widely isolated populations, one in central eastern and the other through central western Australia. They are separated by the dune systems of the Simpson and Strzelecki Deserts, and their origin and divergence from a pan-central Australian ancestor probably dates from the development of those deserts.

The birds forage on the ground in ones or dispersed pairs or small parties like other quail-thrushes, methodically walking a wayward, meandering path, picking up insects and seeds, and keeping contact with occasional thin, high whistles. If disturbed, they may squat out of sight beneath a bush, or run dodging off through shrubbery. When flushed, they whirr up and dash off in rocketing bursts, white tail tips spread and flashing.

Breeding pairs establish a territory each season, the male signalling it with sporadic song through the day from the top of a shrub. Only the female nest-builds, incubates and broods the young, which she has to leave to feed herself. The male later assists with the feeding of chicks and so, too, may other females.

A male Chestnut-breasted Quail-thrush from central western Australia.

Grey-crowned Babbler *Pomatostomus temporalis* (VIGORS & HORSFIELD, 1827)

The Grey-crowned Babbler lines its nest with soft material. It lives in groups of five to 12, all of which help to build the nest and feed the young.

GREY-CROWNED BABBLERS are the largest and most conspicuous of Australia's four babblers. They live and breed in a co-ordinated communal group which may include up to 12 individuals—a pair and its siblings and offspring, both young and adult. Pairs mate for life and are usually the only breeding birds within the group; the other group members help them to build nests and feed the young. Unattended pairs are rare, and it is unusual to find lone birds.

When predators are nearby the group perches motionless in a tree and, if attacked by such birds as Noisy Miners or magpies, huddles in a clump. The group as a whole defends a territory—usually about 12 hectares—all year. Disputes with neighbouring groups are frequent and may last several hours. However, outright fights are rare, and in between bouts of chasing and forming huddles the groups forage with or near one another.

A group forages in a tight cluster over much of its territory for half to three-quarters of the day, spending most of its time on the ground bounding along, rummaging through leaf-litter, probing into soil and turning over small objects such as rocks, sticks or cow-pats. The birds also forage on live or dead trees and shrubs, preferring those with rough bark. Their long, thin, scimitar-like bills enable them to probe deep into crevices and far under branches. They eat insects and spiders, and feed these, as well as lizards, to their young. Grey-crowned Babblers also fly after winged termites but are not efficient at catching them. Flight is a direct, rather laborious fluttering, interspersed with long glides that show a rufous patch in the wings.

Grey-crowned Babblers begin breeding with spring rains. The whole group roosts each night in a roosting nest, and many of these are built and maintained throughout the year. Egg nests and roosting nests look alike but the latter are bulkier and have a wider tunnel-entrance. A new nest is built for each breeding. The pair does most of the building of both types of nest, helped by the other members of the group except the very young birds—those under six months of age. The female incubates band broods the chicks. During this time she is fed by the other birds, both on and off the nest. All the birds in the group carry food to the nestlings but helping is related to age—the breeding male makes most visits, then non-breeding adults, and younger birds the fewest.

During the breeding season birds other than the pair also have functioning reproductive organs but do not usually breed in their own group. When occasional groups contain several breeding pairs, they breed at the same time and in the same nest. On average, large groups raise more young than small groups, but nesting success is often poor. Babblers are apparently long-lived birds.

OTHER NAMES
Cackler, Chatterer, Common Babbler, Happy Family, Happy Jack, Red-breasted Babbler, Twelve Apostles, Dog Bird, Grey-crowned Chatterer, Hopper, Parson Bird, Pine Bird, Rufous-breasted Chatterer, Temporal Babbler.

IDENTIFICATION
LENGTH: *About 250 mm.*
ADULTS: *Sexes similar; male has slightly longer bill. Crown grey bordered by large white eyebrow; back brown-grey shading to brown-black on rump; tail black, broadly tipped with white except central pair of feathers. Wings dark brown, with cinnamon patch in flight feathers exposed in flight. Throat white, grading to cream breast and pale grey-brown flanks and belly throughout eastern Australia west to eastern head of Gulf of Carpentaria, or to rufous-brown breast, belly and flanks to west and northwest; undertail brown-black. Eye pale lemon. Long, downcurved bill black, with ivory line on culmen and base of lower mandible. Feet black.*
IMMATURES: *As adults but bill shorter, gape orange, ear coverts grey and bend of wing rufous; eye dark brown, gradually changing to pale lemon over two or three years.*

VOICE
CALL: *Contact calls chattering repeated* chuck *and loud* wee-oo. *Alarm call to ground predators loud, harsh* shak; *to flying predators high, whistling* woo-oo. *Fledglings squeal while begging and call* wee-uk *while resting.*
SONG: *A loud antiphonal braying; leading female gives* ya – *and leading male answers with* ahoo, *in quick succession, six–eight times.*

NESTING
Breeds July–February. Nest domed, up to 500 mm wide with capacious cavity reached by small tunnel; of strong twigs and lined with fine grass and fur or cow dung; placed in the fork of small branches in outer half of tree, near the top, usually about 4 m above ground. Eggs: usually two–three, up to 14 when several females nesting; glossy pale brown, covered with fine dark brown hair-lines; oval, about 28 x 20 mm. Incubation 18–23 days, by female. Young fledge in about 21 days.

DISTRIBUTION
Northern and eastern Australia, west to the Pilbara region, WA, and southeast to southeastern South Australia, where rare, in open woodland and along streams in cleared areas. Two races: one in west, northwest; the other through east to southern New Guinea.

The White-browed Babbler eats insects, spiders and seeds. It lives in noisy restless groups of six to 10 or 15 birds—a breeding pair and offspring.

White-browed Babbler   *Pomatostomus superciliosus*   (Vigors & Horsfield, 1827)

IN ITS HABITS, THE White-browed Babbler is little different from the Grey-crowned Babbler, though it is smaller and more active. It lives and breeds in groups of up to 15 or so birds—mostly made up of one breeding pair and their offspring—which together build the nest and feed the young.

The groups are sedentary and probably defend a territory of several hectares all year. Members of a group preen each other. They roost in 'dormitory' nests and build separate nests for breeding. Only one female usually lays the eggs—the clutch size varies little—and incubates them and broods the chicks during the three- or four-week nesting period. There are usually two broods a season. When feeding nestlings, adults approach the nest with soft 'mewing' calls.

In its search for food—insects, seeds and spiders—the White-browed Babbler spends more time foraging on the ground than the Grey-crowned Babbler, but will work up to the terminal twigs of trees. Birds forage as a group, bounding along the ground and hopping along branches, rummaging in debris and probing crannies in bark for prey, constantly clucking softly. When one flies to the next patch of foraging cover, the rest follow quickly one by one. Flight is low and direct, of rapid fluttering interspersed with flat glides, spread tails showing their white terminal band.

OTHER NAMES
Happy Family, Kangaroo Bird, Stick-bird, Twelve Apostles, Jumper, Chatterer.

IDENTIFICATION
LENGTH: *180–210 mm.*
ADULTS: *Sexes alike. Crown dark brown-grey bordered by long, thin, white eyebrow edged dusky. Back and wings brown-grey shading into brown-black on rump; tail dusky, tipped broadly white except two central feathers. Throat and all breast white, grading to fawn on belly, undertail and flanks. Eye brown. Long, thin, downcurved bill dusky, with pink-white base to lower mandible. Feet dark grey.*
IMMATURES: *Fledglings as adults but bill short, gape orange and bend of wing rufous for several months.*

VOICE
CALL: *Cacophany of chattering year round. For contact while feeding a soft, repeated* tuk. *In alarm, brisk sharp whistles. Fledglings squeal while begging and give rapid* we-wake-up *while resting.*
SONG: *A long-drawn* miaow, *possibly antiphonal, introduced by short, rising whistles, into a down-slurred grinding churr,* weet-weet- miaaooww.

NESTING
Breeds July–December. Nest and dormitories built of strong twigs and lined with fine grass, wood and feathers; similar to those of Grey-crowned Babbler but only 300–400 mm wide; placed in outer foliaged branches of small tree 1–6 m, usually 2 m, above ground. Eggs: two or three, sometimes five; glossy brown-grey, with dark brown hair-lines; oval, about 24 x 17 mm. Incubation about 16 days, by female.

DISTRIBUTION
Southern Australia east to western slopes of Great Dividing Range, in open forest, woodland, mallee and mulga scrub with shrubby substage. Two races.

Hall's Babbler _Pomatostomus halli_ COWLES, 1964

SURPRISINGLY, HALL'S BABBLER was not discovered until 1963, despite its abundance and wide range in the mulga woodlands of central Queensland and northwestern New South Wales. Earlier observers had evidently confused it with the similar-looking, but noticeably paler, White-browed Babbler—for both species are closely related and have much the same habits, calls and ecology.

Hall's Babblers occasionally move about in pairs but more often form stable flocks of up to 20 birds. The area of their home range may be up to several hectares. Within it, a flock may feed in one pocket of shrubbery for up to half an hour. They forage mostly on the ground, bounding along and probing with their long, curved bills among the debris for insects, or turning over bark or stones, clucking softly all the while in contact. Birds also glean and probe on trunks and branches. Occasionally a bird carries a large prey item to an exposed branch where it shares it with others.

A home range usually contains a clump of roosting nests, each attached securely to small branches just inside the foliage and three–seven metres above the ground. Before entering these dormitories at nightfall, flock members alternately perch close to each other near the nest, and chase each other. The flock may divide between roost nests as well as change their roost on consecutive nights. In the morning, birds emerge silently and sit and preen themselves and each other before flying off to feed.

Hall's Babblers breed after substantial rain outside the breeding season. Only the female incubates; she is usually silent on the nest but gives a series of loud, staccato calls before joining the flock to forage. She may be fed and preened by others, and accompanied back to the nest by attendants which chase intruders away.

Hall's Babblers live in eastern mulga woodlands where they replace their closest relative, the White-browed Babbler.

OTHER NAMES
None.

IDENTIFICATION
LENGTH: _About 200–220 mm._
ADULTS: _Sexes similar. Crown dark sooty brown bordered with very broad white eyebrow. Upper parts dark sooty brown, blacker over rump; tail dusky black tipped broadly white, tips narrow on central feathers. Face dusky; throat and upper breast white, sharply demarcated from dark brown lower breast, belly, flanks and undertail. Eye brown. Bill decurved, black, with pale_ base to lower mandible. Feet black.
IMMATURES: _As adults but duller._

VOICE
CALL: _Cacophany of soft chatterings year round. Soft, repeated clucks in contact; brisk whistles in alarm._
SONG: _Long-drawn, growling miaow as in White-browed Babbler._

NESTING
Breeds mostly July–October. Nest a small, neat spherical dome of fine twigs, 200–300 mm wide; side entrance, lined with finer material; placed in outer foliaged branches of acacias, 3–10 m above ground. Eggs: one or two; creamy brown, marked with fine dark brown hair-lines, more at larger end; oval, about 18 x 24 mm. Incubation by female.

DISTRIBUTION
Dry acacia-covered ridges and plains in central eastern Australia, from at least Boulia–Winton, Qld, in the north, south to near the Barrier Range, NSW, and east to Charleville and Blackall, Qld. No races.

Chestnut-crowned Babbler _Pomatostomus ruficeps_ (HARTLAUB, 1852)

OTHER NAMES
Chatterer, Red-capped Babbler.

IDENTIFICATION
LENGTH: _210–230 mm._
ADULTS: _Sexes similar. Crown and back of neck chestnut, bordered by long thin white eyebrow edged black. Back and wings brown-grey, mottled dusky on_ mantle and with two white bars on wing coverts. Tail dusky, tipped with white. Throat to belly white, edged with dusky line; flanks grey-brown; undertail dusky spotted white; Eye brown. Bill black; lower base bone. Legs dusky.
IMMATURES: _As adults but duller; eyebrow and flanks suffused with rufous._

VOICE
CALL: _Loud upslurred whistles we-chee-chee, in contact in flocks. Chattering chack-a-chack, repeated, when alerted._
SONG: _Series of strident, piping whistles, from high vantage perch._

NESTING
Breeds July–December, or sometimes after substantial rains. Nest a great dome over 400 mm wide, with side entrance, of interwoven sticks and twigs; lined with bark fibres and animal and plant down; placed in open forked branch of tree 5–10 m above ground. Old nests can be used repeatedly. Eggs: three–five, rarely seven; pale grey-brown covered with hair-lines of sepia and dusky; oval, about 26 x 18 mm.

DISTRIBUTION
Open scrubs and arid woodland in southeastern Lake Eyre and western Murray-Darling basins. No races.

This Chestnut-crowned Babbler is taking a centipede to its young.

CHESTNUT-CROWNED BABBLERS OCCUPY drier and more open mallee, mulga and belar _Casuarina_ woodlands in far inland southeastern Australia than do White-browed and Hall's Babblers. Like other Australian babblers, they form permanent flocks of 12–20 birds that keep to the same territory and forage together, hopping noisily about among ground litter and up the branches of trees, rummaging and probing for insects and seeds. If disturbed they fly off, flutter-gliding, low over the ground, but in alarm they dash up to the under-canopy of trees and shrubs, chattering noisily. They are playful, sometimes chasing one another so much around the same bushes that they wear trenches on the ground.

Chestnut-crowned Babblers also roost together in dormitory nests, often disused breeding nests to which they keep adding material. They probably breed communally, too.

Clamorous Reed-Warblers weave their nest from strips of weeds.

Clamorous Reed-Warbler

Acrocephalus stentoreus (LINNÉ, 1758)

OTHER NAMES
Australian Reed Warbler, Reed Warbler, Long-billed Reed-Warbler, Reed-lark.

IDENTIFICATION
LENGTH: *160–170 mm.*
ADULTS: *Sexes similar. Head and upper parts plain tawny-brown; flight and tail feathers darker brown; eyebrow pale buff. Throat dull white, rest of underparts plain pale buff, lighter in centre of belly; flanks cinnamon-buff. Eye brown. Bill brown, buff below. Feet dusky.*
IMMATURES: *Darker brown; short crest.*

VOICE
CALL: *Loud, sharp* chut *in alarm. Also scolding rattle.*

SONG: *Rich, persistent, metallic* tutch-tutch-tutch-dsee-dsee-quarty-quarty-quarty, *with many variations.*

NESTING
Breeds September–February. Nest a deep cup of interwoven strips of reeds and rushes; lined with fine grass and feathers, placed crosswise; firmly attached to two or more upright reeds or to drooping stems in willows. Eggs: three or four; faint blue to pale buff, freckled and spotted with browns and lavender; long-oval, about 20 x 14 mm. Incubation 14-15 days, by female. Young fledge in 14–16 days.

DISTRIBUTION
Beds of reeds and rushes throughout Australia in freshwater swamps. Also New Guinea and Indonesia to southern Asia and northeastern Africa. Over 15 races; one in Australia.

FROM SILENCE IN winter, the brakes of bullrush and cumbungi in freshwater swamps across southern Australia burst into spring song with the arrival of Clamorous Reed-Warblers to breed. Some birds may remain over winter, skulking in the reeds, but most shift north then, to northern Queensland and the Kimberleys, a movement for which their rather pointed wings are well fitted. In September–October they return south, spreading inland along brakes of cumbungi *Typha,* on bore-drains through the Lake Eyre basin. There may even be two immigrant waves of breeding into the southwest, in October–November and December–January.

Near silent in winter, males sing ceaselessly at breeding quarters throughout the day and into the night. They pack into tiny territories of a fraction of a hectare—0.15 hectares of reed bed may support at least five pairs—and they may have to sing constantly to maintain them. Perched on a stem, singing birds puff out their throats and raise their crown feathers. Otherwise they are unobtrusive, living entirely within the cover of reeds and feeding on insects and small aquatic animals there. Flight between banks of reeds is a dashing, low, undulating flutter.

Little Grassbird *Megalurus gramineus* (GOULD, 1845)

OTHER NAMES
Little Marshbird, Striated Grassbird.

IDENTIFICATION
LENGTH: *About 140 mm.*
ADULTS: *Sexes similar. Head and upper parts grey-brown to warm olive-brown, distinctly streaked with dusky black. Wings grey-brown; tail dusky, olive-edged and tapered. Broad white eyebrow. Underparts dull buff-white, spotted and streaked dusky on throat and breast to flanks. Eye mid-brown. Bill pale brown. Feet brown.*
IMMATURES: *Almost plain below.*

VOICE
CALL: *Rapid chattering rattle,* chu-chu-chu-chu, *in alarm.*
SONG: *At breeding, a soft but carrying plaintive three-syllable whistle on same low pitch, first syllable short, second and third drawn out,* pe-peeeee-peeee. *At times first syllable not given.*

NESTING
Breeds mostly August–January, occasionally longer; inland, during wet seasons, may breed at any time. Nest a deep cup of loosely interwoven dry grasses and swamp plant leaves and stems; lined with similar material and feathers, all inserted vertically so that they protrude, arching at top to hide

cavity; placed in grass tussocks, branches of bushes or clumps of broken-down rushes, 0.5–1.5 m above ground. Eggs: three to five; white or pink-tinged, uniformly speckled or dotted with purple-red; long-oval, about 19 x 14 mm.

DISTRIBUTION
From Shark Bay south to Esperance Bay, WA, and from southern Eyre Peninsula through coastal and inland southeastern mainland to Tasmania and southeastern Queensland. Ranges occasionally to inland Western Australia, Lake Eyre basin, Atherton Tableland and Kimberleys. Also New Guinea—maybe vagrant from Australia. Three races: in southwest, southeast, and Tasmania.

DAYLONG MELANCHOLY WHISTLING—rather than dramatic nuptial flight—advertises territory for this bird in its habitat: reed beds, tussocks and shrubbery in and on the edge of freshwater swamps and saltmarsh. There breeding pairs occupy territories of about three-quarters of a hectare. Alone or in twos, the grassbirds sing, hop and run about within cover, tails often part-cocked, gleaning for insects, terrestrial and aquatic molluscs, and spiders. They work through bush after bush, flying low and slowly, wings fluttering continually with tail trailing.

Despite its weak flight, the Little Grassbird often disperses far after breeding. Although much of the population may be sedentary—but silent—over winter in southern Australia, some birds range as far as the Lake Eyre basin and even the Kimberleys then.

The nest of the Little Grassbird is a deep cup of grass and feathers.

The Tawny Grassbird builds its nest in dense clumps of rank grass.

Tawny Grassbird

Megalurus timoriensis WALLACE, 1864

OTHER NAMES
Tawny Marshbird, Rufous-capped Grassbird, Rufous-capped Grass Warbler.

IDENTIFICATION
LENGTH: *About 190 mm.*
ADULTS: *Sexes similar. Crown, nape and rump plain rufous; rest of upper parts rufous-brown streaked with dusky black. Wings and tail rufous-brown, with dusky feather shafts. Eyebrow pale buff. Throat white; rest of underparts plain grey-white. Eye yellow-brown. Bill pink-brown above, paler below. Feet flesh-pink.*
IMMATURES: *Duller than adults, with finer streaking.*

VOICE
CALL: *Single* tchk, *in alarm or for warning.*
SONG: *Rich, loud and varied reel,* ch-ch-ch-zzzzzt-lik-lik, *with a whipcrack effect in some notes, probably given by male.*

NESTING
Breeds August–April. Nest cup-shaped, narrower at entrance at the top, built of dried swamp grasses and lined with finer grasses and rootlets; near ground in any suitable dense cover, such as grass clump. Eggs: usually three, sometimes two; pink, freckled with purple-brown and grey; long-oval, about 20 x 15 mm.

DISTRIBUTION
Ranges from Kimberleys, WA, over most of northern and eastern Australia as far south as Illawarra district, NSW. Occurs mainly on coast, probably not ranging more than 300 km inland; in southeast, range extends westwards to foothills of Nandewar and Warrumbungle Ranges. Also New Guinea to Timor and Philippines. Up to 15 or more races; one endemic to Australia.

TALL RANK GRASSLAND in swampy pockets and flood plains around northern and eastern coastal Australia are the habitat of the Tawny Grassbird. It does enter wetter reed beds and drier heaths and scrubby forest edges, but rarely permanently or regularly. Established pairs may hold territory year round, alongside those of several neighbours in local pockets. Some do wander more widely, however, and there is a common tendency for birds to shift nomadically from area to area according to suitability.

In their habitat, the grassbirds spend most of their time under cover, hopping and running and gleaning for insects. Pairs will chase one another through grass tussocks, fluttering weakly from stem to stem, tails trailing. And they will climb a high stem to look about briefly, bodies and tail twitching.

During breeding, males advertise territory with conspicuous display flights, over the grass with wings quivering and tail down, singing continuously then hovering before dropping back to cover.

Spinifexbird *Eremiornis carteri* NORTH, 1900

OTHER NAMES
Desert Bird, Carter's Desert Bird.

IDENTIFICATION
LENGTH: *150–160 mm.*
ADULTS: *Sexes similar. Head rufous with pale buff eyebrow. Rest of upper parts rufous-brown. Wings and tail darker brown, tail feathers tipped with pale buff. Throat dull white. Rest of underparts plain greyish white, washed pink on flanks. Eye brown. Bill grey-brown above, paler below. Feet grey-pink.*
IMMATURES: *Paler than adults; slightly streaked.*

VOICE
CALL: *Harsh,* t-hut-tchut *or short, sharp* kik, *in alarm and contact.*
SONG: *A loud, high, repeated whistling warble,* cherrywheat, checrit, *and a downslurred* cheeroo, *by male; also rendered* je-swee-ah-voo.

NESTING
Breeds mainly August–November, or after good rains. Nest a deep cup, of fine grasses, sparingly lined with rootlets; generally concealed deep in a clump of spinifex. Eggs: two; pale pink, speckled with lilac and red-brown, particularly at larger end; long-oval, about 18 x 12 mm.

DISTRIBUTION
In spinifex mainly on stony ground, along coastal Western Australia from Hall's Creek and Fitzroy River, south to Minilya River and Dampier and Monte Bello island groups, then eastwards to Alice Springs in south and Newcastle Waters in north, NT, and Cloncurry and Opalton, western Queensland. No races.

A Spinifexbird on a vantage perch in stems atop a spinifex clump.

AS ITS NAME SUGGESTS, the Spinifexbird lives in spinifex, *Triodia*, particularly stands of tall old hummocks among acacia scrub along the slopes and valleys of low stony hills. It is the arid zone equivalent of the rank coastal grasslands occupied by the Tawny Grassbird. In this habitat the Spinifexbird is not rare but very local, and sedentary, established pairs holding to a small permanent territory year round. To defend them, breeding males sing from the tops of bushes or clumps of spinifex.

Spinifexbirds usually forage alone. They work deftly through clumps of spinifex—in which they hide if disturbed—and hop quickly over the ground, tail part-cocked, picking up food as they go. Diet includes insects, mainly small beetles and grasshoppers, and seeds, some of which may be fed to chicks. If alerted, the birds will climb to the top of a clump of spinifex to look about, chattering; in flight, they flutter weakly, straight and low from hummock to hummock, 'heavy' tail trailing and pumping up and down. In its structure the tail is distinctively round-tapered and almost covered with long upper- and undertail coverts.

The Zitting Cisticola is patchily distributed around the far north coast.

Zitting Cisticola

Cisticola juncidis (RAFINESQUE, 1809)

OTHER NAMES
Streaked Cisticola, Fantail Cisticola, Streaked Grass-warbler.

IDENTIFICATION
LENGTH: *95–105 mm.*
MALE: *In breeding plumage, head and upper parts mid-brown, grading to tawny on rump and dusky on wings and tail, dully streaked black on crown and mantle. Tail short, with dull white tip, black subterminal bar and large cinnamon 'windows' on inner webs. Lores and underparts pure white, only thighs tawny. Eye mid-brown. Bill grey-brown above, paler below. Feet brown-pink. In non-breeding plumage, upper parts bright tawny, heavily streaked black, rump plain. Tail long, without cinnamon 'windows'. Lores dull. Underparts cream-white, flanks tawny.*
FEMALE: *As male; duller and more streaked in both plumages.*
IMMATURES: *As non-breeding female; eye dark brown.*

VOICE
CALL: *Soft chattering.*
SONG: *Persistent, dry, tik-tik-tik or lik-lik, rapidly repeated or in doublets, by breeding male.*

NESTING
Breeds December–April, over monsoon. Nest oval, of grass, seed-down and cobweb with longer grass strands drawn in wigwam-style above; entrance near top; inner part of dried grasses lined with fine rootlets and seed-down; about 130 mm high x 60 mm wide externally; near ground in grass clump. Eggs: four or more, usually five; dull pale blue, peppered with red-brown; oval, about 15 x 12 mm.

DISTRIBUTION
Patchy around northern Australian coast, from Ord River, WA, to Rockhampton–Bundaberg, Qld. Also Africa, southern Eurasia, Japan, Philippines, Indonesia and New Guinea. Fifteen races; three in Australia.

RARELY SEEN, THE Zitting Cisticola is confined to pockets of short treeless estuarine and saline grassland around Australia's north coast. After breeding, family groups disperse locally, running quietly on the ground and feeding among the grass stalks, picking up a range of small insects and vegetable matter.

Groups break up with the return of breeding, and males begin conspicuous song-flights to establish territory. Uttering a continuous dry 'ticking', they flutter up straight from the grass to about 30 metres, level off and begin to undulate and circle over their ground. With each undulation, the birds utter a double dry *tik-tik* and fan the tail, exposing its cinnamon 'windows'. This may continue for a minute or more before a male drops in a rushing swoop, sometimes over and after a female, then dives to grass.

Males may be polygynous, for up to five nests have been found in the 100-metre territory of one dominant bird. They construct the nest in three stages, first binding a tear-shaped shell of spiderweb and down on to supporting grass stems, then filling in the walls with short pieces of grass, and finally adding lining.

Golden-headed Cisticola *Cisticola exilis* (VIGORS & HORSFIELD, 1827)

GOLDEN-HEADED CISTICOLAS inhabit taller swampier grassland than the Zitting, usually around fresh water, and are much more widespread through northern and eastern Australia. Living and feeding almost silently on insects on the ground beneath grass swards, it is inconspicuous and rarely seen when not breeding. It does not migrate and is probably little more than locally nomadic then, but it will concentrate in prime foraging grounds, up to 20 or more birds occupying a hectare of field. Flight is weak, fluttering and undulating, low over the grass.

With the coming of spring and summer breeding, males begin song-flights to establish territory. They rise to fly out from exposed bare perches on trees, shrubs and posts, jerking and undulating around at 10–20 metres high over their ground, and singing both there and from vantage perches, until finally pitching to cover. Displays continue sporadically throughout the day.

Both sexes work together in making the nest. The male apparently assists by passing a thread of coarse spiderweb and fibrous material to the female working from inside as they stitch concealing live leaves into its frame. He seldom takes any part in brooding and feeding the young, however. The birds feed mostly on insects which they obtain from the ground.

The Golden-headed Cisticola often sews leaves on to its nest.

OTHER NAMES
Golden Cisticola, Golden-headed Fantail Warbler, Tailorbird, Barleybird.

IDENTIFICATION
LENGTH: *100–110 mm.*
MALE: *In breeding plumage, head plain rusty-rufous; rest of upper parts tawny-brown, streaked black on mantle and wing coverts; wings and tail duskier. Tail short, with faint buff tip and dusky subterminal bar. Underparts cream-white washed rufous over throat, breast and flanks. Iris pale-brown. Bill brown above, flesh below. Feet pink-flesh. In non-breeding plumage, tawny crown and back streaked sharply black; tail* long, tipped off-white; underparts white, with rufous wash only on flanks.
FEMALE: *As non-breeding male; short-tailed when breeding.*
IMMATURES: *As non-breeding female but duller; eye dark brown.*

VOICE
CALL: *Soft nasal* peep *in contact; harsh grating* zeep *in alarm.*
SONG: *Grating, indrawn bzzzt, followed by several loud, metallic, liquid,* plink-plinks, *repeated erratically but incessantly by breeding male.*

NESTING
Breeds September–March. Nest a rounded dome with side entrance near top, often with growing leaves stitched on to outer walls by cobweb threaded through holes; built in grass tussocks, shrubs, swamp vegetation, rushes or vines, near ground. Eggs: three or four; glossy bright blue blotched with red-brown and purple; rounded-oval, about 16 x 12 mm. Incubation by female.

DISTRIBUTION
Coastal and subcoastal northern and eastern mainland, from Pilbara and Kimberleys, WA, to mouth of Murray River, SA, and on King Island, Tas. Also Bismarck Archipelago to China and India. Nine races; about three in Australia.

Rufous Songlark *Cinclorhamphus mathewsi* (IREDALE, 1911)

A female Rufous Songlark at her nest on the ground near a grass tussock or fallen log.

RICH BUT GRINDING metallic reels announce the arrival of Rufous Songlarks in well-grassed woodland across southern Australia to breed in August–September. They are migrants, shifting north in late summer to winter from central-northern Queensland to the Kimberleys. Some birds may remain behind. There is little breeding north of the Tropic of Capricorn.

Males establish and defend breeding territories with frequent song-flights during the day. These are launched from different vantage perches around the territory—a high, exposed bare branch, a post top or even a projecting rock. The bird flutters, circling as it goes, from one perch to another, singing non-stop while it is in the air and sporadically when perched. Unlike the Brown Songlark, it flies horizontally, uses a sequence of tree perches and does not cock the tail. Breeding females are as unobtrusive as males are conspicuous, keeping under grass cover, building the nest, incubating and feeding the young. Breeding territories vary from well-spaced to close-packed, according to the season, each pair occupying from half to five hectares.

Out of breeding, all birds are silent and spend their time foraging alone or in dispersed groups, walking and running unobtrusively among the tussocks, gleaning seeds and insects. Flight is of dashing, looping undulations.

OTHER NAMES
Rufous Singing Lark.

IDENTIFICATION
LENGTH: *Male 180–190 mm; female 160–170 mm.*
ADULTS: *Sexes similar. Upper parts plain brown, with darker shafts; rump rufous. Tail and wing feathers paler edged. Eyebrow pale buff. Underparts plain greyish white, dusky spotting on breast. Eye brown. Bill flesh-brown; black in breeding male. Feet flesh-brown.*

IMMATURES: *As adults; breast streaked.*

VOICE
CALL: *Sharp tik in alarm; scolding rattle.*
SONG: *Repeated rich, grinding, metallic wit-cher wit-cher-witchy-weedle with whip-like effect on first syllables, by breeding male on wing. When perched a long clear falling trill, sometimes ending with explosive* witchy-weedle.

NESTING
Breeds August–February. Nest a cup of grasses; lined with finer strands and sometimes hair; built into hollow in ground, near or under grass tussock in thick herbage and often beside fallen log. Eggs: three or four; pink-white, covered with dark red spots and freckles, in zone at larger end; long-oval, about 23 x 17 mm. Incubation by female.

DISTRIBUTION
Well-grassed woodlands throughout mainland except northern Arnhem Land and Cape York Peninsula where rare. Migratory. No races.

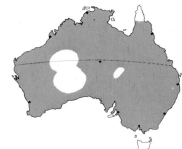

Brown Songlark

Cinclorhamphus cruralis
VIGORS & HORSFIELD, 1827

A BIRD OF ALMOST treeless grass plain and saltbush shrub steppe inland, the Brown Songlark is a desert nomad that follows the rains in the Australian arid zone but nonetheless shifts south to breed in spring. In August and September it appears in the wheat belt across the south to nest in crops; in late summer it moves back across central Australia. There is little breeding north of the Tropic of Capricorn.

Brown Songlarks are ground feeders and roost under shrubs on the ground at night. By day they forage silently among grass and shrubbery, walking and running, gleaning for food: insects, including grasshoppers, beetles and caterpillars, and seeds. When flying from point to point, they dash with low, long dodging undulations just above the shrub or grass cover, closed tail angling up as they dive to land. As a rule they are solitary when not breeding.

As with the Rufous Songlark, the male defends his breeding territory with song-flights by day while the female unobtrusively nest-builds, incubates and rears the young. Males flutter up obliquely from a post or the ground, legs dangling, grinding out their song as they level off, circle a little, then descend clucking, with wings up. They land either on a post or the ground; if on a perch, they may continue to sing, tail cocked like a wren's.

OTHER NAMES
Black-breasted Song Lark, Harvest Bird, Brown Singing-lark.

IDENTIFICATION
LENGTH: *Male 240–250 mm; female 180–190 mm.*
MALE: *In breeding plumage, upper parts, wings and tail mid-brown, mottled dusky on back. Lores black. Underparts plain dusky brown, darker on throat and belly. Eye brown. Bill black. Feet pink-brown. In non-breeding plumage, upper parts cinnamon-brown flecked dusky; wings and tail dusky edged tawny; lores tawny; underparts tawny-brown, with heavy dusky mottling on belly and often throat. Bill grey-brown, paler below.*
FEMALE: *As non-breeding male, but sandier with less dusky ventrally.*
IMMATURES: *As female.*

VOICE
CALL: *Infrequent chattering notes.*
SONG: *Loud, ringing metallic grinding reel, skit-scotcha-wheeler, repeated by male in song-flight and from perch; tick-tock-tick-tock clucks as he descends.*

NESTING
Breeds usually September–February. Nest an open cup of grasses and plant material; on ground hidden under grass tussocks or among crops. Eggs: three or four; pale pink covered all over with numerous freckles of red-brown, particularly at larger end; long-oval, about 23 x 17 mm. Incubation by female.

DISTRIBUTION
Saltbush plains, treeless plains, lightly

The Brown Songlark lives on vast open plains.

timbered grasslands over southern and inland mainland. No races.

Superb Fairy-wren *Malurus cyaneus* (ELLIS, 1782)

JAUNTY COCKED TAIL, iridescent blue plumage and boldness in adapting to urbanisation, parks and gardens have made the Superb Fairy-wren one of the most popular and familiar of Australia's birds. In shrubberies of open forest and woodland around the southeast, it lives in family groups comprising the adult pair, their young of the year and often several additional males. The preponderance of brown birds in such groups gave rise to the idea that each blue-coloured male maintained a 'harem'. Most brown birds, however, are junior males which moult into female-like plumage at the end of summer and back into blue nuptial dress at the start of spring breeding; they nonetheless retain their black bills and dusky lores through winter. Only old males—over four or five years old—may moult directly from one nuptial plumage to another; it is they who tolerate other males in the group, while the parental female drives off members of her own sex.

With the help of additional members, pairs of fairy-wrens regularly raise two or three broods a season, and sometimes even four. All members bring food to the nestlings as they grow, and when they fledge the dominant male and the unattached adults take over their care, leaving the female free to nest again. In their first week out, the fledglings can barely fly and stay hiding, camouflaged in deep shrubbery. Gradually they begin to follow adults and learn to feed, becoming independent in three to four weeks and later returning to help feed the next brood. Despite this fecund reproduction, misadventure and predation take their toll, and less than half of each season's young reach independence.

The female alone builds the nest, incubates, and broods the hatchlings in their first few days; she feeds herself as well. Nest-building usually takes several days, and she may let it lie fallow for a week or more before laying, at 24-hour intervals in the morning, until the clutch is complete. The male stands sentry near the nest, escorts the female on her foraging, and sings constantly to advertise territory. Song battles between neighbours are common. Areas occupied by each group may vary from about half to two hectares. Virtually all the male's displays are directed aggressively to territorial defence: song from vantage perches, flattened and spread plumage with flared ear coverts, and chasing. There is no obviously ritualised courtship, copulation following perfunctorily after a bout of chasing or mutual preening. Males, apparently in courtship, sometimes carry coloured petals.

Superb Fairy-wrens are sedentary birds, remaining paired in a close-knit group year round. Out of breeding they wander beyond territorial boundaries but rarely far. Among the first birds to call in the morning, males begin to sing before daylight, and then, soon after dawn, the groups begin foraging. They hop and flit along, tails cocked and boucing, pecking here and there for food: a wide range of small insects and occasionally fruitlets. During the middle hours, they divert to resting and mutual preening, the whole group perching side by side, one preening another and leap-frogging into the huddle to do so. After another round of feeding later in the afternoon, the group goes to roost on set horizontal perches in tall shrubbery, again huddling together side by side to sleep.

A male Superb Fairy-wren in breeding plumage. Out of breeding, it moults into female-like plumage, except for its pale lores and black bill.

A female Superb Fairy-wren at its grass nest in dense bush. Females of the Splendid Fairy-wren are similar, though their tails are blue.

OTHER NAMES
*Superb Blue Wren, Blue Bonnet, Fairy
Wren, Mormon Wren.*

IDENTIFICATION
LENGTH: *120–150 mm; male larger.*
MALE: *In breeding plumage crown and
upper back sky-blue. Back of neck
through eye to lores, scapulars and
lower back black. Wings grey-brown;
tail dark blue with narrow white tip.
Cheek patch oval, sky-blue. Throat and
breast blue-black; rest of underparts
white. Eye dark brown. Bill black. Feet
flesh-grey. In non-breeding plumage,
upper parts mid grey-brown; lores and
area around eye dusky; underparts
greyish white.*
FEMALE: *As male in non-breeding
plumage; tail browner with green wash;*

bill and feet and area around eye
orange-brown.
IMMATURES: *For first few months
resemble female, except for browner tail.
In autumn young males gain blue tails
and, in the following spring, full
breeding plumage.*

VOICE
CALL: *Staccato* prip-prip *or downwards
trill in contact, repeated; high-pitched
reed-like* seeee *and churring in alarm;
also brooding purr by female.*
SONG: *Loud, rich rippling warble,
descending in pitch, and introduced by
several chirps; by both sexes to advertise
territory and keep group together.*

NESTING
Breeds August–March, rarely after

*January; occasionally in other months
in the drier areas following substantial
rain. Nest a small loose grass ball with
side entrance, about 80–120 mm wide,
of grass stems and blades woven into
framework of cobweb; lined with finer
grasses and feathers; usually in dense
bush or tussock up to 1 m above ground,
occasionally much higher. Eggs: three or
four; white, spotted with red-brown at
larger end; oblong-oval, about 17 x
12 mm. Incubation 13–15 days, by
female. Young fledge in 12–13 days.*

DISTRIBUTION
*Highland southeastern Queensland to
Tasmania and southern Eyre
Peninsula, SA. Generally within 200
km of coast, but also along Murray and
Lachlan River systems. Two races.*

Splendid Fairy-wren *Malurus splendens* (QUOY & GAIMARD, 1830)

IN FULL BREEDING PLUMAGE, the male Splendid Fairy-wren is a brilliant incandescent blue. It replaces the Superb Fairy-wren in the southwestern woodlands but is much less tolerant of human settlement and at the same time more adaptable to aridity: it ranges though the dry mulga *Acacia* scrubs of central Australia to the mallee of inland eastern Australia. In most regions it frequents a rather close-canopied woodland with a fairly open understorey.

Like the Superb Fairy-wren, the Splendid lives and breeds in small groups—with helpers to attend the nest—and is sedentary, maintaining a territory year round. Males, too, moult in and out of nuptial colour in and out of breeding. All members of the group assist in both territorial and nest-site defence. This allows the female to produce several broods. A female breeding for the first time produces more fledglings if she has helpers than if she does not. Groups of Splendid Fairy-wrens include additional adult females as well as adult males throughout the breeding season. Such a situation is rarely found in the Superb Fairy-wren.

The female of the Splendid Fairy-wren does all the nest building, incubating, and brooding of young. Nests take several days to a week or more to finish, more quickly if there is an old nest nearby from which to scavenge material. New nests are built for each brood. Nestlings are fed at the nest by the rest of the group—including their older siblings, if there has been a previous successful nesting that year. When nestlings are newly hatched the female incubates them for long periods and intercepts the food brought to the nest, eating some herself and passing the remainder on to the

OTHER NAMES
Banded Wren, Splendid Wren, Black-backed Blue Wren, Turquoise Wren.

IDENTIFICATION
LENGTH: *115–135 mm.*
MALE: *Brilliant medium to dark cobalt on crown, mantle, wing coverts and narrowly white-tipped tail. Lower back dark cobalt (western race) or black (central and eastern races); scapulars black. Wings grey-brown washed blue. Cheek patch lighter blue than crown, both sky-blue in central race. Band around nape to lores and crossing breast, black. Underparts uniformly deep cobalt (western race), or violet on throat and breast and mid-blue on belly (central race), or uniformly mid-cobalt with centre belly white (eastern race). Eye brown. Bill black. Feet dusky black. In non-breeding plumage, mid- to grey-brown above, with blue wash in wings; tail blue narrowly tipped white; dull white below. Lores and bill dusky.*
FEMALE: *As non-breeding male, but lores and feathers around eye washed rufous; wings plain grey-brown; tail blue-grey, tinged green. Bill light brown; feet dusky brown.*
IMMATURES: *As female but tail brown. During first winter males don nuptial plumage gradually.*

VOICE
CALL: *Staccato, harshly trilled* prip-prip *in contact, repeated; high-pitched reed-like* seeee *and churring in alarm; also brooding purr by female.*
SONG: *Loud rich rippling warble, descending in pitch, introduced by several chirps, by both sexes to advertise territory and keep group together.*

NESTING
Breeds mainly September–January. Nest a loose oval grass ball with entrance two-thirds way up side; lined with plant fibre or feathers; placed in bushy shrub or twiggy branchlets up to 1, rarely 2–3 m above ground. Eggs: usually three, sometimes two or four; white, spotted with red-brown; oblong-oval, about 17 x 14 mm. Incubation 13–16 days, by female. Young fledge in 12–14 days.

DISTRIBUTION
Heathy woodland, mulga and mallee over southwestern, central, and inland eastern mainland. Three races.

A male Splendid Fairy-wren—considered by many the most beautiful of the fairy-wrens—perched on a banksia. The female is grey-brown with a wash of chestnut around the eye.

The black-backed race of the Splendid Fairy-wren which lives in central eastern Australia. Here a male feeds the young in their grass-ball nest.

young. Individuals develop different hunting capacities so that the larger the group, the more varied is the catch brought to nestlings. All members of the group remove the faecal sacs produced by the nestlings, carrying each one at least 20 metres from the nest before dropping it. Of all the eggs laid in one breeding season, only about one-fifth produce young which survive to the following winter. Up to one-fifth of the nesting attempts may be parasitised by Horsfield's Bronze-Cuckoos as well. The young produced in any one year usually stay with their group throughout the winter and some stay even longer. If nest or young are threatened, the adults initiate a distraction display characteristic of all fairy-wrens. They fluff their plumage, lower their tails and run about like mice. The response is known as 'rodent-run'.

In the west, the Splendid Fairy-wren lives in vegetation that is generally more densely shrubbed than its habitat in the centre of Australia and further east. It feeds on a wide variety of insects which it catches as it forages, hopping around in loose groups, along the ground and through and over small shrubs. Sometimes it executes a 'towering flight', which involves making a sortie almost vertically from a bush to seize an insect metres above and then swooping back to cover. As they travel, Splendid Fairy-wrens cock their tails much less than other fairy-wrens and carry them generally at a lower angle.

During the day feeding routines are broken with bouts of bathing, drinking and mutual preening. When preening one another, groups cluster along a horizontal branch, working over their neighbours and leap-frogging into the centre of the group to change partners. They also cluster together, side by side on a set horizontal branch in a high thicket, to sleep at night.

There are three distinctive races of the Splendid Fairy-wren: one dark cobalt with all cobalt back in the west; another sky-blue-headed and -cheeked in central Australia; and the third mid-cobalt and black-backed in the east. All meet at the edges of their ranges and hybridise and intergrade there.

Purple-crowned Fairy-wren *Malurus coronatus* GOULD, 1858

PERMANENT FRESH WATERS, whether billabongs or streams, that are lined with pandan *Pandanus* and canegrass, and overtopped with paperbark trees *Melaleuca*, are the habitat of the Purple-crowned Fairy-wren in northwestern Australia. Despite the ubiquity of this habitat across northern Australia, the fairy-wrens are restricted to only two subcoastal drainage systems, one in the Kimberleys, the other flowing into the southwestern Gulf of Carpentaria, missing Arnhem Land. There they are moderately common, even in the Kimberleys, wherever their habitat has been left undisturbed.

Like other fairy-wrens, the Purple-crowned is sedentary and lives in small family groups of up to five or six or more birds that probably comprise the senior pair, their young of the year and perhaps additional birds. They feed as a loose group, hop-searching through the undergrowth and along the ground, working over piles of flood debris, and sometimes climbing into the mid-strata of paperbarks to poke about. Contact is kept by soft chirping. The birds pick up a variety of small insects, particularly bugs, weevils, ants and wasps, and small quantities of seeds as well. Rounds of foraging are broken with rests, huddling, mutual preening and singing in duets. The group converges on a small twig in the undergrowth, cramming together, each preening the other. The birds probably sleep in such huddles at night.

Breeding peaks in spring and early summer; after it, through the austral winter, males go into eclipse, losing their black collar and all but a hint of their purple crowns. Apparently only the female builds the nest, building a more bulky structure than the other fairy-wrens, with an extended platform entrance, in the crannies of *Pandanus* crowns. She probably incubates unaided, but both sexes—and maybe other members of the group—feed the young. Feeding birds come and go furtively, arriving by a roundabout route and dashing straight off.

OTHER NAMES
Crowned Superb Warbler, Lilac-crowned Wren, Purple-crowned Wren.

IDENTIFICATION
LENGTH: *135–155 mm.*
MALE: *In breeding plumage, crown glistening lilac or purple with centre black, surrounded by broad black band from lores through eyes around nape. Back and wings cinnamon- to grey-brown. Tail greenish to deep blue, all except central pair of feathers tipped broadly white. Throat and breast white shading to rufous-buff on flanks and belly. Eye brown. Bill black. Feet flesh-to grey-brown. In non-breeding plumage, crown dull brownish grey flecked lilac; no collar but black line remaining through eyes; eyebrow flecked white.*
FEMALE: *As male but lacks distinctive crown and black band through face; forecrown bluish grey; white brow and lores ringing eyes like spectacles; broad red-brown cheek patch.*
IMMATURES: *As female; crown wholly dull brown; face duller; tail longer and duller with thin white tipping; bill browner.*

VOICE
CALL: *High-pitched chipping* chirp *in contact, or* sweet; *alarm* churrs; *occasional high-pitched trill.*
SONG: *Shrill bubbling reel,* cheeper-cheeper-cheeper, *first syllable rising, second falling.*

NESTING
Breeds August–January; possibly throughout the year if conditions suitable. Nest a coarse, bulky oval ball of strips of paperbark and pieces of grass; side entrance (usual but not universal) may have small platform; lined with fine rootlets; placed in pandanus crown or in dense clumps of canegrass, at 0.5–4 m above ground. Eggs: two–four, usually three; dull white speckled with mid red-brown, especially at larger end; broad-oval, about 17 x 12 mm. Incubation probably by female.

DISTRIBUTION
Locally on freshwater rivers, streams and lagoons fringed with Pandanus and paperbark Melaleuca in Kimberleys, WA, and southwestern Gulf of Carpentaria. Two races: one with blue tail and sandy back in Kimberleys; the other with green-blue tail and greyer back in Gulf.

A male Purple-crowned Fairy-wren attending a young Brush Cuckoo. The nest, with its entrance platform, is much bulkier than those of other fairy-wrens.

Lovely Fairy-wren

Malurus amabilis GOULD, 1852

LOVELY FAIRY-WRENS LIVE far more in trees than other Australian fairy-wrens, reflecting their habitat: scrubby rainforest and its edges. Although dropping to the forest floor occasionally, they spend most of their time foraging in groups among bushes and the leafy branches of saplings and trees up to 20 metres above the ground. Their rather short, white-tipped tails are carried upright and often slightly fanned as birds hop about the foliage, snatching insects as they go. Family parties comprise up to seven birds, the dominant pair and their young of the year, most of which disperse before the beginning of the next breeding season. Once attaining nuptial plumage, the dominant male never seems to moult out of it. Several of them sometimes gather, hopping about females, carrying yellow petals in courtship.

In their tropical habitat Lovely Fairy-wrens may breed at any time. Unaided, the female takes up to 10 days to construct the nest. Eggs are laid on successive days and incubated by the female once the clutch is complete. Although helped by others in her group, she usually carries most of the burden of feeding the young as well.

The Lovely Fairy-wren lives on Cape York Peninsula. This is a male.

OTHER NAMES
Lovely Wren.

IDENTIFICATION
LENGTH: *120–130 mm.*
MALE: *Crown, mantle and ovate ear coverts azure-blue; lores, nape collar, lower back, throat and breast black; scapular patches rich chestnut; wings dusky black, inner flight feathers edged rufous; tail blue, very broadly tipped white; belly white. Eye brown. Bill black. Feet mid flesh-grey.*
FEMALE: *Crown to lower back smoky blue; wings dark grey; tail smoky blue, broadly tipped white; lores white,*
ringing eyes in mask; ear patches turquoise-blue. Eye, bill and feet as male.
IMMATURES: *As female but duller, greyer. Male may attain nuptial plumage in first year depending on social status.*

VOICE
CALL: *Single, whistled, insect-like* treee *in contact; soft* churr *in alarm.*
SONG: *Short musical trilled warble, descending slightly, without introductory chirps.*

NESTING
Breeds year round, peaking July–
December. Nest a coarse dome with side entrance, about 13 x 9 cm, of grass and skeletonised leaves; lined with feathers, fur, fine grasses and bark; within 1 m of ground in dense undergrowth. Eggs: two to four, usually three; creamy white, very sparingly speckled with red-brown at larger end. Incubation about 13 days, by female. Young fledge in about 12 days.

DISTRIBUTION
Coastal Cape York Peninsula south to near Townsville, in margins of rainforest and associated brushes. No races.

Red-winged Fairy-wren *Malurus elegans* GOULD, 1837

THIS, THE LARGEST OF THE chestnut-shouldered fairy-wrens, is very much a bird of gully and creek-side shrubberies close to water in far southwestern Australia. Sedentary and communal, it lives in small groups of two to five or so birds—mostly a dominant pair and some of their young of the year—in much the same territory year round. The group feeds there unobtrusively, hopping about beneath the shrub cover gleaning a range of insects and occasionally seeds, and carrying their bushy tails cocked high over their heads.

Females build their coarse, larger-than-usual nests in deep tangles of shrubbery and incubate unaided. Other members of the group help in the feeding of young and all can be provoked into 'rodent-run' distraction display by intruders at the nest.

OTHER NAMES
Elegant Fairy Wren, Marsh Wren.

IDENTIFICATION
LENGTH: *135–155 mm.*
MALE: *Crown, mantle and long-pointed ear coverts silvery blue; lores, nape collar and lower back black; throat and breast navy-blue; scapular patches dark chestnut; wings deep grey-brown; tail plain dusky blue; belly greyish white. Eye brown. Bill black. Feet dusky. In non-breeding plumage, as female but lores black.*
FEMALE: *Grey-brown above, greyer over crown; throat and breast white, greyer buff below; lores dark chestnut, not encircling eyes; tail and black bill as male.*
IMMATURES: *As female; tail and bill browner.*

VOICE
CALL: *Soft* treeee *in contact; loud, rapidly repeated* strrrts *in alarm.*
SONG: *High-pitched trilled warble on same pitch, introduced by two–four chirps.*

NESTING
Breeds September–December. Nest a
coarse dome with side entrance, larger than in other fairy-wrens, of leaves, bark fibre and grass; lined with down; usually close to ground, often in a clump of swordgrass Lepidosperma. Eggs: two or three; white, spotted with pink-brown at larger end; oblong-oval, about 15 x 12 mm. Incubation by female.

DISTRIBUTION
Gully and creek-side shrubberies of forests in high rainfall areas in extreme southwest of Western Australia. No races.

The Red-winged Fairy-wren is larger than most chestnut-shouldered wrens.

A male Variegated Fairy-wren with a stick insect. The males of this species lose their colours in the non-breeding season.

Variegated Fairy-wren

Malurus lamberti VIGORS & HORSFIELD, 1827

OTHER NAMES
Purple-backed Wren, Lavender-flanked Wren, Bernier Island Blue Wren, Lambert's Superb Warbler, Lambert Wren, Dulcet Fairy Wren.

IDENTIFICATION
LENGTH: *About 110–145 mm.*
MALE: *Crown and mantle mid to violet-blue, depending on race; long pointed ear coverts distinctly lighter. Lores, nape collar, and lower back black; scapular patches mid-chestnut; wings deep grey-brown; tapered tail dull blue, with narrow white tip. Throat and breast black, with or without wash of violet at sides; belly white, flanks white to tawny grey. Eye brown. Bill black. Feet flesh-grey to dusky. In non-breeding plumage as female but head greyer, breast whiter; lores and bill black.*
FEMALE: *Body colour varies from light to deep grey-brown or grey-blue; lores chestnut encircling eye or white in Arnhem Land; tail grey-blue, with narrow white tip; underparts white or cream-white, grading regionally to russet-grey on flanks; bill red-brown.*
IMMATURES: *As female but upper parts and tail duller until first moult.*

VOICE
CALL: *Long, high single whistle or* tseee *in contact; repeated* churs *in varying degrees of harshness, in contact or alarm.*
SONG: *Soft, dry mechanical-sounding rattling warble on almost same pitch,* yuruyuruya *in Aboriginal alliteration.*

NESTING
Breeds predominantly in spring in all regions. Nest a coarse, dense dome, with side entrance, built of grasses and spiders' egg-sacs; lined with feathers and plant down; generally within 1 m of ground in grass tussock or small bush. Eggs: three or four; white speckled with red-brown at larger end; oblong-oval, about 17 x 13 mm. Incubation 14–16 days, by female. Young fledge in 10–12 days.

DISTRIBUTION
Shrubberies throughout mainland Australia, north to Kimberleys, Arnhem Land and Gulf of Carpentaria, east to Great Dividing Range, crossing it to central east and southeast coast, south to Murray mallee, South Australian gulfs and Western Australian wheat-belt, and west to coast north of Perth and offshore islands. Four races.

MOST WIDESPREAD OF THE FAIRY-WRENS, this species is also one of the most variable and occurs in diverse habitats. In the shrubby forests and heaths of the central east coast is the best-known race, its females mouse-brown and chestnut-lored, and its grey-legged males with light blue crowns and royal blue backs. West of the Great Dividing Range across southern mallee and scrubs to the west coast is another race of almost violet-crowned and -backed males. It ranges north to the Gulf of Carpentaria and southern Kimberleys, the crowns and ear coverts of males becoming lighter blue, and females paler, greyer brown but still chestnut-lored.

The last two races live in the scrubby escarpments of Arnhem Land and the Kimberleys. Both have females with steely grey-blue backs and pure white-bellied males with just a dash of lavender at the sides of the breast. But whereas Arnhem Land females are white-lored, those in the Kimberleys are chestnut-lored and have more broadly white-tipped tails. In all these races younger males moult into dull female-like plumage out of breeding. Wherever they meet, they intergrade, the eastern with the inland through central eastern Queensland and the inland with the two northern through the southern Kimberleys into Arnhem Land.

A moderately dense shrub layer, whether under forest, in heath, through woodland, or in pockets or open plains, is required habitat. In more arid areas the birds are often confined to bushes along ephemeral stream lines. Like other fairy-wrens, they are sedentary and communal, living in small family groups, usually of three–six or seven birds in the same territory or area year round. Rising to sing before dawn, the group moves out to forage in early morning; with tails cocked erect, members keep in contact with high-pitched *tseees* and more frequent harsh *churrs.*

The groups forage mostly by gleaning low within bushes, flying close to the ground and dashing from one shrub to another. Flight is a slightly jerky, tail-dangling flutter. The birds also feed on the ground, hop-searching for insects among the grass, and up into the foliage of low trees, but always close to or under cover. Their bill is broader than that of other fairy-wrens and allows them to take larger prey. They are more generalist feeders, too, than the Superb and White-winged Fairy-wrens in regions where they overlap, taking a variety of insects—bugs, beetles, wasps, grasshoppers, flies, termites—and occasional fruitlets.

Feeding during the warmer hours is broken with rests, sunning, huddles and mutual preening on sheltered branches, and follow-the-leader chases. Basking birds stretch almost prostrate, belly down, along a perch and flare the feathers of the back and sides of the body to let sun and air in. Other fairy-wrens bask in this way.

After young of the year are shed, breeding groups begin to nest with a core pair and sometimes several additional members, mostly males but occasionally females. The parental female builds the nest unaided, constructing a particularly coarse structure in four to six days and sometimes leaving it fallow for up to several weeks before laying. Eggs are laid on consecutive mornings until the clutch is complete, then the female settles to incubate; she continues to brood the nestlings in decreasing periods for several days.

Growing nestlings are fed by all members of the group, coming and going from all parts of the territory with food through the day. Any threat to the nest provokes spontaneous rodent-run distraction displays, the birds running about and over shrubbery, head lowered, feathers flared and tails dragging behind. Young grow fast, often faster than other fairy-wrens, but on fledging can still fly only weakly and spend up to a week hiding, camouflaged, in shrubs. Thereafter they are strong enough to follow adults and learn to forage, becoming independent in another four or five weeks. Parental females, meanwhile, may return to nest a second or third time.

A male of the purple-backed race of the Variegated Fairy-wren. This race lives in arid country right across Australia to the west coast.

Blue-breasted Fairy-wren

Malurus pulcherrimus GOULD, 1844

OTHER NAMES
Purple-breasted Fairy Wren.

IDENTIFICATION
LENGTH: *125–150 mm.*
MALE: *Crown and mantle violet-blue; long-pointed coverts blue. Lores, nape collar and lower back black; scapular patches mid-chestnut; wings deep grey-brown; tapered tail dull blue with narrow white tip. Throat and breast dark violet-blue; belly white. Eye brown. Bill black. Feet flesh-grey. In non-breeding plumage, as female but lores and bill black.*
FEMALE: *Grey-brown above, with chestnut lores encircling eyes; cream-white below. Bill chestnut-red.*
IMMATURES: *As female; browner.*

VOICE
CALL: *Short high-pitched reed-like trills* sriii *in contact; churring alarm* trrrts.
SONG: *High-pitched buzzing reel, without introductory chirps.*

NESTING
Breeds August–September. Nest similar to Variegated Fairy-wren, near ground. Eggs: three; white, spotted with red-brown at larger end; oblong-oval, about 18 x 12 mm. Incubation by female.

DISTRIBUTION
Two populations, one across southwestern Australia; other over Eyre Peninsula, SA, in sandplain heath and mallee. No races.

The Blue-breasted Fairy-wren. This is a male in breeding plumage.

THE BLUE-BREASTED FAIRY-WREN occurs in sandplain heath and heathy mallee across central southwestern Australia and Eyre Peninsula, regions now extensively cleared for wheat farming. As a result, the bird has been confined to a fraction of its former range. Secretive and rarely coming out into the open, it rests, roosts and forages—on beetles, ants, weevils, flies and wasps—under the cover of shrubbery. Much feeding is done on the ground, the birds hop-searching along, tails cocked-high over their heads.

Blue-breasted Fairy-wrens live in communal groups of two to five, rarely more; frequently more than one male and occasionally more than one female helps tend the nest during the breeding season, but the parental female builds and incubates unaided. Groups are resident throughout the year and have territories of about three hectares. Group members keep in contact on their rounds of foraging by uttering a soft single *sreee;* in alarm they keep churring. In the north and east of its range, the Blue-breasted Fairy-wren lives alongside the Variegated Fairy-wren, and in the wetter forested southwest, the Red-winged Fairy-wren.

Red-backed Fairy-wren *Malurus melanocephalus* (LATHAM, 1801)

LIKE OTHER FAIRY-WRENS, male Red-backeds—except old black-winged birds—moult into and out of red-and-black breeding finery with the seasons. During territorial disputes they spread their red feathers across the wings, almost to the belly. Females are courted by males carrying red petals—in contrast to the yellow petals chosen by the Chestnut-shouldered Fairy-wren, and white petals by the White-winged.

The birds are sedentary and communal, breaking up into small groups or pairs to breed and later gathering in loose flocks of 20–30. In their northern and eastern grassland habitat, Red-backed Fairy-wrens forage actively in early morning and evening, hopping cock-tailed along the ground under the sward, gleaning insects.

OTHER NAMES
Black-headed Wren, Orange-backed Wren.

IDENTIFICATION
LENGTH: *100–130 mm.*
MALE: *Black with orange to crimson saddle over back; wings often grey-brown. Eye brown. Bill black. Feet pale brown. In non-breeding plumage, as female; tail shorter.*
FEMALE: *Mid-brown above; cream-white below; lores whitish brown; bill red-brown.*
IMMATURES: *As female but buffier and longer-tailed.*

VOICE
CALL: *Soft lisp,* tssst, *in contact; bubbled churrs in alarm.*
SONG: *Soft, short, rippling warble on same pitch, without introductory chirps.*

NESTING
Breeds August–March; later in north. Nest a grass dome low in grass clump or small bush. Eggs: three or four; white with small red-brown spots at larger end; oblong-oval, about 16 x 12 mm.

DISTRIBUTION
Summer rainfall savanna grasslands of northern and eastern mainland. Two races: one across north; other in east.

A male Red-backed Fairy-wren in breeding plumage; in non-breeding plumage it resembles the female—grey-brown above and white below. The birds live in tropical grasslands in areas of summer rainfall.

White-winged Fairy-wren

Malurus leucopterus DUMONT, 1824

THE COBALT BREEDING PLUMAGE of this fairy-wren is so intense on the Australian mainland that it appears black in some lights and leads to confusion with its two black-plumaged races on islands off the Western Australian coast. On the islands it lives in low heath, but on the mainland it ranges throughout the arid zone in shrub steppes of saltbush, bluebush and samphire.

White-winged Fairy-wrens are sedentary and live in small communal groups that include only one female and rarely more than one coloured male—and even he may moult into female-like eclipse plumage when not breeding. The birds feed predominantly on the outside of bushes, gleaning insects as they hop about the foliage, but they hop-search for insects over the ground as well. If preferred prey—beetles and bugs—is abundant, they will feed almost exclusively on it, but as it becomes scarce they take a wider variety of insects. Moving from bush to bush, they fly in low fluttering dashes, tails trailing, one bird after another.

When breeding, the female builds the nest within four days then lays up to four eggs on consecutive days, commencing incubation when the last egg is laid. After the eggs hatch, she continues to brood for much of the time, while her mate and helpers bring food which she eats herself or passes to her nestlings. Unlike female Superb Fairy-wrens which pass food to the nestlings while still in the nest, the White-winged female hops outside, turns on the edge and pokes her head in to feed the young. There is an hierarchy among the helpers, all of which are sexually mature, with the brown being subordinate to males with any white, then added blue (or black) plumage. A nuptial male may mate with a second female that occupies an adjacent area and has her own helpers.

A male of the blue and white race of the White-winged Fairy-wren.

OTHER NAMES
Black-and-white Wren, White-backed Wren, Blue-and-white Wren.

IDENTIFICATION
LENGTH: *110–135 mm.*
MALE: *Whole body and tail cobalt blue; wing coverts and inner secondaries white, rest of flight feathers mid grey-brown. Races on Dirk Hartog and Barrow Is., WA, black where mainland blue. Eye brown. Bill black. Feet slaty brown. Eclipse and younger males as female but tail bluer, gradually attaining colour over two–three years, starting with white in shoulders, then blue in crown and nape.*
FEMALE: *Pale brown-grey above, white below; lores off-white; tail grey-blue; bill red-brown; feet flesh-grey.*
IMMATURES: *As female but browner.*

VOICE
CALL: *Soft or louder* tsee-tsee *in contact; harsher, louder repeated* trrits *in alarm; soft pips by nestlings and feeders on approach to nest.*
SONG: *Prolonged whirring reel preceded by a few* chips.

NESTING
Usually breeds August–February; any month after substantial rains. Nest a small oval ball of grasses and sometimes wool, lined with down; placed in bush or grass tussock less than 1 m above ground. Eggs: two to four; white, spotted with red-brown at larger end; oblong-oval, about 15 x 11 mm. Incubation about 13 days, by female. Young fledge in about 11 days.

DISTRIBUTION
Shrub steppes and deserts of mainland arid zone, and heaths on Dirk Hartog and Barrow Islands, WA. Three races.

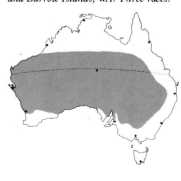

A male of the black and white race of the White-winged Fairy-wren, from Dirk Hartog Island, WA. Unlike the mainland birds, the island races live in low heath.

This Southern Emu-wren is a male; the female's throat, breast and brow are orange-buff. The birds nest in dense shrub, herbage or sedge-tussock.

Southern Emu-wren *Stipiturus malachurus* (SHAW, 1798)

SIX, FIBRUOUS, EMU-LIKE PLUMES compose the tail of the tiny emu-wrens and give them their name. The feathers lack barbicels or tiny hooks which hold the barbs into vanes, and the barbs themselves are sparse. The tail appears cumbersome as it is literally dragged through the undergrowth or flows behind the Southern Emu-wren as it hops or flies through the dense, near-treeless heaths of its habitat around southern Australia. Emu-wrens do cock the tail erect, as fairy-wrens do, but usually only when perched.

Southern Emu-wrens are sedentary, but after breeding, family groups coalesce into larger loose foraging parties of five to 30 or 40 birds over neighbouring territorial grounds. Feeding birds follow routine paths, creeping and hop-searching like mice among twigs, leaves and branches beneath the shelter of a dense shrub canopy for insects—leaf-eating beetles, weevils, plant bugs, and their eggs—and spiders. They work on the ground less frequently and rarely appear on the tops of shrubbery. As they travel they keep contact with soft, whispering *tsuuhs*. If pushed to flight, they flutter laboriously and straight, slowly and low over the heath before dropping to cover, wings whirring, tails trailing. Fleeing birds take refuge in deep undergrowth and even holes in the ground. At night the groups return to the same shrubbery to sleep, probably huddling together as fairy-wrens do.

Breeding birds break up into pairs, occupying small territories which the male defends with regular bursts of song, morning and afternoon. Additional helpers may rarely participate, and although the pair will rear two broods a season, the first may be dispersed before a second nesting begins. The female builds the nest unaided within a week, bringing material wrapped around her bill. She also incubates unaided after laying her clutch on successive mornings, and breaks the routine to feed herself as well. Her tail appears to be an encumbrance as she backs into the nest, tail thrown forward over her head. Both parents feed the young which, after fledging,

huddle almost helpless, camouflaged in deep shrubbery for up to a week, before they are strong enough to follow their parents. Independence comes in about two months.

OTHER NAMES
Button-grass Wren, Emu-wren, Stick-tail.

IDENTIFICATION
LENGTH: *150–190 mm, including 90–120 mm tail.*
MALE: *Upper parts and wings grey to grey-brown, streaked black, tinged rufous on crown. Cheeks grey-brown to brown with white streaks; throat, upper breast and brow pale powder blue; rest of underparts orange-buff, whiter on belly. Tail dusky, long, of six skeletal feathers. Eye shades of brown. Bill dusky. Feet flesh-brown.*
FEMALE: *As male but throat, breast and brow orange-buff; crown browner, more heavily streaked.*
IMMATURES: *As female; duller but juvenile males fledge with pale, blue-grey throat and breast.*

VOICE
CALL: *Soft, reedy chirp* tsuuh *in contact; louder churring* trrrt *in alarm.*
SONG: *A short, descending silvery reel, like that of fairy-wrens but fainter and higher.*

NESTING
Breeds August–January. Nest oval with side entrance; loosely woven of grasses or green sedge-leaves; lined with finer

grasses *and also feathers and fur; placed up to 1 m from the ground in dense shrub, herbage or sedge-tussock. Eggs: two to four; white, sparingly spotted and blotched with mid red-brown and underlying grey, mainly towards larger end; oval, about 17 x 13 mm. Incubation about 10–12 days, by female. Young fledge in 10–11 days.*

DISTRIBUTION
Swamp, wallum and sandplain heaths in Tasmania and around south coast of mainland, north to Tin Can Bay, Qld, and Shark Bay, WA. In local colonies at altitudes up to 950 m. Six races.

Rufous-crowned Emu-wren

Stipiturus ruficeps CAMPBELL, 1899

THIS, THE LIGHTEST-BODIED bird in Australia, weighing five grammes or less, ranges through the spinifex-covered sandplains and low hills of arid western and central Australia. Nesting, roosting, sheltering and feeding within spinifex, Rufous-crowned Emu-wrens also forage up into low acacia shrubs, and their territories often encompass mixed associations of tall hummocks of spinifex and low shrubberies. They are sedentary birds, breeding mostly in pairs and often coalescing in larger, loose, locally feeding groups of 10–20 or more afterwards. On foraging rounds, they hop, gleaning for insects, among the inner branches of shrub foliage and within spinifex, rarely dropping to ground except to run or flutter a metre or two to the next bush and infrequently hopping up to the top of a tussock to peer about, tails cocked. The birds chirp constantly in contact as they travel.

The female builds the nest, taking up to five–seven days to do so: two for the frame, two or three for the walls and one or two for the lining. The male escorts her noisily throughout. She probably incubates and broods unaided as well.

Rufous-crowned Emu-wrens are sedentary birds in spinifex; this is a male.

OTHER NAMES
None.

IDENTIFICATION
LENGTH: *120–130 mm, including 65–75 mm tail.*
MALE: *Upper parts and wings rufous-brown, streaked faintly dusky on mid-back, crown plain bright rufous. All face, brow, throat and breast deep sky-blue; rest of underparts cinnamon-tawny. Tail grey-brown, rather short, of six closely barbed feathers. Eye brown. Bill dusky brown. Feet buff-brown.*
FEMALE: *As male but face streaked white, lores white, throat and breast*

cinnamon-tawny.
IMMATURES: *As Southern Emu-wren, sex for sex, but buffier, less streaked above, and males with whiter throat, soon tinged blue.*

VOICE
CALL: *High, trilled chirp, tsee, often repeated quickly, in contact; sharp churred trrrts in alarm.*
SONG: *Short, warbling trill, on same pitch or downslurred, occasionally by breeding male.*

NESTING
Breeds August–October. Nest small

dome, with side-entrance, of interwoven grass stems and fibre matted with cobweb; lined with down and feathers; hidden in top of spinifex tussock 300–450 mm above ground. Eggs: two–three; dull white, sparsely speckled and blotched pale red-brown, mostly at large end; oblong-oval, about 15 x 11 mm.

DISTRIBUTION
Spinifex fields, on sandplain and low stony hills across centre and central west, from coast of Pilbara, WA, east to Simpson Desert and Opalton area, Qld. No races.

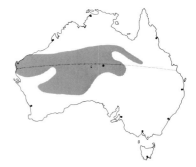

Mallee Emu-wren *Stipiturus mallee* CAMPBELL, 1908

MALLEE EMU-WRENS, which blend the plumage traits of Southern and Rufous-crowned Emu-wrens, are confined to stands of spiny spinifex *Triodia,* under mallee along the South Australian–Victorian border. There they live in pairs or groups of up to five—an adult pair and probably their young—in small pockets of tall unburnt hummocks. Much of their life is spent inside the big tussocks, roosting, nesting, resting, sheltering and feeding. They hop and run with great dexterity, tails lowered, gleaning for insects and

some seeds, and working quickly before fluttering on to the next tussock. Flight is a direct, weak, tail-dragging flutter.

Only the female appears to build the nest, incubate and brood the young, the male attending her and standing sentry. He assists in feeding young, as may other subordinate members of the group.

Young hide, camouflaged, in the week after fledging and any threat to them triggers a 'rodent-run' distraction display from the adults. Usually there is only one brood a season.

A male Mallee Emu-wren. Emu-wrens have long-filamentous tail feathers.

OTHER NAMES
None.

IDENTIFICATION
LENGTH: *130–150 mm, including 80–90 mm tail.*
MALE: *Upper parts and wings grey-brown, streaked dull black, crown plain rufous. All face, brow, throat and breast sky-blue; rest of underparts tawny buff, whiter on belly. Tail dusky brown, medium-long, of six sparsely barbed feathers. Eye brown. Bill dusky black. Feet buff-brown.*
FEMALE: *As male but crown streaked black; lores white; cheeks streaked white; throat and breast dull tawny.*
IMMATURES: *Both sexes plain grey-brown with obscure streaking above, grey-white on throat grading to belly below, flanks tawny, lores white.*

VOICE
CALL: *High, trilled chirp, treeee, in contact; sharp, churring trrrt in alarm.*
SONG: *Short, sharp, twittered descending trill, mainly by breeding male.*

NESTING
Breeds September–December. Nest a small ball with hooded side-entrance, of interwoven fibre, grass stems and spinifex spines matted with cobweb; lined with down and feathers; placed inside spinifex tussock within 400 mm of ground. Eggs: two–three; dull white,

closely freckled red-brown, mostly at larger end; oblong-oval, about 15 x 11 mm. Incubation by female.

DISTRIBUTION
Spinifex hummocks under mallee around South Australian–Victorian border, south of Murray River. Restricted and threatened by fire. No races.

Grey Grasswren *Amytornis barbatus* FAVALORO & McEVERY, 1968

An adult Grey Grasswren removes its chicks' droppings from their bulky nest in swamp canegrass. Both parents share the duties of feeding the young.

NOT DISCOVERED AND IDENTIFIED until 1967, the Grey Grasswren lives in remote, unprepossessing flood pans covered with dense clumps of lignum, *Muehlenbeckia cunninghamii* and swamp canegrass, *Eragrostis australasica,* on the lower Diamantina, Cooper and Bulloo River systems in the eastern Lake Eyre basin.

It is sedentary, like other grasswrens, but appears to be more communal and to forage more up into shrubbery, in the manner of fairy-wrens. Out of breeding the birds band together in locally wandering foraging groups of up to 15, or even 30–40 when concentrated by drought. They chirp constantly in contact, and they eat seeds, insects and water snails. Although hopping and running erratically out over the ground around clumps of lignum when feeding, tails cocked high, they dash back to cover at any hint of

OTHER NAMES
None.

IDENTIFICATION
LENGTH: *180–200 mm.*
MALE: *Mainly light grey-cinnamon above with black-bordered white streaks; eyebrow and face white; black stripe through eye joined to black patch on either side of midline of throat. Wing and long-tapered tail feathers dull black with pale edges. Underparts white with black streaks on breast; flanks cinnamon. Eye brown. Bill black. Feet grey-black.*
FEMALE: *As male but duller.*
IMMATURES: *As adults but duller; face pattern indistinct.*

VOICE
CALL: *Soft, sibilant two- or three–note chirps, twittered constantly in contact. High, piercing* eeep *in alarm.*
SONG: *Apparently twittered triplets.*

NESTING
Breeds July–August. Nest a loose, bulky, semi-dome of grass; lined with softer grass, a few rootlets and one or two small feathers; 300–760 mm above ground in clump of canegrass or lignum. Eggs: two; white or with pink tinge, densely speckled or blotched with cinnamon-brown and red-brown, sometimes in cap at larger end; swollen oval, about 19 x 15 mm.

DISTRIBUTION
Lignum- and canegrass-covered flood pans on lower Diamantina, Cooper and Bulloo River systems, eastern Lake Eyre basin. No races.

danger, often fluttering low, tails trailing. Lignum and canegrass provide their shelter, roosting, feeding and nesting cover. On its top branches, the birds often emerge to look about, twitter in their brief inelaborate songs, and sun on cold mornings.

When breeding, the groups break up into territorial pairs, sometimes with subordinate helpers. With soft twittering, copulation takes place on perches in lignum. Both parents feed the young, often approaching the nest by set routes and chirping noisily.

Carpentarian Grasswren

Amytornis dorotheae (MATHEWS, 1914)

NAMED FOR ITS CONFINEMENT to sandstones of the Carpentarian system at the head of the Gulf of Carpentaria, this grasswren remains one of the least known of Australia's birds. In its rocky habitat, it lives among screes and bouldery plateaux and ravines filled with tussocks of spinifex *Triodia* and *Plectrachne,* and few trees. Sedentary and grouped in pairs or small, loose parties of three to five—mostly an adult pair and their young—they hop and run over the rocks on rapid feeding forays through their territory in the mid-morning, probing and pecking in crevices, under overhangs, and around the edges of over-arching spinifex for both insects (beetles) and seeds.

In manner they are nervously alert, tails well-cocked and twitching constantly this way and that. They dash headlong to cover—a clump of spinifex or a hole under rocks—at the first hint of danger, sometimes part-fluttering with trailing tail, and often stopping behind cover to crane inquisitively back at the cause. When feeding, they chirp constantly in contact, led by the male.

Females apparently incubate and brood unaided but both parents feed the young which remain with them for many months after fledging.

The Carpentarian Grasswren is sedentary, keeping to rocky environments.

OTHER NAMES
Dorothy Grasswren, Red-winged Grasswren.

IDENTIFICATION
LENGTH: *160–180 mm; male slightly larger.*
MALE: *Forehead and face black with thin white streaks, brow chestnut; black line extends from base of bill down sides of neck; crown to upper back chestnut with white streaks, grading to plain chestnut on lower back and rump. Wings dusky brown, flight feathers and coverts edged pale chestnut. Tail slender, dusky, feathers fringed rufous. Throat, breast and upper belly white, grading into pale tawny lower belly and undertail. Eye brown. Bill dark grey with paler base. Feet grey.*
FEMALE: *Like male; flanks and lower belly deep chestnut, separated from white breast by incomplete band of lanceolate white feathers broadly edged black.*
IMMATURES: *Like adults; upper surface duller with less distinct streaks; belly paler tawny in both sexes and lacking breast band in female; bill paler.*

VOICE
CALL: *Soft cricket-like ticking or chirps in contact by both sexes throughout the year; buzzing* tzzzzzt *in alarm.*
SONG: *Long sweet trilled phrases similar to those of White-throated Grasswren, by male all seasons.*

NESTING
Breeds October to February–March. Nest a rather bulky oval dome with side entrance towards top, of closely interwoven dry spinifex stems with some leaves on the base; lined with finer grass stems; built into tip of a clump of spinifex 200–400 mm above ground. Eggs: two or three; rather lustreless, pale pink, sparingly speckled and blotched with red, brown and mauve, often indistinct zone at larger end; rounded-oval, about 20 x 16 mm. Incubation by female.

DISTRIBUTION
Craggy, spinifex-covered sandstone hills inland along southwestern head of Gulf of Carpentaria. No races.

Black Grasswren
Amytornis housei (MILLIGAN, 1902)

OTHER NAMES
None.

IDENTIFICATION
LENGTH: *180–210 mm.*
MALE: *Head and back black, streaked finely white; rump and upper tail coverts chestnut; wings and bushy tail dusky black. Underparts all black, streaked white on throat and breast; no brow. Eye brown. Bill black-grey. Feet grey-black.*
FEMALE: *As male, but lower breast to undertail orange-rufous; chin and eye-rim white; bill and feet paler.*
IMMATURES: *Uniformly dusky, faintly streaked whitish over head and breast.*

VOICE
CALL: *Sharp chirps and purrs in contact; loud ticking and staccato* tsrrrk *in alarm.*
SONG: *Short chattering metallic trills, filling out into brief up-swirling whistles.*

NESTING
Breeds December–March. Nest a bulky dome, of densely interwoven leaves and flower stalks of spinifex; lined with softer grass; built into top of spinifex tussock. Eggs: yet to be recorded.

DISTRIBUTION
Tumbled sandstone outcrops of western Kimberleys, WA, north to Mitchell River, south to Yampi Peninsula. No races.

The Black Grasswren makes its home among sandstone boulders.

ANOTHER 'LOST' SPECIES only recently rediscovered because of its remote, impenetrable habitat is the Black Grasswren. It is confined to the tumbled sandstone outcrops, ravines, and blocks covered with spinifex, *Triodia, Plectrachne,* in the western Kimberleys; the habitat is sparsely treed. Black Grasswrens are also thick-set birds with broad bushy tails that they do not cock much; they look like rats as they scurry over rocks and along crevices.

Sedentary and communal, these grasswrens forage in pairs or small loose groups of up to eight out of breeding, working methodically over the rocks under well-shaded cover from overhangs and shrubbery through their home range each day. They run, hop, flutter and glide with jerky alertness, a few metres apart from one another, stopping here and there to poke into litter and crannies. Both insects and seeds are eaten. To handle large or hard-shelled insects they jump on a rock and bash them against it until manage-

able. Tails are twitched up and down from time to time, and only when the birds pause briefly to look about are they half-cocked.

Males appear to keep the group together at all times. Working ahead, they lead, initiate call-and-answer contact calling, and are the first to bound, tails twitching, to the top of a rock to check along disturbance. Even after the group has dispersed, in headlong dashes among rock crevices, males regather them with snatches of song and contact calls from projecting rocks, heads up as they flirt their tails this way and that.

White-throated Grasswren *Amytornis woodwardi* HARTERT, 1905

OTHER NAMES
None.

IDENTIFICATION
LENGTH: *200–220 mm; male usually larger.*
MALE: *Head, face and upper back black with thin white streaks, grading into chestnut lower back and rump. Lores off-white; black line from base of bill down sides of neck; no brow. Wings dusky black, coverts thinly edged chestnut. Tail long, bushy, dusky black. Throat and breast white, separated from tawny belly and chestnut undertail by band of lanceolate white feathers broadly edged black. Eye brown. Bill grey-black, light towards base. Feet dark grey to grey-brown.*
FEMALE: *Like male; deep chestnut-brown on belly.*
IMMATURES: *Like adults; upper surface duller with less distinct streaks; belly paler tawny in both sexes; breast band not well developed; bill paler.*

VOICE
CALL: *Strong, sharp* trrrrt *or* tzzzt *in alarm, repeated sporadically.*
SONG: *Breeding males sing long sweet rising and falling notes and trills that carry for 100 m or more.*

NESTING
Breeds December–March in wet monsoon. Probably only one brood a year. Nest a bulky oval dome with side entrance towards top; of closely interwoven grass stems, strengthened down back and base with broader leaves; lined with fine grass stems; built in top of clump of spinifex some 350 mm above ground in small rocky breakaways. Eggs: two; matt white-pink, sparingly speckled and blotched with red-brown with underlying markings of purple-grey, forming indistinct zone towards larger end; oval, about 23 x 16 mm.

DISTRIBUTION
Confined to sandstone escarpments of western Arnhem Land, from Spencer Range south to headwaters of South Alligator River and east to central Arnhem Land. In tumbled breakaways and gentle slopes of sandstone rock, clad with tussocks of spinifex and other low shrub growth. No races.

THIS, THE LARGEST and most brilliantly coloured of the grasswrens, is abundant but rarely seen in the limited and remote spinifex-clad sandstone escarpments east of Darwin. Fire, which razes the spinifex, is its only threat. It is sedentary, and like all grasswrens is rather shy and evasive. When not breeding, it associates in small parties of up to six or eight birds. These groups, probably comprising one or two adult pairs and their young of the previous season, feed alertly among clumps of spinifex and over the rocks on small insects and seeds on the ground. The birds dart about each other, raised tails slightly fanned, flirting and waving. Males often lead the group or pair, bounding ahead and jumping up on to rocks to call and sing briefly; generally, however, they are much quieter than the Black Grasswren.

When disturbed, the grasswrens disperse rapidly, running from cover to cover in long and

short bursts and at great speed, with head and tail lowered. They can rarely be flushed from cover, but if they are they perform short, low, direct flights with rapidly beating wings, tail trailing. At times, sheltering birds crane from behind cover to peer inquisitively.

During breeding, the parties separate into pairs, sometimes with an additional helper, and the male takes up a territory which he advertises with singing throughout the day. He sings from a vantage point such as a prominent rock; he throws up his head, droops his wings, and keeps his tail part-raised, twisting this way and that as he beams his voice out in different directions.

The White-throated Grasswren's nearest relatives are the Black Grasswren of the Kimberley Division and Carpentarian Grasswren of the head of the Gulf of Carpentaria. All live in the same habitat and breed at the same time, during the northern Australian wet season.

The White-throated Grasswren lives on spinifex-clad escarpments.

Striated Grasswren *Amytornis striatus* (GOULD, 1840)

The Striated Grasswren is always found in porcupine grass.

ALERT AND NERVOUSLY ACTIVE, the Striated is the most widespread of grasswrens in the spinifex of inland sandplains and mallee and only locally on stony hills. Sedentary and often banding in loose groups out of breeding, it forages for insects and seeds on the ground, bouncing along, cock-tailed, and making running dashes from one patch of cover to another. Flight, rarely undertaken, is a low, weak, direct fluttering, with dragging tail.

Breeding pairs establish territory which the male defends by singing from vantage perches in low trees and shrubs, often near the nest. The female alone nest-builds, incubates and broods, but both parents feed the young, usually rearing only one brood a year.

OTHER NAMES
Rufous Grasswren, Striped Grasswren.

IDENTIFICATION
LENGTH: *140–165 mm.*
MALE: *Brown to rufous above, with fine black and white streaks; tail slender, brown, feathers edged rufous. Light cinnamon below, with white throat and grey and white streaks on breast. Brow and base of remiges rufous; black malar stripe running from bill. Eye brown. Bill and feet black to blue-grey, according to region.*
FEMALE: *As male; chestnut patch on each side of lower breast.*
IMMATURES: *As adults; marks blurred.*

VOICE
CALL: *Reedy chirp,* tseee, *in contact; sharp, burred* tchrot *in alarm.*
SONG: *Sweet up-and-down trilled warbling.*

NESTING
Breeds August–December; perhaps later in regions of summer rains. Nest domed, of porcupine grass, sometimes mixed with shredded bark; lined with plant down, grass seeds and fur; placed in clump of porcupine grass, often towards the top but usually well hidden. Eggs: usually two, sometimes three; white, sparingly speckled and blotched with red-browns and greys, sometimes more at larger end; swollen oval, about 20 x 15 mm. Incubation 13–14 days, by female. Young fledge in 11–12 days.*

DISTRIBUTION
Mallee and sandplain spinifex in inland eastern and mid-western mainland; spinifex on stony hills in Pilbara, WA, and Flinders Range, SA. Three races.

Eyrean Grasswren *Amytornis goyderi* (GOULD, 1875)

KNOWN FROM only one nineteenth century record until 1976, the Eyrean has since been found to be one of the more widespread and abundant of grasswrens. Its habitat—hummocks of dune canegrass *Zygochloa,* mixed with spinifex, on the sand ridges of Lake Eyre basin deserts—is a region rarely penetrated by man.

Eyrean Grasswrens are probably locally nomadic in small communal groups of up to 10 birds. They roost in the clumps of canegrass and feed under them and around their edges, close to cover, on both insects and seeds. Seeds, commonly of the canegrass itself, comprise at least 50 per cent of its diet; the grasswren's short finch-like bill is well suited. Never still, the birds feed by hop-search, running and bounding here and there, tails well cocked and vibrating with each bounce. Contact is kept among the bands by frequent call-and-answer chirping, broken by birds dashing, part-hopping, part-flying to a vantage perch in a bush or low tree to look about briefly or sing before diving back to ground.

Eyrean Grasswrens are most closely related to the Striated Grasswren, replacing it in the Simpson and Strzelecki Deserts.

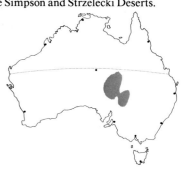

The Eyrean Grasswren lives in the sandhill canegrass of the Simpson and Strzelecki Deserts.

OTHER NAMES
Goyder's Grasswren.

IDENTIFICATION
LENGTH: *140–165 mm.*
MALE: *Cinnamon-rufous above, streaked white and dusky; tail slender, brown, feathers edged rufous. Plain white below, flanks washed faintly cinnamon. No brow; obscure black malar stripe. Eye brown. Thick bill and feet pale blue-grey.*
FEMALE: *As male; deep rufous sash down flanks.*

IMMATURES: *As adults; duller with indistinct markings.*

VOICE
CALL: *High, cricket-like* tseee, sreee *in contact; sharp* zeet *or* zzrt *in alarm.*
SONG: *Jumbled reel of cadences, pips, trills and buzzes, quickly by both sexes.*

NESTING
Breeds August–September. Nest a semi-domed structure, mainly of canegrass leaves and roots; placed in centre of canegrass tussock. Eggs: two; similar to those of Striated Grasswren; swollen oval, about 19 x 15 mm.*

DISTRIBUTION
Canegrass- and spinifex-covered dunes of eastern and southern Simpson and Strzelecki Deserts, SA, Qld, NT. No races.

Dusky Grasswren *Amytornis purnelli* (MATHEWS, 1914)

ROCK-STREWN HILLS and gorges clad with spinifex are the habitat of the Dusky Grasswren in central Australia. More inquisitive and communal than many grasswrens, they travel about their local foraging range in groups of up to a dozen or more—both in and out of breeding—hopping, calling and running over the rocks and among the spinifex like rats, heads down but tails cocked high and quivering. Seeds and a range of insects—ants, beetles, grasshoppers, bugs and flies—are picked from nooks.

Led by males, the birds feed quietly, but whenever they drift apart they begin to chirp and sing in brief bursts. It enables them to regroup. If disturbed, they scatter instantly, dashing and diving in all directions to the cover of crevices and passages under boulders. Flight is rare, the birds relying on their legs to carry them to safety.

Breeding groups are smaller, and often comprise only the dominant territorial pair. Females incubate and brood unaided, and males sing much more than at other times, presumably to advertise territory. They sing mostly from the top of vantage rocks, heads and tails up, swivelling about to beam out their brief songs in different directions. Both sexes feed the young, approaching the nest quietly and furtively along the ground from different directions, and departing quickly with a long hop to the ground. If young are threatened, all members of the group respond with 'rodent-run' distraction display, scrambling about, squeaking, with heads hunched, tails lowered, wings dragging on the ground. Two broods may be raised in a season.

A female Dusky Grasswren of the Queensland race.

OTHER NAMES
Thin-billed Grasswren, Dark Grasswren.

IDENTIFICATION
LENGTH: *150–180 mm.*
MALE: *Head dusky, grading to deep rufous-brown over back and greyer wings, finely streaked white, edged dusky; brow faint rufous, no malar stripe. Tail slender, dusky brown edged rufous. Throat and breast soft, dull rufous, streaked cream, and belly brown-rufous (central Australia) or stiff-feathered, straw-toned, with pale streaking edged black and belly grey*
(Selwyn Range, Qld). Eye brown. Bill and feet dusky.
FEMALE: *As male; patch of rufous at sides of breast (central Australia), or belly flecked dusky with sash of rufous down flanks (Selwyn Range, Qld).*
IMMATURES: *As adults but duller.*

VOICE
CALL: *High, trilled* sreeee, *in contact; sharp chirps* tt-tt-tt *in alarm.*
SONG: *High, staccato, metallic trills, upslurred then downslurred.*

NESTING
Breeds mainly August–October; also to
February–April. Nest a full- or semi-dome, of loosely interwoven grass stems, lined with shredded fibre; in clump of spinifex to 500 mm high. Eggs: two-three; glossy white-pink, closely spotted and blotched with red-browns; swollen oval, about 21 x 15 mm.

DISTRIBUTION
Rocky, spinifex-clad hills throughout central Australia, from Birksgate Range, SA, to Ashburton Range, NT; also Selwyn Range, Qld. Two very distinct races.

Thick-billed Grasswren
Amytornis textilis (DUMONT, 1824)

OTHER NAMES
Western Grasswren, Large-tailed Grasswren.

IDENTIFICATION
LENGTH: *150–200 mm.*
MALE: *Generally drab brown above, including wings, and paler fawn below, grading to whitish on centre of belly, heavily to lightly streaked with white, edged faintly dusky, over head to mid-back and breast. Tail slender, drab brown, faintly edged rufous. No brow or malar stripe. Eye deep brown. Bill dusky. Feet dark grey.*
FEMALE: *As male; chestnut patch at either side of lower breast.*
IMMATURES: *As adults; duller and more diffusely streaked.*

VOICE
CALL: *Soft, cricket-like chirps in contact; squeaks in alarm. Commonly silent.*
SONG: *Short, reedy, metallic trill, filling out into upslurring whistle, sporadically by male.*

NESTING
Breeds August–September, or on to January–April. Nest a flimsy semi-dome, sometimes fully covered or a deep cup, of loosely interwoven grey twigs,
grasses and fibre; lined with finer material, down, fur and feathers; placed within foliage of shrub (saltbush, bluebush) to 600 mm above ground. Eggs: two–three; dull cream-white, closely speckled and blotched all over with red-browns and greys; swollen oval, about 21 x 15 mm.

DISTRIBUTION
Patchy and local in saltbush-bluebush shrub steppe across southern inland mainland, from Shark Bay area, WA, to northwestern New South Wales. Three races: one in west; one through upper Eyre Peninsula, SA; the third through western and southern Lake Eyre–Darling basins, SA, NSW.

The secretive Thick-billed Grasswren lives in saltbush and bluebush.

THE THICK-BILLED IS THE only grasswren to inhabit the shrub steppes of saltbush and bluebush *Chenopodiaceae* of inland Australia. Yet despite the ubiquity of its habitat, its occurrence is patchy and localised and it has disappeared from large areas that it once occupied in western Australia and New South Wales. Overgrazing and trampling by sheep is the suggested cause.

The birds are sedentary, established pairs keeping to the same 20–40-hectare pockets year round, and rarely, if ever, banding together with neighbours in loose foraging groups after breeding. Most feeding is done during the early–mid-morning and later afternoon, the birds foraging on the ground under and around bushes and making blurring zigzagging runs from one patch of cover to the next, heads down, tails erect. As they stop to feed, they hop, picking up a wide range of seeds and fewer insects.

During the hot midday hours, Thick-billed Grasswrens rest and hide under bushes. If disturbed, they scatter in a flash, even diving down rabbit holes.

During breeding the male sings sporadically to advertise territory, hopping up through shrubs to open branches on top, tail-cocked—but he is not as vocal as other grasswrens. The female builds the nest unaided, but the male may assist with incubation; it would be a trait unique in the family. Both parents feed the young which pass through a 'cryptic' phase after fledging before following their parents and learning to feed.

Eastern Bristlebird *Dasyornis brachypterus* (LATHAM, 1801)

The Eastern Bristlebird builds its dome-shaped nest of grasses close to the ground in dense heath.

OTHER NAMES
None.

IDENTIFICATION
LENGTH: *200–220 mm.*
ADULTS: *Sexes similar. Upper parts, rounded wings and bulky tail plain brown, rump rufous-brown, pale buff line above eye. Underparts grey-brown, whitish on throat, breast feathers scaled with pale edges; flanks russet brown. Eye red-brown. Bill dusky. Feet grey-brown.*

VOICE
CALL: *Harsh, sharp* zeet *in alarm and soft* zit.
SONG: *Loud, variable and penetrating series of whistles, it wooa-weet sip.*

NESTING
Breeds August–January. Nest domed with a large side entrance; of coarse dry grasses, lined with fine grass; hidden near ground in grass tussocks, clumps of sword grass or small dense shrubs. Eggs: two; dull pale buff with red- and purple-brown blotches, more at larger end; oval, about 26 x 19 mm.

DISTRIBUTION
Patchy in heaths on east coast and nearby ranges between Cunninghams Gap, Qld, and Marlo, Vic. No races.

A BIRD OF dense heath and tussocky undergrowth, the Eastern Bristlebird lives and nests under the cover, moving through it rather like a rat and foraging mainly on the floor. Rarely does it hop up above a metre within the shrubbery, and it flies only with reluctance and then clumsily on stubby wings for short distances.

Powerful in leg, it runs fast through the undergrowth with flared tail, scratching for food in the litter and on the ground; sometimes it feeds up into low foliage as well. Insects and occasional berries, mainly of epacrids, are taken. The small bristles at the corners of its mouth, from which the bird takes its name, curve back in front of the eyes and may protect them as the bird travels at speed through the shrubbery.

Sedentary and territorial at least when breeding, bristlebirds sing loudly and persistently then, from perches within cover, particularly at dawn and dusk. Breeding territories may occupy about a hectare of prime heath. The birds become quiet through autumn and winter.

Western Bristlebird

Dasyornis longirostris GOULD, 1841

The Western Bristlebird is now localised because of clearing and burning.

FROM A RANGE THAT EXTENDED around the southwest coast north to Perth, the Western Bristlebird is now confined to a few stands of wet, low heath at Two Peoples Bay, Fitzgerald River National Park and Mount Manypeaks just east of Albany, WA. Its decline undoubtedly results from the large-scale clearing of its habitat and to increasing firing of coastal heaths after the arrival of Europeans. It is now a very rare species.

Western Bristlebirds live almost entirely within the cover of heathy undergrowth, roosting, nesting and feeding there. They do hop up to perch on a twig on the top of vegetation to sing, as well as from shrubbery, but only briefly because bouts of song are both short and infrequent. The birds sing throughout the year, increasing their output only slightly during breeding. In each bout, one bird, presumed to be the male, gives a *chip pee tee peeble pet* in a round of about seven repeats; the other responds somewhat less than 60 per cent of the time with a two- or three-note *quick more beer.* If stressed, one bird may give both calls.

Established pairs live in permanent territories of about six hectares with a core area of one–three hectares where the pair spends more than 60 per cent of their time. They move around their territory together, rarely more than 50–100 metres apart. Territories overlap and boundary disputes are rare. Nothing is known of the role of each sex in nest-building, incubation of the eggs and feeding of the chicks. The chick probably stays with the parents for two or more months after leaving the nest.

Western Bristlebirds eat insects and seeds, collected on the ground. They often feed on tracks or other open areas early in the morning or in the late afternoon. Their movements are quick and alert, and they can run very fast if disturbed, and raise and fan the tail. Their powers of flight are feeble and if forced to fly they skim the top of the heath, rarely going farther than five–ten metres before landing on the ground again.

OTHER NAMES
Long-billed Bristlebird.

IDENTIFICATION
LENGTH: *180–200 mm.*
ADULTS: *Sexes similar. Upper parts brown mottled grey over crown and mantle; rump rufous-brown, pale buff eyebrow. Underparts grey-brown, throat and breast feathers scaled with dusky edges; flanks dark brown. Eye red-brown. Bill dusky. Feet grey-brown.*
IMMATURES: *Upper parts olive-brown, no spotting; underparts grey.*

VOICE
CALL: *Harsh, sharp* zeip *in alarm and soft* zit.
SONG: *Two, both variable whistles:* chip pee tee peeble pet *and* quick more beer.

NESTING
Breeds August–September. Nest a dome, 150 x 120 mm, with large side entrance; of coarse dry grasses, lined with fine grass; placed near the ground in tussocks, clumps of sedge or small dense shrubs. Eggs: two; dull buff with purple-brown blotches, more at larger end; oval, about 26 x 19 mm.

DISTRIBUTION
Coastal heaths from Two Peoples Bay to Fitzgerald River National Park, WA. No races.

Rufous Bristlebird
Dasyornis broadbenti (McCOY, 1867)

SUBJECT TO FIRES and the clearing of its coastal heaths, this species may now be extinct in southwestern Australia, where it has not been recorded since 1906. In the southeast, however, it is still moderately abundant in coastal dune scrubs of boobyalla *Acacia sopharae* and heath, mixed with pockets of sedge and paperbarks, blackberries, and forest undergrowth, between the Otway Ranges, Vic., and the mouth of the Murray River.

A ground-living bird, it rarely flies but runs with speed and dexterity through the undergrowth and beneath and around shrubbery. There it picks up its food, not only insects—beetles, moths and larvae—but also seeds and berries, gleaned from both seashore and shrubbery. When paused, the birds flare their tails.

Established pairs occupy small territories which they advertise with year-round singing, perching low in small trees. Both sexes feed the chicks; only one may nest-build and incubate.

A Rufous Bristlebird with its two young. Its song resembles a squeaking cartwheel.

OTHER NAMES
None.

IDENTIFICATION
LENGTH: *230–270 mm.*
ADULTS: *Sexes similar. Head russet-brown; back, wings and long, bushy tail olive-brown, grading to russet-brown over rump. Lores and malar line white. Throat and breast scalloped deep grey and white; belly white, flanks olive-grey. Bill and feet dark brown.*

VOICE
CALL: *Loud, harsh* tweek *in alarm,* often rapidly repeated; also softer alarm zit.
SONG: *Clear, penetrating Pilotbird-like whistle, of three or four pairs of quick short upslurred or downslurred notes, ending in double whipcrack, the last three notes often echoed by female in duet.*

NESTING
Breeds September–December. Large domed nest, with platformed side entrance, of loosely woven rush and fine grasses and rootlets; in tussock or small dense shrub, close to ground. Eggs: two, often only one fertile; whitish, freckled heavily and uniformly red and purplish; oval, about 27 x 21 mm.

DISTRIBUTION
From about Anglesea, Vic., to Murray Mouth, SA, on coast but ranging into Otway Ranges. Also southwest (extinct). Two or three races.

Pilotbird *Pycnoptilus floccosus* GOULD, 1851

OTHER NAMES
Guinea-a-week.

IDENTIFICATION
LENGTH: *About 170 mm.*
ADULTS: *Sexes similar. All upper parts brown with rufous wash. Face to breast ochreish, scalloped brown; flanks brown; belly white; undertail rufous. Eye amber in male, bright red in female. Bill and feet dusky.*
IMMATURES: *As adults; eye grey-brown.*

VOICE
CALL: *Double note with louder second note given during nest building; other single and double notes in alarm and contact.*
SONG: *Loud, ringing, whistled* guinea-a-week, *ending in rising whipcrack.*

NESTING
Breeds August–January. Nest a bulky, untidy dome with side entrance, of bark strips, leaves and roots; lined with feathers after female commences laying; hidden in litter of forest floor, usually on side of bank or under shrub or fallen branch. Eggs: one or two; grey-green to smoky brown, with wash of colour round large end; oval, about 28 x 20 mm. Incubation 20–22 days, by female. Young fledge in 14–18 days.

DISTRIBUTION
Coastal wet forests to subalpine woodland between Blue Mountains, NSW, and Dandenong Ranges, Vic. No races.

The Pilotbird's long legs are indicative of its terrestrial way of life.

A GROUND FORAGER, the Pilotbird hops poking about the litter under ferny cover beneath gully wet sclerophyll and temperate rainforests. Each bird works along, tail part-cocked, turning over debris with its bill for worms, insects and other invertebrates, and occasional berries. A poor flier, it rarely ranges more than a metre up into shrubbery.

Pairs call in brief bursts with a resounding *guinea-a-week,* partly to keep contact and partly to advertise territory, and they exploit ground newly raked over by lyrebirds. This connection between call and a lyrebird's feeding ground has been used as a quick guide to the presence of lyrebirds—hence the name Pilotbird.

Established pairs hold territories year round and expel other birds, including their own young, by displaying agonistically. Only the female builds the nest, taking up to nine days, although finishing replacement nests in three to four. Eggs are laid late into the morning and probably 48 hours apart but incubation does not begin until the second egg. Only the female incubates but is often fed near the nest by the male who calls her off; she will also forage briefly for herself then.

When eggs hatch the male continues to bring food and carries away faecal sacs while the female broods; then as young grow she leaves to bring food herself. After fledging the young first hide under vegetation or debris, but soon begin to roam with the parents or else split up, each tended by one parent. Sometimes as a family, Pilotbirds bathe in shallow pools and also sun themselves—stretching out flat, spreading the wings and raising the feathers.

The Origma uses spiderweb to suspend its domed nest under a sandstone rock-ledge.

Origma

Origma solitaria (LEWIN, 1808)

THE ORIGMA is unique among Australian warblers in constructing its nest in a darkened rock cavern. The nest is delicately suspended from a projection and when the bird alights to feed the young it swings back and forth. There are even records of Origmas placing their nests under wire mattresses in bush shacks.

Sedentary and territorial, Origmas live in pairs, young remaining only for a short time after breeding to form small family parties. They may, however, leave dried-up creeks over summer. Constrained by habitat, they are confined to the central New South Wales coast and fringing ranges. There they occur on the craggy, dissected sandstone cliffs of the Hawkesbury formation and have often been thought limited to them. They do, nonetheless, range on to adjacent limestones. Permanently fresh-watered ravines are the common denominator. Origmas forage over the rock faces, hopping methodically along, moving their bodies from side to side and flicking their tails sideways. Swift dashes over rock faces are broken with creeping into crevices as they poke about. They are even able to work along vertical faces and the underside of overhanging clefts. Most food—a range of insects and seeds—is picked up in crevices and around water-margins, although some insects are caught in the air or prised from tree trunks.

OTHER NAMES
Rock Warbler, Cave-bird, Rock Robin, Sandstone Robin, Cataract-bird.

IDENTIFICATION
LENGTH: *120–140 mm.*
ADULTS: *Sexes similar. Upper parts plain dark brown with rufous wash on rump; tail black. Face and forehead flecked cinnamon-brown. Throat dull white, speckled black; rest of underparts deep rufous. Eye red-brown. Bill dusky. Feet dark brown.*
IMMATURES: *As adults but duller.*

VOICE
CALL: *Slightly liquid rasping notes; harsh scolding churrs in alarm.*
SONG: *Shrill, melancholy* good-bye *given three or four times; also penetrating staccato* pink.

NESTING
Breeds August–December. Nest a suspended dome with side entrance, of rootlets, bark strips, grasses and moss, bound with cobweb; lined with fine grasses, plant down, fur and feathers; hung by cobweb from a minute rock cleft in ceiling of rock cavern, under road-culvert or in tunnel. Eggs: usually three; glossy white, sometimes with faint black specks; oval, about 20 x 15 mm.

DISTRIBUTION
Central east coast and facing ranges north to Scone, and south to Bermagui, NSW; in Hawkesbury sandstone and adjacent limestone formations. No races.

The Australian Fernwren shuffles leaf litter in its search for food.

Australian Fernwren

Crateroscelis gutturalis (DE VIS, 1889)

THE LITTER OF THE FOREST FLOOR under upland rainforests in northeastern Queensland is the foraging habitat of the Australian Fernwren. Spending almost all their time on the ground, the birds work singly or in dispersed pairs, hopping quietly about, probing and turning the litter for food—insects, spiders and snails. For this they have a long bill with partly sealed nostrils.

Sometimes they burrow under thick litter in their searching, and at others they tag along behind Chowchillas or scrubfowl, taking advantage of newly raked ground. As they travel, they occasionally bow and flick the tail.

Established pairs hold territory at least when breeding, and perhaps throughout the year, judged by year-round singing from males at vantage perches in low shrubs. Dependent young accompany adults in their foraging mostly on a one-to-one basis.

OTHER NAMES
Collared Scrubwren, Fernwren.

IDENTIFICATION
LENGTH: *120–140 mm.*
ADULTS: *Sexes similar, or female slightly paler on crown. All upper parts, wings and tail dark olive-brown, duskier on crown; forehead speckled white. Eyebrow, part-eye-ring, and throat white; rest of face olive-grey. Large black crescent across upper breast; rest of underparts mid olive-brown, edged cream under tail. Eye brown, or golden in male. Bill black.*
Feet flesh-brown.
IMMATURES: *As adults; throat pattern dull, grey-white and brown; belly scalloped white.*

VOICE
CALL: *Soft, piping* chip, chirr-ip *in contact; harsh scrubwren-like churrs in alarm and single, surging whistle.*
SONG: *Series of long-drawn whistles, each surged to echoing crescendo.*

NESTING
Breeds September–December. Nest domed with slightly hooded side entrance, of dusky fern rootlets covered with leafy liverworts; lined with finer rootlets; hidden close to ground in ends of fallen logs or under them and in banks. Eggs: two; glossy white, sometimes faintly speckled red-brown at large end; oval, about 22 x 17 mm.

DISTRIBUTION
Tableland rainforests above 600 m, between Cooktown and Paluma Range, Qld. No races.

A Scrubtit, confined to Tasmania and King Island, at its bulky domed nest of dried grass, ferns and moss in a tree fern or a bush near the ground.

Scrubtit *Sericornis magnus* (GOULD, 1855)

SCRUBTITS ARE SEDENTARY BIRDS of the temperate rainforests, taller subalpine thickets, and underbrush of wet sclerophyll forest in Tasmania, and in teatree *Melaleuca* scrub on King Island. There established pairs maintain territories at least during breeding and probably remain in their vicinity all year; young, however, are dispersed during late summer or autumn.

Alone or in pairs, the birds forage in the shady forest or shrubbery midstage, at one to ten metres above the ground, using techniques that help them avoid direct competition with other shrub-gleaning insectivores. Instead of concentrating on foliage, the Scrubtit hop-searches up the smaller trunks of trees and over main branches, like a treecreeper. It works methodically over one tree, then flits to the next, poking and probing into crevices for insects and spiders. For this it has a slender, somewhat down-curved bill. Although the birds do sometimes glean over foliage, at least 70–90 per cent of their feeding time is spent on the larger branches and trunks.

In display, one bird—probably the male—faces its mate at a distance of 30 centimetres on a perch, fans its tail, spreads its wings, lifts them slowly, closes them and repeats the sequence. Then, with feathers fluffed, it bows, tilts and pivots its head, to the accompaniment of quick tinkling.

OTHER NAMES
Fern Weaver, Mountain Wren.

IDENTIFICATION
LENGTH: *110–115 mm.*
ADULTS: *Sexes similar. Upper parts mid-grey, washed russet; wings darker grey, with large white spot on primary coverts. Tail russet-grey, with off-white tip and black subterminal bar. Off-white brow-spot and eye-ring; face greyer. Underparts white, washed russet-grey down flanks. Eye red-brown. Bill dusky. Feet pink-brown.*
IMMATURES: *As adults; washed pale yellow below; eye brown.*

VOICE
CALL: *Scrubwren-like churrings while feeding.*
SONG: *Short, whistled* to-wee-to.

NESTING
Breeds September–January. Nest a large dome about 20 cm high with hooded side entrance about 4 cm in diameter; of loosely woven bark strips, dried grasses, moss and fern rootlets, intermingled with moss; lined with fern rootlets, feathers and fern down; usually hidden on or near ground among plants, in dead fern fronds, a bush or low tree. Eggs: three or four; white, sparsely speckled or finely blotched with red-brown; swollen oval, about 18 x 14 mm.

DISTRIBUTION
Forest undergrowth, beech forests, tall subalpine shrubberies in Tasmania and teatree scrub on King Island. No races.

Atherton Scrubwren

Sericornis keri MATHEWS, 1912

OTHER NAMES
None.

IDENTIFICATION
LENGTH: *120–135 mm.*
ADULTS: *Sexes similar. Upper parts from crown to wings and tail deep flat brown. Face deep flat brown, barely paler than crown. Underparts from chin to crissum cream-buff washed pale yellow, breast faintly streaked in males; undertail olive-tan. Eye deep red. Bill dusky. Feet pale flesh.*
IMMATURES: *As adults but duller; eye brown.*

VOICE
CALL: *Scrubwren-like churring in alarm.*
SONG: *Not described.*

NESTING
Breeds August–December. Nest domed, like that of Large-billed Scrubwren, 150 x 125 mm externally, of fibrous plant material; lined with feathers; placed near ground, well hidden by

vegetation, on bank. Eggs: two; pale purplish white, finely speckled dark brown, forming zone at large end; swollen oval, about 20 x 15 mm.

DISTRIBUTION
Mountain rainforests of northeastern Queensland, from Windsor Tableland to Paluma Range; not below 650 m. No races.

The Atherton Scrubwren is usually seen foraging near the ground.

IT IS NOW COMMON KNOWLEDGE that the high mountain rainforests of northeastern Queensland are inhabited by a second species of plain brown scrubwren that was for long confused with the widespread Large-billed Scrubwren. It was even first described as a race of the Large-billed, although in 1927, G.M. Mathews changed his mind. An expedition of the British Museum proved the point by rediscovering and collecting the species in 1964. Today, Atherton Scrubwrens are known from most mountain top rainforests in northeastern Queensland above 800 metres in altitude, from the Windsor Tableland to the Paluma Range.

Atherton Scrubwrens are a little bigger than the Large-billed and distinctively longer and heavier in 'leg', a trait reflecting their more terrestrial niche. They are also browner, less olive on the back, darker on the face and washed faintly but clearly yellow from throat to belly; some males have faint breast streaks. But the differences are slight and the species easily confused.

They are perhaps easier—or more difficult—to identify by their behaviour and ecology. Whereas Large-billed Scrubwrens forage in pairs or small groups mainly in the forest midstage down to a metre above the ground, Atherton Scrubwrens are more solitary and feed more on their own within a metre or two of the ground. There they hop-search slowly, quietly and methodically over logs, up into the branchlets of low shrubbery, and down on to the litter of the forest floor. Prey—mainly insects and small snails—is gleaned as they go, the birds moving on foot and limiting flight to short flits from log to shrub or shrub to ground.

Sedentary birds, Atherton Scrubwrens also nest close to the ground and, judged by their solitary nature, established pairs may hold permanent territory.

Tropical Scrubwren *Sericornis beccarii* SALVADORI, 1874

THE TROPICAL SCRUBWREN replaces the Large-billed Scrubwren in the rainforests and vine scrubs of Cape York Peninsula and western New Guinea. It feeds and moves in the same lower-middle forest strata as the Large-billed—although descending to the floor in the north; calls and sings in a near identical voice; is communal; nests in the same situations and lays similarly marked eggs.

Where the two 'species' meet around Cooktown and Helenvale they seem to intergrade.

In its plumage markings, the Tropical Scrubwren resembles the White-browed more closely. But the evidence of intergradation with the Large-billed remains, an affinity perhaps more subtly indicated by the red eye and plain tail of the Tropical.

Leaf skeletons are used in this Tropical Scrubwren's nest.

OTHER NAMES
Little Scrubwren, Beccari's Scrubwren.

IDENTIFICATION
LENGTH: *110–115 mm.*
ADULTS: *Northern Cape York Peninsula race: Upper parts olive-brown. Broken white ring around eye and white stripe above lores, edged dusky; lores black (male) or brown (female). Two white bars on dusky wing coverts. Tail plain brown. Underparts plain cream-white. Eye red. Bill grey-flesh; mandible pale flesh. Feet pale flesh.*
Southeastern Cape York Peninsula race: Upper parts and face mid russet-brown. Obscure cream eye-ring and stripe above lores; lores russet in both sexes. Two faint cream bars on dull brown wing coverts. Underparts plain rufous-cream. Bill dusky; lower mandible grey-flesh.
IMMATURES: *As adults of respective races but duller.*

VOICE
As Large-billed Scrubwren.

NESTING
Breeds October–December. Nest as Large-billed Scrubwren, built into

vegetation close to ground or among plants sheltered in trunk buttresses. Eggs: two–four; lustrous pale purple-brown, minutely speckled dark brown in zone at large end; oblong-oval, about 19 x 15 mm.

DISTRIBUTION
Coastal and hill rainforests and vine scrubs of Cape York Peninsula, west to Weipa, southeast to Cooktown, Qld. Also New Guinea and Aru Islands. Two races: one south to Iron Range; the other north to McIllwraith Range, intergrading between.

Large-billed Scrubwren *Sericornis magnirostris* (GOULD, 1838)

LIKE OTHER PLAIN BROWN scrubwrens, the Large-billed lives in rainforest. It is the most widespread of them in Australia, ranging down the entire east coast as far as the Dandenong–Donna Buang Ranges, Vic. In northeastern Queensland it is ubiquitous from the tableland rainforests to the tropical lowlands. Southwards it becomes confined increasingly to pockets of subtropical rainforest, often along gullies, before petering out in Victoria.

Although sedentary and probably territorial when breeding, the scrubwrens commonly band together in small loose feeding parties of five to ten birds. They move through the lower and middle storeys of the forest, chattering constantly in contact, feeding most frequently in the canopies of each layer, only rarely descending into the lower shrub layer and almost never to the ground; throughout their range they feed at heights between about three and 17 metres. Birds often begin low down and work upwards through the foliage, hanging vines or along branches, sometimes suspended upside down while they glean insects off the substrate. The crowns of the plants are often approached from the inside outwards, rather than the reverse. The scrubwrens rarely flutter at the foliage as does the Brown Gerygone with which they share their feeding zone.

As they flit rapidly about, they gather their food—insects and small snails—from leaves, twigs, bark, dangling vines, liana tangles or lawyer-cane. Occasionally they stop to search more closely for prey. In the tropics they are conspicuous in the foraging flocks of mixed species which include Spectacled Monarchs and Little Shrike-thrushes. Each species in such a flock probably catches more insects than it would catch alone because the fluttering of more birds disturbs more insects.

In the lowlands of northern Queensland, where no other scrubwrens occur, Large-billeds construct their own small nests. In southern Queensland and New South Wales, however, where their nests have rarely been found, they occupy those of Yellow-throated Scrubwrens or even Brown Gerygones. Such nests are often old and disused, but Large-billed Scrubwrens will usurp freshly built nests, depositing new lining over abandoned or infertile eggs of the earlier users. Group members sometimes help to feed young.

OTHER NAMES
None.

IDENTIFICATION
LENGTH: *110–125 mm.*
ADULTS: *Sexes similar. Upper parts brown-olive becoming darker and browner on head and warmer brown on rump; tail plain brown with brighter edges. Forehead vaguely scalloped with buff; wing quills edged pale green-buff, the primary coverts dusky edged pale buff. Face pale brown with faint rufous-buff wash of varying intensity around face and throat. Underparts greenish buff with a vaguely yellow wash, more olive on flanks. Eye red. Bill black, slightly upturned. Feet shades of pink-horn.*
IMMATURES: *As adults; generally paler with heavier rufous or warm brown wash on face and underparts. Eye brown; bill smaller.*

VOICE
CALL: *Harsh chattering* s-chew *repeated rapidly, in contact and alarm, softer than churrs made by other east coast scrubwrens.*
SONG: *A soft tinkling twitter* sip-sip-sip.

NESTING
Breeds July–January, sometimes June–February. Nest an oval dome, with side entrance 25 mm diameter; of plant stems, fibre, rootlets, leaf skeletons and moss; lined with fibre and feathers; placed in forks, vines and tree crevices, from close to ground to 10 m high; sometimes old nest of Yellow-throated Scrubwren is used. Eggs: three or four; lustrous, off-white to pale purple-brown, minutely speckled dark brown

forming zone at larger end; oblong-oval, about 19 x 14 mm.

DISTRIBUTION
East coast and nearby ranges of mainland, from Cooktown–Helenvale, Qld, to Dandenong–Donna Buang Ranges, Vic. In rainforest and dense gullies in wetter eucalypt forests. Two races: one Cooktown–Ingham, Qld; the other Clark Range, Qld, and south. Around Cooktown apparently intergrades with Tropical Scrubwren, the forms of which may be treated as races of the Large-billed.

The Large-billed Scrubwren, a bird with a faintly buff face, builds a coarse nest of plants stems, shredded bark and rootlets.

Yellow-throated Scrubwren

Sericornis citreogularis
GOULD, 1838

OTHER NAMES
Devil-bird, Blacknest-bird.

IDENTIFICATION
LENGTH: *120–140 mm.*
MALE: *Upper parts dark olive-brown; darker and browner on crown. Rump warm brown; upper tail dark brown. Wing quills dark grey, primaries edged with green-yellow, coverts dusky with pale green giving a scalloped effect. Forehead, lores, face and ear coverts glossy black; eyebrow white merging into yellow towards back. Chin white; throat and upper breast bright yellow; belly white; side of breast and flanks brown. Eye red-brown. Bill black. Feet flesh-cream.*
FEMALE: *As male; face and forehead all olive-grey-brown.*
IMMATURES: *Upper parts mottled with brown; throat and eyebrow yellow; chest and belly fawn.*

VOICE
CALL: *Single, sharp* tik *in contact; harsh loud chatter in alarm. Feeding call of two single notes followed by a doublet. Adults emit harsh low twitter when approaching nest.*
SONG: *Melodious whistles. Accomplished mimic in southeastern Australia. In courtship, whistles interspersed with mimicked calls.*

NESTING
Breeds August–March. Nest a domed structure with a hooded entrance, of black rootlets, palm fibre, leaf skeletons, twigs, ferns and mosses; lined with feathers; placed either in a vine tangle or suspended from tree branches up to 10 m above ground, often overhanging creeks in which case less moss is used. Eggs: three, rarely two or four; smooth and glossy, pale chocolate pink to chocolate brown with a darker zone or a series thereof at larger end; rounded-oval or long-oval, 26 x 18 mm. Incubation 21 days, by both sexes. Young fledge in about 21 days.

DISTRIBUTION
Subtropical rainforests of east coast except central east coast, Queensland. Mainly mountains and tablelands but down to sea-level in south. Two widely isolated races: one smaller, from Cooktown highlands to Paluma Range, Qld; the other larger, with mimicking song, from about Gympie, Qld, south to Mt Dromedary, NSW.

Of all the scrubwrens, the Yellow-throated Scrubwren is the brightest in colouring, though its colours camouflage it against the rainforest floor, where it lives. It rarely forages higher than the first metre or so of shrub layer.

THE SONGS OF more than 30 other species of birds, from the Variegated Wren to lyrebirds, are mimicked by the Yellow-throated Scrubwren in New South Wales and southern Queensland. This beautiful songster, which will sing for up to half an hour at a time, will even interpolate mimicry into its courtship song. Both sexes sing but the female has a softer voice and is a less accomplished singer than the male.

In northern Queensland there is a separate population of Yellow-throated Scrubwrens, and these have a different voice. Their usual call is loud chattering; otherwise they are rarely heard to give more than a few whistles.

The northern scrubwrens live in mountain and tableland rainforests, rarely occurring below 600 metres above sea level, nor much above 1000 metres. Southern birds also live in mountain rainforests but extend down to the coast.

Despite their bright plumage—these are the brightest of the scrubwrens—its black, yellow and brown patterns camouflage the birds well on the forest floor where they live. Their propensity for this gloomy place is supposed to have inspired their southern Queensland name of Devil-bird. Sedentary and working alone or in pairs, they hop-search methodically over the litter, moving more quickly than the fernwren—with which they share the forest floor in northern Queensland—and picking food more from the surface. Insects and seeds and possibly small snails are taken. Occasionally they work up into undershrubbery as well, though spending only 15–25 per cent of their feeding time there. As

they hop about, they often chatter noisily.

As well as in their call, the northern and southern populations differ also in choice of nest site. The northern birds favour lawyer cane and other vine tangles, whereas in the south most nests are suspended from a tree. These preferences may arise from differences in the vegetation rather than in the birds.

The nest design varies. Some nests are up to one metre in length, and some have more than one nesting chamber in them. Small living rock plants up to 30 centimetres long may be attached to the mossy outside of a nest; sometimes there are four and five plant species on the one nest.

Both male and female nest-build, which usually takes 14 days. In one season they may rear several broods, each in a different chamber of the nest. After the successful rearing of one brood another chamber is lined and used. If the nest has only one chamber, the birds build on another—or else construct a new nest close by.

Both birds take it in turns to incubate their three brown eggs, for 21 days. They sit so tightly on the nest, even when approached closely, that they might easily be captured there. Once the eggs have hatched, Yellow-throated Scrubwrens become wary and advertise their presence as little as possible. Both birds feed the young, chiefly on beetles and moths. The young leave the nest after about 21 days.

The Fan-tailed Cuckoo often lays its eggs in the nests of the Yellow-throated Scrubwren. Old Yellow-throated Scrubwren's nests may also be used by Large-billed Scrubwrens.

White-browed Scrubwren *Sericornis frontalis* (VIGORS & HORSFIELD, 1827)

THE WHITE-BROWED SCRUBWREN is one of the most widespread, abundant and familiar of Australia's small ground-feeding birds, occurring from northern Queensland, south around the coast to Tasmania and Shark Bay, WA. Throughout that vast range it lives in one type of habitat—close and usually moist shrubberies, along creeks or the sides of ridges or the fringes of mangroves and coastal heath and mallee scrubs. It even persists in pockets of blackberries after surrounding vegetation has been cleared.

In their habitat the scrubwrens are sedentary. Established pairs hold to a permanent territory of one–five hectares year round but often include several additional adults and immatures in their group, probably some of their young of previous nestings. The group forages as a loose party, hop-searching briskly over the shrubbery floor and occasionally up among low branches, gleaning a range of insects—beetles, weevils, bugs and moths—as well as spiders and seeds. Most feeding is done under cover, the birds moving from patch to patch of shrubbery with short dipping flights within a metre of the ground. Members of a band keep up a constant soft chattering as they travel, to maintain contact. This changes to harsh staccato churring if they are disturbed, one or two

birds then climbing up into shrubbery to check the cause.

Most groups often include only one adult female, the mate of the dominant male. She may build and incubate unaided, but the male and other members of the group assist in feeding the young. If they survive their first year as inexperienced juveniles, White-browed Scrubwrens may live as long as 15 years.

Geographical variation in plumage marks and tones matches the wide distribution of this species. There are at least nine races which fall into four main groups. One occurring down the east coast of Queensland to the New South Wales border has a plain buff-white throat and breast, a clear black-and-white face pattern with dusky running over the ears, and a white-tipped tail. Another ranging around the mainland coast from the Queensland border to Mt Lofty Ranges, SA, is similar but has a black streaked throat, facial black restricted to the lores (males), and a brown-tipped tail. In Tasmania is a third group, larger and darker, with obscure face pattern and dark-tipped tail. Lastly, there is the 'Spotted' Scrubwren around the western coast from Shark Bay east to the South Australian gulfs; it has the face pattern of eastern races, a heavily black-spotted throat and breast and white-tipped tail.

OTHER NAMES
Buff-breasted Scrubwren, Brown Scrubwren, Spotted Scrubwren.

IDENTIFICATION
LENGTH: *110–140 mm.*
MALE: *Plumage variable according to geographical range. Upper parts dark olive-brown to mid cinnamon-brown, crown darker; rump lighter. Wing coverts dusky to black with two dull to white bars of varying extent. Tail has indistinct or clear subterminal black band near tip and at times a white tip. Face patterned with distinct white brow, a white spot under eye and white malar line, dull in one race; lores black or dusky, extending over ears in one race. Throat and breast white to pale*

yellowish cream or buff-grey, plain, lightly streaked or heavily spotted black; rest of underparts dull white or buff; flanks cinnamon to olive-grey. Eye cream. Bill dusky with paler under base. Feet pink-brown.
FEMALE: *Duller, with brown lores.*
IMMATURES: *Head smoky brown, upper and underparts washed chocolate-brown; face markings much duller.*

VOICE
CALL: *Soft churrs and chips in contact; harsh repeated staccato churring tzz-tzzz-t-tzzz in alarm.*
SONG: *Soft, rapidly repeated series of whistled notes on same pitch, t'seer-t'seer-t'seer; often many other notes are given in softer undertones.*

NESTING
Breeds July–January. Nest a coarse dome, with rounded side-entrance, of bark strips, rootlets and grasses; usually lined with feathers; hidden on or near ground amid tangled undergrowth, in a clump of grass, under bank, wedged between tree-trunks or behind hanging or fallen bark. Eggs: two or three; colour varies from grey-white to pale buff, finely speckled with darker spotting, and a well-defined zone at larger end; oval to oblong-oval, about 19 x 14 mm. Incubation probably by female.

DISTRIBUTION
From Atherton Tableland, Qld, south around coast and adjacent mountains to Shark Bay and offshore islands, WA;

also Tasmania and islands of Bass Strait. About nine races.

A black-lored male White-browed Scrubwren at its dome-shaped nest hidden in the base of a staghorn fern. Nests of White-browed Scrubwrens are usually hidden amid tangled undergrowth, tussocks, a fork of a shrub or behind loose hanging bark. This is the race found in mainland southeastern Australia.

Chestnut-rumped Hylacola *Sericornis pyrrhopygius* (Vigors & Horsfield, 1827)

The Chestnut-rumped Hylacola is an accomplished mimic. This is a male.

ALERT, EVASIVE, COCK-TAILED birds of the undergrowth, Chestnut-rumped Hylacolas occur in dense heath shrubberies around southeastern Australia. Where they abut on the range of the Striated Calamanthus, as on the sandstone tablelands along the south coast of New South Wales, the sedentary hylacolas keep to the drier upland and stony heaths.

Pairs or small loose groups forage on the ground, bounding briskly among and beneath shrubberies, tails well-cocked at 50–70 degrees, picking up a range of insects and seeds. If alarmed, they disperse like bouncing rubber balls. Flight is dashing but brief, of swift low undulations to cover.

Hylacolas are gifted singers. Quiet during summer and autumn, they begin to sing regularly at the beginning of winter. It is then that chasing and pairing occurs among groups and territory is

OTHER NAMES
Heath Wren, Chestnut-rumped Heath Wren, Chestnut-rumped Ground Wren.

IDENTIFICATION
LENGTH: *135–140 mm; male noticeably larger.*
MALE: *Upper parts mid-brown; rump dull rufous, washing on to back. Wings grey-brown, with faint speculum and grey-white tips to primary coverts. Tail dark brown with black subterminal band and pale grey tip. Eyebrow dull white. Underparts dull white, heavily streaked dusky; undertail mid-rufous. Eye yellowish-brown. Bill black-brown. Feet pale brown.*
FEMALE: *As male; brow and undersurface buff, finely streaked dusky.*
IMMATURES: *Upper parts russet brown, intensifying down back; underparts plain grey-white, washed rust over breast and flanks.*

VOICE
CALL: *Single staccato chip or zeet when disturbed or in contact.*
SONG: *Varied sequence of trills, warbles, whistles and silvery cadences, swelling in volume, with calls of other birds interwoven.*

NESTING
Breeds June–November. Nest domed with small spout-like entrance near top, of bark strips, rootlets and dried grass stems; lined with feathers and fur; hidden on or near ground under grass tussock, tangled undergrowth or shrub. Eggs: two or three, sometimes four; pale pink, freckled and blotched with dark brown, particularly at larger end; oval, about 19 x 14 mm. Incubation by female.

DISTRIBUTION
Southeastern mainland, from granite belt, Queensland to southeastern South Australia, Kangaroo Island, and Mt Lofty–Flinders Ranges, SA. No apparent races.

established or reaffirmed. Males perch up in low bushes—rarely on top—with tail cocked, beaming out song for half an hour at a time to advertise territory at all times of the day. In and out of the strain they weave their own song and those of other birds in mimicry; females may join in a duet.

Nests—of bark strips, rootlets and dried grass stems—are usually hidden near the centre of the territory. The female alone appears to incubate but both parents tend the young and respond with distraction displays to intruders, running about rapidly in crouched posture. Second broods are sometimes attempted.

A male Shy Hylacola foraging for insects among thick ground cover.

Shy Hylacola

Sericornis cautus (Gould, 1843)

SHY HYLACOLAS REPLACE the Chestnut-rumped in the heathy mallee of southern Australia. Their ranges come to within five kilometres of one another north of Bendigo but there is no hint of intergradation; the species are separated by habitat, the Shy keeping to whipstick mallee thicket. Only in the southwest does it spread into coastal dune scrub and sandplain heath. Clearing of mallee has reduced the bird to a fraction of its former range.

A sedentary ground forager like the Chestnut-rumped, the Shy Hylacola feeds singly or in pairs, bounding cock-tailed along the ground around, among and beneath shrubbery, picking up small insects and, occasionally, seeds. The small feeding parties that sometimes remain together after breeding are probably an adult pair with their young of the year.

Young are dispersed before the next season, and the birds nest as pairs. While the female incubates, the male maintains territory, singing from perches in bushes, and often beginning before dawn. His song is as varied and full of mimicry as that of the Chestnut-rumped. Both sexes feed and tend nestlings and fledglings.

Belying its name, the Shy Hylacola is no more or less 'shy' than the Chestnut-rumped. Both are timid and elusive.

OTHER NAMES
Shy Heath Wren, Mallee Heath Wren.

IDENTIFICATION
LENGTH: *135–140 mm; male larger.*
MALE: *Upper parts deep brown, darker on lower back; rump rich chestnut. Wings with large white speculum. Tail with black subterminal band and white tip. Eyebrow bright white. Underparts bright white, streaked boldly black; undertail chestnut. Eye yellowish brown. Bill dark brown. Feet mid-brown.*
FEMALE: *As male; brow and*

undersurface cream, coarsely streaked dusky; speculum small.
IMMATURES: *As adults; dully streaked and washed russet below.*

VOICE
CALL: *Loud, sharp calls tchak when feeding or disturbed.*
SONG: *Varied sequence of trills and cadences, chee-chee-chick-a-dee, with calls of other birds interwoven.*

NESTING
Breeds August–November. Nest a dome with spout-like side entrance, of fine

twigs, grasses and bark strips; lined with fine grasses and down; hidden on or near ground in prickly shrub or amid plants at base of shrub or tree. Eggs: two or three; pale olive-grey, minutely freckled with brown, often forming zone at larger end; oval to tapered-oval, about 20 x 14 mm. Incubation by female.

DISTRIBUTION
Heathy mallee from Murchison River, WA, eastwards to Wyalong and Round Hill Nature Reserve, NSW. Probably no races.

Redthroat *Sericornis brunneus* (GOULD, 1841)

A male Redthroat at the entrance to its well-hidden nest. The female lacks the chestnut throat patch.

THIS SOBERLY COLOURED bird of the arid and semi-arid regions of Australia is not only an accomplished singer but it also mimics, incorporating the songs of a variety of birds into its own. With the approach of the breeding season both members of a pair call, often from the top of a bush, even on moonlit or rainy nights. Only the female incubates, while the male rarely approaches the nest. Once the eggs hatch, both birds bring food to the young. Occasionally the Redthroat fosters a Black-eared Cuckoo.

Redthroats occur in taller pockets of shrubbery in saltbush-bluebush steppe, in scrubby undergrowth in mulga *Acacia,* belar *Casuarina* and sometimes mallee *Eucalyptus* woodland, often on low hills. Where they impinge on the range of the Rufous Calamanthus, they occupy the better wooded uplands.

Although occasionally gathering in small parties and flocks of up to 30, Redthroats are usually solitary, living in sedentary pairs in the same territory year round. There they forage individually, hopping briskly, tails down, along the ground beneath and around shrubbery; also up into the branches of bushes. Insects, including beetles and ants, and seeds are gleaned as they go. Flight is low and dashing among shrubbery, the tail fanning during undulations.

Rufous Calamanthus *Sericornis campestris* (GOULD, 1841)

DRY, LOW, near-treeless shrub-fields, from sandplain heath to samphire around salt lakes and saltbush–bluebush steppe inland are the habitat of the Rufous Calamanthus. Despite its wide range, it is patchy and local.

Sedentary birds, Rufous Calamanthus live in pairs or small family parties after breeding, and forage apart from one another in rapid, cock-tailed hop-searches over the ground around shrubbery. They feed on insects and seeds. If disturbed, they run at speed and will seek refuge in a burrow. Flight, taken only if the birds are pushed, is a low fluttering dash. During breeding, less at other times, males hop to the top branch of a bush, tail cocked, to sing sporadically through the day, advertising territory.

A Rufous Calamanthus at its perch.

Speckled Warbler *Sericornis sagittatus* (LATHAM, 1801)

SOMBRE STREAKED PLUMAGE and a habit of freezing when disturbed give the Speckled Warbler camouflage in its woodland habitat in southeastern Australia. Outside the breeding season individuals, pairs, or small parties of these sprightly birds hop, foraging among the litter around and under bushes and trees, without any tail-cocking. If disturbed they often fly to the lower branches of a nearby tree or bush, where they bound from branch to branch uttering a scolding churring chatter, returning to the ground once the cause has passed.

Sometimes loose mixed feeding-flocks form as Speckled Warblers mingle with Yellow-rumped Thornbills or Buff-rumped Thornbills. Speckled Warblers eat insects, their larvae, other invertebrates of the leaf-litter layer, and also seeds.

By the beginning of the breeding season the young of the previous year have dispersed and most territories contain only a pair of birds. Occasionally, however, there are two females that are attended by one male. One female usually nests before the other and at this time the male assists in feeding the young nestlings and fledglings of the first female. Later he helps to tend the young of the second female.

Speckled Warblers may act as hosts to the Black-eared Cuckoo whose egg resembles that of its host. As many as four Speckled Warblers have been seen carrying food to one cuckoo nestling.

The Speckled Warbler, unlike its relatives, does not cock its tail. This is a black-browed male.

OTHER NAMES
Blood-tit, Speckled Jack, Chocolatebird.

IDENTIFICATION
LENGTH: *About 120 mm.*
MALE: *Upper parts grey broadly striped black-brown; rump fawn. Tail brown-black, broadly tipped white on both feather vanes. Crown and forehead grey-brown, finely streaked white and bordered with black stripe on either side of head; eyebrow, lores and feathers around eye white. Face and underparts cream; throat, breast and flanks boldly marked with black arrow-like streaks; undertail tawny-brown. Eye grey-brown. Bill grey-brown. Feet blue-grey.*
FEMALE: *As male; hidden russet line above and behind eye.*
IMMATURES: *As adults; head duller and less streaked; eyebrow dull rufous; black markings of underparts smaller, more tear-shaped.*

VOICE
CALL: *Harsh* churring *chatter, in alarm.*
SONG: *Soft but rich trilled and chirruping warble; often mimics.*

NESTING
Breeds August–January. Nest domed of dried grasses and bark strips; lined with fur and feathers; hidden in a slight hollow in the ground under thin cover; side entrance enables bird to walk directly inside. Eggs: three or four; chocolate-red with darker zone at larger end; oval, about 19 x 15 mm.

DISTRIBUTION
Eucalypt woodlands, gullies and rocky ridges with open, shrubby understorey throughout southeastern mainland, from Suttor Creek, Qld, to around Grampians, Vic. No races.

The Striated Calamanthus hides its nest under tussock or dense bush.

THE STRIATED CALAMANTHUS replaces the Rufous Calamanthus in the swampy heaths and tussock fields around southeastern coastal Australia. Larger and tawnier, with wedge-shaped bill, it is nonetheless a bird of the ground and undershrubbery.

It is sedentary, and established pairs—together with their young after breeding—may keep to the same territorial area of several hectares year round. They feed somewhat apart, working through the undergrowth and over the ground like rodents, cock-tailed and hopping, picking up insects and seeds as they go. If flushed they flutter in a low, direct dash to cover; more often they hop to the top of a bush to investigate any disturbance. Males sing in territorial advertisement from such vantage perches, tail cocked and flicking this way and that. Song is intermittent throughout the day during breeding, but afterwards the birds fall silent.

Because the birds reputedly emit an odour that distracts quail dogs, they have been called Stinkbirds.

Striated Calamanthus
Sericornis fuliginosus (VIGORS & HORSFIELD, 1827)

OTHER NAMES
Striated Fieldwren, White-lored Fieldwren, Fieldlark, Mock Quail, Stinkbird.

IDENTIFICATION
LENGTH: *130–140 mm.*
MALE: *Upper parts tawny-olive, washed rufous on forehead, heavily streaked black; tail with black subterminal band and dull grey tip. Brow, lores and throat white, streaked black. Rest of underparts pale tawny, streaked black. Eye red-brown. Wedge-shaped bill dusky horn, with paler under base. Feet dark flesh-grey.*
FEMALE: *As male; brow buff, lores and throat tawny as breast.*
IMMATURES: *As female; more dully marked.*

VOICE
CALL: *Soft chatter, in contact; generally silent.*
SONG: *Trilled and chirruped warble, chip-chip, followed after pause with chik-chik-whirr-reee, the last syllable rising, repeated intermittently in burst of up to 20 seconds or more.*

NESTING
Breeds August–December. Nest a compact dome with small side entrance, of coarse grass and fibre; lined with finer grasses, feathers and down; hidden on ground under tussock or dense bush. Eggs: three–four; light chocolate to purplish brown, faintly speckled and shaded dark at large end; oval, about 23 x 16 mm.

DISTRIBUTION
Coastal swamp heaths and tussock fields of southeastern mainland, from Sassafras Range, NSW, to southeastern South Australia, and Tasmania. Three races.

Weebill *Smicrornis brevirostris* (GOULD, 1838)

OTHER NAMES
Brown Weebill, Yellow Weebill, Yellow Tree-tit, Short-billed Scrub-tit, Short-billed Tree-tit, Southern Weebill.

IDENTIFICATION
LENGTH: *80–90 mm.*
ADULTS: *Sexes similar. Head greyish and upper parts dull olive-brown to bright olive-yellow, particularly on lower back and rump. Off-white stripe extends from forehead over eye and, in some forms, rufous-brown spot in front of eye. Tail ash-brown with broad black bar and distinct white spot at tip of inner webs of all except central one or two pairs of tail feathers. Wings brown; flight feathers edged ash-olive to olive-yellow. Chin and throat dull- to yellow-white, sparsely striped with black in some forms, merging into plain yellow-buff to rich light yellow on breast and belly; colour deepest on belly and flanks. Eye straw to pale cream-yellow. Bill pale grey to flesh-brown, lower mandible paler than upper. Feet and claws pale grey to flesh-brown.*
IMMATURES: *As adults; eye greyer.*

VOICE
CALL: *Harsh, sharp, buzzing* chiz *in contact, mostly in flight; repeated often.*
SONG: *Lively, surprisingly strong song of usually four whistled slurs, last two higher and drawn-out, repeated rapidly several times with little variation:* weebill, weebill, weebee *or* willy-weet, willy-weetee; *by both sexes throughout the year.*

NESTING
Breeds August–February in south; October to April–May in north; in central Australia depends on rains but probably coincides with southern population. Nest neat, round to pear-shaped dome, with narrow spout-like entrance near top; of wiry grass and plant stems closely and tightly bound with cobweb and spiders' egg sacs; lined with feathers and plant down; attached to slender, leafy branchlets 1–10 m or more above ground. Eggs: two, sometimes three; matt cream-buff, finely speckled with buff-brown to purple-brown, particularly at larger end; oval, about 15 x 11 mm. Incubation about 12 days, by female. Young fledge in about 10 days.

DISTRIBUTION
Widespread in eucalypt woodlands and open forests throughout mainland Australia. No races.

THE SHORTEST BIRD in Australia, the Weebill abounds in eucalypt woodlands and open forests, feeding in the outer foliage at one to 20 metres above the ground. Denser forests and woodlands of trees other than eucalypts are generally shunned. Sociable and vocal, the birds glean among leaves in pairs or in loose parties of up to about 10, searching for small insects and their larvae. Usually they flit about, hopping among and clinging to the foliage, often well above the ground in the canopy, but they will hover as well over leafy branchlets, wings beating rapidly, to snap up small flying insects.

As it feeds, the Weebill moves systematically from tree to tree—usually eucalpyts—often in company with other small birds such as thornbills and pardalotes. Feeding parties keep in communication with strong, sharp buzzing notes, and individual birds will sing sporadically as well, at all times of the day. Sedentary birds with established foraging ranges, groups of Weebills remain permanently in one locality.

During breeding, males usually attend females and sing about the nest site but do not assist much in building the nest. The song is usually repeated several times with little variation and is often the only song to be heard at midday in the hot eucalypt woodlands. The birds display to each other at the nest site with much tail-fanning and with slight bowing and wing-quivering. Incubation—by the female—lasts about 12 days. The young fledge about 10 days after hatching, often fed by several birds of the local group in addition to their parents. Two or more broods are raised each year.

Weebills range widely across Australia—nowhere else—and their plumage colours change with the region. Those around southern Australia are dark, with mid olive-green backs, grey heads and creamy underparts spotted dusky on the throat. In central Australia they maintain the contrast between upper and underparts but become much paler. And across the north they are suffused with yellow, without throat marks. Populations grade into one another so imperceptibly that no races can be distinguished.

Weebills resemble thornbills in their flocking and contact calls and are like the gerygones in their songs, feeding and tail-markings; their eggs are marked like those of the scrubwrens.

The Weebill, the shortest bird in Australia, is only 80–90 mm long. The colouring differs throughout the country.

Green-backed Gerygone *Gerygone chloronota* GOULD, 1842

ALTHOUGH THE GREEN-BACKED GERYGONE—pronounced *jer-rig'-ony*—is confined to the limited pockets of monsoon rainforest in northwestern Australia, it is abundant there. And in the Kimberleys it extends inland along streams lined with paperbark *Melaleuca* into eucalypts. It is rather solitary, but is sometimes seen in pairs or with other birds in loose feeding flocks. It feeds vigorously, gleaning insects in the outer foliage of the canopy and leafy middle stages, rarely going close to the ground.

In most parts of its range the Green-backed Gerygone is sedentary, though it may wander locally when not breeding. At that time it often enters the mangroves along the coast of Arnhem Land.

It seems likely that, as with other gerygones, the female constructs the nest and incubates the eggs with some assistance from the male. There is usually only one brood a year.

The Green-backed Gerygone builds its nests in the same way as the Brown but, like the White-throated and the Fairy, it spends more time shaping the nest cavity. Like the Fairy Gerygone, the Green-backed often builds its nest near a wasp nest.

The side-entrance hood of this Green-backed Gerygone's domed nest forms a funnel.

OTHER NAMES
Green-backed Warbler, Green-backed Flyeater.

IDENTIFICATION
LENGTH: *90–100 mm.*
ADULTS: *Sexes alike. Head and face mid grey-brown; back and rump dull yellow-green. Wings like back, but flight feathers darker grey-brown, edged dull yellow-green. Tail plain grey-brown. Underparts white, often faintly grey on throat and washed pale lemon on flanks. Eye rich red. Bill black. Feet slate to dark grey.*
IMMATURES: *Like adults but duller. Eye brown; bill dark horn.*

VOICE
CALL & SONG: *Rapid high-pitched twittering reel of whistled notes around same pitch, repeated over and over. Males and possibly females sing at all times of day throughout year, but more when breeding.*

NESTING
Breeds mainly October–April; probably also sporadically throughout year. Nest a rounded, compact oval dome, with short tail and side-entrance hood usually extended into funnel; of bark strips and grasses bound with cobweb sparsely adorned with bark and spiders' egg sacs; lined with vegetable down and sometimes feathers; suspended from a stem among leafy end branchlets of small trees 1–15 m above ground. Eggs: two, usually three; matt white, speckled all over with red-brown, often in zone at larger end; oval, about 18 x 13 mm. Incubation about 12 days, mostly by female. Young fledge in about 10 days.

DISTRIBUTION
Pockets of monsoon rainforest and fringing mangroves around Arnhem Land and offshore islands, NT, and inland along paperbark-lined streams to eucalypt gorges in Kimberleys, WA. Widespread in New Guinea. Four races; two in Australia.

A Brown Gerygone brings an insect to its young; both parents feed the young, which fledge in 15–16 days. These birds sometimes raise two broods a year.

Brown Gerygone *Gerygone mouki* MATHEWS, 1912

LIKE OTHER AUSTRALIAN WARBLERS, the Brown Gerygone builds its nest in three stages. First, it makes a hanging, solidly interwoven mass of fibre bound with cobweb, gradually building it up to become longer and thicker. Then it makes a hole in the side— usually towards the top—which it hollows out and enlarges by shuffling and turning in the cavity; in the process it pushes out the walls of the nest. Lastly, it roofs the entrance hole all around. The ultimate shape of the nest depends very much on the time spent on each of these stages. It is usually about 250–300 mm long, including the 70–120 mm 'tail'.

The unobtrusive yet incessant twitterings of the Brown Gerygone are among the characteristic sounds of the rainforests of eastern Australia. The bird is abundant in these forests, where it lives year round. Singly, in pairs, or in loose threes or fours out of breeding, it feeds quietly but energetically through the inner and outer foliage of the trees, at two–20 metres above the ground. The birds frequently join foraging groups of other species to wander through the thick growth fringing the rainforests.

Like all Australian gerygones, the Brown gleans its insect food from leaves and branches, but occasionally darts out like a flycatcher to capture insects on the wing, or takes them in flight while hovering with rapid wing-beats about the outer foliage. While feeding it has a tendency to shake its wings and flick its tail. Both sexes call while breeding, but the males twitter more loudly and insistently, often perching close to where the female is constructing the nest. This call seems to maintain contact and announce territory, though it does not seem to have become as specialised for the latter purpose as in other Australian gerygones. Brown Gerygones, from coastal New South Wales to northeastern Queensland, lack the sweet, sibilant song of the others.

They also differ in that display between the sexes is more mutual. The birds bow slightly and delicately and fan their tails to reveal white spots at the tip. Only the female incubates, but both sexes—and sometimes additional helpers—feed the young.

OTHER NAMES
Northern Warbler, Brown Flyeater, Citron Bird, Brown Warbler.

IDENTIFICATION
LENGTH: *90–110 mm.*
ADULTS: *Sexes alike. Upper parts rich, deep olive-brown, often toned rusty, with distinct white stripe on side of forehead extending back towards but hardly over eye; indistinct white eye-ring, dark lores; cheeks grey finely scalloped with white. Wings as back, flight feathers greyer-brown. Tail grey-brown, with broad black bar near tip and distinct white spot at inner tip of all tail feathers except central pair. Underparts cream to soft grey on throat,* neck and breast, with or without red-brown wash on sides of belly. Eye rich red-brown. Bill black. Feet deep olive-grey to black.
IMMATURES: *As adults; eye brown.*

VOICE
CALL & SONG: *Three- to five-syllable soft twitter,* diddle-it-did-dit, *around same pitch, repeated rapidly and incessantly throughout the day, even when not breeding.*

NESTING
Breeds September–February. Nest a slender dome, with long bulky tail and projecting side-entrance hood extended into a funnel; of soft-bark fibre, rootlets, grass and moss, bound firmly with cobweb, adorned with lichen or green moss; lined with soft plant down or, rarely, fur or feathers; slung from a slender stem among hanging branchlets or lawyer-vines in rainforest 1–15 m above ground, often near water. Eggs: two or three; matt white to pink, freckled, spotted and blotched with dull to bright red and purple-red, often in a zone at larger end; oval, about 17 x 12 mm. Incubation 16–19 days, apparently by female. Young fledge in about 15–16 days.

DISTRIBUTION
Cool, subtropical rainforests and their fringes in eastern coastal Australia and

adjacent ranges to about 1200 m high, from near Cooktown, Qld, south to Gippsland, Vic., and inland to Carnarvon Range. Three races.

Mangrove Gerygone *Gerygone laevigaster* GOULD, 1843

THE SWEET SONG OF THE Mangrove Gerygone carries through the mangroves of northern and eastern Australia during much of the day. Its wayward chromatic cadence is given all year—except towards the southern end of its range in New South Wales, where it sings mainly when breeding. There it appears to be less sedentary, moving in only over spring and summer, to nest.

The Mangrove Gerygone—its name is pronounced *jer-rig'-ony* —is abundant in tidal mangroves, but it will forage out into fringing eucalypt- and rainforest and even through gardens around Brisbane. Where it occurs with other mangrove-inhabiting gerygones—such as the Large-billed and Dusky—it usually keeps to the shrubbier landward stands of white mangrove *Avicennia*.

It forages alone or in pairs, and rarely bands into small, loose feeding groups. Small insects are its food and it searches vigorously for them in the outer branchlets and foliage of the mangroves, both close to the ground and well above it. It will hover to catch flying insects it has disturbed but it does this less than other gerygones, spending more time among the foliage.

Established pairs hold territory when breeding. Males advertise it throughout the day with sustained singing from sheltered perches. They attend their mates constantly during nest-building, singing nearby and displaying with slight but often rapid flicking of wings and tail. They also fan the tail and make bowing movements. It seems likely that Mangrove Gerygones pair permanently. Both sexes feed the young.

There are two different races of Mangrove Gerygone in Australia: a western one, *Gerygone laevigaster laevigaster,* in which the birds are small and whiter on the breast, and an eastern one, *G.l. cantator,* which is larger, with a rusty tinged back and only the barest white wash in the base of the tail.

OTHER NAMES
Buff-breasted Warbler, Mangrove Flyeater, Mangrove Warbler, Queensland Canary.

IDENTIFICATION
LENGTH: *100–110 mm.*
ADULTS: *Sexes alike. Head and upper parts grey washed variously brown; clear white stripe on either side of forehead extending over eye and merging with white eye-ring; lores dusky; neck grey. Flight feathers grey-brown, edged fawn. Tail dark grey-brown washed white at base of outer one or two pairs of feathers, with broad black bar and large white spots at tip of inner webs of all except central feathers. Underparts grey- to pure-white; greyer on flanks. Eye red to brown-red. Bill black. Feet black.*
IMMATURES: *As adults, but face, eye-ring, sides of neck, throat and breast washed lemon-yellow. Eye brown; bill brown, pale horn at base of lower mandible.*

VOICE
CALL: *Soft chattering occasionally in contact by both sexes when feeding.*
SONG: *Sustained, carrying series of slow, rising and falling whistled chromatic cadences, by male.*

NESTING
Breeds September–April; sporadically throughout year in north. Nest compact, pear-shaped dome, 180–250 mm long including a short 50–100 mm tail and short side-entrance hood; of coarse strips of bark, grass stems, seaweed and rootlets, firmly bound into smooth surface with cobweb, usually adorned with cocoons and spiders' egg sacs; lined with vegetable down and feathers; suspended from a stem among ends of leafy branchlets 1–8 m above ground. Eggs: two or three; matt, warm white to pink-buff, densely speckled red-brown, often in zone at larger end; oval, about 17 x 12 mm. Incubation 12 days, probably by female. Young fledge in about 10 days.

DISTRIBUTION
Tidal mangroves and adjacent coastal scrub, from southwestern Kimberleys east around Cape York Peninsula to Princess Charlotte Bay, Qld, and from about Townsville, Qld, south to Lake Macquarie, NSW. Also southern New Guinea. Three races.

The white eyebrow of the Mangrove Gerygone is one of its main distinguishing marks. This gerygone makes its nest of bark, grass stems, seaweed and rootlets, binds it with spiderweb, and suspends it from leafy branchlets, usually in mangroves.

Western Gerygone *Gerygone fusca* (GOULD, 1838)

OTHER NAMES
White-tailed Warbler, White-tailed Flyeater, Western Warbler, Western Flyeater, Inland Warbler, Fuscous Warbler, Fuscous Flyeater, Sleepy Dick.

IDENTIFICATION
LENGTH: *100-110 mm.*
ADULTS: *Sexes alike. Head and upper surface dull grey washed faintly olive or cinnamon, with indistinct, off-white stripe on forehead extending back towards but rarely over eye, merging with indistinct white eye-ring; lores dusky; neck grey. Flight feathers grey-brown, often with paler edges. Tail dark grey-brown with broad white band across base of outer three to five pairs of feathers, broad black bar near tip and large white spots at tip of all except central pair. Throat and upper breast pearly grey to cream; rest of underparts off-white. Eye rich red to brown-red. Bill black. Feet dark grey to black.*
IMMATURES: *As adults, but face, eye-ring, sides of neck, and undersurface generally faint lemon-yellow; eye cream to buff or brown; bill brown, pale horn at base of lower bill.*

VOICE
CALL: *Soft chattering in contact, by both sexes occasionally when feeding.*
SONG: *Soft but far-carrying, slow chromatic cadence of whistled notes, first rising and then falling away, finishing prematurely; apparently only by male.*

NESTING
Breeds August–January; in central and northern Australia may be geared to rains. Nest a compact, well-formed oval dome, 200–250 mm long, including a 120 mm long tail; short hood projects over side entrance; of bark fibre, grass stems and other vegetable matter, bound with cobweb and adorned with spiders' egg-sacs; lined with feathers; suspended from a stem among leafy branchlets of a tree 2–10 m above ground. Eggs: two or three; matt white to flesh, sparingly spotted and speckled with dull red-brown, mainly at larger end, often forming zone; oval, about 18 x 13 mm. Incubation about 12 days, by female. Young fledge in about 10 days.

DISTRIBUTION
Short, open eucalypt woodlands, mallee and mulga Acacia *scrubs of inland Australia. Three races.*

A broad band of white at the base of the tail distinguishes the Western Gerygone from other grey gerygones.

DURING THE BREEDING season the male Western Gerygone signals his territory by singing his sweet, whistled song throughout the day. While the female is building the nest the male is in constant attendance. He perches nearby, singing, occasionally bowing slightly, fanning his white-marked tail and flicking his wings up and down in display. Pairing seems to be permanent. Only the female incubates the eggs, for about 12 days. The young, fed by both sexes, fledge about 10 days after hatching. Horsfield's Bronze- and Black-eared Cuckoos often cuckold its nest.

The Western is the only gerygone to range around Australia to the southwest and to occupy dry habitat, from coastal eucalypt forest in the southwest to mallee in the east and mulga woodland in the centre. Its silence and unobtrusiveness when not breeding has suggested that it is migratory in southern regions, but it seems in fact to be rather sedentary except in the southwest, where part of the population shifts as far north as the Kimberleys in winter.

The Western Gerygone gleans its food—small insects and aphids—in the outer foliage of trees, usually well above the ground. It often hovers about the crowns of trees to capture small flying insects which it has disturbed. It works alone or in pairs or, rarely, in small, loose groups. Rather restless in its movements, it frequently shakes itself as if its feathers are wet.

Despite the fact that its habitat is widespread, the Western Gerygone is limited today to three rather isolated populations. One race, *Gerygone fusca fusca,* occurs in southwestern Australia, dispersing north to the Kimberleys and east to the Victoria Desert in winter and recurs in isolation on southern Eyre Peninsula. Another race, *G.f. exsul,* lives in central eastern Australia from central Victoria north along the western slopes of the Great Dividing Range and adjacent western plains to the foot of Cape York Peninsula; vagrants may reach the Mount Lofty Ranges, SA. A third race, *G.f. mungi,* inhabits a broad band of semi-desert scrub across central Australia, from the Selwyn Range, Qld, west and northwest to the Pilbara and Kimberleys, WA.

Large-billed Gerygone *Gerygone magnirostris* GOULD, 1843

SMALL AND INCONSPICUOUS in the outer foliage of trees where they live and feed, the various gerygones—pronounced *jer-rig'-ony*—pose an ecological question. How do they co-exist? Focussing this question is the Large-billed Gerygone, for over its range it lives alongside three other gerygones in closed forest: the Fairy, Green-backed and Mangrove. Subtle partitioning of habitat and foraging is probably the answer. Thus the Large-billed keeps mainly to the taller stands of *Rhizophora* mangroves where it meets the Mangrove. And, with its stronger bill, it may take heavier, hard-shelled insects where it overlaps the Green-backed and Fairy in riverine rainforests and paperbark galleries along streams. There it is limited by nesting site, hanging its untidy nest low over water; the nest looks so much like flood debris that the species

The dull Large-billed Gerygone.

has been called Floodbird.

The Large-billed Gerygone is like other gerygones in behaviour. It is sedentary, and singly or in dispersed pairs—rarely threes or fours—it gleans small leaf insects for much of the day in the upper strata of closed forest. It works vigorously but unobtrusively more on the inside than the outside of foliage, but will hover to take insects on the wing.

The male assists in nest-building but spends much of his time singing close by. The nest and branchlets at the nest site seem to be the main place for mutual displays between paired birds, which perform slight bowing movements and fan the tail to expose the markings at its tip. Nests are often built near hornets' nests. Probably only the female incubates, but both sexes feed the young, often rearing two broods a year.

OTHER NAMES
Large-billed Warbler, Large-billed Flyeater, Floodbird, Brown-breasted Flyeater.

IDENTIFICATION
LENGTH: *105-115 mm.*
ADULTS: *Sexes similar. Head and upper parts warm-brown, with indistinct white spot on either side of forehead and indistinct white eye-ring in otherwise plain face. Wings as back but flight feathers greyer brown. Tail grey-brown with brown-black bar near tip and off-white spots at top of inner web of outer two to four pairs of feathers only. Underparts cream-white, washed pale buff or cinnamon-brown on breast and*
flanks. Eye rich red to red-brown. Bill black. Feet grey.
IMMATURES: *As adults; eye, bill brown.*

VOICE
CALL: *Soft chattering in contact.*
SONG: *Sweet, short whistled notes, lively and jerky, rising and falling, uttered in rapid succession for short periods by both sexes.*

NESTING
Breeds September–April. Nest a 500–700 mm long, straggling structure with egg chamber towards base, a ragged tail and short side-entrance hood; of shreds of bark, grass stems, rootlets and leaf skeletons, often adorned with spiders'
egg-sacs; lined with feathers and down; slung from low, slender branchlets often overhanging or near water, 2–10 m or more above. Eggs: two or three; matt pale pink, freckled, spotted and blotched with red and sometimes purple-grey, often in indistinct zone at larger end; oval, about 17 x 12 mm. Incubation 12–14 days, probably by female. Young fledge in about 10–11 days.

DISTRIBUTION
Mangroves, riverine rainforest and paperbark galleries, from western Kimberleys, WA, to Broad Sound, Qld; broken at Gulf of Carpentaria. Also New Guinea and offshore islands. About 12 races; two in Australia.

Dusky Gerygone *Gerygone tenebrosa* (HALL, 1901)

The Dusky Gerygone—the largest Australian gerygone—forages for insects among the foliage of mangroves.

THE LARGEST AND LEAST-KNOWN Australian gerygone, the Dusky is limited to mangrove groves and shrubbery. In this habitat Dusky Gerygones often band together into loose feeding groups of up to four or five which hop vigorously among the foliage picking insects from the leaves. Most feeding is done in the upper branchlets of the mangrove canopy, but occasionally they come to ground.

Where the Dusky Gerygone occurs in the same forests as the Mangrove Gerygone it seems to restrict itself, like the Large-billed Gerygone, to the taller, denser, seaward mangroves, while the Mangrove Gerygone occupies the patchier landward edges.

The Dusky Gerygone is sedentary, moving only locally. It is probably similar in its breeding behaviour to other gerygones.

OTHER NAMES
Dusky Warbler, Dusky Flyeater.

IDENTIFICATION
LENGTH: *About 115 mm.*
ADULTS: *Sexes alike. Head and upper parts mid-grey, washed light olive-rufous, particularly on rump. Indistinct white stripe on either side of forehead extends back towards eye, merging with indistinct white eye-ring in otherwise plain face. Wings darker grey-brown. Tail grey-brown with dull dusky bar and small faint brown-white spots on inner tips of outer one or two pairs of feathers. Underparts grey-white. Eye white. Bill black. Feet black.*
IMMATURES: *As adults; underparts and sides of neck washed pale yellow; eye, bill brown.*

VOICE
CALL: *Soft, rapidly repeated ticking or chatting in contact when feeding.*
SONG: *Soft, sweet plaintive whistles and descending trills, similar to Large-billed Gerygone but not as jerky or vigorous; both sexes probably sing.*

NESTING
Breeds mainly September–March. Nest a rather compact, hanging oval dome 200–250 mm long, including short, thin tail, with side-entrance hood; of strips of bark, closely bound with cobweb; slung among leafy mangrove branchlets, 2–5 m above ground. Eggs: two, perhaps three; matt white spotted with red-brown, particularly at larger end; oval, about 18 x 12 mm.

DISTRIBUTION
Coastal mangroves from Shark Bay northwards to King Sound–Collier Bay, WA. Two or three races.

Fairy Gerygone

Gerygone palpebrosa WALLACE, 1865

OTHER NAMES
Black-throated Warbler, Black-throated Flyeater, Fairy Warbler, Fairy Flyeater.

IDENTIFICATION
LENGTH: *100–110 mm.*
MALE: *Head and upper parts dull olive, browner or greyer on crown and sides of face. Distinct white spot on either side of forehead and white 'moustache' stripe down sides of throat. Flight feathers grey-brown. Tail plain grey-brown, with faint dusky subterminal bar. Throat dusky to pale brown or white. Breast and belly yellow. Eye red to orange-red. Bill black, often with pale grey tip. Feet black.*
FEMALE: *As male, but throat always white; little hint of 'moustache' stripes.*
IMMATURES: *Like adults, but throat dull yellow like breast; no white 'moustache' stripe; forehead spots reduced; eye browner; bill paler; feet slate-grey.*

VOICE
CALL: *Soft consistent chatter and twittering, by both sexes in contact in feeding groups.*
SONG: *Lively protracted reel of up-and-down whistled notes, by male all day throughout year, more animatedly when breeding.*

NESTING
September–March, but may breed sporadically throughout year. Nest a short, often spherical dome, with slender tail and projecting, sometimes funnel-like, side entrance hood; of strips of bark and other plant fibre, bound with cobweb, adorned with spiders' egg-sacs and pieces of lichen and moss, lined with vegetable down and slung from stem of leafy end-branches of small tree 2–10 m or more above ground. Eggs: two, sometimes three; matt, pale pink freckled with red-brown and dull purple red, often forming zone at larger end; oval, 18 x 13 mm. Incubation about 12 days, probably by female. Young fledge in about 10 days.

DISTRIBUTION
From Cape York Peninsula south to Mary River, Qld, in lowland rainforests, particularly their edges, and mangroves, and also enters fringes of more open woodland through scrub along creeks on higher tablelands. Also New Guinea and nearby islands. Five or six races; two in Australia.

This Fairy Gerygone is a male of the dusky throated race in the rainforests and mangroves on Cape York Peninsula.

AMONG AUSTRALIAN gerygones, the Fairy is not only the brightest in colouring but the one species in which there is an obvious difference in plumage between male and female. The female always has a white throat but the males differ markedly in the two Australian races. Abundant birds, they live and feed in the upper foliaged edges of lower altitude rainforest and vine thicket in northeastern Queensland.

In the race on Cape York Peninsula south to about Cooktown, the males have a dusky brown or black face and throat on which white 'moustache' stripes contrast conspicuously. South of Ravenshoe and Innisfail, Qld, the males are white-throated like females, but some have a black spot on the chin. Between these areas they intergrade.

The Fairy Gerygone is more sociable in its behaviour than other warblers. It occurs alone or in pairs, but frequently bands together into small parties and mixes with other small forest birds to forage. With soft, continuous twitterings, it gleans vigorously in the outer foliage of shrubbery and the crowns of trees to capture insects on the wing.

This bird's behaviour when breeding is territorial and much like that of other gerygones. Males attend their mates and sing from around the nest site—which is often near a wasp nest—while the female does most of the work of nest construction. Probably only the female incubates, but both sexes feed the young. The nestlings have erectile head plumes, the function of which is not known. One, or infrequently two, broods are produced each year.

Two cuckoos, the Golden Bronze-Cuckoo and the Little Bronze-Cuckoo, often lay their eggs in the nests of the Fairy Gerygone.

White-throated Gerygone *Gerygone olivacea* (GOULD, 1838)

A White-throated Gerygone of the race which occurs in eastern Australia. After breeding it migrates northwards.

OTHER NAMES
White-throated Warbler, White-throated Flyeater, Bush Canary, Native Canary.

IDENTIFICATION
LENGTH: *100-110 mm.*
ADULTS: *Sexes alike. Head and upper surface mid ash-grey, sometimes faintly tinged olive, with distinct white spot on either side of forehead. Wings like back but flight feathers darker grey-brown, edged ash-grey. Tail grey-brown, with broad to faint white band in base, broad black band near tip and white spot at inner tip of all feathers except central pair. Throat pure white, breast and belly rich yellow. Eye rich red. Bill black. Feet black to slate.*
IMMATURES: *Like adults but throat pale yellow like breast and belly. Forehead spots reduced or absent. Eye brown; bill dark brown; feet grey.*

VOICE
CALL: *Infrequent shortened, softened song, in contact by both sexes.*
SONG: *Long, reeling trill of quick, sweet whistled notes, first rising briefly, then cascading chromatically down and up the scale. Songs of northern races more abbreviated than in the east.*

NESTING
Breeds mainly August–January; more spread in northern Australia. Nest an oblong-oval to pear-shaped dome, with slender tail 100–150 mm long and shortly projecting side-entrance hood; of strips and shreds of bark closely matted and bound with cobweb, lined with down, feathers or both, and slung from a stem among outer leafy branchlets 2–15 m above ground. Eggs: three, sometimes two; matt white to pink, speckled and spotted with dull red, red-brown and purple-red, often forming zone at larger end; oval, about 18 x 13 mm. Incubation about 12 days, mostly by female. Young fledge in about 10 days.

DISTRIBUTION
Widespread in taller, open eucalypt woodlands around northern and eastern mainland. On southern migration straggles occasionally southwest to southeastern South Australia but is rare west of Melbourne in winter. Also southeastern New Guinea. Three races; all in Australia.

EACH SPRING THE rippling cadences of the White-throated Gerygone—pronounced *jer-rig'-ony*—herald the bird's arrival in the southernmost parts of its range to breed. At other times it is quiet and solitary, keeping to the upper leafy branches of trees in eucalypt woodlands and open forests, where it lives and forages when feeding. At that time, White-throated Gerygones move singly, in pairs or, occasionally, family groups, through the outer foliage, gleaning insects along stems or under leaves. They will often hover over trees to capture the insects they have disturbed.

When breeding, males advertise their territory with day-long song. They help the female to build the nest but they spend more time singing near the nest while she is brooding. Nest-building takes 11–14 days. Both the male and, to a lesser extent, the female, display about the nest site, bowing and spreading their tails. They may mate permanently, at least in the north of their range where they appear to be rather sedentary.

Most, if not all, the incubating is done by the female, but both parents feed the young, raising one or two broods each season. The Golden and Horsfield's Bronze-Cuckoos both lay their eggs in the nests of White-throated Gerygones.

The White-throated is apparently the only regular migrant among Australian gerygones but it seems that only one race is involved. This is *Gerygone olivacea olivacea,* which occurs throughout eastern Australia and is deep olive-toned on the back and has a distinctly white-tipped and -based tail. It migrates southwards in spring, straggling occasionally southwest to southeastern South Australia and the Mt Lofty Ranges near Adelaide.

There are two other races, both smaller birds. In the northwest, as far east as the Gulf of Carpentaria, *G.o. rogersi* is greyer on the back and has indistinct white tips and bases to the tail feathers; *G.o. lavigaster,* which lives on Cape York Peninsula, is also pale but has distinct white tips on the tail feathers.

Brown Thornbill *Acanthiza pusilla* (SHAW, 1790)

BROWN THORNBILLS PRODUCE a greater variety of calls than any other thornbill, even though they never dominate the sounds of the bush. The grey broad-tailed race inland is particularly varied in its voice, whistling and chipping in contact, churring harshly in alarm, and giving protracted trills and whistles in song, with perhaps occasional mimicry.

Ranging across much of southern Australia and the inland, Brown Thornbills are sedentary birds in a variety of habitats, from rainforest to arid mulga *Acacia* woodland. The thornbills are not spread evenly through their vegetations but occur in pockets, common to all of which is a taller close shrub layer one to five metres high. Established pairs hold territories of a quarter to five hectares there year round, advertising them with regular singing even when not breeding, though not so frequently. Young forage with their parents in family parties in the months after breeding but are expelled from the territory during autumn and early winter. Many wander into unusual habitat then and most perish. Those that survive to find territory of their own may live for 10 years or more.

Day by day, Brown Thornbills spend most of the morning and afternoon foraging through the mid and upper strata of their shrubberies, infrequently coming close to the ground. They hop-glean briskly among foliage and along twigs, working through one bush before flitting jerkily to the next. Insects, and occasionally seeds, are picked from leaves, under bark and sometimes the ground. The birds also take advantage of flowers, such as those of the spikes of grass trees *Xanthorrhoea*. Working its way up a spike, each bird inserts its bill into each flower and holds it there for several seconds, probably taking nectar. Outside the breeding season Brown Thornbills join mixed feeding flocks of other birds—particularly of White-browed Scrubwrens, and Buff-rumped and Striated Thornbills—within the vicinity of their territories.

Only the female builds and incubates, but the male commonly sings nearby in territorial defence. Then and in excitement, the birds will cock and flush their tails like wrens, particularly the inland race. Both Horsfield's and Golden Bronze-Cuckoos and, occasionally, Fantailed Cuckoos parasitise them.

Often regarded as a separate species, the greyer 'Inland' or 'Broad-tailed' thornbill of the arid zone is now treated as a race of the Brown. First to propose this were the ornithologists Ernst Mayr and D.L. Serventy in 1938, partly on the grounds that olive-toned Brown Thornbill-like birds with russet scalloping on the forehead in extreme southwestern Australia intergraded there with greyer, russet-rumped birds of the inland type, with white scalloping on the frons. Mayr and Serventy's suggestion was not followed at the time because it was thought that the two forms did not intergrade where they met in the east. Recently it has been found that they do, wherever they come in contact along the western watersheds of the Great Dividing Range: at Tenterfield, Cobbora and Temora, NSW, in the Big Desert, Vic., and in the upper South-East and Adelaide plains, SA.

OTHER NAMES
Inland Thornbill, Broad-tailed Thornbill, Red-rumped Thornbill, Whitlock's Thornbill, Brown Tit, Whitlock's Tit, Tanami Tit, White-scaled Tit, Lake Way Tit, Brown-rumped Tit, Browntail, Scrub Thornbill, Tit-bat.

IDENTIFICATION
LENGTH: *100-110 mm.*
ADULTS: *Sexes similar. Upper parts generally rich olive-brown to brownish grey, according to race; rump more rufous-brown or rich russet in grey race. Wings darker grey-brown, with paler edges. Tail dark grey-brown with black subterminal band and grey-buff to white tips on inner webs of all but central pair of feathers. Face flecked olive- to pale-grey, scalloped russet to white on forehead. Underparts cream- to pure-white grading to olive-brown, grey or yellowish on flanks and undertail; throat and breast clearly to heavily streaked grey-black. Eye red. Bill black. Feet dusky brown.*
IMMATURES: *As adults but duller and more lightly streaked on breast; eye brown. Adult plumage gained at general body moult in first autumn.*

VOICE
CALL: *Soft chips and a plaintive whistle, seee, (inland race only) in contact; harsh staccato buzzing churring in alarm.*
SONG: *A series of whistled twitters, ending in short swirled metallic trill; mimicry often interwoven and more varied and protracted in inland grey race.*

NESTING
Breeds June–December; in colder areas starts as late as September. Nest untidy dome, with slightly hooded side entrance near top; of shreds of bark, coarse grasses and fern bound with a little cobweb; lined with finer grasses, fur and feathers; built in low branches, shrubberies, fern thicket or under tussocks on edge of banks. Eggs: two, usually three; white to pale flesh, liberally speckled and blotched with red-brown, mostly at large end; oblong-oval, about 16 x 12 mm. Incubation 17–21 days, by female. Young fledge in about 15 days.

DISTRIBUTION
Shrubberies, from under rainforest to arid zone woodland, throughout southern and inland mainland north to 20°S, and also Tasmania and other offshore islands. Seven races: five olive-brown with russet frons scalloping around coastal mainland, King Island and Tasmania; one grey with white frons scalloping throughout inland and southern mallee; one intermediate on Kangaroo Island, SA.

A Brown Thornbill of the greyer inland race at its domed bark and grass nest in shrubbery.

The Mountain Thornbill's nest is a large domed structure with a slightly hooded entrance, slung from leafy twigs, and covered with green moss.

Mountain Thornbill *Acanthiza katherina* DE VIS, 1905

THE MOUNTAIN THORNBILL in the montane rainforests of northeastern Queensland is the link between the Australian Brown Thornbill group and New Guinea's only thornbill, a similarly cream-eyed species in that island's cloud forests. This small warbler-like bird lives among the foliage of the mid and upper strata of rainforest. It feeds there on a range of leaf insects in small parties of two to eight or more, hopping briskly among the branchlets at five–25 metres above the ground, gleaning prey from foliage and twigs, and flitting in short, undulating dashes from one tree to the next. As they move about, the birds keep up a constant twittering in contact.

Ranging from 400 to 1200 metres altitude, the Mountain Thornbill overlaps the Brown Gerygone, another small foliage-gleaning insectivore, on lower hills. Where it does, it keeps to the upper forest strata, above 15 metres. Whether this has any connection with their polymorphic changes in plumage is not clear. Mountain Thornbills at lower altitude tend to be brighter green above and yellower below than duller birds at higher elevations.

OTHER NAMES
None.

IDENTIFICATION
LENGTH: *100 mm.*
ADULTS: *Sexes similar. Upper parts green-olive, brighter on lower back, tawny on upper tail coverts. Tail grey-brown, the outer feathers banded dusky and white on inner webs at tip. Wing quills grey-brown edged green-olive. Forehead scalloped buff. Chin, throat and upper breast cream, faintly scaled with grey; sides of face flecked cream-grey; rest of underparts cream washed lemon. Eye white to cream. Bill black. Feet deep grey-brown.*
IMMATURES: *As adults but duller.*

VOICE
Resembles Brown Thornbill.
CALL: *Single chips in contact; buzzing chaah, cha, chaaah in alarm.*
SONG: *Sweet, short metallic trills, often introduced by several short falling whistles tchu-tchu-tchu-tchu.*

NESTING
Breeds September to December–January. Nest a bulky dome with hooded side-entrance closely interwoven; of grass and tendrils, covered with green moss; lined with finer material; slung from twig or stem 5–15 m above ground in leafy branchlets or under bank. Eggs: two; pinkish white, spotted and blotched with brown, red-brown and underlying grey, often in zone at large end; oval, about 17 x 12 mm.

DISTRIBUTION
Mountain rainforests above 350 m between Cooktown and Paluma Range, Qld. No races.

Slaty-backed Thornbill *Acanthiza robustirostris* MILLIGAN, 1903

OTHER NAMES
Robust Thornbill, Thick-billed Thornbill, Robust-billed Thornbill.

IDENTIFICATION
LENGTH: *100–110 mm.*
ADULTS: *Sexes similar. Upper parts rich grey with slight blue tone; fine black streaks on crown; rump dull russet. Wings darker grey-brown. Tail dusky with white inner tips on all but central pair of feathers. Underparts plain white. Eye red. Bill and feet black.*
IMMATURES: *As adults; eyes browner.*

VOICE
CALL: *High, plaintive whistled seee, seee in contact. Harsh two-note churr in alarm.*
SONG: *High-pitched up-and-down warbled and whistled twittering, resembling Brown Thornbill's.*

NESTING
Breeds July–November; at other times depending on rainfall. Nest domed, often with a poorly constructed top, and side entrance with a slight hood; of dried grasses lightly bound with cobweb and cocoons; lined with hair, feathers and soft plant materials; generally placed in twigs and foliage of low bush. Eggs: two or three; white with pink tinge, speckled finely with rust-red markings, often forming zone at larger end; oblong-oval, about 16 x 12 mm.

DISTRIBUTION
Mulga Acacia woodlands and scrubs of inland west and central mainland east around northern Simpson Desert to far-western Queensland. No races.

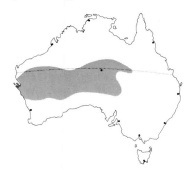

The Slaty-backed Thornbill generally places its domed nest in the foliage of a low bush.

A THORNBILL OF THE MULGA woodlands of central-western Australia, the Slaty-backed forages in the same feeding zone as the grey, inland race of the Brown Thornbill: the outer branchlets and foliage of shrubs and trees at about one to five metres above the ground. Like the Brown, it appears to be rather sedentary and to feed alone or in pairs or small family groups, without banding together in larger foraging flocks as other thornbills do.

The birds are brisk but rather quiet in their feeding, hop-gleaning along twigs and among leaves, picking off insects, larvae and spiders, and often hanging upside down beneath foliage or fluttering to do so. Often they forage in mixed flocks with Chestnut-tailed and Brown Thornbills; the usually clean white breast of the Slaty-backed is one of its most reliable identifying features.

Many aspects of this thornbill's biology are still confusing. Although it forages mainly in mid-height foliage, it does come to ground, perhaps to dust-bathe. And it may wander locally according to seasonal conditions.

Tasmanian Thornbill *Acanthiza ewingii* GOULD, 1844

TEMPERATE RAINFOREST AND wet sclerophyll shrubberies in Tasmania and islands in Bass Strait are the habitat of this thornbill. Hopping and flitting actively about throughout the day, it feeds mostly on insects gleaned from the leaves and outer branches of shrubs and trees from a metre up to the forest canopy, and rarely visits the ground.

In the wet forests there it occurs side by side with two other small, insectivorous 'warblers'—the Scrubtit and White-browed Scrubwren—but these generally occupy different feeding zones. The White-browed Scrubwren forages in shrubberies close to the forest floor, while the Scrubtit feeds more on the trunks and larger branches of trees.

In winter these three species form noisy mixed feeding parties that flit and hop locally through the undergrowth, each searching out prey within its own niche. Up to 20 Tasmanian Thornbills can be present and their musical twittering mixes confusingly with the calls of the scrubwren and Scrubtit.

The Tasmanian Thornbill is sometimes found with another closely related insect-eater, the Brown Thornbill, but mostly they live in different habitats: the Brown keeps generally to drier, more open forests and heaths, with little overlap. This is probably a consequence of the island having been invaded at different times by thornbills from the mainland. First came the ancestors of Tasmanian Thornbills, at a time when cold wet forests offered the only niche. Later, the Brown Thornbill arrived to establish itself in drier forests under a warmer climatic regime.

The two birds are similar in plumage but the Tasmanian Thornbill- can be distinguished by its more uniformly washed russet forehead, its mottled rather than streaked breast, pure white undertail coverts and a dash of russet-ochre on the flight feathers.

In courtship, one bird—probably mostly or only the male—faces its mate on perches about 30–50 centimetres apart and bows repeatedly, spreading its wings slightly and fanning its tail to show the terminal pattern.

A Tasmanian Thornbill at the entrance hole of its compact, dome-shaped hanging nest.

OTHER NAMES
Ewing's Thornbill, Ewing's Tit.

IDENTIFICATION
LENGTH: *About 100 mm.*
ADULTS: *Sexes similar. Upper parts generally olive-brown; upper tail coverts washed russet. Wings dark grey-brown; primaries edged broadly russet, contrasting with black coverts. Tail dark grey-brown with black subterminal band and grey-buff tips to inner webs of all but central pair of feathers. Forehead washed chestnut, faintly scalloped dusky. Face grey-brown with lighter flecks and pale grey lores. Throat and breast grey-white, flecked and mottled dusky grey; lower breast to flanks and belly buff-grey with white centre; undertail coverts white. Eye red. Bill dusky black. Feet dusky brown.*
IMMATURES: *As adults but paler; undertail coverts greyer; eye dark brown.*

VOICE
CALL: *Thin, reedy, twittered tsirp tsirp, repeated three or four times, in contact; soft staccato buzzing churring in alarm.*
SONG: *Whistled warbling, twitters, often starting with contact call followed by short, swirled metallic trill.*

NESTING
Breeds September–January. Nest a compact dome with open side entrance near top, of grass, bark and moss bound with cobweb; lined with fine grass and a thick mat of feathers and fur; hung by the top from a thin twig in outer foliage or branches of a small tree or shrub, usually 2–4 m above ground, rarely to 8 m. Eggs: three or four; pinkish white finely speckled with red-brown, mainly at larger end; oblong-oval, about 18 x 13 mm.

DISTRIBUTION
Common in wet sclerophyll forest and temperate rainforest throughout Tasmania, particularly in west. Also in wet gullies in dry sclerophyll forest and coastal heathland, on King, Flinders and Maria Islands. No races.

Chestnut-rumped Thornbill *Acanthiza uropygialis* GOULD, 1838

The Chestnut-rumped Thornbill nests in holes and crevices in a variety of places, from trees and logs to fence posts and buildings.

VERSATILITY DESCRIBES THE feeding strategy of the Chestnut-rumped Thornbill. Over its range through the dry mallee, mulga, black box and belar woodlands of inland southern Australia, this thornbill lives alongside other small insectivorous thornbills—the Brown, Slaty-backed, Yellow and Yellow-rumped—and often joins them in mixed feeding parties. Indeed, the Chestnut-rumpeds may be catalysts for such groupings.

But whereas the other thornbills are rather sedentary or permanently territorial and keep to particular foraging strata, Chestnut-rumpeds wander about much and feed at all levels of the vegetation, from leafy tree tops to the ground. They even venture into the edges of cleared fields and around farm buildings. Working in small, loose parties of two to 10 or more, rarely alone, they flit and hop actively along, gleaning among upper foliage, hovering outside the crown or next to the trunk, poking into crevices in bark, and searching around fallen debris on the ground for food: insects, spiders, larvae and some seeds and vegetable matter. As they go they keep up a constant twittering—reminiscent of the Buff-rumped's—in contact. At night they retire to low shrubbery and tangles of undergrowth to roost.

Quick movers, the groups travel rapidly through the scrub although rarely very far. Chestnut-rumped Thornbills may be local nomads, particularly out of breeding, but they do not seem to undertake large-scale seasonal movements. Even so, wanderers are occasionally recorded outside the species' normal range. Flight, of low, undulating dashes, is like that of other thornbills; in each undulation the tail is spread, flashing its white tip and black subterminal band to contrast with its russet rump.

In keeping with their nomadic habit, Chestnut-rumped Thornbills are communal. Not only parents, but sometimes other adults as well, assist with feeding and rearing of young. They are also versatile in their choice of nest sites—holes in walls and fence posts as well as chinks under bark and spouts in trees.

Breeding birds twitter in territorial song in short bursts throughout the day, hopping and twisting non-stop from bare vantage perches well up in trees.

OTHER NAMES
Chestnut-tailed Thornbill, Chestnut-rumped Tit.

IDENTIFICATION
LENGTH: *About 100 mm.*
ADULTS: *Sexes similar. Upper parts plain mid grey-brown; rump rich russet. Wings dusky brown. Tail dusky with narrow white tips to inner webs of all but central pair of feathers. Forehead feathers scalloped white on brown-black; face mottled brown and white. Underparts from chin to undertail off-white, washed greyer from sides of neck to flanks. Eye white. Bill and feet dusky. Birds in south of range grade slightly darker than those in north.*
IMMATURES: *As adults; eye brown.*

VOICE
CALL: *Quiet, constant twitter of single and run-together* chips *from feeding flocks; also soft, carrying, plaintive whistles* pseee, pseee *in contact; churring buzzing chips in alarm.*
SONG: *Prolonged chirping twittering, throughout year but mostly during breeding; mimicry included.*

NESTING
Breeds July–December, but not during drought. Nest a dome of dried grasses, bark fibres and occasionally some cobweb with side entrance; lined with feathers, fur and soft plant material; placed in hole in tree, log, fence post, or building 1–6 m above ground. Eggs: three; pale pinkish white, minutely freckled all over with red-brown, particularly at larger end where a zone is usually formed; oblong-oval, about 16 x 12 mm.*

DISTRIBUTION
Abundant in arid mulga, mallee, black box and belar woodlands and scrubs throughout southern inland mainland, north to about 22°S and no farther east than lower western slopes of Great Dividing Range. No races; northern inland birds only grading gradually paler than those in south and southeast.

The Western Thornbill builds its dome-shaped nest close to the ground.

Western Thornbill

Acanthiza inornata GOULD, 1841

THE LEAST COLOURFUL OF the thornbills, the Western resembles the Buff-rumped in habits and behaviour. It occurs in the same habitats too—heathy woodland and close-shrubbed open forest—in southwestern Australia where it replaces the Buff-rumped. Both species probably arose from a common ancestral stock that was once widespread across southern Australia. Changing climates that became drier split it and its habitat into two pockets in the southeast and southwest of the continent; from them Buff-rumped and Western Thornbills evolved.

Active feeders, Western Thornbills forage by hop-gleaning at all levels, from the lower tree canopy down to the ground. Much time is spent in and around undergrowth and ground debris searching for insects, mainly beetles and bugs. The birds are communal and band together in small feeding parties of up to a dozen or so after breeding. These groups wander locally, often out into the edges of farming land and frequently in company with other insectivores.

OTHER NAMES
Bark-tit, Plain-coloured Tit, Master's Tit.

IDENTIFICATION
LENGTH: *90–100 mm.*
ADULTS: *Sexes similar. Upper parts plain olive-grey, including wings and tail duskier grey, the tail feathers tipped narrowly buff except centre pair. Forehead scalloped and face flecked with buff-white. Underparts buff-cream, flecked faintly grey at sides of breast. Eye greyish white. Bill dusky, paler below. Feet dusky grey.*

IMMATURES: *As adults; duller with obscure forehead markings.*

VOICE
CALL & SONG: *Rapid ringing staccato twittering in erratic bursts on the same pitch, similar to that of Buff-rumped Thornbill.*

NESTING
Breeds August–December. Nest a dome of grasses and bark strips, with some dried leaves and binding cobweb; lined with feathers, fur, hair, or plant down; hidden close to ground behind loose

bark of tree, in stumps, knot-holes, post holes and even under tussock of grass. Eggs: usually four; pale flesh-white, with pale red to rich brown freckles and spots, often forming a zone at larger end; oblong-oval, about 16 x 12 mm. Incubation about 20 days.

DISTRIBUTION
Open forest, heath, scrubby woodland and their edges in southwest of mainland. No races.

Slender-billed Thornbill

Acanthiza iredalei MATHEWS, 1911

OTHER NAMES
Slender Thornbill, Dark Thornbill, Samphire Thornbill.

IDENTIFICATION
LENGTH: *90–100 mm.*
ADULTS: *Sexes similar. Upper parts light olive-grey to dark brown-olive; rump and base of tail broad buff-yellow to narrow yellow-olive. Wings and tail darker grey-brown, black subterminal band and grey-white tip on all but central pair of tail feathers. Forehead and cheeks scalloped and flecked pale to deep cream. Underparts uniformly cream-white to deep cream-buff washed and flecked olive-grey, more so on flanks. Eye cream-white. Bill dusky black. Feet black. Some variations in shade but not in overall pattern; birds of western salt lakes palest, those around St Vincents Gulf, SA, darkest.*
IMMATURES: *As adults.*

VOICE
CALL & SONG: *Reedy, tinkling, whiteface-like twittering on same pitch, usually from perches on tops of bushes.*

NESTING
Breeds July–November. Nest a rather small dome with side entrance at top, often of swamp grasses and bark strips, seaweed in coastal areas and bound

with cobweb; lined with vegetable down, fur or other soft materials; placed low in foliage towards top of small bush, often samphire or blue-bush, within a metre of the ground. Eggs: three; white, speckled with spots of red-brown, particularly at larger end; oblong-oval, about 15 x 11 mm.

DISTRIBUTION
Samphire and chenopod shrub-fields around salt lakes and on flood pans across inland southwest and around South Australian gulfs. Also sandplain heaths of Ninety Mile, Big and Little Deserts, SA, Vic. Two or three races.

TREELESS EXPANSES OF SHRUB-FIELD, whether samphire and blue-bush around salt lakes or metre-high heath on sandplain, are the habitat of the Slender-billed Thornbill. In pairs or small loose parties of up to eight or 10, the birds forage quickly, hop-gleaning in and among the foliage and twigs of one shrub before flitting in low, bouncing undulations on to the next. In this way they cover much country quickly but, keeping to shrubs, they rarely come to ground. Throughout, they twitter constantly to one another to stay in touch. Leaf insects and spiders are their prey.

To what extent local groups are nomadic or sedentary is not clear. Those on salt lakes inland may wander according to season

The Slender-billed Thornbill rarely comes to ground; it forages for insects and spiders in the samphire and blue-bush shrub-fields of the inland.

and drought, but those in samphire around the South Australian gulfs and in the sandplain heaths straddling the Victorian–South Australian border are present locally all year round. There they break up into breeding pairs from August to October and forage in groups of four to 10 from November into winter.

Buff-rumped Thornbill

Acanthiza reguloides
VIGORS & HORSFIELD, 1827

OTHER NAMES
Buff-tailed Thornbill, Varied Thornbill, Bark Tit, Buff-rumped Tit-warbler, Buff-tailed Thornbill, Scaly-breasted Tit.

IDENTIFICATION
LENGTH: *100–110 mm.*
ADULTS: *Sexes similar. Upper parts dark olive-brown (southern populations) to mid olive-green (northeastern); rump and base tail dull pink-cream buff (southern) to mid-yellow (northeastern). Wings greyer brown. Tail dusky black, with narrow buff (southern) to pale yellow (northeastern) tips to all tail feathers except central pair. Forehead and face scalloped and flecked buff-white to yellowish cream respectively. Underparts buffy cream flecked grey on throat and sides of breast (southern) to plain yellowish cream (northeastern) with colour deepening on flanks. Eye greyish white. Bill dusky brown, paler below. Feet dusky grey.*
IMMATURES: *Duller than adults, lacking distinct facial and forehead markings; immature plumage moults out at first autumn moult, about three months after fledging.*

VOICE
CALL & SONG: *Rapid ringing, staccato, double-syllabled, twittering chips, pit-ta, pit-ta, pit-ta, around same pitch, repeated in rapid, quick-fire bursts; given both in contact in feeding flocks and as song in territorial or individual advertisement.*

NESTING
Breeds August–December. Nest a dome of grasses and bark strips and some dried leaves, bound with some cobweb; lined with feathers, fur, hair or plant down; placed close to ground in or under a shrub or low tree, under bark on sides of tree trunks or in hollows on the ground beneath tussocks. Eggs: three–five, usually four; flesh-white, with tiny freckles and larger spots of pale red to rich red-brown, often forming a zone at larger end; oblong-oval, about 16 x 12 mm.

DISTRIBUTION
Drier open eucalypt forests and close heathy woodlands and copses of coastal eastern and southern Australia and nearby ranges, from Atherton Tableland, Qld, south and west to Mt Lofty Ranges, SA. Possibly two, perhaps three races.

The Buff-rumped Thornbill makes a looser nest than most thornbills and often places it on or near the ground.

THE BUFF-RUMPED THORNBILL is a bird of the dry, open eucalypt forests and heathier woodlands of the eastern coast and nearby ranges. Ground cover affects the zones where the thornbills feed. In southern regions, where the understorey is shrubbier, patchier and littered with debris, the birds spend much time on the ground, among the litter and on rough-barked tree trunks, hopping and flitting along in small groups, gleaning and poking for a range of small insects and occasionally seeds.

Perhaps, too, they avoid competition from Striated Thornbills there. In the north, along the coastal Queensland ranges, the ground is covered with a tall grass sward, and there the birds forage higher in the twigs and foliage of smaller trees up to 20 metres above the ground, particularly in pockets of *Casuarina.*

Buff-rumped Thornbills are sedentary and after breeding form local clans of up to 20 birds which merge their breeding territories to form one large clan territory of about 15 hectares. When feeding, each clan mixes with other insectivorous species but expels other clans of its own. As the birds work through their territory each day, they keep up a constant twittering to maintain contact. Ground-feeding flocks flush with spread tails, apparently to flash their coloured rumps as a deterrent to predators.

Young remain with the clan until the beginning of the next spring breeding, when it breaks up into smaller breeding units of a single female to one–three males in re-formed small nesting territories. Surplus young females disappear, but young males usually join their parental breeding group. The female incubates alone—after constructing a larger, rougher nest than other thornbills—but all members of the unit share in feeding the young. Much of their foraging is arboreal then, even in southern regions.

White head streaks and brow distinguish the Striated Thornbill from allies.

Striated Thornbill

Acanthiza lineata GOULD, 1838

LIKE YELLOW THORNBILLS, Striateds are completely arboreal, feeding, roosting and nesting in trees; but unlike Yellows, they live almost exclusively in eucalypts, particularly forest eucalypts around the southeastern seaboard. Abundant birds, they forage mainly in the canopy at up to 50 metres above the ground, hop-gleaning quickly through the outer foliage of one tree, then flitting on to the next, chipping constantly to keep contact. Rarely do they stay long in one tree. Leaf beetles, weevils, bugs, caterpillars and spiders are all eaten but scale insects are staple. These they pluck from the leaves while hovering.

Striated Thornbills are sedentary and communal, territorial birds spending all the 10–12 years of their lives within the same few hectares of forest. Out of breeding they band into clans of up to 25 birds in an enlarged clan territory of about six hectares, and often catalyse other species of birds to feed along with them there. With the coming of spring, the clans break up into breeding groups of one female to one–three males. Mainly the female nest-builds and she alone incubates; both sexes, and the helper males, feed the young which later join the clan until the next spring.

OTHER NAMES
Striated Tit, Striped Tit, Striped-crowned Thornbill.

IDENTIFICATION
LENGTH: *About 100 mm.*
ADULTS: *Sexes similar. Upper parts plain dull olive; crown washed russet and streaked white. Wings browner; tail olive-brown with black band near tip. Brow white; cheeks streaked white. Underparts dull white, streaked dusky on throat and breast; flanks washed olive-grey to pale yellow. Eye grey-white. Bill dusky; base pale grey. Feet* grey-brown.
IMMATURES: *Duller than adults; throat mottled.*

VOICE
CALL: *Soft, buzzing* tiz *or* tiz-tiz, *repeated almost non-stop, in contact.*
SONG: *Quiet, fast, high-pitched trill, only during breeding.*

NESTING
Breeds July–December; starts a little later in mountains. Nest a neat oval or pear-shaped dome, 100 mm long and 75 mm broad, with round, spout-like entrance near top; of fine bark strips, grasses, spiders' egg sacs and cobweb; lined with feathers, fur or soft fibre; suspended from top, in outer branch of eucalypts, 5–10 m above ground. Eggs: three; pale pink-cream with red-brown spots, particularly at larger end; oblong-oval, about 17 x 12 mm. Incubation 15–17 days, by female.

DISTRIBUTION
Wet and dry eucalypt forests around southeast coast and ranges, from Kroombit Tops, Qld, to Mt Lofty Ranges, SA. Three races.

Yellow-rumped Thornbill *Acanthiza chrysorrhoa* (QUOY & GAIMARD, 1830)

A bright yellow rump distinguishes the Yellow-rumped Thornbill from all other thornbills.

MOST WIDESPREAD of the thornbills, the Yellow-rumped also occurs in the most open woodlands and scrubs. It commonly frequents 'edge' habitat, where woods and shrubberies fringe clearings with much bare ground, using the bushes for shelter, roosting and nesting and the ground for foraging. Most feeding is on the ground, the birds working along in loose lines in jerky hops, picking up a range of insects, spiders, caterpillars and occasional seeds. If flushed, they fly to cover in short, jerky undulations, chipping to keep contact and fanning the tail to flash the yellow rump.

Sedentary and communal, Yellow-rumped Thornbills have a social organisation like that of the Buff-rumped. Out of breeding, they band together in clans of 10–30 with an enlarged defended clan territory, often feeding with other species of insectivores then. The clans break up into small groups to breed—with one female to several males—rearing up to four broods in good seasons. A very bulky nest is built for each brood, with a characteristic 'false nest' or cup in the top and a concealed side entrance. All members of the breeding group brood and feed the young, but only the female incubates.

OTHER NAMES
Yellow-tailed Thornbill, Yellow Tail, Chigaree, Tomtit.

IDENTIFICATION
LENGTH: *110–115 mm.*
ADULTS: *Sexes similar. Upper parts mid-brown often with olive wash; rump and base tail yellow. Wings grey-brown. Tail black, with white tips to all outer feathers. Forehead black spotted with white; eyebrow white; lores dusky; cheeks flecked dusky and white. Underparts plain dull white, flanks buffier. Eye grey-white. Bill black. Feet* dark grey.
IMMATURES: *As adults but duller.*

VOICE
CALL: *Sharp repeated* tchip *in contact in flight; softer chips and subsong for contact calls in flocks; harsh single-note alarm.*
SONG: *Descending rich twittered warble, repeated rapidly two or three times in cycles.*

NESTING
Breeds July–December. Nest domed with false upper nest and chamber with concealed side entrance beneath, of grass and plant fibre bound with cobweb; lined with down and feathers; slung in outer foliage, 1–5 m above ground. Eggs: three or four; pale flesh-coloured, sparingly dotted at larger end with red-brown; oblong-oval, about 18 x 13 mm. Incubation about 19 days, by female. Young fledge in about 18 days.

DISTRIBUTION
Forest clearings, open woodlands, shrubbery edges throughout north to about 18°S. Two races.

Yellow Thornbill

Acanthiza nana
VIGORS & HORSFIELD, 1827

OTHER NAMES
Little Thornbill, Yellow-breasted Tomtit, Yellow Dicky, Little Tit.

IDENTIFICATION
LENGTH: *90–100 mm.*
ADULTS: *Sexes similar. Upper parts plain rich to pale olive-green; primaries dull brown-grey edged with olive-yellow. Tail browner, with black bar near tip. Dull white spots over lores and white shaft streaks on cheeks. Chin and throat yellow washed with buff; rest of underparts plain pale to rich yellow; flanks darker. Eye brown. Bill pink-brown or black. Feet dark grey-brown.*
IMMATURES: *As adults; slightly duller.*

VOICE
CALL: *Stereotyped harsh clipped double-note chip,* tzid-id, *sometimes varied with extra chips,* tzid-id, tis-tis— *carrying and repeated at regular intervals, perhaps both in contact and to advertise territory. More animated buzzing chipping in group interactions. No song.*

NESTING
Breeds August–December. Nest oval or spherical dome with narrow entrance near the top; about 90 mm high by 65 mm across, smaller than that of Striated Thornbill; of thin strips of dried bark and fine grasses matted with cobweb, ornamented outside with spiders' egg sacs and green mosses; lined with fine dried grasses, plant fibres and feathers; placed among outer twigs or leaf clusters in acacias, native pines, or tea-trees at 3–12 m above ground. Eggs: usually three; flesh-white with red-brown freckles and a few lilac spots; oblong-oval, about 16 x 12 mm.

DISTRIBUTION
Groves and copses of acacia, casuarina, native pine, tea-tree and chenopod shrubs throughout coastal and near-inland eastern mainland, including denser brigalow and mulga scrubs. Avoids rainforest and higher, colder mountain country; infrequent in eucalypts except black box. Visits orchards, parks and gardens. Sedentary. Three races.

This Yellow Thornbill has added threads to the usual grass and strips of bark in its nest, here in a tea-tree.

HARSH, CLIPPED, DOUBLE-NOTE chips, repeated at intervals and loud for so small a bird, are the first clue to the presence of Yellow Thornbills. For otherwise the birds are unobtrusive, foraging alone or in dispersed pairs or small family parties of five to eight without forming large clans as other thornbills do, and not often joining feeding flocks of mixed species.

They are almost wholly arboreal, feeding, roosting and breeding in the mid and upper stages of woodlands, open forest, mallee and denser eastern mulga at one–10 metres above the ground, but also foraging in bushes. Unlike the Striated Thornbill and the similar-looking Weebill, they usually avoid eucalypts, keeping to thickets of *Acacia, Casuarina, Callitris, Melaleuca* and chenopod bushes—all trees and shrubs with bushy foliage. There they methodically, hop-gleaning for insects in among the leaves, working quickly but remaining for some time in each shrub and calling regularly in contact and territorial defence.

They are sedentary, established groups remaining in the same small groves of a few hectares year round. Each group may have only one permanent breeding female, but all members will help in the feeding of young.

Banded Whiteface *Aphelocephala nigricincta* (NORTH, 1895)

GREGARIOUS LIKE OTHER WHITEFACES, the Banded is a local nomad, wandering about in small feeding parties and often mixing with other species. Its range overlaps the other whitefaces on the steppes of far-inland Australia but the Banded generally keeps to the most desolate, bare gibber-plains and sandy ridges, with few shrubs and almost no trees. There it forages on the ground in short hops, picking up seeds, spiders and insects which provide its water.

Nesting may be communal, several pairs building nests close by, and both parents and helpers feeding young. Males have a breeding song-flight, rising to flutter and sing, then dropping back to cover.

OTHER NAMES
Black-banded Whiteface, Black-banded Squeaker.

IDENTIFICATION
LENGTH: *110–120 mm.*
ADULTS: *Sexes similar. Crown grey-brown, flecked dusky; rest of upper parts bright cinnamon-rufous. Wings grey-brown, secondaries and coverts edged cinnamon-white. Tail dusky with white tip. Forehead and face white,* separated from crown and ears by dusky line in front of eyes. Underparts off-white with narrow black band across breast; rufous flecking on flanks. Eye white. Bill black. Feet dusky.
IMMATURES: *Probably resemble adults.*

VOICE
CALL: *Staccato twittering, in contact, more tinkling than in Southern Whiteface.*
SONG: *Soft, weak bell-like notes, often in flight.*

NESTING
Breeds February–August, influenced by rain. Nest a large globe or cylinder with long entrance tunnel; made mostly of densely interlocked small twigs; lined with feathers and down; in bush or low tree, 1–2 m up. Eggs: two to four; dull white to light brown, thickly freckled with red-brown blotches; oblong-oval, about 18 x 13 mm.

DISTRIBUTION
Saltbush plains and low spinifex ridges in central inland, from central Lake Eyre basin, Qld, SA, to southern Pilbara, WA. No races.

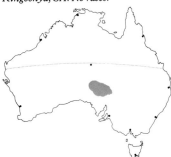

The Banded Whiteface lives on the dry far-inland plains of Australia, where it is locally nomadic.

Chestnut-breasted Whiteface *Aphelocephala pectoralis* (GOULD, 1871)

NOT DESCRIBED UNTIL 1871, the Chestnut-breasted Whiteface has remained one of Australia's least known and seen birds; its nest and eggs were not found until 1968. One reason is its rarity and another its apparent nomadism. It occurs on the stony, shrubbed steppes and low tablelands around the western fringes of the Lake Eyre basin, in near-treeless vegetation of sparse saltbush and bluebush, mixed with desert annuals.

Out of breeding, Chestnut-breasted Whitefaces are gregarious, gathering in small loose wandering bands of up to 10 or so birds, their movements apparently governed by seasonal conditions. They forage on the ground, hopping in short bursts as other whitefaces do, picking up seeds and small insects.

Flight, too, is like that of other whitefaces, of low, swift undulations, carrying the birds to the cover of shrubs if they are flushed. The groups sometimes associate with mixed feeding flocks of Banded and Southern Whitefaces. If good seasons prompt breeding, however, they may disband into pairs to nest, sometimes returning to the same site in successive years.

OTHER NAMES
Chestnut-breasted Tit.

IDENTIFICATION
LENGTH: *110-120 mm.*
ADULTS: *Sexes similar. Crown grey-brown, flecked dusky; rest of upper parts cinnamon-rufous. Wings grey-brown, secondaries and coverts edged cinnamon-white. Tail dusky with white tip. Forehead and face white, separated from crown and ears by dusky line in front of eyes. Underparts dull white with broad chestnut band across breast; rufous flecking on flanks. Eye white. Bill black. Feet dusky.*
IMMATURES: *As adults; breast band narrower, edged dusky. Juveniles with only fine black breast band.*

VOICE
CALL: *Erratic, staccato twittering in contact, like that of Southern Whiteface.*
SONG: *Described as soft, plaintive whistles.*

NESTING
Breeds August–September; influenced by rainfall and seasonal conditions. Nest a globe with rounded side entrance near top, loosely made of dead twigs; lined with feathers and wool. The only occupied nest yet described was built into a Maireana shrub 300 mm above ground, and was similar to that of Banded Whiteface but without entrance tunnel. Eggs: three; matt, pale pink, covered with purple-grey markings, especially at larger end; oblong-oval, about 17 x 13 mm.

DISTRIBUTION
Shrub steppe on elevated gibber-plains around western fringes of Lake Eyre basin, between Granite Downs, Oodnadatta, Lyndhurst and Kingoonya, SA. No races.

The rarely seen Chestnut-breasted Whiteface is restricted to a small area.

Southern Whiteface *Aphelocephala leucopsis* (GOULD, 1841)

The Southern Whiteface has a sturdy bill that enables it to eat seeds as well as insects. Feeding mainly on the ground, it also probes dead tree-trunks.

THE SOUTHERN WHITEFACE is one of a group of three Australian acanthizine warblers that has taken to feeding much on seeds. For this they have stout finch-like bills and thickly muscled stomachs part-filled with grit to help grind the seeds. Insects and plant shoots are taken as well, all picked up from the ground, where the birds use their bills to turn over pieces of dung and debris, prising underneath, then pushing up as do turnstones and starlings to expose food.

Of the three species, the Southern is much the most abundant, occuring generally in better-watered open, sparsely shrubbed woodland right across southern inland Australia, from the east coast to the west. It almost completely overlaps the range of the other two species, but where this happens, one of the others at least—the Banded—tends to replace it, notably in the Gibson Desert, WA, and central Lake Eyre basin–Simpson Desert, SA. This at once suggests that the two species compete and that the Banded is at advantage in the driest desert habitats.

Although feeding mainly on bare ground, the Southern Whiteface also occasionally works up on to the trunks of dead trees, probing into cracks and knotholes. It is a gregarious bird, banding together in small foraging parties of 10–15, occasionally 50 or more, and mixing with other feeding species such as Yellow-rumped Thornbills. The whitefaces forage over the ground in short half-hops, one foot in front of the other, picking up food as they go.

If flushed, they either fly further on then drop to continue feeding or perch up on dead trees, twittering constantly in alarm and to keep contact. Even when perched they are rarely still, hopping forward and back and from side to side along bare limbs. Flight is a swift, undulating dash, low over the ground.

Southern Whitefaces are sedentary, and groups probably forage in much the same area year round. During breeding, the groups do not seem to break up much into obviously territorial nesting pairs; breeding could be communal. They choose nest sites different from those of the other whitefaces: holes in stumps, trees, and posts, wherever they are available. Young, after fledging, go through a cryptic phase for several days, huddling in a bush, before beginning to follow their parents and learning to feed.

There are two distinct races of the Southern Whiteface, one eastern, the other western. They have not always been appreciated because the eastern ranges well into Western Australia. The western race, with a broad sash of rufous down its flanks, is limited to the southern Pilbara and northern Goldfields district, WA, east to the western fringes of the Gibson and Great Victoria Deserts. The eastern race, with brown on white flecking on its flanks, ranges west across most of southern Australia, to the eastern fringes of the Gibson and Great Victoria Deserts and right through the Nullarbor Plain to about 124°E. There the two races meet and intergrade through a bottleneck.

OTHER NAMES
Eastern Whiteface, Western Whiteface, Chestnut-bellied Whiteface, White-faced Titmouse, White-faced Squeaker.

IDENTIFICATION
LENGTH: *110–120 mm.*
ADULTS: *Sexes similar. Upper parts deep grey-brown, crown flecked dusky. Wings plain deep grey-brown, secondaries edged duller. Tail dusky, with white tip on all but central pair of feathers. Forehead and face white, separated from crown and ears by dusky line in front of eyes. Underparts all cream washed olive-grey on breast to pure white. Flanks either flecked mid-*brown on white (eastern race) or sashed plain rich rufous. Eye white. Bill black. Feet dusky.*
IMMATURES: *Similar to adults.*

VOICE
CALL: *Twittering notes,* tweet-tweeter, *in erratic bursts in contact when feeding, sharpened to more staccato* wit-wita-wit-wit, *rapidly repeated in bursts, in alarm and flight.*
SONG: *Soft, tuneful bell-like notes; probably modified contact call.*

NESTING
Breeds June–November; influenced by rain in interior range. Nest a large, untidy dome of bark strips and grasses; lined with feathers, fur, wool and sometimes plant down; secreted in tree hollows, mortice-holes in fence posts, low foliage of shrubs or trees, and even large stick nests of birds-of-prey. Eggs: two to five; dull white to buff, lightly marked with brown to red freckling—at times spotting is indistinct; oblong-oval, about 19 x 14 mm.*

DISTRIBUTION
Open woodland, savanna, and shrub steppe across southern Australia, throughout inland north to 23°S. Two races.

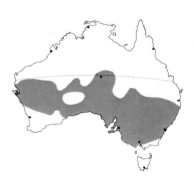

A female Varied Sittella of the black-capped southern race. All sittellas can hang upside down like this with ease to feed the young.

Varied Sittella

Daphoenositta chrysoptera (Latham, 1801)

OTHER NAMES
Treerunner, 'Nuthatch', Barkpecker.

IDENTIFICATION
LENGTH: *120–130 mm.*
ADULTS: *Variable but generally brown-grey above and white below, with or without streaking. Head black, white or sooty, or a mixture. Back mid grey-brown with or without black streaks. Rump plain white. Wings black with a complete cinnamon (southern races) or partial white (northern) bar across flight feathers. Tail black, tipped white to all except central pair of feathers. Throat white, black or streaked; breast and belly white with or without dusky streaks; undertail white chevroned black. Eye yellow to orange; eye-ring yellow. Bill long, black with buff base (southern) or short, yellow with black tip (northern). Feet yellow, claws dusky. Orange-winged race: sooty head, 'orange' wing bar, streaked above and below; Black-capped race (larger than rest): black cap with white (male) or black (female) face, 'orange' wing bar, no streaking; White-winged race: head as Black-capped, white wing bar, back only streaked; Striated race: head black to throat (female) or streaked white on face (male), white wing bar, boldly streaked above and below; White-headed race: as Orange-winged but all head white.*
IMMATURES: *As adults but white tips on primary coverts (first year). Juveniles mottled white over head and back, less streaked below; feet dull brown.*

VOICE
CALL: *Single, whistled chip repeated monotonously while foraging. Incubating females and young give shrill chatter.*
SONG: *High drawn-out double-whistle, the first syllable higher pitched,* seee-weee, *in twittered chorus by moving groups.*

NESTING
Breeds September-January in south; July–October and again February–March in Queensland. Nest an unusual tubular cup of fibre bound with cobweb, coated with camouflage flakes of bark and lichen; built into two-pronged fork of upright dead branch 5–25 m above ground. Eggs: three or two; dull bluish or greyish white, boldly blotched and spotted with greyish and reddish brown and dusky slate, more at large end; oval, about 17 x 14 mm. Incubation 18–20 days, by female. Young fledge in about 20 days.

DISTRIBUTION
Woodland and open forest of all mainland; also montane New Guinea. About nine races, five in Australia: Orange-winged in southeast; Black-capped in west and south; White-winged in northwest; Striated in northeast; White-headed in central east.

VARIED SITTELLAS ARE tree-living birds both when foraging and at rest. In small parties these stocky little birds scurry non-stop in all directions over tree-trunks and branches searching for food: beetles, bugs, spiders, bees and caterpillars. Finishing in one tree they flit quickly to the next, close together, floating and dipping like butterflies on rounded wings, and keeping in touch in a chorus of thin, high whistles. If frightened, they dive to cover, hiding in cracks in bark or hanging motionless upside-down in branchlets, resembling a leaf.

Sittellas range throughout the woodlands and open forests of the mainland, most abundantly in areas of rough-barked eucalypts, and avoid only rainforests. Parties seem to keep year round to the same home or breeding range which may nonetheless be so large that local sittellas can give the impression of being nomadic.

Their foraging behaviour differs in many respects from those other bark-foragers, the treecreepers. They commonly climb down the trunk head-first, and do not work along the underside of branches though they often hang upside-down. They move over branches in a characteristic zigzag fashion, leaning over and peering to one side then the next, at times flickering one or both wings, probably to scare cryptic prey. After reaching the end of a branch, they often turn around and hop quickly back towards the trunk. The bill is slightly upturned, and used for probing crevices and prising off flakes of bark for prey beneath—particularly on dead branches. Males have longer bills than females and generally work the inner, more thickly barked parts of the tree. After catching a large insect, they will use one foot—mostly the left one—to pin it down while stabbing it with the bill. Ants, the staple food of treecreepers, are rarely eaten.

At rest, sittellas often sit together and preen themselves or each other. If three birds huddle together, the outer two will simultaneously groom the middle one, which goes into a seeming trance. One of the outer birds may then try to squeeze into the middle position but occasionally lifts one of the other birds off their perch by squeezing between its legs.

Before dusk the birds fly to one of their roost-sites—usually the base of a dead branch. After the first two have settled, the other group members arrive, and one by one wedge themselves in between those present, each pushing the outer bird farther along the branch. This process continues into the night with much jostling of positions until all fit.

Sittellas are usually grouped in pairs or parties of up to 12, but larger, temporary aggregations of up to 30 gather after breeding. All members of the group join in building the beautifully camouflaged nest, and feed the incubating female and her young. Even birds less than three months old may feed the young of later broods. Queues often form as birds wait their turn to visit the nest. Unfortunately so much activity makes the nest easy to locate and many are destroyed by predators. The young are fed for up to 11 weeks after fledging, by which time they have almost lost the mottling on their upper parts. Two broods may be raised in a season.

The five Australian races of the Varied Sittella are distributed in a circular chain around mainland Australia. Each is distinctive in colouration but wherever it comes into contact with another they interbreed freely; all forms are connected in central Queensland by a hybrid population.

A Varied Sittella of the white-headed race in central eastern Queensland. Bark camouflages the nest.

White-throated Treecreeper

Cormobates leucophaea (LATHAM, 1801)

TREECREEPERS ARE SMALL, brownish birds with rather long curved bills, large feet, and a pale buff bar in the wing which shows in flight. Confined to Australia and New Guinea, they hunt for food on tree trunks and large branches which they climb without using their tails for support. Their method is simple. They work steadily up the tree, moving straight up or sidling around from side to side; reaching an end point, they fly and plane down to the base of the next tree to repeat the process. Flight is direct, of bursts of whirring stiff-winged beats interspersed with planing glides. At night they sleep, clinging upright, on the surface of tree trunks in bark crevices, or burnt-out basal hollows; even crevices in the walls of buildings have been used.

A bird of the wetter forests of the east coast and outlying ranges, the White-throated is much the most solitary of the treecreepers, to the point of being antisocial. It feeds alone except briefly during breeding and even mated birds keep well away from one another at most times. Trespass is met with aggressive chases, loud calls and a strange clicking noise made by abrupt spreading of the tail.

The White-throated Treecreeper is the most acrobatic member of its family. When moving along an outward-sloping limb, it works as much along the underside as the upper, investigating areas inaccessible to most birds. As it moves up the tree it explores crevices or cracks in the trunk and areas of peeling bark, probing and testing the surface with its rather thin bill—which is thinner and slightly more down-curved than those of other treecreepers. It sometimes hammers briefly at a particularly likely looking spot, or even probes with its tongue into deep crevices the bill cannot plumb. Occasionally it snatches an insect from a leaf or thin twig, and on rare occasions it may even probe into a flower, such as a banksia, as a honeyeater does. Treecreepers feed on a wide variety of insects and spiders, but ants—the most conspicuous and numerous of tree-trunk insects—are the chief item in their diet. Unlike other treecreepers, the White-throated hardly ever feeds on the ground; it feeds on prevailingly rainforest trees and rough-barked eucalypts: stringybarks, peppermints and ironbarks. In rainforests, clumps of arboreal moss and lichens are probed.

White-throated Treecreepers—like all treecreepers—climb in an unusual way. The bird holds one foot in front of the other, then moves the lower foot up to the front foot, then the one in front moves higher up the trunk so that one foot retains the lead. At times the left foot will be ahead, at others the right, but the bird does not walk up the tree with one foot ahead of the other in sequence, nor does it hop, with both feet together. Rather, the gait is a shuffling, slow gallop, the feet, with front toes partly bound by skin, gripping like callipers. The bird's large, strong feet and claws also enable it to hang vertically upwards on a trunk, but like other treecreepers it cannot reverse itself and hang downwards like a sittella. Occasionally it will shuffle backwards down the tree, but normally it only moves upwards.

Pairs maintain an exclusive territory year round which both sexes advertise with ringing song-calls from any perch on trunks or branches. With each measured note the singer jerks its tail sharply downwards. Early in breeding the male feeds his mate frequently, first announcing his offering with a fast trill. From selected perches he gives whistled crescendos and a spectacular pre-mating display. With each call, the head is lowered and the wings shivered. If the female arrives he spreads his wings horizontally and raises his tail, then slowly rocks from side to side, waving one or both wings. Copulation may follow.

Only the female builds the nest and incubates, laying each egg of the clutch at 48-hour intervals. When she emerges after a sitting she often emits a single loud note, then forages with her mate, uttering a soft twitter periodically. Both sexes care for the young, which beg loudly with a distinctive chatter, audible from some distance. Nests are normally built in tree-holes or stumps, but this treecreeper will also build behind loose pieces of bark and in artificial nest-boxes. Usually only one brood is reared a season.

The northernmost race of this species, the Little Treecreeper *C.l.minor*, is largely confined to highland rainforests (above 300 metres) but also inhabits eucalypt forests on the ranges in northern Queensland. Compared to the White-throated Treecreeper of the southeast it is smaller and darker, but in other respects, such as voice, it is similar. The two forms are linked by intermediate populations in central and southeastern Queensland to northeastern New South Wales. The Papuan Treecreeper of montane New Guinea rainforests is also sometimes treated as a race of the White-throated, but it is much smaller and more russet brown, with a brown rump and differently marked crown.

This White-throated Treecreeper is a male; the female has a rusty-orange spot on its ear coverts.

OTHER NAMES
Little Treecreeper, 'Woodpecker'.

IDENTIFICATION
LENGTH: *140–170 mm.*
MALE: *Upper parts deep olive-brown; rump grey; forehead and forecrown feathers edged buff, giving scaly appearance; lores off-white. Wings dusky, with buff band across flight feathers and pale grey trailing edge. Tail mid-grey with broad black subterminal band on all but central pair of feathers. Throat and centre breast white becoming creamy yellow on belly; variable wash of brown-grey across breast; sides of breast and flanks drop-spotted cream-white on dusky. Undertail buff-white with broken black crossbars. Eye brown. Bill dusky; base of lower mandible grey-white. Feet deep olive-grey-brown. Northeastern Queensland races south to Eungella, darker above, throat grey-white, broad deep brown-grey breast band, belly heavily mottled olive-brown, cream and dusky.*
FEMALE: *As male; a rusty-orange spot on lower cheek, larger in young birds.*
IMMATURES: *As adults, but black-edged whitish streaks on scapulars in most birds; upper parts barred faintly dusky in males; rump bright rufous in females. Adult plumage gained gradually at first annual moult several months after fledging.*

VOICE
CALL: *Series of piping whistles quickly repeated, the first descending in pitch then flattening out, or uttered singly, by both sexes, probably both to advertise territory and maintain contact; also soft buzz and kookaburra-like chuckle.*
SONG: *Males give repeated series of up to 10 upward-inflected whistled notes*

with slight crescendo in display, as well as rapid trills and soft upward-inflected hit, quickly repeated. Females give melodious succession of whistled notes, descending scale and slowing down; during incubation period, soft morse-code-like notes. Juveniles give a soft trill reminiscent of Fantailed Cuckoo.*

NESTING
Breeds August–December. Nest in tree hollow, often filled with debris; a cup, lined with hair, moss, fur or feathers. Eggs: two or three, rarely four; white to creamy white, sparingly dotted with dark red-brown or purplish-black, mostly at larger end; oval, about 22 x 17 nm. Incubation 22–23 days, by female. Young fledge in about 26 days.

DISTRIBUTION
Rainforests and wet and dry sclerophyll forest with rough-barked eucalypts around east coast of mainland and nearby ranges, north to tablelands near Cooktown, Qld, and southwest to southeast and Mt Lofty Ranges, SA. Restricted to montane forests north of 25°S. Five races.

Red-browed Treecreeper *Climacteris erythrops* GOULD, 1841

OTHER NAMES
*Red-eyebrowed Treecreeper,
'Woodpecker'.*

IDENTIFICATION
LENGTH: *145–160 mm.*
MALE: *Upper parts dark brown; crown
and nape blackish; rump mid-grey.
Wings with pale buff band across
flight feathers. Tail mid-grey with
broad black subterminal band on all
but central feathers. Foreface and
eyebrow rust-red. Throat dull white;
upper breast plain brownish grey;
lower breast to belly boldly striped
black-and-white; undertail buff-white
with broken black crossbars. Eye
brown. Bill dusky. Feet dark
olive-grey.*
FEMALE: *As male; upper breast striped
rufous and dull white.*
IMMATURES: *As adults but face grey;
underparts plain grey-buff with
sporadic white streaks.*

VOICE
CALL: *Rapid sibilant chatter
descending in pitch; often immediately
answered by a sharp descending two-
or three-syllable trill from another
bird. Also harsh grate. Juveniles give
high-pitched, strident notes, at times
monotonously.*
SONG: *Shrill, upward-inflected note,
quickly repeated up to four times.*

NESTING
*Breeds August–January. Nest a cup of
bark, covered with layer of fur; placed
in a tree hollow, particularly a hollow
dead branch of a eucalypt, 2–30 m
above ground. Eggs: two; delicate pale
pink with close red-brown and dull
purple blotching all over, especially at
larger end; oval, about 22 x 17 mm.
Incubation 18 days, by female. Young
fledge in 26 days. Sometimes
double-brooded.*

DISTRIBUTION
*Cool eucalypt forests on ranges and
coast around southeastern mainland,
north to near Gympie, Qld, southwest
to Daylesford, Vic. No races.*

The Red-browed Treecreeper nests in a tree hole, particularly in a dead eucalypt. This is a female.

COOL, TALL, EUCALYPT FORESTS along the Great Dividing Range
and southeast coast are the core habitat of the Red-browed
Treecreeper. It does enter drier forests locally as well as subalpine
snow gum woodland, but avoids rainforest unless there are
overtopping eucalypts for it to feed in.

Throughout its range, the Red-browed Treecreeper occurs side
by side with the White-throated. Most competition for food—both
are mainly ant-eaters—is averted by the Red-browed's foraging in
different sites. It often comes down to work over fallen logs, and in
the trees it keeps to the smooth-barked eucalypts, spending much
time rummaging in accumulated debris hanging in forks. Even
when visiting rough-barked eucalypts, it concentrates on the
smoother outer branches where the bark peels away.

Red-browed Treecreepers are communal, small family groups
holding permanent territories up to three times as large as those of
the White-throated. The dominant breeding pair tolerates young
males in the territory for up to three years, but females usually
leave in their first. Nest building is begun by the female, but other
members then bring lining and feed the incubating female and her
young in the nest. As they forage, contact is kept by feeding in the
same tree or by antiphonal call-and-answer.

At night they roost mainly in hollows in dead tree branches.

White-browed Treecreeper *Climacteris affinis* <small>BLYTH, 1864</small>

THE DESERT-DWELLING White-browed Treecreeper is the quietest and least conspicuous of its group. Its core habitats are the denser mulga and belah or blackoke *Casuarina* woodlands of the arid zone, but it also enters mixed woodlands which include other acacias, native pines *Callitris* and occasional eucalypts.

In the east and southwest of its range it overlaps both Brown and Rufous Treecreepers which also forage in similar ways on the trunks of trees for the same basic food: ants and occasional other insects. At times when they meet the larger Brown will aggressively chase the White-browed. Extensive competition, however, is unlikely because the Brown and Rufous keep to groves of mallee and creek-bed eucalypts and feed much on the ground in open areas. The White-browed Treecreeper, by contrast, keeps more to the interior of mulga and belah and is primarily arboreal, spending less than a quarter of its time on the ground.

Although closely related to the communal Red-browed Treecreeper, the White-browed is rather solitary like the White-throated. Pairs are sedentary and probably hold large territories year round, from which young are dispersed soon after breeding. Even when paired, male and female forage alone except during breeding; contact then is kept with soft cricket-like chirrups. Like other treecreepers, they hop-gallop methodically up tree trunks and main branches, probing in crannies and crevices for food, then flutter-plane off to the base of the next tree to start again.

Early in breeding, males advertise territory by chirruping stridently but sporadically from vantage perches. Only the female incubates, but the male supplies her with food as well as carrying lining to the nest. Both sexes feed the young but there are no reports yet of additional attendants helping at the nest. Two broods may be raised in a season.

OTHER NAMES
White-eyebrowed Treecreeper.

IDENTIFICATION
LENGTH: *135–150 mm.*
MALE: *Upper parts earth-brown, greyer on crown and nape; rump mid-grey (eastern race) or brown (western race). Wings dusky with pale buff band across flight feathers. Tail mid-grey (eastern) to browner (western), with broad black subterminal band on all but central feathers. Eyebrow white; ear coverts streaked black and white; lores dusky. Throat dull white; upper breast plain mid-grey; lower breast and belly boldly striped black and white; undertail buff-white with broken black crossbars. Eye brown. Bill and feet dusky black.*
FEMALE: *As male but rusty red wash over eyebrow and lores; upper breast striped rufous and dull white.*
IMMATURES: *As adults; eyebrow greyish and indistinct. Adult plumage gained at first annual moult several months after fledging.*

VOICE
CALL: *Usually silent. Weak, short, descending, cricket-like, sibilant trills or chirrups, of two to four notes, in contact between pair or family party during breeding. Nestlings give low-pitched strident trill.*
SONG: *Strident chirrup by male, repeated from vantage perch.*

NESTING
Breeds August-December. Nest of grass or strips of bark formed into cup, at times built up with animal dung; lined with fur, hair or down; placed in a deep hollow limb or trunk, sometimes down to ground level. Eggs: two or three; pale pink, closely spotted and speckled all over with red-brown and purplish red; oval, about 22 x 17 mm. Incubation by female. Young fledge in about 22-23 days.

DISTRIBUTION
Mulga and blackoke woodlands of southern arid zone north to about 24°S. Two races: one western, east to northern Simpson Desert, western Lake Eyre basin and Flinders Ranges; the other eastern, west to northern Murray mallee and western Darling basin.

The White-browed Treecreeper lives in drier areas than the other treecreepers, but like its relatives it nests in tree hollows; two broods may be raised each season. The brown rump on this bird indicates that it belongs to the western race.

The male Black-tailed Treecreeper has a black throat streaked with white. Black-taileds live in northern Australia, with an isolated race in the west.

Black-tailed Treecreeper *Climacteris melanura* GOULD, 1843

IN FLIGHT, THE PALE WING-STRIPE of the Black-tailed Treecreeper contrasts with its near-black plumage. It replaces the Brown Treecreeper in the eucalypt woodlands and open forests of northwestern Australia, occupying permanent territories there.

Like the Brown Treecreeper it is communal and spends up to half its foraging time feeding on the ground and fallen timber. In loose groups of two to six, it hops briskly along, picking up mainly ants, and bobbing its tail as it goes. It also works over the trunks and lower branches of trees as other treecreepers do. Feeding groups keep in touch with sharp piping whistles, often duetting, both simultaneously and antiphonally. During breeding, helpers assist with nest building and the feeding of young.

OTHER NAMES
Allied Treecreeper, Chestnut-bellied Treecreeper.

IDENTIFICATION
LENGTH: *155–170 mm.*
MALE: *Upper parts plain dusky; ear coverts faintly streaked white. Wings dusky with pale buff band across flight feathers. Tail dusky with blacker subterminal band. Throat and upper breast black, streaked white; rest of underparts brown-dusky, with black shaft streaks, washed rufous in Pilbara, WA; blacker barred white on undertail.*
Eye brown. Bill and feet black. Western race isolated in Pilbara, WA, lighter on back and washed on underparts.
FEMALE: *As male; throat white, ringed with rufous-and-white striping on upper breast.*
IMMATURES: *Uniformly dusky black; chin white edged black.*

VOICE
CALL: *Strident, piping-whistled* spink, *given singly in contact.*
SONG: *Same notes rushed together, often higher-pitched and descending a little, spaced erratically after first surge.*

NESTING
Breeds September–January. Nest a cup of grass and bark; lined with fur and feathers; in hollow limb or trunk. Eggs: two–three; flesh-white, almost obscured with red-brown and purple-red spots and blotches; oval, about 24 x 18 mm.

DISTRIBUTION
Eucalypt woodlands and open forests of northwestern mainland between Kimberleys, WA, and head of Gulf of Carpentaria, Qld; rufous isolate in Pilbara, WA. Two races.

Brown Treecreeper *Climacteris picumnus* TEMMINCK, 1824

A male Brown Treecreeper searching a tree trunk for insects. Treecreepers hop up trees with one foot in front of the other, probing cracks and crevices.

THE ARRESTING STACCATO CALLS of the Brown Treecreeper are characteristic of much of the eucalypt woodlands, mallee, and drier open forest of eastern Australia. Brown Treecreepers, largest of their group, overlap the ranges of the White-throated and Red-browed there—even living with them in the same copse. Browns nonetheless keep to more open woodland with much open ground and fallen timber, so benefiting from clearing by man.

Brown Treecreepers are communal and sedentary. Pairs to groups of three to six hold to the same large territory of about five to 10 hectares year round and spend about half their foraging time feeding—hopping, one foot in front of the other, in the litter on open ground. They turn over leaves and debris, and work over fallen logs and spiral up tree trunks as well, pecking and probing cracks, crevices and peeling bark for food: beetles, bugs, larvae, but mainly ants. As they go, they fly low from point to point, on stiffly whirring wings punctuated with planing glides, and call constantly in contact. If flushed from the ground they fly to a tree or stump. Machine gun-like alarm churrings are given whenever the birds mob potential predators or nest-robbers, such as snakes.

Each local group comprises a breeding pair and one or two subordinate males. With the coming of breeding the dominant male gives a pre-mating display. Facing the female as she crouches with quivering wings, he bows back and forth in front of her before sidling behind to mount, still bowing. All males join in building the nest, feeding the incubating female and caring for the young.

Some members of a group also attend other nests in adjacent territories—even on the same day. This reflects a relaxation of territoriality when young are present. And some birds continue to attend nests in their natal territory after they become breeders with their own. Thus young may be fed not only by their parents but also older siblings and occasionally unrelated birds.

The northernmost populations of Brown Treecreepers at the foot of Cape York Peninsula are rather small and dusky backed and have higher-pitched calls than those to the south; they were once regarded as a separate species, the Black Treecreeper. In other aspects of their biology, they are like the Browns; as they intergrade southwest of Townsville, they are now treated as the same species.

OTHER NAMES
Black Treecreeper, 'Woodpecker'.

IDENTIFICATION
LENGTH: *160–180 mm.*
MALE: *Upper parts plain earth-brown, greyer on crown and neck. Wings greyer brown with pale buff band across flight feathers. Tail earth-brown with broad black subterminal band on all but central pair of feathers. Eyebrow and face pale sandy-buff; lores dusky; ear coverts streaked brown and buff. Throat off-white grading to cream-buff on upper breast; centre of lower throat freckled black; lower breast, flanks and belly pale buff-brown streaked finely dusky and white; undertail buff-white with broken black bars. Eye brown. Bill and feet dusky. The Black Treecreeper (race melanota) is similar below, but uniformly dusky black above; the tail band is obscured. Eyebrow, throat and cheeks are creamy white, contrasting sharply with blackish crown and line through eye.*
FEMALE: *As male, but slightly smaller; rufous freckling instead of black on centre of lower throat, often hidden.*
IMMATURES: *Darker brown above with greyer head, including eyebrow; throat of males white, bordered below with black markings; flanks, belly and undertail coverts washed rufous.*

VOICE
CALL: *Single, strident, staccato whistles,* spink, *with slight upward inflexion, often repeated in contact. Machine gun-like churring or chatter in alarm. Juveniles give adult contact notes, but even higher-pitched.*
SONG: *Includes a succession of slightly falling notes, followed by rising rattles or canary-like whistles (often from different birds); also a rapid series of*

six–10 piping whistles repeated at short intervals (pre-mating call).

NESTING
Breeds June–December; earlier inland, later near coast. Nest a cup of dried grasses, bark and dung; usually lined with fur, feathers or plant down; placed in a hollow limb or trunk 1–3 m up, sometimes as high as 15 m or more— fence-post holes are often used. Eggs: two or three; pale pink, densely spotted and blotched with red-brown and underlying lavender; oval, about 23 x 18 mm. Incubation 16–17 days, by female. Young fledge in 26 days, but often forced to leave as early as 20 days.

DISTRIBUTION
Eucalypt woodland and drier open forest, including mallee and river gum galleries inland throughout eastern mainland west to Mt Lofty–Flinders Ranges and Coopers Creek, SA, and north to foot of Cape York Peninsula, Qld, with local pockets north to Weipa. Two intergrading races: one dusky backed north of Townsville– Hughenden; the other brown everywhere else.

Rufous Treecreeper

Climacteris rufa GOULD, 1841

OTHER NAMES
'Woodpecker'.

IDENTIFICATION
LENGTH: *150–170 mm.*
MALE: *Upper parts plain ash-brown,
more rufous on rump; crown and neck
greyer. Wings greyer brown with pale
buff band across flight feathers. Tail
rufous-brown, with broad black
subterminal band on all but central
pair of feathers. All face including
brow rufous-ochre; lores dusky. Throat
to belly plain rufous-ochre, with grey
wash across breast and black freckling
in centre of lower throat; undertail
pale rufous with broken black bars.
Eye brown. Bill black. Feet dusky.*
FEMALE: *As male but slightly smaller;
rufous freckling instead of black on
centre of lower throat.*
IMMATURES: *Slightly darker brown
above, darker below with greyer
throat.*

VOICE
CALL: *Single, thin whistle, peeep,
repeated erratically in contact, higher-
pitched and less strident than in
Brown Treecreeper. Harsh churring in
alarm. Juveniles give low-pitched,
downslurred notes.*
SONG: *A rapid, falling series of piping
whistles, faster and higher-pitched
than in Brown Treecreeper.*

NESTING
*Breeds July–November. Nest a cup of
dried grasses and bark; lined with fur,
feathers or plant down; placed in a
hollow limb or trunk, occasionally in a
hollow log. Eggs: one–four, usually two
or three; pale pinkish-white, thickly
marked all over with red-brown and
dull purple; oval, about 24 x 19 mm.
Probably raises two broods in good
seasons.*

DISTRIBUTION
*Eucalypt woodland, open jarrah forest
and mallee in southwest, north around
Nullarbor Plain to central Eyre
Peninsula, SA. Apparently two races;
despite the tenuous connection with the
west north of the Nullarbor, Eyre
Peninsula treecreepers are consistently
larger and more brightly rufous.*

THE RICHLY COLOURED Rufous Treecreeper is the only member of its family found in southwestern Australia. It is closely related to the Brown Treecreeper of the southeast and, like it, lives in open woodland. The Rufous also lives in humid jarrah forests where it is quite common, although it tends to retreat as areas are settled.

The Rufous Treecreeper, like the Western Yellow Robin and the Blue-breasted Fairy-wren, is one of the southwestern birds that ranges east to Eyre Peninsula, SA. The Eyre Peninsula treecreepers have, however, become rather rare, being restricted to 'bull' mallee where there are trees old and large enough to produce nesting hollows. It was once thought that the Eyre Peninsula treecreepers were isolated by many hundreds of kilometres from the rest of the population in the west, but it is now known that they are thinly connected through mallee sand-plain around the north of the Nullarbor Plain.

The Rufous Treecreeper hunts for its insect food by pecking and probing into cracks, crevices and peeling bark on the trunks and main branches of trees. It can only climb upwards, which it does in sharp hops with one foot ahead of the other, flashing its tail laterally as it goes. It also spends much time feeding among litter on the ground, mainly on ants.

Rufous Treecreepers are often seen in groups of three, rather than the usual pairs, occupying large territories. Probably the third bird is a male of the previous brood. All three birds help feed the nestlings.

Their courtship display is probably like that of the Brown Treecreeper. The male faces the female while she crouches with quivering wings. He bows in front of her, then sidles behind her, still bowing, and copulation follows.

The most brightly coloured treecreeper, the Rufous Treecreeper of southwestern Australia lives in open woodland, mallee and humid jarrah forests. The tree hollows it nests in are generally near the ground.

Red Wattlebird *Anthochaera carunculata* (SHAW, 1790)

NAMED FROM THE LOBES of skin on their cheeks, Red Wattlebirds are large members of one of Australia's largest and most typical family of birds, the honeyeaters. Honeyeaters are aggressive tree- and shrub-living birds with diving undulating flight and four-pronged brush-tipped tongues for rifling nectar and pollen from flowers. They are versatile foragers, taking a variety of insects and fruit as well, and many are nomadic or migratory—they have to be—following the cyclic and seasonal flushes of flowering around the countryside.

Red Wattlebirds are no exception. Widespread in the eucalypt woodlands and forests of southern Australia, they gather in loose nomadic bands of five to 100 or more after breeding to roam on established flight paths in search of concentrations of flowering rich enough to support their energy requirements: flowering eucalypts, banksias, grevilleas and hakeas which produce copious amounts of nectar and attract many insects. The birds frequently establish feeding territories around these sources, advertising them with much raucous calling and chasing other wattlebirds and smaller honeyeaters away. Insects are caught on the wing or gleaned from leaves and bark; even honeybees are hunted as they fly in and out of hives.

Wattlebirds commonly enter well-shrubbed urban gardens and orchards, sometimes becoming pests. They remain as long as there is food, moving on when it dwindles and generally vacating higher altitudes and travelling north in winter; in areas of stable supply, some remain year round. The flocks disband during breeding, pairs—possibly permanent—often or always nesting away from others. Pair bonds are kept firm by frequent duet calling between male and female, mostly during breeding. Young are fed—on insects—by both parents for some weeks after fledging.

OTHER NAMES
Gillbird, Wattled Honeyeater.

IDENTIFICATION
LENGTH: *320–350 mm, tail tapered.*
ADULTS: *Sexes similar. Upper parts grey-brown, shaft-streaked white, blacker on crown. Wings and tail grey-brown with narrow and broad white tipping respectively. Cheeks plain grey-white, with rounded pink-red wattle. Throat to breast, flanks and undertail pale brown-grey heavily streaked white; centre belly plain yellow. Eye red. Bill black. Feet pink-flesh.*

IMMATURES: *As adults but face duller, wattle vestigial, eye browner; wattle fills out in first year.*

VOICE
CALL: *Hacking coughs* chok-ch-chok *or* yak-yak-yak *in contact when feeding; higher* tew-tew-tew *from female. Single loud* chok *in alarm.*
SONG: *Mellow, ringing* tew-tew-tew-tew *by female injected with harsh deep coughing* chork-ch-chok-ch-ch-chock *by male, in duet; often introduced by bill snapping.*

NESTING
Breeds mainly July–December; sometimes autumn. Nest a rough, small cup of grass and twigs; lined with feathers, hair or down; perched in outer foliage of tree or bush 3–10(-20) m up. Eggs: two–three; pink-buff with sparse red-brown and purplish spots; oval to tapered-oval, about 33 x 22 mm.

DISTRIBUTION
Eucalypt woodland, forest and mallee heaths of southern near-coastal mainland. No races or one on mainland and one on Kangaroo Island, SA.

Yellow Wattlebird *Anthochaera paradoxa* (DAUDIN, 1800)

THE LARGEST OF ALL HONEYEATERS is the Yellow Wattlebird, named for the pendulous orange-yellow wattles that hang from its cheeks. Males may reach more than 500 millimetres in length and weigh more than 250 grams. This and their nectarivorous diet make them good eating whenever they fatten up on late-flowering eucalypts at the end of summer; because of this and their depredations in orchards they were subject to an open shooting season each autumn until 1972.

Endemic to Tasmania and King Island, Yellow Wattlebirds are birds of tall mature eucalypt forest, but they do range out into woodland heath, gardens and orchards to feed. They are opportunistic foragers, converging in groups of 10–20 on pockets of flowering eucalypts, rifling nectar from blossoms, gleaning insects and spiders from foliage, lapping sugary exudates from stems, and pecking fruit, both in orchards and on native shrubs—*Cyathodes* and *Astrodoma*—to within a metre of the ground.

Most feeding is done in the forest canopy, the birds travelling in loose bands during autumn and winter, moving from tree to tree without stopping long in any one. In this way, some groups work through the same local pocket of forest day after day, others wander randomly, and still others follow regular seasonal paths—from mountains to lowlands in autumn and back again in spring. As they travel, they 'cough' regularly in contact, usually upon landing from a short flight through or over the tree tops.

During breeding, flocks break up into territorial pairs or small groups. Pair-bonds are affirmed by frequent duetting in trees.

OTHER NAMES
Long-wattle Bird, Tasmanian Wattlebird.

IDENTIFICATION
LENGTH: *Male about 480 mm; female 440 mm; very long tapered tails.*
ADULTS: *Sexes similar. Crown to mantle boldly striped grey and white; back, rump and wings browner grey, with dusky and white shaft streaks and edging, flight feathers tipped narrowly white. Tail grey-brown, tipped broadly white. Face hairy grey-white with 30–40 mm long orange-yellow wattles hanging from cheeks; dusky malar line. Throat bearded pale grey, grading to grey-white, dusky-shafted breast, flanks and undertail; centre of belly yellow. Eye dark brown. Bill black. Feet dull yellow.*
IMMATURES: *As adults but belly dull, tail and wattles shorter.*

VOICE
CALL: *Discordant* kuk, quok *or* ku-kuk *by male for contact.*
SONG: *Gargling by female interspersed with harsh croaks from male, in duet.*

NESTING
Breeds July–January. Nest a substantial untidy cup, of bark, twigs and leaves; lined with feathers, down, and fine grass; placed in upright fork 5–30 m high. Eggs: two–three; pale salmon-pink finely and sparsely spotted with red-brown and purple-grey; oval to tapered-oval, about 36 x 24 mm. Incubation 14–16 days. Young fledge in about 18 days.

DISTRIBUTION
All Tasmania except rainforested west coast; also King Island. Eucalypt forests and woodland. No races.

The Yellow Wattlebird, a honeyeater from Tasmania, has long pendulous yellow wattles on the sides of its face.

Red Wattlebirds are common across southern Australia. They often enter suburban gardens to feed on nectar from the flowers of native shrubs.

This Little Wattlebird is feeding on the nectar and pollen from Dryandra flowers. The bird is common in western heathlands and forests.

Little Wattlebird *Anthochaera lunulata* <small>GOULD, 1838</small>

REPLACING THE BRUSH WATTLEBIRD in southwestern Australia is the Little—indeed, the two have long been treated as one species under the name Little Wattlebird. Like the Brush, the western Little inhabits coastal heaths, shrubby forests and even urban gardens in small—though more spaced out—sedentary colonies; it seems similarly dependent on nectar for most of its energy. Insects are gleaned from foliage and young are fed almost exclusively on them, to build protein.

Little Wattlebirds differ from the Brush in many small ways that add up to several major differences in colour pattern and biology. They have a clutch of a single egg and much more protracted bubbling songs. Females again are the sopranos, often sparking duets with males with high-pitched up-and-down twittering; males chime in with bill snapping and clattering *choks* that fill out into long, friarbird-like cacklings and chucklings.

In form, too, Little Wattlebirds have fine white wing tips, more slender bills, plain brownish heads contrasting with bright whitish cheek sashes, and chestnut eyes. Eye colour is the most obvious clue to specific status, for wherever other similar-looking honeyeaters that differ in eye colour meet—such as the New Holland and White-cheeked Honeyeaters, and the species of *Ptiloprora* in New Guinea—they behave as separate species.

OTHER NAMES
Western Wattlebird, Lunulated Wattlebird, Mock Wattlebird.

IDENTIFICATION
LENGTH: *270–300 mm, with tapered tail.*
ADULTS: *Sexes similar; male distinctly larger. Generally brownish grey, with narrow white, droplet-shaped shaft streaks over back and all underparts, but crown and mantle plain. Sash on side of face bright grey-white; large white tufts at sides of breast. Flight feathers with area of rufous in base of primaries, showing in flight; tips finely white. Tail tipped broadly white. Eye chestnut. Bill black. Feet dusky.*
IMMATURES: *As Brush Wattlebird.*

VOICE
CALL: *Cheeping* weep *by feeding adults and fledglings; squawking croaks—* chwaaak—*by male, high twittering by female as territorial markers.*
SONG: *High twittering by female; bill snapping and clattering* choks *and bubblings by male, developing into protracted ringing cackles and chuckles. Frequently in duet, the female leading.*

NESTING
Breeds mainly July–November through spring. Nest a small, rough saucer of interwoven stems and twigs; lined with fine grass and down; supported in outer branchlets of tree or shrub 1–5 m up. Eggs: one; salmon-buff, sparingly spotted with chestnut-red and underlying purple-grey; long oval, about 29 x 21 mm.

DISTRIBUTION
Heaths and shrubby woodlands and forest with flowering proteads in southwestern mainland.

Brush Wattlebird *Anthochaera chrysoptera* (<small>LATHAM, 1801</small>)

BRUSH WATTLEBIRDS—which lack wattles—are very much birds of coastal forests and heaths around the southeastern mainland, wherever there are stands of tall banksias. They do enter heathy eucalypt scrub and urban gardens and will wander seasonally to flushes of flowering, but in pockets of banksias—particularly *B. serrata* and *B. integrifolia* in which there is some flowering year round—they form near-permanent sedentary colonies of 10–30 or more birds.

Brush Wattlebirds appear to depend largely on a diet of nectar. They also take manna and insects for protein, and hawk for midges and gnats in near vertical sorties, but these tiny insects provide little energy and the birds only seek them much at times of abundant nectar-flow. The main sources of nectar are banksias, eucalypts, grevilleas, mistletoes and epacrids.

Around their food sources the birds establish individual territories—the males taking over larger patches than the females—from which they chase other wattlebirds and smaller honeyeaters.

Feeding colonies are incessantly noisy as birds hop about rifling flowers and swoop from perch to perch and tree to tree. At any one time some birds will be giving soft submissive feeding *weeps,* others rasping *choks* or squeaks as territorial markers, and still others protracted bill-snapping and chuckling in territorial advertisement. Male and female often duet in the long calls, the female sparking them with 'soprano' metallic shrieks and the male joining in with 'basso' chuckling squawks.

Such duets accompany courtship. Male and female face one another on a perch, the male fluffing his feathers and fanning his tail as the female, also with feathers fluffed, swings below the branch. Then both sway and claw with one foot at one another. The female lays two eggs consistently but one often fails to hatch. She incubates alone, but the male assists in feeding young—as may others in local groups—for several weeks after fledging.

OTHER NAMES
Little Wattlebird, Biddyquock, Cookaycock, Mocker, Mock Gillbird, Mock Wattlebird.

IDENTIFICATION
LENGTH: *270–320 mm, with tapered tail.*
ADULTS: *Sexes similar; male distinctly larger. Generally deep grey with white, droplet-shaped shaft streaks over all upper and lower parts, including crown. Sash on side of face obscure pale grey; small white tufts at sides of breast. Flight feathers with area of rufous in base of primaries, showing in flight; tips broadly white. Tail tipped broadly white. Eye pale blue-grey. Bill black. Feet dusky.*
IMMATURES: *As adults but browner grey with obscure fine streaking; eye dusky.*

VOICE
CALL: *Soft cheeping* weep *when feeding, also by fledglings; loud rasping* tehaak *or squawk by male, high-pitched squeaks by female as territorial markers, often repeated.*
SONG: *Soft metallic high double-note shriek by female,* tschee-heee, *the second note lower, often quickly repeated; bill snapping and spaced guttural rasping squawks and* choks *by male, often repeated in descending sequence. Frequently given in duet, the female leading.*

NESTING
Breeds opportunistically all months, mainly July–December. Nest a rough cup of woven twigs, grass and plant fibre; lined with wool, fibre and feathers; supported in outer branchlets of tree or shrub, 1.5–3.5(–15) m up. Eggs: two, sometimes three; pink-buff, irregularly spotted red-brown and purplish red, mainly at large end; oval, about 28 x 21 mm. Incubation about 16 days, by female. Young fledge in about 16 days.

DISTRIBUTION
Shrubby forest and tall heath on coast and nearby ranges—with Banksia *—from near Rockhampton, Qld, southwest to Adelaide and Kangaroo Island, SA, and Tasmania. Three races.*

Brush Wattlebirds form sedentary colonies in coastal pockets of banksias.

Like most birds, the Striped Honeyeater feeds larger prey to its young than it eats itself because young can disarticulate the lower jaw.

Striped Honeyeater *Plectorhyncha lanceolata* GOULD, 1838

WITH ITS SHORT, DAGGER-LIKE bill, the Striped Honeyeater of eastern inland woodlands is more an insect- and fruit-eater than a nectar-eater. In small, fairly sedentary colonies of two to eight, it spends much of its time foraging in the middle inner strata of trees, often native pines inland and casuarinas on the central coast, but also eucalypts and acacias. There it hops briskly about under cover, picking over leaves and probing branchlet stems for insects and caterpillars and taking any berries, including those of mistletoes and peppercorns *Schinus*. Having a brush-tipped tongue, it will take nectar from the flowers of eucalypts, eremophila and native tobacco *Nicotiana*.

Flight is limited to erratic, undulating dashes between food trees and cover or to splash-bathe and drink; song flight is rare.

Despite much local wandering and sporadic irruptions, pairs may keep permanent territory in consistently productive habitat. This they advertise with rollicking bubbling song at any time of the day. Often the pair duet, perched almost side by side on high but sheltered branches. Both adults feed the young, are pugnacious in defence of their nests and attack trespassers, whistling shrilly and landing on branches, tail rising and falling.

The Striped Honeyeater is not obviously related to any other member of its family. It has a generally streaked appearance, with long and spiky feathers on the throat and upper breast which gave rise to its scientific name, *lanceolata*.

OTHER NAMES
Lanceolated Honeyeater.

IDENTIFICATION
LENGTH: *210–230 mm.*
ADULTS: *Sexes similar. Head and face to upper neck white, boldly striped black; lores and brow white. Back grey-brown striped dusky. Wings and square-cut tail plain grey-brown. Throat to upper breast white with spiked feathers; lower breast to undertail off-white finely streaked dusky, flanks greyer. Eye brown. Bill pale blue-grey, dark tipped. Feet pale blue-grey.*
IMMATURES: *As adults but duller.*

VOICE
CALL: *Rollicking trills that rise and fall, as calls or as song when protracted and often duetted:* cherree-cherree-chirrarip-chirrarip-cheeree-chew.

NESTING
Breeds August–January. Nest a deep cup, 75 x 95 mm inside, of fine dry grass or thin dry grass stems, covered outside with plant down or wool and often decorated with emu feathers; lined with grass; suspended at several parts of rim from thin leafy twigs at end of a drooping branch 1–10 m above ground. Eggs: three or four; dull white, usually marked with brown-red and underlying pale purple-grey, sometimes forming cap or zone at larger end; oval, about 23 x 17 mm.

DISTRIBUTION
Moderately common in woodlands and scrubby country of inland eastern Australia. Sedentary, or nomadic in autumn. No races.

Spiny-cheeked Honeyeater *Acanthagenys rufogularis* GOULD, 1838

THIS LARGE AND ELEGANT honeyeater, with striking pink-and-black bill, seems to replace the wattlebirds in the arid scrubs of inland Australia. There it ranges through dry mallee and shrubby mulga, along creek washes and out into dune thickets. It is as much a fruit- as a nectar-eater, taking the drupes of chenopods and mistletoes and even cultivated fruits and peppercorns along the central Murray River. Even insects are snapped up, either gleaned from foliage or, just as often, on hawking flights around the tree- or shrub-tops.

Nectar and manna is nonetheless staple diet, the birds wandering locally—even regionally in the north—and congregating in loose gatherings of 100 or more at seasonal flushes of flowering eucalypts, mistletoes and eremophilas. Whether rifling flowers or picking fruit, the Spiny-cheeks stay under cover, working quickly to the outside of foliage from within. Flight from thicket to thicket is a swift, undulating dash low over or usually among and between trees. Feeding groups are noisy, and individuals often break off to throw up their heads in territorial song—an unusual mixture of whistles, gurgling trills and whines.

Like other honeyeaters, Spiny-cheeks hold feeding as well as breeding territory and chase off trespassers. Song flights affirm territory, the birds fluttering near vertically up from the top of a tree or bush for 10–20 metres, singing, then swoop-gliding back to cover. Wherever there is a fairly consistent year-round supply of nectar and fruit, individuals and pairs establish a permanent territory of several hectares from which they exclude other birds. Only the female may brood, but both parents feed the young, primarily on a range of insects to build protein.

OTHER NAMES
Spring-cheeked Honeyeater.

IDENTIFICATION
LENGTH: *230–260 mm.*
ADULTS: *Sexes similar; male larger. Upper parts except rump mid brown-grey streaked with dusky, plainer on crown; rump off-white. Wings deeper grey-brown, the feathers finely edged citrine-white. Tail dusky grey, broadly tipped white on all except central pair of feathers. Dusky line from lores through eye across side of head; broad swathe of white spiny feathers across cheeks; dusky malar line from mouth to sides of neck, becoming flecked dusky and white. Chin to upper breast plain cinnamon; lower breast to undertail yellowish cream, streaked with drops of grey-brown. Eye china blue; eye-ring greyish pink. Bill with black tip and pink-red base and gape. Feet dark grey.*
IMMATURES: *As adults but slightly duller, cheeks washed yellow, eye browner. Cheeks whiter over several months.*

VOICE
CALL: *Brief, bubbled trills, gurgles and whines as territorial markers; sharp, clipped* tok *in alarm and in contact between pairs.*
SONG: *More protracted bubbled trills, gurgles and whines, often beginning with a rising* widit, wid-ll-id-ll-it, *and ending in falling whines,* pee-peer, pee-peer, pee-peer. *Given both in song-flight and from perches, and often in duets by both sexes.*

NESTING
Breeds July–January in eastern and southern Australia; elsewhere irregular. Nest a lightly built cup, 75 x 50 mm inside, of long grasses and plant stalks, often worked in from rim to bottom crossing each other, held together by cobweb and fastened at rim to thin forked branches 1–13 m above ground. Eggs: usually two; pale cream-brown or light olive, sparingly marked with dark brown and underlying blue-grey usually at larger end, sometimes all over; oval, about 25 x 18 mm. Incubation about 14 days, by female. Young fledge in about 15 days.

DISTRIBUTION
Woodland and scrubby dune desert in dry inland regions, south to central south coast and Kangaroo Island, SA. Sedentary or locally nomadic in south, with more marked northward movements in winter in north to Selwyn Range and Gulf district, Qld. No races.

Spiny white feathers give the Spiny-cheeked Honeyeater its name. Inhabiting arid inland scrubs, the bird holds permanent territory in good areas.

Silver-crowned Friarbird *Philemon argenticeps* (GOULD, 1840)

The Silver-crowned Friarbird forages noisily in flowering trees. Its metallic rolling whistles resound through the tropical woodlands of the north.

ONE OF THE FIRST VOICES in the dawn chorus in the tropical eucalypt forests and woodlands of far northern Australia is the rolling
clanking of the Silver-crowned Friarbird. In Arnhem Land, the
Kimberleys and around the Gulf of Carpentaria it is the common
large honeyeater in those habitats; on Cape York Peninsula, where
it is represented by a different race with small bill 'knob' and overlaps the range of the Noisy as well as the Helmeted Friarbird, it is
rarer and more restricted to local pockets.

Identified by a narrow stripe of silvery cream feathering over the
top of the head to the hind-neck, they resemble Helmeted
Friarbirds but are smaller and paler. Singly, in pairs or small groups
of up to 10 or more, they feed noisily in the upper foliage of trees—
mainly eucalypts and paperbarks *Melaleuca*—rifling flowers for
nectar, gleaning insects from bark, twigs and leaves, and picking
fruit. They take a higher proportion of insects than do Helmeted
Friarbirds, often sallying out in short flights to snatch them in
midair. Beetles, grasshoppers and chafers are main food,
augmented with weevils, ants, wasps, mantids and spiders.

Silver-crowned Friarbirds are regional nomads and follow
flushes of flowering in both eucalypts and paperbarks, congregating to feed in them in loose groups alongside other honeyeaters and
lorikeets. In these gatherings, the friarbirds are usually the noisiest
members, chasing poachers from their small feeding territories and
clanking and chuckling often in advertisement. At times they break
off to bathe in rock pools and springs—and even garden sprinklers
at Darwin—diving down, hitting the water and fluttering back to
a perch without landing. They drink in this manner too.

Groups break up to breed in isolated pairs. The female does
most nest-building and incubates unaided, but both sexes feed the
young. Nests are often parasitised by the Common Koel.

OTHER NAMES
Silvery-crowned Friarbird.

IDENTIFICATION
LENGTH: *270–310 mm.*
ADULTS: *Sexes similar; male larger.
Forehead, crown, and heavily tufted
nape silver-white, side of face bare black
skin; ear coverts furry black-brown.
Back, shoulders and rump mid fawn-
brown. Flight feathers and square tail
darker brown, paler below. Chin, throat
and upper breast silver-white with
scaly feathering; belly vent and
underwing coverts plain fawn. Eye red.
Bill black with large oblong knob at base
of upper mandible. Feet dark slate-grey.*
IMMATURES: *As adults but throat and
breast washed yellow, mantle, shoulders
and rump flecked white, bill casque
smaller, eye browner; juveniles before
first annual moult several months after
fledging are more like adults, without
yellow wash or white flecking,
but fluffier.*

VOICE
CALL: *Metallic whistled clankings softer
than Helmeted Friarbird's.*
SONG: *Raucous, clanking more
tobacco, uh-more tobacco-uh, often in
duet or antiphonally.*

NESTING
*Breeds September–December;
sometimes later. Nest a bowl of strips of
bark, bark fibre and cobweb; lined with
grass stalks and other plant matter; rim
of nest firmly woven over thick-forked
branch usually in drooping outer
foliage 2–11 m above ground. Eggs: one
or two, rarely three; fine, matt pale pink
to white, sparingly and vaguely spotted
with pale sepia, purple-brown and
slate, often more at larger end; tapered-
oval, about 30 x 21 mm. Incubation
by female.*

DISTRIBUTION
*Tropical eucalypt and paperbark
Melaleuca open forests and close
woodland around coastal and subcoastal northern mainland, from
Kimberleys to Cape York Peninsula.
Nomadic, following flowering, and may
irrupt outside range in eastern
Queensland. Two races: one widespread;
the other limited to northern and
eastern Cape York Peninsula.*

Helmeted Friarbird *Philemon buceroides* (SWAINSON, 1838)

LARGEST OF AUSTRALIAN FRIARBIRDS, the Helmeted is a bird of the rainforest edge, wherever it occurs throughout its vast range, from New Guinea across northern Australia to the Lesser Sundas. It does feed out into fringing eucalypt woodlands in northern Queensland and streamside galleries of paperbarks *Melaleuca* in Arnhem Land, and it commonly frequents nests in mangroves along the Darwin coast, but nowhere is it ever far from core pockets of rainforest and monsoon vine thicket.

Helmeted Friarbirds feed in the upper strata of trees and aggressively chase off any poachers. They usually forage alone or in pairs but sometimes congregate noisily in blossoming trees in groups of 10–30. At times they flutter, cackle and squabble boisterously in the canopy foliage, and at others sit quietly feeding among the leaves, picking up a range of insects, spiders, fruit and nectar. They also hawk out to catch insects on the wing, particularly termites, but nonetheless eat more fruit than other friarbirds. Flight

from tree to tree is erratically undulating, tail flirting above and about, giving the impression that the bird is blown along by wind. They also dive down to bathe in pools and spend much time preening afterwards.

After wandering locally by day when not breeding, the friarbirds return to rainforest to roost in the canopy, spaced out one by one. They announce their positions there at dusk—and again when waking at dawn—with monotonous, mournful double-note cries, often rendered *poor devil*. During breeding, pairs are more sedentary and secretive near the nest site. The female builds the nest—sometimes in close association with other species of birds—and may be seen tearing off small strips of bark from trees and flying back with them streaming behind. She incubates the eggs, while the male stays close by. Both sexes feed the young. Pairs advertise breeding and feeding territory by cackling duets sporadically through the day. Other birds may join in as well.

OTHER NAMES
Melville Island Friarbird, Sandstone Friarbird.

IDENTIFICATION
LENGTH: *310–360 mm.*
ADULTS: *Sexes similar; male larger. Crown, lightly tufted nape, back, wings and tail fawn-brown to mid-brown. Sides of face of bare, slaty black skin; ear coverts dusky-haired. Throat and breast of silvery brown scale-like feathers with dark shafts; belly to undertail fawn-brown. Eye dark red. Bill black with small to large bulbous knob. Feet slate-grey.*
IMMATURES: *As adults but back, shoulders and rump edged white; edges of flight and tail feathers washed citrine; throat and breast washed yellow; bill knob small. Juveniles before first annual moult two-three months after fledging as adults but fluffier; throat unscaled; eye brown.*

VOICE
CALL: *Mournful, double-note, downslurred chant,* poor devil, *as position call mainly at dawn and dusk. Also* chillank-chillank *cackles and squawks during fighting and feeding site advertisement.*
SONG: *Series of measured cackles and guttural wails and clankings, often by both sexes in duet or antiphonally.*

NESTING
Breeds August–January; sometimes later. Nest a loose, bulky cup of bark strips and occasionally leaves, interwoven with vine tendrils and twigs; lined with finer tendrils and twigs; situated on well-camouflaged outer limb or in fork among foliage; 2–14 m above ground. Eggs: one to five, usually two or three; cream to light pink, closely freckled and blotched with red-brown, purple-red and lilac-grey; tapered-oval, about 34 x 23 mm. Incubation by female.

DISTRIBUTION
Melville Island, NT, and adjacent mainland in mangroves, monsoon forests and paperbark swamps; western Arnhem Land from Oenpelli to Mary River in broad-leafed gullies and creek courses; coastal Queensland from Cape York to Sarina at low altitudes. Also New Guinea and Lesser Sundas. About 10 races; three in Australia.

A Helmeted Friarbird of the brown Queensland race. It is an aggressive bird which cackles and squabbles often.

Noisy Friarbird *Philemon corniculatus* (LATHAM, 1790)

THE TONSURED HEAD OF THIS big honeyeater gives the friarbirds their name, with the Noisy Friarbird having the barest head. All the other knob-billed friarbirds have partly feathered heads.

Every spring and summer in southeastern Australia, the open eucalypt forests and woodlands ring with the day-long chuckling cackles and bubblings of this noisy bird. It calls and sings— perched with bill thrown up—to advertise feeding as well as breeding territory, and does so year round in northeastern Queensland where it is only locally nomadic. But south of 30°–35°S it is migratory, shifting off mountain tops to low altitudes and travelling north as far as central eastern Queensland in March–April and returning in late August–September. The birds move north in small loose groups of up to 30–40, flying straight and high, often well over the tops of trees. On their return they trickle south in ones and twos through forest and woodland.

Like other honeyeaters, Noisy Friarbirds are versatile feeders, taking nectar, insects and fruit—including grapes, blackberries and even syrup that oozes from sugar cane after it has been fired; often the birds become a pest in stone-fruit orchards in late summer and are shot illegally.

Flushes of flowering bring them to congregate in loose groups with other honeyeaters, particularly Little Friarbirds. They are boisterously noisy and aggressive then, each bird defending its own feeding branches, chasing off other competitors, and calling loudly in a cacophony of sound.

All feeding is arboreal, the birds bouncing around in the branches, picking off fruit, gleaning under bark, along twigs and among leaves for insects, and often hanging upside down on the outside of foliage as they probe flowers for nectar, from one to 30 metres above the ground. Flowering proteads and eucalypts provide most of their energy needs. Noisy Friarbirds also hawk for insects, fluttering up, catching prey in midair, then swooping back to the cover of foliage.

When flying from tree to tree they sometimes undulate and dive this way and that, tail angled and twisted about; at other times flight is straight and direct.

Groups spread out to roost at night, individual birds sleeping alone in tree crowns and signalling their position to one another at dusk and when awaking at dawn with a repeated rolling *ya-kob*. Pairs also break off to nest in territories of their own. Only the female may incubate but both sexes attend the young.

OTHER NAMES
Knobby-nose Leatherhead, Four o'clock Pimlico, Poor Soldier.

IDENTIFICATION
LENGTH: *300–340 mm.*
ADULTS: *Sexes similar; male larger. Head and upper neck of bare black skin, with narrow line of grey-brown feathering over eye and triangle of silver-grey feathering on chin. Back, rump and shoulders mid fawn-brown. Wings mid-grey. Tail mid-grey, square-ended with narrow white tip. Lower throat and upper breast of a ruff of lanceolate silvery white feathers with dark shafts; lower breast to undertail pale fawn. Eye red. Bill black with small black triangular knob at base of upper mandible. Feet dusky grey.*
IMMATURES: *Neck and back of head feathered; mottled grey and edged white on shoulders, back and side of neck. Flight feathers and tail indistinctly edged green-yellow; flight feathers tipped white. Throat and breast lack lanceolated feathers. Knob not obvious; eye browner.*

VOICE
CALL: *Rolling, double-note chant* ya-kob *or* poor soldier *as position call; harsh, cackling* tabacco, tobacco *and* four o' clock *at feeding sites; loud brassy shout in pursuit.*
SONG: *Rippling, chuckling cackles, often in duet or antiphonally between sexes at set perches; voice of female higher pitched.*

NESTING
Breeds July–February. Nest a large deep, open cup of narrow strips of stringybark at times interwoven with dry grasses, cobweb and pieces of cloth; lined with finer grasses, wiry plant stems and wool; built in outer branches, camouflaged in thick foliage, 1.5–17 m above ground, occasionally in lower saplings. Eggs: two or three, rarely five; light to dark pink-buff, vaguely spotted and marbled with pale slate, chestnut or violet-grey, particularly at larger end; oval to tapered-oval, about 33 x 22 mm. Incubation by female.

DISTRIBUTION
Coastal regions of mainland from Cape York south to eastern Victoria, in open areas in wet and dry sclerophyll forest, and open woodlands. West of range occurs in wooded areas, along watercourses. Also in New Guinea. No races.

Noisy Friarbirds build a large, deep cup nest in outer branches up to 17 metres above ground. The female incubates, but both sexes tend the young.

This Noisy Friarbird has pollen from a grevillea on its bill. Most friarbirds have a knob on their upper bill, and the Noisy Friarbird has the roundest.

Little Friarbird *Philemon citreogularis* (GOULD, 1837)

The Little Friarbird is the only Australian friarbird without a knob on its bill. It lives in open forests and woodlands and feeds on insects, nectar and fruit.

LIVING IN EUCALYPT WOODLANDS alongside Noisy and Silver-crowned Friarbirds around much of eastern and northern Australia, the Little may feed with them but generally keeps to more open habitat. A smaller bird—and without a bill casque—it is the loser in any fighting and squabbling for flowering food branches, although it does chase off honeyeaters smaller than itself.

Rather, it is a specialist in exploiting smaller pockets of flowering eucalypts and paperbarks rarely visited by the larger friarbirds. There it feeds in the outer foliage of trees and shrubbery, often hanging upside down to rifle nectar from blossom, and picking up fruit and insects which it may hawk after on the wing. It drinks and bathes daily, skimming the surface of pools or fluttering through sprays, and rarely strays far from water.

Like other friarbirds, it is a local, flower-following nomad across the north and largely migratory in the east. Many populations south of about 25°S move to northeastern Queensland over winter and then return in spring to breed in small loose groups along the river systems west of the Great Dividing Range.

OTHER NAMES
Yellow-throated Friarbird, Little Leatherhead.

IDENTIFICATION
LENGTH: *250–290 mm.*
ADULTS: *Sexes similar; male larger. Head grey-brown; darker wash extends above eye and around neck; nape light smoky grey, back and shoulders grey-brown with blue tinge; rump lighter. Flight feathers dark grey-brown with outer edges lighter; underwing coverts scalloped brown and white. Tail mid brown-grey, paler tip, lighter below. Chin has silky silver-white hair-like feathers; throat and upper breast grey with silver-white drop-streaks on breast; belly lighter; vent white. Eye mid grey-brown. Bill black. Feet dark slate-grey.*
IMMATURES: *Similar to adults, but plumage and naked skin lighter. Back, shoulders and rump mottled with white. Chin and throat usually washed yellow; broad yellow scallops on sides of breast; indistinct grey band across breast. Flight feathers indistinctly edged green-yellow.*

VOICE
CALL: *Raucous* ar-cooo, rockety crook-shank; *abrupt alarm call. Jumbled notes when squabbling and feeding in groups.*
SONG: *Liquid* chewip, *repeated with slight variations.*

NESTING
Breeds June–December; sometimes later. Nest usually open cup of shreds of bark, dry grass stems and rootlets woven tightly and bound with pieces of cobweb, silky cocoons and occasionally hair; lined with finer grasses and rootlets; suspended by rim in hanging outer foliage 2–11 m above ground or at times over water. Eggs: two or three, occasionally four; pale pink to grey-pink, well marked with lines, blotches and spots of red-brown, slate or purple-grey, at times forming zone at larger end; oval to tapered-oval, about 28 x 20 mm.

DISTRIBUTION
Open eucalypt forests and woodlands, visiting flowering Melaleuca *in north; inland along tree-lined watercourses and adjacent flowering scrub. Avoids heavy forest. Also in New Guinea. Two races: one across north; the other in east.*

Regent Honeyeater *Xanthomyza phrygia* (SHAW, 1794)

THE DECLINE OF THIS BRILLIANT black-and-yellow honeyeater has been alarmingly subtle. Where once it occurred commonly in congregations of 50–100 in flowering eucalypts around southeastern Australia 20 and 30 years ago, today it is found only singly, in pairs or small groups of no more than 10, and then infrequently. The cause of its decline is not clear, for the extent of its habitat—well-shrubbed eucalypt woodland and open forest flanking the Great Dividing Range—has changed little over the past 30 years.

Regent Honeyeaters are irruptive and partly migratory, shifting generally northwards in autumn and winter, returning south to breed in spring, and congregating anywhere at flushes of blossoming. In districts where they have been few or absent for many years they will suddenly appear in numbers. Nectar is their main food and energy source—rifled from various box and ironbark eucalypts and occasional banksias and mistletoes—but they also take insects, manna, lerps and fruit. The birds feed aggressively and quickly in the outer foliage—chasing or being chased—and fly swiftly from tree to tree, wings often clattering. Manna and honeydew are gleaned from leaves, and insects are captured by probing crevices in bark or on aerial sallies.

As the birds go, they give frequent ringing metallic chinking in contact, often from set perches with bobbing and stretching movements of the head, or in flight.

Although sometimes breeding in loose colonies, Regent Honeyeaters usually nest in isolated pairs. The female apparently incubates unaided, but the male stands sentry high in a nearby tree for much of the time and later helps in the feeding of young.

OTHER NAMES
Embroidered Honeyeater, Warty-faced Honeyeater, Flying Coachman, Turkeybird.

IDENTIFICATION
LENGTH: *200–220 mm.*
ADULTS: *Sexes similar; male larger. Head and upper and lower neck black, with pink-buff bare warty skin around eye. Back, scapulars and rump black scalloped cream-yellow. Wings black, feathers edged patchily broad yellow. Tail black, outer feathers bright yellow. Lower breast and belly cream scalloped black; undertail cream-white. Eye red-brown. Bill black. Feet dusky grey.*
IMMATURES: *As adults but duller, black browner; bill buff to base.*

VOICE
CALL: *Metallic, bell-like chink.*
SONG: *Rolling, oriole-like clink-clank or tink tink-tink, from perch or in song-flight.*

NESTING
Breeds mainly August–January. Nest a thick-walled cup of bark strips bound with cobweb; lined with fine dry grass and bark shreds, about 65 x 50 mm inside; supported in thick vertical fork, upright forked branch or horizontal branch of tree or bush, or knots in mistletoe clumps, 1–19 m above ground. Eggs: usually two, sometimes three; red-buff, darker towards larger end, with small purple-red and violet-grey markings, usually forming zone at larger end; oval to tapered-oval, about 24 x 18 mm. Incubation by female.

DISTRIBUTION
Eucalypt woodland and open forest on both flanks of Great Dividing Range, north to about Brisbane, Qld, and southwest to Bendigo, Vic., with outlier in Mt Lofty Ranges and Kangaroo Island, SA. Nomadic and irruptive; declining. No races.

Black and cream scallops on back and breast distinguish the Regent Honeyeater from other black, white and yellow honeyeaters, which are streaked.

Blue-faced Honeyeater *Entomyzon cyanotis* (LATHAM, 1801)

AMONG THE larger honeyeaters, the Blue-faced is miner-like in its communal gatherings and feeding. It does take fruit—sometimes damaging bananas and pears—and often mixes with other honeyeaters to hang in foliage rifling nectar from flowering paperbarks and grevilleas or to glean syrup from burnt sugar cane, but the bulk of its diet is insects. Working in small loose groups of two–10, rarely more or less, Blue-faced Honeyeaters hop about branches and cling to trunks, probing and prising under bark for prey: click- and leaf-beetles and weevils and, less frequently, ants, chafers, shield bugs and spiders. Often they hawk out to catch insects in midair, particularly over water. Most feeding is done in the early morning and late afternoon.

Communal groups seem to be close-knit. At dawn and dusk, individual birds sing sweet plaintive notes from the top branchlets of roost trees. During the day they feed close to one another in the upper foliage and branches of trees, keeping in touch with soft chirps, and following one another in direct, strong-flapping flights as they work from tree to tree. Like

miners, they will glide on hunched wings and perch head-down, craning at an intruder. And if alarmed, they may bunch together, hopping about one another, on branches, piping loudly.

Foraging routines are often broken by bathing and drinking, the birds diving down and back to perch, little more than splashing the surface of pools.

During breeding, communal groups establish themselves in pockets of productive habitat in the eucalypt woodlands around northern and eastern Australia, usually along watercourses. Instead of building their own nest, breeding females often occupy deserted roosting nests of Grey-crowned Babblers. These are always readily available because of the babblers' propensity to build many bulky nests which last well. All the Blue-faced Honeyeater does is rebuild the lining at the top; if its clutch is destroyed, it can shift to a new site, rebuild the lining and lay again within seven days.

After breeding, communes wander locally, taking advantage of flowering, and in the southeast often shifting northwards during winter.

OTHER NAMES
Banana-bird, Pandanas-bird.

IDENTIFICATION
LENGTH: *240–300 mm.*
ADULTS: *Sexes similar. Crown, hind-neck and line around face black; broken white crescent around nape. Back to wings and tail deep yellowish green; flight feathers with (northern races) or without concealed white dollar, white or cinnamon on underside; underwing coverts black; tail feathers broadly tipped white except central pair. Grey-black gorget from chin to upper breast. White line from sides of mouth down sides of neck to all plain white lower breast, belly and undertail. Eye cream-white; eye skin turquoise, grading cobalt. Bill black with pale grey-blue base. Feet leaden-grey.*
IMMATURES: *Resemble adults. Head and nape dark brown; throat duller grey. Eye brown-yellow; eye skin green with yellow tinge; bill dark grey with lemon-yellow base; feet olive-grey.*

VOICE
CALL: *Mewing chirps in contact. A miner-like alarm chattering, harsh mew, ky-owt or teeu repeated often.*
SONG: *Strong, strident piping notes, mainly in early morning.*

NESTING
Breeds June–January; mostly August–November. Nest an untidy deep, thick-walled cup, of bark strips, grass and rootlets; lined with finer bark fibres, rootlets and grass stems; placed in upright fork or broad branch of tree, 3–18 m above ground. Also uses deserted nest of Grey-crowned Babbler, sometimes relining it; or may build on top of nest. Occasionally uses old nests of miners or Noisy Friarbird. Eggs: two, rarely three; white to pale buff-pink with large purple-red and chestnut spots and blotches with underlying slate-grey marks; oval, about 32 x 22 mm.

DISTRIBUTION
Eucalypt, paperbark, and Pandanus *woodland to edge of rainforest and mangroves around north and east, from Kimberleys, WA, to southeast of South Australia. Also southern New Guinea. Three races.*

A Blue-faced Honeyeater feeding at a grevillea. This bird becomes pugnacious during the breeding season.

Bell Miner *Manorina melanophrys* (LATHAM, 1801)

OTHER NAMES
Bellbird, Bell Mynah.

IDENTIFICATION
LENGTH: *180–190 mm.*
ADULTS: *Sexes similar; male slightly larger. Upper parts from head to rump plain dark olive-green, darkest on crown. Wings and tail plain browner olive, the flight feathers edged citrine. Forehead, line over eye and malar stripe dusky black; lores light yellow-green; small patch of bare orange-red skin behind and under eye. Underparts uniformly mid yellow-green. Eye mid-brown. Bill and feet waxy yellow.*
IMMATURES: *Similar to adults; eye-patch olive-yellow for first three months, changing to orange at six to eight months.*

VOICE
CALL: *Sharp, repeated* jak-jak-jak; *complaining Noisy Miner-like chirping* kwee-kwee-kwee *in aggression; scolding churring in alarm; and mewing shrieks in distraction display. Fledglings beg with repeated soft* yeek, yeek, *without wing-flutter.*
SONG: *Continual, single-note, metallic, high, bell-like* tink *or* plink, *explosive at close quarters and far-carrying, given day-long as position-contact call between members of colonies; varies in pitch between individuals.*

NESTING
Breeds mainly July–February; also April–June. Nest a loosely woven cup of thin twigs, grasses and shredded bark; lined with rootlets and occasionally downy seed; bound to branches with cobweb, suspended by the rim, sometimes close to the ground, but normally 4–5 m up in sapling or tree. Moss, lichen, leaves, insect egg cases or cocoons often attached to exterior. Eggs: two, sometimes one or three; pale pink spotted with chestnut, red or purple-brown; oval, about 24 x 16 mm. Incubation about 15 days, by female. Young fledge in 12–15 days. Commonly host to Pallid Cuckoo.

DISTRIBUTION
In discrete colonies in edge and gullies of wet and dry sclerophyll forest, usually near water, along east coast and coastal scarps of Great Dividing Range, north to near Gympie, Qld, and southwest to near Melbourne, Vic. No races.

The Bell Miner is famous for its metallic call, which echoes like a bell through eastern eucalypt forests.

THE HIGH, BELL-LIKE NOTES of the Bell Miner, which have inspired much poetry, are single plucked notes given by each bird in turn in their close-packed colonies. The purpose of these far-carrying calls seems to be to maintain contact and distance among birds in a group; they are given non-stop day-long throughout the year.

Each colony occupies a territory of up to two hectares and comprises a number of discrete groups of birds, each with its own feeding range of as little as 50 metres square but usually more. The groups themselves are made up of a mated pair plus up to eight additional members.

Bell Miner colonies are sedentary, remaining in the same densely shrubbed gullies in wet eucalypt forest for many years in southeastern Australia. Hopping and fluttering about in the middle strata of the forest, down to the shrubbery and up into the lower canopy, the birds glean mainly lerps—sap-sucking scale insects on foliage and their protective sugary coating. This link between the birds and their food has led to their being used as indicators of infested forest. The miners may tolerate other insectivores in the forest under-shrubbery but drive off all foliage-feeding competitors by chasing and mobbing.

Only the female builds the nest, incubates and broods the young, although the male often escorts her while she is building. Other members of the group also attend the nest, even perching on the rim while she works in material. Later, when young hatch, they all join in their feeding, often queuing to wait and feeding two nestlings on one visit, then carrying off faecal sacs. To distract intruders, adults wave their wings and call harshly, then drop suddenly into low undergrowth to repeat the performance.

Young fledge erratically and at first may return to the nest to sleep. Huddled in the tops of shrubbery close by, they continue to be fed by all members of the group until about four weeks old and roost together with them in dense shrubbery at night.

Yellow-throated Miner *Manorina flavigula* (GOULD, 1840)

MINERS ARE medium-sized, yellow-billed and -footed honeyeaters that live in tight communal groups and feed mainly on insects. Most widespread of them and ranging through the open woodlands of the inland, the Yellow-throated is also the most nomadic. Some colonies in better-watered areas may be sedentary year round, but those in drier mallee and mulga scrubs wander locally after breeding. Local communes of only up to a dozen or so birds coalesce then in flocks of 50 or more.

Yellow-throated Miners, like all miners, have strong legs and sharp claws and can hang for some time in bizarre, inverted poses on trunks and branches. They forage there, hopping about prising and poking under bark and gleaning among foliage for insects and also spend much time on the ground, walking and working over litter and even dung for beetles, ants, wasps, bees, bugs, weevils and caterpillars. Fruit and seeds are picked up on occasion as well and nectar may be rifled from eucalypt and other blossom, though not often. Foraging bands will feed, play and fly in slow fluttering and gliding about one group of trees for some time, then fly several hundred metres to the next. Like other communal miners, they have a complex vocabulary of soft twitterings and whistled squeaks to keep contact and to signal intentions.

Yellow-throated Miners breed in close-knit colonies which, probably smaller than those of the Noisy Miner, comprise several individual groups of a pair plus helpers which nest simultaneously. There is co-operative care of the young; males, coming in singly, may feed the nestlings of several females. Fledglings stay together after leaving the nest and continue to be fed by adults. They beg noisily and squeak during each feeding but without fluttering their wings, a characteristic of all honeyeaters.

OTHER NAMES
Dusky Miner, Black-eared Miner, White-rumped Miner, Bun-Bun, Mickey.

IDENTIFICATION
LENGTH: 250–280 mm.
ADULTS: Sexes similar; male slightly larger. Much geographic variation in size and colour. Crown to mid-back mid to dark grey, flecked white on nape; forehead washed variably citrine. Rump off-white to mid-grey. Wings deep grey washed citrine. Tail dark grey broadly tipped white. Face with broad black sash through eye with or without white edge; malar line and chin white or dusky; bare yellow skin at gape, sides of chin and behind eye. Throat to undertail white, mottled grey-dusky on breast, with or without yellow wash on sides of neck. Eye deep brown. Bill yellow. Feet yellow-orange.
IMMATURES: As adults but buff edging on back and wing coverts.

VOICE
CALL: Territorial flight call teu-teu-teu-teu, similar to Noisy Miner's. Nasal whistled chatter to ground predators; pure whistle to flying predators. Soft twitters and whistled squeaking in social and feeding groups.
SONG: A pre-dawn chorus of whistles.

NESTING
Breeds July–December; sometimes in response to rain. Nest a bulky cup, thick walls often contain wool as well as twigs and grasses; lined with wool, fur or hair; cobwebs bind nest to branches, usually in fork of sapling or near outer branches of a low tree. Eggs: usually three or four; pink to red-buff with specks or blotches of red or purple-brown, mostly at larger end; oval, about 26 x 18 mm.

DISTRIBUTION
Copses in drier open woodlands—mulga to mallee and river gums on watercourses—throughout mainland west of Great Dividing Range; locally to central east coast, Queensland. Three races: two dark-faced and -rumped in southwestern and southeastern mallee previously regarded as separate species but now hybridising and intergrading with white-rumped race; southeastern 'Black-eared' race now being hybridised out of existence due to opening-up of mallee.

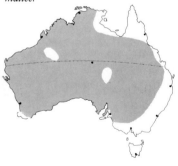

The Yellow-throated Miner, like other miners, has strong legs and needle-sharp claws, which enable it to hang in bizarre inverted positions. It prises loose bark from the trunk of trees in its search for insects.

A communal honeyeater of eastern eucalypt woodland, the Noisy Miner is noted for its loud and frequent crying and scolding calls.

Noisy Miner *Manorina melanocephala* (LATHAM, 1801)

GARRULOUS IN SEDENTARY COMMUNES, the Noisy Miner is perhaps the best-known honeyeater in eastern Australia, replacing the Yellow-throated Miner there in better-watered woodlands on both sides of the Great Dividing Range. Following the river gum woodlands of the Murray River, it reached the Mt Lofty Ranges and suburbs of Adelaide around the turn of the century where, as elsewhere, it now enters urban gardens with large eucalypts.

Noisy Miners feed mainly on insects and other invertebrates, gleaning, hopping and fluttering about the mid-strata of woodland, poking along branches and prising under bark for prey, and even dropping to work over litter on the ground. They also take fruit—occasionally becoming a pest in orchards during drought—and will harvest nectar from blossom and other sugary products among foliage, such as lerps, manna and honeydew from sap-sucking insects. In places they have learnt to invade houses and picnic grounds for jam, butter and bread.

Social organisation in the communes is complex, with a number of territorial groups of six to 30 birds combined in a loose colony of up to several hundred. Males outnumber females. Miners unite to mob predators, and are particularly noisy when ganging up on snakes or goannas. They also attack other species of birds that enter their territory, and are successful in driving out most species, occasionally killing some.

In these attacks miners use the same threatening behaviour and displays as they do with members of their own species. The patch of bare yellow skin behind the eye comes into play here—by fluffing the feathers over its edge or by sleeking them back, the miner can change the effective size of the patch. In a frontal stare, the yellow patches look like two large, intimidating eyes.

Noisy Miners have other boisterous social displays or 'corroborees'. Many birds come together and greet each other by opening their beaks and lifting their tongues while slowly waving their wings. Such social greetings occur mainly among birds of the same territorial group. Noisy Miners indulge in many other types of communal activity, feeding, bathing and sleeping together. A communal song is uttered for about 10 minutes before sunrise between May and January, its pure whistling contrasting with the harsh squeaks and chatters given in daily socialising.

The female builds the nest alone, finishing it in about six days and often dismantling an old nest to do so. She advertises the location of the nest with a stereotyped display flight as she brings material, fluttering along with head held high and back. Males may accompany her and pick up twigs but always drop them in foliage

or forks short of the nest itself. Eggs are laid at daily intervals from two to 10 days after the nest is finished; incubation begins with the laying of the second.

Up to 10 or more males may visit a nest while the female is incubating and join in feeding the nestlings; in any one season one female may be helped by as many as 24 males, and feeding visits to the nests often exceed 50 an hour. After fledging, young remain together huddled in foliage and continue to be fed for another five weeks. Several broods may be reared in a season.

OTHER NAMES
Micky, Noisy Mynah, Squeaker, Soldier-bird.

IDENTIFICATION
LENGTH: *250–290 mm.*
ADULTS: *Sexes similar; male larger. Crown black, extending down over ears to sides of throat and chin. Hind-neck to rump mid-grey, mottled dusky and flecked white on nape. Wings mid-grey edged citrine. Tail dark grey, broadly tipped white. Forehead white-grey, lores whitish; patch of bare yellow skin behind eye. Underparts white, mottled grey on throat and breast. Eye brown. Bill yellow. Feet brown- to orange-yellow.*
IMMATURES: *As adults; a suffusion of light brown on back, rump and wing coverts.*

VOICE
CALL: *A complex repertoire. Territorial call a rhythmic, repeated two- or three-syllable* teu-teu-teu-teu *uttered in short, undulating flight. Females may utter four or five throaty, chuckling notes in sequence, with pitch of the last rising questioningly; often in answer to territorial call of male. Nasal whistled chatter to ground predators; pure whistle to flying predators. Soft twitters and whistled squeaking in social and feeding groups.*
SONG: *Before sunrise at onset of or during nesting, pure whistles and antiphonal notes emitted in chorus.*

NESTING
Breeds mainly June–December; can occur all months. Nest a cup, often flimsy, of twigs, grasses and leaves, bound by cobweb and cocoons, sometimes lined with hair; lining a felt-like pad of silk from moths' cocoons or wool in the bottom; supported in upright outer branches up to 20 m, sometimes as low as 0.5 m. Eggs: two to four, rarely five; cream-white, spotted heavily with red-brown, mostly at larger end; oval, 27 x 18 mm. Incubation 15–16 days, by female. Young fledge in about 16 days.

DISTRIBUTION
Sedentary colonies in eucalypt woodland and open forest with clear understorey throughout eastern mainland, north to Atherton Tablelands, Qld, south to Tasmania, southwest to Mt Lofty Ranges, SA. Two races: one on mainland; the other in Tasmania.

Tawny-breasted Honeyeater *Xanthotis flaviventer* (LESSON, 1828)

ONE OF THE FEW HONEYEATERS of New Guinea's tropical rainforests to reach Australia is the Tawny-breasted. It is limited to the rainforests and riverside galleries of vine scrub on Cape York Peninsula, replacing Macleay's Honeyeater there.

Like Macleay's, it forages unobtrusively in the middle and upper strata of the forest beneath the canopy, working through hanging clumps of dead vegetation and leafy vines and poking into crevices on trunks and branches. Progress is deliberate and methodical. The birds usually feed alone or in loosely associated pairs and sometimes small parties. Arboreal insects are their main prey, but they also take some fruit and nectar rifled from clusters of flowers, for example in mistletoes. For this they have a conventional honeyeater's tongue—a long, protrusible channelled structure split into four brush-tipped filaments at the apex.

It is mainly when moving from point to point in the forest that the birds descend to lower levels, flying in swift dashing undulations among the tree trunks. From perches well up they call often throughout the day, even in the hot middle hours when other species are quiet. They frequently feed out to the edge of rainforest and follow the canopy edge down to low shrubberies there, but rarely forage into adjacent eucalypt or paperbark forest.

Like most honeyeaters, the Tawny-breasted builds a hanging cup-shaped nest that is fastened at its rim into a horizontal fork in leafy foliage. The female usually builds the nest and incubates the eggs unaided, laying at daily intervals and beginning to sit with the laying of the second egg. Young hatch within 24 hours of one another, after 13–16 days incubation. Fed by both parents they fledge in the rather shorter time of 10–14, rarely 16 days.

OTHER NAMES
Buff-breasted Honeyeater, Streaked Honeyeater, Streak-naped Honeyeater.

IDENTIFICATION
LENGTH: *180–220 mm.*
ADULTS: *Sexes similar. Upper parts dark brown with olive tinge, becoming darker on crown; nape vaguely spotted pale grey. Wing and tail quills dark brown-grey edged outside with ochre and inside with brown-buff; wing coverts edged ochre. Naked area of skin behind eye yellow-pink; sash from bill to ear coverts dusky, lined narrowly white above, tipped with small yellow ear-tuft. Throat and sides of neck grey* becoming tawny brown on breast and belly with pale streaks. Eye dark brown. Bill black. Feet leaden-grey.
IMMATURES: *Similar to adults; wing coverts more heavily edged brown-ochre; plumage slightly darker above and paler and greyer below.*

VOICE
CALL: *Series of single repeated whistles cycling up and down in pitch. Also chatters and scolds.*
SONG: *Loud whistling.*

NESTING
Breeds November–February. Nest a cup of bark strips and fibre, lined with finer fibre; slung from rim in horizontal fork in foliage, 4–20 m above ground. Eggs: two; smooth, pale flesh-coloured, sprinkled sparsely with red-purple spots, particularly at larger end; oval, about 27 x 17 mm. Incubation 13–16 days, by female. Young fledge in 10–14 days.

DISTRIBUTION
Rainforest, galleries of vine scrub and fringing mangroves—rarely edge of more open eucalypt forests—on Cape York Peninsula, south to Malaman Creek on west coast and the McIlwraith Range and the Edward River on the east. Also New Guinea and offshore islands. About seven races: one in Australia shared with southern New Guinea.

In Australia, Tawny-breasted Honeyeaters live only on Cape York Peninsula. They keep mainly to the middle and upper strata of rainforest and vine scrub.

Macleay's Honeyeater eats mainly insects and spiders which it finds among dead leaves or on the surfaces of large leaves in the canopy of rainforest.

Macleay's Honeyeater *Xanthotis macleayana* (RAMSAY, 1875)

OTHER NAMES
Yellow-streaked Honeyeater, Mottle-plumaged Honeyeater, Buff-striped Honeyeater.

IDENTIFICATION
LENGTH: *180–210 mm.*
ADULTS: *Sexes similar. Forehead, crown* and nape brown-black, nape feathers have white shafts; mantle streaked brown and yellow; rump yellow-brown; scapulars brown with cream triangular tips; wing and tail quills brown with yellow-green outer and ochre inner edges. Naked skin around eye yellow-grey; side of head to behind eye black; dark line from bill to yellow-white ear plume. Chin and throat grey, blending into yellow-streaked upper breast; lower breast feathers brown with buff triangular tips; belly grey-yellow. Eye brown. Bill black. Feet leaden-grey.
IMMATURES: *Duller than adults. Slight indication of white nape spots; markings on back less distinct; front of neck and upper breast dull olive-yellow.*

VOICE
In territorial advertisement, a loud rapid, strident five-note call, each note upslurred: tchu-wi, tchu-wi-wii. *Also single chip and cycling whistles.*

NESTING
Breeds October–January. Nest a deep cup of plant fibre, dead leaves, bark, leaf skeletons, cobweb and cocoons; lined with plant fibre; slung by rim in horizontal fork, usually fairly high up in canopy but sometimes as low as 2 m above ground. Eggs: two; smooth, slightly lustrous, pale flesh-buff, dotted and freckled with chestnut, particularly at larger end where grey markings also occur; oval, about 23 x 17 mm.

DISTRIBUTION
Northeastern Queensland, from Cooktown to Townsville, in rainforest but also mangroves, gardens and, rarely, nearby eucalypt forest. Most abundant in lowlands. Endemic. No races.

COMPARED WITH OTHER honeyeaters, Macleay's Honeyeaters are quiet and unobtrusive birds. They live singly or in pairs in the middle and upper layers of the rainforest canopy in northeastern Queensland, where their deliberate movements and foraging by probing are more suggestive of riflebirds.

The diet of Macleay's Honeyeater consists of about 70 per cent insects and spiders, 20 per cent nectar and 10 per cent fruit. It finds most of its insects in hanging bunches of dead leaves and vine tangles and in the search for them often buries its entire front half in the dry vegetation, the rustling of the leaves betraying its presence. It also gleans insects from the surfaces of the large leaves of plants such as silver basswood *Tieghemopanax murrayi,* and occasionally hovers to catch an insect or pluck a fruit.

Flowers of the umbrella tree *Schefflera* attract Macleay's Honeyeater, and because umbrella trees are frequently grown as ornamental trees, this bird is often attracted into gardens.

Lewin's Honeyeater feeds on insects and fruit as well as nectar.

Lewin's Honeyeater

Meliphaga lewinii (SWAINSON, 1837)

RANGING FROM THE McILWRAITH RANGE almost to Melbourne, Lewin's is the most widespread honeyeater of Australia's eastern coastal rainforests. In the south it extends down to the coast, and north to Townsville it keeps to montane rainforest above 200 metres; wherever it occurs it is rather sedentary. Individuals and pairs hold to much the same territory year round which they advertise with distinctive machine-gun chattering through the day. Only during winter do they wander much beyond.

Lewin's Honeyeaters forage singly or in loose pairs in the mid and upper strata of rainforests, only gathering in larger loose groups to rifle blossom or pick fruit in profusely flowering or fruiting trees. They commonly spiral up trees picking out insects from crevices in the bark, or hover to glean from the end of a twig. They also visit orchards and gardens, where they feed on pawpaws, oranges and mandarins. Aggressive birds, they spend much time chasing one another and other species away from feeding places.

OTHER NAMES
Yellow-eared Honeyeater, Bananabird, Brasseye, Orangebird.

IDENTIFICATION
LENGTH: *190–210 mm.*
ADULTS: *Sexes similar; male larger. Upper parts, wings and tail plain mid to dark olive-green; dusky shafts on back; forehead washed grey. Line from base of bill to below eye cream-white; malar area and cheeks to edge of ear coverts dull grey; ear coverts with flared cream-yellow patch. Underparts uniformly mid to pale olive-green with faint dusky grey mottling. Eye mid blue-grey. Bill black; gape cream-white. Feet grey-horn.*
IMMATURES: *As adults; fluffier with dorsal streaking and ventral mottling obscure; eye browner.*

VOICE
CALL: *Loud rolling staccato chatter, sometimes likened to machine-gun fire.*
SONG: *Single harsh tchuuu like call of Yellow-spotted Honeyeater but softer.*

NESTING
Breeds August–January. Nest cup-shaped, of bark strips, leaves, moss, and cobweb, size inside 100 x 50 mm; suspended by rim in foliage 2–6 m above ground, in gully or over a stream. Eggs: two or three; cream with red or purple spots forming zone at larger end; oval to long-oval, about 26 x 18 mm. Incubation 14–15 days. Young fledge in 14–15 days.

DISTRIBUTION
Rainforest and fringing growth on east coast and ranges between McIlwraith Range, Qld, and Melbourne. Two races: one in McIlwraith Range; the other everywhere else.

Yellow-spotted Honeyeater *Meliphaga notata* (GOULD, 1867)

ENDEMIC TO NORTHEASTERN QUEENSLAND, the Yellow-spotted Honeyeater lives in lowland rainforests and their edges. It enters mangroves and congregates with other honeyeaters to feed on nectar in blossoming trees in eucalypt forests and nearby gardens.

Like other honeyeaters it is noisy, aggressive and feeds in the foliage of trees and shrubs—singly, in pairs or small loose groups—from close to the ground up to the canopy. Insects, nectar and fruit are taken, particularly berries of lantana and wild raspberry. The birds seem to be sedentary throughout their range.

OTHER NAMES
Lesser Lewin Honeyeater.

IDENTIFICATION
LENGTH: *170–190 mm.*
ADULTS: *Sexes similar; male larger. Upper parts, wings and tail plain deep olive-green; forehead and lores dusky olive. Line from base of bill to below eye yellow-cream; malar area and cheeks to edge of ear coverts dusky olive; ear coverts with flared cream-yellow patch. Underparts plain mid olive-green. Eye mid-deep brown. Bill black; gape yellow-cream. Feet grey-horn.*
IMMATURES: *As adults but duller.*

VOICE
CALL: *Territorial advertisement call a loud, sharp repeated bark— chua-chua-chua-chua-chua— descending in pitch and each note measured, not rattled out as in Lewin's Honeyeater. Liquid chip in contact. Loud, ascending scolding notes. Queek-queek-queek in alarm.*
SONG: *Harsh tchu-chua, often falling in pitch.*

NESTING
Breeds September–February. Nest a deep cup, of palm fibre, bark, rootlets, grass and leaves bound with cobweb; lined with plant down or fine grass; suspended in foliage 1–4 m up in rainforest edge or nearby. Eggs: usually two; smooth, white with small, sparse red-black and brown spots, mostly at larger end; oval, about 23 x 16 mm. Incubation about 15 days. Young fledge in about 15 days.

DISTRIBUTION
Rainforests and their edges, at low altitudes up to 600 m in coastal Cape York Peninsula, southeast to near Townsville. Two races.

The Yellow-spotted Honeyeater is similar to Lewin's Honeyeater but has rich brown, not blue-grey eyes.

Graceful Honeyeater

Meliphaga gracilis
(GOULD, 1866)

OTHER NAMES
Lesser Yellow-spotted Honeyeater,
Grey-breasted Honeyeater.

IDENTIFICATION
LENGTH: *140–160 mm.*
ADULTS: *Sexes alike. Upper parts, wings and tail plain mid olive-green; forehead and lores duskier green. Line from base of bill to below eye yellow-cream; malar area and cheeks to edge of ear coverts olive-green; ear coverts with flared cream-yellow patch. Underparts pale to mid plain olive-green. Eye mid to deep brown. Bill black; gape yellow-cream. Feet grey-horn. Closely resembles Yellow-spotted Honeyeater but distinctly smaller, slightly paler and with a proportionately longer and slender bill: width at base of bill is 3.4–4.4 mm, compared with 4.5–5.5 mm in Yellow-spotted.*
IMMATURES: *As adults but faint yellow wash on underparts; base of under mandible buff-brown.*

VOICE
CALL: *Sharp* tuck *or* tick *in contact.*
SONG: *Thin whistle, rarely given.*

NESTING
Breeds October–February. Nest a cup about 70 x 70 mm outside, of palm fibre, bark, rootlets, grass and leaf skeletons, bound with cobweb, covered with moss and lichen; lined with plant down or soft grass; suspended by rim of tree or bush, 2–6 m above ground, on rainforest edge or over water. Eggs: usually two; smooth glossy; salmon-flesh with chestnut and purple-red spots forming zone at large end; oval, about 20 x 15 mm. Incubation about 14–15 days. Young fledge in about 14–15 days.

DISTRIBUTION
Lowland rainforests, mangroves, their edges and gardens mostly below 300 m altitude in coastal northeastern Queensland, from Lower Archer River around Cape York Peninsula southeast to near Townsville. Also New Guinea and offshore islands. Three or four races; two in Australia.

The Graceful Honeyeater builds its nest in a tree or bush at the edge of rainforest or in open forest nearby.

THIS IS AUSTRALIA'S THIRD member of *Meliphaga,* a group of rainforest-inhabiting honeyeaters which, centred in New Guinea, has plain olive-green plumage, yellow-cream gape line and a flared yellow or white spot on the ear coverts.

In all aspects of its behaviour, diet and breeding, the Graceful Honeyeater resembles the Yellow-spotted, with which it lives in the lowland rainforests and mangroves of northeastern Queensland. Both birds forage in foliage from near the ground to the forest canopy and along its edges out into eucalypts and gardens, seeking insects, fruit and nectar.

The Graceful is the smaller and more slender-billed of the two and is particularly acrobatic, often hanging upside down, flitting about or hovering to pick a fruit or snap up an insect. Generally it works in ones and twos through the upper strata of the forest, feed-ing more consistently in the canopy than the Yellow-spotted, and sometimes gathering there in loose aggregations to rifle blossom in profusely flowering tree crowns. The birds come and go continually in these food trees.

Contact is kept—and position identified—by a sharp, single *tick* call, given day-long. It is easily distinguished from the harsh *tchu-chua* call of the Yellow-spotted Honeyeater.

Graceful Honeyeaters appear to be sedentary throughout their Australian range, and keep to the lowest most tropical altitudes of all northeastern Queensland meliphagas. Only in the McIlwraith Range on Cape York Peninsula do they occur regularly above 500 metres. Unlike Yellow-spotted Honeyeaters, they occur in New Guinea where they are widespread in lowland rainforests and mangroves around its south and east coasts.

White-lined Honeyeater *Meliphaga albilineata* (H.L.WHITE, 1917)

The White-lined Honeyeater spends much of the day foraging for insects, fruits and seeds.

CHASMS AND RAVINES filled with broad-leaved scrub and pockets of monsoon vine forest among sandstone escarpments are the habitat of the White-lined Honeyeater in remote parts of Arnhem Land and the Kimberleys. Feeding usually in ones and twos, it is an aggressive forager, chasing off smaller birds; it otherwise stays within the cover of crowns of trees and shrubs as it hops about, gleaning fruit and a range of insects—termites, bees, beetles, flies, wasps, weevils and grasshoppers—and spiders.

Groups of up to a dozen or so congregate, according to circumstance, to drink and bathe in rock pools during mid-afternoon, and will even flutter through the spray of waterfalls. At other times they gather, with other honeyeaters, in flowering food trees—*Melaleuca, Allosyncarpia, Agonis, Xanthostemon*—to rifle nectar.

Local populations appear to be rather sedentary, rarely wandering far after breeding. Established pairs may be permanently territorial, judged by year-round singing, and both members feed the young. Territorial song is given at all times of the day, from sheltered perches in the canopy of trees and shrubs. The songs given by the two isolated races, one in Arnhem Land, the other in the Kimberleys, are quite different. Arnhem Land birds utter three or four long-drawn rising-and-falling whistles; those in the Kimberleys fire out 10–12 quick chirruping whistles in the same time.

OTHER NAMES
White-striped Honeyeater.

IDENTIFICATION
LENGTH: *180–200 mm.*
ADULTS: *Sexes similar; male larger. Upper parts, wings and tail uniformly deep brownish grey; flight and tail feathers with or without citrine wash, according to race. Lores, area through eye, malar line and cheeks dusky grey, split by narrow white line from bill under eye; ear coverts with small flared patch of white. Underparts greyish white, heavily mottled grey-brown over throat and breast. Eye blue-grey. Bill black; gape pale yellow. Feet leaden.*

IMMATURES: *As adults. Juveniles plain olive-grey brown above; plain grey-white below; wing coverts tinged rufous; flared yellow patch over ears in otherwise plain face.*

VOICE
CALL & SONG: *Ringing whistles in territorial advertisement: in Arnhem Land, three to five long-drawn clear rising-and-falling whistles, tuuheeer-tuuu-tuuu-uu-eeee; in Kimberleys up to 12 up- and down-slurred chirruping whistles in quick-fire bursts.*

NESTING
Breeds August–January. Nest a deep cup, about 60 x 60 mm, of fine dry stems, bound with cobweb; lined with finer stems and fibre; suspended at rim by binding cobweb to low fork in shrubbery 1–3 m above rock. Eggs: two; pale salmon with wreath of dark salmon and red dots at large end; oval, about 21 x 15 mm.

DISTRIBUTION
Shrubberies and pockets of vine forest in ravines in tumbled sandstone escarpments in western Arnhem Land, between Wellington Range and Katherine Gorge, NT, and in northwestern Kimberleys, WA. Two races.

Yellow-faced Honeyeater *Lichenostomus chrysops* (LATHAM, 1801)

YELLOW-FACED HONEYEATERS are among Australia's most conspicuous migrants. Each autumn thousands leave their breeding grounds in southeastern Australia to travel north along the Great Dividing Range. From March–May flocks of up to 100 or more fly low along established flyways, one after another, often in company with White-naped Honeyeaters. Most movement occurs in the morning and often in zigzag directions as the birds shift out of high country.

At the end, the large restless flocks congregate to wander about coastal New South Wales, mid-eastern Queensland and parts of South Australia over winter. In a range of habitats from coastal scrubs to open woodland, they follow flushes of blossoming for manna before heading back south in spring to breed. The return movement is less conspicuous, but small flocks drift south between August and October, eventually finding their nesting grounds of the previous summer in wet and dry sclerophyll forests.

Active birds, Yellow-faced Honeyeaters are arboreal foragers, gleaning insects from twigs and foliage and even hawking for them in short sallies among the canopies of trees and shrubs. They also rifle nectar from the flowers of eucalypts, banksias, grevilleas and heaths. Their flight is strong, swift and undulating.

The flocks break up as nesting pairs establish their own territories in spring. These they defend with much singing from vantage perches in the tops of shrubbery and tree branches throughout the day. Yellow-faced Honeyeaters nest late, most beginning in December and some not until February in the south.

OTHER NAMES
Chickup, Quitchup, Yellow-gaped Honeyeater.

IDENTIFICATION
LENGTH: *160–170 mm.*
ADULTS: *Sexes alike. Upper parts, wings and tail plain grey-brown; underwing coverts cinnamon. Yellow stripe under eye ending in white tuft, bordered above and below by black lines; small white spot over eye. Underparts off-white obscurely striped pale grey-brown. Eye blue-grey. Bill black. Feet grey-brown.*
IMMATURES: *As adults but duller.*

VOICE
CALL: *Repeated single clipped clip in flight contact; peevish descending whistle kree in contact at perch or when feeding.*
SONG: *Brisk, descending, ringing chickup-chickup-chickup.*

NESTING
Breeds July–March; most nesting October–January. Nest a small cup of fine grasses and bark bound with cobweb, sometimes camouflaged with moss or lichen; bound to small fork of outer branches of tree or shrub, up to 7 m above ground. Eggs: two or three, rarely four; light pink, blotched with browns and reds, more at larger end; oval, about 21 x 14 mm. Incubation about 14 days. Young fledge in about 13 days.

DISTRIBUTION
Coast and ranges of eastern Australia from Atherton Tableland, Qld, to Mount Lofty and southern Flinders Ranges, SA. During breeding season, primarily in denser dry sclerophyll and wet sclerophyll forests. Also common along creeks. No races.

A Yellow-faced Honeyeater at a Christmas Bell. Like other honeyeaters, it has a brush-tipped tongue—an adaptation to feeding on pollen and nectar.

Bridled Honeyeater

Lichenostomus frenatus (RAMSAY, 1875)

A Bridled Honeyeater in the depths of northern Queensland rainforest.

OTHER NAMES
Mountain Honeyeater.

IDENTIFICATION
LENGTH: *190–210 mm.*
ADULTS: *Sexes similar; male larger. Upper parts, wings and tail dark brown-grey, with white shafts on back; forehead dusky; flight and tail feathers edged citrine, ochreish underneath. Bare line of buff skin beneath eye; large white spot behind eye; malar line and ear coverts black, finely tipped yellow at ear; sides of neck tipped buff. Chin and throat dusky, crossed by inverted thin yellow V. Rest of underparts mid grey-brown, mottled paler, grading to pale buff on belly and undertail. Eye blue-grey. Bill black with chrome-yellow base. Feet dusky grey.*
IMMATURES: *Like adults but more rufous-brown; more yellow on throat.*

VOICE
CALL: *Harsh squeak,* chaaarh, *when feeding.*
SONG: *Rippling descending chirps—* tchew-tchew-tchew-tchew-tchew, *run rapidly together and sometimes bubbling up and down.*

NESTING
Breeds September–January. Nest a brown cup of vine tendrils, plant stems and ferns, 110 x 50 mm; lined with paler plant fibre; hung in twigs or tangles of vines up to 8 m. Eggs: two; smooth matt white with minute dots of purple-blue and grey-brown mostly at larger end; tapered-oval, about 25 x 15 mm.

DISTRIBUTION
Montane rainforests of northeastern Queensland, between Cooktown and Paluma Range. No races.

TAKING ITS NAME FROM the yellow 'bridle' extending from its bill to its ears, the Bridled Honeyeater is an active, aggressive nomad in the rainforests of northeastern Queensland. For much of the year it wanders locally in small foraging bands of up to a dozen or so birds, often descending to low altitudes around mountain ranges in winter. As a rule, however, it keeps to montane forest above 300 metres, feeding there in the canopy and mid-strata, gleaning fruit and arboreal insects among the foliage and nectar from blossoms whenever it can.

Bridled Honeyeaters are the main nectar-feeding honeyeaters of the upland rainforests of northern Queensland. The birds will converge in numbers at profusely flowering trees and climbers, particularly scheffleras and mistletoes, even entering gardens and visiting nearby paperbarks in open forest. There they hop and flutter about, calling noisily, often hanging upside down in outer foliage and sprays of blossom to probe the flowers. Their behaviour and ecology is little different from the honeyeater *Lichenostomus subfrenatus* in montane New Guinea.

Eungella Honeyeater *Lichenostomus hindwoodi* (LONGMORE & BOLES, 1984)

PROBABLY THE LAST BIRD SPECIES to be discovered on the Australian mainland is the Eungella Honeyeater. It had been known since the early 1960s from the high rainforested tablelands of the Clarke Range west of Mackay, Queensland—and confused then with the Bridled Honeyeater from further north. But its distinctiveness was not recognised until the late 1970s and then not formally described until 1984.

Despite its limited range, the Eungella Honeyeater is moderately abundant along the summit rainforested ridges of Clarke Range and down along its wooded eastern slopes, into which it spreads during winter on flowering eucalypts.

Eungella Honeyeaters forage in small, locally nomadic enclaves of up to a dozen or so birds in the middle and upper strata of rainforest and its edges. There, like Bridled Honeyeaters, they feed on fruit, insects and, wherever it is available, nectar. Fruit, particularly of *Alphitonia,* is picked from outer foliage and insects are gleaned there too, and on short hawking flights under and out from the forest canopy. Nectar is taken from blossoming trees and mistletoe, and in eucalypts on the edges of the rainforest. Both sexes sing territorially from their feeding areas throughout the day, from high but sheltered vantage perches.

The Eungella Honeyeater was not formally described until 1984.

OTHER NAMES
None.

IDENTIFICATION
LENGTH: *180–200 mm.*
ADULTS: *Sexes similar; male larger. Upper parts, wings and tail slightly mottled deep grey-olive, duskier over crown; underwing coverts ochreish. Face dusky, with feathered white line from gape to under eye; small white spot behind eye; ear coverts dusky, extensively tipped white and lined yellow above in elongate plume. Underparts light grey, washed brown, the feathers with grey-white shafts, appearing streaked; undertail grey-brown edged off-white. Eye blue-grey. Bill all black; gape pale flesh. Feet leaden.*
IMMATURES: *As adults but duller.*

VOICE
CALL & SONG: *Short but carrying, high-pitched, up-and-down tinkling, the notes of organ-grinder or music box quality and unlike those of any other Australian bird. Given in position and territorial advertisement.*

NESTING
Breeds probably September–January. Nest and eggs unknown.

DISTRIBUTION
Summit rainforests of Clarke Range, Qld, mainly above 600 m but also down forested coastward gullies to near sea-level at least in winter. No races.

Singing Honeyeater *Lichenostomus virescens* (VEILLOT, 1817)

RARELY SEEN NEAR URBAN centres on the east coast, the Singing Honeyeater is nonetheless Australia's most widespread honeyeater, ranging across the continent west of the Great Dividing Range. Some reference texts claim that it also occurs in northern New Guinea, confusing it there with a pale race of the Varied Honeyeater. Throughout its range it frequents open scrubby shrubberies, whether in mallee or mulga or even coastal heaths.

Singing Honeyeaters may wander in poor seasons but are usually rather sedentary in small enclaves of two to five or six birds which feed solitarily. Most of their foraging is done in shrubbery and low tree foliage where they switch between nectar, insects and fruit as the opportunity offers, but the birds also hop along the ground and steal eggs and young from finch nests. Insects taken include beetles, weevils, moths, caterpillars, wasps, ants, flies and lerps. The honeyeaters also eat the fleshy fruits of more than 40 species of native shrubs, particularly of chenopods. The seeds are swallowed but not digested, so the birds act as dispersing agents.

Belying their name, Singing Honeyeaters are not accomplished singers but do advertise territory in rollicking duets between pairs, usually from vantage perches on the tops of bushes. A variation of the song is trilled out sweetly in the dawn chorus. Pallid Cuckoos often parasitise their nests.

OTHER NAMES
Black-face Honeyeater, Grey Peter, Grape eater, Forrest's Honeyeater.

IDENTIFICATION
LENGTH: *170–210 mm.*
ADULTS: *Sexes similar. In drier areas populations paler; also washed greener in southeast, browner in southwest, and largest in Rottnest Island, WA. Upper parts brown, washed olive; forehead and crown grey-brown; wings and tail brown with feathers edged olive-yellow. Broad black band from bill through eye down to side of neck; parallel yellow streak below, edged underneath with white broadening into large patch on side of neck. Underparts off-white,* streaked dusky grey, washed browner over breast. Eye brown. Bill black. Feet dark grey-brown.
IMMATURES: *As adults; face pattern and ventral streaking much lighter.*

VOICE
CALL: *Dry, whistled* creeee *in contact; soft, trilled* prrit-prt-prrrit *when alerted.*
SONG: *Rollicking, rolling trilled* crik-crikit-crik-crikit, *often in rattling duet.*

NESTING
Breeds July–February; at other times following heavy rains. Nest a cup of interwoven grasses and sometimes bark strips, matted with cobweb; 55 x 39 mm inside, lined with fibrous rootlets, sometimes fur or hair; suspended by rim in small branches of bush or low tree, usually 0.5–5 m above ground. Eggs: two–three; pale pink or buff-white, usually with darker cap or band at larger end; occasionally with few small brown spots; oval, about 22 x 16 mm. Incubation 12–15 days, by female. Young fledge in 10–13 days. Often two broods a season.

DISTRIBUTION
Pockets of shrubbery throughout inland woodlands west of Great Dividing Range, reaching west and south coast and penetrating regularly to east only in central Queensland. Endemic; rather sedentary or nomadic in deserts. No races.

The Singing Honeyeater can be identified by its faintly streaked grey breast. Contrary to its name, it usually makes creaking or chattering noises.

Varied Honeyeater *Lichenostomus versicolor* (GOULD, 1843)

The Mangrove race of the Varied Honeyeater at its nest among low mangrove branchlets. The nest can be slung as little as one metre above water.

THAT BIRDS SO DIFFERENT from one another in appearance as the Varied and Mangrove Honeyeaters can intergrade as one species shows how unreliable plumage can sometimes be as an indicator of species. In this case the yellowish, streak-throated Varied Honeyeater of northeastern Queensland coasts intergrades and merges with the brown, scaly-throated Mangrove of the mid and south coasts between Bowen and Cardwell. Here behaviour and ecology are better clues to relationships. Both races live in coastal mangroves, although the Mangrove will feed on blossoms of fringing eucalypts and banksias, and the northern Varied does enter coastal gardens and coconut groves on offshore islands for nectar. Indeed, much of its life is spent in low dashing undulating flights between these island feeding groves and roosting and nesting grounds in mangroves.

Both races also live in sedentary communal groups of two to seven or eight birds and forage among the branchlets and foliage in the mid and upper strata of mangroves. There they glean leaves and crevices along branches for insects, even working down towards mud-level for small crabs, and probe the small white mangrove flowers for nectar. The birds are noisy and aggressive in defence of both feeding and breeding territories. Smaller birds are driven off in dashing chases through and around shrubbery. And often during the day, members of territorial groups gather to sing rollicking duets in advertisement, clustered together, heads thrown up, on vantage perches in the crowns of mangroves, on coconut fronds, or in other trees nearby.

Both Fantailed Cuckoos and Little Bronze-Cuckoos occasionally parasitise the nest of Varied Honeyeaters. Only the female builds the nest and incubates, but both parents and possibly other members of their group may feed and care for the young.

OTHER NAMES
Mangrove Honeyeater, Fasciated Honeyeater, Scaly-throated Honeyeater, Island Honeyeater.

IDENTIFICATION
LENGTH: *180–210 mm.*
ADULTS: *Sexes similar; male larger. Crown to back olive-green streaked black, with forehead plainer grey and rump plainer olive-brown (northern race); or crown to rump plain deep brown-grey, greyer on forehead. Wings and tail grey-brown, extensively (northern race) to narrowly (southern race) washed and edged citrine. Broad black stripe from lores through eye down sides of neck; parallel yellow streak below to over ears, tipped with white plume running into broad white patch on side of throat. Throat yellow, faintly streaked (northern race); or lightly barred brown, producing scaling (southern race). Breast to undertail pale yellow, lightly streaked grey-brown (northern race); or off-white heavily striped dusky, the stripes coalescing in brown-grey breast band (southern race). Eye blue- to brown-grey. Bill black. Feet dark grey.*
IMMATURES: *As adults of respective races; more dully and lightly marked; eyes browner.*

VOICE
CALL: *Scolding chatter, maybe in alarm.*
SONG: *Loud, rollicking, rolling, fluted trills, resembling those of Singing Honeyeater, but louder and more varied; more protracted in northern race.*

NESTING
Breeds April–December, mainly August–November. Nest a scanty cup of dry grass, seaweed and rootlets, bound with cobweb and adorned with cocoons; lined with finer rootlets and plant down; slung by rim in horizontal fork usually among low mangrove foliage or in slightly isolated beachside tree, standing in or near saltwater, 1–5 m above ground. Eggs: two; lustrous pink-buff, with a few tiny spots of red-brown and purplish, mainly at larger end; oval, about 23 x 17 mm. Incubation and fledging times probably as Singing Honeyeater.

DISTRIBUTION
Mangroves, and fringing seaside groves, gardens and offshore islands, on northeast coast of mainland, from Cape York and Torres Strait south to mouth of Hastings River, NSW. Also coastal New Guinea and islands. About four, possibly five races; two in Australia.

The Varied race of the Varied Honeyeater visits seaside gardens for nectar.

White-gaped Honeyeater

Lichenostomus unicolor
(GOULD, 1843)

OTHER NAMES
River Honeyeater, Erect-tailed Honeyeater.

IDENTIFICATION
LENGTH: *180–200 mm.*
ADULTS: *Sexes similar. Upper parts plain dark grey with hint of green; feather shafts on crown darker. Wing and tail quills grey-brown, edged green-lemon. Lores dark grey to black. Underparts mid plain grey, sometimes with a vague lemon wash. Eye grey to grey-brown. Bill black with conspicuous white gape flange. Feet leaden.*
IMMATURES: *As adults but heavier lemon wash on underparts and edges of wing quills. Gape yellow.*

VOICE
CALL: *Explosive* chiew *or* chop, *miner-like peeping.*
SONG: *Series of rollicking, trilled whistles, resembling those of Singing and Varied Honeyeaters.*

NESTING
Breeds September–March, sometimes later. Nest cup-shaped, of bark strips, particularly inner bark of Melaleuca, *grasses, rootlets and hair and bound with cobweb and cocoons; lined with fine grass; usually suspended by rim in fork of a small tree, often over water. Eggs: two; smooth, slightly lustrous white to pale flesh with freckles of red and purple, particularly at larger end; oval, about 22 x 17 mm.*

DISTRIBUTION
Tropical Australia from Broome, WA, to Townsville, Qld. Humid thicket in woodland, such as paperbark swamps,

The White-gaped Honeyeater is a noisy bird easily recognised as it has no adornment except its white gape.

vegetation along rivers, pandanus and freshwater and estuarine mangroves. Visits suburban parks and gardens. Common. No races.

NOISY AND AGGRESSIVE LIKE MOST honeyeaters, the White-gaped occupies the streamside thickets and shrubberies throughout the tropical eucalypt woodlands of northern Australia. Wherever it occurs it is sedentary, established pairs and small groups seeming to hold to much the same small foraging range year round. This they defend with active chasing and loud chirruping songs, often in duet, from vantage perches in the cover of shrubbery.

White-gaped Honeyeaters feed under shrubbery and within the canopy of trees, hopping actively with tails often part-cocked, picking fruit and gleaning insects and spiders from twigs, trunks and foliage. They occasionally join other honeyeaters to rifle nectar from flowering trees. Flight, from shrub to shrub, is low and more erratic and jerky than that of other honeyeaters.

Both sexes feed the young. A male approaching the nest with food calls loudly, to which the female replies and leaves the nest. If no bird is brooding, approaches are silent. Parents swallow the faecal sacs of newly hatched young but later carry them off.

Yellow Honeyeater

Lichenostomus flavus (GOULD, 1843)

THE RICHLY TONED YELLOW Honeyeater replaces the White-gaped in the streamside thickets and woodlands of coastal eastern Queensland. Where they overlap—between Townsville and the Gulf of Carpentaria—is the only area where the White-gaped is scarce in northern Australia. The two are alike in feeding habits and rollicking songs which they give to advertise feeding as well as breeding territory.

The presence of Yellow Honeyeaters is heralded by their loud cheery calls and their scolding chatter. They also draw attention to themselves by their jerky movements. They are rarely still and keep constantly on the move, usually in pairs but occasionally singly or in small groups.

They are locally nomadic and sometimes gather in large groups at flowering trees along with other honeyeaters. They search busily from the shrub layer to the treetops, for nectar in blossoms and insects and fruit among the leaves and branches.

The Yellow Honeyeater is distinguished by its loud, cheery calls.

OTHER NAMES
None.

IDENTIFICATION
LENGTH: *170–190 mm.*
ADULTS: *Sexes similar. Upper parts bright green-yellow; wing and tail quills dark grey-brown, edged externally with bright yellow and internally with buff. Line above and below eye bright saffron-yellow; lores and ear coverts dark grey-green; faint stripe on side of throat green-yellow. Underparts bright saffron-yellow, darker with green tinge on sides of breast and flanks. Eye light brown. Bill*

dark brown to black; gape yellow, no flange. Feet green-horn to grey.
IMMATURES: *Duller than adults; bill paler.*

VOICE
CALL: *Cheery, metallic* whek-whek *in contact; chattering and scratchy* jab *in alarm.*
SONG: *Rollicking trilled whistles,* t-wheee-a, t-wheee-a, *often rather piercing.*

NESTING
Breeds September–March. Nest a cup of plant fibre, bark strips and binding

cobweb; lined with fine bark or other soft material; suspended by the rim to twigs 0.5–10 m above ground in foliage of tree or shrub. Eggs: two; smooth, matt white to pink thickly blotched with chestnut, red and purple-grey, particularly at larger end, forming zone; oval, about 22 x 16 mm.

DISTRIBUTION
Northern Queensland, from Cape York Peninsula to Broad Sound. Common in eucalypt forest close to creeks, riverine vegetation, paperbark swamps, parks and gardens. No races.

Yellow-tufted Honeyeater *Lichenostomus melanops* (LATHAM, 1801)

THROUGHOUT THEIR RANGE in heathy eucalypt woodlands and open forest in southeastern Australia, Yellow-tufted Honeyeaters live and breed in discrete colonies of 10–100 birds or more, often along creeks. There is often much variation in appearance between birds in different colonies, those in high mountains or southern latitudes in particular being larger than others elsewhere. Even so, there are only two clear-cut races.

The larger and more brilliantly coloured of the two is the Helmeted Honeyeater, *L.m. cassidix,* previously regarded as a distinct species. Once widespread in western Gippsland, Vic., it is now restricted, through clearing of its habitat, to a tiny area on Woori Yallock Creek near Yellingbo. Today the population probably numbers no more than 100–150 birds. Recent shifts in local drainage there have affected the eucalypt woodland in which the birds live and made them more susceptible to insect attack. This in turn has brought in the pugnacious Bell Miner, which specialises in taking sap-sucking insects—but which also competes with and drives out the smaller Helmeted Honeyeater.

The other race, *L.m. melanops,* is shorter-tailed and tufted on the forehead, has a paler back and less clear-cut cream-tipped tail. It ranges along both scarps of the Great Dividing Range in New South Wales north into southern Queensland and southwest to the Grampians, Vic., and the southeast of South Australia. Between it and the Helmeted Honeyeater along the southeastern gullies of the Range in central and eastern Gippsland is an extensive intergrading population, formerly treated as a separate race, *L.m. gippslandica.* Whatever their differences in appearance, all colonies are similar in calls, habits and behaviour.

Coastal colonies, including Helmeted and *gippslandica* honeyeaters are sedentary and permanent in creekside eucalypts. Those in the summit gullies and along the western scarps of the Great Dividing Range, wander in autumn and winter, generally shifting northwards and down to lower altitudes.

Everywhere they feed in foliage on insects and their sugary secretions: honeydew lerp, and—particularly during breeding—manna, the sugary sap that exudes from damaged plant tissue. Nectar is also taken, the coastal colonies exploiting it only when local trees are in flower, and those inland roaming more widely to follow blossoming. Most insects are taken by gleaning over leaves in the mid and upper strata of trees, but in summer and autumn Helmeted Honeyeaters shift to the shrub layer to forage. Then, too, all populations hawk occasionally for flying insects. Often they capture insects on tree trunks, like treecreepers. Some colonies spend up to 30 per cent of their time foraging in this way.

Roaming groups return to parental breeding grounds to nest each spring and summer, up to 50 pairs in about 10 hectares of territory. Both parents feed the young and helpers may assist as well.

OTHER NAMES
Helmeted Honeyeater, Black-faced Honeyeater, Yellow Whiskers, Whisky.

IDENTIFICATION
LENGTH: *170–230 mm.*
ADULTS: *Sexes similar. Forehead, crown and nape green-yellow shading into darker back; forehead feathers form tuft of varying length. Back various shades of brown-olive; flight feathers and tail dark brown with green-yellow edges; cream tips to tail feathers. Broad black sash through eye to ear coverts; ear tuft chrome-yellow; lower cheeks and throat yellow, with dark central line from chin to upper breast. Rest of underparts yellow-green with dark streaks—heaviest on breast. Eye red-brown. Bill black. Feet dark grey.*
IMMATURES: *As adults but yellow areas greener and duller; gape flange cream to lilac.*

VOICE
CALL: *Loud harsh* tchurr *comprises bulk of repertoire, used for contact and in chorus in group displays (apparently for colony advertising). Alarm note similar but harsher, more urgent.*
SONG: *Infrequent, sweet, whistling.*

NESTING
Breeds June–March, mostly August–January. Nest a cup of bark strips and grass, bound with cobweb and cocoons; lined with finer strips of bark, grass, feathers or hair; suspended from rim usually in low shrubs or small trees 0.3–4 m above ground in horizontal fork or where several stems interlace. Eggs: two, rarely three; smooth, dull flesh-buff to white, spotted and blotched with chestnut, purple-red and purple-grey, mainly on larger end in zone; oval, about 23 x 16 mm. Incubation about 14 days. Young fledge in about 13 days.

DISTRIBUTION
In colonies in shrubby eucalypt forest and woodland, often along creeksides, on coast and inland scarps of Great Dividing Range, north to Carnarvon Ranges and Blackdown Tablelands, Qld, and southwest to Grampians, Vic., and southeastern South Australia. Two races, intergrading in central and eastern Gippsland.

The White-eared Honeyeater has a loud ringing call.

UNLIKE MOST OF ITS RELATIVES, the White-eared Honeyeater is not communal, rarely gathers in any number at flowering food trees and never forms coherent colonies. Rather, established males or pairs hold large, well-spaced territories year round, rarely wandering far except in the Australian alps which they vacate for lower altitudes in autumn and winter. Even there some birds remain in cold months. Habitats occupied are varied, from coastal heath to wet sclerophyll forest, alpine woodland and mallee inland around southern and eastern Australia, but close-packed eucalypts and shrubberies are common to all. There the birds feed, usually singly, from the middle of shrubs into the lower tree canopy. Much gleaning is done in foliage, where the birds take manna and honeydew from insect-damaged leaves. They also spend more time than other

White-eared Honeyeater

Lichenostomus leucotis (LATHAM, 1801)

OTHER NAMES
None.

IDENTIFICATION
LENGTH: *170–210 mm.*
ADULTS: *Sexes similar; male larger. Crown and hind neck rich grey streaked black. Rest of upper parts, wings and tail deep citrine-green. Face, throat and upper breast black with white ear patch. Rest of underparts pale yellow-green. Eye blue-grey. Bill black. Feet deep grey.*
IMMATURES: *Duller than adults; olive-green crown, dusky grey face and throat, cream-yellow ear patch.*

VOICE
CALL: *Loud resounding* chok; chop; cherry-bob; cher-up—*notes rolled. A lighter ringing* cherrywheet, cherrywheet *inland. Rapid rattling. No sustained song.*

NESTING
Breeds mostly August–December. Nest a cup of bark strips and grasses bound with cobweb; lined with fur or hair; slung from rim 2–3 m above ground in small bush or shrub or among fallen debris. Eggs: two, sometimes three; white lightly spotted with red at larger end; oval, about 21 x 15 mm.

DISTRIBUTION
Sclerophyll forests, alpine woodland, mallee and coastal tree-heaths around southern and eastern mainland; in west, north to about mulga line. Two races.

honeyeaters on the trunks and main branches, hopping sideways along, probing in and under bark for insects—particularly beetles—and spiders. Their bills being short, they do not visit flowers much for nectar. When they do, however, they often use the ploy of all short-billed honeyeaters, that of poking a hole into the base of a flower through which to suck nectar.

Established males or pairs advertise territory with resounding *chop* and *cher-up* calls year round—but mostly during breeding—from vantage perches in the crowns of trees and shrubs.

The Yellow-tufted Honeyeater builds its cup-shaped nest in a low shrub, small tree or vine tangle where stems interlace, in eucalypt forests or woodland. Both sexes feed the chicks, and occasionally helpers assist. The young leave the nest 13 or 14 days after hatching.

Yellow-throated Honeyeater *Lichenostomus flavicollis* (VEILLOT, 1817)

RESTRICTED TO TASMANIA and Bass Strait Islands, the Yellow-throated Honeyeater occurs through a wider range of habitats there than any other honeyeater. Wet and dry sclerophyll forest, coastal heaths, alpine woodland, and even well-shrubbed gardens are occupied. Like its close relative, the White-eared Honeyeater, it is rather solitary, only remaining in family groups temporarily after breeding in autumn and gathering on cider gum to feed on manna exuding from foliage. During winter too, coastal populations swell with birds—females and immatures—from probably higher altitudes, most visiting the same feeding quarters each year.

Territorial males are sedentary, and hold much the same range year round, advertising it with loud, machine-gun-like *tonk-tonk-tonks* sporadically from vantage perches through the day. They seem to mate temporarily with females, then drive them and young off, only to remate and nest again in the same season. Pairs nest alone. Both partners are reported to build and incubate —though this needs confirmation—and both feed the young and defend the vicinity of the nest aggressively, flying at intruders and driving them off. Building birds often become bold and pull hair and fur from stock and household pets to line their nests.

Also like the White-eared Honeyeater, the Yellow-throated is a bark- and crevice-forager. Indeed, its abundance in any area can be linked with the number of large eucalypts providing extensive foraging surfaces. The birds work over the cracks and crannies on trunks and branches, hopping and fluttering actively, gleaning out into foliage and down through shrubbery to the ground. Spiders and insects—beetles, flies, wasps, and caterpillars—are staple prey, and are augmented with scale insects, their sugary secretions and manna from insect-damaged foliage. The birds even hawk out for small moths and butterflies. Flight between trees is an erratic, twisting, undulating dash.

Insects provide 80 per cent of this honeyeater's diet. Nectar and fruit are taken rarely, although young birds are sometimes attracted to eucalypt blossoms and fruit.

OTHER NAMES
Linnet.

IDENTIFICATION
LENGTH: *190–210 mm.*
ADULTS: *Sexes similar; male larger. Head, nape and sides of neck rich grey, faintly flecked black on crown. Rest of upper parts, wings and tail citrine-green. Lores and lower cheeks black-grey to silver-grey upper cheeks and ear coverts with small yellow ear tuft. Chin and throat rich yellow, bordered blackish grey, grading into paler grey breast and belly which is washed yellow in centre; undertail olive, tipped yellow.*

Eye claret-red. Bill black. Feet slate-grey.
IMMATURES: *As adults but duller; throat pale yellow; eye hazel.*

VOICE
CALL: *Advertising call loud, resonant, machine-gun-like* tonk, *usually repeated three or four times. Other calls are whirring* churr *ending with sharp* chop *note and loud* pick-em-up. *Very harsh* churr *in aggression. Many local dialects.*
SONG: *Variety of soft warbling notes uttered at dawn or dusk, mainly during breeding season.*

NESTING
Breeds July–January. Nest a deep bark cup, interwoven with grasses; lined with fur, wool and sometimes feathers; usually placed in a grass tussock, bracken bush, up to 1 m above ground. Eggs: two or three; pale buff-pink, delicately spotted and flecked with red-brown and purple-grey, mostly at larger end; oval, about 23 x 16 mm. Incubation about 15 days. Young fledge in about 14 days.

DISTRIBUTION
Common in most habitats throughout Tasmania and Bass Strait islands, *particularly shrubbed wet and dry sclerophyll forests. Two races; King Island birds duller.*

The Yellow-throated Honeyeater, which lives in Tasmania and on Bass Strait islands, is clearly distinguished from other honeyeaters by its yellow throat.

The Purple-gaped Honeyeater is restricted to mallee thickets in small areas.

Purple-gaped Honeyeater

Lichenostomus cratitius (GOULD, 1841)

OTHER NAMES
Lilac-wattled Honeyeater, Wattle-cheeked Honeyeater.

IDENTIFICATION
LENGTH: *160–170 mm.*
ADULTS: *Sexes similar; male larger. Upper parts plain olive-green, washed greyer on crown and citrine on wings and tail. Dusky black sash from lores over ears, ending in an acute yellow ear plume; bare lilac flange from gape down cheeks; malar line yellow. Underparts plain pale yellow-grey. Eye brown. Bill black. Feet dark grey.*
IMMATURES: *As adults but duller; gape flange pale yellow.*

VOICE
CALL: *Sharp chirps and* twit *in contact. Also clicks and whistles.*
SONG: *Harsh chattering, of rapidly repeated* chuk-chuk-chuk-chuk-chuk, *to mark territory.*

NESTING
Breeds July–December. Nest a cup of
bark strips and grass bound with cobweb; lined with soft fibre and down; slung from rim in dense foliage below 2 m up. Eggs: two; white-pink, with sparse red-brown spotting, more at larger end; oval, about 21 x 15 mm.

DISTRIBUTION
'Whipstick' mallee thicket around south coast and subcoast of mainland, in pockets east to Bendigo, Vic. Two races.

Purple-gaped Honeyeaters are rather solitary. Males or established pairs keep to a loose territory year round which they advertise, like the related Grey-headed Honeyeater, with sporadic chattering from vantage perches in the crowns of mallee. The birds feed on insects which they glean from foliage or prise out from beneath strips of bark in the outer foliage. Honeydew and manna from insect-infected foliage and nectar from blossom is taken too, from shrubs of grevillea, heaths and *Correa* as well as mallee eucalypts. The long tubular flowers of *Correa* are pierced at the base and the nectar sucked out from there.

THE PURPLE-GAPED HONEYEATER is confined to stands of dense, low 'whipstick' mallee and its fringing heaths around the southern Australian coast and near-inland. There it is sedentary, moving only locally to flushes of flowering and only then gathering in loose aggregations of up to five or six birds.

Grey-headed Honeyeater *Lichenostomus keartlandi* (NORTH, 1895)

GREY-HEADED HONEYEATERS INHABIT the low scrubs in rocky breakaways, clefts in ranges and on desert dunes across the arid mid-northern mainland, replacing there their close relative, the Purple-gaped Honeyeater.

Like Purple-gaped Honeyeaters, they usually occur in small sedentary groups of two to five or six birds in low, mallee-like eucalypts, gleaning insects from their branchlets, honeydew and manna from their foliage, and nectar from their flowers. Most feeding is done in the canopy. To mark their territory, the groups do not make song flights, but chatter regularly through the day from vantage perches in the crowns of shrubs and trees.

Often after protracted breeding in a good season, roving bands of 100 or more may follow flushes of blossoming.

OTHER NAMES
None.

IDENTIFICATION
LENGTH: *150–160 mm.*
ADULTS: *Sexes similar; male larger. Upper parts pale fawn-grey; crown pale grey; wings and tail washed citrine. Dusky grey wash from lores over ears, ending in acute yellow ear plume. Underparts light yellow, streaked faintly brown on breast. Eye brown. Bill black. Feet grey-brown.*
IMMATURES: *Duller than adults.*

VOICE
CALL: *Single* chek, chek *in flight contact; weak 'alarm-clock' trill in alarm.*
SONG: *Chattering* kwoyt-kwoyt-kwoyt, *repeated rapidly on same pitch.*

NESTING
Breeds July–November or after rain. Nest a flimsy cup of bark strips and grass bound with cobweb and slung from rim in foliage, 1–5 m up. Eggs: two; whitish, lightly spotted with red-
browns, more at larger end; oval, about 20 x 14 mm.

DISTRIBUTION
Desert eucalypt shrubs on dunes and hills across mid-northern mainland, from Pilbara, WA, to central Queensland. Mainly sedentary. No races.

Grey-headed Honeyeaters are found in much of inland northern Australia.

Yellow-plumed Honeyeater

Lichenostomus ornatus (GOULD, 1838)

OTHER NAMES
Mallee Honeyeater.

IDENTIFICATION
LENGTH: *150–165 mm.*
ADULTS: *Sexes alike. Upper parts, wings and tail dark green-grey. Face dull green; lores dusky; black streak below ear edged with pointed yellow plume tuft. Underparts white, heavily streaked dark grey. Eye brown. Bill black or base becoming buff—like black eye-ring—out of breeding. Feet grey-horn.*
IMMATURES: *As adults but duller; base of bill and eye-ring buff.*

VOICE
CALL: *Repeated chip in contact when feeding; flat, machine-gun-like chirping in alarm.*
SONG: *Rapid, rattling wi-te-te-te-tet, falling slightly in pitch, and ringing, whistled chick-o-wee, from perches. Rapid, trilled whistles hit-jo-jo, hit-jo-jo repeated in climbing song-flight.*

NESTING
Breeds July–December. Nest a neat cup of grasses, bark strips and cobweb, usually suspended in sapling. Eggs: two or three; salmon-pink minutely freckled with red-brown, particularly at larger end; oval, about 20 x 14 mm.

DISTRIBUTION
Mallee and fringes of adjacent woodland across southern mainland, east to Temora–West Wyalong, NSW. No races.

The Yellow-plumed Honeyeater is similar to the Grey-fronted Honeyeater, but underparts are more boldly streaked.

SIMILAR IN ITS FEEDING habits and behaviour to White-plumed and Grey-fronted Honeyeaters, the Yellow-plumed replaces those species in the wetter mallee of southern Australia. It is almost entirely confined to mallee, spreading into taller eucalypt woodland and open forest only in southern Western Australia and entering barely the fringes of mulga scrub further inland.

Yellow-plumed Honeyeaters are sedentary in pairs or small colonial groups, rarely gathering in large aggregations or wandering more than locally to exploit flushes of blossoming eucalypts, mistletoes and eremophilas for nectar. Most feeding is done in the upper foliage of mallee, the birds hopping and gleaning over leaves, along branchlets and under bark for insects and lerps. Flying insects are also caught in short sallies on the wing.

Feeding and breeding territory is advertised by males both in song from vantage perches and with rapid, trilled whistles in near-vertical song-flights above the mallee.

Grey-fronted Honeyeater *Lichenostomus plumulus* (GOULD, 1841)

OTHER NAMES
Yellow-fronted Honeyeater.

IDENTIFICATION
LENGTH: *150–160 mm.*
ADULTS: *Sexes similar; male larger. Upper parts, wings and tail mid green-grey. Face yellowish green, with narrow grey forehead; lores dusky; black streak below ear edged with broad yellow plume. Underparts cream-white, lightly streaked faint grey. Eye brown. Bill black. Feet grey-horn.*
IMMATURES: *As adults but duller.*

VOICE
CALL: *Repeated clit in contact.*
SONG: *Rattled it-wt-wt-wt, from perch and in song-flight.*

NESTING
Breeds July–January, or after rains. Nest a small cup of fibre and bark bound with cobweb; slung or often supported in upright fork of bushy foliage, 1–3 m up. Eggs: two–three; pale pink, spotted red-brown at larger end; oval, about 20 x 14 mm. Incubation about 14–15 days, probably by female.

DISTRIBUTION
Bushy mallee and woodland on stony hills and dunes in arid zone. No races.

A pair of Grey-fronted Honeyeaters attending their young; most nests are suspended from mallee twigs and made of finely shredded bark bound with spiders egg-sacs and cobwebs.

GREY-FRONTED Honeyeaters replace Yellow-plumed Honeyeaters in stunted desert mallee and eucalypt woodland in a ring around arid Australia, both on low stony hills and spinifex-clad dunes. Where they overlap in the south, the Grey-fronteds keep to bushier mallee regrowth.

Singly, in pairs or small groups of up to about eight, they are locally nomadic and sometimes swarm on flushes of blossoming mallee, taking both nectar and insects attracted to the flowers.

Lerps, aphids, nectar and berries are also eaten, gleaned from the upper foliage.

Males advertise feeding as well as breeding territory by singing from vantage perches just under the canopy and in near-vertical song-flights, calling strongly before suddenly diving back to cover. Most nests are built in the tips of bushy mallees, supported by near-upright twigs, unusual for honeyeaters. Both sexes attend the young, but probably only the female incubates.

Yellow-tinted Honeyeater *Lichenostomus flavescens* (GOULD, 1840)

The northern race of the Yellow-tinted Honeyeater.

IT WAS THE DANISH ornithologist Finn Salomonsen in his revision of the world's honeyeaters who first realised that the 'Fuscous' and 'Yellow-tinted' Honeyeaters were merely races of one and the same species. To Australian ornithologists familiar with the large brown-plumaged 'Fuscous Honeyeaters' in southeastern Australia and the small, sulphur-washed 'Yellow-tinteds' in the tropical north, it was difficult to understand. But available to Salomonsen in the large museums of America and Europe were specimens of linking populations through eastern Queensland barely represented in collections in Australia. His conclusion solved at least one problem for field ornithologists familiar with both 'Fuscous' and 'Yellow-tinted' races in the wild: why they were so alike in their calls.

Throughout their range, Yellow-tinted Honeyeaters live in small to large colonies in well-shrubbed eucalypt woodland and open forest, often along creeks. In most regions they are rather sedentary except for colonies in the extreme southeast and Australian alps. There they shift completely out of the high country in winter down to the coast or further north, returning each September–October to former breeding sites to nest.

The birds feed variously on insects, lerps, honeydews, manna, nectar and occasionally fruit, all gleaned in foliage and branchlets from the middle of shrubs to the tops of trees. Most feeding is done in the middle strata and canopy of the woodland, the birds hopping and fluttering actively about and flying in undulating dashes from one tree to the next. Flying insects are also caught on the wing.

Groups are both aggressive and playful, often chasing one another in twisting aerial acrobatics. Often they gather at water pools to drink and bathe, diving down, splashing into the surface of the water, then fluttering back to a perch.

During breeding, colonies may comprise a number of territorial pairs, each holding ground 100–200 metres in diameter. Males mark territory both by singing from high vantage perches and in aerial song-flights, flying up at an angle above the trees, singing, then diving back to the cover of the canopy. Birds additional to the resident pair may help in the feeding of their young.

OTHER NAMES
Fuscous Honeyeater, Pale-yellow Honeyeater, Yellowish Honeyeater.

IDENTIFICATION
LENGTH: *150–170 mm.*
ADULTS: *Sexes similar; male larger. Upper parts, wings and tail pale to mid olive-brown, washed citrine on flight and tail feathers and over crown according to race. Face grey-brown with dusky eye-ring to pale yellowish without dark eye-ring; below ear a black streak edged with short to long yellow plume. Throat and breast cream-white with coarse dull brown streaks to cream-yellow with finer, fainter streaks; belly and undertail plain white to creamy yellow. Eye dark brown. Bill black or with cream-yellow base and gape out of breeding in southeastern population. Feet grey-horn.*
IMMATURES: *As adults but duller; faint breast streaks, fawn rumps and buff bills.*

VOICE
CALL: *Single whistled* chip, *by feeding birds, in contact. Harsh, rapidly repeated whistled chirps in alarm.*
SONG: *Repeated, dry, rattling* twit't't't *on same pitch from perches, often ending in harsh* taw-taw-taw, *particularly in southern race. In song-flight a ringing* tiu-tiu-tiu-tiu *or* porra-chew, porra-chew, porra-chew-chew, chi-porra-chew *as bird climbs. Local variations in dialect.*

NESTING
Breeds July–March, mainly August–December. Nest a cup of bark fibre, grass stems and down, bound with cobweb; lined with finer grass stems, rootlets, wool and hair, 40 x 25 mm inside; suspended by rim from horizontal fork in leafy branchlet 1–15 m above ground. Eggs: two, sometimes three; light flesh to salmon-buff, with small sparse spots of red-brown, purplish red and paler grey, often in zone at large end; oval, about 19 x 14 mm. Incubation about 14 days.

DISTRIBUTION
Open eucalypt forests and woodlands, often along creeks, along Great Dividing Range (both scarps) and across most of tropical north except far-north of Arnhem Land and much of Cape York Peninsula, Qld. Also southeastern New Guinea. About five races; probably all in Australia.

'Fuscous' race of Yellow-tinted Honeyeater showing the yellow-orange eye-ring typical of juveniles and non-breeding adults.

White-plumed Honeyeater *Lichenostomus penicillatus* (GOULD, 1837)

OTHER NAMES
Greenie, Native Canary, Chickowee.

IDENTIFICATION
LENGTH: *150–170 mm.*
ADULTS: *Sexes alike. Upper parts plain grey-brown washed olive to citrine, particularly on wings and tail. Face and lores mid- to yellow-green; thin black cross-line below cheek, edged with white plume. Underparts plain cream-grey, washed strongly yellow in western race. Eye dark brown. Bill and eye-ring black. Feet horn-brown. Inland birds paler, and western yellower than those in southeast.*
IMMATURES: *As adults but duller with buff-yellow bill and eye-ring.*

VOICE
CALL: *Soft, squeaky* chip, *constantly in contact by feeding birds; rapid strident trilling of chirps on same pitch in alarm.*
SONG: *Repeated, squeaky-whistled* chik-a-weee *from vantage perches. Loud, tremulous* wit-e-chu *or* choo-i-choo *repeated continuously in rising song-flight.*

NESTING
Breeds any time, peaking spring and autumn. Nest a neat deep cup, of interwoven grass, bark strips, rootlets, down and binding cobweb; lined with finer fibre, down and sometimes feathers; slung from rim in drooping foliage in eucalypt, often over water, 1–20 m above ground. Eggs: two–three; pink-white, sparsely spotted with red-brown, purple-brown and grey, often in zone at large end; oval, about 20 x 15 mm. Incubation by female.

DISTRIBUTION
Close and open woodlands over eastern mainland and across inland on eucalypt-lined watercourses; often near water; enters urban parks and gardens. Three races.

The White-plumed Honeyeater darts noisily about the trees in eucalypt woodland in southeastern Australia.

THIS IS ONE OF THE most widespread of honeyeaters. It is abundant in the taller eucalypt woodlands of eastern Australia, establishing itself in many urban areas and ranging inland across the continent on river systems lined with gums, *Eucalyptus camaldulensis.* Wherever it occurs it is sedentary and communal, pairs and small groups of up to 10 or so holding permanent territory which they advertise with year-round singing and spectacular song-flights, particularly when breeding. Individual birds do wander occasionally—mainly juveniles dispersed from their natal colonies—and have been known to travel as far as 300 kilometres.

Rarely still, White-plumed Honeyeaters feed in the outer branches and crowns of tall shrubs and trees, mainly eucalypts, bouncing around among the foliage and uttering soft *chips* incessantly to keep in touch with one another. Often they dash from one tree to the next, one after the other, in darting, twisting undulations or short glides with wings half-opened and up-held. Even when perched on bare twigs they are rarely still, reversing their bodies continually and pointing heads and tails this way and that. It is then that colony members often converge in brief, twittering huddles. The birds are aggressive and concerted in defence of their territory. Shrill alarm notes from one member will send the rest diving into foliage, to sit motionless at the approach of a predator; they will gather to mob intruders much larger than themselves. Ploys vary with the circumstances; when defending advanced nestlings, one adult will flutter to the ground while another dives at the intruder, both calling loudly.

Like other short-beaked honeyeaters, White-plumed are gleaners, picking up manna and honeydew augmented with occasional insects—beetles, lacewings, bees, ants, weevils, aphids, bugs, flies and lerps—from eucalypt foliage. Manna provides over 90 per cent of the diet in some areas in summer. Blackberries are also eaten and nectar from blossoms of a variety of trees and shrubs, even from tubular flowers longer than their 11-millimetre bills. As in all honeyeaters, the tongue is muscled so that it can protrude far from the bill and is tipped with more than 50 fine bristles that soak up sugary fluids; the birds insert their bills into flowers, extend the tongue and lick up nectar at about 10 licks per second.

When breeding, females build and incubate while males attend and make frequent song-flights, fluttering slowly upwards on a near-vertical line above the tops of trees, singing non-stop for about 10–20 metres before stopping and diving back to cover. Both parents and additional colony members help feed the young.

Black-chinned Honeyeater *Melithreptus gularis* (GOULD, 1837)

THE BLACK-CHINNED IS ONE of a small natural-group of honeyeaters with black heads, a white crescent around the nape, and a spot of coloured bare skin above the eye. They are grouped in the genus *Melithreptus*. All have short, wedge-shaped bills and spend much more of their time gleaning in foliage and on tree branches than in rifling blossom for nectar.

The Black-chinned is the most sedentary of the group and lives in the smallest communes, of two to 12 birds, rarely more. But because the feeding territory of each colony is so large, the birds often appear locally nomadic. Their colonies are thinly distributed around the drier open eucalypt woodlands of the Australian main-land, mainly along the western slopes of the Great Dividing Range and across the mid-north where they range into spinifex scrubs.

Like the more nomadic Brown-headed Honeyeater of denser scrubs, the Black-chinned works quickly from tree to tree, mostly eucalypts, foraging rapidly along outer twigs, the underside of branches, and even trunks, probing in crannies and under bark for insects. Much honeydew is also gleaned from foliage in summer. Contact is kept by frequent calling, and the birds break the routine during the middle hours of the day to drink and bathe.

Breeding can be communal, with additional members of the colony helping the senior parental pair in feeding their young.

OTHER NAMES
Golden-backed Honeyeater, Black-throated Honeyeater.

IDENTIFICATION
LENGTH: *155–170 mm.*
ADULTS: *Sexes similar. Head black to sides of cheeks, with white band around nape to eyes. Back and rump dull olive-green to rich lemon-yellow across northern Australia, varying according to race; wings and tail mid grey-brown washed lightly citrine. Chin black, running on to centre of upper throat; lower cheeks and malar sash white. Rest of underparts white, with grey bloom in eastern race. Eye deep brown, with spot of bare skin above eye turquoise-blue in eastern race, and turquoise-green toned yellow in northern. Bill black. Feet flesh-brown.*
IMMATURES: *As adult but crown dusky brown, nape band buff-white, eye skin dull grey, and bill dull buff.*

VOICE
CALL: *High-pitched bubbling croaks* prrrp, prrrp, *often in concert among groups and in flight, for contact.*
SONG: *Ringing bubbling trill, ch-reee, ch-reee, repeated several times and often developing out of* prrrps *in duet but usually given by only one bird, from vantage perch; sometimes between individuals when landing from flight.*

NESTING
Breeds July–December. Nest a deep, beautiful felt-like cup, of strips of grass and bark closely bound with down and cobweb; lined with plant down; suspended from rim in ends of hanging leafy branchlets, at 3–15 m above ground. Eggs: one–two; salmon-pink, spotted sparsely with rich chestnut, red-brown, mostly at larger end; oval, about 22 x 16 mm. Incubation probably 14–15 days. Young fledge in 13–14 days.

DISTRIBUTION
Open eucalypt woodland and fringing forest and desert scrub, mainly along western slopes of Great Dividing Range and across near inland north to Pilbara, WA. Small declining outlying population in Mt Lofty Ranges, SA. Two races: one golden-backed across north of mainland; the other more olive-backed in east, intergrading broadly through central northeastern Queensland.

The Black-chinned Honeyeater lives in open eucalypt woodland in northern and eastern Australia.

Strong-billed Honeyeater *Melithreptus validirostris* (GOULD, 1837)

The Strong-billed Honeyeater finds larval and adult insects by prising bark off trees with its stout bill. It builds a deep cup-shaped nest of bark, grass, wool and cocoons in the outer branches of a eucalypt. Strong-billed Honeyeaters are confined to Tasmania and Bass Strait islands.

THE CRACKLING OF BARK being prised from eucalypts is one of the sounds that indicate the presence of a flock of Strong-billed Honeyeaters working a patch of forest in search of their insect food. Confined to Tasmania and Bass Strait islands, the birds wander about in nomadic bands, giving their rattling calls constantly to keep in touch.

Unlike many other honeyeaters the Strong-billed almost never hawks for insects and is seldom attracted to nectar-carrying blossoms. Spiders, beetles, ants, bugs and weevils, taken almost entirely from crevices in tree trunks, are its most important food. It is one of the most specialised feeders among the Tasmanian honeyeaters, even though it gleans manna from foliage in winter and sometimes goes to ground to take swarming caterpillars.

The eucalypts whose bark it favours are the stringybark *Eucalyptus obliqua,* the gum-topped stringybark *E. delegatensis,* the mountain ash *E. regnans,* and the blue gum *E. globulus.* With its stout, chisel-like bill, this honeyeater has developed a feeding technique not unlike that of the treecreepers *Climacteris* of mainland Australia. It prises pieces of bark off the trunk and larger limbs of eucalypts in its search for insects, though it flies from place to place on the tree and does not hop up the trunk in the manner of a treecreeper. It also seems more haphazard in its coverage of each tree but, without fully developing the treecreeper's technique, it has filled the vacant treecreeper niche in Tasmania.

The Strong-billed Honeyeater, the largest member of the genus *Melithreptus,* is noisy and gregarious. It is easily recognised by the white crescent around the nape and by its call. It lives both in wet and dry sclerophyll forest but mostly shows a preference for the taller wet forest. It frequents dry forest in winter when roaming with foraging parties, often in association with the Black-headed Honeyeater. It resembles, and is closely related to, the Black-chinned Honeyeater of mainland Australia.

Both sexes may build the nest and incubate the eggs, and both feed the young. Whether Strong-billed Honeyeaters have helpers at the nest when rearing the young is not certain, but it seems likely as they nest in the same loose associations as other species of the same genus in which this practice occurs.

OTHER NAMES
Bark Bird.

IDENTIFICATION
LENGTH: *160–180 mm.*
ADULTS: *Sexes similar; male larger. Head black to sides of cheeks, with white band around nape to eyes. Rest of upper parts, wings and tail deep grey-brown with pervading olive wash strengthening on rump and tail. Chin black, running on to centre of grey-white upper throat; lower cheeks and malar sash broad white. Rest of underparts mid-grey, tinged buff on flanks and belly and streaked white on undertail. Eye deep red, with pale turquoise eye-ring and crescent of bare skin above eye. Bill stout, black. Feet buff-brown.*
IMMATURES: *Similar to but generally duller than adults; nape crescent and sides of throat lemon-yellow and head sooty brown. Eye mid-brown; eye-ring and bare skin patch above eye orange. Bill orange with darker tip; feet pale orange.*

VOICE
CALL: *Harsh* churr *in alarm; at nest soft contact call* cheep.
SONG: *A loud staccato* cheep *as single or double note or in rattling cadence of notes rolled into each other.*

NESTING
Breeds July–December. Nest a deep cup of woven bark, grass, wool and cocoons; lined with fine grass, wool, fur and sometimes feathers; strung on to outer stems of branch of mature eucalypt, or placed in top of forest understorey tree, always among leaves and usually 5–25 m above ground. Eggs: two–three; pale flesh-coloured, spotted and speckled with red-brown and purple-grey, particularly at larger end; oval, about 22 x 17 mm. Incubation about 15 days. Young fledge in about 15 days.

DISTRIBUTION
Common in wet and dry sclerophyll forest throughout Tasmania and King, Flinders and Cape Barren Islands. Also in rainforest, subalpine forest and coastal heathland. No races.

Brown-headed Honeyeater   *Melithreptus brevirostris*   VIGORS & HORSFIELD, 1827

OTHER NAMES
None.

IDENTIFICATION
LENGTH: *120–140 mm.*
ADULTS: *Sexes alike. Head dusky brown, with grey-white band around nape. Back, wings and tail grey-brown washed dull olive. Chin dusky; rest of underparts pale buff-grey. Eye brown, eye skin cream-green. Bill dusky. Feet buff-brown.*
IMMATURES: *Much duller; bill buff.*

VOICE
CALL: *Sharp, chattering ktt, ktt, ktt, repeated in chorus in contact.*
SONG: *Call notes run together as bubbling trills.*

NESTING
Breeds August–December. Nest a thick cup of bark, hair, grass and binding cobweb, slung in outer foliage of tree or sapling. Eggs: two–three; pale pink, speckled red-brown; oval, about 16 x 13 mm.

DISTRIBUTION
Drier forests and woodlands across southern mainland to mideastern Queensland. Four races.

A Brown-headed Honeyeater at its cup-shaped nest of bark, grass and cobweb hung in a native pine *Callitris*.

DRY SCLEROPHYLL FOREST, alpine woodland and mallee across southern Australia are the habitats of Brown-headed Honeyeaters, wherever the canopy is close. The birds live in communal groups of 10–20, each occupying large and sometimes overlapping foraging ranges of up to five or more square kilometres. The groups wander far through their territories each day, feeding rapidly together along and under the outer branches and twigs of one tree, flicking off bark and probing fissures, then flying quickly on over the forest to the next, often 50 metres or more away, chipping constantly in contact. Spiders, insects and their larvae are chief food, but they also glean manna, honeydew and lerps from foliage, particularly in winter.

The groups are close-knit societies. Members often preen one another and all huddle to roost side-by-side in outer foliage at night, the younger members protected in the middle. All share in incubation and in feeding the young of the parental breeding pair. The senior laying female, however, builds most of the nest herself and is the only bird fed by others as she broods.

White-throated Honeyeater   *Melithreptus albogularis*   GOULD, 1848

White-throated Honeyeater.

OTHER NAMES
White-chinned Honeyeater.

IDENTIFICATION
LENGTH: *130–150 mm.*
ADULTS: *Sexes similar. Head to upper cheeks black, with white band round nape to eyes. Back, shoulders and rump citrine-green; wings and tail deep grey-brown, washed citrine. Chin, lower cheeks and malar sash white. Rest of underparts white. Eye red-brown, skin around eye white with blue tinge above. Bill black. Feet flesh-brown.*
IMMATURES: *Similar to adults. Head, nape and shoulders light to mid-brown, darker on sides of face; white crescent indistinct. Back duller; rump washed brown.*

VOICE
CALL: *Sharp tip, repeated in flight in contact; harsh rasping sherp-sherp and*

rarely, soft mewing notes in feeding contact; trilled *si-si-si-si-si in alarm.*
SONG: *Rapid, piping, whistled p'pit-p'pit-p'pit-p'pit repeated rapidly in bursts on same pitch.*

NESTING
Breeds January–October. Nest cup-shaped, of bark strips interwoven with plant down, cobweb and spiders' egg sacs, lightly lined with finer bark fibre; suspended by rim to thin fork in outer foliage, 5–9 m above ground. Eggs: usually two; occasionally glossy, pink to pale buff, lightly freckled with red-brown and mauve, particularly at larger end; oval, about 19 x 14 mm.

DISTRIBUTION
From Derby, WA, across northern Australia to about Kempsey, NSW. Mainly eucalypt woodlands and forests but also along watercourses and in

paperbark swamps and mangroves. Also southern New Guinea. Three races; two in Australia: one across north to Cape York Peninsula; the other larger and duller-backed down east coast.

THE WHITE-THROATED HONEYEATER replaces its temperate counterpart—the White-naped Honeyeater—in the tropical eucalypt forests and woodlands of northern Australia and southern New Guinea. Although more sedentary than the White-naped, it feeds in the high outer foliage of trees in the same way. Pairs and small loose flocks of three to eight birds probe actively along twigs and among leaves, gleaning manna, honeydew and insects, often hanging upside down to do so. Only infrequently do they work over bark on large branches and trunks as Black-chinned and Brown-headed Honeyeaters do. Leaf beetles, ants and flies are main prey. The blossoms of flowering trees, particularly of paperbarks, are sometimes visited as well, for nectar and insects, the birds mixing with other species of honeyeaters.

White-throated Honeyeaters nest in pairs or small communal groups in which other members help the senior nesting pair feed and rear their young. Males and females advertise breeding and feeding territory with a rapid piping whistling from high vantage perches, particularly in the dawn chorus.

White-naped Honeyeater *Melithreptus lunatus* (VIEILLOT, 1802)

THE CANOPY OF TALL EUCALYPT forests in southwestern and eastern Australia right along the Great Dividing Range are the foraging grounds of the White-naped Honeyeater. There, in pairs and small communal groups, they feed in the outer branches and foliage, spending almost three-quarters of their feeding time gleaning over leaves, craning up or hanging upside down among them. Manna and honeydew—the sugary secretions of leaf insects and damaged leaves—are their main food, making up to 60 per cent or more of all intake. But the birds also pick up quantities of insects, their larvae and spiders, and visit blossoming eucalypts for nectar.

Groups are fairly sedentary in most parts of their range, but in the high mountains of the southeast, between Canberra and Melbourne, they are spectacularly migratory.

Each autumn, in March and April, they band in groups of 30 to 50 and travel north, west and east along the coast in thousands. Sometimes they mix with migrating Yellow-faced Honeyeaters and at other times move alone. How far they go is not known. The farthest recorded movement is about 250 kilometres, so it is likely that they rarely spread further than southeastern Queensland and the South Australian gulfs. The return migration in spring, from late August into September, can be just as massed but it often follows different routes. Whatever the path, breeding birds return to the same locality each year.

The birds nest in pairs and small communal groups, in which the senior breeding pair is helped to feed and rear the nestlings. Nests are defended with vigorous aggression by all members.

A White-naped Honeyeater feeding the young Pallid Cuckoo that it has fostered. White-naped and other honeyeaters are often parasitised by this cuckoo.

OTHER NAMES
Black-cap, Black-capped Honeyeater, Lunulated Honeyeater.

IDENTIFICATION
LENGTH: *140–150 mm.*
ADULTS: *Sexes similar. Head black to sides of cheeks, with white band around nape to eyes. Back, shoulders and rump citrine-green; wings and tail deep grey-brown, washed citrine. Lower cheeks and malar sash black, extending under chin. Rest of underparts and underwing coverts white. Eye brown, with bare skin around top of eye scarlet (eastern race) or chalky white (southwestern race). Bill black, mouth rich orange. Feet buff- or flesh-brown.*
IMMATURES: *As adults but head russet-brown, nape band buff, underparts cream. Eye skin as adults of respective races but duller; bill orange-buff at base.*

VOICE
Soft, mellow, mewing tsew-tsew-tsew *and harsh grating* sherp-sherp, *often repeated, from perches when feeding or in flight. Soft, tense, trilled* pew-pew-pew *in alarm. No song.*

NESTING
Breeds July–January. Nest a delicate deep cup of fine grass, strips of bark and plant down, closely bound with cobweb; lined with down; hung in hanging foliage, usually in eucalypt, at 5-20 m above ground. Eggs: two–three; pink to pale buff, finely spotted all over with red-brown and grey, mainly at large end; oval, about 18 x 14 mm. Incubation about 14 days. Young fledge in about 14 days.

DISTRIBUTION
Wet and dry sclerophyll forests of eucalypts in southwestern Australia and along Great Dividing Range and its slopes in east, north to Atherton Tableland, Qld, and southwest to Mt Lofty Ranges, SA. Two races: one in southwest; the other in east, differing in colour of eye skin and size.

Black-headed Honeyeater *Melithreptus affinis* (Lesson, 1839)

OTHER NAMES
Black-cap, Black-capped Honeyeater, King Island Honeyeater.

IDENTIFICATION
LENGTH: *Male 145 mm; female 130 mm.*
ADULTS: *Sexes similar. Entire head and throat plain black, with black sash running from sides of neck down sides of breast. Back, rump and upper parts dull olive-green; shoulders (wing coverts) and flight feathers plain deep grey. Breast to undertail and flanks and underwing white, grading greyer white below. Eye dark brown, with crescent of turquoise-green skin above. Feet purplish-flesh.*
IMMATURES: *General plumage similar to adults but paler. Nape, crown, forehead and back olive-brown. Face sooty-brown; chin, throat and breast dusky grey-brown; sides of neck pale lemon-yellow. Bill dark brown; feet pale fawn-pink.*

VOICE
CALL: *Harsh grating* sherp-sherp. *Contact call at nest-site a soft chip.*
SONG: *High-pitched whistle given as double note, or rapidly repeated notes of rising inflection.*

NESTING
Breeds October–January. Nest a deep cup of bark strips, wool and moss, bound with cobweb; lined with hair, fur and feathers; suspended among outer leaves of tree or sapling, 5–20 m above ground. Eggs: two–three; pale, flesh coloured, finely spotted and speckled with red-brown and purple-grey, mostly at larger end; oval, about 19 x 14 mm. Incubation about 15 days, by both sexes. Young fledge in about 15 days.

DISTRIBUTION
Dry and wet sclerophyll forest, low and high altitude eucalypt woodland and coastal heaths throughout Tasmania, King Island and Furneaux Group. Abundant. Largely absent from rainforests and heaths of western Tasmania. No races.

The Black-headed Honeyeater is found in Tasmania and on islands in the Bass Strait. With no white nape band, it is one of the most easily recognised honeyeaters.

THE BLACK-HEADED HONEYEATER replaces the White-naped Honeyeater in the dry and wet sclerophyll forests of eucalypts in Tasmania and Bass Strait islands. Rainforests, however, are avoided. Like the White-naped, it is rather gregarious and lives in loose flocks, smaller and more sedentary during breeding, and larger and widely nomadic after, in autumn and winter. It is then that Black-headeds join in mixed feeding associations with Strong-billed and other honeyeaters, pardalotes and thornbills.

It is an active and noisy feeder, calling continually as it works over the outer foliage of eucalypts, from middle branches to the forest canopy. It spends most of its time gleaning among leaves, leaving the cracks and crannies in bark and larger branches to its heavier-billed, more robust relative, the Strong-billed Honeyeater. Finishing in one tree, flocks and individuals fly on to the next in a buoyant, undulating dash through the tree crowns, giving two-note whistles between wing-beats to stay in touch.

As with the White-naped Honeyeater, foliage insects—beetles, flies, wasps, ants and caterpillars—and spiders and honeydew are principal dietary items; indeed the birds spend 75 per cent of feeding time in search of them. Nectar is rifled from flowering eucalypts only occasionally, and though the birds sometimes work over the trunks of manna gum *Eucalyptus vimihales* and feed down to the ground, they almost never hawk after insects on the wing.

Breeding is communal. Both male and female build the nest, incubate the eggs and feed the young; any other subordinate adults in their group assist in the rearing as well. The birds have to work particularly hard whenever, as often happens, they are parasitised by Pallid Cuckoos to rear foster cuckoo chicks.

With an all-black head and throat, no nape crescent, grey shoulders, and very short stubby bill, the Black-headed is the most easily identified of the *Melithreptus* honeyeaters. It ranges as far north as King and Flinders Islands, but on Deal Island, further on towards Victoria in Bass Strait, its ecological niche is filled by the White-naped Honeyeater from the mainland.

Green-backed Honeyeater

Glycichaera fallax SALVADORI, 1878

The Green-backed Honeyeater lives in rainforest on Cape York Peninsula.

OTHER NAMES
White-eyed Honeyeater, Puff-backed Honeyeater.

IDENTIFICATION
LENGTH: *110–120 mm.*
ADULTS: *Sexes alike. Upper parts dull olive-green, greyer on crown. Tail dusky edged olive. Flight feathers grey-brown edged olive; underwing coverts pale yellow. Face grey-green; faint narrow ring of white feathers around eye; throat white. Underparts yellow-green, washed or streaked more olive on breast. Eye white to pale grey. Bill dusky horn, lower mandible paler. Feet blue-grey.*
IMMATURES: *As adults but duller.*

VOICE
CALL & SONG: *Contact call a small twittering, usually ascending slightly. Feeding call a single* peep. *When chasing out other birds, a* tick, *several of which may be run together to form a short call, similar to that of Graceful Honeyeater.*

NESTING
Unknown.

DISTRIBUTION
Outlying population of a species rarely seen but widespread in New Guinea and on nearby islands. In rainforest, occasionally nearby eucalypt forest at Claudie River and other rainforest patches at tip of Cape York Peninsula south to McIlwraith Range, Qld. Four races; one in Australia.

WIDESPREAD IN THE LOWLAND rainforests of New Guinea, the Green-backed Honeyeater is confined in Australia to tropical rainforests on northern Cape York Peninsula. It feeds there almost exclusively on insects gleaned from leaves, although it will visit blossoming palms or eucalypts on the rainforest edge.

Its short, rather straight bill is better fitted for picking off insects than probing flowers.

Working singly, in pairs or small loose groups of three to eight,

Green-backed Honeyeaters forage in foliage, from shrubbery to the rainforest canopy, mainly on the outside of the forest and along its edges where growth is densest. Movement is tirelessly non-stop as the birds hop, flutter, tumble, hover and hang upside-down to get at insects; in this way, they travel quickly through the foliage, *peeping* frequently to stay in touch, and never remain in one site for long. Flight, through and under the canopy, is a swift, slightly undulating dash, with occasional erratic twists.

Brown Honeyeater

Lichmera indistincta
(VIGORS & HORSFIELD, 1827)

ACROSS TROPICAL AUSTRALIA and down east and west coasts where climate is benign, Brown Honeyeaters frequent thicket, shrubbery and pockets of scrub, whether along creeks, under woodland or on the edge of rainforest and mangroves. They are abundant and locally nomadic.

The birds, with their long bills, are opportunistic nectar-feeders; they converge on profusely blossoming trees—particularly paperbarks and mangroves—to rifle flowers at all levels, from near the ground to the crown. There males sing constantly from branches to advertise feeding territory but are often chased off themselves by larger honeyeaters. When there is no local flowering, the birds turn to insects, catching them among foliage and in midair in short flights out from high branches.

Brown Honeyeaters nest in solitary pairs, occupying much the same nesting territories year after year. Only the female builds, incubates and appears to feed the young; the male, which develops a black gape flange then, merely sings in defence and keeps watch on a nearby branch.

The nest of the Brown Honeyeater is suspended from a thin branch.

OTHER NAMES
None.

IDENTIFICATION
LENGTH: *110–150 mm.*
ADULTS: *Sexes similar; male much larger. Upper parts, wings and tail dull brown, washed greyer on crown and citrine on flight and tail feathers. Lores and around eye duskier, with triangular spot of spangled yellow and white behind eye. Throat and upper breast pale brownish grey, grading brownish white over belly, flanks and undertail. Eye grey-brown. Bill black, with yellow gape flange. Feet* grey-brown.
IMMATURES: *As adults; yellower brown above, yellow-cream below.*

VOICE
CALL: *Squeaks and chips in contact;* grating churr *in alarm.*
SONG: *Sequence of strong, metallic notes:* swiit-swiit-quarty-quarty-chee-chee-chee. *Often only first two notes.*

NESTING
Breeds June–January. Nest a cup of bark strips, grass, down and wool, bound with cobweb and cocoons; lined with down and hair; slung in foliage or fronds less than 2 m above ground, often over water. Eggs: two; matt white, freckled faint brown, mostly at large end; swollen oval, about 17 x 13 mm. Incubation about 14 days, by female. Young fledge in about 14 days.

DISTRIBUTION
Thickets, pockets of shrubbery and mangrove edge throughout tropical Australia south in west to south coast and in east to Hunter Valley, NSW. Also New Guinea and Lesser Sunda Islands. About five races; one in Australia.

White-streaked Honeyeater *Trichodere cockerelli* (GOULD, 1869)

The White-streaked Honeyeater is found only on Cape York Peninsula.

FOUND ONLY LOCALLY on Cape York Peninsula, the White-streaked Honeyeater is an extremely active bird. Singly, in pairs or small groups, it moves rapidly through the upper part of the crowns of low eucalypt and paperbark trees, feeding on nectar and insects they take from the leaves and branches.

Paperbark blossoms attract White-streaked Honeyeaters in large numbers and the flowering of these trees and eucalypts is reported to be followed by the somewhat-nomadic birds. Individuals and pairs space themselves 70–100 metres apart and sing in defence of feeding and breeding territory, from vantage perches in trees.

OTHER NAMES
Brush-throated Honeyeater, Cockerell's Honeyeater.

IDENTIFICATION
LENGTH: *160–180 mm.*
ADULTS: *Sexes similar. Crown and lores dusky grey, grading to mottled brown over back, wings and tail; rump paler; wing coverts dusky tipped white to yellow; flight and tail feathers edged yellow. Face flecked grey; yellow ear tuft, extending in line down sides of neck; short yellow line under cheeks. Throat and breast with hairy, grey-edged feathers shafted white; rest of underparts plainer off-white. Eye brown. Bill black, gape flange blue-grey. Feet leaden.*
IMMATURES: *Upper parts dull-brown; ear coverts grey; chin pale yellow. Underparts off-white with yellow tinge except for white throat.*

VOICE
CALL: *Metallic scolding* churrr.
SONG: *A pleasant, often four-note whistle.*

NESTING
Breeds January–May. Nest a deep, flimsy, thin-walled cup of fine rootlets and plant stems bound with cobweb; usually slung in fork low in a bush or small tree, often in paperbark over water. Eggs: two; smooth, slightly lustrous, cream-buff to pink with zone of purple-red or brown freckles at larger end; swollen oval, about 17 x 14 mm.

DISTRIBUTION
Endemic to northern and eastern Cape York Peninsula, Qld, in tropical heath and woodland with heathy substage; also edges of rainforest and mangroves. Erratically southeast to Helenvale. No races.

Painted Honeyeater

Grantiella picta (GOULD, 1838)

PLUMAGED IN CONTRASTING BLACK, white and yellow, the Painted Honeyeater feeds almost exclusively on the drupes of mistletoe. It has been recorded feeding on no more than five species of mistletoe *Amyema,* and to keep itself in food it follows their fruiting nomadically north and south over inland eastern Australia.

At the beginning of breeding, males may arrive several weeks before females and establish territory with tree-top singing and near-vertical song-flights. Competitors are driven off in silent, weaving flights low among trees. Both sexes construct the nest, taking up to three weeks, and both share incubation, changing over within hourly intervals. Both also feed the young, on insects as well as mistletoe drupes, and rear two broods in a good season.

OTHER NAMES
None.

IDENTIFICATION
LENGTH: *155–160 mm.*
MALE: *Head, upper parts, wings and tail black; flight and tail feathers broadly edged yellow; tail tipped white; white ear tuft. Underparts white, streaked black on flanks. Eye brown. Bill pink, dusky tip. Feet slate.*
FEMALE: *As male but upper parts greyer, flanks plainer.*
IMMATURES: *As female.*

VOICE
CALL: *Undulating whistle;* churr.
SONG: *Sing-song, stridently whistled* tort-tee, tort-tee *or* et-tee, et-tee.

NESTING
Breeds October–March. Nest a frail cup, 50 x 45 mm inside, of fibrous rootlets, casuarina needles or grass bound with cobweb; attached to leafy twigs at end of drooping branch 3–20 m above ground. Eggs: two; salmon-pink, with small spots of red-brown and lilac, particularly at larger end; oval, 20 x 15 mm. Incubation 14–15 days, by both sexes. Young fledge in 12–14 days.

DISTRIBUTION
Open forest and woodland in much of inland eastern Australia. Uncommon and nomadic. No races.

The Painted Honeyeater is uncommon and nomadic in eastern Australia.

New Holland Honeyeater *Phylidonyris novaehollandiae* (LATHAM, 1790)

IN APPEARANCE AND HABITS, the New Holland Honeyeater closely resembles the White-cheeked Honeyeater. Both are birds of heaths and densely shrubbed woodlands around much of coastal southwestern and eastern Australia but where they overlap they separate into rather different habitat; the New Holland, as a rule, keeps to the more closely shrubbed and forested vegetation. Other traits that distinguish the two are their song-flights. In contrast to the protracted warbling flight of the White-cheeked, the New Holland flies up rapidly for a few metres above the shrubbery, whistles briefly, then dives back to cover. It also calls from exposed perches on top of shrubs.

New Holland Honeyeaters feed almost exclusively on nectar taken from blossom in shrubs and small trees. This they augment with sugary manna and honeydew gleaned from foliage. And for protein they hawk out for insects in brief flights, although spending as little as 10 minutes a day on that activity. Their tiny thin-walled stomachs cannot digest much hard food.

To extract nectar, New Holland Honeyeaters—like other long-billed honeyeaters—force their faces into the mouths of the flowers, brushing against anthers, and becoming dusted with pollen. This they transfer to the next flower—and the next plant—so effecting pollination. Visiting over 100 species of plants, New Hol-

land Honeyeaters are particularly important agents.

Five to 10 New Holland Honeyeaters may gather per hectare in prime habitat, each spending three to 10 hours a day harvesting nectar and holding small feeding territories which they mark with song-flights morning and afternoon. In many parts of their range, different plants come into flower at different times in a year-round cycle. There the honeyeaters are permanent residents, simply switching from one shrub species to another as each blooms. When flowering falls or fails, dominant individuals—usually males—expand their territories and force others—females and juveniles—to search elsewhere. It is then that groups disperse to wander the countryside. Flight, at all times, is of low dashing undulations, with whizzing turns.

Pairs of New Holland Honeyeaters often nest in a loose communal group centred in a fraction of their combined foraging territories. Both male and female feed the young. The birds first collect nectar, then catch a number of insects, holding them in line in the bill before darting off to feed the young, first with insects, then regurgitating the nectar. Sometimes the male takes over the care of fledglings completely after they are about 25 days old, leaving the female free to build and nest again. In this way, two or three broods may be raised in a season.

OTHER NAMES
Yellow-winged Honeyeater, White-bearded Honeyeater, White-eyed Honeyeater.

IDENTIFICATION
LENGTH: *165–185 mm.*
ADULTS: *Sexes similar; male larger. Upper parts—head to wings and tail—dusky black, greyer striped black and white on back; flight and tail feathers edged broadly yellow; tail tipped white. Face black with white hairy tufts over nostrils, white hind eyebrow, white malar tuft, and white ear tuft. Throat black, with long white hairs (beard).*

Breast to undertail white streaked black. Eye white. Bill black. Feet dusky.
IMMATURES: *As adults but black greyer-brown, white washed yellow; eye grey.*

VOICE
CALL: *Harsh tjik in contact and as marker when feeding. Harsh chattering in aggression. Rapid high, whistled piping in alarm.*
SONG: *Single, high, whistled phseeet in song-flight and from perches.*

NESTING
Breeds any time according to food supply, mainly July–December,

March–May. Nest a tightly woven cup of twigs, fibre, bark, grass and cobweb; lined with down and fur; supported in leafy fork in shrub or low tree 1–5 m above ground. Eggs: one–three; pink-buff with belt of chestnut-red and browner spots at large end; oval, 21 x 15 mm. Incubation 14–15 days, by female. Young fledge in 10–14 days.

DISTRIBUTION
Heaths, heathy woodlands and heath pockets in sclerophyll forest around coastal southern mainland north to Conondale Range, Qld. Also Tasmania and southeastern islands. Four races.

Crescent Honeyeater *Phylidonyris pyrrhoptera* (LATHAM, 1801)

A male Crescent Honeyeater; the female is olive-brown.

CONFINED TO SOUTHEASTERN AUSTRALIA, Crescents live in wetter sclerophyll forests than any other of the *Phylidonyris* honeyeaters. Throughout their range—except in South Australia—they shift altitudinally with the seasons, moving down close to coasts in autumn and returning to higher mountain gullies and forests in spring to breed.

Like its relatives, the curve-billed Crescent Honeyeater is primarily a nectar-feeder. Flowering eucalypts, banksias, telopeas and heaths attract loose aggregations of the birds, which feed from under shrubbery to the tops of trees, but mainly in the middle strata. Males, but not females, defend feeding territories with loud *e-gypt* calls, giving them from high bare vantage perches or while

OTHER NAMES
Chinawing, Egypt, Horseshoe Honeyeater.

IDENTIFICATION
LENGTH: *Male 150–160 mm; female 130–140 mm.*
MALE: *Head, back, wings and tail plain grey-black; flight and tail feathers edged broadly yellow; tail tipped white. Face dark grey, with white hind eyebrow. Throat and centre breast white streaked grey; sides of breast with broad black crescents, edged white; flanks and belly pale grey; undertail mottled grey and white. Eye red-brown. Bill black. Feet dark grey.*
FEMALE: *Duller than male with indistinct crescent. Where male is darker female is olive-brown; wing patches dull olive-yellow.*
IMMATURES: *Similar to adults but duller and crescent obscure.*

VOICE
CALL: *Soft notes in contact.*
SONG: *Loud, metallic ke-jilk (e-gypt), repeated with emphasis on second syllable, often mixed with twittering.*

NESTING
Breeds July–January; sometimes

March–April. Nest cup-shaped, of bark strips and twigs lined with grass or other soft material; usually placed in a shrub within 2 m of the ground. Eggs: two–three, rarely four; pale pink with bold spots of reds and browns; swollen oval, about 19 x 15 mm. Incubation about 14 days, by female. Young fledge in about 13 days.

DISTRIBUTION
In wet sclerophyll forests from just south of Newcastle, NSW, around coast and mountains to southeast of South Australia. Isolated populations in Mt Lofty Ranges, Kangaroo, King and Flinders Islands and Tasmania. Two races.

feeding; they do not seem to have a marked song-flight.

Manna and honeydew excreted by sap-sucking insects are also important sources of food. These the birds obtain by gleaning among foliage and under bark on the outer branches of rough-barked eucalypts. Insects are taken less often and usually in flight, the honeyeaters picking them up in short flights from high perches. Flight from tree to tree is a fast, undulating dash.

Pairs nest alone, the female building and incubating unaided and both sexes feeding the young.

A New Holland Honeyeater feeding on nectar from a banksia. Like other honeyeaters it is particularly attracted to the blossoms of banksias and eucalypts.

White-cheeked Honeyeater *Phylidonyris nigra* (BECHSTEIN, 1811)

The White-cheeked Honeyeater builds its nest low in dense vegetation in woodlands and heaths. When food is plentiful, these birds nest in loose colonies.

WARM, MUSICAL WARBLES fill the air as groups of male White-cheeked Honeyeaters advertise the onset of the breeding season. To mark his territory the male delivers his main song in flight, beginning with a few chirps and whistles as he climbs from his perch near the nest. The sound reaches full volume when the bird reaches the apex of his flight and then stalls in midair, his wings quivering. His song delivered, he descends more slowly than he rose and finishes with a few chirps and whistles.

When nectar and insects are available White-cheeked Honeyeaters nest in loose colonies, and the males spend much time singing or sitting on a strategic covered perch near their nests while females build and incubate. White-cheeked Honeyeaters are not strictly territorial but the males defend the nest site and a few vantage perches against other honeyeaters. The male's singing becomes less frequent after the eggs hatch, when both parents are occupied catching insects to feed to the young.

Successful nesting depends upon an abundance of nectar—the main food of adults—not only as food for the nestlings but as a source of energy for the parents which spend much time hawking for insects for the nestlings. They make hurried visits to nectar-rich flowers of plants such as banksias and dryandras and also to the blossoms of eucalypts, angophoras, grevilleas, tea-trees and paperbarks. The parents continue feeding the young after the family leaves the nest to wander through heath or forest understorey.

Family groups appear to keep to themselves for some time after fledging, but when the young are fully grown, larger groups of young and adult birds often gather. During the non-breeding season adults join young birds in wandering bands seeking blossom. Aggregations of White-cheeked Honeyeaters are exceptionally animated and noisy, for they are seemingly bold birds which advertise their presence with loud chattering and noisy squabbles and chases among themselves.

In eastern Australia the White-cheeked Honeyeater is a common resident of coastal heaths and woodlands with a dense understorey of flowering plants. However, in southwestern Australia its distribution is patchy; it is abundant in some parts of the range and rare in others. It can be distinguished from the similar New Holland Honeyeater by its large white cheek patch and dark brown eye.

OTHER NAMES
Moustached Honeyeater.

IDENTIFICATION
LENGTH: *160–180 mm.*
ADULTS: *Sexes similar; male slightly larger. Upper parts—head to wings and tail—black, thinly striped white on back; flight and tail feathers edged broadly yellow; tail tipped white. Face black with long, broad white brow; broad white cheek patch which is flared (eastern race) or tapered (western race). Throat plain black; breast to undertail white steaked black. Eye black-brown. Bill black. Feet dark grey.*
IMMATURES: *Browner and greyer than adults; eyebrow broader; yellow tint on lores.*

VOICE
CALL: *Harsh, metallic* chak-a-chak *or* chip-choo *from perch; chattering* tee-tee-tee, *rapidly repeated, probably in alarm.*
SONG: *Loud prolonged whistled* chip-choo-chippy-choo *coupled with musical* twee-ee-twee-ee *in flight or from perch.*

NESTING
Nests any time, mostly August–November and March–May. Nest a cup of plant fibre, bark and grass tightly woven together; lined with soft material such as banksia flowers, or cobweb and soft plant material; placed low in dense vegetation and usually within 1 m of the ground. Eggs: one–three, usually two; pale buff with pink or red-brown spots at larger end; oval, about 21 x 15 mm. Incubation 14–15 days, by female. Young fledge in 12–14 days.

DISTRIBUTION
Coastal heaths and heath woods in southwestern mainland and from Atherton Tablelands, Qld, to Wallaga Lake, NSW, in east. Two races; one in east; one in west.

White-fronted Honeyeater   *Phylidonyris albifrons* (GOULD, 1841)

LIVING IN AUSTRALIA'S ARID zone, with its erratic rainfall, White-fronted Honeyeaters are nomads. They arrive in large numbers where nectar-rich shrubs are coming into flower, nest, and then leave as blossoming falls off. Like other species of *Phylidonyris* honeyeaters they are primarily nectar-feeders, exploiting flowering eucalypts, mistletoes, grevilleas and hakeas as well as eremophilas.

Honeydew and insects are also taken, the insects mostly in midair in short flying sallies. Flight, from thicket to thicket, is of long, swift undulations.

White-fronted Honeyeaters nest in pairs in loose colonies, the males making song flights to advertise feeding and breeding territory; they defend their territories vigorously.

OTHER NAMES
None.

IDENTIFICATION
LENGTH: *160–180 mm.*
ADULTS: *Sexes similar; male larger. Crown dusky, flecked faintly white; hind-neck to shoulders and rump grey-brown streaked black; wings and tail grey-brown, edged dull yellow. Forehead and lores to ring around eye white, with small red wattle behind eye; ear coverts grey with white hind plume; white malar line. Throat and upper breast black with fine white centre streaks; rest of underparts white*
streaked black on upper breast, flanks and undertail. Eye dark brown. Bill black.
IMMATURES: *As adults but plainer brown on head and back; wings and tail edged browner; throat whitish brown, mottled over breast.*

VOICE
CALL: *Single metallic, canary-like* kweet *or* kwaak *as marker; scolding harsh* dik-dik-dik *in alarm.*
SONG: *Metallic* pert-pertoo-weet *or* quak-peter-peter, *the first note harsh, the rest loud and melodic; given as advertisement.*

NESTING
Breeds August–December, and after rains. Nest a cup of grass or bark strips interwoven with cobweb; lined with wool or vegetable matter; usually suspended in fork of bush or small tree, within 2.5 m of ground. Eggs: two–three; pale buff spotted at larger end with red-brown and underlying purple; oval, about 20 x 14 mm. Incubation about 14 days. Young fledge in about 14 days.

DISTRIBUTION
Dry inland scrubs and mallee and dry coastal parts of south and west. No races.

This White-fronted Honeyeater is nesting amid bark, but usually these honeyeaters suspend cup-shaped nests from thin branches in a bush or tree.

Tawny-crowned Honeyeater *Phylidonyris melanops* (LATHAM, 1801)

HIGH ABOUT THE HEATH, male Tawny-crowned Honeyeaters rise in spectacular song-flights in spring to mark their breeding and feeding territories. They flutter almost vertically up, then spiral back down on outstretched wings and tail, like a falling leaf, filling the air with their metallic fluting. They also sing in shorter bursts from the top of exposed vantage perches. The birds often gather in loose colonies to breed, but seem to nest in pairs.

After breeding, the groups often disperse and wander locally, but rarely travel far. Living in coastal heaths and mallee scrubs around southern Australia, they feed mainly on nectar in low shrubberies of epacrids, proteads, bottlebrushes, myrtles and *Xanthorrhoea*, among others. Much feeding is done low within thickets, even on the ground, the birds hopping along and craning up to probe overhanging sprays.

They also take many insects, catching most in the air in short sallying flights out from vantage perches and picking up others flying past or from the ground during foraging forays.

Occasionally the honeyeaters also enter forest to take nectar from blossoming eucalypts and to probe bark and crevices for the honeydew excreted by insects sheltering there.

A Tawny-crowned Honeyeater feeding on nectar from the flowers of a Mangles' kangaroo paw.

OTHER NAMES
Fulvous-fronted Honeyeater.

IDENTIFICATION
LENGTH: *150–170 mm.*
ADULTS: *Sexes similar; male larger. Crown tawny-rufous, edged white around forehead and over brow. Hindneck to rump brown-grey, streaked dusky on mid-back. Wings and plain tail deep grey-brown, edged dull yellow; underwing coverts tawny-rufous. Broad black sash from lores, through eyes, over ears and down sides of breast; small, flared white ear tuft. Underparts pure white, washed fawn-grey with dusky chevrons on flanks and undertail. Eye dark brown. Bill black. Feet leaden grey.*
IMMATURES: *Brown streaked cream-buff over head and back; black facial sash restricted to face, replaced with dusky, russet-washed stripe down sides of breast; ear tuft yellow; breast and flanks shortly striped brownish over white.*

VOICE
CALL: *High, fluted e-peer-peer-pee-pee spaced and ascending gradually in pitch; given throughout year.*
SONG: *Introduced by call and developing into series of run-together rich metallic trilled whistles, falling in pitch and cyclic; given in song-flights and from vantage perches during breeding.*

NESTING
Breeds July–March; mostly September–November. Nest a cup of bark fibre and grass; lined with soft material, often wool; placed on ground or in low scrub sometimes as high as 2–3 m above ground. Eggs: two, rarely three; white or pale pink sparingly spotted and blotched with red-brown; oval, about 21 x 14 mm.

DISTRIBUTION
In southwest, ranges from near Shark Bay to Israelite Bay; and in southeast from Eyre Peninsula north to mouth of Richmond River, NSW. Also Kangaroo Island, Bass Strait islands and Tasmania, where rare. Two races: one on mainland; the other in Tasmania.

Brown-backed Honeyeater *Ramsayornis modestus* (GRAY, 1858)

A Brown-backed Honeyeater removes a nestling's faecal sac. Brown-backed Honeyeaters live in northeastern Queensland and New Guinea.

WIDESPREAD ACROSS SOUTHERN New Guinea, the Brown-backed Honeyeater is limited in Australia to wetter, riverside woodland, vine thicket and paperbark swamps in coastal northeastern Queensland. There it is nomadic and probably migratory. Loose flocks arrive along the coast between Cooktown and Townsville to breed in August–September and leave in April–May. At the same time they withdraw from drying swamps on Cape York Peninsula, suggesting that most fly to New Guinea to winter. Perhaps they move at night because no passage migrants have been recorded on Torres Strait islands so far. Members of travelling bands keep in touch with one another by continual calling, *mik, mik, mik.*

On their breeding grounds, Brown-backed Honeyeaters spread out in pairs to nest along well-shrubbed waterways. Often they associate in dispersed colonies, where the proximity of nests may aid efficient food gathering—and also parasitism by the birds' chief host, the Brush Cuckoo. In northeastern Queensland—but rarely elsewhere—Brush Cuckoos lay white, black-speckled eggs that closely mimic those of the Brown-backed Honeyeater.

Feeding alone or in dispersed groups, Brown-backeds forage much on insects gleaned from foliage, from under bark on branchlets and, particularly, on the wing in short hawking sallies. The birds work from low shrubbery to the tops of trees.

Nectar is also rifled from blossom, mostly from flowering paperbarks *Melaleuca,* Black Bean *Castanospermum,* and *Calophyllum.* Brown-backeds mix then with other feeding honeyeaters, such as Brown and Dusky.

OTHER NAMES
Unadorned Honeyeater, Modest Honeyeater.

IDENTIFICATION
LENGTH: *120–130 mm.*
ADULTS: *Sexes similar. Upper parts warm brown, faintly lined on crown and mottled on back with dusky. Wings and tail darker, greyer brown. Face warm brown, with short cream-white bar under eye; obscure brown malar line. Underparts uniformly white; creamier and scalloped faintly brown on breast; flanks faintly streaked brown. Eye red-brown. Bill deep brown-flesh. Feet brown-flesh.*
IMMATURES: *As adults but back washed ochreish; breast strongly streaked brown.*

VOICE
CALL: *Sharp* chit *when feeding, rapidly repeated, perhaps in alarm; repeated, soft* mik, mik, mik *in contact in flight.*
SONG: *Lively chattering* shee-shee-shee-shee.

NESTING
Breeds August–March. Nest a rough, deep cup, roofed over at top, of strips of melaleuca bark; lined with finer strips; hung from twigs and foliage, usually 2–4 m above water. Nest either solitary or in loose colonies of up to 18–20. Eggs: two–three; matt white, unmarked or very sparsely spotted with minute black dots which sometimes form dark cap at larger end; tapered-oval to long oval, about 20 x 13 mm.

DISTRIBUTION
In paperbark swamps, mangroves, riverine vegetation and eucalypt woodland in coastal northeastern Queensland from tip of Cape York to Ayr. Also in southern lowland New Guinea and offshore islands, including Aru Islands. No races.

Bar-breasted Honeyeater

Ramsayornis fasciatus (GOULD, 1843)

GALLERIES OF PAPERBARK woodland and forest along streams are the core habitat of Bar-breasted Honeyeaters throughout their range across northern Australia. Where the birds overlap the Brown-backed Honeyeater, they keep more to drier woodland.

Although often nesting in loose colonies, Bar-breasted Honeyeaters are rather solitary feeders and wander nomadically in search of blossoming paperbarks, eucalypts and grevilleas after breeding. They do glean insects among foliage—and often catch them in short aerial sallies—but nectar is their primary food. They work quietly but aggressively at all levels of flowering trees, creeping about among the blossom from near the ground to the canopy, and gathering in loose groups with other honeyeaters there. Feeding territory is marked by sharp squawks from perches.

The Bar-breasted Honeyeater lives in paperbark swamps and woodland.

OTHER NAMES
Fasciated Honeyeater, White-breasted Honeyeater.

IDENTIFICATION
LENGTH: *130–140 mm.*
ADULTS: *Sexes similar. Crown black, scalloped finely white; rest of upper parts, wings and tail deep grey-brown, shading to cinnamon on rump, streaked dusky over back. Face white; clear black malar line. Underparts white, with coarse black scalloping across breast and black streaking down buff-washed flanks. Eye pale red-brown. Bill dark brown, tipped black. Feet brown-flesh.*

IMMATURES: *As adults but crown plain dusky brown; wing coverts edged buffy; breast as well as flanks streaked dusky.*

VOICE
CALL: *Soft mew in contact; shrill rapidly repeated piping in alarm.*
SONG: *Loud, metallic squawks, in a clatter.*

NESTING
May breed year round according to conditions; peaks in August–January. Nest a deep cup, roofed over at top, coarsely constructed of bark strips; slung in hanging foliage or twigs of

usually a paperbark, 1–5 m above ground and usually overhanging water. Double nests are recorded. Eggs: two–three; matt white, closely blotched mid red-brown, more at larger end, often forming zone; tapered-oval, about 21 x 14 mm.

DISTRIBUTION
Across northern Australia from about Broome, WA, to Rockhampton, Qld, in paperbark swamps, savanna woodland, particularly near water, and riverine vegetation. No races.

A Rufous-banded Honeyeater perches above its well-hidden nest.

Rufous-banded Honeyeater

Conopophila albogularis (GOULD, 1843)

IN COASTAL POCKETS of monsoon vine scrub, mangroves and swampy paperbark forests around Arnhem Land and Cape York Peninsula, Rufous-banded Honeyeaters forage actively all day long for nectar and insects. There they are semi-nomadic. Working alone or in loose pairs, they dash, hopping and fluttering, through the outer foliage of the scrub mid-strata, two–five metres above the ground, gleaning prey: spiders, beetles, flying termites, and flies. They are noisy when feeding, twittering constantly and giving short bursts of song, and often breaking off to chase one another from contested feeding branches. Many insects are caught in midair in short hawking flights up from branches.

Blossoming trees, particularly paperbarks along coastal streams, attract local gatherings of five or six, or sometimes even 20 or so to rifle the flowers for nectar. It is then that Rufous-bandeds mix with other species of foraging honeyeaters: Bar-breasted, Rufous-throateds, White-throateds and Duskys.

The female builds the nest alone, taking 15 to 16 days. Then, and while she incubates, the male spends much time perching nearby and singing. She is not fed on the nest but leaves the eggs for short intervals in the warm middle hours of the day to forage herself, close by. The male escorts her and both join in frequent twittering duets; other birds may attend too. Returning to the nest, she sidles down the branches, then drops in, leaving only her head and tail exposed. She continues to brood the young unaided but the male assists in their feeding, never staying long after depositing food. Fledglings remain in the nest for several weeks.

OTHER NAMES
White-throated Honeyeater, Rufous-breasted Honeyeater.

IDENTIFICATION
LENGTH: *120–130 mm.*
ADULTS: *Sexes similar. Crown and side of face smoky grey; back, shoulders and rump mid-brown with buff tinge. Wings and tail grey-brown with outer webs of flight and tail feathers edged golden yellow. Chin and centre of throat white; broad red-brown band extends across breast to side of neck; rest of underparts white; flanks buffier. Eye grey-brown. Bill dark grey-brown; lower mandible lighter. Feet slate-grey.*
IMMATURES: *As adults but crown and*

face dull brown as back; underparts uniformly cream-white, often washed yellowish; bill paler, buff at under base.

VOICE
CALL: *Hard s'veee by male; cheeps, continual musical twittering.*
SONG: *Twittering* sweeta-swee *or* swee-whit-chee-tee, *often in rondo-like duets.*

NESTING
Breeds September–April; probably two broods, at beginning and end of wet season. Nest deep, sturdy purse-shaped cup, of bark fibre and plant down interwoven with cobweb; lined with fine

dry grass and bark fibre; suspended from thin horizontal fork in outermost foliage, entrance usually protected by overhanging leaves, 1–6 m above ground. Eggs: two–three, rarely four; white, spotted and freckled with fine red-brown, occasionally purple-brown, particularly at larger end; tapered-oval, about 18 x 13 mm. Incubation about 12 days, by female. Young fledge in 10–11 days.

DISTRIBUTION
Two isolated populations in coastal Arnhem Land and Cape York Peninsula, in monsoon vine scrub, paperbark swamps, mangroves, urban gardens and fringing woodland. Also

southern coastal New Guinea and Aru Islands. No races.

Rufous-throated Honeyeater *Conopophila rufogularis* (GOULD, 1843)

IN NOMADIC BANDS, from small family groups to loose flocks of several hundred, Rufous-throated Honeyeaters range through the eucalypt woodlands and forests of northern Australia when not breeding, following blossom. Movements often have a seasonal basis, some groups moving south in Queensland each August and others into coastal western Arnhem Land in November.

They are aggressive when foraging and often fight among themselves and even occasionally with other small honeyeaters when joining them in mixed feeding flocks at flushes of flowering. Larger honeyeaters are rarely attacked because in such mixed flocks a peck order system operates, based on size and aggressive ability. Fighting is preceded by a threat display in which the Rufous-throated Honeyeater, jerkily lifting its beak, holds itself upright and fluffs out the red-brown feathers of its throat so that they become particularly striking—even immature birds lacking the rufous throat marking practise this display—or it raises its wings, displaying the golden-yellow wing bands. The birds peck at each other until the loser flies away. Both sexes appear to fight.

Rufous-throated Honeyeaters are tree-living birds but they are not restricted to the tall eucalypts where they feed on nectar and insects in the upper branches. They visit flowering bauhinia bushes and *Xanthostemon,* fly out to catch insects on the wing and hover to catch swarming ants and termites or other ground insects; during the monsoon months they chase cicadas.

These birds spend a great deal of time around water, drinking and bathing. Sometimes they bathe in the shallows but they prefer to fly out over the water, hover for a few seconds, then alight on the surface and dip before returning to a branch to preen.

To breed, the flocks break up to nest in isolated pairs, each holding a territory of about 0.2 hectares. The male accompanies the female in search of nest materials and defends the territory but does not take part in nest construction. Over about 14 days the female builds the external nest structure, which hangs slackly between the forks of a branch, and then adds a lining of pliable grass blades or roots which stiffen and shape the nest.

The female lays her eggs about two–four days after completing the nest and begins incubating after the second egg is laid. She leaves the nest for short periods at regular intervals and, on returning to brood, hops down into the nest so that—except when the bill and tail show above the rim—she completely disappears. The male helps to feed the nestlings from about the third day after hatching, but the female brings them about twice as much food as he does. Both sexes defend the nest and the young. Nesting by immature birds, lacking adult colouring, has been reported.

OTHER NAMES
Red-throated Honeyeater.

IDENTIFICATION
LENGTH: *120–140 mm.*
ADULTS: *Sexes similar. Crown light grey-brown; shoulders, nape, back and rump, wings and tail fawn-brown; flight and tail feathers edged golden yellow. Smoky grey suffusion from bill base to ear coverts, joining at middle of breast where it becomes indistinct grey-brown band. Chin and centre of throat deep rust-red; belly, vent and underwing coverts white, flanks slightly buffier. Eye grey-brown. Bill dark grey-brown, mid-grey towards base of lower mandible. Feet slate-grey.*
IMMATURES: *As adults, but crown browner, throat white, bill and feet paler.*

VOICE
CALL: *Sharp* zit-zit, *in contact and/or alarm.*
SONG: *Twittering chatter, often in duet.*

NESTING
Breeds September–April; varying according to season and localities. Nest a deep purse-shaped cup, one side higher than other, of bark, grasses, stems, plant fibres and cobweb; suspended at end of leafy branch, 1.5–7 m above ground, frequently near water. Eggs: two–three; white to grey-white, with fine to coarse pink-red to purple-brown spots; oval to tapered-oval, about 18 x 13 mm. Incubation about 13 days, by female. Young fledge in about 12 days.

DISTRIBUTION
From Kimberleys, WA, across northern mainland to central Cape York Peninsula and Noosa, Qld. Along tree-lined river courses and in nearby eucalypts, occasionally in more open woodlands. During wetter months disperses farther inland throughout eucalypt woodlands and forests. Nomadic or, in Queensland, regularly migrates north–south in non-breeding months. No races.

The Rufous-throated Honeyeater suspends its nest—a deep, purse-shaped cup—from the end of a leafy branch, often near water. It bathes frequently.

Grey Honeyeater *Conopophila whitei* (NORTH, 1910)

A Grey Honeyeater feeding its chick. The nest is a flimsy cup of plant fibres and webs slung between low twigs in trees and bushes.

OTHER NAMES
None.

IDENTIFICATION
LENGTH: *110–120 mm.*
ADULTS: *Sexes alike. Upper parts uniformly grey-brown; flight feathers edged citrine; tail tipped narrowly white. Underparts uniformly white, with broad grey wash across breast. Eye brown. Bill and feet dusky.*

IMMATURES: *As adults but back and breast band washed russet; broken cream eye-ring.*

VOICE
CALL: *Harsh, loud* cre-seek.
SONG: *Twittering trills, of* tee-te-deee *or* tsee-u-ee, *much repeated.*

NESTING
Breeds August–November or after
rains. Nest a frail cup of plant fibre and cobweb; lined with plant down; slung in branchlet tips within 3 m of ground. Eggs: two; white, dotted red-brown, particularly at large end; tapered-oval, about 17 x 12 mm. Both sexes incubate and tend young.

DISTRIBUTION
Mulga woodlands of western central Australia. No races.

ONE OF AUSTRALIA'S least-known birds, the Grey Honeyeater is a nomad of the mulga belt of western central Australia. They are largely insectivores and glean briskly, in ones, twos and small groups, through the foliage of low mulga trees and other shrubby acacias, taking fruits of mistletoes as well. Nectar is also rifled from blossoming eremophilas on occasion, the birds piercing and probing the base of the flowers. As they work through mulga woodland, they sometimes associate in mixed foraging flocks of Western Gerygones and Yellow-rumped Thornbills.

Banded Honeyeater *Certhionyx pectoralis* (GOULD, 1841)

The Banded Honeyeater lives in northern Australian forests and woodlands.

OTHER NAMES
None.

IDENTIFICATION
LENGTH: *120–130 mm.*
ADULTS: *Sexes similar. Crown, mantle, wings and tail black; nape freckled grey; lower back grey; rump and upper tail coverts white. Underparts white with black band across breast. Eye dark brown. Bill black. Feet grey-black.*
IMMATURES: *Crown pale brown; mantle mid-brown streaked darker; rump white; wings and tail grey-brown edged pale brown; line through eye dark; yellow area from bill to ear coverts over lower cheek. Chin yellow; rest of underparts off-white with brown breast band. Bill grey-brown. Most birds have combination of adult and immature plumage.*

VOICE
CALL: *Chirping* trrp *and finch-like* tweek *in contact.*
SONG: *Clear, descending chattering, often in song-flight.*

NESTING
Breeds October–April. Nest a small
flimsy open cup of fine bark strips, grass or hair, bound with cobweb; hung in horizontal fork of small branch up to 3 m above ground. Eggs: two; smooth, matt cream with buff zone of dusky brown freckles at larger end; swollen oval, about 17 x 12 mm.

DISTRIBUTION
From Kimberleys, WA, to all Cape York Peninsula, Qld, in eucalypt forests and woodland, melaleuca swamps and riverine vegetation, avoiding rainforests and mangroves. No races.

IN LARGE NOMADIC BANDS of up to 50, Banded Honeyeaters follow the flowering of eucalypts and paperbarks through the tropical Australian woodlands. Travelling flocks fly high over the woodland in slow, jerky, chat-like undulations, chirping constantly in contact.

Nectar is their main food, and in their chase for it Banded Honeyeaters mix with other honeyeaters in the mid and higher foliage of blossoming trees. Insects are eaten too, many of them caught on the wing on short aerial sallies.

Apparently mated permanently, pairs break off from flocks to nest separately. To mark territory, males give a short song-flight, climbing swiftly in an up-curve for four–six metres from a high branch, then swooping down in the same line. Young do not attain pied adult plumage until their first annual moult and even then retain brownish black-striped backs for another year or so.

Black Honeyeater

Certhionyx niger (GOULD, 1838)

OTHER NAMES
None.

IDENTIFICATION
LENGTH: *100–120 mm.*
MALE: *Upper parts, head, throat to stripe down centre of belly, wings and tail sooty-black; rest white. Eye dark brown. Bill and feet black.*
FEMALE: *All upper parts mid-brown, edged paler on shoulders; brow paler; underparts white, mottled and washed brown on throat and breast.*
IMMATURES: *As female.*

VOICE
CALL: *Chattering chirps.*
SONG: *Thin, whistled* seep *or* see-see, *from high perch or in song-flight.*

NESTING
Breeds September–December; probably any time after suitable rains. Nest a coarse cup of twigs, grass and cobweb; supported in fork of horizontal branch close to the ground. Eggs: two or three;

buff with dusky purple spotted zone near larger end; swollen oval, about 15 x 12 mm. Incubation by female.

DISTRIBUTION
Acacia, mallee and spinifex scrubs of all arid zone. Nomadic. No races.

The female Black Honeyeater builds a frail cup-shaped nest of grass and spiderweb in a tree fork close to the ground.

BLACK HONEYEATERS ARE TINY desert nomads that follow the blossoming of *Eremophila* shrubs. They do visit other flowers—particularly of eucalypts and grevilleas—and they often take small insects, many in short sallies on the wing, but nectar from eremophilas is staple diet. Just as their flowering in the arid zone is erratic, so are the movements of Black Honeyeaters; the bird's numbers in any area vary greatly from year to year. There is a seasonal influence in the movements, most regional populations shifting north in autumn–winter and south in spring–summer. For their long flights, the birds have rather pointed wings with a vestigial outer primary.

Black Honeyeaters concentrate their feeding on those species of eremophila with flowers no longer than their bills, such as *E. longifolia.* The birds hop among the blooms vigorously, and even hover in front. Larger flowers may be pierced at the base.

Flight from bush to bush is fast, of dipping, zigzagging undulations, and usually low.

Black Honeyeaters often travel and breed in dispersed colonies.

To mark territory, breeding males display in dipping song-flights, just over tree tops. At the top of each dip, the wings are held stiff and slightly downwards and the head raised as the bird whistles; sometimes the bird drops vertically, wings folded and tail slightly fanned. Only the female builds the nest and incubates, but the male helps in the rearing of the young.

The male Black Honeyeater. He leaves nest-building and incubation to his mate, but shares in the care of the young. They live in inland regions.

Pied Honeyeater *Certhionyx variegatus* LESSON, 1830

The male Pied Honeyeater is distinguished from the similar male Black Honeyeater by its much larger size and white on rump, wings and tail.

AS NOMADIC AS BLACK Honeyeaters and depending also on nectar from eremophila bushes, Pied Honeyeaters follow erratic flowering through Australia's arid zone in small bands of two to six or eight birds. Local flushes can bring many groups together to breed in one small area; then, as blossoming declines, the birds disperse—perhaps not returning for several seasons. There is no seasonal pattern to the movements. Pied Honeyeaters have slender, pointed wings—the outermost primary is reduced, if not vestigial as in the Black Honeyeater—and fly long distances effortlessly in long, low, sweeping undulations.

Although feeding mainly on eremophilas, probing with their curved bills, Pied Honeyeaters are not limited to them. They will also take nectar from shrubs of *Brachysema*, fruit from chenopods, and occasional insects, frequently caught in short hawking sallies.

Breeding males mark territory with a spectacular song-flight, climbing vertically then diving straight back, wings closed, tail fanned, singing as they drop. Both sexes build, finishing the nest in two or three days; both incubate. Females disturbed from the nest drop to the ground and feign injury to draw off attention.

OTHER NAMES
None.

IDENTIFICATION
LENGTH: *150–180 mm; male larger.*
MALE: *Head, throat, sides of breast, back, wings and inner webs of upper tail coverts black; also two central tail feathers and tip of tail black. Wing coverts, secondaries, rump, outer webs of upper tail coverts, underparts and remaining tail feathers white. Small pale blue wattle under eye. Eye brown. Bill blue-grey. Feet black.*
FEMALE: *All upper parts mid-brown, faintly mottled darker; wing coverts edged off-white; brow paler; underparts white, mottled and washed brown on throat and breast. Feet grey.*
IMMATURES: *As female.*

VOICE
CALL: *Usually silent.*
SONG: *In song-flight a piercing, drawn-out whistled* te-titee-tee-tee.

NESTING
Breeds September–February or after rains. Nest a loose cup of twigs, grass and cobweb; supported in fork in low bush. Eggs: two to four; buff-grey, clearly spotted and blotched dusky; oval, about 22 x 16 mm. Incubation about 12–13 days, by both sexes. Young fledge in about 10 days.

DISTRIBUTION
Acacia, mallee and spinifex scrubs of all arid zone. Nomadic. No races.

This female Pied Honeyeater has nested in a wattle. Both sexes build the nest and incubate the eggs.

Eastern Spinebill *Acanthorhynchus tenuirostris* (LATHAM, 1801)

SPINEBILLS ARE SMALL, ACTIVE honeyeaters with particularly long bills for probing tubular flowers for nectar. They also have long, protrusible almost tubular tongues tipped with short serrations, better fitted for licking and capillary flow than brushing. Eastern Spinebills put this organ to good effect in the wet shrubberies around eastern Australia. Although they do take insects—and feed young almost exclusively on them, for protein—they depend largely on nectar for their own needs. In coastal and northern localities they are rather sedentary but in the southern mountains they shift to lowlands over winter, often entering urban gardens.

Working alone or in loose aggregations at flushes of flowering, the birds forage in shrubs in forest understorey and through taller heaths, mostly within a metre or two of the ground. They flutter about nonstop, perching to probe a flower, then dashing to the next shrub in swooping zigzag undulations with noisy wing-whirr, tail flirted and flashing white. Flowers of epacrids, *Correa, Banksia, Billardiera* and eucalypts are visited most.

When breeding, the male defends a small territory with wavering climbing song-flights while the female builds the nest and incubates. He may also bring nest material and perhaps relieves occasionally in incubation; later he assists in feeding the young.

A male Eastern Spinebill, with black crown and long awl-like bill.

OTHER NAMES
Cobbler's Awl, Spine-billed Honeyeater.

IDENTIFICATION
LENGTH: *150–160 mm; bill 30 mm.*
MALE: *Crown and sides of face to below eye glossy black; collar russet, grading to grey-brown back, rump grey. Wings and tail glossy black; outer tail feathers tipped broadly white. Throat and breast white, flanked by broad black crescents; centre of throat with deep chestnut-brown patch. Rest of underparts tawny rufous. Eye crimson. Bill and feet black.*
FEMALE: *As male but crown satin grey.*
IMMATURES: *Upper parts plain olive-brown; throat cream grading to tawny belly, without black. Eye browner.*

VOICE
CALL: *Soft rapidly repeated piping whistles on same pitch, in bursts, for contact and position.*
SONG: *Quick-fire, three-syllabled twittered whistles, pi-pi-dee, pi-pi-dee, in cyclic bursts, from perch and in song-flight.*

NESTING
Breeds August–March, peaking October–January. Nest a cup of grasses and plant fibre; lined with feathers or hair; attached to twigs at rim, 1–5 m above ground in bushy shrub or tree. Eggs: two or three; buff or buff-pink with chestnut or red-brown spots towards larger end; oval, about 17 x 13 mm. Incubation about 14 days, mainly by female.

DISTRIBUTION
On tablelands inland from Cooktown, Qld, south to Tasmania, Mt Lofty Ranges and Kangaroo Island, SA, reaching coast around all southeast. Four races.

Western Spinebill *Acanthorhynchus superciliosus* GOULD, 1837

A male Western Spinebill; the female has a plain brown head and buff-brown throat and breast.

OTHER NAMES
None.

IDENTIFICATION
LENGTH: *140–150 mm; bill 25 mm.*
MALE: *Crown and sides of face dusky, with broad rufous collar; back olive-grey, greyer on rump and wings. Tail grey-black; outer feathers broadly tipped white. White hind eyebrow and long white malar line. Chin to upper breast rich rufous, subtended by white, then black bands across breast; rest of underparts pale buff-grey. Eye crimson. Bill and feet black.*
FEMALE: *Plain brown-grey above with rufous collar and grey, white-tipped tail; dull white hind eyebrow; plain creamy buff below.*
IMMATURES: *As female but duller.*

VOICE
CALL: *Loud, metallic kleet-kleet.*
SONG: *Fluted metallic whistles and twitterings.*

NESTING
Breeds September–January. Nest a small cup of bark fibre, fine stems and binding cobweb; lined with fibre and Banksia fur; supported in upright fork in low bush. Eggs: one–two; pink-white, spotted and blotched brown and red-brown, mostly at large end; oval, about 18 x 13 mm. Incubation mainly by female.

DISTRIBUTION
Southwestern mainland from Jurien Bay to Israelite Bay, in heath and shrubby woodland. No races.

AS ITS NAME SUGGESTS, the Western Spinebill replaces the Eastern in the well-shrubbed woodlands and heaths of southwestern Australia. Its bill is shorter than the Eastern's but is still furnished with a tubular tongue for soaking up nectar. Insects are often taken, both gleaned from shrubbery and caught in short sallies on the wing, but nectar is staple diet. The birds visit flowering shrubs as they bloom—dryandras, banksias, various myrtles and other proteads, and particularly kangaroo paws, *Anigozanthos*. When sidling up stems or hovering to probe into the hanging flowers of kangaroo paws, the spinebills become coated with pollen over their backs. At the next flower spray, stigmas brush against the back—and so pollination is effected.

Some shrubs are always in flower locally, so the birds rarely move far with the seasons. They generally forage alone, hopping and fluttering in one shrub, then dashing off in whirring zigzag undulations to the next, tail flirting and flashing its white tips.

Breeding males hold small territories and mark them with song-flights, fluttering up near vertically for about 10 metres, twittering, then diving to cover. The female builds the nest and incubates with little or no assistance; both parents feed the young.

Dusky Honeyeater *Myzomela obscura* GOULD, 1843

The Dusky Honeyeater common in the denser forests of northern Australia.

OTHER NAMES
None.

IDENTIFICATION
LENGTH: *120–140 mm.*
ADULTS: *Sexes similar. Plumage uniformly mid dusky brown or slightly paler on underparts, with faint russet cast in Queensland populations; wings and tail greyer dusky brown. Thin dusky black line down centre of throat. Eye dark brown. Bill black. Feet dark grey-brown.*
IMMATURES: *Similar to adults but duller; lower mandible grey-orange tipped darker.*

VOICE
CALL: *Variety of squeaks; rapid tit-tit-tit-tit in chases and rapid soft trills.*
SONG: *Dawn song of four whistled chirps* tip-tip-eee-chip, *third note longer and descending; repeated from perches.*

NESTING
Breeds August–January. Nest an open cup of fine rootlets and plant tendrils, bound with cobweb and lined with fine grasses; suspended in fork, from about 2 m above ground to top of forest canopy. Eggs: two; slightly lustrous, white freckled with pale and dark rust-red, particularly at larger end; oval, about 17 x 13 mm.

DISTRIBUTION
Denser forest pockets and galleries in Arnhem Land, from Port Keats to Roper River, NT, and from Cape York Peninsula to Wide Bay, Qld. Also southern New Guinea to Moluccas. Nine races; three in Australia.

DESPITE ITS SOMBRE PLUMAGE, the Dusky has all the other traits of the small, tropical *Myzomela* honeyeaters: no territorial song-flight, white eggs spotted rust-brown, and a brush-tipped tongue split into four segments, in which the lateral splits are deeper than the median.

It also keeps to the denser wetter forests in northern Australia, whether rainforest, monsoon vine forest or mangroves and only forages out into fringing eucalypt and paperbark *Melaleuca* to harvest nectar from blossoming trees. There it usually occurs singly or in small groups in the crowns of trees, but will gather with other honeyeaters at flushes of flowering. An aggressive feeder, it is nonetheless often chased off by larger honeyeaters.

Dusky Honeyeaters are locally nomadic, their movements depending on their immediate habitat. In rainforest they are virtually sedentary, never travelling far and eating mainly insects gleaned from leaves and branchlets or caught in short hawking sallies. Flowering trees—eucalypts, paperbarks, grevilleas, kapoks *Bombax* and coral trees *Erythrina*—attract them into more open forest to rifle nectar. And sometimes they eat small fruit.

Like other *Myzomela* honeyeaters, they forage briskly, flitting rapidly through the foliage, hanging upside down and hovering to extract nectar from blossom.

Red-headed Honeyeater
Myzomela erythrocephala GOULD, 1840

A male Red-headed Honeyeater; the female has only a scarlet wash.

OTHER NAMES
Bloodbird, Mangrove Red-head, Myzomela.

IDENTIFICATION
LENGTH: *110–130 mm.*
MALE: *Head, side of neck, lower back, rump and upper tail coverts glossy scarlet. Lores black; back, wings and tail brown-black with olive-yellow edges to flight feathers and tail. Breast black-brown; belly and vent brown-grey; underwing coverts white. Eye red-brown. Bill black. Feet brown-grey.*
FEMALES: *Crown, back and rump brown; wings and tail grey-brown. Forehead, chin and lower cheeks lightly washed scarlet. Side of face, throat and breast smoky grey; belly, vent and underwing coverts off-white.*
IMMATURES: *Similar to adult female. Bill and feet lighter.*

VOICE
CALL: *Shrill, whistled* chiew, chiew, *buzzing chirps, whistled squeaks when feeding.*
SONG: *Metallic jingling twittering, by male from vantage perch.*

NESTING
Appears to breed March–September; possibly two broods—at beginning and end of wet season. Nest a small cup of bark strips and fibre interwoven with cobweb, especially at the rim where it is suspended from a thin horizontal fork; lined with fine vegetable fibre. Eggs: two, rarely three; matt-white or cream freckled and blotched with rust-brown or red, particularly at larger end; oval, about 16 x 12 mm.

DISTRIBUTION
Mangroves of northern coastal mainland, from Broome, WA, to Princess Charlotte Bay, Qld. Also southern New Guinea, Aru and Torres Strait Islands, and Sumba. Two races; one in Australia.

THEIR SCARLET HEADS glistening, male Red-headed Honeyeaters brighten the sombre green of mangrove thickets across coastal northern Australia. Red-headeds are virtually confined to mangroves where they wander locally, in one and twos, or rarely small loose flocks, to sources of food. Like other *Myzomela* honeyeaters, they take both insects and nectar, hunting actively, flitting about in fast, bouncy undulations and never staying in one position for long.

The birds do much of their foraging among the foliage within the mid and upper strata of mangroves. Gleaning over leaves and probing crannies in branchlets, they pick up not only beetles, flies, ants and caterpillars but also large numbers of spiders. When mangroves and other shrubs flower, the birds rifle nectar, often venturing out into adjacent flowering eucalypts or paperbarks then and mixing with other feeding honeyeaters. To probe for nectar, they hang over the flowers or hover in front; as they feed they whistle-chirp frequently.

Scarlet Honeyeater *Myzomela sanguinolenta* (LATHAM, 1801)

A male Scarlet Honeyeater brings an insect to its chicks in their nest in a wattle. The female Scarlet Honeyeater is brown with a scarlet-washed chin.

MALE SCARLET HONEYEATERS GLISTEN like tiny red jewels as they forage among the cream-white blossom in the crowns of flowering eucalypts and paperbarks. Dependent on nectar, they wander nomadically, locally or widely, up and down the Australian east coast and adjacent ranges in search of blossom. North of Townsville they are more abundant in the mountains, and south of Brisbane more frequent the coast; south of Sydney they appear only erratically. Everywhere they frequent the canopy of tall flowering trees—eucalypts, callistemons, melaleucas, turpentines, banksias, coral trees—often in gully galleries and on the edge of rainforest.

Smallest of Australia's honeyeaters, the birds congregate in loose groups in food trees, mixing there with other honeyeaters. They work briskly, hopping about foliage, hanging head-down rifling blossom, hovering in front of flowers to probe, and flitting in fast bouncing undulations from branch to branch, non-stop. Sometimes they break off to pick fruit or flutter out in short sallies to catch insects—midges—in midair. All the while males sing their wayward tinkling songs to mark feeding territory.

While the male holds territory, the dull brown female builds and incubates. To gather bark for the nest, she pulls off fine strips from trees with her bill, clinging to the side of a trunk and bracing herself with her tail. Both parents feed the young.

OTHER NAMES
Bloodbird, Crimson Honeyeater, Sanguineous Honeyeater.

IDENTIFICATION
LENGTH: *100–110 mm.*
MALE: *Head, neck, centre back and rump scarlet; lores black. Shoulders and wings black, with outer feathers edged white. Tail black. Throat and upper breast scarlet, lower breast becoming mottled scarlet and grey; rest of underparts light grey-white. Eye black-brown. Bill black. Feet dark grey.*
FEMALE: *Upper parts plain brown tinged with olive. Throat and breast pale brown with chin washed red; rest of underparts off-white.*

IMMATURES: *Resemble female. Scarlet feathers first appear on young males about chin and sides of head and down centre of back; about same time black feathers develop on shoulders; scarlet feathers appear last on front of neck and breast.*

VOICE
CALL: *Male gives various short tinkling twitters; female squeaks.*
SONG: *Clear silvery tinkling by male, in stanzas of half a dozen notes, rising and falling erratically.*

NESTING
Breeds July–January. Nest a frail cup of fine bark strips, rootlets, stems and cobweb; 38 x 32 mm inside, sparsely lined with finer material; usually attached at rim to thin horizontal fork of tree where another thin stem crosses to form a triangle, enabling nest to be fastened by cobweb at rim on three sides; 1–15 m above ground in foliage. Eggs: usually two; white, generally spotted with rust-brown and some yellower and greyer tones, densest at larger end; swollen oval, about 16 x 12 mm. Incubation by female.*

DISTRIBUTION
In coastal and range forest and woodland on east coast of Australia, from Cooktown, Qld, to far eastern Victoria; also on some offshore islands. Erratic south of Hunter Valley. Also on islands from Sulawesi to New Caledonia. About 11 races; one in Australia.*

Crimson Chats build a cup-shaped nest, often in saltbush. This is a male in breeding plumage; the female has a mottled red breast and light brown head.

Crimson Chat *Epthianura tricolor* GOULD, 1841

ONE OF AUSTRALIA'S DESERT NOMADS, the Crimson Chat wanders the Australian arid zone following the erratic rains that provide its food and water. It is a gregarious bird and travels in flocks of tens to hundreds, keeping more to well-shrubbed mulga, acacia and mallee scrubs than the other chats. Movements tend to be northwards in autumn–winter and southwards in spring–summer, to breed, but there are many fluctuations and erratic irruptions.

Crimson Chats feed mainly on the ground. There flocks work rapidly through a patch of scrub, birds running quickly, picking up insects, then suddenly taking wing as a group to fly 100 metres or more to the next site, in swift jerky undulating flight. As well as insects, the chats occasionally sweep nectar from ground-flowering herbs, for which they have short-brushed, honeyeater-like tongues —a clue to their probable ancestry.

They also drink whenever they can, taking only fresh water and even gleaning dew from leaves. The Crimson Chat has a more economical body water balance and lower metabolic rate than the White-fronted Chat. Also, it breeds later, into the warmer months, than the latter where they overlap, indicating that it is a better desert-adapted bird than the White-fronted.

Non-breeding males are dull mottled birds resembling females, but during breeding they don vivid red crowns and breasts. Such nuptial plumages, gained by a second annual body moult, are rare in Australian passerines and matched only in two other chats, the White-winged Triller, Brown Songlark, and the fairy-wrens.

Crimson Chats often nest in loose colonies, within which a male defends first his mate, then their territory of about 20 metres radius. In advertisement, he flies from a bush on one side to one on the other. Climbing steeply he puffs out his coloured underparts while uttering a vigorous oscillating call. Then at the top he folds his wings and glides down to a *tee-whee* call, levels off and lands. Intruders are chased off in long flights lasting for 20 seconds or more, well beyond the territory boundary.

In courtship, the male swoops towards the female with wings and tail spread and crown raised. He also accompanies her as she collects material and constructs the nest and assists her in incubation and in feeding the young. If the nest is threatened, both flutter to ground, feigning injury. After young fledge, neighbouring families may group together and so flocks re-form.

OTHER NAMES
Crimson-breasted Nun, Tricolour Chat.

IDENTIFICATION
LENGTH: *110–120 mm.*
MALE: *Crown scarlet; hind-neck and back dark brown; rump scarlet. Wing feathers brown-black with white edges; tail feathers brown-black with white spot on inner web of each feather at tip, except middle pair. Face dusky; throat white; rest of underparts scarlet, becoming white under tail. Eye cream-yellow. Bill has upper mandible black, lower light horn. Feet slate-grey.*
ECLIPSE MALE: *As female but forehead washed red; breast blotched more heavily red.*
FEMALE: *Wings, rump and tail as male. Head and back plain mid grey-brown. Underparts white with irregular blotching of pale red over breast.*
IMMATURES: *Crown, back and edges of wing feathers light brown; rump orange-red; underparts white, washed buff-brown on breast and flanks. Eye light brown.*

VOICE
CALL: *Common call, probably in contact, high silvery chiming* swee, *usually repeated three to six times. Soft* dik-it, dik-it *or brisk* chek, chek *in flight, in contact.*
SONG: *Harsh oscillating rattles and silvery trills.*

NESTING
Breeds mainly August–October in south; variable in north. Nest a cup of fine dry grass, fine twigs and plant stalks; lined with fine rootlets and hair; usually 100–750 mm above ground in saltbush, grass tussock, forb or similar low cover. Eggs: three or four; white, scattered with red-black, purplish and grey spots, particularly at larger end; oval, about 17 x 14 mm. Incubation 12 days, by both sexes. Young fledge in about 14 days.

DISTRIBUTION
Scrubby shrub savanna and tree savanna of inland plains. During coastward irruptions may enter cultivated areas and gardens. Nomadic. No races.

Orange Chat

Epthianura aurifrons GOULD, 1838

THE BRILLIANT ORANGE CHAT is nomadic and gregarious in Australia's arid zone, like the Crimson Chat, and the two sometimes feed in mixed parties when not breeding. But there are differences. The Orange rarely gathers in flocks of more than 50 birds, and frequents different habitat: low saltbush-bluebush (chenopod) steppe and samphire around dry salt lakes.

Orange Chats forage on the ground, where they run rapidly along, feeding exclusively on insects. Like the Crimson Chat they conserve body fluid with a lowered metabolic rate and cope with their need for fresh drinking water by nomadism; they simply fly in low, dipping undulations until they find it. At the same time they seem to withstand dry conditions better than Crimson Chats, remaining and breeding longer at any site.

With the coming of breeding in late winter, the flocks break up into territorial pairs. Males, gaining brilliant nuptial plumage for the event, establish a territory while the female builds the nest. Any intruder is chased off in flights low over bushes, the occupant male clicking his bill and squeaking but without making contact. To advertise his territory he perches on top of a tall bush, nape hackles raised, and turns his head jerkily in all directions; the tail is spread to expose his orange rump. Males present the orange and black areas of their faces and backs to all opponents before giving chase, sparked by intrusions as little as 30 metres from the nest.

Males attend their mates closely up until egg-laying and then share in incubation. Relieved birds usually forage well away from the territory, and males slip off to chase away intruders at the slightest provocation. Both parents feed the nestlings, and both drop to the ground to feign injury if the nest is threatened.

On fledging, young at first stay in the territory where they crouch motionless under bushes, protected by injury-feigning adults. After a few days, the whole family moves off to join local flocks where young continue to be fed by their parents.

OTHER NAMES
Orange-fronted Chat, Orange-fronted Nun, Saltbush Canary.

IDENTIFICATION
LENGTH: *105–120 mm.*
MALE: *Head, side of face, lower back, rump, and all underparts yellow, tinged orange on forehead and centre of breast and belly; lores and throat black. Back and shoulders olive-yellow streaked black. Wings and tail dusky, feathers edged and tipped white respectively. Eye brick-red to orange-brown. Bill and legs black.*
ECLIPSE MALE: *As nuptial male but paler, purer yellow; black bib reduced.*
FEMALE: *Upper parts uniform greenish grey-brown, streaked dusky on crown and mantle; rump pale yellow. Underparts plain yellow with grey-brown wash on breast.*
IMMATURES: *As female, in first year.*

VOICE
CALL & SONG: *Metallic* tang; *flight call a mellow* cheek cheek.

NESTING
Breeds July–April; mainly August–December. Nest a cup of dry grass and fine twigs, lined with fine rootlets, flower-heads and hair; usually placed in saltbush or cotton-bush up to 25 cm from ground. Eggs: usually three, sometimes four; white, sometimes with faint pink tinge, scattered with spots of red-black, sepia and red-brown, mainly at larger end; oval, about 18 x 13 mm. Incubation about 12 days, by both sexes. Young fledge in about 10 days.

DISTRIBUTION
Saltbush plains, samphire around salt lakes and shrub-dotted gibber plains through arid Australia; also coastal marshes in west. Nomadic. No races.

A male Orange Chat at its nest in a low saltbush, *Atriplex,* in the arid chenopod steppes of inland Australia. Both sexes incubate.

Yellow Chat

Epthianura crocea CASTELNAU & RAMSAY, 1877

OTHER NAMES
Yellow-breasted Nun.

IDENTIFICATION
LENGTH: *110–120 mm.*
MALE: *Upper parts yellow-olive to olive-grey lightly streaked dusky; wing and tail feathers dusky with white or green-yellow edging and tips. Forehead, face, underparts and rump bright yellow. Black bar of varying intensity across breast. Eye cream or grey-cream. Bill and feet grey-black.*
ECLIPSE MALE: *As nuptial male but paler yellow; breast bar incomplete.*
FEMALE: *Similar to male; yellow parts paler and lacks black breast bar. Bill dark grey, paler towards base.*
IMMATURES: *Paler grey-brown above; white below, washed pale yellow. Eye tan.*

VOICE
CALL & SONG: *Metallic* tang; *cricket-like churrs; two or three-note musical* pee-eep.

NESTING
Breeds November–January. Nest a

small cup of thin dried stalks of herbaceous plants, lined with fine wiry grasses and rootlets; placed in thick grass or low bush. Eggs: three; white with blotches of olive-brown and light red-brown or minute spots of black-red; oval, about 17 x 13 mm.*

DISTRIBUTION
Open grassy swamps of northern mainland, mostly west of Great Dividing Range, and reeds of bore-drain swamps in interior. Nomadic, depending on water. Two races.

The Yellow Chat is a nomad, and offers little chance for observation.

LEAST KNOWN OF THE CHATS, the Yellow is an irruptive nomad on the open, well-grassed swamplands of northern Australia, particularly those in semi-arid regions that are prone to dry out. The development of bore drains in the Great Artesian basin has increased its habitat inland, and following the drains, local groups have now reached northeastern South Australia. There and on the Alligator River flood-plain in the Northern Territory it is more sedentary but it still wanders locally from swamp to swamp as they dry out or become broken up by buffalo.

The chats frequent the banks of reeds, sedge, samphire and sub-shrubs that fringe the edges of surface waters, occurring there in small bands of two–10 or so birds. Larger gatherings are rare but flocks of up to 50 or more have been recorded. They feed on the ground, at the shore, running about individually between shrubs and under sedge and reeds, picking up insects. Insects—small flies, caterpillars, beetles, bugs, lacewing larvae, and ants—seem to be their exclusive food. If disturbed the birds fly up to the tops of bushes or reeds to perch and crane to inspect the cause, and often use such perches for brief sallies after flying insects.

Nesting in loose groups on the edges of well-grassed swamps, Yellow Chats are probably like other chats in their breeding biology. And like other chats, they have brush-tipped tongues.

White-fronted Chat *Epthianura albifrons* (JARDINE & SELBY, 1828)

The White-fronted Chat frequents low shrubberies across southern Australia and nests close to the ground.

OTHER NAMES
Baldyhead, Tang, Tintack, Bumps, Moonbird, Ringneck, Single-bar, Thistlebird, White-fronted Nun.

IDENTIFICATION
LENGTH: *120–130 mm.*
MALE: *Forehead, face, throat and breast white encircled by broad black band from crown across breast. Back mid-grey. Wings and tail black, with white spot on inner tip of each tail feather except middle pair. Rest of underparts white. Eye white to light orange. Bill and feet black. No eclipse plumage.*
FEMALE: *Duller than male; crown, face and back grey-brown; underparts white with dusky band across breast.*
IMMATURES: *As female but breast band fainter; flanks buffier.*

VOICE
CALL & SONG: *Nasal* tang, *given singly, but tossed about in flocks in contact, particularly in flight. Other fussy notes.*

NESTING
Breeds mainly July–January. Nest a cup of fine twigs, rootlets and plant stalks, lined with fine grass, hair and sometimes flower-heads; placed near ground in saltbush, samphire, reed-clump or similar cover. Eggs: two–four; white with sparse spots and blotches of black, red-black and grey or various shades of red-brown, particularly at larger end; oval, about 18 x 14 mm. Incubation 13–14 days, by both sexes. Young fledge in 14–15 days.

DISTRIBUTION
Low shrubberies of samphire and saltbush of estuarine flats and salt lakes, moist grassland, edges of swamps and marshes, and low heath across southern Australia to Tasmania. Sedentary, and nomadic. No races.

WHITE-FRONTED CHATS are the familiar, widespread chat of southern rural Australia, living there in open fields, heaths and the low shrubberies around lakes and swamps. After breeding it gathers locally in nomadic flocks of five to 50 or sometimes several hundred birds, flying from one feeding area to another in high, slow, jerky undulating flight on broad, rounded wings. The birds forage on the ground, running about individually, taking insects exclusively and drinking regularly.

Gregariousness extends to breeding when the birds often nest in loose colonies, sometimes only metres apart. Each pair neverthe-less holds a small discrete territory which the male defends by sit-ting on a vantage perch on top of a shrub, flashing his white front in different directions, and chasing intruders. The female builds the nest but both sexes incubate and feed the young, and both feign injury if the nest is threatened. All foraging is done well away from the nest, after which non-brooding birds return to keep watch from a prominent twig nearby. Only males chase off intruders.

Gibberbird *Ashbyia lovensis* (ASHBY, 1911)

THE SONG-FLIGHT OF THE Gibberbird is unique among chats. It is performed during the breeding season, probably by the male. The bird rises almost vertically in steps to more than 30 metres. During the short upward part of each step a high, piercing *weet weet weet* is uttered. At the top of its ascent the bird falls directly to earth, to almost the same spot from which it rose.

Gibberbirds are also unique in their habitats and habits. Living on the exposed waterless gibber plains in the driest, most irradiated part of Australia—the Lake Eyre basin—they are Australia's most complete desert bird. How they cope with those extreme conditions is not known. They belong to a group of birds that need to drink regularly to maintain body fluids, yet they can hardly drink themselves unless they harvest dew. They pant in the shade of rocks and bushes on hot days, cooling by evaporation from their mouths, but this results in water-loss.

To compensate they may have lower metabolic rates than even Orange Chats. Nomadism is a strategy used by other chats to escape environmental deprivation but Gibberbirds are not great wanderers. They may shift about locally, but hardly ever do they range beyond the Lake Eyre basin, only moving a little south in years of extreme drought or floods.

Among Australian chats, Gibberbirds are also complete ground-dwellers, feeding, roosting and nesting there. In ones, pairs or small loose groups of up to 10 or so, they walk and run among the gibber stones picking up spiders and insects: beetles, caterpillars, moths, cicadas and grasshoppers. Sometimes they run swiftly after low-flying prey or leap into the air to snap up any passing overhead, and they pick up blowfly larvae that drop off sheep.

Moving from point to point they fly rapidly low over the ground, undulating and zigzagging this way and that, a habit shared with other chats, but with tail often held down in the manner of pipits. To land, moreover, they pitch not onto the top of a bush but onto the ground or a stone, peering about and teetering up and down, also like a pipit.

Nesting is often loosely colonial, two or three pairs nesting within 100 metres or so. Both sexes nest-build and incubate the eggs; on hot days the brooding bird may spread its wings to shade

the young. The sitting bird usually performs a distraction display if an intruder approaches the nest. It runs or crawls along in a crouched position with wings spread and drooped close to the ground, covering the legs. It flops over large gibbers, sometimes rolling its body from side to side. If it stops to face the intruder it may fluff out its yellow breast feathers.

OTHER NAMES
Desert Chat, Gibberchat.

IDENTIFICATION
LENGTH: *125–130 mm.*
MALE: *Crown grey, centres of feathers with dark mottling; back and rump grey-brown with dark mottling. Wings dark grey-brown, flight feathers with pale edges. Tail dusky, with white tips on inner webs of all but central pair of feathers. Forehead, lores, eyebrow, face and underparts yellow, suffused lightly grey-brown on breast and flanks. Eye white to yellow. Bill dark brown to black. Feet grey-brown to brown. No eclipse plumage.*
FEMALE: *Similar to male; browner above and breast band heavier.*
IMMATURES: *Crown, back and wings buff-brown; throat pale yellow; breast buff-brown; belly yellow. Bill horn.*

VOICE
CALL: *Musical chatter, probably in contact. Alarm call a series of five or six high piercing notes.*
SONG: *Squeaky weet, weet, weet, uttered during song-flight.*

NESTING
Breeds June–December; at other times following sufficient rain. Nest a cup about 60 cm in diameter and 40 cm deep; of dry grass, twigs and rootlets, built in depression in ground, sometimes scratched out by the birds;
lined with fine rootlets and fine dry grass and often with up to 10 cm wide platform of dried material extending out from lip of nest; sometimes placed in shelter of low bush. Eggs: two–four; white, sometimes with pink tinge, and spotted olive-brown, red-brown and pale-grey; oblong-oval, about 20 x 15 mm. Incubation by both sexes.*

DISTRIBUTION
Locally fairly common on sparsely vegetated stony plains of Lake Eyre basin and adjoining regions. Mainly sedentary though there are some local movements in non-breeding season. No races.

The Gibberbird is more robust than the similar Orange Chat, and its bill and legs are stouter. This is a male but, unlike the other chats, there is little difference between the plumage of the sexes. True to their name, Gibberbirds live on gibber plains on the Lake Eyre drainage basin.

Yellow-bellied Sunbirds form established pairs. These acrobatic birds of tropical Queensland flit about flowering shrubs searching for nectar.

Yellow-bellied Sunbird *Nectarinia jugularis* (LINNÉ, 1766)

THE MIX OF COLOUR as tiny Yellow-bellied Sunbirds flit about red-flowering shrubs with the blue Emperor butterfly, *Papilo ulysses,* in a tropical Queensland garden is vivid indeed. Although unrelated to humming birds, sunbirds are their nearest ecological replacement in the old world tropics, and of them only one reaches Australia: the Yellow-bellied. Like honeyeaters they have long curved bills and protrusible brush-tipped tongues for rifling nectar, but the structure of the brush is different, more shortly toothed, and the edges of the tongue are rolled to form a complete fine tube, so that nectar can be sucked up by capillarity.

In tropical Queensland, sunbirds live as much in gardens as in mangroves and the margins of rainforest and regrowth nearby, wherever there are nectar-bearing flowers, native or introduced. The birds even enter houses in search of spiders and insects and hang their nests from all sorts of man-made structures. Nectar and spiders—many plucked from webs by hovering birds—are their staple diet, and the birds are constantly on the move, darting here and there to find them. To take nectar from different flowers, sunbirds use a variety of techniques. In front of small flowers they simply hover and insert the bill. With large open flowers, they cling to the front, tearing the petals to get at the nectar; with narrow trumpet-shaped flowers longer than their bills, they get to the nectar by piercing the base of the corolla.

Yellow-bellied Sunbirds are locally nomadic and may be extending their range south with the opening up of the Queensland coast. Before the main breeding season, males congregate in groups of eight–10 and often intrude into the territories of established pairs. After spending some hours chattering and chasing one another, they suddenly stop and sit together in line on a perch, heads sunk back and bills pointing skywards. In this position they stay for a few minutes or as long as an hour, then just as suddenly fly off and disperse. The function of this display—perhaps to test territory holding or to recruit females—is not clear.

Established pairs hold territory which the male protects while the female nest-builds and incubates. He attends her while she is building but provides little help. Nests around human habitation are well protected from the weather under eaves, verandas or in sheds. The same site may be used year after year, for 15 years, and old nests are renovated until they fall down; in them the birds may rear up to three broods a season. After young hatch, the female continues to brood and tend them for another six to eight days before the male begins to join in their feeding.

OTHER NAMES
Olive-backed Sunbird, Yellow-breasted Sunbird.

IDENTIFICATION
LENGTH: *100–115 mm.*
MALE: *Upper parts plain olive-green. Wing quills dusky edged olive-yellow; tail dusky, tipped white on inner webs. Face olive-yellow; lines above and below eye brighter yellow. Chin, throat and upper breast metallic blue-black, glossed at edges with purple tinge in centre; rest of underparts deep yellow, washed orange on sides of breast. Eye dark brown. Bill and legs black.*
FEMALE: *Underparts plain deep yellow; no orange tinge on breast.*
IMMATURES: *As female but duller yellow below. Immature males develop line of metallic blue on throat.*

VOICE
CALL: *Animated high-pitched tzit-tzit-tzit-tzit in contact when feeding and in flight.*
SONG: *Hissing whistle drawn out into trill, sometimes runs into shower of descending notes; often in display.*

NESTING
Breeds July–March, but nests all months. Nest long, spindle-shaped, with hooded side entrance, of bark, plant fibre, dead leaves, grass, cobweb and cocoons, and strings of caterpillar droppings; lined with plant down and feathers; hung from trees, under eaves, powerlines and clotheslines. Eggs: two, rarely three; smooth, lustrous green-grey to ash-white, covered with brown freckles, sometimes forming band at larger end; oval, about 17 x 12 mm. Incubation by female.

DISTRIBUTION
Rainforest edges, mangroves and suburban gardens in coastal Queensland from Cape York to about Gladstone. Also from Andaman Islands through southeastern Asia to New Guinea and Bismark Archipelago. About 23 races; one in Australia.

A female Yellow-bellied Sunbird clings to its spindle-shaped nest to feed young. The male has a blue-black throat.

Mistletoebird

Dicaeum hirundinaceum (SHAW, 1792)

THE LIVES OF THE Mistletoebird and mistletoes are inextricably linked. The bird is Australia's only member of a widespread tropical family of flowerpeckers which feed almost exclusively on the fruits of mistletoes; it, in turn, is the basic disseminator of the plants within Australia. The seed and accompanying flesh are squeezed with the bill and swallowed. The seeds are soon defaecated—within 25 to 60 minutes after ingestion—and are very viscid, adhering to any surface. Almost all seeds germinate and if these have lodged on compatible host trees or shrubs, a mistletoe plant may establish.

The digestive systems of the Mistletoebird and other flowerpeckers are adapted to the specialised diet of mistletoe fruits: the stomach has become a blind sac able to digest little else than a few insects and the alimentary canal facilitates the quick passage of seeds.

Just as mistletoes set fruit at different times in different areas, so Mistletoebirds are locally nomadic. They forage alone and fly from one clump of mistletoe to the next in high bullet-like flight among and over the tops of trees, often calling as they go. The birds do take other fruit and insects but only rarely.

Nesting in pairs, the female builds and incubates unaided and both parents feed the young. First fed on insects, young are weaned on to mistletoe drupes in several days.

A female Mistletoebird feeding a chick on a mistletoe berry. Both parents feed the young.

OTHER NAMES
Australian Flowerpecker.

IDENTIFICATION
LENGTH: *100–110 mm.*
MALE: *Upper parts glossy blue-black. Chin, throat and undertail coverts scarlet; breast and belly grey-white with broad central black streak. Eye dark brown. Bill and feet black.*
FEMALE: *Upper parts plain grey-brown. Underparts plain off-white; undertail coverts pale scarlet. Bill and feet dark horn-grey.*

IMMATURES: *As female; orange bill and gape.*

VOICE
CALL: *High-pitched, sharp, whistled szit or dzee in contact, often in flight.*
SONG: *Two or three, rising and falling whistled notes—witu-witu, tzee-zit, tsew-wit-zit—given from vantage perch.*

NESTING
Breeds mainly October–March. Nest a neat, downy, hanging purse, with narrow side entrance; of plant down matted with cobweb and covered with dried flowers, lichens and insects; suspended from horizontal twig in foliage, up to 10 m above ground. Eggs: usually three; plain white; oval, about 17 x 11 mm. Incubation by female. Young fledge in about 15 days.

DISTRIBUTION
Throughout mainland Australia. Also islands in Arafura Sea. Four races; one in Australia.

The Mistletoebird builds a neat, soft, pear-shaped nest of plant down and spiderweb. Mistletoebirds live wherever mistletoe grows; this is a male.

Red-browed Pardalote *Pardalotus rubricatus* GOULD, 1838

The Red-browed Pardalote lives in arid woodlands in mainland Australia. Their long legs enable them to hop and run quickly through high foliage.

PARDALOTES ARE SMALL, FOLIAGE-GLEANING birds that are endemic to Australia. They have short, scoop-shaped bills and use them to prise sugary lerps—the white scaly coating of psyllid insects— from leaves and to pick up manna and small insects from twigs. Feeding almost exclusively in eucalypts, they have long legs and hop, run and creep quickly through high foliage like mice. Plumage is a mixture of bright and dull tones, where white spotting on the heads and wings in most species has given them the name, Diamond Bird. In flight they dart bullet-like from tree to tree, stumpy-tailed and with rather pointed wings. This, their general form and vestigial outermost primary have led many ornithologists to associate them with the Asian flowerpeckers, Dicaeidae. Recent evidence from molecular studies suggests, however, that they are allied to the Australian scrubwrens and thornbills, Acanthizidae.

Red-browed Pardalotes are widespread through the lower scrubbier, drier eucalypt woodlands of northern Australia, ranging south along tree-lined watercourses into the Lake Eyre basin. There they feed in the outer foliage of eucalypts, gleaning insects, lerps, and other arthropods. They are solitary feeders, perhaps holding extended foraging territories year round. To advertise them, males call in bursts sporadically throughout the day, singing from sheltered vantage perches under the tree canopy. Daily routine is a continual alternation between bouts of feeding and bouts of singing.

Throughout their range Red-browed Pardalotes overlap the bulkier Striated Pardalote. Competition between them is largely averted, however, by their use of different habitats and breeding sites. Red-browed Pardalotes occupy lower, shrubbier eucalypt woodlands than Striateds, and nest strictly in tunnels in earth banks, often in the sides of watercourses.

Helped by the male, the female digs out the nest tunnel, scraping with her feet, and builds a deep cup of bark fibre in a cavity at the end. She may also carry out most of the incubation, the male perching above in a nearby tree for much of the time, singing territorially. Both parents feed the young.

OTHER NAMES
Fawn-eyed Diamond Bird, Red-lored Pardalote.

IDENTIFICATION
LENGTH: *100–110 mm.*
ADULTS: *Sexes similar. Crown black, thickly spotted white; eyebrow buff-yellow, with orange flash at front. Back and scapulars fawn-brown, lightly to heavily flecked dusky, becoming washed yellow over rump. Wings dusky, the bases and outer edges of flight feathers washed yellow-orange in broad bar; inner flight feathers narrowly edged white. Tail dusky, tipped white on inner vanes. Face and underparts pale white-fawn, with large spot of yellow in centre breast. Eye pale yellow. Bill dusky above, flesh-white below. Feet leaden grey.*
IMMATURES: *Crown faintly mottled dusky and white; eyebrow olive-cream; rest of upper parts plain fawn-olive; underparts uniformly pale yellow.*

VOICE
CALL & SONG: *Soft but carrying series of five–six whistled notes, the first two or three spaced and upslurred, each at a higher pitch than the preceding, and the last three run together quickly, at the same pitch as the third—apparently by male in territorial advertisement;* sometimes in call-and-answer between separated pairs.

NESTING
Breeds July–December and after rains in arid regions. Nesting site a tunnel bored 500–800 mm into a bank with nest chamber at end. Substantial cup nest built in chamber, of thin bark strips, sometimes lined with fine grasses. Eggs: three, four or sometimes two; plain white; rounded-oval, about 19 x 15 mm. Incubation mainly by female.

DISTRIBUTION
Eucalypt scrubs and low eucalypt-lined watercourses across drier parts of northern and inland mainland. Two races.

Spotted Pardalote *Pardalotus punctatus* (SHAW, 1792)

TINY WHITE JEWEL-LIKE SPOTS ADORN the crown, wings and tail of the male Spotted Pardalote and the wings and tail of the female—and because of these spots, the species is commonly called Diamond Bird. Like other pardalotes, it gleans for lerps, manna and insects in the foliage of eucalypts, moving rapidly like a mouse through tree crowns, but it also differs in many of its habits.

It is the tiniest of the pardalotes and frequents denser, wetter eucalypt forests around temperate southern Australia, ranging north to the Atherton Tablelands along the Great Dividing Range where climate is cool. Even where its yellow-rumped race ranges through mallee, it keeps to the denser, wetter tracts with a close canopy. Not needing tree hollows for nesting, it is not limited to mature forest and forages through saplings and regrowth, even to the ground, sites not often visited by Striated Pardalotes.

Out of breeding, Spotted Pardalotes gather in loose feeding flocks of 10–20, or even 100 or so individuals, to forage nomadically. Most movements are fairly local, but in the colder mountains of the southeast and Tasmania there is a general exodus to lowlands, inland and northwards in autumn. Many groups reach the central Queensland coast then, a major non-breeding refuge for the species through winter. Travelling groups keep contact with high mewing whistles as they move while feeding but not in flight.

The flocks return and disperse with the onset of breeding. Unlike Striated Pardalotes, individual pairs take up and defend much the same territory that encompasses foraging range as well as the nest area. The male advertises it by singing frequently throughout the day from a bare vantage perch at mid-heights in trees. He stands high on his toes, head stretched erect and chin tucked in as each long note is uttered, turning to beam his voice in different directions. Both sexes—but mostly males—chase off intruders in long twisting flights, and will attack planted models, pecking at the yellow throat patch. They themselves are in turn chased by larger pardalotes and, particularly, honeyeaters.

Spotted Pardalotes nest almost exclusively in terrestrial burrows excavated in low banks or walls. The male generally takes the initiative in selecting the site and both partners excavate and build the nest, occasionally breaking off to sit at the entrance and spread their wings in display. Both also share incubation and the feeding of young. Arriving birds dive into the nest-hole in full flight.

Two distinct forms of the Spotted Pardalote—one ochre-rumped in wet coastal forests and the other yellow-rumped in mallee—have often been regarded as separate species. Recent studies have shown that they hybridise and intergrade from the Mt Lofty Ranges, SA, through the lower Murray mallee, to near Bendigo, Vic. On the high tablelands in northeastern Queensland is a third smaller race, its males blending the russet rumps of the wet forest race with the greyer, more finely spotted back of the mallee form.

A male of the southeastern race of the Spotted Pardalote at its nest burrow.

OTHER NAMES
Yellow-rumped Pardalote, Yellow-tailed Pardalote, Diamond Bird, Pardalote, Diamond Dyke, Ground Diamond, Spotted Diamond Bird.

IDENTIFICATION
LENGTH: *90–100 mm.*
MALE: *Crown black, spotted white; hind-neck flecked grey. Mantle, scapulars and mid-back brown coarsely spotted buff to grey more finely spotted white; lower back and rump ochre-red to bright yellow, edged glossy crimson at base over tail. Wings and tail black, the feathers tipped white. Face flecked grey and white; long white eyebrow. Throat dark to bright yellow; breast and belly cream-buff to cream-white; undertail dark to bright yellow. Eye grey-brown. Bill black, greyish at underbase. Feet flesh-brown.*

FEMALE: *As male, but crown spots buff-yellow all races, back brown spotted coarsely to finely cream-buff all races; eyebrow buffier all races; throat cream-white.*
IMMATURES: *As female but crown olive-grey, spotted buff-yellow; dorsal spotting sparser; rump and undertail duller ochreish. Adult plumage gained at first annual moult.*

VOICE
CALL: *Short series of mewing whistles, slower and dropping in short* weep *call and faster and rising in long* weep *call, given in contact. Fast chipping in aggression at nest, and whistled* wheee *in alarm there. Young beg with short fast chirps.*
SONG: *Explosive, penetrating three- or four-syllabled piping whistles by male:* sa-weet ba-beee *in ochre-rumped race, the second syllable high-piercing and the last longer drawn; or* wit wee-eee *in yellow-rumped race, in simpler form and often with first syllable elided.*

NESTING
Breeds August–January. Nest a dome of loosely woven bark fibre and grass; sometimes lined with feathers; placed at end of sloping burrow, 500–1500 mm long, excavated into creek bank, sandy ground, side of cliff and even wall of a building. Eggs: three to six, usually four; plain white; oval, about 16 x 13 mm. Incubation 14–16 days, by both sexes.

DISTRIBUTION
Wet and dry sclerophyll forests and wetter mallee, infrequently more open woodland, around southern and eastern coastal and subcoastal Australia, from Darling Ranges, WA, to Atherton Tableland, Qld. Three races.

A male of the yellow-rumped mallee race of the Spotted Pardalote. These pardalotes dig a sloping burrow in level sandy ground, which leads to a nest dome of loosely woven bark fibre and grass.

Forty-spotted Pardalote *Pardalotus quadragintus* GOULD, 1838

The Forty-spotted Pardalote usually has 40 white spots—20 on each wing. It is restricted to dry sclerophyll forest in Tasmania and islands in Bass Strait.

EXTINCTION MAY BE FACING the Forty-spotted Pardalote, which is found only in Tasmania. Its total numbers are already low—probably not more than 1000 individuals scattered between six or seven relict populations on islands and peninsulas in the southeast and east of Tasmania and in Bass Strait. Apparently it has never been a common bird but it had a much wider distribution in Tasmania—from 1838 when naturalist John Gould described it—up until the 1920s. Since then the decrease in its numbers and the contraction in its range have been dramatic; the only apparently viable colonies are on Bruny and Maria Islands.

Reasons for the overall decline are complex but may reduce to two central issues: quality of habitat and competition from other pardalotes. Wherever they survive today, Forty-spotted Pardalotes live in rather sedentary colonies in mature mixed eucalypt forests with many hollow trees, fallen logs and stumps to provide nest sites. Manna gums *Eucalyptus viminalis* are often dominant. Widespread clearing of such forest has pushed them back.

With short, rounded wings, they are not strong fliers as are other pardalotes, disperse little—even out of breeding—and are faithful to local areas, each pair nesting in the same hollow or one nearby year after year. Experiments have shown that they do not accept change easily.

Their main competition comes not from the more closely related but smaller Spotted Pardalote but the large Striated Pardalote. Forty-spotteds forage in the same way for the same food in the same trees as Striateds, working methodically through the higher outer foliage in mixed forest and hanging on twigs—even more so—as they glean lerps and manna from eucalypt leaves. They also nest in tree hollows and stumps. Straying Forty-spotteds are chased off by Striated Pardalotes and honeyeaters and do not seem to be able to maintain themselves outside large colonies; even there broods may be lost because adults spend so much time in defence. So the chances of establishing new colonies and expanding under present 'natural' conditions are slim.

Forty-spotted Pardalotes feed consistently in the crowns of eucalypts, usually more than 10 metres above the ground, where as well as lerps and manna they pick up a range of small spiders and insects: beetles, wasps, flies, weevils, leaf bugs, millipedes and termites. They work more slowly than other pardalotes. Although some birds—probably young of the year—do wander locally during autumn and winter, most birds are so set in their feeding pattern—foraging on a regular beat through just two or three trees—that they can be found almost in the same pocket of foliage year round. Small groups of up to 10 or more gather in winter, however, calling spiritedly, fluttering their wings and posturing as they play-chase through the trees.

Occurring in colonies, Forty-spotted Pardalotes nest in loose association, their nests no more than 10 metres apart. Pairs apparently mate permanently, most keeping their bonds through winter, and returning to the same nest site. The female probably builds the nest and both adults incubate the eggs and feed the young. Because of the long fledging time of apparently 25 days, only one brood may be reared a year.

OTHER NAMES
Tasmanian Diamond Bird, Many Spotted Pardalote.

IDENTIFICATION
LENGTH: *95–100 mm.*
ADULTS: *Sexes similar. Upper parts dull olive-green faintly scalloped with black; upper tail coverts yellow-green scalloped with black. Tail black with white tip. Wings and wing coverts black, feathers tipped white. Face and undertail coverts lemon-yellow; throat pale grey with yellow tinge; breast pale yellow-grey with darker grey mottling; belly buff-grey. Eye dark brown. Bill short, stubby, notched, black. Feet fawn-pink with purple tinge.*
IMMATURES: *Similar to adults; face and undertail coverts duller yellow.*

VOICE
CALL & SONG: *Normal call a repeated, soft, nasal* whi-whi *or* whi-oot, *with stress on first syllable. In breeding season male has loud, nasal territorial call* twint. *Both sexes utter soft* whi *contact call at nest.*

NESTING
Breeds September–January. Nest dome-shaped or cup-shaped, depending on size of nest cavity, made of fibre from stringybark, lined with fine Poa *grass, wool and feathers; placed in hollow branch or tree trunk up to 20 m from ground or, occasionally, in a hole in the ground. Eggs: three to five; lustrous white; oval, about 17 x 13 mm. Incubation about 16 days, by both sexes. Young fledge in 25 days.*

DISTRIBUTION
Total population perhaps less than 1000; in colonies in southeast and islands off coast there. Found only in sclerophyll forest, with preference for white gum Eucalyptus viminalis *as a food tree. Probably extinct on King and Flinders Islands. No races.*

Striated Pardalote *Pardalotus striatus* (GMELIN, 1789)

LARGEST OF THE SMALL PARDALOTES, the Striated is also the most widespread and nomadic. It frequents more open eucalypt forests and woodlands than other pardalotes, and, following the river gum galleries along watercourses, it ranges right across the inland. Throughout the north it is more sedentary, dispersing locally after breeding but apparently rarely wandering far. Many southern populations, however, shift north, inland and to lower altitudes in autumn and winter, often forming loose flocks of 100 or more as they travel. Most but not all Tasmanian birds cross Bass Strait then to winter on the mainland as far north as southeastern Queensland. The stubby-tailed groups travel quickly from clump to clump of trees, flying high and bullet-like.

Like other pardalotes, the Striated feeds in the crowns and outer foliage of eucalypts, creeping and running like a mouse, picking lerps and other insects—bugs, grasshoppers, beetles, cockroaches, thrips, weevils, ants, bees, wasps, flies and caterpillars—from the leaves and outer twigs. As they work the birds trill softly and frequently in contact.

Males announce the coming of breeding with loud punctuated chip songs from high, often bare vantage perches. Flocks return and disperse into pairs and small groups of three–six to nest in traditional areas. No territory is defended, just the immediate vicinity of the nest, whether a hole in a tree or stump, as is usual in southern populations, or a burrow in the ground. The central pair works the nest, incubates the eggs and feeds the young, and may be helped by additional members of their groups. All of them often cluster and display with wing-waving around the nest entrance. Northern black-headed populations, which usually nest in banks, begin breeding earlier than elsewhere to take advantage of dry ground during the winter dry season.

The races of Striated Pardalotes have often been regarded as distinct species, but hybridise and intergrade wherever they meet.

OTHER NAMES
Eastern Striated Pardalote, Black-headed Pardalote, Yellow-tipped Pardalote, Red-tipped Pardalote.

IDENTIFICATION
LENGTH: *100–120 mm.*
ADULTS: *Sexes alike, or crown of female scalloped fawn in north. Crown black, with or without white streaks. Back grey-brown, or rufous or yellow on rump. Wings black, with small red to yellow spot at shoulder tip; outer flight feathers with narrow or broad white stripe; inner flight feathers edged rufous or white. Tail black, tipped white. Brow stripe rich yellow to white over eye; black stripe through eye over cheeks plain or flecked grey-white. Underparts all cream-white with yellow line down centre throat forking over sides of breast. Eye tan-grey. Bill black. Feet dusky brown.*
IMMATURES: *As adults but crown and face olive-grey; brow all cream.*

VOICE
CALL: *Repeated soft trills in contact; soft* cheeoo *or* pee-ew, pee-ew.
SONG: *Loud, sharp, stuttered chips, run together in two to four syllables on same pitch, repeated in raped-fire bursts—*chip-chip *or* pik-pik *or* pik-it-up *or* wi-di-dup *or* wi-di-di-dup. *Much dialectic variation, even in local populations.*

NESTING
Breeds June–January. Nest cup-shaped, partly domed or domed; of grasses, bark fibre and rootlets, sometimes lined with feathers; placed in hollow of post or tree 10 m or higher, or at end of nest burrow dug into side of cliff, creek bank, roadside cutting or building. Eggs: three to five, usually four; white; oval, about 19 x 15 mm. Incubation by both sexes.

DISTRIBUTION
Almost the whole of Australia and Tasmania, in open eucalypt forest and woodland. Six races.

The black-headed form of Striated Pardalote is common in the north and northeast of Australia. This one has made its nest in a bank.

The yellow-tipped form of the Striated Pardalote breeds in Tasmania and visits the southeast of mainland Australia—as far as southeastern Queensland—in the winter months. This pardalote is at the entrance to its nest.

A red spot can be seen at the base of the narrow wing stripe on this Striated Pardalote. It is the common form in coastal southeastern Australia and here is seen at the entrance to its nest. Another race west of the Great Dividing Range has a broad white wing stripe.

Pale White-eye *Zosterops citrinella* BONAPARTE, 1850

OTHER NAMES
Pale Silvereye, Pale-bellied Silvereye.

IDENTIFICATION
LENGTH: *100–110 mm.*
ADULTS: *Sexes similar. Upper parts* plain light citrine-green, yellower on forehead. Wing and tail feathers dusky grey edged citrine. Eye-ring narrowly white; lores to line under eye black. Throat to upper breast and undertail clear deep yellow; lower breast and belly off-white, washed grey on flanks. Eye mid-brown. Bill black-grey, greyer at lower base. Feet leaden grey.
IMMATURES: *As adults but duller; throat lemon-yellow.*

VOICE
CALL: *Single, soft chirped whistles in contact.*
SONG: *Rich but soft series of warbles, whistles and trills, as in other white-eyes; given from perch in thickets.*

NESTING
Mainly wet season, December–June. Nest deep, cup-shaped, of dried skeletons of leaves bound with cobweb; lined with fine grass and covered on outside with broad, thin strips of paperbark; about 80 mm in diameter and 50 mm deep, suspended from horizontal fork of shrub. Eggs: two to four; pale blue-green; oval to tapered-oval, about 17 x 13 mm.

DISTRIBUTION
Small wooded islands in Torres Strait and off eastern Cape York Peninsula south to Palfrey Island, near Cooktown, Qld. Locally common. Also Lesser Sundas and Tanimbar. Three races; one in Australia.

IN AUSTRALIA, PALE WHITE-EYES are limited to small offshore islands along the east coast of Cape York Peninsula and in Torres Strait. There they inhabit shrubby thickets in small parties of up to about six and forage among the foliage of low trees and shrubs for insects and berries. Their calling, as they feed, is a soft whistled mewing, typical of white-eyes, and is often given to keep contact as they dash in undulating swoops from shrub to shrub.

Remote and difficult to identify, Pale White-eyes have been seen by few ornithologists; almost nothing is known of their habits. Brightly coloured Silvereyes have occasionally been mistaken for them in northeastern Queensland, but the White-eyes can be distinguished by their richer deep yellow throats and plain citrine backs; Silvereyes there have a grey band across the back.

Yellow White-eye *Zosterops lutea* GOULD, 1843

OTHER NAMES
Yellow Silvereye, Gulliver's White-eye.

IDENTIFICATION
LENGTH: *95–110 mm.*
ADULTS: *Sexes alike. Upper parts plain citrine-green; wings and tail duskier. Eye-ring white, lores black. Underparts plain lemon-yellow. Eye brown. Bill dusky slate. Feet leaden.*
IMMATURES: *As adults but duller.*

VOICE
CALL: *Single, mewing whistles, in contact.*
SONG: *Strong warbled whistles and trills.*

NESTING
Breeds October–March. Nest a small, neat cup about 65 mm in diameter, of fine grass or thin bark shreds and cobweb; lined with finer material; hung from low horizontal twigs among outer leaves of mangrove. Eggs: three or four; pale blue or green-blue; oval to tapered-oval, about 17 x 13 mm. Incubation by both sexes.

DISTRIBUTION
Mangroves and adjacent shrubland from Shark Bay, WA, to near Weipa, Cape York Peninsula, also near Ayr, Qld. Two races.

The Yellow White-eye lives in tropical coastal mangroves in the north and northwest of Australia.

YELLOW WHITE-EYES, readily identified by their uniformly yellow toning, are birds of mangroves around the northern Australian coast. Although they often wander inland along riverine galleries of paperbarks and eucalypts and fringing acacia scrubs in Western Australia when not breeding, they are still centred in mangroves and return to them to nest.

Travelling in close-knit groups of five to 30 or even more after breeding, Yellow White-eyes move nomadically through the outer foliage branchlets of mangrove thickets, at one–10 metres above the mud. They glean for food briskly, hopping about and hanging upside down to pick items from leaves and twigs, then dashing in short swooping undulations on to the next patch of shrubbery. All the while they keep contact with soft whistled chirps, each bird answering the other in a constant low chorus of sound. Insects are staple diet, particularly beetles, bugs, ants, but small fruits and even nectar from flowers are picked up as opportunity offers.

Pairs apparently leave groups to breed on their own. They sing much then from sheltered branches near the nest, giving both subsong and the full sibilant songs typical of white-eyes. Both sexes build the nest, incubate and feed the young.

Silvereye *Zosterops lateralis* (LATHAM, 1801)

OTHER NAMES

Grey-breasted Silvereye, Eastern Silvereye, Grey-backed Silvereye, Western Silvereye, Green-backed White-eye, Grinnell.

IDENTIFICATION

LENGTH: *110–130 mm.*
MALE: *Upper parts generally citrine-green with grey back and duskier, citrine-edged flight and tail feathers. Underparts grey or white with white eye-ring and dusky lores. Wide plumage variation in subspecies. Central and southeastern Australian race Z.l. familaris has citrine-green head, shoulders and rump; back grey; throat pale yellow or yellow-green; breast pale grey to white on belly; pale yellow undertail. Northeastern race Z.l. ramsayi is brighter with yellower throat and undertail. Capricorn Island race Z.l. chlorocephala similar but much larger. Tasmanian race Z.l. lateralis has throat usually pale green-grey, breast grey to white undertail; flanks vary from deep chestnut to dull chestnut-brown. Western Victorian-South Australian race Z.l. halmaturina has grey-white throat and grey breast, with pale rufous flanks and white undertail. Western Australian race Z.l. gouldi has whole of upper parts—head, back and rump—plain citrine-green. There is no winter plumage; only plumage changes are due to deterioration between moults.*
FEMALE: *Paler than male in any pair, but may be brighter than male of neighbouring pair.*
IMMATURES: *As adults or duller. Juveniles have soft, downy plumage which is quickly moulted.*

VOICE

CALL: *Drawn-out, peevish whistled chirp* peeeh *in contact; sharper* pyeeew *during night migration.*
SONG: *Loud song of stereotyped whistled and trilled warbles; also more protracted and varied subsong, whispering, with interwoven mimicry.*

NESTING

Breeds August to January–February. Nest a small cup, 65 mm in diameter, of fine grasses, rootlets, cobweb, hair, occasionally animal fur; lined with hair or finer material such as casuarina leaves; usually suspended from small, almost horizontal branch in outer foliage 1–5 m above ground. Eggs: two–four, usually three; plain pale blue or blue-green; oval to tapered-oval, about 17 x 13 mm. Incubation usually 10–13 days, by both sexes. Young fledge in nine–12 days.

DISTRIBUTION

Common in Tasmania and throughout most of coastal and adjacent areas of mainland except north and northwest, from near Carnarvon, WA, to eastern Cape York Peninsula. Also common in suburban parks and gardens, where it breeds in native and exotic plants, shrubs and trees. Also in New Zealand and subtropical Pacific Islands to Fiji. Fourteen races; six in Australia.

SILVEREYES, named for the ring of white feathers that encircles their eyes, are among the most familiar of Australia's garden birds. Ranging around the wetter parts of the south and east, they enter almost every habitat, from rainforest to mallee thicket. Everywhere pockets of shrubbery provide them with shelter and foraging.

Each year hundreds of thousands of Silvereyes migrate from Tasmania and southern Victoria north as far as southern Queensland. They begin to move towards the end of summer, after breeding, when they congregate in flocks. Some flocks wander erratically, even reaching the Adelaide plains, and others migrate northwards along definite routes. Most follow the eastern coastal plain where vast numbers feed in heaths and gardens, in company with many honeyeaters. Migrating groups travel mainly at night, flying high and calling constantly in their whistling chirps to keep contact. By day they simply drift along through shrubberies, feeding as they go.

Not all populations of Silvereyes move so much after breeding. Most in Queensland are locally nomadic at best, and others in southern and western Australia may shift only a little inland. Nor do all Tasmanian birds leave in winter; those remaining are probably older breeders with long established territory.

Working through thickets and low foliage in trees, and sometimes hopping on the ground, Silvereyes are brisk, versatile feeders. They glean over leaves and twigs for insects— beetles, bugs, wasps, flies, and aphids—visit flowering plants for their nectar, pick up occasional seeds, and hang upside down to pick fruit, a trait which makes them a pest in orchards.

No sooner do they finish foraging in one thicket than they fly to the next in fast, low, dipping undulations. Silvereyes usually feed in small flocks, and as they go, all members whistle-chirp constantly to one another to keep contact. Foraging routines are broken regularly to drink and bathe, particularly on hot days.

Juvenile Silvereyes usually pair permanently in their first winter. Older pairs stay closer to their territories then but still allow other birds to forage there. Even during breeding, nesting birds will feed outside their territories, particularly when feeding nestlings and fledglings.

Silvereyes nest in discrete pairs and sing to advertise territory; song is most voluble during breeding. The birds sing their loud songs from bare exposed vantage perches, particularly at dawn, and give whispered subsongs from under sheltering foliage often through the day. Both male and female build the nest and share incubation and the feeding of young, rearing sometimes two or three broods a year. Young are fed first on insects and later on fruit, and if they fledge successfully, may live 10 years or more.

Silvereyes of the eastern race that breeds in Tasmania feeding on a persimmon. The birds pair permanently.

European Goldfinch *Carduelis carduelis* (LINNÉ, 1758)

The European Goldfinch is common in cities and on settled agricultural lands in southeastern Australia. It eats seeds, and sometimes insects.

INTRODUCED TO AUSTRALIA IN THE 1850s and 1860s, European Goldfinches spread rapidly through temperate rural districts. Releases at Melbourne in 1863 and possibly 1857 were followed by others at Adelaide in 1879, at Sydney before 1886, and around Hobart in the early 1880s or before. By the early 1900s the birds had established themselves throughout their present range in southeastern Australia, only to stop and even decline over the past 20 or so years.

Goldfinches have only been able to prosper in areas of cultivated and cleared land that carry traditional food plants—exotic weeds, particularly thistles, Asteraceae—and local copses of trees for nesting and roosting. These resources are now limited by changing farming practices and herbicides. In the southwest, the birds have followed the same rise and fall as in the east. Released at Perth in 1912 and later at Albany in 1955 they first spread slowly and locally and then stopped and are now infrequently seen there.

Goldfinches are gregarious and live year round in small groups called charms. These amalgamate after breeding—from March to early September—in flocks of 200 or more to forage over the countryside. The birds are primarily seed-eaters, feeding on the ground or low plants gleaning grain from exotic herbs and forbs. Small quantities of insects—caterpillars, aphids and beetle larvae—are taken as well, particularly during breeding when nestlings need protein for growth. When feeding, the entire flock advances systematically over the ground as birds from the rear hop over others to feed at the front.

Throughout August there is an upsurge in courtship activity, marked by more singing, increased aggressiveness between birds, and frequent aerial chases. By late August pairing is complete and the winter flocks fragment in September as groups of goldfinches take up breeding quarters, to rear, rarely, up to three broods a year.

Early in breeding, the male vigorously defends his territory which is just a small area immediately around the nest; several pairs may nest in the same tree and share a communal feeding range. Nests, which are built by the female throughout the day but with peaks in the early morning and late afternoon, are usually placed in exotic trees. Nest-building takes about a week, and then

an egg is laid daily soon after sunrise until the clutch is complete.

The female incubates unaided, seldom leaving the nest and being fed by her mate. At the brooding stage the male brings food to the nest, where it is regurgitated to the female and then fed to the young. Twelve to 15 days after hatching, the now well-feathered young climb from the nest into the surrounding cover and from there make their first flights. They remain dependent on their parents for food for another three or so weeks.

OTHER NAMES
Goldfinch, Thistle-finch.

IDENTIFICATION
LENGTH: *125–135 mm.*
ADULTS: *Sexes similar. Crown black, running in crescent down sides of head. Hind-neck to rump brown-buff. Wings black, with gold bar and white tips to flight feathers. Tail black with white tip. Face a crimson disc, larger in male. A white patch runs from ear to ear under the neck. Underparts white, washed buff-brown down sides of breast and flanks. Eye brown. Bill bone with black tip. Feet buff.*
IMMATURES: *As adults but lack brightly coloured head and face. Body plumage flecked with fine stripes.*

VOICE
CALL: *Drawn-out, canary-like* tu-leep *in alarm. In flight a repeated tinkling* tswitt-witt-witt, *in contact.*
SONG: *Short twittered warbling,* twiddlee-ee-twiddle-ee-dee.

NESTING
Breeds late September to March. Nest a tightly woven cup of rootlets and soft fibres lined with down and often decorated with lichens; built in end branchlets of conifers and other introduced trees, 2–12 m above the ground. Eggs: three–six, usually four or
five; blue-white with sparse red-brown spotting; oval, about 16 x 13 mm. Incubation 12–13 days, by female. Young fledge in 12–15 days.

DISTRIBUTION
Urban and settled agricultural lands of temperate southeastern Australia. Small colonies of aviary escapees have become established in Perth and Albany. Natural range is from British Isles to central Russia and northwestern Africa. Up to eight races; one introduced in Australia.

European Greenfinch *Carduelis chloris* (LINNÉ, 1758)

EUROPEAN GREENFINCHES were introduced into Australia at the same time as the European Goldfinch but have not spread so widely through the temperate southeast. Successfully released at Melbourne between 1863 and 1873, at Adelaide in 1879 and possibly at Sydney before the 1890s, they had established themselves at those centres by the turn of the century. By 1910 they had reached Albury and Bathurst, but their spread has been gradual and limited to urban habitats of hedges, gardens, orchards, parks and plantations of exotic conifers; the main southeastern population is still barely linked with the centre around Adelaide and the Mt Lofty Ranges. Only in Tasmania has the European Greenfinch expanded quickly. First reported there in 1941, it has now spread throughout the east and along the coast in the wilder west.

Greenfinches usually travel in small groups. During the non-breeding months of winter they venture locally into woodland, heath and open farmland where, denied their traditional European food of elm, yew and hornbeam seeds, they feed, hopping on the ground, on weeds in open wasteland and fallow. Seeds are husked with a strong, powerful bill, and the birds pick up occasional insects—beetles, ants and aphids—as well.

In late September, the breeding season is forecast by their return to nesting areas. The males' drawn-out *birrzz* call, from high exposed perches, announces them. They begin nesting in early October, in loose colonies of two–six pairs, building their nests close to each other; each male defends a small territory around his nest. While the female is occupied with nesting duties the male often gives an overhead aerial display, in which he circles the nest area with a lazy, flapping bat-like flight, twittering in song and uttering his call.

At breeding time the greenfinch is often aggressive towards other species, such as the goldfinch. Their breeding habitat sometimes overlaps and the larger, more quarrelsome greenfinch often succeeds in expelling goldfinches by, among other things, pirating nesting material or puncturing goldfinch eggs in an unattended nest. The nest is built entirely by the female, usually on the outer part of the branch, in a conifer or, sometimes, another exotic tree. The female, fed at the nest, incubates alone, and after young hatch she spends most of her time brooding while the male continues to bring food, a mixture of insects and the pulp of crushed seeds. Two broods are often reared in a season.

OTHER NAMES
Greenfinch, Green Linnet.

IDENTIFICATION
LENGTH: *140–160 mm.*
MALE: *Generally citrine-green over upper and underparts; rump and belly washed yellower. Wings duskier, outer flight feathers broadly edged yellow, forming band, inner broadly edged mid-grey. Tail dusky, outer feathers broadly edged yellow towards base, forming band on either side. Eye brown. Bill bone-white. Feet pale pink.*
FEMALE: *Similar to male but duller and browner; reduced yellow banding in wings and tail; faint streaking over back.*
IMMATURES: *Brownish grey-green above and below, clearly streaked dusky brown; wings, tail as adults. Adult plumage gained at first annual moult, in autumn after fledging.*

VOICE
CALL: *Loud, rapid twitter* chichichichi; *usually on wing; monotonous nasal* birrzz *rising at end, from perch; canary-like* tsooeet *in alarm.*
SONG: *Twittering running into and out of spaced-out chirps—* cheu-cheu-cheu—*interspersed with* birrzz *call.*

NESTING
Breeds early October–January, sometimes later. Nest a bulky cup of tightly woven twigs, rootlets and soft fibres; lined with plant down; in fork usually on outer part of branch of conifer or other exotic tree, 2–12 m above ground. Eggs: four–six; blue-white with red-brown spots and mottlings; oval, about 21 x 15 mm. Incubation 13–14 days, by female. Young fledge in 13–16 days.

DISTRIBUTION
Common in urban gardens and parks of southeastern Australia. Natural range from northwestern Africa to Britain and all Europe to Afghanistan, Caucasus and Urals. Four races; one introduced in Australia.

The European Greenfinch lives in town parks and gardens in southeastern Australia. This is a male.

House Sparrow *Passer domesticus* (LINNÉ, 1758)

A female House Sparrow. House Sparrows were introduced from Europe last century.

THE HOUSE SPARROW was introduced to Australia from Europe from 1863 to 1870, following successful releases at Melbourne, Adelaide and Hobart; it expanded throughout eastern Australia to reach islands in Torres Strait by the late 1970s. Its spread into Western Australia and the Northern Territory has been checked there by the fauna authorities. A commensal of man, it never occurs far from human habitation and rarely enters forest of any sort.

These noisy little birds live in flocks in the trees and on the ground, feeding on seeds, insects and scraps and hopping about with wings often drooped and tails part-cocked and flicking. They also eat insects, particularly when feeding young. At night they roost, often tightly packed, in shrubs or vines and under eaves.

House Sparrows cram their untidy nests into crevices in trees and buildings. The female does most of the incubating and both parents feed the young, from the bill and by regurgitation. Breeding commences in early spring; the birds are monogamous and form permanent pairs. An integral part of the breeding cycle is a group display, in which up to a dozen males chase a single female in rapid, close flight, eventually disappearing into cover amid loud chirruping. Because of the volume, these displays are often called 'sparrow parties'. The display lasts up to a minute and stimulates the female to breed.

OTHER NAMES
English Sparrow.

IDENTIFICATION
LENGTH: *140–160 mm.*
MALE: *Crown and rump dark grey; rest of upper parts dark chestnut-brown with black streaks. Wings brown with dull white bar on shoulder; tail dusky brown. Lores, throat and upper breast black forming bib; cheeks and rest of underparts light grey-white. Eye brown. Bill dusky. Feet light brown. In non-breeding eclipse, bib reduced.*
FEMALE: *Duller brown above; crown brown; buff bar on shoulder; throat and rest of underparts brown-white; bill grey-horn.*
IMMATURES: *As female but duller and mottled on crown.*

VOICE
CALL & SONG: *Noisy; variety of chirrupings such as* cherr'p *and harsh twittering.*

NESTING
Breeds in spring and summer and at other times if conditions suit, raising several successive broods in a season. Nest an untidy dome of grass, with side entrance; lined with feathers and plant down; placed in crevices in buildings, under bridges, in thick bushes and trees or in hollow limbs. Eggs: three–six; usually grey-white, blotched with brown and grey; oval, about 24 x 16 mm. Incubation 12–14 days, by female. Young fledge in 14–15 days.

DISTRIBUTION
Common throughout eastern mainland Australia to western Queensland and Nullarbor Plain, particularly in association with human habitation. Also Tasmania. Occurs naturally in Eurasia and North Africa. Eleven races; one introduced in Australia.

The male House Sparrow is the more strikingly patterned bird. House Sparrows are found wherever humans live in eastern and southeastern Australia.

The Tree Sparrow usually makes its nest in a tree hollow. Tree Sparrows resemble House Sparrows, but male and female are similarly plumaged.

Tree Sparrow *Passer montanus* (LINNÉ, 1758)

SINCE ITS INTRODUCTION from Europe at Melbourne in 1863–4, the Tree Sparrow has not spread far, reaching only western Gippsland and the southeastern Riverina, NSW, as far north as Cowra. Although not as tied to man as the House Sparrow, it still keeps to urban parks and gardens planted with exotic trees and shrubs and has not intruded into natural woods and forests.

Tree Sparrows resemble House Sparrows in appearance and habits but are slimmer, have chestnut crowns and black cheek spots in both sexes, and are more retiring. Gregarious birds, they feed in small groups on the ground and in shrubbery on seeds, insects and scraps, and at night cluster to roost in holes in trees, crevices in buildings and dense thickets. Throughout the day they chirp and chatter quietly in higher, shriller tones than House Sparrows, and deliver a simple chirruping song from a tree perch, sometimes in chorus. Flight, as in the House Sparrow, is fast and direct, on rapidly beating wings and sometimes slightly undulating.

The birds nest through spring and summer, pairing permanently. Males court their mates by bowing, spreading their wings, raising crown feathers and chasing with tails cocked. Copulation is repeated and, between each act, males hop about, without any of the soliciting from females that happens in House Sparrows. Both sexes share nest-building, incubation and the feeding of young, often rearing two broods a season.

OTHER NAMES
Mountain Sparrow.

IDENTIFICATION
LENGTH: *140–150 mm.*
ADULTS: *Sexes similar. Crown chestnut; rest of upper parts chestnut-brown streaked black. Wings and tail brown, wing coverts with two white bars. Cheek white with black spot on ear coverts; underparts grey-white with small black bib on throat. Eye red-brown. Bill black. Feet light brown.*
IMMATURES: *Duller than adults.*

VOICE
CALL: *Mixture of twittering chirrups and chirps, cherr'p. In flight a hard tek.*
SONG: *Series of chirruping chirps.*

NESTING
Breeds September–January. Nest a compact dome of grasses, with side entrance; lined with feathers; usually placed in a tree hole, in a bush or, less frequently, a crevice in a building. Eggs: four–six; glossed, brown-white

with fine dots of brown or chestnut; oval, about 20 x 14 mm. Incubation 12–14 days, by both sexes. Young fledge in 12–14 days.

DISTRIBUTION
Urban central Victoria, including Melbourne, to eastern Riverina, NSW. Natural range Europe to eastern Asia and Moluccas. Seven races; one introduced in Australia.

Diamond Finch *Stagonopleura guttata* (SHAW, 1796)

The Diamond Finch is usually seen in a group, in southeastern open woodlands. This is a male.

OTHER NAMES
*Diamond Firetail, Diamond Sparrow,
Spotted-sided Finch.*

IDENTIFICATION
LENGTH: *120–130 mm.*
MALE: *Head grey; back and wings ash-
brown; rump and upper tail coverts
shining crimson; tail black. Lores black;
throat, lower breast, belly and undertail
coverts white; black band across upper
breast, extending back along flanks
where white spots occur on upper
margin. Eye and bare eye-ring red. Bill
red-pink; base blue-tinged. Feet dark
grey.*
FEMALE: *Similar to male; lores
browner; breast band narrower.*
IMMATURES: *Mainly olive-brown above,
head greyer; rump and upper tail
coverts crimson; underparts white with
dull wash over breast and down flanks
flecked white. Eye red-brown; bill
grey-black.*

VOICE
CALL: *Drawn-out, plaintive, nasal
twooo-heee, with first syllable
descending and second ascending and
whistled; given in contact and
identification by both sexes, higher
pitched in female. Also low, snoring
calls between birds during nest relief.*
SONG: *Long series of low, rasping notes,
by male in display.*

NESTING
*Breeds August–January; in colonies of
three–12 pairs. Nest large, flask-shaped
with bulky spherical nest chamber and
entrance tunnel of variable length, 240–
300 mm long, 10–20 mm high, 120–
170 mm wide; made of long grass blades
and stems; lined with fine grass stems
and white feathers; placed in thick
foliage in mistletoe clump, eucalypt tree
or shrub up to 10 m above ground.
Eggs: four–seven; pure white; oval,
about 18 x 13 mm. Incubation 12–
15 days, by both sexes. Young fledge in
10–12 days.*

DISTRIBUTION
*Woodland and open grassland with
scattered timber in southeastern
mainland Australia, north to
Carnarvon and Expedition Ranges,
Qld, and southwest to Kangaroo Island
and southern Eyre Peninsula, SA.
No races.*

DIAMOND FINCHES, DAPPER IN white, black, grey and red, live in scattered groups of five to 40 birds, occasionally to 150, in the open eucalypt woodlands and fringing mallee of southeastern Australia. In many areas its numbers have declined, partly due to clearing of habitat and partly to trapping—for Diamond Finches are popular cage birds. Local populations through the Mt Lofty Ranges, SA, were almost exterminated by trapping in the 1950s but have partly recovered since. Others that ranged north to the Atherton Tablelands before then have apparently been wiped out.

In their habitat, Diamond Finches—unlike the firetails—feed exclusively on the ground, hopping briskly along, feet together, as they search for ripe and part-ripe seeds and occasional insects. Water and trees are always near, for drinking and for shelter. The birds drink frequently throughout the day, not by scooping but by sucking as other dry-country finches do. At dusk the feeding flocks disperse to roost, small tight groups going to dense shrubbery or to nests specially built for sleeping. Roosting nests are smaller, and built lower and closer than breeding nests, and are made of coarse green and dry grasses.

When taking wing, the finches rise with a whirring and fly strongly, straight and silent, to their trees, displaying their crimson rumps as they go. Flight is fast and direct with few undulations, on rapidly beating wings; over short distances the birds fly rarely more than a few metres above the ground, manoeuvring around trees and bushes. In large flocks they tend to fly in a long line with lead birds close together, or in a Y-formation, with the younger birds at the rear. Isolated or lost individuals often utter plaintive identity calls which other members of the flock answer.

With the coming of breeding, the loose flocks that have amalgamated through autumn and winter break up as groups leave to nest in small colonies on their own. Even there Diamond Finches are much more social than the firetails, and several nests—even a dozen or so—are often grouped in one or two bushes and trees. Defended territory extends around the nest site only.

Male courts female in an elaborate ritual. Picking up a long grass stem at one end, he flies to a high bare dead branch. The female follows and the male begins to sing his raspy song and bob. Inclining

his head forward and down, bill to breast, and fluffing his plumage to almost double his size, he begins to bounce up and down. Legs bend and straighten alternately, without feet leaving the perch. The attracted female comes close and as she does, the male bends his head down and towards her, offering his open beak and grass stem. In response, she may invite copulation by quivering her tail, there or at the nest.

This ceremony contains the themes of nest-building (the grass stem) and the feeding of young (imitation of begging), both basic elements in the courtship of many birds. Its objective is to stimulate and synchronise sexual responses in the female, which are also tuned by frequent long bouts of calling and answering between male and female early during breeding.

Each pair takes about 10 days to build its bulky nest, both sexes bringing grasses, and pausing in a nearby tree before landing at the nest site; but only the female does the weaving. The female lays her first egg before the nest is fully lined, and both parents incubate the completed clutch and later share in feeding the nestlings, sleeping with them at night in the nest. In wetter years two broods may be attempted in one season. After fledging, young birds spend about a week in the breeding area before joining a larger flock to forage wherever food sources are abundant. Many young exist as nomads during the winter months, not constructing roost nests and moving on as the food source becomes depleted.

Beautiful Firetail *Emblema bella* (LATHAM, 1801)

ONE OF AUSTRALIA'S RAREST finches, the Beautiful Firetail frequents dense stands of heathy growth around southeastern Australia, along streams, steep gullies or swampy flats where water is permanently at hand and where pockets of grassland provide feeding. It is sedentary there and not particularly gregarious. The small groups of up to a dozen or so that do consort through autumn are either parents and their young or groups of immatures that gather, pair and then disperse to find territories of their own.

Adult pairs, mated permanently, keep to a large foraging range of several square kilometres with a core breeding centre. Other birds are tolerated in the feeding but not the nesting area, particularly during breeding when they are driven off by the male. In threat, he raises and fans his tail, opens and drags his wings and hops at the intruder, sometimes following up with an aerial chase.

The pair work through their foraging range in rotation, spending several days feeding at one spot, then moving to another. With one often sitting guard, they forage mostly on the ground in both heath and fringing grassfield, staying near and under cover as they hop rapidly along in high jumps, feet together. Seeds of various grasses are picked up as they go, and flower petals and the seeds of sheoaks *Casuarina*. Occasionally the birds work up into low foliage as well, gleaning aphids, psyllids and other insects.

There is a regular daily routine. The birds fly out to feed soon after dawn, forage for several hours, then break off to drink, bathe, build and rest in roost nests through the middle hours before another bout of feeding in late afternoon. They drink often, by scooping, both from dew and pools; they bathe as well, usually immersing themselves completely. Afterwards they cluster on branchlets to preen, not only themselves but also one another.

At dusk the pair returns to sleep together in a roost nest. Flight is low, direct and arrow-like on rapidly beating wings, with few undulations; there is no flight call. The birds rise with a whirr, dodge easily among the bushes, and dive bullet-like straight into cover. Roost nests, small temporary balls of grass 130–150 mm in diameter in the middle of shrubs, one–two metres above the ground, are occupied for a few months at a time before being abandoned. Then the pair moves to a new foraging sector.

Beautiful Firetails nest late, at the beginning of summer, and usually rear only one brood a season. Courtship, desultory through autumn and winter, quickens. Low in shrubbery, the male attracts his mate with a long piece of grass, nodding his head up and down in bursts of three. When she approaches, he crouches low, leans forward, fans his tail and lowers his wings to show his crimson rump. Then, again in bursts of three, he bounces up and down in long, arching bobs and sings a strange, cricket-like *caw,* open-billed, at each bounce. The female responds by hopping closer with tail towards him but without any of the quivering of other finches. Copulation may follow there or after a quick flight into bushes.

Both sexes construct the breeding nest in 10–13 days, the male not only carrying in material from long distances but assisting in the weaving as well. By about day five the nest chamber is walled and the female continues with its lining while the male finishes the outer structure. Both parents share incubation, changing over at about 90-minute intervals during the day and signalling it by calling; the arriving bird does not enter the nest chamber until its call has been answered. At night both birds roost in the nest, the non-brooding bird sleeping in a cup-shaped vestibule in the entrance tunnel. Its droppings, and those of young which are placed there, help to give the active nest an air of dereliction.

Both parents also feed the young, flying straight into the entrance without stopping. After fledging, young—herded by the male—return to the breeding nest in the first two or three nights, then abandon it for a roost nest. For a week or so they are fed at perches under shrubbery, then gradually learn to feed themselves. Self-sufficiency comes at two weeks, but young remain with the adults for another two–three weeks before being evicted by the male. Then they move out to peripheral areas, group with other free young, pair, and begin to build their own roost nests.

OTHER NAMES
Firetail Finch.

IDENTIFICATION
LENGTH: *120–130 mm.*
MALE: *Crown, back and wings mid brown-grey, finely barred with black; rump and upper tail coverts crimson; tail brown-grey barred faintly dusky. Lores and around eyes black; underparts light grey with close black bars; centre of belly and undertail coverts black. Eye hazel; naked blue* eye-ring. Bill pink-red. Feet pink-brown. In breeding birds, plumage darkens, belly and undertail blacken, eye-ring becomes bluer and wing tips whiten.*
FEMALE: *Similar to non-breeding male; no black in centre of belly.*
IMMATURES: *Duller than adults, with indistinct bars; bill black.*

VOICE
CALL: *Mournful, penetrating whistle* weeee, *in identification. Low-pitched* cherrr-it *in contact. Alarm call a loud* tup, tup, tup, *in triplets. At brooding change-over, two or three whistle-chirped* two-eee's *or* tit-e's.
SONG: *Cricket-like* caw-caw-caw, *in triplets accompanying bob by male.*

NESTING
Breeds November–January. Nest a bulky dome, with spherical egg chamber, a long side-entrance tunnel, and cup depression adjacent to chamber; 250–450 mm long, height and width each 150–200 mm; of green grass stems overlaid with dry twigs and stems; lined with fine grass and occasionally feathers; placed in close shrubbery or branchlets within 2 m of the ground. Eggs: two–six, usually four–five; white; oval, about 18 x 12 mm. Incubation 20–22 days, by both sexes. Young fledge in about 23 days.

DISTRIBUTION
Uncommon to rare on mainland southeastern Australia, north to Hunter Valley, NSW, and west to Mt Lofty Ranges and Kangaroo Island, SA; in thick coastal belts of heath, tea-tree scrub and casuarinas not far from water; more plentiful in Tasmania and on offshore islands. Probably no races.

The Beautiful Firetail lives in coastal heathlands of southeastern Australia; it is more plentiful in Tasmania.

Red-eared Firetail *Emblema oculata* (Quoy & Gaimard, 1830)

THE RED-EARED FIRETAIL IS the most solitary of all Australian grass finches. Mated pairs establish a permanent territory; any flocking is temporary, of a few young birds or adults outside the breeding season. Found only in the southwest of Western Australia, these finches inhabit dense heath and undergrowth in heavy forest along the coast and nearby ranges where they have been adversely affected by human settlement.

Territories are generally 100–200 metres across and contain all the resources needed by occupant pairs, including water for drinking and bathing. Only the area around the nest is strongly defended. Like other firetails, Red-eareds have long bills well suited to probing and they spend much time foraging among low branches and fallen twigs. There they hop and fly with great agility, pivoting this way and that in their feeding without any of the tail flicking of other finches. Seeds of grasses and sedges are staple diet, but the birds also pick seeds from trees and shrubs and occasionally pluck insects and spiders off foliage, particularly when feeding young. Often foraging 100 metres or more apart, members of pairs keep contact with an occasional mournful identity call. Such calls, given through closed bill and often repeated in bursts, are always answered and may help to advertise and mark territory as well.

At night the pair flies to sleep together in roost nests, small unlined balls of green grass built in shrubbery and which are regularly changed. Flight then, as at all times, is low, steady and direct on quick-beating wings, with little or no undulation.

Courtship is initiated by the male high in trees. He hops between branches at the top of a tree holding a long grass stem that swings pendulum-like, and gives nest-site *oooweeee a-a-a-a* calls when he lands. Eventually he stops near the female, fluffs out his feathers and bounces up and down on the perch with his bill pointed upwards or head arched down. In reponse, the female may invite copulation by quivering her tail up and down.

Both male and female build the breeding nest, but the male only brings material. Nipping off long grass stems at ground level, he carries each to the female; she works them into the bottle-shaped structure constructing first the chamber, then the entrance tunnel and a cup-shaped vestibule. Both birds incubate, in about two-hour shifts, changing over inside the nest, and at night both sleep in the nest. Both also share caring for the nestlings, carrying off the egg shells at change-over as they hatch. After fledging, the male takes the lead in tending young for their first three or four weeks before expelling them from the territory.

In good seasons two broods may be reared in succession. Juveniles begin to moult into adult plumage six weeks after hatching and complete the process by four months.

OTHER NAMES
Red-Eared Finch, Red-eared Firetail Finch.

IDENTIFICATION
LENGTH: *120–130 mm.*
MALE: *Head, back and wings mid brown-grey finely barred with black; rump and upper tail coverts crimson; central tail brown-grey barred faintly dusky. Lores and around eyes black; crimson patch behind eye, becoming darker in breeding. Breast buff-brown finely barred with black; lower breast, belly and undertail spotted white on black. Eye red-brown; naked blue eye-ring. Bill scarlet. Feet dark brown.*
FEMALE: *Similar to non-breeding male; ear coverts duller.*
IMMATURES: *Duller than adults with no crimson ear patch or spots on belly; bill black.*

VOICE
CALL & SONG: *At least five: a mournful whistled* oowee, *singly or repeated in series for identification and contact—more quavering in female;* twit-twit *greeting on approach to nest at change-over, answered with* tweet-tit-tit-tit *from bird within nest; quickly repeated nasal* cherk *in chase; bursts of six-syllabled nasal whistles when searching for nest site; harsh clucking in alarm.*

NESTING
Breeds September–January. Nest a substantial, horizontal, bottle-shaped structure with a spherical entrance chamber and long, narrow entrance tunnel, 350–400 mm long, 160 mm high, 150–200 mm wide. Outer walls strongly built of twining green stems; inner walls of softer shorter stems lined with feathers; placed 7–15 m high in trees and shrubs. Eggs: four–six; pure white; oval, about 18 x 12 mm. Incubation 12–14 days, by both sexes. Young fledge in 21–24 days.*

DISTRIBUTION
Uncommon; in dense heath and uncleared gullies in southwest, from Darling Range to Esperance. No races.

The most solitary of the Australian grass finches, the Red-eared Firetail lives in dense heath and uncleared gullies in southwestern Australia.

Painted Firetail *Emblema picta* GOULD, 1842

Painted Firetails are found in the northern interior among rocky gorges and stony hills with permanent waterholes. In this pair the bird on the left is a male.

MAKING THE BEST OF ITS ARID environment, the Painted Firetail lives along gorges and among stony, spinifex- and acacia-clad hills through northern inland Australia. There it establishes small loose sedentary groups of five–30 birds on permanent waterholes. Pairs do not seem to hold permanent territory as other firetails do, nor are their bonds particularly close. Body contact is avoided, even during breeding, and they do not preen one another.

Never far from water, Painted Firetails drink regularly, scooping water and tilting back their heads to swallow, not sucking as most Australian finches do. Flight is strong and low with marked undulations. Long tapered bills enable the birds to probe under herbage and crannies in rocks as they feed, hopping briskly over the ground, never in bushes or seeding tussocks. Fallen grass seeds are staple diet. Communication among feeding groups is kept by

low calling which sharpens in flight. The birds do not build roost nests and at night sleep near one another in low bushes and under tussocks; even when breeding, only the female roosts in the nest.

Painted Firetails breed in small loose colonies, but without clustering their nests. They court on the ground, twisting their tails towards each other more than other grass finches do. In introduction both partners pick up and drop stems and stones. Then the male fluffs out his face and breast colours and, stretching up without bouncing, begins to sing, pivoting his head. As he does so he hops up in front of the female. Both birds wipe their bills often during the ceremony.

Both sexes bring material for the nest, the female first laying down a platform of bark, twigs and stones, then constructing a small flimsy dome upon it. Both sexes also feed the young.

OTHER NAMES
Emblema, Mountain Finch, Painted Finch, Emblema Finch.

IDENTIFICATION
LENGTH: *110–120 mm.*
MALE: *Crown dusky; back and wings mid-brown; rump and upper tail coverts crimson; tail dusky brown. Face, lores, forehead, chin and upper throat scarlet. Front of neck, breast, sides of belly and flanks black with white spots; all centre of belly scarlet; undertail black. Eye white. Upper mandible black with red tip; lower red with pale blue base. Feet pink-brown.*
FEMALE: *Face brown, scarlet only about bill; small scarlet patch on belly; more*
heavily spotted on breast and flanks.
IMMATURES: *Similar to female but duller; no scarlet on head and breast; ventral spotting smutty; bill black above, grey below with whitish base.*

VOICE
CALL: *Loud, harsh chirped* chek *or* chek-did-did-dit *for identification and contact, sometimes soft, sometimes loud, staccato and repeated, especially in flight. Loud rattling* terrait *in alarm by female; male gives louder contact call.*
SONG: *Wheezy chattering followed by long whistles,* che che che-che-che-che-werreeeee-oooeeeee, *by male with up-pointed part-opened bill. Repeated in bursts.*

NESTING
Breeding months vary, depending on rainfall. Nest globular, with open side entrance; 110 mm long, 110 mm high, 130 mm wide; of twigs, bark, rootlets and spinifex stalks, built on platform of twigs, stones and bark; inner walls of soft grass stems, lined with hairy seeds and feathers; placed near the ground in spinifex tussock. Eggs: three or four; plain white; oval, about 14 x 11 mm.

DISTRIBUTION
Locally common in rocky gorges and stony hills in northern interior, south to Everard and Birksgate Ranges, SA; erratically reaches Flinders and Gawler Ranges, SA, and the eastern Murchison
district, WA; extends to coast in Pilbara, WA. No races.

Star Finch *Neochmia ruficauda* (GOULD, 1837)

Star Finches, from the north of Australia, feed in flocks of five to sometimes 200 birds. The male (topmost bird) has more red on his face than the female.

THIS CENTURY HAS MARKED a serious decline in the Star Finch. From a range that once extended right across northern Australia to New South Wales, the bird has withdrawn almost completely to pockets in the northwest, from Arnhem Land to the Pilbara. The causes are probably disturbance to its habitat—rank streamside grass and reeds in scattered eucalypt woodland—and trapping.

Star Finches flock to feed, drink and roost, in small groups of up to 20 or sometimes larger. Apart from occasional insects taken on the wing during breeding, they feed mainly on ripe and green seeds from the heads of tall grasses. The birds rove agilely among the stems, clinging and holding down a flower spike to pick out seeds. Only when the grasses dry off do they go to ground to forage. They drink regularly at pools, by sucking, and at night they roost together in thickets; no roost nests are built. In their socialising, only members of pairs touch in contact and preen one another. The birds fly arrow-like in compact flocks, turning sharply in concert, but undulate more slowly when flying on their own.

Male or female may initiate pairing. The male confronts different females and sings until one responds, but the female flutters back and forth in front of perched males, holding a long grass stem. In courtship, the male also displays with a long green grass stem. He fluffs out his flanks and face and, twisting his tail towards the female, bobs up and down on a perch, bowing deeply between bobs and singing. Both partners select the nest-site in an elaborate ceremony, sitting on it together and simultaneously bowing deeply with their tails twisted. Then they pivot around the perch. In other aspects of their breeding they resemble Crimson Finches. Both partners share incubation and brooding, with only the female staying in the nest at night; both feed young at the mouth of the nest.

OTHER NAMES
Red-faced Finch, Red-tailed Finch.

IDENTIFICATION
LENGTH: *110–120 mm.*
MALE: *Upper parts yellow-olive; upper tail coverts dull crimson with white spots; tail dull crimson-brown. Front half of head crimson; face and upper throat crimson with white spots. Rest of underparts pale yellow-olive spotted white, plain yellow over belly and white undertail. Eye light red. Bill scarlet.*
FEMALE: *Duller than male with less crimson on head and face.*
IMMATURES: *Upper parts olive-brown; head and face grey; underparts plain pale olive, belly whiter.*

VOICE
CALL: *Loud identity call* sseet *mainly in flight; soft call* pslit *in contact while feeding or in small groups.*
SONG: *Soft, high, toneless twitter.*

NESTING
Breeds December–August; mainly March–April. Nest rounded dome with no entrance tunnel; 110 mm long, 90 mm high, 130 mm wide; of either coarse green or dried grass; lined with wool and feathers; placed in grass tussocks or in small bushes and trees 6 m up. Eggs: three–six; pure white; oval, about 14 x 12 mm. Incubation 12–14 days, by both sexes. Young fledge in about 15–17 days.

DISTRIBUTION
Brakes of rushes and tall grasses around wooded creeks and swamps in northern Australia, mainly between Gulf of Carpentaria and Pilbara, WA. Possibly two races; one extinct.

Crimson Finch *Neochmia phaeton* (HOMBRON & JACQUINOT, 1841)

KEEPING APART IN PAIRS OR family groups, the Crimson Finch rarely forms flocks. The birds fight constantly, driving one another away from perches and fencing with their bills. Even pairs do not perch touching together or preen each other. Squabbling birds erect their face feathers and fan their tails; in fights they raise one wing vertically. This aggressiveness does not extend to territory and several pairs may nest close to one another.

Crimson Finches range across northern Australia in pockets of tall wet grassland mixed with pandans and trees along streams. There they have also occupied patches around settlements with their own wells and troughs. The birds are never still, hopping up among grass stems, flitting about—but never far—and constantly twittering their penetrating identity calls. The birds accompany every move with continuous flicks of their long tapered tails; whenever they lower them they expose their bright red rumps.

Crimson Finches eat seeds of a wide variety of grasses and herbs and, during the breeding season, many insects. They rarely feed on the ground, foraging mainly high on grass stems and gathering seeds by climbing nimbly among the stalks. Although living near open water they rarely drink from it, scooping drops of dew and rain from the tips of grass blades instead.

No roost nests are built and at night the birds sleep individually on perches in thickets.

The female Crimson Finch has a special flight display with which she invites pairing, flying with deep, fluttering wing-beats to and fro between perches at a prospective nest site. Courtship is elaborate. Both birds perch close, sitting parallel with their heads and tails turned towards each other. Holding a piece of grass in his bill, the male fluffs his feathers and squats horizontally and then, as he sings, bobs up and down without bowing. Finally raising himself erect, he copulates, received with much tail quivering. He also finds the nest site, giving loud calls in enticement. The female follows and the pair settle with an elaborate nesting ceremony. They sit together bowing with head and tails turned towards each other, wiping their bills and whining loudly.

Although building mainly in pandans, Crimson Finches are also known to nest in cracks and crevices in buildings. Only the male brings material but both construct the nest. Both also incubate and brood, changing every hour or so during the day; at night only the female stays in the nest, the male roosting often well away. After being brooded for about a week, young are fed at the mouth of the nest by both parents, not inside. They are more advanced than other finches at fledging.

OTHER NAMES
Blood Finch, Pale Crimson Finch, White-bellied Crimson Finch.

IDENTIFICATION
LENGTH: *130–140 mm.*
MALE: *Crown dusky grey; back and upper wing coverts grey-olive tinged with crimson; upper tail coverts (rump) bright crimson. Centre of tail dull crimson, outer feathers dull red-brown. Whole face, throat, breast and flanks crimson, with fine white spots on flanks. Belly and undertail coverts black or white (Cape York Peninsula race). Eye brown-yellow. Bill red; base white or blue. Feet brown-yellow.*
FEMALE: *Plain olive-brown above, paler below; face, throat, rump, tail and bill crimson, duller on tail.*
IMMATURES: *Mostly grey-brown above, with rump and tail dull crimson; pale brown below. Bill dusky.*

VOICE
CALL: *Loud, penetrating sibilant chatter,* tsee-tsee-tsee-tsee-tsee, *soft and one- or two-syllabled in contact, or loud and repeated rapidly in alarm or identification.*
SONG: *Soft, rapid rasping ending in three low descending notes.*

NESTING
Breeds September–May in Queensland; January–April in Western Australia and Northern Territory. Nest a bulky dome with no entrance tunnel, about 130 mm wide, 100 mm high, 140 mm wide, of coarse grass, bark and leaves; lined with feathers; built in pandanus palm, or eaves and inside buildings when available. Eggs: five–eight; plain white; oval, about 14 x 12 mm. Incubation 12–14 days, by both sexes. Young fledge in about 20–21 days.

DISTRIBUTION
Pockets of wet wooded grassland on streams of coastal plains and valleys across north, from Kimberleys to Mackay, Qld. Also in southern New Guinea. Two, possibly three races.

A male Crimson Finch of the black-bellied form; another form is white-bellied. All females are olive-brown with crimson face, rump and tail.

Red-browed Finch *Neochmia temporalis* (LATHAM, 1801)

THE RED-BROWED FINCH or Waxbill is Australia's most familiar finch. Widespread around the eastern seaboard and now introduced near Perth, it lives in wetter woodlands and open forests, wherever there are pockets of seeding grasses and herbage. Wandering locally for food it often enters parks and gardens.

It is also much the most social of the blood finches, and the only one of them to build roosting nests, small round balls in shrubs with no tunnel entrance or lining. Red-browed Finches live in tight-knit flocks, smaller during breeding and larger afterwards; several pairs will even nest in the same bushes. Pair bonds are strong. The birds mate permanently and stay close year round, preening one another and roosting together at night in roost nests, often with several others. Flock members keep in touch with constant high-pitched calling, both while feeding and in flight.

Red-browed Finches feed on a variety of ripe and half-ripe seeds of grasses and herbs, which they supplement with fruitlets and insects, particularly when breeding. Insects are gleaned from foliage rather than caught in the air. Usually the birds forage on the ground, hopping about here and there, but occasionally they balance on swaying stalks to peck at seed heads. Feeding is broken by frequent visits to water where they drink by scooping. If disturbed, they fly off low as a group to the cover of shrubbery in strong, slightly undulating flight, flirting the tail as they land.

In courtship, the male holds a grass stem at one end and, standing stiffly erect, jumps up and down, tail pointed towards the female which sidles towards him. As they close, she throws up her head as he does. Copulation follows or the male goes into the second stage of his routine, crouching tail up and rocking up and down as he wipes his bill rapidly and sings.

Both partners share incubation and brooding by day and roost together in the nest at night. Fed inside the nest, young beg with quivering wings, a trait unique in Australian grass finches.

OTHER NAMES
Red-browed Firetail, Waxbill, Red-brow, Temporal Finch.

IDENTIFICATION
LENGTH: *110–120 mm.*
MALE: *Back and wings olive-green; rump and upper tail coverts crimson; tail dusky brown. Head mid-grey; olive-yellow patch on side of neck; lores and eyebrows crimson. Throat, ear coverts and entire underparts pale grey-buff. Eye red-brown. Top and bottom of bill lined black; sides red. Feet flesh-coloured.*
FEMALE: *As male; eyebrow thinner.*
IMMATURES: *Rump dull crimson; brow plain; underparts ash-brown. Bill black.*

VOICE
CALL: *Piercing high-pitched repeated sseee-seee accompanying most movements, in contact and alarm.*
SONG: *Simple rhythmic repetition of call note.*

NESTING
Breeds August–January in south; December–April in north. Nest flask-shaped with tunnel entrance at side, sometimes only a hood, constructed of stiff green and/or dry grass, occasionally with pieces of bark or leaves; 200–280 mm long, 140 mm high, 100–130 wide; lined with white feathers; placed mainly in bushes—often thorny—to 8 m up. Eggs: four-six; pure white; oval, about 16 x
12 mm. Incubation 13–14 days, by both sexes. Young fledge in about 15–17 days.

DISTRIBUTION
Grassy areas interspersed with dense shrubberies, in wet woodland and open forest, from Mt Lofty Ranges, SA, northwards to Cape York Peninsula on rainforest edges. Introduced in Darling Ranges, WA. Two, probably three races.

The Red-browed Finch is common along the east coast of Australia where grassy areas are interspersed with dense shrubs, even entering parks and gardens in its search for food. Nests are flask-shaped, and often placed in thorny bushes.

Plum-headed Finch *Neochmia modesta* (GOULD, 1837)

Closely related to the Star Finch, the Plum-headed Finch occurs in eastern streamside grassland. They need to drink almost hourly.

ALTHOUGH PLUM-HEADED FINCHES have declined in numbers over the past 50 years, it is difficult to estimate their status because they are so nomadic. Where they occur along the western tablelands and slopes of the Great Dividing Range in central eastern Australia they shift generally north in winter, occasionally as far as the Atherton Tableland, and south in summer, sometimes as far as the northern Riverina and Canberra. Because the birds need to drink regularly, almost every hour, drought and wet seasons can turn their movements into erratic irruptions. Plum-headeds will suddenly appear in numbers, in areas where they have not been seen for many years, and then vanish again just as quickly. Throughout their range they frequent open, lightly wooded, well grassed flats, often along streams and always near water.

Very like the closely related Star Finch in habits and behaviour, Plum-headeds live in flocks, small during breeding and in large nomadic aggregations of up to several hundred or more afterwards. Within the flocks, however, contact is only close between mated male and female and even then they only cluster and preen one another much when breeding. Pairing is permanent. The birds do not build roost nests, sleeping instead on twigs and grass stems in thickets. Cohesion within flocks is kept by much contact calling. Smaller flocks are sometimes rather silent, but larger gatherings keep up a constant murmur of soft *tlips* in contact while feeding.

These change to a chorus of louder, long-drawn *pyiiits* when birds stray and flocks take wing. The birds fly in compact groups with strong, slightly undulating flight, and usually rise up into the higher open branches of trees when disturbed.

Plum-headed Finches feed on or near the ground on ripe and part-ripe seed, hopping quietly along, feet together, or skilfully climbing grass stems to pluck seed heads. A bird pulls one head down, then another with its bill, then holds them in its feet as it proceeds to pick out the grain. To drink, the birds alight on grass stems over water and bend down their heads to sip water.

Plum-headed Finches engage in a typical song-and-dance courtship ceremony. The male holds a grass stem in his bill and perches near the female. He twists his tail towards her, bobs up and down on the spot and sings a few phrases of his song. He then drops the stem and fluffs out his belly feathers and sings with his bill wide open and pointing down. Between song phrases he constantly wipes his bill and shakes his body. The female eventually responds with tail quivers which signal the male to mount.

Both sexes bring material for the nest, the female undertaking the bulk of construction. Both also take turns in incubating and brooding by day, although only the female sleeps in the nest at night. Brooding finishes within a week or so, after which both parents feed the young inside the nest until they fledge.

OTHER NAMES
Cherry Finch, Diadem Finch, Plum-capped Finch, Plumhead.

IDENTIFICATION
LENGTH: *105–115 mm.*
MALE: *Upper parts and wings all mid brown-olive; rump and upper tail coverts barred white; wing coverts and inner flight feathers tipped white. Tail black. Top of head, forehead and chin claret-red; lores black; ear coverts white streaked brown; cheeks white. Underparts white with thin brown-olive bars from throat to sides of belly; centre belly and undertail plain white. Eyes dark brown. Bill black. Feet pink-brown.*
FEMALE: *Duller than male on face; no*

claret-coloured chin; white line above eye.
IMMATURES; *No claret-red head markings; underparts white with almost no bars. Adult plumage gained at first annual moult several months after fledging.*

VOICE
CALL: *Loud tinkling whistle* pyiiit *in identification and flight; soft murmured* tlip *in close contact.*
SONG: *Very soft high-pitched chirping and gargling trills which become louder and more flute-like towards end.*

NESTING
Breeds September–January in south; August–March in north. Nest a small

round, laterally compressed chamber of mostly green grass, with side entrance but not tunnel, 110 mm long, 130 mm high, 75 mm wide; with or without feather lining; placed in tall grass stems where some blades built into nest walls; also found in thick bushes, usually close to ground. Eggs: four–seven, usually five or six; pure white; oval, about 17 x 12 mm. Incubation about 12–14 days, by both sexes. Young fledge in about 21 days.

DISTRIBUTION
Savannas along low tablelands and western, less often eastern slopes of Great Dividing Range, north to Townsville-Atherton, Qld, south to Lachlan valley, NSW, and Canberra;

favours grass, reeds and bushes along margins of creeks and rivers. Seasonally nomadic. No races.

Zebra Finch *Taeniopygia guttata* (VEILLOT, 1817)

MIDDAY STILLNESS IN Australia's interior is often broken by the nasal, twanging *tiah-tiah* of Zebra Finches as they feed in flocks on the ground, drink, or hop about in sheltering shrubbery through the hot hours. The smallest and most widespread finch in Australia, they range across dry short grasslands and fields of spinifex studded with shrubs and small trees. The grass provides grain food and the thickets shelter and nest sites.

Centred in Australia's arid zone, Zebra Finches have adapted to dry environments in various ways. Their metabolic rate is lower than in other finches, reducing water turnover and loss. They also excrete less water in their faeces and can drink brackish water not tolerated by other birds. Like most seed-eating birds, however, they need to drink regularly, preferably every hour or two. Because of this Zebra Finches live sedentarily close to pools and watering points; the establishment of these for stock and irrigation has probably increased their numbers and range at least several-fold in the present century. The birds drink by immersing their faces in the water and sucking.

Zebra Finches are social birds, living in close-knit flocks of 10–100 or more year round and even staying together when breeding. Individual pairs may have their own nest bush, but where habitat is limiting, up to a dozen or so will build in the same shrub. Pairs mate permanently and stay close all year, roosting together and with others in communal roost nests—either old breeding nests or small round unlined structures built specially.

The flocks feed during much of the morning, hopping about on the ground, feet together, picking up fallen seeds, mostly of grasses.

Sometimes they reach up to pluck overhanging seed heads but never hold the stalks in their feet. Insects are also taken— particularly to feed young—caught in shrubbery, on the ground, and in flight. Mostly in late afternoons each flock gathers around a central watering point, flying in groups in their fast, direct slightly undulating flight. There they drink, bathe, huddle together on perches and preen one another to restore social bonds.

A three-stage courtship, usually on bare twigs, leads to copulation. Male and female begin by dancing about one another, the male without a grass stem and both wiping their bills and twisting their tails towards one another. Then the male approaches his stilled mate in a rhythmic pivoting dance, singing with open bill. At the end, the female crouches and invites mounting by quivering her tail up and down.

The female chooses a nest site from several potential ones selected by the male by sitting in it, then both begin to build, the male bringing material and the female constructing, forming first a platform, then the walls and roof, and finally the entrance tunnel. Nests are finished in one to two weeks. The female lays eggs at daily intervals, beginning incubation with the next to last. Both sexes brood in one- to two-hour shifts by day, calling to one another to change outside the nest; both sleep in the nest at night.

Fledged young are led back to the nest to roost at night until abandoned by their parents. They are independent at 10 days, gain adult plumage in nine–10 weeks, and are able to breed then. To cope with their environment, Zebra Finches breed opportunistically and continuously, halted only by drought and winter cold.

OTHER NAMES
Chestnut-eared Finch.

IDENTIFICATION
LENGTH: *About 100 mm.*
MALE: *Head grey; back and wings plain grey-brown; rump white. Tail and side coverts barred black and white. Face white, with black tear-marks; cheeks rusty. Throat and upper breast pale grey barred finely black; flanks russet spotted white; belly and undertail white. Eye, bill and feet orange-red.*
FEMALE: *As male but cheeks, throat, breast and flanks plain grey-white; bill paler.*
IMMATURES: *As female, but eye grey-brown, bill black, feet grey.*

VOICE
CALL: *Nasal twang, tiah, often in flight. Soft, repetitive* tet *in close contact; hissing* wsst *in chases.*
SONG: *Harsh, nasal trill in series of phrases, each one–two seconds.*

NESTING
Breeds in most months. Nest flask-shaped with spherical nest chamber 120–200 mm in diameter, and a side entrance tunnel, 50–250 mm long, of grass stems; lined with feathers and down; built in twigs of bushes and low trees, occasionally in hollows or on ground. Eggs: four–five (–seven); pure white; oval, about 15–11 mm. Incubation about 12–14 days, by both sexes. Young fledge in about three weeks.

DISTRIBUTION
All dry wooded grasslands. Also Lesser Sunda Islands. Two races; one in Australia.

Zebra Finches are common in all habitats except wet coastal forest, and have adapted in various ways to their arid environment. The male, with a pale chestnut ear patch, is at left.

The Double-barred Finch occurs in small pockets of grassy woodland where there are thickets for shelter and surface water for drinking.

Double-barred Finch *Taeniopygia bichenovii* (VIGORS & HORSFIELD, 1827)

WIDESPREAD IN THE BETTER-WATERED grassy woodlands of northern and eastern Australia, the Double-barred Finch is one of the few birds that seems to be expanding in the settled southeast. Since the turn of the century it has reached the New South Wales coast on a broad front and the Murray River along the western slopes of the Great Dividing Range. Everywhere it occurs in local pockets, with thickets for shelter and streams and pools for drinking. Like the Zebra Finch it needs to drink regularly, even hourly, and not being a strong flier, never lives far from water. It drinks standing at the edge of pools, immersing its face and sucking.

Double-barred Finches are also as highly social as Zebra Finches, grouping in small flocks of up to about 40 birds, or usually less, year round. Members greet one another during the day by bowing with twisted tails and opening and shutting their bills quickly. The groups are so close-knit that component pairs—which mate permanently—rarely stand out until breeding. All feed and drink together, huddle and preen one another on twigs in bushes and low branches, and sleep together at night, up to six at a time cramming into a tiny, domed, unlined roost nest specially built for the purpose in thickets. Even during breeding contact is kept, several pairs often nesting in the same bush. Afterwards the groups sometimes join with others in larger, locally nomadic flocks of several hundred or more, but usually only under drought conditions and rarely for long.

The birds feed mostly on the ground, hopping energetically about picking up the fallen seeds of grasses and herbs and jumping up to pull down and pluck half-ripe grain from overhanging seed heads; stalks are not held down with the feet. Many insects are also taken, gleaned from foliage and the ground rather than caught in flight. If disturbed, Double-barred Finches flit up to the nearest thicket for cover, hopping and jumping about, and uttering nasal squeaks to signal identity and keep contact. Agitated birds constantly flick their tails in a semi-circle.

Courtship is inconspicuous and subdued with no dancing nor stem-holding by the male. Instead the male simply fluffs himself into a ball, crouches on a perch by his mate, bodies parallel, and begins to sing and bill-wipe over and over. As song develops he hops towards the female, body pivoting from one side to the other in the manner of Zebra and Masked Finches.

Both sexes contribute to the nest, the male bringing most of the material while the female constructs. Sometimes they take over and renovate derelict nests of other birds, such as babblers. Both also incubate, changing over at rather long two- to three-hour intervals during the day; they sleep together in the nest at night. Young beg with active head movements and, after fledging, hold up one wing when being fed to shield off their siblings.

OTHER NAMES
Black-rumped Double-bar, Banded Finch, Bicheno Finch, Black-ringed Finch, Double-bar Finch, Owl-faced Finch, Ringed Finch.

IDENTIFICATION
LENGTH: *100–110 mm.*
MALE: *Crown to mid-back mid brown-grey with fine black barring; upper rump black; lower rump and upper tail coverts white in eastern race, black in northwestern race. Wings black, finely spotted white. Tail black. Face and upper breast white-cream; thin black ring from forehead above eye, around face and across lower throat; another thin black bar across lower breast. Lower breast and belly cream; undertail black. Eye dark brown. Bill blue-grey. Feet slate-grey.*
FEMALE: *As male; black barring often narrower.*
IMMATURES: *Duller than adults; barring indistinct above and below, and upper parts tinged olive-grey.*

VOICE
CALL: *Short low nasal* tat *in close contact; longer, louder nasal* tiaat *in identification, alarm and flight; high-pitched squeaking at nest.*
SONG: *Soft repetitive sequence of nasal identification notes.*

NESTING
Breeds mostly spring and autumn in southeast, extending through summer; June–November in Queensland; January–March in northwest, towards end of wet season when seeding grasses abound. Nest almost spherical, 140 mm long, 120 mm high, 90 mm wide, with short side-entrance tunnel; of dry grass stems, coarser outside, finer inside; lined copiously with feathers in east or plant wool in northwest; in twiggy branchlets in small shrubs and trees or, occasionally, stumps and hollows at 1–4 m above ground. Eggs: usually four or five; plain white; oval, about 16 x 11 mm. Incubation about 12–14 days, by both sexes. Young fledge in about 21 days.

DISTRIBUTION
Small pockets of grass, thicket and surface water in woodland and open forest around coastal and near inland northern and eastern Australia, from Kimberleys, WA, to Murray River, NSW. Range extends towards southeastern coastal regions where bird has adapted to human settlement. Two races: one black-rumped in northwest; one white-rumped in east; intergrade around Gulf of Carpentaria.

Masked Finch *Poephila personata* GOULD, 1842

LIVING IN CLOSER GRASSY woodland and open forest than other grass finches across northern Australia, Masked Finches shelter during the hot part of the day in the shade among branches of tall eucalypts. They spend most of their time feeding on the ground on the fallen seeds of grasses, eating a wide variety of ripe and half-ripe seeds, and supplementing them regularly with the insects that make up the bulk of their diet during the breeding season. Many insects are caught in flight. Masked Finches drink by sucking, and like Long-tailed and Black-throated Finches hang to reach water inaccessible to other small birds. They drink in the mornings and evenings and may congregate in flocks of hundreds, even thousands, with other finches there. They flick their tails sideways when excited.

Masked Finches are social, grouping in loose colonial flocks of 10–20 during the breeding season, and in slightly larger bands in the non-breeding season. Sexual partners are closely associated in the flock and, towards the breeding season, become even closer. During the day the birds come together at a certain tree, but do not head-bob as Long-tailed and Black-throated Finches do. As each pair arrives they welcome one another with chattering calls, and quiver their tails up and down. Each bird preens its mate, and then they swap partners. After some

time the pairs re-form and fly back to their nests. In this way each member of a colony restores bonds. At night pairs cluster to roost in small round unlined dormitory nests, low in trees and bushes, using the same one for up to a year.

The birds court in the topmost branches of all eucalypt trees. Bending their tails towards each other, the partners dance back and forth along a branch while the female gives loud *tiat* calls. She then stops and quivers her tail up and down, emitting high-pitched copulation calls. The male continues to dance, then sings for a short period, after which he mounts. Courtship normally begins again immediately and multiple copulations follow.

The male Masked Finch searches for possible nest sites, and when he has found one, hops back and forth with short, loud, whining calls. The female selects the final site and the two set about building the nest, one ferrying material and weaving as much as the other and taking several weeks to finish it. Both sexes incubate, beginning with the laying of the fourth egg, and both brood the young for nine–12 days, relieving one another inside the nest chamber. Young are reared on a mixture of seeds and insects and although independent within a week of fledging, may be fed by their parents for several weeks more. Only one brood is reared a year.

OTHER NAMES
Masked Grass Finch, White-eared Finch, White-eared Grass Finch.

IDENTIFICATION
LENGTH: *130–140 mm.*
MALE: *Head, back and wings deep sandy brown; upper rump with black bar running down across flanks; lower rump and upper tail coverts white. Tail black and shortly pointed with attenuate central feathers. Forehead, lores, front of face and chin black. In northwestern Australian race, ear coverts, breast and flanks sandy buff; lower belly to undertail white. In Cape York Peninsula race, Poephila personata leucotis, ear coverts and mid-flanks white; breast pink-buff; belly and undertail white. Eye brown. Bill buff-yellow. Legs red-orange.*
FEMALE: *Similar to male; black face mask smaller.*
IMMATURES: *As adults but much duller brown, suffused grey; face mask partly grey. Bill and feet black. Adult plumage gained at first annual moult, about three months after fledging.*

VOICE
CALL: *Soft nasal* twet, twet, *repeated between birds in close contact when feeding and preening; loud, nasal chirp* tiat *in identification and contact between individuals and groups at distance, often in flight or when landing; a hissing* wsst *in aggressive chases, to which chased bird responds with high, plaintive 'fear' note, also given in alarm; male selecting nest sites for female whines rapidly in enticement.*
SONG: *Loud, rapid, sharp nasal notes in monotone, with few inflections. Both calls and song have a toneless quality resembling those of Zebra and Double-barred Finches.*

NESTING
Breeds March–June, after the wet monsoon when grass seeds drop. Nest flask-shaped, 110–160 mm long, 100–130 mm high, 110 mm wide, with bulky and globular chamber entered by short side-entrance tunnel; of long dead grass stems elaborately interwoven; lined with plant fibre, feathers and sometimes fur; pieces of charcoal frequently added to nest chamber by both sexes; placed in bushes and trees or grass at 2–8 m above the ground. Eggs: four–six; pure white; oval, about 17 x 12 mm. Incubation about 13–14 days, by both sexes. Young fledge in about 22 days.

DISTRIBUTION
Moderately common in closely wooded grassland across northern Australia, from Kimberley Division, WA, to Cape York Peninsula, Qld. Two races: one Poephila personata leucotis in Cape York Peninsula; the other P.p. personata across rest of north and northwest, east to head of Gulf of Carpentaria.

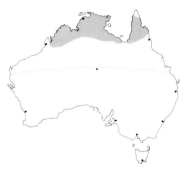

This is the white-eared race of Masked Finch, which is found on Cape York Peninsula.

Long-tailed Finch
Poephila acuticauda (GOULD, 1840)

The Long-tailed Finch lives in dry savanna grasslands, especially along creeks, in northwestern Australia.

THE LONG-TAILED FINCH is restricted to tropical northwestern Australia, where it is common in savanna grasslands, especially in and around eucalypts along creeks and rivers. There the dainty birds are easily identified by their black bibs and high-pitched flock and identity whistle, which seems to hang in the air as it is given from a perch.

Long-tailed Finches drink by sucking, reaching for water that would be inaccessible to most birds. They can draw off drops of dew from blades of grass and catch drops of falling rain; they can even suck water while hanging upside down. The birds drink in the mornings and evenings only.

Long-tailed Finches are highly social, forming small, loose sedentary colonial flocks of 10–15 pairs. Like Black-throated Finches they bob the head up and down a few times when they land. When one bird alights near another they perform their most conspicuous bobs, accompanying them with a soft cackling. This ritual seems to be in appeasement, preventing any agonistic behaviour from developing. At night the birds sleep in pairs in small, round, unlined roost nests high in tree foliage.

Long-tailed Finches eat mainly ripe and half-ripe seeds that have fallen to the ground; occasionally they jump up and pull spikes of seeds. They sometimes hawk out to pick off flying insects, including termites and ants, especially during breeding.

Long-tailed and Black-throated Finches have the strongest pair-bonds of all Australian finches. Male and female are always together, never more than a metre apart on the ground, and almost as close in flight, as they dash in direct whirring flutters between ground and trees. When landing in a tree they greet each other with a series of head bobs and cackles and, bibs flared, follow this with mutual preening. One bird invites its mate to preen by pointing its bill skyward and exposing and fluffing out the black throat patch. The partner responds and after a few minutes the pair reverse roles. Only mated birds preen in this way and the process is thought to strengthen the pair-bond.

Courtship is elaborate. On about one third of occasions, it is preceded by a vertical dance performed by the male. He holds a long grass stem in his bill and bobs up and down on his perch, turning his tail towards the female and sometimes singing a few phrases. The female is attracted and courtship proper begins. Both birds perform a long horizontal dance, hopping around each other among the twigs at the top of a tree, bobbing their heads, wiping their bills and bowing and pivoting. Stopping suddenly, the male sings a few song phrases with bib flared and the female crouches and invites mounting with quivers of her tail. After copulation the birds greet each other with head bobs, bows and loud cackles.

As with the Black-throated Finch, the female picks a nest site from many proposed by the male. Both contribute to the nest, the male bringing mostly loose grass from the ground and the female weaving it in. Both also share incubation and brooding, changing over at one–two hour intervals during the day in the entrance to the nest and feeding the young by regurgitation with a mixture of green seeds and insects—for protein. At night all sleep in the nest until young fledge.

Nestlings are brooded for nine–12 days and, although soon independent, remain with their parents for another three weeks after fledging. Up to three broods are reared in a season.

Black-throated Finch *Poephila cincta* (GOULD, 1837)

NOT ONLY RESEMBLING THE Long-tailed Finch in appearance and behaviour—but for its rounded tail—the Black-throated also lives in similar habitat: open timbered grasslands with continuous and often deep sward and sparse but often tall overtopping eucalypts and paperbarks. The two species represent each other geographically, the Black-throated replacing the northwestern Long-tailed in the northeast, from northern New South Wales to Cape York Peninsula. There it occurs in two intergrading races, one black-rumped north of the Burdekin Valley and the other white-rumped to the south. The black-rumped race is abundant but the white-rumped has declined markedly since the turn of the century and withdrawn northwards. It is all but extinct in New South Wales.

Black-throated Finches live in loose sedentary flocks of 10–30 which may breed throughout the year as a dispersed colony. The flock is social and often drinks, bathes, rests, clusters and allopreens together, but the pair or family is the basic unit and the pair bond permanent. Both partners keep sexual rivals at a distance. Mates greet each other throughout the day with cackling and profuse head-bobbing, their bibs fluffed out, and spend much time on high bare perches preening one another's heads. The nodding greeting is derived, in an evolutionary sense, from the bobbing courtship of other Australian finches.

Much of the day is spent feeding on the ground on ripe and part-ripe grass seeds. Mostly the birds eat fallen seed but they also often jump up, pull down a spike, and clamp it to the ground with one foot while they pluck out the seeds. Insects are a small but regular part of their diet—often caught in midair—and spiders and ants are occasionally picked up as well. The birds drink—by sucking—at irregular intervals during the day and often only twice, morning and afternoon.

In courtship there is no tail twisting and no stem carrying, except by young males. Both sexes begin by hopping to and fro between two high, bare branches, bobbing their heads as they alight and wiping their bills. When the female stops, the male—with bib fluffed out—starts to hop-dance towards her, bowing often, head bobbing constantly and singing or not. She crouches and quivers her tail, inviting copulation which is brief. After it both birds bow, bob and cackle in a way matched only by the Long-tailed Finch.

The male selects nest sites by flying from the female to one site, then another, whining and bowing on them—until she settles on one. It is confirmed when they sit together at it. Building begins within hours, the male bringing the bulk of the material and the female weaving it in. Both sexes incubate and brood, changing over every hour or so in the nest entrance during the day; both sleep in the nest at night until young fledge. Afterwards all roost in round dormitory nests.

Young are brooded in the nest until nine–12 days old and fed by regurgitation on half-ripe seeds and insects. They become independent within about two weeks of fledging but remain with their parents, even as they raise one or two more broods in a season.

OTHER NAMES
Parson Finch, Diggle's Finch, Black-rumped Finch, Black-tailed Finch, Black-throat.

IDENTIFICATION
LENGTH: *120–130 mm.*
MALE: *Head blue-grey; back and wings fawn-brown, black bar on rump extends across lower flanks; upper tail coverts black in northern race, white in southern; tail black. Lores black; ear patch blue-white. Throat and upper breast bib black; lower breast, belly and flanks cinnamon-fawn; undertail white. Eye dark brown. Bill black. Feet orange-red.*
FEMALE: *Similar to male; black throat patch slightly smaller.*
IMMATURES: *As adults but duller.*

VOICE
CALL: *Loud, harshly whistled* teeweet *in identification; soft* tet *in conversational contact; hissing* wsst *in chases.*
SONG: *Soft flute-like squeezing notes in series of phrases, ending in long mournful whistle.*

NESTING
Breeds all months; mainly autumn in north and spring in south. Nest flask-shaped with long side-entrance tunnel, of dead grass stems; 250 mm long, 140 mm high, 110 mm wide; lined with down, feathers and occasionally charcoal; in outer eucalypt twigs and also hollows, termite mounds and base of hawk nests 1–15 m up. Eggs: four or five; oval, about 17 x 12 mm. Incubation 12–14 days, by both sexes. Young fledge in about 21 days.

DISTRIBUTION
Woodland savanna through northeastern Australia between Cape York Peninsula and Dumaresque River, NSW, where rare. Three races.

The Black-throated Finch lives in woodland savanna where water is available. It eats mainly grass seeds.

Pictorella Mannikin *Heteromunia pectoralis* (GOULD, 1841)

Pictorella Mannikins live in northern Australia, where they visit the drier inland parts of their range after the summer rains.

AMONG THE OLD-WORLD TROPICAL mannikin finches, the Pictorella stands apart in its adaptations to dry, open habitat. Across northern Australia it frequents the more arid acacia-dotted savannas of the near inland, even ranging into spinifex. Although the birds may drink once or twice a day, water is not necessarily close. They are nomadic and irruptive, following food, but as a rule disperse south and inland during the summer wet season and concentrate north towards receding coastal waters in the dry. They mix then in large flocks of several hundreds with other finches, flying in dense swarms and chipping in a shower of calling.

Pictorellas climb expertly up and down grass stems for seeds like most mannikins, but nonetheless feed mainly on the ground like grass finches. There, hopping about, they pick up a range of fallen grass grains or reach up to pluck overhanging heads. They also take many insects both in the air and on the ground, particularly during the wet season when insects are abundant and growing young need protein. To drink, Pictorellas scoop quickly, tilting their heads up to swallow in rapid succession. This may help the birds keep watch for predators; whereas other grass finches have perhaps solved the problem by sucking, Pictorellas have coped by speeding up conventional sipping. At night they roost in tussocks or thickets; no roost nests are built.

With the coming of the wet season, Pictorellas disperse inland in small groups to breed. As in Painted Finches, male courts female on the ground. After preliminary ground-pecking from both partners, the male holds up a straw by one end, fluffs his feathers, fans his tail and commences to dance and sing in an arc in front of his mate. Gradually he closes until he is hopping up and down just in front of her. Then he drops the stem, stands beside her and bows towards her, tail fanned, only to step around behind her to the other side to repeat the performance. Bowing and singing continues until the female invites copulation by quivering her tail.

Both sexes incubate and brood, changing in regular shifts by day; only the female sits in the nest at night.

OTHER NAMES
Pictorella, Pictorella Finch, White-breasted Finch, Pictorella Munia.

IDENTIFICATION
LENGTH: *110–120 mm.*
MALE: *Upper parts warm grey-brown; wing coverts finely spotted white; rump and tail duskier. Face and throat glossy black edged around ear coverts with pale cinnamon-buff. Breast white flecked black; belly and undertail coverts pale purple-buff. Eye dark brown. Bill pale blue-grey. Feet flesh coloured.*
FEMALE: *Throat and face brown-black; breast more heavily flecked black.*
IMMATURES: *Plain dull grey-brown, lighter below. Bill dusky.*

VOICE
CALL: *Communication call sparrow-like chip. Loud identity call* tlit.
SONG: *Undeveloped. Soft, nasal, bisyllabic* g'ee, *repeated two seconds apart.*

NESTING
Breeds January–May, in late wet season. Nest untidy bottle-shaped with vestigial side-entrance tunnel; 250 mm long, 120 mm high and 120 mm wide; of dry grass stems and twigs; little lining; placed in low bushes or tussocks of spinifex, close to ground. Eggs: four to six; plain white; oval, about 16 x 11 mm. Incubation by both sexes.

DISTRIBUTION
Drier northern tropical grasslands, from Kimberleys, WA, to Gulf of Carpentaria. Nomadic. No races.

The Chestnut-breasted Mannikin breeds in dense colonies and builds a spherical nest close to the ground. They are common in wet grassfields.

Chestnut-breasted Mannikin *Lonchura castaneothorax* (GOULD, 1837)

A TYPICAL REED FINCH, the Chestnut-breasted flocks in groups of up to several hundred birds. They bunch into tight-flying packs, calling and executing all manoeuvres in rapid unison. They also feed, drink, rest, sleep and sing together; fighting is rare and ritualised. Yet they do not preen one another and never build roost nests, clustering instead to sleep in brakes of reeds. Bonds and coherence in flocks are kept by 'jingling' and peering.

Chestnut-breasted Mannikins inhabit banks of rank grasses and reeds on the margins of swamps, mangroves and rivers around northern and eastern coastal Australia. There they are locally nomadic, more so in the northwest than the east. They have adapted well to cultivation, even becoming pests on crops.

They mostly eat half-ripe grass seeds, gathered while clambering nimbly among seeding stems, one foot after the other. They land among the upright stems, reach out for a laden spike, pull it down and clamp it with one foot while they pick out the seeds. Finishing one spike they begin on the next until four or five stripped stalks collect under their feet. At the start of the breeding season they also catch flying termites on the wing. Drinking is by scooping, the birds tilting their heads back to swallow.

Courtship is typical of the mannikin finches, without any grass stem being held by the male. In mannerisms varying from bird to bird, the male first performs a song-and-dance ritual on grass stems. He ruffles head, breast and rump feathers, points his bill downwards—holding it wide open when whistling loudly—and dances up and down, often shaking his body and wiping his bill. Approaching the female slowly, he stops singing and sits beside her. Both fluff their belly feathers, turn their tails towards each other, and bow a number of times. Copulation follows.

The birds breed in dense colonies with the small nests only a few metres apart. Nest-building, incubation and rearing resembles those of other Australian grass finches, both sexes sharing all duties but only the female sleeping in the nest at night.

OTHER NAMES
Chestnut-breasted Finch, Barley Bird, Barley Sparrow, Chestnut Finch, Chestnut-breasted Munia.

IDENTIFICATION
LENGTH: *110–115 mm.*
ADULTS: *Sexes similar. Crown and back of neck flecked grey-brown; back and wings russet; upper tail coverts and central tail feathers straw-brown; outer tail feathers brown. Face, chin, throat and undertail coverts black; breast pale chestnut with lower edge bordered black (this band sometimes narrower in female); belly white with flanks barred black. Eye brown. Bill blue-grey. Feet leaden-grey.*
IMMATURES: *Olive-brown above; pale buff below with brown-buff breast.*

VOICE
CALL: *Bell-like* teet *or* tit, *in contact.*
SONG: *Long (12 seconds) toneless phrase of four spaced segments: clicks, harsh notes in two series, whistles at end.*

NESTING
Breeds all months; mainly summer and autumn. Nest spherical, compressed at sides, somewhat resembles a bottle on its side with neck sloping downwards; *130 mm long, 120 mm high, 90 mm wide; of dry blades of grass; lined with fine grass stems; built within 2 m of ground, in dense clumps of grass and reeds, some worked into nest; also bushes. Eggs: four–six; white; oval, about 17 x 12 mm. Incubation 12–13 days, by both sexes. Young fledge in 21–22 days.*

DISTRIBUTION
Rank grasses, reeds fringing rivers, swamps and mangroves around coast, from Kimberleys, WA, to Nowra, NSW. Also New Guinea. About five races; probably one in Australia.

Yellow-rumped Mannikin *Lonchura flaviprymna* (GOULD, 1845)

THE RATHER RARE AND BEAUTIFUL Yellow-rumped Mannikin was first discovered by naturalists of HMS *Beagle*—the famous ship that carried Charles Darwin—on its voyage of exploration along the northwest coast of Australia in the late 1830s. Today the bird still occurs only on swampy, well-grassed flood plains there, centred on the Ord, Victoria, Daly and upper Roper Rivers.

Despite its distinctive appearance, the Yellow-rumped is very closely related to the Chestnut-breasted Mannikin. It seems to have evolved from ancestral Chestnut-breasted stock after colonising the northwestern river systems at some time in the past. Since then its range has been re-invaded by Chestnut-breasted Mannikins. Both Yellow-rumped and Chestnut-breasteds now mix freely there, feeding, bathing, roosting and breeding together.

In any mixed flock, Chestnut-breasteds usually outnumber Yellow-rumpeds at about two to one. They also interbreed with them, about 10 per cent of pairs being obviously mixed. Almost 50–60 per cent of birds that look like Yellow-rumpeds show in fact some Chestnut-breasted marks, usually a darkened face and a hint of a dusky band on the lower breast. These marks also seem to develop with age: birds that appear to be 'pure' Yellow-rumpeds when young become part-Chestnut-breasted as they grow older. It is a problem for bird dealers trafficking—now illegally—in these increasingly rare mannikins.

If the Yellow-rumped interbreeds so freely with the Chestnut-breasted, why should they be treated as a separate species? The point is that interbreeding may not be so free. Unlike the cases of the White-cheeked Rosellas, Black-eared Miners and Australian Magpies—in which almost every bird in the hybrid zone shows traits of mixed parentage—nearly 50 per cent of the Yellow-rumpeds appear to be 'pure'. This, at least, is the indication of present evidence. Furthermore, their calls are deeper and aspects of behaviour differ slightly, notably in courtship.

Along the northwestern rivers, the Yellow-rumped Mannikin is sedentary or somewhat nomadic, tending to congregate on the more permanent coastwards swamp fields in the dry season and dispersing further inland in the wet when rain spreads the growth of grasses. In general it tolerates drier habitat than the Chestnut-breasted.

It is highly social at all times. Mixing in flocks of up to 100 or more with Chestnut-breasteds, it flies in tight-packed bands, fast and straight with wings whirring, turning sharply this way and that in perfect co-ordination, then landing in the same habitat from which it rose, a sward of grass. On their own the birds fly more like grass finches, with slight undulations.

Yellow-rumped Mannikins feed on the ripe and part-ripe grains of a variety of grasses; *Echinochloa colonum, Chloris virgata,*

Sehima nervosum, Panicum zymbirforme and *Oryza sativa* all contribute to their diet. The birds climb adeptly up and down grass stems, feet moving alternately as in walking or running. Alighting on stalks just below a seeding spike, they proceed to pick out the grains; then, as they finish, they pull the spike down underfoot and proceed with the next. In this way up to four or five empty spikes collect under the birds' feet. During breeding they also catch flying insects such as termites.

Feeding routines are broken, as in the Chestnut-breasted Finch, with drinking, bathing and socialising. Although they do not preen one another, members of groups restore their bonds by peering at one another and 'jingling', males often singing in duets and trios perched along grass stems. Pairs do not stand out in the groups. To drink, the birds perch on the edge of water and scoop, tilting their heads back to swallow. No roost nests are built and at night the flocks sleep clustered on perches in brakes of reeds.

In preliminaries to courtship, male and female hop to and fro around one another on horizontal perches, holding grass stems in their bills. Then, dropping his stem and calling sharply, the male lands in front of the female. He ruffles his whole plumage and starts to bob up and down, body erect or horizontal, and bill open and pointing down as he sings all the while. Between each bob he wipes his bill vigorously once or twice on the perch and as he concludes he pivots his head from side to side. Copulation follows bowing and tail-twisting from the female. Overall, the performance is more exaggerated than that of the Chestnut-breasted Mannikin, with more bill-wiping and fluffing of plumage.

Nesting in the latter half of the wet season when food abounds, Yellow-rumpeds can rear two broods in quick succession. Both parents incubate, brood and feed the young, but only the female sleeps in the nest at night, the male roosting nearby on stems of reeds. Young are fed on a mixture of half-ripe seeds and insects.

OTHER NAMES
Yellow-tailed Finch, White-headed Finch, Yellow-rumped Finch, Yellow-rumped Munia.

IDENTIFICATION
LENGTH: *110–120 mm.*
ADULTS: *Sexes similar. Crown pale grey; back and wings cinnamon-brown; rump, upper tail coverts and central tail feathers golden straw; edges of outer tail feathers brown. Face plain cream-buff, becoming fawn-buff over breast and belly; undertail black. Eye dark brown. Bill and feet pale blue-grey.*
IMMATURES: *Rump dirty yellow; back*

and throat dark brown; underparts buff-grey.

VOICE
CALL: *Bell-like* teet, *short versions for communication, louder, longer ones for identity signals.*
SONG: *Protracted. Introduced by rhythmic clicks of the bill, followed by harsh toneless phrases* weeee-weeee-teuu-teuuu-cheeonk-cheeonk-ching-ching, *and ending with long drawn-out whistles,* weeeeee, *as in Chestnut-breasted Mannikin. Each phrase preceded by silent mandibulation.*

NESTING
Breeds January–March. Nest spherical, compressed at its side entrance without a tunnel, 30 mm long, 120 mm high, 90 mm wide, of dry blades of grass; lined with fine grass stems and feathers; placed in tussocks of grass and reeds, the stems of which are often interwoven into the nest. Eggs: four or five; white; oval, about 17 x 12 mm. Incubation about 12–13 days, by both sexes. Young fledge in about 20–22 days.

DISTRIBUTION
Uncommon; on riverine grass plains from eastern Kimberleys, WA, to western Arnhem Land, NT; centred on Victoria and Ord River systems. During wet season moves south into drier country where it breeds. No races.

The highly social Yellow-rumped Mannikin lives in river grasslands in northwestern Australia.

Nutmeg Mannikin *Lonchura punctulata* (LINNÉ, 1758)

OTHER NAMES
Spice Mannikin, Nutmeg Finch, Rice-bird, Spotted Munia, Nutmeg Munia.

IDENTIFICATION
LENGTH: *110–120 mm.*
ADULTS: *Sexes similar. Crown, back, wings and rump rich brown with faint pale shafting. Tail and upper tail coverts grey-yellow. Throat dusky chestnut; rest of underparts white heavily scalloped dark brown. Eye brown-red. Bill and feet blue-grey.*
IMMATURES: *Pale brown above; dull yellow-brown below with no scalloping.*

VOICE
CALL: *Soft* chp *in contact; loud, variable* kit-leeee *in identification; sharp* tret-tret *in alarm.*
SONG: *Almost inaudible; soft descending notes followed by high flute-like whistles and bill rattles, ending with a long descending whistle.*

NESTING
Breeds in colonies, all months in northeastern Queensland; spring and summer in south. Nest a sphere with large chamber and short side entrance tunnel, 170–220 mm long, 170–200 mm high, 120–150 mm wide, of green grass and leaves; in foliage of shrubs and trees. Eggs: four–seven; pure white; oval, about 17 x 12 mm. Incubation about 12–13 days, by both sexes. Young fledge in 20–22 days.

DISTRIBUTION
Introduced and established on east coast between Cooktown, Qld, and Sydney; inland on Darling Downs. Natural range Pakistan to Sulawesi and Lesser Sundas. Twelve races; one in Australia.

The Nutmeg Mannikin is an introduced species, which first became established in the 1930s, in Brisbane. Its range is extending, and Nutmeg Mannikins are now one of the most frequently seen birds along the Queensland coast.

ONE OF THE MOST ABUNDANT birds along the east coast of Australia today, the Nutmeg Mannikin inhabits long grasses and rank herbage along roads and river banks, and the cane fields and crops around farms. Several dozen will pass flying straight and fast in tight formation, only to suddenly make a perfectly co-ordinated turn and descend into long grass, where they completely disappear from view. It is behaviour characteristic of mannikins.

Native to southeastern Asia, Nutmeg Mannikins have been introduced to Australia, first at Brisbane in the late 1930s, then at Sydney in the 1940s and later at Townsville and Rockhampton, in 1950 and 1954 respectively. Most if not all releases have been of aviary birds. Their spread in the north has been dramatically fast; in 1960 they were established around Cairns and Mackay and through most of the country in between, and by 1961 they had reached Cooktown. In the south they have moved more slowly, their breeding restricted to longer cool winters. It took them 20 years to reach Grafton from Brisbane, and around Sydney they are still localised. Rural rather than urban habitats are colonised.

An ability to eat seeds of almost any grass and herb and to breed continuously underlies their success, particularly north of the Tropic of Capricorn where nesting is almost year round. And it makes them potentially overwhelming competitors against native finches in tropical grasslands. Like other mannikins they climb nimbly among stalks in pasture to glean grain from grass- and herb-heads. Few insects are taken and young are fed almost exclusively on half-ripe seeds; the birds do, however, scavenge for scraps around farms and garbage dumps, and some populations have taken to picking at the flesh of road-killed animals.

Nutmeg Mannikins are extremely social, feeding, flying and sleeping in small to large but always close-knit groups. They call incessantly in contact, perch touching together to preen one another, and 'jingle' and peer. Tails and sometimes wings are flicked sideways constantly. Males not only sing in courtship but 'jingle' at any time, on their own, in duets or trios. Both sexes, young and old, peer, flying up to a solitary bird and staring in its face. It seems to strengthen group bonds. At night the birds cluster to sleep in special roost nests in bushes and trees, as many as 15–20 cramming in at a time.

Courtship begins with both partners picking up and dropping small pieces of grass as they zigzag back and forth around each other between small branches. The male then lands near the female, drops his grass stem, wipes his bill a number of times and assumes posture for singing. He ruffles the feathers of his head and belly and lowers his tail, bobs up and down, and pivots his whole body from side to side. As he does so, he keeps his level bill partly closed, only opening it widely to pour out the louder notes at the end of the phrase. This upright posture alternates with bends and twists of his body towards the female. At the end, the female invites him to mount by quivering her tail.

Even during breeding, Nutmeg Mannikins remain social, nesting in dense colonies in trees and shrubs fringing their feeding grounds and rearing brood after brood in succession. Nests sometimes touch one another but are usually about three metres apart and well camouflaged. Both sexes share nest-building, incubation, breeding and the feeding of young as other grass finches do, passing on food by regurgitation. Young fledge in about three weeks.

Gouldian Finch *Erythrura gouldiae* (GOULD, 1844)

A pair of the common black-headed form of the Gouldian Finch. The male, in front, has the brighter plumage.

BOLD COLOURING HAS BROUGHT the brilliant Gouldian Finch fame as a cage bird and misfortune in the wild. Once widespread through the grassy subcoastal woodlands of northern Australia, from the Kimberleys to Cape York Peninsula, it has now withdrawn from nearly half its range. The colonies around the Gulf of Carpentaria and on Cape York Peninsula have almost gone. Even in the Kimberleys and Arnhem Land, where it is still locally common in savannas dotted with tall trees around permanent waters, the flocks of thousands that flourished 50 years ago have dwindled to tens and hundreds. The causes may be trapping for the bird trade and too-regular firing of feeding grounds.

Gouldian Finches feed on a range of seeding grasses, not on the ground but by climbing and clinging to vertical spikes to pick out grains as mannikins do. They are also expert at catching flying ants in midair and during breeding become almost entirely insectivorous, feeding young on a protein-rich diet. Following their food, Gouldian Finches are partly migratory. In the winter dry season they shift coastwards as grasses die off inland, then follow the rejuvenating rains back in the summer wet to breed.

Like most mannikins, Gouldian Finches are social birds, living together in small to large flocks. If flushed, they fly as a group to the very tops of nearby trees to sit and hop about with blue rumps conspicuously displayed and tails flicking deeply up and down. They also join in daily bouts of sun-bathing and drinking at pools; drinking is by sucking. There is no huddling or allo-preening, however, nor do they sleep together in roost nests.

Pairs court on horizontal twigs in the middle of trees. The male may hold a grass stem in pre-play but soon drops it. Fluffing his head and breast and raising his tail to highlight his colours, he sits in front of the female and bows and shakes, moving his bill rapidly to and fro over the perch and occasionally wiping it. Then he jerks quickly erect and, tail depressed, begins a whisper song with bill held down and head swinging from side to side. After repeats, male and female fly to the nest and copulate inside.

Gouldians are the only Australian finches to nest exclusively in hollows in trees or termite mounds. They are poor nest-builders—putting together only the rudiments or not even that—but they do nest socially in loose colonies. Up to six pairs will nest in a single tree, some in the same hollow together. Each rears two or three broods a season. Both parents incubate and brood in shifts, relieving one another inside the nest; only the female sleeps in the nest at night. After fledging, young may retain their juvenile plumage for six months or more, even breeding in it.

The less often seen red-headed form of the Gouldian Finch.

The Blue-faced Finch lives in northeastern rainforests and mangroves. These nomadic birds are uncommon in Australia, and rarely seen.

Blue-faced Finch *Erythrura trichroa* (KITTLITZ, 1833)

NO MORE THAN AN OUTLIER, the Australian range of this Melanesian finch is limited to the rainforests of northeastern Queensland, from eastern Cape York Peninsula to the Atherton Tableland. Like other finches, Blue-faceds are seed-eaters, yet they find their food not in grassland but in rainforest trees, shrubbery and glades within the forest, in both middle and upper strata. Insects are picked up there too. If the birds do feed on grass seeds and other herbage it is only at the forest edge, close to cover. Seeding bamboo is favoured and, following it, the finches are nomadic, both locally and regionally. Movements tend to oscillate between tablelands over summer and coastal lowlands through winter. Because of this and their small numbers in the northeastern rainforests, they are rarely seen.

Blue-faced Finches are social birds, like the related mannikins, but are not so communal as some finches. Flocks of up to 20 or 30 —both juveniles and adults—sometimes amalgamate after breeding, but usually the birds occur as small groups of three–five or six, or even just a pair. They fly with the swift directness of mannikins through the forest mid-strata, co-ordinating their movements in unison. Although they do not cluster on perches to touch and preen one another, groups do build roost nests into which they cram to sleep at night.

Courtship is elaborate. The male approaches his mate on hori-zontal twigs, singing, his body erect and tail twisted towards her. She responds by bending her tail towards him while he hops up and down. Then she flies off, uttering her loud identity trill, and he gives chase singing as he goes. Each time he lands besides her she flies off again, repeating it up to 20 times before allowing him to approach. The entire ritual, as in all courtship, serves to synchron-ise the responses of the partners for copulation. Eventually the female invites mounting by quivering her tail and emitting a series of soft calls. Copulation follows, the male grasping his mate's head feathers seemingly roughly in his bill.

Soon after mating the pair begins to search for a nest-site together. The male calls the female to one after another until she settles on one by sitting on it. He joins her and then leaves to return with a strand of fibre or moss to cement the choice. Both partici-pate in making the nest, the male bringing most of the material and the female working it in. Both also take shifts in incubation and brooding but in a rather irregular manner. Often the female broods for most of the day and at night both sleep in the nest.

Young are not fed for at least 24 hours after hatching, until two iridescent turquoise nodules develop at either side of the gape of their bills. These luminous markings help to guide feeding parents to their mouths in the dark interior of the nest. Young Gouldian Finches also have these nodules.

OTHER NAMES
Blue-faced Parrot-finch, Tricoloured Parrot-finch.

IDENTIFICATION
LENGTH: *120–130 mm.*
MALE: *Upper parts and wings grass-green, the outer flight feathers dusky; rump and upper tail coverts dull crimson; tail olive-brown edged with dull scarlet. Face and forehead cobalt-blue. Underparts all light grass-green with golden-olive tinge on thighs. Eye dark brown. Bill black. Feet brown.*
FEMALE: *Slightly duller than male; less blue on head.*
IMMATURES: *Dull green all over,* including face, paler greyer-green below; bill dusky grey.

VOICE
CALL: *Communication call a short, high-pitched single reedy chirp; identity call a low trill.*
SONG: *Two series of high-pitched trills, followed by a single whistle that falls then rises at the end. Soft and spaced out.*

NESTING
Breeds November–April, in wet and pre-wet season. Nest pear-shaped or rounded with side entrance near centre of one side, 250 mm long, 150 mm wide, 150 mm high, of moss, fern rootlets, fungus and vines, or plant down; lined with soft grasses; placed in foliaged forks in trees and shrubs, usually within a few metres of the ground but sometimes up to 7 m or more. Eggs: three or four; pure white; oval, about 18 x 13 mm. Incubation 12–14 days, by both sexes.

DISTRIBUTION
Uncommon in Australia; in grassy glades in rainforest along coastal plains and foothills of northeastern Queensland, between Helenvale and Ravenshoe on tablelands and adjacent coast. Also in New Guinea, Celebes, Moluccas, Solomon Islands, Caroline Islands, New Hebrides and Loyalty Islands. Ten races; one in Australia (and New Guinea).

Metallic Starling *Aplonis metallica* (Temminck & Laugier, 1824)

AUSTRALIA'S ONLY NATIVE STARLING, this bulging-red-eyed bird arrives along the tropical northeast coast of Queensland each August–September to breed. Most—but not all—leave again in March and April for winter quarters in New Guinea. Their presence is brief but conspicuous, for they are colonial birds and travel in big noisy flocks. Fruiting rainforest trees—and orchards—draw them from all directions to feed and groups come and go all day long. At any one time several hundred or more shuffle about on the foliage, picking fruit and often knocking off as much as they eat. Although the starlings glean and sally after occasional insects and rifle nectar, fruit comprises 95 per cent of their diet.

Replete birds sit out in lines on branches, sunning themselves, picking at one another and jockeying for position. All the while they keep up a constant wheezy chattering to maintain contact and identity. At dusk and at times during the day, they fly back to breeding colonies or roosting sites which are sometimes street trees or overhead wires. Flight is swift and direct, the flocks hurtling through and over rainforest, calling as they go.

Breeding colonies can number thousands. They festoon their bulky nests from the branches of a single huge rainforest tree, often an emergent on the edge of a clearing, to which they return year after year. Under it a thick layer of excreted seeds, decomposing nests and other debris builds up in time, augmented by branches that sometimes break off under the weight of the nests. Flocks come and go in a day-long stream, making a deafening noise. Each pair may raise two, perhaps three broods in a season.

OTHER NAMES
Shining Starling, Australian Shining Starling, Glossy Starling.

IDENTIFICATION
LENGTH: *210–240 mm.*
ADULTS: *Sexes similar. Glossy black with green reflections and purple iridescence of crown, nape, upper back and upper breast. Neck feathers long, spiky; tail long, tapered. Eye orange-red. Bill and feet black.*
IMMATURES: *Back glossy black; underparts white with black streaks. Before gaining full adult plumage they develop a black breast band.*

VOICE
CALL: *Jumble of nasal, metallic wheezes, chants and chattering.*
SONG: *Short, canary-like trilling and fluting.*

NESTING
Breeds August to December–January, in colonies. Nest globular and bulky, tapered above, with a side entrance sometimes extended into a spout, 250–500 mm long x 200–250 mm wide, made of tendrils; lined with strips of palm leaf; hung in dense packs from branches of isolated tall rainforest tree.

Eggs: *two or three, rarely four; glossy pale blue- to green-white, freckled with red-brown and purple-grey, particularly at larger end; oval, about 30 x 21 mm.*

DISTRIBUTION
A breeding migrant from Cape York to Repulse Bay, Qld; straggles farther south, occasionally to Sydney region. Mainly in lowland rainforest and its fringes and occasionally mangroves, but visits gardens for cultivated fruit. Also in Moluccas and Banda arc through New Guinea to Solomons. Five races; one in Australia.

A pair of Metallic Starlings at their nest. These starlings nest in dense colonies, in some of which thousands of nests hang from the branches of one tree.

Common Starling *Sturnus vulgaris* LINNÉ, 1758

ALONG WITH THE HOUSE SPARROW, the Common Starling is one of Australia's most familiar introduced birds. Releases at Melbourne in the late 1850s were followed at Hobart in 1860, Brisbane in 1869–70, Sydney in 1880 and Adelaide in 1881. Between 1880 and 1900 it had reached Eyre Peninsula and Kangaroo Island and by 1926 had occupied all rural areas of New South Wales.

Although starlings are occasionally recorded north to about Innisfail, tropical climate has halted its spread from Brisbane. The main movement is west, to uncolonised Western Australia. So far the few birds that have crossed have been destroyed by authorities, including 2000 at Nullarbor Station in 1980–81.

In Australia, Common Starlings frequent rural and urban habitat, where pasture, lawn and clearing allow them to feed, and trees and buildings provide shelter and roosting. They avoid heavy forest. Gregarious birds, they swarm in large flocks through autumn and winter and sleep at night in thousands in communal roosts—in a bushy tree or under the eaves of a building or bridge.

The birds feed mainly on the ground, standing erect and walking jerkily. Working in groups they probe the ground for insects—beetles, weevils, earwigs and larvae—and spiders, worms and molluscs that make up about half their diet. Much of the rest is fruit, the birds causing considerable damage in soft fruit orchards.

With the coming of breeding the flocks break up into pairs which themselves sometimes nest in loose colonies. Males advertise by singing and wing-waving on vantage perches, and pairing follows earlier bouts of chasing. To solicit copulation females crouch slightly and droop and quiver their wings.

Common Starlings nest in holes of any kind—under eaves, on walls, in tree hollows, and in crevices in the dense crowns of palms. To buildings they bring lice and to tree hollows they bring conflict with native birds. Many of the smaller species that depend on hollows for nesting—grass parrots, kingfishers, treecreepers and owlet-nightjars—are driven out by the more aggressive and persistent starlings. As a result, their breeding success has probably been held in check. The starlings, though, rear one, often two broods a year; both sexes share incubation and feeding of young.

This Common Starling has new plumage; the speckles are feather tips, which wear off, leaving black plumage.

OTHER NAMES
European Starling, Starling, English Starling.

IDENTIFICATION
LENGTH: *210–230 mm.*
ADULTS: *Sexes similar; female slightly duller. Black all over with green and purple iridescence except for brown wash on wings and tail. In new plumage (autumn), speckled buff above and white below over black. Speckles (feather tips) wear off by beginning of spring breeding, leaving even glistening black plumage. Eye brown. Bill yellow (breeding) to dull brown (non-breeding). Feet dirty brown.*
IMMATURES: *Grey-brown above, slightly paler below, throat off-white; gape flesh-yellow.*

VOICE
CALL: *Harsh, rasping tch-cheer, in alarm; also sharp dik or chik-ik-ik by squabbling birds.*
SONG: *Prolonged series of wheezes, clicks and rattles, interspersed with long descending whistles and much mimicry of other birds' calls.*

NESTING
Breeds mainly August to December–January. Nest untidy cup, of grass, twigs, leaves, feathers, as well as man-made materials, generally placed in tree hollow, cliff hole, crevice in building or bridge. Eggs: four–eight; pale blue; oblong-oval, about 30 x 21 mm. Incubation 10–12 days in Australia, by both sexes; slightly longer in Europe. Young fledge in about three weeks.

DISTRIBUTION
Common from central Queensland throughout southeastern Australia and Tasmania, as far west as Eyre Peninsula, SA, to fringes of Nullarbor Plain. Birds reaching southern Northern Territory and Western Australia are exterminated. Eurasian species, introduced into many parts of the world. About 11 races; one introduced to Australia, from the British Isles.

Common Mynah *Acridotheres tristis* (LINNÉ, 1766)

The Common Mynah was introduced from Southeast Asia and is now plentiful in eastern Australian cities. It scavenges in streets and parks.

INTRODUCED AT MELBOURNE FROM Southeast Asia in 1862, the Common Mynah quickly established itself and became the core for releases elsewhere. In 1883 they were introduced to the cane fields of northeastern Queensland—ostensibly to combat insects—and soon spread locally, reaching the Atherton Tableland. Releases at Sydney and Toowoomba followed, covering metropolitan areas there and at Brisbane by the 1940–50s. Two releases in Tasmania, one in 1900 and another in 1955 at Launceston, both failed, as has another in Adelaide in the late 1950s. Canberra fared better—or worse—where since the late 1960s the bird has established itself in central southern suburbs. Today mynahs are common in most urban centres along the eastern Australian seaboard, but have remained there without spreading far into rural countryside.

Common Mynahs are scavengers of urban parks, gardens and streets. Walking, hopping and strutting along, they poke into nooks and crannies on the ground and in buildings and gutters, and sort through refuse, eating almost anything: insects, scraps, fruit and vegetable matter. They even catch and eat fledgling sparrows, and are a nuisance in market gardens, picking off seedlings.

They forage by day in scattered pairs or small family groups and rest often, perched on poles or roof tops. At night they congregate to sleep in noisy communal roosts under bridges, in dense trees or within the rooves of large empty buildings; several thousand birds may be involved, creating serious nuisance.

Common Mynahs mate for life and, breeding in holes, compete with native birds for nesting hollows on the edges of settlements. As breeding progresses, the size of communal roosts fall as the birds disperse to nest and females become occupied with incubating and brooding; smaller temporary roosts even form. The birds leave the roosts earlier then, and arrive back later, kept away by the demands of food for nestlings as well as themselves. The birds fly to and fro with easy, direct, round-winged flapping flight.

OTHER NAMES
Indian Myna, Calcutta Myna, Myna.

IDENTIFICATION
LENGTH: *230–250 mm.*
ADULTS: *Sexes similar. Head, neck and throat dark chocolate brown with green sheen. Rest of upper parts deep fawn-brown; wings duskier, with large white oval in flight feathers conspicuous in flight; tail dusky, tipped white. Breast and flanks lighter fawn-brown; centre belly to undertail white. Eye yellow; dull yellow patch of bare skin behind and around. Bill and feet pale yellow.*
IMMATURES: *Duller, ragged-looking.*

VOICE
CALL: *Mellow liquid note on taking flight; harsh* scairr *in alarm.*
SONG: *Raucous creaks, growls and rattles strung together and mixed with loud* o-kik, o-kik, *at roosts and perches.*

NESTING
Breeds mainly October–March. Nest untidy, of grass, leaves, feathers and rubbish placed in a hollow tree limb, hole in building, under bridge or in thick vegetation. Eggs: three–six, usually four or five; glossy pale blue; oblong-oval, about 31 x 22 mm. Incubation by female.

DISTRIBUTION
Most cities and towns of east coast, from Mossman, Qld, to Ballarat, Vic., and some subcoastal centres. Natural range Turkestan to India, Andamans and Ceylon. Two races; one introduced to Australia.

Figbird *Sphecotheres viridis* VIEILLOT, 1816

A male Figbird of the eastern race. Males of the northern race have yellow underparts.

FIGBIRDS ARE BULKY orioles that have warty buff face skin that reddens in excitement, eat fruit exclusively, and build very flimsy nests. They are also colonial, living in small groups even when breeding and gathering in large flocks of 20–50 or more afterwards. In Australia they range around the north and east coast, and keep to gallery monsoon forest, pockets and edges of rainforest, and parks and gardens, wherever their food plants occur: figs, native cherries and raspberries, ink-weed, lantana, tobacco-bush and bananas, pawpaws, guavas and mulberries in cultivation. Following their foods, the flocks are locally nomadic, but rarely travel far.

Figbirds are arboreal and pick all their fruit from branchlets in the crowns of trees and shrubs. Flocks are noisy and active and concentrate on a single tree until they virtually strip it, birds even hanging upside down on the ends of twigs to get at the last fruit. They will also swing upside down from perches during rain squalls to bathe. Immatures predominate in the larger flocks, older birds keeping to their own smaller, more sedentary groups.

Figbirds usually breed in pairs, although extra males may bring food to the nestlings and brood them. Both parents share incubation and feeding as well. Fruit is regurgitated and held momentarily in the bill before being passed on.

OTHER NAMES
Southern Figbird, Northern Figbird, Green Figbird, Yellow Figbird, Grey-breasted Figbird, Banana-bird, Mulberry-bird.

IDENTIFICATION
LENGTH: *280–290 mm.*
MALE: *Head glossy black, with buff to red naked face skin. Rest of upper parts yellow-green; flight feathers black edged grey-green; tail black, tipped broadly white on outer feathers. Chin to belly plain yellow (northern race) or chin and breast deep grey, extending around collar and belly green-yellow; undertail white. Eye red-brown. Bill black; nostrils flesh. Feet flesh-buff.*
FEMALE: *Upper parts olive-brown streaked darker; face skin grey; underparts white, streaked brown.*
IMMATURES: *As female; no tail tip.*

VOICE
CALL: *Emphatic, downslurred whistle,* tchieuw *or* see-tchieuw, *repeated erratically; loud* scluk.
SONG: *Mellow* tu-tu-heer, tu-heer, tu-heer *and squeaky notes.*

NESTING
Breeds October–February. Nest a light saucer of vine tendrils and a few twigs; slung from a horizontal fork near end of a branch usually fairly high. Eggs: usually three; shades of dull green, with brown and purple spots; oval, 32 x 24 mm. Incubation by both sexes.

DISTRIBUTION
Humid coastal districts of northern and eastern Australia from near Derby, WA, to Illawarra district, NSW. Also New Guinea, Timor, Wetar and Kai Islands. Six races; two in Australia.

A female Figbird with her chicks in their flimsy saucer-shaped nest. The females of both races look similar.

The Yellow Oriole builds a cup-shaped nest of bark fibre and other plant matter, and fastens it to a thin horizontal fork in the outer branches of trees.

Yellow Oriole *Oriolus flavocinctus* (VIGORS, 1827)

THE CARRYING BUBBLING CALLS of the Yellow Oriole echo along the vine-forested streams of northern Australia in the hottest hours on most days. Sedentary birds, established males sing sporadically throughout the day year round to mark territory. One bird may call from a sheltered perch inside the tree canopy for up to two hours at a time, almost non-stop.

Yellow Orioles are birds of gallery rainforests and monsoon vine thicket, particularly those lining permanent, running streams. Solitary or in pairs, they feed almost exclusively on fruit in the middle and upper strata of the forest, keeping within the shelter of the canopy. They work slowly and methodically, feeding and sitting in one tree for several hours or more before flying off to another 100 or

more metres away in direct, deep undulations. Apart from bursts of protracted singing, they are quiet birds and easily remain neither seen nor heard amid blending foliage.

The female undertakes most of the incubation and brooding, but both parents feed the young, mainly on fruit and by regurgitation. After fledging, family groups remain together for a few weeks, then young are dispersed. In the months that follow they can wander rather widely, entering marginal habitats such as mangroves, paperbark galleries and gardens, and they often follow streams inland. At such times small groups of six or eight will gather with adults in profusely fruiting trees, particularly at the end of the dry season when resources are short.

OTHER NAMES
Yellow-bellied Oriole, Green Mulberry.

IDENTIFICATION
LENGTH: *260–280 mm; male larger.*
MALE: *General plumage bright moss-green, yellower on belly and undertail coverts; plumage finely streaked black, from a few streaks on foreparts to more all over; mantle always heavily marked with broad arrow-shaped streaks. Primaries black; secondaries and upper wing coverts black, edged and tipped with pale lemon-yellow to white; tail feathers black, edged with olive and tipped with lemon-yellow; central tail feathers browner than others. Eye red. Bill dull pink-red. Feet dark grey.*

FEMALE: *Similar to male but yellower and more streaked.*
IMMATURES: *Upper parts pale green, underparts bright yellow, all coarsely streaked black. Yellow eyebrow contrasts with green streaked head. Wing and tail feathers brown. Eye grey-brown. Bill black to brown.*

VOICE
CALL: *Clear* pee-kweek; *harsh* scarab *in aggression.*
SONG: *Rich, deep bubbling* yok-yok-yoddle. *Sustained subsong of soft warblings.*

NESTING
Breeds October–March. Nest cup-

shaped, of bark fibre, grass, dried leaves and plant tendrils, bound with cobweb; lined with finer plant material; usually fastened to a thin forked horizontal branch in outer branchlets of trees, 2–20 m above ground. Eggs: two or three; light cream to pale brown, variably blotched with dark brown and grey; oblong-oval, about 34 x 23 mm. Incubation mainly by female.

DISTRIBUTION
Coastal northern Australia and offshore islands from Sarina to Normanton, Qld, and from Broome, WA, to eastern Arnhem Land. Also in southern New Guinea and on Aru Islands. Two or three races; one in Australia.

Olive-backed Oriole *Oriolus sagittatus* (LATHAM, 1801)

WIDESPREAD ACROSS NORTHERN AND eastern Australia, the Olive-backed Oriole overlaps the Yellow Oriole throughout its range. The two, however, do not compete, because of their different needs in habitat, feeding and movements. Olive-backed Orioles are birds of eucalypt woodland and open forest, living and feeding in the upper foliagè and branches, singly and in dispersed pairs, in much the same way as the Yellow Oriole does in vine forest.

Olive-backed Orioles are mainly fruit-eaters but do take insects, all gleaned from outer foliage and twigs: leaf beetles, ants, mantids and caterpillars. In their movements, the birds are much more nomadic than Yellow Orioles, and in the southeast even migratory.

Those south of about 27°S shift north to central and northeastern Queensland in autumn and south again in spring to breed. Strays from these movements sometimes reach the Mt Lofty Ranges, SA. Flight is swift, silent and undulate through tree tops.

Established pairs sing regularly to one another throughout the year; it may help to maintain bonds. The female builds the nest in up to 14 days and then incubates; the male merely makes brief visits prior to hatching. Both parents feed the young, by regurgitation. In plentiful seasons, the male may later take over care of the fledglings while the female nests a second time. Young are dispersed almost as soon as they become independent.

OTHER NAMES
'Green Thrush', Oriole, Cedar Bird.

IDENTIFICATION
LENGTH: *250–280 mm.*
MALE: *Upper parts from head to scapulars and rump rich olive-green with very faint black streaks. Wings and wing coverts dusky, the feathers broadly edged and washed mid-grey. Tail mid-grey, the outer feathers narrowly to broadly tipped white. Chin grey-green streaked black, grading into white underparts clearly marked with short black streaks. Eye orange-red. Bill dull brick-red. Feet leaden grey.*
FEMALE: *As male but more clearly streaked on back and more coarsely streaked below; also slightly smaller.*
IMMATURES: *Dull olive-brown above, often with faint russet wash on grey wings; faint buff eyebrow; tail tips buff; underparts dirty white, heavily and coarsely streaked dusky. Eye red-brown; bill dusky.*

VOICE
CALL: *Rolling, mellow, bubbled* olio *or* orry-ol *in contact. Harsh scolding note.*
SONG: *Extension of contact calling, a rippling rolling, carrying* olly-olly-olly-o-lol *and variations. Shallower, less resonant, and more protracted than in Yellow Oriole. Also subsong of scratchy warbles and mimicry.*

NESTING
Breeds September–January. Nest deep and cup-shaped, of bark strips, leaves, grass, wool, or other soft plant material; suspended by rim from thin fork in outer foliage of tree or shrub. Eggs: two–four; cream, spotted and blotched with grey and brown; oval, about 32 x 22 mm. Incubation about 17–18 days, by female. Young fledge in 15–17 days.

DISTRIBUTION
Eucalypt woodlands and open forests— infrequently rainforest pockets— of coastal and near-inland northern and eastern Australia, from Broome, WA, to southeast of South Australia, with outliers about Adelaide. Also southern New Guinea. Two races, both in Australia: one across north to Cape York Peninsula; the other through east, north to foot of Cape York Peninsula.

A male Olive-backed Oriole bringing food to its chicks. The nest is a deep cup-shaped structure of bark strips, grass and wool, suspended by the rim from a thin fork in the outer foliage of a tree.

Spangled Drongo

Dicrurus bracteatus
GOULD, 1843

OTHER NAMES
Drongo, Fish-tail, Drongo-shrike, King-crow.

IDENTIFICATION
LENGTH: *300–320 mm, including 140 mm tail.*
ADULTS: *Sexes similar; male larger. General plumage glossed metallic black with indistinct blue-green spangles or iridescent spots on head, neck and breast; green reflections on wings and tail. White fleck-barring on undertail. Long tail forked, with upturned outer tips. Eye red. Bill and feet black.*
IMMATURES: *Head and nape dull black, spangled with metallic blue; back, rump and wings dull dusky; tail black edged with blue; cheeks and underparts dull black.*

VOICE
CALL: *Harsh, metallic chattering or cackling; a tearing shshashashash while perched and in flight.*
SONG: *Brief metallic chattering, hissing and twanging, with interwoven mimicry.*

NESTING
Breeds September–March. Nest open, shallow or saucer-shaped, of vine tendrils, plant stems and various fibres; attached to slender horizontal fork of thickly foliaged tree, up to 25 m above ground. Eggs: three–five; pale pink to purple-grey, spotted and streaked with red and purple; long-oval, about 29 x 21 mm. Incubation by both sexes.

DISTRIBUTION
In rainforest, vine scrub and fringing open forest and mangroves, from Kimberleys to Arnhem Land, and from Cape York Peninsula to northeastern Victoria; accidental in western New South Wales, Tasmania and South Australia. Also Moluccas, New Guinea, New Britain, Solomons and Lesser Sundas. About 13 races; one in Australia.

The Spangled Drongo is distinguished from other black birds by its curling forked tail and strange metallic calls.

DRONGOS, IRRESPECTIVE OF VERNACULAR connotations, are sleek birds of the Old World tropics, only one of which reaches Australia: the Spangled Drongo in the rainforests and marginal woods around the north and east coasts. A heavy, bristled bill, tapered wings, fish-forked tail and small, weak feet fit them for one particular life style, that of catching insects on the wing.

Working singly or in pairs, they sally out from set perches through the middle forest strata, flying in gracefully tight aerial manoeuvres, circling, banking, weaving and hovering. Many insects are picked and gleaned from foliage and more on the wing, most of them large and hard-shelled: beetles, cicadas, grasshoppers, dragonflies and mantids. On perches the birds are much less able. After landing—usually on an exposed bare branch from which they can see and launch easily—they usually rest and wait, tail hanging, before darting off to resume the hunt.

Drongos are sedentary in northwestern Australia but nomadic and part-migratory in the east. A core breeding population along the coast of Queensland disperses both north and south in March–April after nesting. Travelling in bands of 10–30, most move north to southern New Guinea, then return to breed in October–November. A few others drift south over winter, however, reaching the Victorian border; still others remain stationary year round.

Breeding birds usually display near the nest before copulating. The male alights in the tree close to the nest-building female, wipes his bill several times, approaches in weak hops and pecks at her feet and body. She wing-quivers, then flies closer to the nest to crouch and quiver again. The male follows, perching beside her, and gives her a peck, then hops to the other side and pecks again. Several repeats may precede mounting, accompanied by wing-beating from both birds. Both sexes incubate, brood and feed the young.

Golden Bowerbird *Prionodura newtoniana* De Vis, 1883

OTHER NAMES
Golden Gardener, Newton's Bowerbird.

IDENTIFICATION
LENGTH: *230–250 mm; male larger.*
MALE: *Head, chin, back and wings
yellowish olive-brown, with short
glistening yellow crest and patch on
mantle; flight feathers duskier. Tail
long, forked, with central tail feathers
dusky olive, three outermost pairs
orange-yellow. Underparts rich golden
to orange-yellow with opalescent sheen.
Eye yellow-white. Bill olive-brown with
pale under base. Feet black.*
FEMALE: *Head, upper parts, wings and
tail dull olive-brown; underparts ash-
grey with faint throat and breast
streaks.*
IMMATURES: *Like female but eye deep
brown. Immature males don adult
plumage starting gradually on the back;
mature in three years.*

VOICE
CALL & SONG: *Breeding male utters soft,
far-carrying wheezing croaks,
churrings and mechanical chatterings
throughout day; also mimics. Female
utters similar sounds; less animated.
Otherwise silent, or harsh rasp when
feeding.*

NESTING
*Breeds September–January, to
beginning of monsoonal wet season. Nest
a compact, rather deep, coarsely
constructed cup of dry leaves, twigs and
strips of bark, bound with rootlets and
vine tendrils; lined with finer leaves,
rootlets and twigs; placed in tree hole or
tree fork 1–3 m above ground, distant
from bower, in deep forest. Nest 160 mm
across, 110 mm deep, with cup 90 x
60 mm. Eggs: usually two, sometimes
one; slightly lustrous, cream; oval,
about 36 x 25 mm. Incubation by female.*

DISTRIBUTION
*Mountain rainforests above 900 m from
near Cooktown to Paluma Ranges,
north of Townsville, Qld. No races.*

A male Golden Bowerbird; the female is dull olive-brown above, ash-grey below. They live in mountain rainforests.

THIS, THE SMALLEST OF THE bowerbirds, builds the biggest bower for its nuptial displays. Occurring only in the montane, mist-draped rainforests of northeastern Queensland above 900 metres, it is Australia's representative of a group of maypole-building bowerbirds found in the mountains of New Guinea. The Golden Bowerbird, however, builds not one but two towers of sticks. It is perhaps the sort of structure from which both maypole and avenue bowers—as built by Satin and Spotted Bowerbird groups—have sprung in the course of evolution.

On a sloping hillside the male builds twin towers around two saplings about a metre apart. These are bridged by a low branch or buttress on which he displays to females. The towers are one–three metres high, and usually unequal; the twigs that form them are glued with saliva and adorned with moss, grey-green lichens, green and white flowers and fruit.

The birds live in loose clans, with as many as 10–15 in 40–50 hectares. Each is the property of a single nuptially plumaged male or several uncoloured males that come and go. Holding them year after year, adult males defend their bowers and tend them through most months, constantly refurbishing and adding to the structure.

During breeding, males spend much of the day perching watchfully in trees over the bower, giving intermittent pulsating buzzes and churrs which probably serve to identify themselves and ownership. Like most bowerbirds they are polygynous and mate with itinerant females. To attract females a male displays in his bower in glittering performances that highlight his glistening yellow plumage, unique among bowerbirds. On the display perch he hops from side to side, jerking his head, flaring his short crest and sometimes fanning his tail, breaking the routine by suddenly hanging and flapping his wings. At other times he hovers about the bower, body suspended vertically and tail opening and shutting to flash its brilliant margins.

Copulation may take place in the bower. After it the female leaves to build her nest unaided well distant from the bower, and incubates and rears her young alone.

In the montane rainforests of northern Queensland, Golden Bowerbirds are sedentary, even females and immatures which sometimes drift temporarily to lower altitudes in winter. They are rather solitary birds and feed actively from the upper forest strata to the floor on a variety of fruits and occasional insects.

Satin Bowerbird

Ptilonorhynchus violaceus (VIEILLOT, 1816)

IN AUTUMN AND WINTER Satin Bowerbirds leave their breeding quarters in the edges of rainforest and dense wet sclerophyll along the eastern Australian seaboard to forage in roving flocks. Bands of up to 50 or more move into nearby woodland and orchards then, raiding for fruit, shoots and insects picked from the crowns of trees and bushes. The birds travel silently and furtively, or occasionally hissing softly, flying rapidly but heavily from tree to tree.

With the coming of spring breeding, they disperse into smaller clans and return to the forests, apparently occupying the same territories year after year. In one clan territory there may be up to 20 bowers, sub-bowers and clearings on the forest floor. Each primary bower is the property of a single male, which tends and protects it through much of the year, calling from branches overhead and relaxing only through late summer and autumn. Young males are usually driven off to use communal 'practice' sub-bowers.

Main bowers are neat avenues of thin sticks woven upright into two walls aligned north–south, and usually painted black with a mixture of charcoal dust and saliva dabbed on with the bill. Platforms at both ends are decorated with flowers, feathers, berries and various man-made objects—mostly blue. A male displays actively only in the presence of females. Whenever one enters the avenue, he begins to prance and bound about stiff-legged, in exaggerated postures of begging and aggression. He flares his tail, grabs objects in his bill, flings his wings about and hisses and churrs, his eyes bulging.

Copulation takes place in the bower, with any female that visits. Females then leave to nest-build, incubate and rear young alone, well away.

The male Satin Bowerbird collects mainly blue objects to decorate his bower.

A female Satin Bowerbird; she builds a nest well distant from the bower.

OTHER NAMES
Satin bird.

IDENTIFICATION
LENGTH: *270–330 mm; male a little larger.*
MALE: *Entirely black with soft, glossy, purple-blue sheen. Eye gleaming lilac to sapphire-blue. Bill short and thick, dull blue with yellow-green tip. Feet light green-brown with yellow tint.*
FEMALE: *Head and upper parts dull grey-green with faint blue tinge. Wings dull brown to dull green on coverts, inner flight feathers often tipped white; underwing washed buff-yellow; underwing coverts barred. Tail dark grey-brown above, washed yellow below. Underparts cream to buff-white, strongly marked with crescents of dark olive-grey to dusky grey, giving spotted appearance to throat and scalloped look to breast and belly. Eye gleaming lilac-blue. Bill dark grey-brown. Feet and claws pale grey-brown.*
IMMATURES: *Like adult female, but first-year birds whiter below, with white streaks on mantle and wing coverts. Older males—from third and fourth years—become more uniformly green over breast and throat, finely marked white. Full adult male plumage attained in sixth or seventh year.*

VOICE
CALL: *Contact and alarm call a harsh, wheezing hiss. Feeding flocks may make continuous croaking sounds, explosive churrings and whirring rattles, but are often silent in non-breeding season.*
SONG: *In display, males emit harsh chatterings, buzzing and creaking churrings, interspersed with loud ringing notes and mimicry of local birds.*

NESTING
Breeds September–January. Nest a bulky, shallow saucer of twigs and some dry leaves, lined with finer dry leaves; 2–35 m above ground in upright branches of outer foliage, clumps of mistletoe, or against a trunk, well distant from display bower. Eggs: one-three, usually two; cream to buff-brown, heavily spotted, blotched and sometimes lined with umber, purple-grey and ink-grey; oval, about 44 x 29 mm. Incubation 21–22 days, by female. Young fledge in 19–22 days. After fledging they are conducted to a nursery area where the female tends them for another eight–nine weeks.

DISTRIBUTION
Rainforests and edges of sclerophyll forests of east coast and adjacent ranges. Two main populations: one, P.v. violaceus from the Dawes Range and Bunya Mountains, Qld, south to the Dandenong and Otway Ranges, Vic., down to sea level; the other, P.v. minor, occurs above about 500 m altitude, from Helenvale southwards to the Paluma Range, north of Townsville, Qld.

Regent Bowerbird *Sericulus chrysocephalus* (LEWIN, 1808)

THIS BOWERBIRD OF THE MID-EASTERN coastal rainforests exemplifies the general rule that the brighter the plumage, the less elaborate the bower. Its brilliant males build simple avenues of upright twigs and hide them in tangles of ferns and lawyervines on the forest floor. Here plumage may play as important a role as the bower in attracting females for mating, for like all bowerbirds, Regents are polygynous. Males set up their arenas for display, and females come to mate and then leave to nest on their own.

Several adult males and immatures may attend a bower which is built on loose platforms of sticks about a metre in diameter. Its parallel walls are about 150–200 mm long, up to 300 mm high and 60–90 mm apart, and they are painted yellow with saliva and juice from crushed leaves. The runway between the walls is adorned with snail shells, berries, galls, pebbles, leaves and rat faeces, all of red-black yellow-brown tones; even orange peel is added.

The male starts to display when a female approaches or enters the avenue. He bounds and prances about the bower, twisting and turning his flashing head and bulging eyes towards her. He prostrates himself in front of her with tail fanned, while spreading, drooping and sometimes beating his wings to display their brilliant bands, all the while churring, chattering and wheezing. Mating may take place in the bower or on arena-like clearings which the male makes throughout the forest and where he also displays.

Regent Bowerbirds are fruit-eaters and live mainly in the mid and upper levels of forest, descending to the ground only for bower-making, display and mating. When not breeding, they often band into loose feeding flocks of 10–30 or more birds—immatures, females and adult males—to roam locally into more open country.

OTHER NAMES
Australian Regent Bird, Regent Bird.

IDENTIFICATION
LENGTH: *240–280 mm; male smaller.*
MALE: *Brilliant black and yellow. Crown to upper mantle rich golden yellow, sometimes tinted carmine, the feathers short, crisp and plush. Rest of back black with subtle purple gloss. Wings black with broad band of golden yellow across flight feathers. Tail black, with bow-like pointed outer feathers. Underparts and side of head black with black line over eye. Eye bright yellow. Bill yellow. Feet and claws black.*
FEMALE: *Head dull brown with fine dusky spots; dull soot-black patch on hind-crown. Back and rump fawn-brown, feathers broadly scalloped with white, black-edged crescents towards upper back. Wings dull brown; flight feathers with paler edges, washed underneath with dull yellow-grey; wing coverts barred. Tail dull brown. Underparts cream-white except for black spot on throat, mottled and scalloped with brown edges to feathers, especially on upper breast; scallops change to fine bars on belly and flanks. Eye dull yellow; bill, feet and claws dusky.*
IMMATURES: *Like adult female but with dusky brown eyes.*

VOICE
CALL: *Harsh churring squawk,* te-aar, *and similar squeaky notes uttered by both sexes as contact and alarm calls.*
SONG: *Soft whisper songs; low, explosive chatterings and hisses; possibly some mimicry by adult males during* breeding *as part of display rituals and, to a lesser extent, by females and immatures.*

NESTING
Breeds October–January. Nest a loose, fragile saucer of twigs, concealed in dense tangles of vines 3–25 m up, often within 20 m of bower. Eggs: two, rarely three; pale buff-grey, with delicate brown to black scrawls and blotches and some underlying marks of lavender; oval, about 37 x 26 mm. Incubation about 18 days, by female. Probably one brood a season.

DISTRIBUTION
Subtropical rainforests and their edges in eastern Australia, from Clarke and Berserker Ranges, Qld, where isolated, and Dawes Range south to the Hawkesbury River, near Sydney. *No races.*

A male Regent Bowerbird in its small bower. The female is a dull brown bird with darker scallops on its upper parts and breast.

Fawn-breasted Bowerbird *Chlamydera cerviniventris* GOULD, 1850

A Fawn-breasted Bowerbird on the platform in front of its bower. This bird has ornamented the structure with bunches of green fruit.

WIDESPREAD THROUGH THE SAVANNAS of New Guinea, Fawn-breasted Bowerbirds are restricted in Australia to the east coast of northern Cape York Peninsula. There, as elsewhere, they live in pockets and galleries of vine forest and mangroves amid grassland and eucalypt woodland. They are sedentary birds, and usually solitary, but occasionally band together in small loose parties of up to 10 to roam locally for food. Groups gather at any time of the year in profusely fruiting figs and other food trees to pick fruit and occasional insects, including green tree ants. Like other members of their genus, they are wiry frugivorous birds, bounding actively among tree crowns when feeding, and flying from pocket to pocket of scrub in swooping glides—wings to body—that alternate with heavy wing-beats.

This rather dull-plumaged bowerbird builds a particularly complex bower for its courting and mating. The foundation of the bower is a raised oblong platform of interwoven, crisscrossed sticks with sloping sides. On this is erected a narrow avenue of sticks with upright walls only 80–100 mm apart, barely wide enough for the bird to squeeze between. The walls are 300–400 mm long and about 300 mm high, and they are oriented from north–south to east–west. The platform varies in size but is up to about 1500 mm long, 700 mm wide and 400 mm high. The bird paints the walls of the avenue with green vegetable matter which dries to a colour ranging from dull grey to red-brown. The walls and the northwestern end of the platform are adorned with fruits, flowers and occasional leaves, all of a grey-green or green tone.

The male bird builds the bower in a pocket of closed forest or shrubs along the fringes of open grassland or woodland. Construction and ornamentation begin in April and May, at the start of the monsoonal dry season, and continue until the bower is abandoned in December, at the close of breeding. The next year a new bower is built on the site of the old one. Each bower seems to be the property of one male, which constantly attends it, even though other males and immatures may display in it.

Arrival of a female at the bower triggers display by the male. This is a sequence of strained and exaggerated postures, prancing and bounding about the platform and overhanging branches, accompanied by churring and hissing. It is similar to the displays of the Spotted Bowerbird and the Great Bowerbird, even to the point of flicking and twisting the back of the head towards the female, despite its lacking the opalescent lilac bar of those species.

It is not known whether the male Fawn-breasted Bowerbird performs peripheral and central displays in the same way as other members of its group, but this seems likely because of the bounding display about the bower and the tendency to restrict himself to the end of the platform facing the avenue. Females enter the avenue and mating probably takes place there. Each male may mate with any number of itinerant females which leave to nest on their own.

OTHER NAMES
None.

IDENTIFICATION
LENGTH: *260–290 mm.*
ADULTS: *Sexes similar. Head and neck grey-brown with faint off-white streaks on forehead and sides of neck. Back and rump dark grey-brown scalloped with white. Wings dark grey-brown with broad white tips on inner flight feathers and wing coverts. Tail dark grey-brown above, paler below, with pale buff tip. Throat and upper breast brown-grey with pale buff streaks; rest of underparts ochre-fawn, sometimes faintly scalloped on breast and barred on flanks. Eye dark brown. Bill black; mouth yellow. Feet grey-brown.*
IMMATURES: *Like adults but back and wing coverts more broadly scalloped with pale buff; sides of breast and flanks sometimes more barred; feet pale grey. Full adult plumage in second year.*

VOICE
CALL: *Harsh, rasping contact and alarm churrs; weak, harsh grasshopper-like hisses.*
SONG: *Displaying males utter harsh, metallic churrings, explosive chatterings and hisses, and sometimes mimic other birds. Females hiss softly.*

NESTING
Breeds September–December, but also sporadically through year. Nest a loose, flimsy shallow cup of roughly interwoven twigs, vine tendrils and bark strips, lined with finer twigs and rootlets; placed in fork of tree, well-hidden in deep foliage, 2–10 m above ground, usually on edge of clearings and over 100 m from bower. Nest measures 190 x 100 mm. Eggs: one, very rarely two; pale green-olive to cream, scrawled all over with umber, purple-grey and black thread-like lines; about 36 x 26 mm. Incubation by female.

DISTRIBUTION
Edges and pockets of vine, coastal scrub and mangroves in wooded grassland, on east coast of Cape York Peninsula south to Silver Plains. Also New Guinea. No races.

Spotted Bowerbird

Chlamydera maculata (GOULD, 1837)

DURING BREEDING—AND THROUGH THE rest of the year—the male Spotted Bowerbird spends much time tending, watching and singing over its bower: twin parallel walls of finely interwoven dry stems, about 200–500 mm high, 400–700 mm long and 150–200 mm apart, set in a foundation-mat of crossed sticks, and oriented north–south on the ground under sheltering shrubbery. With its bill the bird dabs a red-brown mixture of saliva and grass juice on the inner walls; at each end of the bower it clears up to a metre of ground and adorns it with neat piles of white and pale green objects—bones, pebbles, snail shells, seeds, berries and even glass, cartridge cases and can tops.

At the arrival of a female, the male displays animatedly in two ways. Either he runs and bounds cock-tailed in circles round the bower while the female sits behind the bower walls, or he cavorts on his ornamented platform, facing the female at the bower entrance. In both displays the male strikes erratic, stiff and violently contorted postures, attacks bower ornaments and hisses, clicks and churrs explosively, mixed with extraordinary mimicry. He opens and droops or raises his wings, gapes at the female, and flashes his raised and expanded lilac neck bar by flicking his head sideways and forward.

Mating takes place in the bower with any number of females which then leave to nest and rear their young. When not breeding or attending bowers, Spotted Bowerbirds range locally, singly or in small groups, through the warmer near-inland woodlands in eastern Australia. They feed primarily on fruit and occasional insects in the crowns of trees and shrubberies, drink daily, and fly in long swooping undulations, with wing-tips upswept.

This male Spotted Bowerbird has used berries, bits of white and green glass and can tops to decorate its bower.

OTHER NAMES
Mimicbird, Cabbage-bird.

IDENTIFICATION
LENGTH: *280–300 mm.*
ADULTS: *Sexes similar; female more streaked on crown, with smaller nape bar and longer tail. Crown and face brown streaked ochre; broad nape bar of dense lilac plumes. Mantle plain brown. Rest of upper parts, wings and moderate tail dusky brown spotted ochre at tips of all feathers. Throat and breast brown-grey mottled ochre-cream, grading to plain cream over belly; barred grey on* flanks and undertail. Eye brown. Bill horn-brown; mouth yellow. Feet olive-brown.
IMMATURES: *As adults; no nape bar.*

VOICE
CALL: *Penetrating, drawn-out, rasping note for contact and alarm.*
SONG: *Male in display splutters, clinks, hisses and mimics other noises. Female may hiss softly in bower.*

NESTING
Breeds September–February. Nest a loose, frail saucer of thin, interlocking leaves, vines and twigs, 130–200 mm x 90 mm; lined with needles and tendrils; placed on horizontal fork in shrubbery or mistletoe 2–15 m up, usually far from bower. Eggs: two–three; pale buff-grey with dusky zigzag lines; oval, about 38 x 27 mm. Incubation by female.

DISTRIBUTION
Well-grassed woodlands of mid-eastern Australia, south to central Murray River, north to mid-Queensland coast and foot of Cape York Peninsula, and west to Georgina River system, Qld. No races.

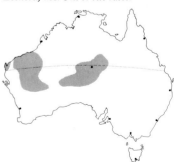

The Western Bowerbird is distinctly smaller than the Spotted Bowerbird.

REPLACING THE SPOTTED BOWERBIRD in the desert hills and ranges of central and Western Australia is the Western Bowerbird. The two are alike in their bower-building and behaviour, although the Western often raises its avenue of sticks on a higher platform 150–200 mm above the ground. They resemble one another, so much so that they have been regarded as races of one species.

Nevertheless, the Western is a distinctly smaller, more richly coloured bird. Both its bill and tail are shorter and a different shape. Its crown is scalloped, not streaked, and it lacks all traces of the plain mantle patch that is the particular characteristic of the Spotted. Nor is there any evidence that they intergrade where they all but meet around the northern Simpson Desert.

Throughout their range, Western Bowerbirds keep to breakaways where there is water for drinking and copses of leafy trees for

Western Bowerbird

Chlamydera guttata GOULD, 1862

OTHER NAMES
Guttated Bowerbird.

IDENTIFICATION
LENGTH: *250–270 mm; female larger.*
MALE: *Crown dusky, closely scalloped ochre and leaden; broad nape bar of dense lilac plumes. Rest of upper parts, wings and short tail dusky black, spotted ochre at tips of all feathers, finer on mantle. Face and throat dusky, spotted ochre; rest of underparts yellow-cream, faintly barred and variably washed russet on flanks and undertail. Eye brown. Bill black; mouth yellow. Feet olive-grey.*
FEMALE: *As male but crown scalloped plain ochre, nape bar reduced, throat more heavily spotted, tail longer.*
IMMATURES: *As female; nape bar absent.*

VOICE
Similar to Spotted Bowerbird.

NESTING
Breeds September–December. Nest a loose saucer of dry twigs; lined with finer twigs and needles; placed in horizontal fork in tree foliage 2–10 m up. Eggs: usually two; pale grey-green, covered with winding scrawls of brown and occasional darker blotches; oval, about 32 x 26 mm.

DISTRIBUTION
Central Australian ranges, between Birksgate, Warburton, Macdonnell and Jervois Ranges, and Pilbara east to edge of Gibson Desert and south to Cue-Leonora, WA. One or two races.

shelter and feeding. Although taking insects, they are mainly fruit-eaters, picking drupes of sandalwoods and mistletoes within the crowns of shrubs and trees. In many areas the bird is limited to pockets of the fig, *Ficus platypoda.*

Great Bowerbird *Chlamydera nuchalis* (Jardine & Selby, 1830)

THROUGHOUT THE TROPICAL WOODLANDS of northern Australia, the Great Bowerbird fills the niche of other *Chlamydera* bowerbirds elsewhere. Usually solitary, it is primarily a fruit-eater, bounding alertly within the crowns of bushy trees and shrubs—rarely down to the ground—picking off a range of fruits and occasional insects. Profusely fruiting trees attract loose groups of up to 20 or so, particularly out of breeding, and the birds may also come and go in twos and threes at waterholes where they come to drink on most afternoons. Flight is of high, swooping undulations on rounded upturned wings through and over the tops of trees.

Males build bowers in loose clans, each bower the property of a single bird which tends it through much of the year, either refurbishing it constantly or rebuilding a new one nearby each season. Concealed under low foliage, bowers are open or over-arching avenues of twigs and grass—thicker than those of Spotted and Western Bowerbirds—supported on a mat of sticks in a cleared space about two x one-and-a-half metres. The walls of the avenue, about 300–450 mm high, 600–1000 mm long and 200 mm apart, are aligned north–south and may be painted on the inside, although this does not show. The avenue itself and its lips are littered with white objects—shells, bones, stones, fruit, leaves, flowers and even bleached dung.

On the arrival of a female, the male goes into peripheral display, circling the bower, or central display, cavorting on its northern lip, depending on her position. He parades with wings lowered until they touch the ground, raises tail and crest, flicks his head and gapes to reveal his yellow mouth, churring harshly. If the female sits in the bower, he may offer green fruit as they meet. Mating takes place in the bower, with any number of females which then leave to nest and rear young on their own.

OTHER NAMES
Queensland Bowerbird, Great Grey Bowerbird.

IDENTIFICATION
LENGTH: *330–370 mm.*
ADULTS: *Sexes alike; female faintly barred on belly and lilac nape bar reduced or missing. Head mid grey-brown or flecked white on crown according to race; broad bar of thick lilac plumes on nape, edged by curled, white-tipped feathers. Back, wings and tail mid grey-brown, scalloped faintly to heavily grey-white over back and shoulders; underwings washed pale buff; tail tipped narrowly white. All underparts paler grey-brown, barred* darker on undertail. Eye deep brown. *Bill deep olive-brown; mouth yellow. Feet deep olive-brown.*
IMMATURES: *As adults but lack nape bar; faintly barred on lower breast, belly and flanks.*

VOICE
CALL: *Harsh, drawn-out asthmatic rasp, in contact and alarm.*
SONG: *In display or song from perches over bower, males give a range of hisses, churrs, rasps, twangs and gratings, and mimic superbly.*

NESTING
Breeds August–February; predominantly October–January. Nest a flat, coarse, loosely constructed shallow cup of sticks and twigs, 240 mm across by 130 mm deep, placed—not often well hidden—in the branches of trees or shrubs 1–10 m above ground, and far from bower. Eggs: one, sometimes two; lustrous grey-green to cream covered with umber, purple-grey and black lines, squiggles and spots; oval, about 42 x 29 mm. Incubation by female; one brood a season.

DISTRIBUTION
Pockets of vine scrub, paperbark and eucalypt thicket in woodland and open forest across northern Australia. Two races: one from Kimberleys to eastern head of Gulf of Carpentaria; the other on Cape York Peninsula south to Mackay, Qld, except wet eastern coastal fringe.

This Great Bowerbird has a good collection of bleached snail shells, bones and pebbles decorating its bower—a structure only used for display and mating.

Green Catbird *Ailuroedus crassirostris* (PAYKULL, 1815)

OTHER NAMES
Spotted Catbird, Black-eared Catbird.

IDENTIFICATION
LENGTH: *240–320 mm; smallest on Cape York Peninsula, largest on mid-east coast.*
ADULTS: *Crown and nape black spotted buff (Cape York race) to plain green speckled white on nape (mid-east coast race). Rest of upper parts, wings and tail emerald green; inner flight feathers, wing coverts and all tail feathers except central pair tipped white. Face mottled dusky, white and buff with plain black ear coverts (Cape York) to green-brown speckled cream, with white half-ring behind eye and white patch on side of neck (mid-east coast). Chin dusky, throat white, breast dusky brown with coarse buff-white spots and belly, flanks and undertail plainer cream-buff (Cape York); to brownish green on chin and throat grading to green over breast and flanks and lemon on belly and undertail with fine whitish spotting on throat, and fine white streaking on breast and flanks (mid-east coast). Eye vermilion. Bill bone-cream. Feet grey.*
IMMATURES: *As adults but head duller and greener, less mottled in northern races; rest of upper parts duller, with blue tinge; breast and belly greener with finer spotting (northern races) or coarser streaking (mid-east coast race); eye brown, remaining so for several years. Adult plumage gained in second year.*

VOICE
CALL: *Sharp, carrying clicking* tk *when feeding, repeated at intervals, possibly in contact. Harsh rasping in alarm and maybe display.*
SONG: *Not elaborated; territorial call a nasal, grinding drawn-out wail, like cat's miaow or baby's cry,* yiiaaooow, *often first falling, then rising in pitch, repeated at intervals; shorter in northern races than in south. In dawn display, several clicking notes ending in two or three guttural cries.*

NESTING
Breeds September–January. Nest a large, bulky deep cup 220–250 mm across, 120–150 mm deep, of large dry leaves and twigs, bound with leaves and vine tendrils, sometimes surrounded by mass of loose leaves and twigs; lined with leaves, stems and vine tendrils; placed in upright fork in dense tree foliage, vine tangle or crown of tree fern, 2–23 m above ground. Eggs: one–three, usually two; slightly lustrous plain cream or cream-buff; oval, about 39–44 x 25–30 mm. Incubation 23–24 days, by female. Young fledge in about three weeks.

DISTRIBUTION
Tropical and subtropical rainforest along east coast and adjacent ranges, in three tracts, from Iron Range to McIlwraith Range, Cape York Peninsula, Helenvale to Paluma Range, Qld, and Dawes Range, Qld, to Narooma, NSW. Also New Guinea, Aru Islands and Misool. About nine or 10 races; three in Australia.

The southern, green race of the Green Catbird, eating fruit. They particularly favour figs.

A Green Catbird of the southern green-headed race feeds its young. The nests are the bulkiest of all the bowerbirds.

THE GREEN CATBIRD, named 'catbird' because of its wailing territorial cries, is a bowerbird that pairs monogamously and does not build a formal bower for courtship. Individual birds—probably males—have been found to pluck green leaves and place them upside down in a rudimentary clearing, after the manner of the Tooth-billed Bowerbird, but they have no ceremonial attachment to it. This suggests that, far from being primitive bowerbirds unskilled in the art of arena display, they have discarded the habit and reverted to conventional pairing.

In Australia there are three isolated populations of Green Catbirds, all in the rainforests of the east coast—on Cape York Peninsula, in the Helenvale–Ingham tract in northeastern Queensland, and along the central east coast south to Narooma, NSW. Size and plumage may differ between the populations but habits and behaviour are the same everywhere.

Australian Green Catbirds are rainforest birds, and rather sedentary and solitary. Established pairs hold permanent territory year round and have been retrapped at the same site over periods of at least nine years. Groups of up to 10–15 occasionally gather to wander locally after breeding, visiting fringing eucalypt forest and orchards, but these are probably young of the year and unattached adults without territory.

Territories are marked by loud wailing raspings for which this bird is renowned. Both sexes give them, from perches on horizontal branches in the forest mid-strata. They are uttered sporadically through the day during breeding but usually develop into choruses at dawn and dusk, the only time that the calls are given at other times of the year. Unlike other bowerbirds, Spotted Catbirds do not sing. At night members of pairs roost in vines and dense foliage in separate trees near to one another.

Green Catbirds are mainly fruit-eaters. Working in ones and twos, they hop and flit heavily through all forest strata, from the floor litter to just under the high canopy, picking mostly figs but also other fruits. Usually a catbird tugs off a fig and then swoops out of the tree to eat or store it at a site in another tree. Insects and

their larvae, occasional leaves, shoots and flower heads, frogs, and nestlings of other birds are also taken. If flushed in shrubbery, catbirds often bound heavily upwards from branch to branch into the canopy, or fly off through upper strata on rounded wings in swift laboured undulations.

During breeding the male actively defends a small area of about 15–20 metres in diameter around the nest, usually built in a densely foliaged understorey tree. Courtship is simple, the male clicking and rasping sporadically from a low display perch and chasing the female from branch to branch, each pausing to wail from time to time and bob head and body. Chasing is interspersed with preening and feeding. Pairing is probably permanent.

Only the female builds and incubates, but both sexes feed the young and defend the nest by injury-feigning, dropping to the forest floor and fluttering along as though with broken wings. While the female broods, the male brings much food—mainly fruit, particularly figs and some tamarinds. Animals constitute about one third of the diet—arthropods, mostly beetles, and a few nestling birds. One brood is usually reared a season.

Opinion differs as to whether there are one or two species of Green Catbirds in Australia; the second is the small, dusky-headed, coarsely mottled 'Spotted' race in northeastern Queensland. A reassessment of the problem suggests that it is not a question of one or two species, but of one or three. The plain green, finely spotted population on the central coast is distinct enough and so is the black-headed, coarsely spotted, buff-breasted population on Cape York Peninsula, itself no more than a diminutive version of black-eared Green Catbirds in New Guinea. Between them in the Cooktown–Ingham tract, however, is a population of intermediate appearance in intermediate geographical position. It has the dark head marks of the Cape York population but the pattern is dull dusky brown; it has the green-white toned ventral spotting of the mid-east coast population but in the coarser form of populations to the north; and it is intermediate in size. Given these trends and connections, it seems wisest to treat all as races of one species.

Tooth-billed Catbird *Ailuroedus dentirostris* (RAMSAY, 1876)

MOUNTAIN RAINFORESTS OF northeastern Queensland ring with the brilliant song of male Tooth-billed Catbirds during spring breeding. Their song is an astounding medley of rich limpid twitters and whistles and high-pitched chatters and burrings which seem so varied that some of them may be mistaken for mimicry of other birds. The song stops and starts as neighbouring territorial birds sing in turn. Song comes from either the bower or vantage perches from one-half to six metres above it inside the forest where the male spends much of the day in watchful attendance. As he sings, he throws his head up, bill open, and sometimes bobs from side to side.

The bower itself is a flat circular or oval clearing one–three metres in diameter on the forest floor between tree buttresses and under small palms and saplings. It is swept clean of litter by the attendant male which then adorns it with eight–15 large green leaves snipped off the stalk with its double-notched bill. The leaves are specially chosen for their pale grey undersides and are placed upturned on the bower stage so that they glow palely in the gloom.

Rearrangement is constant and as soon as a leaf withers it is replaced by a fresh one.

Males gather into loose clans to establish their bower-stages each season. Each bower—the property of one male—is within hearing distance of the nest and all are lined out along ridges, often up to 20 per kilometre. Apart from cleaning the floor and replacing and rearranging the leaves, the male spends little time on the bower stage itself until visited by a female. Then he advances across it in erratic crouching hops. His breast fluffs into a broad ruff, his wings flick, his tail jerks upwards and his beak gapes, burring and sputtering. Leaves may be picked up and head bobbed as he sings. Males apparently mate with more than one female, each of which usually rears only one brood each season.

When not breeding, Tooth-billeds live quietly in the upper forest strata, planing through and over the canopy from tree to tree to feed in ones and twos on a range of fruits, leaves and occasional insects and their larvae. Their notched bills are well-fitted for chewing and strip-cutting leaf blades, major items in their diet.

OTHER NAMES
Tooth-billed Bowerbird, Stage-maker, Leaf-turner.

IDENTIFICATION
LENGTH: *260–270 mm.*
ADULTS: *Sexes similar; male slightly larger. Upper parts from head to wings and tail plain deep olive-brown, washed faint russet on flight feathers. Face streaked brown and buff. Underparts dark cream edged thickly brown, appearing streaked; undertail with brown chevrons. Eye deep brown. Bill dusky, with double-notch at tip;* *mouth orange-yellow. Feet dark olive-grey.*
IMMATURES: *Upper parts browner than adults; throat and breast paler and mottled.*

VOICE
CALL: *Harsh, short* chuck *to maintain contact within the clan, and for identification.*
SONG: *Rich, varied whistling and high chirping, long burrs, sputters and chattering, interwoven with liquid notes, varied whisperings and maybe mimicry.*

NESTING
Breeds September–January. Nest rather frail, shallow saucer of sticks lined with finer twigs; 190 x 110 mm deep; in thick vegetation among vines, 3–25 m above ground. Eggs: two; slightly lustrous cream or buff-cream; oval, about 42 x 29 mm. Incubation by female.

DISTRIBUTION
Montane rainforests above 500 m between Cooktown and Paluma Range, northeastern Qld. Locally nomadic. No races.

A Tooth-billed Catbird on a bower stage—a circular or oval space decorated with large green leaves. There can be up to 20 bowers within one kilometre, and each one is the property of a single male, which he maintains and sometimes uses for display.

Paradise Riflebird *Ptiloris paradiseus* SWAINSON, 1825

A female Paradise Riflebird; the male is black with an iridescent crown, a patch of metallic green on its throat, and belly feathers edged with green.

OTHER NAMES
Riflebird.

IDENTIFICATION
LENGTH: *280–300 mm; male slightly larger, but shorter in bill.*
MALE: *Crown iridescent metallic green; upper parts velvety black with purple tones; wings black with papery texture. Tail short, square and black with metallic green on upper surface of two central feathers. Chin to upper breast velvety black with small central triangular gorget of metallic green. Rest of underparts black, the feathers broadly edged with V-shaped iridescent oil-green. Eye dark brown. Bill black; mouth lime-yellow. Feet black.*
FEMALE: *Head and tail grey-brown*
with fine streaks of pale buff and cream eyebrows. Upper parts mid-brown with rufous wash on flight feathers and tail. Underparts buff-cream, plain on throat, marked with large black crescents and chevrons on breast and belly and with bars on flanks and undertail. Bill dusky. Feet slate-grey.
IMMATURES: *As adult female; immature males shorter-billed.*

VOICE
CALL: *Raucous, explosive, long-drawn rasping yaa-a-a-ss, probably uttered by both sexes, but mostly by males, to declare themselves and identify their territory in breeding season. Also long, mellow, upslurred whistle.*
SONG: *Soft rasps and churrs in display.*

NESTING
Breeds September–January. Nest a rough, bulky bowl of broad dry leaves, palm fronds, bark, twigs and sometimes paper; bound with vine tendrils, about 210 mm across x 120 mm deep; outside, especially rim, sometimes decorated with green fern fronds, moss, orchids and sloughed snakeskin; lined with finer leaves and fibres; placed in a mass of vines or leafy branchlets well up in forest canopy 5–30 m above ground. Eggs: usually two; lustrous rich pink-cream, boldly and uniformly marked and striped with chestnut-red, purple-brown and grey; oval, about 36 x 24 mm. Incubation 15–16 days, by female. Young fledge in about four weeks.

DISTRIBUTION
Subtropical rainforests between Berserker Range and Kroombit Tops, Qld, to Gloucester and Barrington Tops, NSW. No races.

PARADISE RIFLEBIRDS OF THE mid-eastern coastal Australian rainforests are among the few birds-of-paradise occurring outside New Guinea. Males advertise themselves during breeding with strident calls from display perches. Like other birds-of-paradise, they are polygynous. The males expend their breeding energy in flamboyant display while the females build the nests, incubate the eggs and rear the young without assistance.

The male Paradise Riflebird holds not a breeding territory, but a display territory in the form of one or more thick, horizontal branches high above the ground in a tall forest tree. There he spends much of the day, either calling or in solitary display. When displaying he extends and fans his wings upwards, flings back his head to show the metallic, slightly erectile feathers on his throat, and throws out the glistening scalloping on his belly and flanks into a circle. He moves his head rhythmically from side to side, bill

open to flash the lime-yellow mouth, while raising and lowering his wings to produce a sharp, rustling sound.

When a female arrives on the display bough the male becomes even more animated. He encircles her with outstretched wings and claps their tips together repeatedly as he dances backwards and around with her. Young males changing into adult plumage don colour irregularly over body, wings and tail over a period of a year or so. They do not appear to start this until at least three years old.

Quiet and solitary in their feeding, Paradise Riflebirds forage over upper branches like big treecreepers, hopping along and probing into crevices and under bark and ruffling through hanging litter for spiders and insects and their larvae. They work from tree to tree, flying in direct undulations under the canopy. Profusely fruiting trees attract them in twos and threes to feed in their crowns where the birds pick methodically and hang acrobatically.

Victoria's Riflebird *Ptiloris victoriae* GOULD, 1850

THIS RIFLEBIRD OF THE mid-northeastern Queensland rainforests eats much fruit in the mid and upper forest strata. Some of this it skins by holding the fruit with one foot and slipping off the rind with its bill. It also eats insects, which it finds by probing, shuffling and pulling with its bill in bark or among debris in tree forks and branches. Foraging birds will spiral up trunks like treecreepers. They fly rapidly in direct undulations for short distances through the forest, the wings of the males rustling like silk, or they glide away through the tree tops.

Males display solitarily throughout the breeding season, keeping to small territories of about two hectares in which they dominate all vantage points. A male will perch on a thick, near-vertical stump in the crown of a tree, stand erect, and raise his wings until the tips meet over his head or forward like an umbrella under his chin. He sways and pivots his body backwards and forwards, with green-tipped body plumes fanned out in a circle and tail cocked forward. He opens his bill and throws his head back and moves it rhythmically from side to side in a scintillating display.

In duet display, two swaying birds face each other with breasts almost touching. Each raises an outstretched wing forward in alternation and in increasingly rapid succession while throwing back its head and moving rhythmically from side to side to meet the other bird's upswinging wing. Ultimately the male encircles the female with both wings and copulation follows.

There is no pairing. A male may mate with any number of itinerant females which leave to nest and rear young on their own, usually rearing one brood a season. Females and immatures are not territorial as are adult males and wander locally.

A female Victoria's Riflebird with its long bill buried in the soft flesh of a pawpaw. These birds eat much fruit.

OTHER NAMES
Lesser Riflebird, Queen Victoria Riflebird.

IDENTIFICATION
LENGTH: *230–250 mm; male slightly larger but bill shorter.*
MALE: *Crown iridescent metallic green; rest of upper parts velvety black; wings black with papery texture. Tail short, square and black, with metallic green over central feathers. Chin to lower breast velvety black with small central triangular gorget of metallic green, smaller than in Paradise Riflebird. Rest of underparts black, the feathers broadly edged with rounded oil-green scallops. Eye dark brown. Bill black; mouth lime-yellow. Feet black.*
FEMALE: *Head mid grey-brown with fine buff streaks on crown and pale buff eyebrow. Upper parts mid brown-grey with light wash of rufous in wing quills. Underparts rich rufous-buff, spotted and marked with small arrows of dusky grey to undertail, paler and plain on throat with narrow brown streaks running down on each side from base of bill; flanks lightly barred grey. Bill dusky. Feet slate-grey.*
IMMATURES: *As adult female; immature males shorter-billed, not gaining adult plumage until about fourth year.*

VOICE
CALL: *Raucous, rasping, carrying yaa-a-rr uttered particularly by male in advertisement from high perches.*
SONG: *Soft rasps and churrs in display.*

NESTING
Breeds September–January. Nest a rough, open bowl of thick rootlets, leaves and tendrils, 170–180 mm x 80–90 mm deep, sometimes decorated with sloughed snakeskin; lined with broad leaves and a few fine sticks; placed in top of pandanus or other palms or in dense tree foliage 2–30 m above ground. Eggs: usually two; lustrous pink-flesh or pink-buff marked with longitudinal streaks and smudges of red, red-purple, umber and purple-grey; oval, about 34 x 23 mm. Incubation by female. Young fledge in about four weeks.

DISTRIBUTION
Rainforests in northeastern Queensland and adjacent offshore islands from Helenvale near Cooktown, to Paluma Range, near Townsville, Qld. No races.

Magnificent Riflebird *Ptiloris magnificus* (VIEILLOT, 1819)

A female Magnificent Riflebird.

OTHER NAMES
Albert's Riflebird, Prince Albert's Riflebird.

IDENTIFICATION
LENGTH: *Male 300–330 mm; female 260–280 mm, bill shorter than male's.*
MALE: *Crown iridescent dark blue-green; face and upper parts velvety black; wings black, outer flight feathers bowed and pointed, inner flight feathers broadly square-tipped. Tail black with blue sheen on central feathers. Chin and upper breast covered with long triangular gorget of short, metallic blue-green feathers, separated from purple-black lower breast and belly by a narrow band of velvet black and yellow-green; feathers of flanks and belly finely plumed. Eye dark brown. Bill black; mouth lime-yellow. Feet black.*
FEMALE: *Head grey-red-brown with faint buff stripes on crown and off-white eyebrow. Upper parts dull red-brown, richer on wings and tail. Underparts off-white with close black bars, plainer,* paler and more speckled on throat with a brown streak from either side of bill. Bill dusky. Feet blue-grey.
IMMATURES: *As adult female, but males distinctly larger.*

VOICE
CALL: *In Australia, loud, hoarse double-syllabled hooting whistle, the first upslurred, the second usually down-slurred, mostly by adult males— but also by females and immatures— to advertise territory or position. Also harsh, rasping growls.*
SONG: *Blowing, croaking and swishing by male in display.*

NESTING
Breeds September–February; possibly sporadically throughout year. Nest a rough, shallow cup, about 200 mm across x 140 mm deep, of broad dead leaves and vine tendrils; lined with dry leaves and plant fibre; placed in dense vegetation, often in crown of palm, 3–15 m above ground. Eggs: usually two; lustrous cream to buff, boldly marked with thick longitudinal streaks and underlying smudges of brown, blue-black and pale grey; oval, about 34 x 23 mm. Incubation about 15–16 days, by female.

DISTRIBUTION
Tropical rainforest and galleries from Cape York to Weipa and McIlwraith Range, Qld. Also New Guinea. Three races; one endemic in Australia.

RESTRICTED IN AUSTRALIA to the rainforests of Cape York Peninsula, Magnificent Riflebirds live solitarily in the forest canopy or gather in ones and twos at fruiting food trees or to bathe in pools. They also feed on a range of insects, bounding up vertical branches and trunks, probing, riffling and pulling at bark and debris for prey. Flight is straight and direct through the forest mid-strata, the wings of males rustling as they go.

Each adult male appears to hold a small several-hectare territory year round, advertising it with explosive whistles throughout the day. In display he performs alone on horizontal, often exposed branches and vines, from the mid-strata to the forest canopy. He stands erect and rapidly opens and shuts his wings, producing a loud rustling from his textured wings. Or with outstretched wings he will circle on foot, hissing and croaking. The arrival of a female or encroaching male elicits a similar response. Standing erect and with tail cocked, he throws his wings out and head back to expose his gorget, and then begins to swing the head from side to side, blowing with each movement. Each display only lasts up to 15 seconds. Itinerant females are attracted, mate, and then leave to nest and rear their young unaided.

Trumpet Manucode *Manucodia keraudrenii* (LESSON & GARNOT, 1826)

OTHER NAMES
Trumpet Bird, Manucode, Australian Bird of Paradise.

IDENTIFICATION
LENGTH: *280–320 mm.*
ADULTS: *Sexes similar; male larger, more brightly glossed with longer plumes on back of head. Plumage black glossed all over with oil-green, sometimes tending to purple, except under wings and tail. Feathers of nape, neck and throat narrow, long and pointed, forming slender tufts of plumes on each side of back of head. Eye vermilion. Bill and feet black.*
IMMATURES: *Less glossy than adults, plumage softer; head plumes shorter; slightly smaller.*

VOICE
CALL: *Single, loud, deep croak* gronk, *repeated at intervals for contact, identification, and marking territory by male; low, drawn-out* aaa-a-a-a-a *like heavy door squeaking, probably by male.*
SONG: *Loud trumpeting in display, by male. Female responds with soft chirping* chee-eee.

NESTING
Breeds mainly October–January; possibly sporadically throughout year. Nest an open, shallow, flimsy cup, about 170 mm across x 110 mm deep, of vine tendrils and twigs; lined with similar materials; placed 10–20 m up to often more, in upright to horizontal fork in canopy of tall rainforest trees. Eggs: one or two; very pale dull purplish pink, spotted and finely blotched all over with red-brown, umber and violet-grey, often in zone at larger end; oval, about 37 x 24 mm. Incubation 15–16 days, by both sexes.

DISTRIBUTION
Pockets of rainforest from Cape York southwards to Rocky River and McIlwraith Range. Also in New Guinea and on Aru Islands. Six or seven races; one endemic in Australia.

The Trumpet Manucode lives in rainforests on Cape York Peninsula.

TRUMPET MANUCODES ARE ABERRANT birds-of-paradise that breed in monogamous pairs, lack patches of metallic colour, and have, in males, a long coiled windpipe running under the skin over the muscles of the breast. This coiled windpipe apparently produces their loud carrying territorial croaks and squeaking jarrs.

Limited in Australia to the tropical hill and lowland rainforests of Cape York Peninsula, Trumpet Manucodes spend much time feeding on the forest canopy. They are fruit-eaters—although taking occasional insects and larvae—and they bound and fly through the tree tops with jerky, heavy-footed furtiveness, twisting and craning, never still. Following fruiting trees, they are locally disappearing and then congregating in twos to fives at flushes of food. But they do not migrate to New Guinea.

Males hold territory, marking it with loud croaks from high perches. Courtship is spectacular. Male chases female, both landing from time to time on high exposed branches. There the male faces his mate, crouches, fluffs his feathers into a ball and spreads his wings, trumpeting. The female responds with soft chirping.

Both sexes share incubation and the feeding of the young and often site their nests close to those of Black Butcherbirds. They will also usurp the new nests of other birds but probably without relying on the original owners to brood and rear their young.

White-winged Chough *Corcorax melanorhamphus* (VIEILLOT, 1817)

FEW AUSTRALIAN BIRDS LIVE such a close-knit communal life as the White-winged Chough—pronounced 'chuff'. These large sooty black birds with thin curved bills and strong legs form groups of two–20—usually five to ten—that hold to permanent feeding territories of about 800–1000 hectares in the better-watered woodlands and open forests of southeastern Australia. Being ground-feeders they keep to forests with open under-shrubberies and much litter, and because of this have adapted well to plantations of exotic conifers; it partly compensates for the clearing of much of their habitat for farming. In winter, up to 100 or more may gather temporarily at flushes of food, but they soon disperse and revert to their component groups.

Each group comprises one or more adults of each sex plus the young of several years—young choughs do not mature sexually until their fourth year—and they all eat, sleep, rest, play and breed together. Even if one bird uncovers a cache of food in its foraging, the rest run in to share. By day the choughs spend much time in rounds of feeding, working and reworking several hectares of their territory for a week or so, then moving elsewhere to repeat the procedure. When feeding they walk along in spread-out formation, searching methodically in their teetering gait, heads nodding forward and back and tails waving up and down. Insects, spiders, snails and even grain and freshwater mussels are their quarry and they find them by probing and scratching in the ground and among litter; litter is constantly shuffled and tossed aside by sideways flicks of the bill.

Rounds of foraging are broken by drinking, sunbathing, anting or simply resting together in a shady tree during the hot hours. At night all gather to sleep in one or two adjacent trees, bounding up among leafy branches well above the ground. They fly from point to point also as a group, in slow flapping flight interspersed with short flat glides on stiff, rounded wings with upswept tips. In flight the white patches in their wings flash prominently.

The birds are quiet or chatter softly to one another as they go about their routines, but if alarmed or flushed, or even in unprompted flight, they pipe and churr loudly. The eyes of adults can bulge red in excitement then.

Groups withdraw to a small defended territory of about 20 hectares to breed, using a nest of previous years or building a new one. All members of the group join in nest-building, constructing the nest in stages because, being of mud, each has to harden before more is added. A stem or piece of bark is first dabbled in mud, then carried to the nest to be 'trowelled' into place and trimmed by a rapid scissoring of the bill held sideways to the nest. A lasting structure results, which although appearing to be solid mud, is about seven per cent fibre by weight.

All members of the group also help to incubate the eggs and brood and feed the nestlings; sometimes more than one adult female will lay in the nest. Nestlings fledge before they can fly properly, fluttering to the ground to be with their elders. Stillness and camouflaging buff-covered down over the eye help them to avert capture by predators then and they respond instantly to the piping alarm call of other flock members.

At night they clamber up a sloping tree trunk or bush to shelter and sleep; by day they beg incessantly.

At about 60 days of age, young can fly as strongly as their parents and the down on the head is moulted. The young birds, however, still continue to beg and need much help in foraging; many die in their first winter. Occasionally two broods are reared a season, yet despite this and the assistance of helpers, fewer than two offspring reach independence in most years. For choughs to survive such a low rate of recruitment, the survivors must live long—and many do, for more than 10 years.

Although holding their own in most areas, White-winged Choughs fall prey to introduced predators such as feral cats and foxes. They are also easy targets for shooters.

The White-winged Chough uses several layers of mud to build its durable basin-shaped nest.

OTHER NAMES
Black Jay, Black Magpie, Jay, Apostlebird.

IDENTIFICATION
LENGTH: *430–470 mm.*
ADULTS: *Sexes similar. Uniformly soft, fluffy sooty black except for concealed white patch through outer flight feathers. Eye red, with orange inner ring in birds over four years old. Bill black, downcurved and thin. Feet black.*
IMMATURES: *Until eight or nine weeks old have two lines of buff down above eye. Eye brown in first-year birds.*

VOICE
CALL: *Single and double descending piping whistles in contact and alarm; an ear-shattering scream in extreme alarm; throaty churring* cree-ee-eek *or* kthrrrrr *in aggression; soft throaty clicks among feeding groups.*
SONG: *None.*

NESTING
Breeds August–December; sometimes as early as June and as late as March. Nest a pudding basin-sized bowl of mud and fibre; lined with fibre; placed on horizontal limb 4–14 m above ground. Eggs: three–five, up to 10 if two females contribute; cream, sparingly blotched brown, black and grey; oval, about 40 x 30 mm. Incubation about 19 days, by group. Young fledge in about 25 days.

DISTRIBUTION
Woodland and open forests in eastern and southern Australia; also enters pine plantations. No races.

Apostlebird _Struthidea cinerea_ GOULD, 1837

The adult Apostlebird has several helpers—progeny from previous breeding seasons—to help it construct the mud nest and share in nesting duties.

THE NAME APOSTLEBIRD STEMS from impressions that these birds live in groups of 12 wherever they occur through the well-grassed woodlands of inland eastern Australia. Their clans in fact comprise usually about eight–16 individuals—a parental breeding pair and their young of several years—and may grow to 20 or more if the clan stays intact for long enough. Although they may join with others in foraging flocks of 40–50 or more in marginal areas during hard winters, most clans are sedentary and rarely wander much more than a kilometre beyond their 10–15 hectare territories. All territories have watering points, and the clan needs them both for drinking and nest building.

Garrulous and restless, the clans are close-knit and their members share noisily in everything. When drinking and dust bathing, they all go together; when preening, they sit alongside one another on a branch and preen each other as well as themselves; when roosting they line up close together on a branch. They also play, engaging in follow-the-leader chases around trees, each bird crouching low and trying to nip the bird in front as it darts away. Several birds will cling together, claws locked and wings flapping, to roll over and over in the dust, pecking and calling. Young birds even challenge older by running about holding a leaf high in the bill. Tugs-of-war ensue, reducing the leaf to tatters, and the challenger may only escape attack if it is less than six months old.

Apostlebirds are weak in wing and strong in leg. They fly as a group slowly and directly, interspersing a few quick wing-beats with flat glides on rounded upswept wings. To ascend trees they do not fly but hop up from branch to branch. On the ground they move with ease, running, hopping and walking with a teetering gait, head nodding forward and tail bouncing up and down. They forage on the ground, fanning out in a loose group to pick up insects, larvae, spiders, other invertebrates, shoots and a few seeds in summer, and mainly seeds, herbs and grasses in winter. Here differences in their appearance from the closely related White-winged Chough are partly explained. The slender-headed, long-billed chough is a prober and digger; the shaggy, bull-headed Apostlebird, with its finch-like bill, is a surface picker.

Apostlebirds are just as communal in their breeding. All members of the clan build the mud nest, constructing it in the same way as White-winged Choughs do. And all share in incubation—sometimes sitting on eggs laid by several females—and later join in the feeding of young and removal of droppings from the nest.

OTHER NAMES
Grey Jumper, Happy Family, Lousy Jack, Twelve Apostles, CWA Bird.

IDENTIFICATION
LENGTH: _290–330 mm._
ADULTS: _Sexes similar. Uniformly mid-grey with brownish wings and black tail; head, back and breast shaggy with pale grey tipping. Green sheen to upper back and tail when newly moulted. Eye grey with pearly ring. Bill and feet black._
IMMATURES: _Smaller, duller and shorter-tailed than adults; eye brown._

VOICE
CALL: _Variety of harsh chattering_ ch-kew ch-kew, creechew, creechew, chereer chereer; _rasping alarm call._
SONG: _None._

NESTING
Breeds August–February. Nest a bowl about 150 mm in diameter, of mud reinforced with fibrous matter; lined with fine dry grass; plastered to a near horizontal branch about 2–17 m above ground. Eggs: two–five; glossy white, sparingly blotched with brown, black and grey; oblong-oval, about 29 x 22 mm. Incubation about 18 days, by group members. Young fledge in 13–18 days.

DISTRIBUTION
Common in mulga scrubs, Murray pine, brigalow and lancewood areas throughout inland eastern Australia between Gulf of Carpentaria and Riverina, NSW, to Mt Lofty Ranges, SA, with outlier in southern Arnhem Land, NT. Two races.

Australian Magpie-lark *Grallina cyanoleuca* (LATHAM, 1801)

An adult male Australian Magpie-lark with chicks—all of which have a white eyebrow. The female has a white forehead and throat, but no white eyebrow.

THE FAMILIAR MAGPIE-LARK—or Peewee—occurs anywhere in Australia but Tasmania, wherever there is pasture and mud bark for feeding, trees for roosting, and surface water to provide mud for nesting. Usually in pairs or locally nomadic parties, the birds spend much of their time foraging on the ground or puddling on the edge of shallow water, picking up insects and their larvae and, less often, earth worms and freshwater molluscs. When feeding they walk along bobbing the head back and forth in time with the feet. Progress is sedate, but if pushed the birds run; if stopping or agitated, they wave rump and tail up and down. Flight is buoyant, slow and direct, on rounded, evenly flapping wings.

Established pairs are permanently territorial, males defending territories of about eight–10 hectares in aerial skirmishes, fluttering about, lifting and dodging. When breeding, territorial display and courtship become intertwined. Male and female stand side by side on a high vantage perch and call rapidly in antiphonal duets, each bird raising its wings above its head and fanning its tail. Then they fly about, one after the other, calling liquidly and flapping with arrested pulsing wing-beats, only to return to a perch and display. Standing half a metre or so apart, they call alternately and posture. The head is dropped, bill points to the ground and tail fanned and flipped up. Bowing to one another is accompanied with flicks of part-fanned tails.

Both members of a pair select the nest site and carry mud and other materials to construct the nest. During the day both birds share incubation in shifts of about 15–30 minutes up to as long as an hour. The female usually incubates at night; more than one brood may be raised a season. Young magpie-larks are clothed in grey down when they hatch, unlike hatchling White-winged Choughs and Apostlebirds which are naked. Fed by both parents, they fledge in a distinctive pied plumage which is not lost for three or four months, soon after they join non-breeding flocks.

Having no territorial ties, non-breeding flocks are nomadic and shift with the seasons, mainly north in autumn–winter and south in spring–summer; some reach Arnhem Land and Cape York Peninsula. After breeding, the flocks may grow to several thousand with arriving young—and all roost together at night.

OTHER NAMES
Magpie-lark, Mudlark, Murray Magpie, Peewee, Peewit.

IDENTIFICATION
LENGTH: *260–300 mm.*
MALE: *Upper parts black with broad white band through shoulder of wing to base of inner flight feathers; rump, base and tip of tail white. Face and throat black; eyebrow and small bar below eye white; white patch on sides of neck joining lower breast to undertail white. Eye cream. Bill off-white, tipped black. Feet black.*
FEMALE: *Similar to male; forehead and throat white encircled by black band; no white eyebrow.*
IMMATURES: *Broad white eyebrow; white throat encircled by black band to forehead. Eye dirty brown; bill dark grey.*

VOICE
CALL: *Variety of loud piping calls,* peewee peewee *and high* doodit doodit *with variations throughout the range. Strident* pee-pee-pee *in alarm. Scolding chatter by young birds.*
SONG: *Liquid lower-pitched version of piping call,* cloo-it, cloo-it *sung by mated birds in flight.*

NESTING
Breeds mainly August–December but any month. Nest a bowl of plant fibre bound with mud, about 150 mm in diameter; lined with grass, fur, feathers; plastered to horizontal branch or man-made structure or pole 4–20 m above ground. Eggs: three–five; pink-white, marked with red- and purple-brown spots and blotches; oblong-oval, about 20 x 21 mm. Incubation 17–18 days, by both sexes. Young fledge in 18–23 days.

DISTRIBUTION
Very common in most parts of Australian mainland, usually near water; avoids heavily forested areas. Also in Timor, southern New Guinea and on Lord Howe Island. No races.

Black-faced Woodswallow *Artamus cinereus* VIEILLOT, 1817

LIKE OTHER WOODSWALLOWS, Black-faceds are aerial insect-catchers, replacing the Dusky Woodswallow on the open, shrubbed plains of inland Australia and in the drier tropical northern woodlands. They are neat birds with a smoky bloom to their plumage, the result of grooming with power downs hidden in the birds' flanks. Flight is effortless, on broad, pointed wings with short wrists, but feet are weak. On branches the birds can no more than shuffle and on the ground—which they land on to pick up swarming insects or nest material—they hop weakly.

Black-faced Woodswallows are rather sedentary birds despite their often unpredictable environment, keeping to the same local foraging range year in, year out. Like Dusky Woodswallows, they live in small communal groups of only several pairs plus immediate progeny. Bouts of foraging are broken with occasional huddles and mutual preening as several birds land to sit together, tails wagging and rotating, on a bare branch—although they are usually more spaced out than other woodswallows. At night all members cluster to roost, cramming in a tight ball into sheltering hollows and tree crotches.

When hunting, they rarely hawk high for long periods but sally out in brief low sorties from vantage perches—the top of a post or bush or a dead branch top. They circle and soar, hover and float, catching insects with bills and feet in midair and eating them there. In this way groups work through their range each day, twittering constantly on the wing and from perches to keep contact.

Like other woodswallows with white-tipped tails, pairs court by mutual wing-waving and tail-rotation. Nests are built in about six days. Both parents build, incubate, and feed the young and may be helped in feeding by other unmated birds in their group.

OTHER NAMES
Grey-breasted Woodswallow, White-bellied Woodswallow, White-vented Woodswallow.

IDENTIFICATION
LENGTH: *180–190 mm.*
ADULTS: *Sexes similar. Head and back light smoky grey; rump black. Wings bluer grey, whiter grey beneath. Tail black, all feathers except central pair tipped broadly white in Australia. Lores and small area around eye and chin black. Underparts pale smoky grey; black or white on vent and undertail coverts according to race. Eye dark brown. Bill pale blue-grey with black tip. Feet mealy black.*
IMMATURES: *Coarsely speckled cream on grey-brown as nestlings; speckling persists to first moult, several months after fledging.*

VOICE
CALL: *Soft, sweet, scratchy chirps in contact, chiff, chiff or chap, chap, given singly or in doublets; harsher chattering in alarm and when mobbing predators.*
SONG: *Soft, short twittering, including mimicry.*

NESTING
Breeds August–January; sometimes after rain in arid areas. Nest a shallow, skimpy bowl of twigs, grass stems and rootlets; placed in a well-hidden fork in a bush, or in crotch on a stump or fence post, 1–5 m above ground. Eggs: three or four; white with purple-brown blotches concentrated at larger end; oval, about 22 x 17 mm. Incubation 14–16 days, by both sexes. Young fledge in 18 days.

DISTRIBUTION
Common throughout drier open woodlands and steppes of Australia mainly west of Great Dividing Range. Also in Timor and New Guinea. Largely sedentary, though locally nomadic outside breeding season. Three races; two in Australia.

Black-faced Woodswallows are common throughout the drier and northern areas. They breed after drought-breaking rain, but more usually in spring.

Masked Woodswallow

Artamus personatus
(GOULD, 1841)

A male Masked Woodswallow at its loosely built nest. The female has a dusky face and more pink-grey breast.

THE MASKED IS ONE OF THE TWO Australian woodswallows that flock in numbers, feed for long periods high in the sky, and make long nomadic flights, north across the continent in autumn and south in spring to breed. The other woodswallow is the White-browed. Of the two, the Masked predominates over the western two-thirds of the continent; both mix in flocks of hundreds or more. Flocks keep together by chirping continuously. They may flutter and circle for hours in the sky, catching their insect food and eating on the wing, only to suddenly swoop into tree foliage to rest or glean insects and nectar. Nesting is colonial but not communal, and the birds do not cluster-roost at night.

OTHER NAMES
Blue 'Martin', Bush 'Martin', Skimmer.

IDENTIFICATION
LENGTH: *190–200 mm.*
MALE: *Upper parts plain mid-grey, white tip on tail. Forehead, face, throat black, edged white. Underparts and underwing pale grey. Eye dark brown. Bill pale blue, tip black. Feet mealy black.*
FEMALE: *As male but face and throat dusky; underparts vinous grey.*
IMMATURES: *Upper parts and face finely speckled cream-white.*

VOICE
CALL: *High, descending chirrup in contact; chattering when mobbing.*
SONG: *Soft twittering, with mimicry.*

NESTING
Breeds August–December. Nest a loose shallow bowl of twigs, grass stems, rootlets; usually 1–2 m above ground, in bushes or on stump or fence post. Eggs: two or three; white with purple-brown and grey blotches; oval, about 22 x 17 mm. Incubation about 12 days, by both sexes.

DISTRIBUTION
Open woodlands mainly over western two-thirds of continent; erratic east of Great Dividing Range. Moves nomadically north–south, generally breeding south of Barkly Tableland and Kimberleys. No races.

Little Woodswallow *Artamus minor* (VIEILLOT, 1817)

LITTLE WOODSWALLOWS, the smallest of the genus, live in small communal groups of about six–20 around rocky outcrops and hilly woodlands through much of inland and northern Australia. There they are sedentary; only in the east where they extend into rolling, grassy woodlands are they rather nomadic. Although visiting plants for insects and nectar, Little Woodswallows feed mainly on the wing, in local sorties from bare vantage perches. They float, dip and dive in easy curves and hang-glide over cliff faces, rarely far above the ground, catching and eating insects on the wing.

At night the woodswallows cluster to roost in tight packs in hollow trees and under rock overhangs. Perching birds often huddle and preen one another, wagging their tails in rotation. Tail-wagging continues in courtship, the birds fluttering their wings as well. Both parents nest-build and brood, and other members of the group help them with the feeding of young.

OTHER NAMES
None.

IDENTIFICATION
LENGTH: *120–130 mm.*
ADULTS: *Sexes similar. Upper and all underparts dark chocolate; rump black-grey. Wings slate-grey above, pale below. Tail black-grey, outer feathers tipped white. Eye dark brown. Bill blue-grey with black tip and stripe down under bill. Feet mealy black.*
IMMATURES: *Speckled cream on brown generally; bill brownish. Speckling persists to first moult, several months after fledging.*

VOICE
CALL: *Soft, chirping peet-peet in contact, often repeated in flight.*
SONG: *Soft twittering on perch.*

NESTING
Breeds August–January; after rain in arid areas. Nest an open bowl of fine twigs, stems and rootlets; placed in crevice of rock ledge, sometimes a dead stump. Eggs: three; cream with grey and brown blotches and spots at larger end; oval, about 20 x 14 mm. Incubation by both sexes.

DISTRIBUTION
Rocky outcrops and hills in northern half of Australia; also plain woodlands in east. No races.

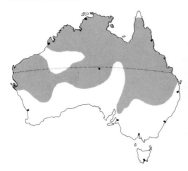

The Little Woodswallow here has built its nest in a dead tree stump.

White-browed Woodswallow *Artamus superciliosus* (GOULD, 1837)

A pair of White-browed Woodswallows at their nest; the male is on the left. Although predominantly insect-eaters, these birds will take nectar.

TRAVELLING IN SWARMING FLOCKS of several hundreds or more, White-browed Woodswallows wander up and down the wooded inland of eastern Australia. Movements are generally northwards in autumn to winter quarters through central Queensland into the Northern Territory. In spring the flocks shift south to breed, spreading regularly to Eyre Peninsula and sometimes spilling over to Tasmania. Southerly irruptions are erratic and affected by seasonal conditions; swarms that appear in one year may not reappear for many more.

Throughout their range, flocks mix with varying numbers of Masked Woodswallows—more in the west. Both species even nest in colonies together but with little hybridisation.

The feeding flocks usually fly high, birds fluttering and wheeling in all directions, chirruping constantly in contact, and catching and eating flying insects on the wing. Prey is caught in both beak and foot. The birds stay aloft for hours, then suddenly dive down to converge in a swarm in the crown of a tree to rifle blossom and glean insects, often hanging acrobatically upside down to do so. Their shortly brush-tipped tongues may help in taking nectar. The flocks cluster, chirrup and flutter in the tree for a while, or drop to the ground to feed on swarming insects, then just as suddenly take off again. At night they do not come in to sleep until almost dark, pitching into foliage and shrubbery to roost near, but not clustered against, one another.

Nesting colonies develop rapidly if conditions are suitable and are abandoned just as quickly if they fail. Pairs nest almost side by side in every available tree crotch and post hole, both sexes building the nest in a few days and incubating and rearing the young. No other birds, however, assist in feeding the young.

OTHER NAMES
Blue 'Martin', Skimmer, Summer-bird, White-eyebrowed Woodswallow.

IDENTIFICATION
LENGTH: *190–200 mm.*
MALE: *Upper parts from head to tail uniformly deep bluish grey; broad white brow over eye; underwing and undertail white-grey; tail tipped narrowly white. Throat deep blue-grey; rest of underparts dark chestnut. Eye dark brown. Bill pale blue; tip black. Feet mealy black.*
FEMALE: *As male but upper parts paler mid-grey; white brow finer; breast to undertail mid-rufous.*
IMMATURES: *Upper parts grey finely speckled with cream-white, persisting on wings; underparts brown-grey. Bill brownish. Wing spotting persists after first moult, several months after fledging.*

VOICE
CALL: *High descending twittered chirrup* chp, chap, *in contact, given singly among flying birds and at perches; chattering when mobbing; miner-like squeaks.*
SONG: *Soft twittering; mimicry.*

NESTING
Breeds mainly August–January. Nest a shallow bowl of twigs, grass stems and rootlets; up to 3 m above ground, but usually lower in fork in shrub or small tree, or on stump or fence post. Nests usually in a loose colony of 10 or more pairs. Eggs: two or three; white with purple-brown and grey blotches concentrated at larger end; oval, about 22 x 17 mm. Incubation about 12 days, by both sexes. Young fledge in 13–15 days.

DISTRIBUTION
Open eucalypt and acacia woodlands of inland eastern Australia, only erratically east of Great Dividing Range and west of Eyre Peninsula and Alice Springs, NT. Rarely breeds north of Tropic of Capricorn but spends winter as far north as Gulf of Carpentaria. Nomadic, reaching eastern tablelands and Victoria in times of drought inland. No races.

White-breasted Woodswallow *Artamus leucorhynchus* (LINNÉ, 1771)

White-breasted Woodswallows are sociable, and often sit side by side.

OTHER NAMES
White-rumped Woodswallow.

IDENTIFICATION
LENGTH: *170–180 mm.*
ADULTS: *Sexes similar. Head and upper parts to short tail dark slate-grey; rump white. Throat slate; rest of underparts and underwing white. Eye dark brown. Bill grey-blue; tip black. Feet mealy black.*
IMMATURES: *Upper parts flecked buff; throat whitish, breast faintly russet.*

VOICE
CALL: *Chirruped chirps, pert, pert, singly but often, in contact; strident chattering in alarm.*
SONG: *Soft twittering, with mimicry.*

NESTING
Breeds August–January. Nest a substantial open bowl of twigs, grass and rootlets; often in an exposed crotch or spout of tree 10-30 m above ground or inside magpie-lark's mud nest. Eggs: three or four; white with purple-brown blotches concentrated at larger end;

oval, about 23 x 17 mm. Incubation by both sexes.

DISTRIBUTION
Close to water in woodland from Shark Bay, WA, around north of Australia to Manning River, NSW; farther inland, in east along rivers. Also from Malaysia through Indonesia and New Guinea to Fiji. Eleven races; one in Australia.

THE WHITE-BREASTED WOODSWALLOW seldom lives far from fresh or brackish water and is mainly a bird of tropical woodlands. It moves south in winter in Western Australia, where it lives among mangroves, and generally shifts south in spring in eastern Australia. Flocks of as many as 100 birds travel as far as the Murray–Darling River system, where they breed. In the north, breeding generally follows the summer rains.

White-breasted Woodswallows appear to be more sociable than other woodswallows and often 10–50 or more cram together sitting side by side, along a bare branch, preening one another. It is in such a position that they roost at night, usually under sheltering foliage. They rarely land on the ground and feed mostly by catching insects in the open bill as they fly, circling, soaring and fluttering high over tree tops and surface water. They usually swallow even large prey whole but sometimes dismember it and, with the foot, carry pieces

to the mouth in flight. They are quieter than other woodswallows but still chirp almost continuously in contact. The call becomes more strident when danger threatens and builds into a vocal barrage when the birds mob a potential predator.

Unlike the other five Australian woodswallows, this woodswallow has no white tip to its tail and it does not fan and rotate its tail in courtship display. This suggests that the tail movement serves to emphasise the white tip in the other species. White-breasted Woodswallows display only by waving their wings, and the pair sit close together throughout. Copulation soon follows and afterwards the birds often sit side by side and preen each other. Sometimes the male feeds the female before they mate. Both sexes build the nest, incubate the eggs and feed the nestlings, often helped by others in their group. Young stay with their parents for many weeks after leaving the nest.

Dusky Woodswallow *Artamus cyanopterus* (LATHAM, 1801)

DUSKY WOODSWALLOWS OCCUR AROUND coastal eastern and southern Australia, in denser eucalypt woodlands and forests than any other woodswallows. Yet they still forage in the same way, hawking on the wing for flying insects in graceful glides, soars, flutterings and circles between and over the tops of trees. For launching into their sallies, they settle on high bare branches on the edges of clearings and open woodland, sitting there, often together and preening one another, tails rotating nonstop.

Like Black-faced Woodswallows, Duskys live in small communal flocks of 10–30 and cluster together to roost in a tight ball-like mass in tree hollows. In winter the flocks amalgamate and several hundred or so may jam then into tree chimneys to sleep. Such clustering is thought to conserve body heat and therefore energy. Birds will even go into huddles on chilly days.

Unlike Black-faced Woodswallows, Duskys are migratory in southeastern regions, most shifting north in autumn as far as central Queensland and south again in spring to breed. Virtually the entire Tasmanian population leaves to winter on the mainland. Groups return to traditional areas where pairs re-establish small territories. They do not spread out over the countryside but nest close together in 'neighbourhoods'. This enables adjacent pairs, even the whole flock, to join in defence of a threatened nest, mobbing the predator amid a chorus of scolding chattering.

In courtship, the pair perches on the same branch and the male offers the female food. She faces her mate and adopts a begging position with the body depressed, extended wings quivering and head thrust forward with bill open. Both birds utter a low continuous call throughout. Mating is preceded by a conspicuous, silent display. One bird begins fluttering its wings up and down and then rotates its partly fanned tail, emphasising the white-tipped feathers. The other joins in with identical display.

Male and female share all the nesting duties, from building the nest to tending the fledglings. Sometimes one or more birds— not necessarily progeny of previous years—help the parents to feed the

young. The nestlings remain in the nest for 16–20 days, depending on the weather, the availability of food and the number of nestlings involved. They leave the nest before they are able to fly properly, but are well camouflaged by mottled plumage, and have strong, sharp claws with which they can cling to branches. Young birds usually stay in the parental flock.

OTHER NAMES
Bee Bird, Bluey, Jacky Martin, Skimmer, Sordid Woodswallow, Woodswallow.

IDENTIFICATION
LENGTH: *170–180 mm.*
ADULTS: *Sexes similar. Upper and underparts deep greyish brown; rump and undertail dusky. Wings slate, the outer edge of outer primaries lined white; underwing white-grey. Tail dusky, outer feathers tipped white. Eye dark brown. Bill grey-blue with black tip and stripe down under bill. Feet mealy black.*
IMMATURES: *Coarsely speckled cream on brown; bill brownish. Fading gradually, speckling persists to first moult, several months after fledging.*

VOICE
CALL: *Brisk, chirrupping chirp, pirrt, pirrt, tossed about incessantly between pairs and in flocks for contact, both at perches and in flight; also a vigorous, harsh mobbing chattering when harassing larger birds.*
SONG: *Chirrupping chirps and pirrts.*

NESTING
Breeds August–January. Nest a small basket of twigs, grass, stems and rootlets; often lined with a few green plant stems;

placed in exposed positions 1–11 m above ground, on top of broken stump, behind piece of half-shed bark, on top of fence post or in fork of horizontal branch. Eggs: three or four; cream with purple-brown spots and blotches, particularly at larger end; oval, about 23 x 17 mm. Incubation about 16 days, by both sexes. Young fledge in 16–20 days.

DISTRIBUTION
Two separate populations: one eastern from Atherton Tableland, Qld, (where sedentary) to Tasmania and South Australia; the other western in extreme southwest of Western Australia. In east, the birds regularly move north for winter and south again in spring. Apparently two races.

This Dusky Woodswallow has built its nest in a tree hollow, though the species sometimes chooses a more exposed nest site, such as the top of a fence post.

Black Butcherbird *Cracticus quoyi* (LESSON & GARNOT, 1827)

The Black Butcherbird is moderately common in mangroves, monsoon forests and rainforest scrub in the north and northeast of Australia.

OTHER NAMES
Rufous Crow-shrike, Black
Crow-shrike.

IDENTIFICATION
LENGTH: *420–440 mm (Arnhem Land
and Cape York Peninsula race); 340–
380 mm (eastern Queensland race).*
ADULTS: *Sexes similar; male larger.
Wholly black, outer feather edges with
metallic sheen. Eye dark brown. Bill
black with light grey-blue base. Feet
and claws black.*
IMMATURES: *Two colour phases, both
produced in one brood: one dull black,
occasionally tinged brown, and found
everywhere; the other generally rufous,
limited to northeastern Queensland. In
rufous phase, upper parts variable,
usually dusky with heavy rufous-*
*brown streaks; flight feathers and tail
mid to dark brown-grey. Throat cream
becoming light cinnamon on breast,
indistinctly scalloped with black; belly
vent and underwing cinnamon-rufous.
Eye brown. Bill dark blue-grey, base
lighter. Feet slate-grey tinged olive.
Mating has been recorded in this
plumage.*

VOICE
CALL: *Loud, quick clonking*
grong-gronk *on same pitch, by male in
identity call. Loud cawing in alarm,
and range of other caws and flutings in
contact.*
SONG: *Repetitive fluting yodel,
basically* caw-caw-kuk-a-kuk, *the first
two notes up-slurred and the rest
yodelled at lower pitch.*

NESTING
*Breeds September–February. Nest a
bowl of sticks and twigs, occasionally
lined with rootlets; in forked branch
5–10 m above ground down to 2 m
above ground in mangroves. Eggs: two
or three, sometimes four; variably dull
green-grey sparingly spotted and
lightly blotched with red-brown,
lavender and brown-black, mostly
towards larger end; oval, about
35 x 25 mm. Incubation by both sexes.*

DISTRIBUTION
*Rainforests, mangroves and fringing
growth around coast and adjacent
tablelands of northern Australia:
Arnhem Land between Port Keats and
Blue Mud Bay, Cape York Peninsula
between Archer and Stewart Rivers,*
*and northeastern Queensland between
Cooktown and Ingham, with isolated
population around Mackay-Proserpine.
Also New Guinea and offshore islands.
About three races; probably two in
Australia.*

LARGEST AND MOST POWERFUL of the butcherbirds, the Black is also the only one that lives almost exclusively within rainforest. In Australia it ranges around the coastal rainforest galleries and mangroves between northeastern Queensland and Arnhem Land. Sedentary in habit, established pairs occupy permanent territories that may be as large as 10 hectares or more. These the males identify with long clonking calls from vantage perches high under the forest canopy in early morning and late afternoon, as well as with sporadic singing during the day. Both sexes sing in call-and-answer duets then and to stay in touch.

Black Butcherbirds forage through all strata of the forest, even working opportunistically out to its fringes and down to the ground, where, in mangroves, they will walk about at low tide searching for crustaceans. The birds hunt on their own with a quiet stealth, fluttering from branch to branch, diving down to pounce on prey and probing into cracks and crannies. Small birds and their eggs, large insects, crustaceans, and occasional reptiles and frogs are all eaten; even fruit is taken. Most animal prey is captured in short swooping dives; to eat it the birds will wedge it in a tree fork and then dismember it with the great hooked bill.

Both sexes share in nest-building, incubation, and the feeding of nestlings. After fledging, young are usually dispersed within several months, soon after gaining independence. Because territorial space is fully occupied, few survive.

Grey Butcherbird *Cracticus torquatus* (LATHAM, 1801)

The Grey Butcherbird is common in wooded country throughout Australia.

CARNIVOROUS BIRDS NEEDING exclusive control of their resources, no butcherbird overlaps the niche of its sister species. The separation is most subtle in the Grey and Pied Butcherbirds which range through the more open forests and woodlands around Australia. Wherever they meet, the Grey holds to the denser thickets with closer tree canopy.

Spry, bold but wary, the Grey hunts by perch-and-pounce like all butcherbirds, sitting watchfully on a vantage perch one–10 metres up, then diving to the ground or through trees after prey. Flight is direct and swift with quick shallow wing-beats. Large items are carried back to a perch in the bill and often wedged in a fork. Because its legs are short and weak, it does not anchor prey with its feet. Insects are its main food, but small birds, nestlings, reptiles and mice are all taken, as well as a few fruits and seeds.

Grey Butcherbirds are rather solitary in their feeding, and sedentary. Established pairs hold permanent territories and nest in much the same site year after year. Both sexes advertise territorial boundaries with vigorous antiphonal singing from a high tree at the opening of breeding. Either bird may initiate the song in which each sex has its individual signature phrases. After breeding, song is more sporadic and often mingled with subsong and mimicry from lower branches; immatures often join in.

Only the female incubates, fed on the nest by the male, but both parents feed the young and defend the nest fiercely. After fledging, young may stay with their parents for some time even into the next breeding season when they help to feed the new brood. Full adult plumage is not gained until their second year in southern races. Usually only one brood is reared a year.

The Black-backed Butcherbird lives in woodland on Cape York Peninsula.

Black-backed Butcherbird

Cracticus mentalis SALVADORI & d' ALBERTIS, 1876

THE BLACK-BACKED BUTCHERBIRD replaces the Grey Butcherbird on Cape York Peninsula and in southeastern New Guinea. Like the Grey it lives in territorial pairs and hunts through the mid-strata of open eucalypt forest and woodland. Although diving onto terrestrial prey from vantage perches, it also spends much time poking into cracks and crannies along branches and among shrubbery. Large insects, arboreal lizards, small birds and nestlings are its main prey, but *Acacia* seeds are also picked up. To advertise territory, particularly during breeding, the partners sing antiphonally, each contributing part of the complete song in turn.

Pied Butcherbird *Cracticus nigrogularis* (GOULD, 1837)

THE SUSTAINED FLUTED PIPING of the Pied Butcherbird is one of the purest sounds uttered by any Australian bird. Ringing through the morning air, it is given by male and female—often in antiphonal duets—from high set perches at dawn to signal territory. The birds stand with heads thrown up, ducking and stretching with the flow of notes. During breeding, singing continues sporadically through the day and even into the night.

Pied Butcherbirds live in more open woodland than other butcherbirds and have spread in southwestern Australia with clearing for farming. Arboreal and hunting by perch-and-pounce, they sit out in open places, often on posts in ploughed fields or pasture,

and spiral down onto prey. From point to point they fly swiftly and low in long undulations, usually swooping steeply up to a perch with wings spread to show their back pattern; it signals their new position. They are aggressive hunters, picking off large insects, mice, nestlings and reptiles, and even chasing small birds in flight. Pairs often hunt together, one backing up the other.

Pied Butcherbirds hold permanent territories but are more communal than other butcherbirds, and often live in family parties of three to five—the breeding pair and their young of several years. Young birds do not gain adult plumage until their second annual moult and help their parents feed later broods of siblings.

OTHER NAMES
Black-throated Butcherbird, Black-throated Crow-shrike, Break-o'day Boy, Organbird.

IDENTIFICATION
LENGTH: *320–360 mm.*
ADULTS: *Sexes similar. Head, neck, upper back, throat and breast black. Collar, rump, lower breast and belly white. Wings black with broad white bar through secondary coverts to secondaries; base primaries edged white. Tail black, tipped white on outer feathers. Eye dark brown. Bill blue-grey, tip hooked and black. Feet black.*
IMMATURES: *Black areas of adults dull brown; eyebrow buff-brown. Very young birds have no sign of darker 'bib' on off-white throat.*

VOICE
CALL: *Strident shriek, reek, in alarm.*
SONG: *Superb. Of sustained far-carrying fluted pipings, often in duet, with one sex calling higher, the other lower in mellow tones.*

NESTING
Breeds August–December; in tropical areas May–November. Nest a cup of sticks; lined with rootlets and fine grass; placed upright in fork of tree 5 m or more above ground. Eggs: three–five; dull green, spotted with brown or black; oval, about 33 x 24 mm.

DISTRIBUTION
Open woodlands throughout warmer parts of mainland, south in west to south coast and in east to about Murray River. Absent from sandy deserts and South Australian gulfs. No races.

The Pied Butcherbird builds a cup-shaped nest of sticks and lines it with rootlets and fine grass. The female usually lays four dull green brown-spotted eggs.

Australian Magpie *Gymnorhina tibicen* (LATHAM, 1801)

An Australian Magpie at its nest. The various subspecies of Australian Magpies have black, white or grey backs. This is a male of the western race.

TAKING ITS NAME FROM an unrelated pied crow in Europe, the Australian Magpie is essentially a butcherbird that feeds on the ground, has become insectivorous, and lives in communal groups. To suit its different niche, it has long powerful feet for walking, running and hopping, a short tail that keeps out of the way of the ground, a straightened bill for probing and grasping, and long pointed wings for flying over open spaces quickly.

Daily routines are simple. The birds leave their roosting trees in the early morning, usually after several carolling duets to reaffirm territory, and fly and glide down to open fields, spreading out to feed. They stay there for most of the day, walking methodically about, stopping and looking, head on side, then jabbing the bill into soft ground, under cow pats or into crevices to grasp a range of invertebrates. Only during hot midday hours or rainy weather do they go to shelter in trees.

Magpies are sedentary and live in territorial groups of three to about 24 birds in southwestern Australia and two–40 hectares—or even more inland—depending on the number of birds in the group and the quality of the habitat. The group depends on the territory not only for food but also for safe nesting and roosting sites; all members defend it year round. Territories of the right size with sufficient resources—open field plus trees—are at a premium.

Magpies cope with these limitations by social stratification. At the top is the permanent territorial group, large enough to defend its territory capably without depleting resources. Females usually predominate and one of the males dominates the rest, mating with

any or all of the females during breeding. Next come marginal groups whose territories are lower in quality and which rarely nest successfully. Below them are more mobile groups whose members are not fixed and which roost away from their feeding areas.

On the bottom rung are loose non-territorial flocks—of immatures evicted from parental territories, adults without territorial status, and older birds whose territorial groups have disintegrated. These flocks can grow to hundreds, specially in autumn and winter at local flushes of food, and they never attempt nesting.

The coming of breeding brings much jockeying for social position and territory, and song battles grow between neighbouring groups as their members gather on high perches to sing in chorus. Within groups, subordinate males try to steal matings with females. These females nest on their own, building and incubating unaided. Usually only one is fed by the dominant male, and then not much because of his preoccupation with defence of territory and his other females. It is rare for nests other than those supported and made secure by him to produce hatchlings.

Even after young hatch, the burden of their brooding and feeding remains largely with their parental female until they fledge, before they can fly properly. For the next several months, young follow any adult in sight for food, and their cawing begging becomes one of the familiar sounds of early summer. By autumn they can care for themselves and then are usually driven forcibly out of the group—chased, grappled and pecked by adult members—to join the floating non-territorial flocks.

OTHER NAMES
Black-backed Magpie, White-backed Magpie, Western Magpie, Long-billed Magpie, Flute Bird, Piping Crow-shrike.

IDENTIFICATION
LENGTH: *380–440 mm.*
MALE: *Face and head black. Hind-neck, back and rump white or with broad black back band in northern and eastern Australia north of mid-Victoria; scapulars black. Wings black; upper and underwing coverts white. Tail white with broad to narrow black tip. Underparts uniformly black. Eye red-brown. Bill grey-white; tip black. Feet black.*

FEMALE: *As male of respective race but white of back and on hind-neck flecked grey or, in southwestern Australia, feathers of back centred black with white edges; bill shorter.*
IMMATURES: *Dusky parts of adult plumage scalloped buff for first year, greyer in second; white parts flecked grey; buff-white eyebrow after first moult.*

VOICE
CALL: *Loud shout and descending caw in alarm or warning; shrieking yodel in aggression, often in flight to fights. Young beg with whining cawing.*
SONG: *Organ-like fluted carolling, often in group duets. Subsong by individual*

birds includes some mimicry.

NESTING
Breeds June–December. Nest a basket of sticks, plant stems, even wire; lined with wool, hair and grass; placed in outer canopy of eucalypt or other tree, even telegraph pole, 5–20 m above ground. Eggs: one–six, usually three–five; blue or green, blotched and streaked with red-browns; oval, about 38 x 27 mm. Incubation 20 days, by female. Young fledge in about four weeks.

DISTRIBUTION
Eucalypt woodlands throughout most of Australia. Also southern New Guinea. About six races; probably five in

Australia, differing mostly in patterning of back—black or white—but all hybridising and intergrading where they meet.

Pied Currawong *Strepera graculina* (SHAW, 1790)

Pied Currawongs are common in southeastern Australia. They live in tall forest in summer and move to the plains and to towns in the winter months.

IT HAS BEEN ESTIMATED that there are a million Pied Currawongs in the forests of southeastern Australia alone. The nests are less frequently seen, however, for the birds breed as scattered pairs in thick tall forests in the Great Dividing Range. Some currawongs stay in the high country all year round but most winter on lower tablelands and plains. They wander nomadically and tend to form flocks which can number more than 100 birds. Some birds, particularly non-breeding adults and immatures, may travel as much as 300 kilometres. During winter many of them invade cities and towns to forage on lawns, and fly each evening to communal roosts, with undulating deep lapping wing-beats. Further north to coastal Queensland they are more sedentary.

Pied Currawongs are omnivorous scavengers, and hunt for food anywhere, bounding about the branches of trees poking into foliage and crevices, or walking, running or hopping, one foot in front of the other, over the ground to peck, probe and jab. They often walk with tail part-cocked and one wing drooped. Carrion, small birds, insects, caterpillars, lizards, snails and berries are all eaten; stick insects are specially favoured and the birds concentrate on local plagues of them.

During breeding both members of a pair defend a territory and gather most of their food within its boundaries. Both also gather nesting material, but only the female seems to build, selecting sticks more carefully and working mostly in mid-morning to finish the structure in about 14 days. She incubates unaided but is fed at the nest by the male. Both parents feed the young until some weeks after they fledge, and the family continues to occupy the territory until the end of the summer season. Only one brood is raised.

OTHER NAMES
(Pied) Bell Magpie, Black Magpie, Chillawong, Currawong, Mountain Magpie.

IDENTIFICATION
LENGTH: *440–480 mm.*
ADULTS: *Sexes similar. Generally sooty black with white band at base of primaries and tail, and white tip on tail; undertail coverts white. Eye yellow. Bill heavy, aquiline and black. Feet black.*
IMMATURES: *Paler and browner.*

VOICE
CALL & SONG: *Variations on loud, ringing several-syllabled croak,* krik-krik-bewaiir, *the last note down-slurred, or guttural, wailing* jabawok-jabawok *in north, given in identification, often in flight. Also long-drawn falling whistle at perch; shorter whistles and guttural croaks in 'conversation'.*

NESTING
Breeds August–January; commences in July in north. Nest a cup of sticks, lined with roots, grasses and bark; placed 7–25 m above ground in fork in outer branch of eucalypt. Eggs: usually three; light brown marked with blotches and freckles of darker brown; oval, about 42 x 30 mm. Incubation about three weeks, by female. Young fledge in about 30 days.

DISTRIBUTION
All eastern seaboard ranging up to 400 km inland from Cape York Peninsula to Grampians, Vic. Breeds in tall forest but moves to plains and townships in winter. Also Lord Howe Island. Three races; two in Australia.

Black Currawong

Strepera fuliginosa (GOULD, 1837)

SHORT-TAILED, CROW-LIKE Black Currawongs represent the Pied Currawong in Tasmania. Like the Pied, they nest in isolated pairs in wetter mountain forests and high tablelands in summer, and flock to wander more widely in autumn and winter. Sometimes several hundred gather and move down to milder valley farmland then, visiting orchards, parks and gardens for scraps.

Although bounding about tree branches to poke and glean, Black Currawongs spend much time feeding on the ground, even wading in shallow water and probing seaweed on beaches. They eat carrion, insects, berries and small vertebrates, sometimes wedging them in crevices to butcher. In flight, they float high with the loose lapping wing-beats and swoops characteristic of currawongs.

OTHER NAMES
Black Bell Magpie, Black Magpie, Black Jay, Mountain Magpie, Sooty Currawong.

IDENTIFICATION
LENGTH: *470–490 mm.*
ADULTS: *Sexes similar. Black with small white bar in primaries and white tips to wings and tail. Eye yellow. Bill and feet black.*
IMMATURES: *Duller; mouth yellow.*

VOICE
CALL & SONG: *Rending, long-drawn rolling croak in identification, often in flight. Also soft croaks and whistles in 'conversation'.*

NESTING
Breeds August–December. Nest a bulky cup of sticks; placed high in a forest tree.

Eggs: two–four; grey-buff blotched with red-brown and purple; oval, about 40 x 29 mm.

DISTRIBUTION
Confined to Tasmania and Bass Strait Islands. No races.

The Black Currawong is common in the wetter forests of Tasmania.

Grey Currawong *Strepera versicolor* (LATHAM, 1801)

THE RINGING CALL OF THIS currawong at once draws attention to its presence in the sclerophyll forests and denser mallee and mulga woodlands of southern Australia. An even leaner, more rakish bird than the Pied Currawong, it is also more solitary, living in rather sedentary pairs or as single birds within the forests and rarely emerging into open woodlands except, sporadically, in winter. Only in Tasmania does it flock much and then in loose groups no larger than 30–40 in winter.

Grey Currawongs explore all levels of the forest for food, from upper branches to the ground, picking up a range of insects, small vertebrates, eggs and young birds robbed from nests, and many berries. Whether in trees or on the ground, the currawongs bound about heavily; in flight they float through the trees in the deep swooping undulations characteristic of currawongs, but with even slower lapping wing-beats.

The Grey Currawong has a more slender, pick-like bill than the Pied Currawong, and uses it to feed in different ways. Commonly it clings to the trunks of eucalypts and levers off bark to get at insects underneath. On rocky ground, it will also crook its head to one side and force the bill under a stone, turning it over for insects and reptiles beneath. Insects in the litter of the forest floor and under tree bark, however, are its main prey.

Grey Currawongs breed in isolated pairs in a large defended territory. Only the female incubates but both parents feed the young which remain dependent for several months through summer. Only one brood is raised a year.

OTHER NAMES
Squeaker, Bell Magpie, Black-winged Currawong, Bell Crow-shrike, Brown Currawong, Brown Crow-shrike, Grey Bell-magpie, Grey Crow-shrike, Grey Magpie, Rainbird.

IDENTIFICATION
LENGTH: *450–510 mm; size varies throughout range: largest birds are in Tasmania (S. v. arguta).*
ADULTS: *Sexes similar. Body colour variable, from mid-grey with duskier tail in New South Wales and Victoria (S.v. versicolor) to dusky in Tasmania and Murray Mallee–Mt Lofty Ranges, SA, (S.v. melanoptera) and dark-grey in central and Western Australia and Yorke and Eyre Peninsulas, SA (S.v. plumbea). Undertail coverts and tip of tail white; white band at base of wing primaries in all but Murray Mallee–Mt Lofty Ranges race. Eye yellow. Bill and feet black.*
IMMATURES: *Similar to adults, but duller.*

VOICE
CALL & SONG: *Ringing double-note kring-kring or chling-chling on same pitch in east or more protracted kreee-ling in South Australia, keer-keer-kink or klink-klank in Tasmania, often in flight. Also soft mewing notes and trumpet-like squeaks.*

NESTING
Breeds July–November. Nest a shallow cup of twigs; lined with coarse rootlets and grass; placed in horizontal foliaged tree fork 3–14 m above ground. Eggs: two or three; stone-brown to pink-buff with dark brown, red-brown and lilac-grey spots and blotches; oval, about 42 x 30 mm. Incubation by female.

DISTRIBUTION
Coastal and subcoastal open forests, close woodlands, mallee and close mulga around southern Australia, from Shark Bay, WA, to about Hunter Valley, NSW. Also isolated populations in central Australian ranges and Tasmania. Four races.

The black-winged race of Grey Currawong, of the Murray Mallee.

Australian Raven *Corvus coronoides* Vigors & Horsfield, 1827

THE PASTORAL INDUSTRY, by providing frequent watering places and an abundance of carrion, has probably benefited the Australian Raven. This big black bird, the largest member of the crow family in Australia, is frequently responsible for clearing up carrion. Its large bill can penetrate the carcasses of animals up to the size of sheep, and it has been widely blamed for killing young lambs. Careful examination of thousands of lamb carcasses, however, has shown that the vast majority of lambs on which Australian Ravens had fed were either already dead or almost dead. During the warmer months, Australian Ravens eat mainly insects, and their diet includes such agricultural pests as grasshoppers and army worms. They are birds of open pastures around southern Australia and the northeastern inland, and rarely forage in forests.

Australian Ravens do not breed until they are three or more years old. Until then they forage nomadically in flocks of 30 or more. Once they pair, they occupy a territory of about 100 hectares, within which they find most of their food, and roost and breed. Australian Ravens pair for life and breeding pairs occupy their territory year round. Husbanding its resources, they even larder food in crannies in trees.

Each morning, soon after sunrise, the pairs reaffirm the boundaries of their territories by patrolling and calling. On a still morning the countryside resounds with their wailing calls.

Australian Ravens have no courtship displays apart from mutual preening by members of the pair and occasional chasing flights. In flight, the birds often flutter along on quivering wings, quite distinct from the deep, cuckoo-like undulations of the crows. They breed in spring, irrespective of latitude. Both sexes build the nest, frequently working together. A nest is usually completed in two–three weeks. If a clutch fails and the pair attempt again, the nest may be ready in five days but in this case it is usually an old nest refurbished. Only the female incubates but the male feeds her on the nest, sometimes once every half-hour. Breeding is seasonal, irrespective of latitude, and begins in July.

After leaving the nest, the young birds remain in their parents' territory for three to four months, fed at first by their parents but becoming increasingly independent. In the summer these young birds join passing nomadic flocks which feed on grasshoppers or spilt grain in fields of stubble, and family ties are broken. The parents are heavily in moult at that time and their defence of the territory is at a minimum.

Sixty-two per cent of Australian Ravens die before they are one year old but after that mortality decreases. It has been found that in more closely settled areas, such as the Canberra district, annual mortality among Australian Ravens is about 23 per cent, but as little as 15 per cent on large pastoral stations inland.

OTHER NAMES
Crow, Kelly, Raven.

IDENTIFICATION
LENGTH: *480–540 mm.*
ADULTS: *Sexes alike. Plumage wholly black, with purple and green gloss; underdown dusky grey. Throat feathers of long, round-tipped hackles that are flared conspicuously in a shaggy bag as bird calls; flanked by narrow areas of bare black skin running down either side of chin from base of underbill. Eye white, with blue inner ring. Massive bill black. Feet dusky black.*
IMMATURES: *As adults, but breast and belly sooty black; underdown paler greyish; eye brown.*

VOICE
CALL & SONG: *Powerful, high, nasal, wailing cawing,* aah-aah-aahaah, *mainly in series of three, the last note long-drawn, falling and fading; given in territorial advertisement, sometimes in flight but usually on perch, the bird standing horizontal, head forward and hackles flared. Also softer, shorter warbled caws in contact and 'conversation', but usually tenor in tone.*

NESTING
Breeds July–September. Nest a large stick basket; lined with bark and wool felted together in a thick mat; usually more than 10 m above ground in a tree fork providing good all-round lookout. Substantial nests may last for several years. Eggs: four or five; green, heavily blotched and spotted with dark olive-brown; oblong-oval, about 45 x 30 mm. Incubation 20 days, by female. Young fledge in about 43 days.

DISTRIBUTION
Better-watered pastoral areas of southwestern and all eastern Australia north to Gulf of Carpentaria, where more abundant inland than on more tropical east coast north of Hunter Valley, NSW. Two races.

The Australian Raven can be distinguished from other ravens and crows by its long throat feathers and wailing call.

The Forest Raven is the only member of the family that lives in Tasmania.

Forest Raven

Corvus tasmanicus MATHEWS, 1912

OTHER NAMES
None.

IDENTIFICATION
LENGTH: *520–540 mm.*
ADULTS: *Sexes similar. Plumage wholly black, with green and purple gloss; underdown dusky grey. Throat hackles short and indistinct. Eye white, with blue inner ring. Bill and feet black.*
IMMATURES: *As adults; breast and belly feathers sooty brown; underdown paler greyish; eye brown.*

VOICE
CALL & SONG: *Deep short, basso cawing, korr-korr-korr-korr, last note drawn out, in territorial advertisement; also short deep 'conversational' caws.*

NESTING
Breeds August–November. Nest a large stick basket; lined with bark and wool in mat; placed high in a tree, usually in an upright fork. Eggs: usually four; pale green blotched and spotted with dark and olive-brown; oblong-oval, about 46 x 31 mm. Incubation by female.

DISTRIBUTION
Tasmania and islands in Bass Strait; southeast coast between western Gippsland, Vic., and southeastern South Australia; New England Tableland and adjacent coast between South West Rocks and Port Stephens, NSW. Two races.

THE MOST CHARACTERISTIC feature of the Forest Raven is its short deep baritone cawing which resounds through the forest. It is the biggest of the ravens and the only one occurring in Tasmania. On the mainland there are small populations along the southeast coast as well as in northern New South Wales on the New England tableland and adjacent coast. Such scattered populations suggest that the range of the species was once much wider, and that it has been pushed back by changing habitat and more effective competition from other adaptable corvids.

The New England race, which has larger wings and tail than others, defends territories against Australian Ravens and Torresian Crows, as well as against others of its own species. Adult birds of all three species live in their territories year round, but they breed at slightly different times of the year, forage in different places, and have strikingly different calls. Only the Forest Raven, for example, feeds consistently below a closed canopy of trees.

The south coast race of Forest Raven can be distinguished from Australian and Little Ravens there by its very much shorter tail. In Tasmania, it exploits all the opportunities available to a large omnivorous bird, feeding on carrion, insects and plant material in about equal quantities, even foraging on beaches. It is sometimes a pest in vegetable crops, damaging seedlings, potatoes and maize.

Forest Ravens appear to live in nomadic flocks until they pair and take up residence in a territory that covers 40 hectares or more.

Little Raven *Corvus mellori* MATHEWS, 1912

SO SIMILAR ARE THE Little Raven and the Australian Raven in appearance that for many years the former was not recognised as a separate species. The two live side by side throughout the open woodlands of southeastern Australia where the range of the Little is almost completely overlapped by the Australian. Competition between them, however, is largely avoided because of differences in their way of life and behaviour.

The Little Raven is nomadic, sociable and flocks. While adult Australian Ravens hold permanent territory exclusively in pairs in the most productive habitat, Little Ravens shift about to forage over marginal habitat as well, congregating to exploit any sudden flushes of food. In well-watered agricultural areas, movements are usually small, and breeding adults almost sedentary. But in inland New South Wales, flocks of up to several hundred—mostly subadults and non-breeders—travel southeast in summer to better-watered foothills and mountains. Some birds travel more than 400 kilometres, flying high in cohesive groups in a consistent direction. The birds that breed in the Snowy Mountains move differently. As summer draws to a close they desert the alpine region for fringing forests and woodlands, where they feed largely on stick insects, before moving to adjacent plains.

Little Ravens are as omnivorous as the Australian Raven and will eat carrion, but their slender bills make it virtually impossible for them to kill dying lambs. They eat instead very large quantities of insects gleaned from foliage and branches in trees as well as from the ground. Insects can account for 60 per cent of their diet, compared with 15 per cent carrion and 25 per cent plant matter, much of it grain spilt in stubble at harvest time.

Breeding habits also differ from the Australian Raven's. Little Ravens nest in groups in tightly clustered territories and feed far beyond their boundaries. Several pairs may even nest in one tree although most territories, held only during breeding, are about two–three hectares. Often the territories overlap those of Australian Ravens, but the two do not compete even there because the Little usually forages well away and builds in smaller trees.

Little Ravens advertise their territories with short cawings and shuffle their wings above their backs while doing so. Courtship takes the form of a strutting promenade. Often nesting a month later than the Australian Raven, Little Ravens are more adaptable in timing their breeding. Inland they generally lay in August–September, but in alpine regions their feeding grounds are still under snow then and they seldom begin laying before late September and may continue into December.

The Little Raven is only slightly smaller that the Australian Raven.

OTHER NAMES
None.

IDENTIFICATION
LENGTH: *480–500 mm.*
ADULTS: *Sexes alike. Plumage wholly black, with green and purple gloss; underdown dusky grey. Throat hackles indistinct. Eye white, blue inner ring. Bill and feet black.*
IMMATURES: *As adult but sooty ventrally; underdown whitish grey; eye brown.*

VOICE
CALL & SONG: *Guttural baritone cawing,* kar-kar-kar-kar *or* ark-ark-ark, *in contact and advertisement.*

NESTING
Breeds August–September or as early as May; in alpine regions September–December. Nest a substantial stick basket; lined with bark, wool and frequently Emu feathers; placed at junction of three stems in tree or, in treeless areas, on telegraph poles and bushes. Eggs: four or five; pale green, boldly marked with dark and olive-brown blotches and spots; oblong-oval, about 44 x 30 mm. Incubation 19–20 days, by female. Young fledge in 35–41 days.

DISTRIBUTION
Woodlands and fields of southeastern mainland, also King Island. No races.

Little Crow *Corvus bennetti* NORTH, 1901

IN MANY INLAND TOWNS Little Crows may be seen perching on roofs and telephone wires. They are typically nomads of the arid inland but in Western Australia they are common right along the midwestern coast and during summer usually migrate into the coastal plain between Perth and Bunbury. Elsewhere they only move towards the coast when conditions are particularly bad inland. Some have been recorded travelling over 600 kilometres.

Little Crows are sociable, and birds of all ages mix in small to large flocks of up to several hundred. Flying flocks often carry out spectacular aerial displays. In unison they spiral upwards on the thermal and then plummet earthwards and pull out of a dive, with a whistling rush of wings, only 30–40 metres above ground. When calling in flight they often undulate steeply like cuckoos, holding wings to body through the bottom of each swoop. On perches, they flick the wings up and tail down with each cawing note.

Like other Australian corvids, Little Crows are omnivorous and scavenge much around refuse tips and towns inland. Diet comprises about 26 per cent carrion, 48 per cent insects and 26 per cent plant matter. With their finer bills they can pick residual morsels from carcasses relinquished by larger corvids and kites.

Little Crows breed mainly in spring, but if halted by drought they can nest in response to the return of favourable conditions. They most commonly breed in loose colonies with nests only 20–50 metres apart. The clutches are usually laid within a few days of one another. Where trees are scarce inland, Little Crows nest on telephone poles, an unpopular practice for the nests often contain wire and can cause short-circuits. Nests are unlike those of all other Australian crows and ravens, the birds adding lumps of clay to the stick foundation, under the lining. Because of this, they invariably breed within reach of some surface water.

Little Crows feed their nestlings mainly on insects. Both parents tend them, although in the early stages, before they grow feathers, the female spends much of her time brooding. Food brought by the male is passed first to the female which in turn feeds the nestlings. It is a pattern that continues for about two weeks, the female also depending on the male for her food then.

Little Crows have warbling and creaking calls which they utter during their midday resting period, presumably to keep contact.

OTHER NAMES
Kelly, Small-billed Crow.

IDENTIFICATION
LENGTH: *450–480 mm.*
ADULTS: *Sexes similar. Plumage wholly black, with purple and green gloss; underdown pure white, clearly demarcate. No hackles. Eye white, with blue inner ring. Bill and feet black.*
IMMATURES: *As adults but breast and belly sooty brown; underdown greyish white; eye brown.*

VOICE
CALL & SONG: *Nasal baritone cawing,* nark-nark-nark *or* k'larp-k'larp-k'larp, *the notes short and clipped, in contact and advertisement, from perch or in flight. Also bubbled guttural warble and soft jarring caw in close contact.*

NESTING
Breeds July–October, but also after good rains. Nest a solid basket of sticks, well lined with wool, feathers and bark; often a layer of mud between lining and sticks; usually placed in three-way fork of tree, 1–10 m or more above ground. Eggs: three–six, usually four; pale green boldly marked with dark and olive brown spots and blotches; oblong-oval, about 39 x 27 mm. Incubation 17–19 days, by female. Young fledge in 29–31 days.

DISTRIBUTION
All inland areas north to about 20°S and Barkly Tableland, NT; reaches coast in Western Australia. No races.

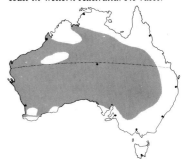

The nest of the Little Crow is distinctive in that it is lined with clay overlain with a pad of wool, feathers and bark fibre.

The Torresian Crow is common across tropical Australia, through the dry inland and along the northeast coast, maintaining permanent territory.

Torresian Crow *Corvus orru* BONAPARTE, 1851

ACROSS THE NORTH OF Australia, the Torresian Crow occupies much the same ecological niche as the Australian Raven in the south. Where they meet through inland northeastern Australia, both defend territories against one another and others of their own species. Conflict is only reduced where the crow breeds a month or two later than the raven and nests in less particular sites.

Like the ravens, Torresian Crows are sedentary and live territorially in premium habitat that provides all their needs for food, roosting and nesting. It is a mixture of pasture, field and treed woodland or open forest around the coast and eucalypt-lined watercourses and hill valleys in the drier inland. Although roaming flocks of 50–60 form in autumn and winter—mostly of immatures and non-breeding adults—established pairs hold a permanent territory. Territories commonly cover 100–200 hectares.

Torresian Crows feed mainly on the ground, walking about or hopping one foot in front of the other to move faster or before taking flight. Like other Australian corvids they are omnivorous and will scavenge almost anything anywhere. They visit refuse dumps and slaughter yards, pick at carcasses of road-killed animals, and land on crops to pick grain. Maize and sorghum are attacked in this way, and the birds also take other seeds and fruit on the ground. Their diet, overall, comprises about 26 per cent carrion, 43 per cent insects, and 31 per cent plant material.

When travelling, the crows fly easily through and over tree tops with shallow loping wing-beats, much as do Little Crows. They call often, in rather staccato caws, both on the wing and from perches to advertise territory and to maintain contact among pairs and groups. In flight, calling birds often undulate steeply, wings to body, like cuckoos; on perches they stand with head thrown forward and wings jerking up and tail down as each note is uttered.

As is usual in corvids, only the female incubates but both adults feed the young. Nests are often parasitised by Channel-billed Cuckoos, a fate unknown in any other Australian crow or raven. Fledged young remain with their parents for several months before being driven out and dispersed.

Until about 20 years ago it was thought that this species, the Little Crow and the Australian Raven were the only corvids in Australia. Now it is known that there are five. Their similarity to one another and their white eyes—which are unique among the world's crows—suggest that all evolved from a common ancestor that arrived fairly recently, in geological terms, in Australia.

How they split off from one another makes for fascinating conjecture. The first split probably developed between the crows in the northern Torresian forests and the ravens in the Bassian south. Not only do both crows have pure white feather bases but they also often undulate like cuckoos when calling in flight. None of the ravens seem to have these traits.

The evolution of species within the crows and the ravens might then be explained most simply by sequences of east–west invasions north and south of a central desert region. In the north, past changes in climate broke up habitat and separated ancestral crows into two populations, one in the east, the other in the west or centre. The one in the west then evolved in isolation into the Little Crow and the one in the east into the Australian Crow. When climate later ameliorated and allowed the birds and their habitat to spread and overlap once more, the two crows kept apart, perhaps no longer able to interbreed.

The sequence in the south was more complicated because three species of raven are involved. What could have happened is that ancestral ravens across southern Australia were first split into progenitors of the Forest Raven in the east and the Little Raven in the west. Then climate changed, allowing ancestral Little Ravens to colonise the east, only to change again and cut them off.

The eastern isolate became the Little Raven as we now know it; the remnant in the west developed into the Australian Raven which has since spread east once more.

OTHER NAMES
Australian Crow, Crow, Kelly, Large-billed Crow.

IDENTIFICATION
LENGTH: *480–540 mm.*
ADULTS: *Sexes similar. Plumage wholly black, with green and purple gloss; underdown pure white, clearly demarcated. Throat hackles short and inconspicuous. Eye white, with blue inner ring. Bill and feet black.*
IMMATURES: *As adults but breast and belly sooty brown; underdown greyish white; eye brown. Eye does not whiten until third year, as in other Australian corvids.*

VOICE
CALL & SONG: *Nasal, high-pitched cawing uk-uk-uk-uk-uk or ok-ok-ok-ok-ok-ok, the notes short and clipped, in contact and advertisement, from perch or in flight; never an aaa sound as in Australian Raven. Occasionally more long-drawn caws, resembling those of Little Crow. Western birds give long garbled yodelling caw in flight, possibly as territory marker.*

NESTING
Breeds August–October in south; farther north eggs are still laid in February. Nest of finer twigs than in other crow nests; scantily lined; usually placed in tree canopy, presumably for shade; 4–9 m above ground. Eggs: usually five; pale green, lightly or boldly marked with dark and olive brown spots and blotches according to race; oblong-oval, about 44 x 30 mm. Incubation by female.

DISTRIBUTION
Common and widespread across tropical Australian woodlands. Northern population extends west to Kimberleys, southwest to central Australian ranges and southeast to coastal New South Wales (Port Stephens). Isolated by Great Sandy and Simpson Deserts, western population ranges from Pilbara south to beyond Kalgoorlie. Also Moluccas, New Guinea, New Britain and Tanimbar. Four or five races; probably two in Australia.

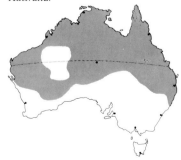

Rare visitors, escaped captives . . .

In addition to the birds that breed in or regularly visit Australia, others come only rarely, as wandering vagrants or off-course migrants. There are also birds that have escaped from captivity or been released intentionally. All these are described briefly below.

Many migrants are difficult to identify and verify on sight; only those accepted by the Records Appraisal Committee of the Royal Australasian Ornithologists Union and that Union's Atlas of Australian Birds are included here.

Rare visitors

South Georgian Diving-Petrel
Pelecanoides georgicis
As Common Diving-Petrel; slit-like nostrils. Breeds off New Zealand and sub-antarctic islands; straggles off southeastern and southwestern mainland.

Bullers Albatross *Diomedea bulleri*
Resembles Grey-headed Albatross; smaller; white forehead. Breeds on islands southeast of NZ; occasional off southeastern Australia.

Antarctic Petrel *Thalassoica antarctica*
Brown-grey above, white below, broad white upper wing stripe. Breeds in Antarctica; five records off southeastern Australia.

Mottled Petrel *Pterodroma inexpectata*
Grey-bellied, diagonal black underwing stripe. Trans-Pacific migrant breeding off NZ; straggles to southeastern Australian waters.

Cook's Petrel *Pterodroma cookii*
Resembles Black-winged Petrel; paler above, thin black edge to underwing. Trans-Pacific migrant breeding off NZ; three records off NSW.

Snow Petrel *Pagodroma nivea*
A white, black-billed petrel of Antarctic pack ice; several records off southeast coast.

Grey Petrel *Procellaria cinerea*
Plain grey-brown, paler underparts. Breeds on subantarctic islands; straggles to waters off southern mainland.

Black Petrel *Procellaria parkinsoni*
Black, pale-billed. Breeds in NZ; migrates east–west in southern Pacific; one record at Sydney Heads, 1875.

Westland Petrel *Procellaria westlandica*
As Black Petrel; larger. Breeds locally in NZ; visits eastern Australian coast sporadically.

Manx Shearwater *Puffinus puffinus*
As Fluttering or Hutton's Shearwater; larger; pure white 'armpits'. Trans-Atlantic and eastern Pacific migrant; one Australian record at Venus Bay, 1961—a bird banded in Wales.

Leach's Storm-Petrel *Oceanodroma leucorhoa*
White-rumped, fork-tailed. Breeds in northern Atlantic and Pacific; migrates south of equator; stragglers off southwestern and southeastern Australia.

Sooty Storm-Petrel *Oceanodroma matsudairae*
All sooty, fork-tailed. Breeds in northwestern Pacific; migrates to Indian Ocean; reaches northwestern shelf.

King Penguin *Aptenodytes patagonicus*
Very large; orange-eared; of subantarctic waters; infrequently straggles off southwestern and southeastern mainland in winter.

Gentoo Penguin *Pygoscelis papua*
Moderately large; white band around hind-crown from eye to eye. Breeds in Antarctic, subantarctic waters; three records from Tasmania.

Chinstrap Penguin *Pygoscelis antarctica*
Pied, black line around face under chin. Breeds in Antarctica; has wandered to Tasmania at least twice.

Snares Penguin *Eudyptes robustus*
Recumbent crest, bulbous red bill, white gape. Breeds on Snares Islands; several records from Tasmania and southeastern mainland.

Macaroni Penguin *Eudyptes chrysolophus*
Recumbent yellow crest, plain red bill. Stragglers of whiter-faced race from Macquarie Island sometimes reach southeastern waters.

Magellanic Penguin *Spheniscus magellanicus*
The pied jackass penguin; black-and-white banded throat. Breeds off subantarctic South America; one record from Phillip Island, 1976.

Christmas Frigatebird *Fregata andrewsi*
Very large; black head, white belly. Breeds only on Christmas Island; once blown to Darwin by storms, January 1974.

Cape Gannet *Morus capensis*
Like Australasian Gannet; tail blacker, thick black stripe under chin. Breeds southern Africa; one individual in colony of Australasian Gannets on Wedge Island, Port Phillip Bay, 1981-3.

Yellow Bittern *Ixobrychus sinensis*
Resembles Little Bittern; bill longer, male brown-backed. Ranges from central eastern Asia to Papuasia; straggles to Australia by accident: Kalgoorlie and maybe Queensland.

Garganey *Anas querquedula*
Shoveller-like teal; white eyebrow, dusky foreneck, white belly. Breeds in Eurasia; migrates to New Guinea; overshoots sporadically across northern Australia.

Northern Shoveller *Anas clypeata*
Green head, white breast (males). Holarctic migrant wintering in tropical America and southern Afro-Asia; stragglers have reached Australia at least twice.

Red-legged Crake *Rallina fasciata*
Large; plain russet head and neck, black-and-white banded breast, belly and wings. Breeding migrant through southeastern Asia; straggled once to Broome, WA.

Corncrake *Crex crex*
Large; brown, black-mottled. Breeds northern Eurasia; migrates to Africa; stragglers twice recorded: Sydney 1893, off Fremantle 1944.

Pheasant-tailed Jacana
Hydrophasianus chirurgus
Plain-headed, black band from eyes across breast in non-breeding plumage. Breeds in southern Asia; one straggler at Paraburdoo, WA, in 1974.

Little Ringed Plover *Charadrius dubius*
Orange-legged, ring-breasted, white wing bar. Breeds Eurasia southeast to New Guinea; Asian migrants reach northern Australian shores in most summers in very small numbers.

Ringed Plover *Charadrius hiaticula*
Larger; orange-legged; ring-breasted without white wing bar. Breeds in Holarctic; migrates to Africa and southern Asia; reaches Australia sporadically, across north and down east coasts.

Caspian Plover *Charadrius asiaticus*
As Oriental Plover in non-breeding plumage; underwing white with black trailing edge. Breeds across central Eurasia; migrates to Africa; one confirmed record from Pine Creek, NT, in 1896.

Upland Sandpiper *Bartramia longicauda*
Small plover-like curlew; erect stance, straight bill. Breeds in northern America; migrates to South America; one Australian record: Sydney, 1848.

Redshank *Tringa totanus*
Medium-sized, long-billed; reddish legs, white rump and tail, white trailing edge to wings. A Palaearctic migrant wintering in Africa and southern Asia; sporadic in northern and southern coastal Australia over summer.

Lesser Yellowlegs *Tringa flavipes*
Resembles Greenshank; head darker, upper rump brown, 'legs' orange-yellow. Holarctic migrant; once recorded at Geelong, January-March 1983.

Baird's Sandpiper *Calidris bairdii*
Medium-sized; scaly plumage, dusky tail, white wing bar. Breeds in eastern Holarctic; migrates to southern America; rare stragglers to southeastern Australian coast.

White-rumped Sandpiper *Calidris fuscicollis*
Medium-sized; scaly plumage, white rump, faint wing bar, dark legs. Breeds in Nearctic; migrates to southern America; rare vagrants on eastern Australian coast to southwest.

Little Stint *Calidris minuta*
As Red-necked Stint; whiter throat, more brightly patterned upper parts in breeding plumage. Breeds in northwestern Eurasia; migrates to southern Afro-Asia; several records in Port Phillip Bay.

Cox's Sandpiper *Calidris paramelanotos*
Maybe no more than a hybrid between Dunlin and Sharp-tailed Sandpiper. Migratory wader known only from sporadic stragglers in non-breeding plumage in southeastern Australia in summer; all Australian records of Dunlins, *Calidris alpina*, seem to be of this 'species'.

Buff-breasted Sandpiper *Tryngites ruficollis*
Plover-like; buff toning, black bar on white underwing. Breeds from eastern Siberia to northwestern America; migrates to South America; accidental stragglers reach southeastern Australian coast.

Stilt Sandpiper *Micropalama himantopus*
Rather large; greyish, long yellowish legs, no wing bar. Breeds in Nearctic tundras; migrates to southern America; strays recorded Darwin area.

Grey Phalarope *Phalaropus fulicarius*
In non-breeding plumage grey-rumped, white wing-bar, plain grey back. Breeds in far Arctic, pelagic when not breeding; one Australian record at Swan Hill, Vic., summer 1976.

Wilson's Phalarope *Phalaropus tricolor*
In non-breeding plumage, plain grey upper parts, white rump. Breeds inland in northern America; migrates to South America; straggles erratically to southeastern Australia.

Pintailed Snipe *Gallinago stenura*
Rather small; 24–28 tail feathers, the outermost blackish narrow 'pins'. Breeds in Siberia; migrates to winter from Africa to southeastern Asia; straggles to far northwestern Australia, from Dampier Land to Pilbara.

South Polar Skua *Catharacta maccormicki*
As Great Skua; smaller; often paler buff-grey. Breeds in Antarctic; migrates north of equator; stragglers pass through eastern and western Australian seas.

Long-tailed Jaeger *Stereorarius longicauda*
Resembles Arctic Jaeger; more tern-like, slender. Breeds in Arctic Circle; migrates to waters off western and eastern South America; straggles to southeastern Australia.

and unsuccessful introductions

Black-tailed Gull *Larus crassirostris*
Medium-sized; dark-backed, pale-headed, black tail band. Breeds along eastern Asian coast; wanders south; stragglers recorded several times in Port Phillip Bay, Vic.

Franklin's Gull *Larus pipixcan*
Small; dark-backed, dark-headed. Breeds in North America; migrates to South America; straggles to southeastern and southwestern Australia in summer.

Black Tern *Chlidonias nigra*
Resembles White-winged Black Tern; black collar out of breeding, dark grey upper wings in breeding. Holarctic breeder; migrates to southern America and western Africa; two records from central coast, NSW.

Grey Ternlet *Procelsterna albivittata*
Tiny; pale blue-grey noddy. Breeds in Pacific Ocean southeast to Norfolk and Lord Howe Islands; straggles to eastern Australian waters over summer.

White Tern *Gygis alba*
All-white, black-billed noddy. Same breeding range as Grey Ternlet; straggles to eastern Australian seas.

Glossy Swiftlet *Collocalia esculenta*
Metallic blue-black; white belly. Widespread in western Pacific tropic archipelagos. Sporadic records from Cape York Peninsula to Mackay; small local breeding colonies possible.

Uniform Swiftlet *Aerodramus vanikorensis*
All dusky. Ranges from Sulawesi to western Pacific islands. One confirmed Australian record, on Cape York Peninsula, September 1913.

House Swift *Apus affinis*
Small; square-tailed; clear white rump. Ranges from southern Europe and Africa to southeastern Asia; one record from Darwin, March 1979.

Blue-winged Pitta *Pitta moluccensis*
Buff-breasted, white throat, pale buff eyebrow. Breeds in southeastern Asia; migrates south through Malay Peninsula to Greater Sundas; two records in northwestern Australia: 1927, 1930.

Yellow-tailed Wagtail *Motacilla citreola*
Broad yellow frons and brow. Breeds in northern central Asia; migrates southeast to winter; one recorded near Sydney, July 1962.

Grey Wagtail *Motacilla cinerea*
Yellow underparts, grey upper parts. Breeds throughout Palaearctic; migrates south to Afro-Asia; straggles to northeastern Australia—mostly Cooktown to Townsville.

White Wagtail *Motacilla alba*
Grey-and-white. Breeds through Eurasia and northern Africa; migrates south and east, reaching southeastern Asia; straggles to western Australian coast between Kimberleys and Perth.

Great Reed-Warbler *Acrocephalus arundinaceus*
Resembles Clamorous Reed-Warbler; bill deeper, throat faintly steaked. Breeds through Palaearctic; migrates to southeastern Asia; straggles to northwestern Australian coast (Kimberleys to Arnhem Land) regularly in summer.

Introductions and escaped captives

Ostrich *Struthio camelus*
Released in South Australia in 1870; relict population survives northeast of Port Augusta.

Spur-winged Goose *Plectropterus gambensis*
Liberated in southwest between 1912–1920; failed to establish.

Canada Goose *Branta canadensis*
Released in southwest between 1912–1920 and later; no survivors.

Egyptian Goose *Alopochen aegyptiacus*
Introduced on Rottnest Island early this century; disappeared before 1956.

Mandarin Duck *Aix galericulata*
A pair liberated on Macedon Reservoir, Vic., in 1960s; failed.

Common Quail *Coturnix coturnix*
Twelve 'Madagascar Quail' imported into Victoria in 1862; fate and identity unknown.

Feral Chicken *Gallus gallus*
Released in Plenty and Dandenong Ranges, Vic., and on Phillip Island in 1860s and on Rottnest Island in 1912; all failed. Other stocks introduced on North-West and Heron Islands, Qld, in 1880 and 1900 may still survive.

Silver Pheasant *Lophura nycthemera*
Released in Tasmania and Porongorup Ranges, WA; first failed; second exterminated 1970s.

Crested Fireback Pheasant *Lophura ignita*
Liberated in Dandenong Ranges, Vic., in 1871; failed.

Impejan Pheasant *Lophophorus impejanus*
Liberated in Dandenong Ranges and at Phillip Island, Vic., in 1871; failed.

Common Turkey *Meleagris gallo-pavo*
Introduced to Prince Seal Island, Furneaux Group in Bass Strait; still present in 1950.

Chukar Partridge *Alectoris graeca*
Introductions in Victoria in 1864, 1865, 1872 and around 1874 all failed. Establishment at Gulgong, NSW, in 1970s may be successful.

Red-legged Partridge *Alectoris rufa*
Released at Colac, Vic., 1860s–70s and possibly near Melbourne in 1873; all failed.

Barbary Partridge *Alectoris barbara*
Introduced in Victoria in 1873; failed.

European Partridge *Perdix perdix*
Released at Gembrook and Phillip Island, Vic., in 1871–2, in southwest in 1897 and 1912, in Tasmania in 1936; all disappeared.

Helmeted Guinea fowl *Numida meleagris*
Released in numbers at Gembrook, Vic., and nearby in 1870–3, in southwest and at Rottnest Island early 1900s; none survived. Stocks introduced on Heron Island in 1960s–70s still breed in Capricorn group, Qld.

Pintailed Sandgrouse *Pterocles alchata*
This or the Imperial Sandgrouse, *P. orientalis*, released at Phillip Island, Vic., 1864; failed.

Common Sandgrouse *Pterocles exustus*
Introduced around Melbourne and on Phillip Island, Vic., 1863, 1864, 1872, without success.

Common Turtle-Dove *Streptopelia turtur*
Released about Melbourne in 1872; failed.

Collared Turtle-Dove *Streptopelia decaocto*
Escapees at Sydney in 1946 failed; a small colony established in Perth in 1975 were destroyed.

Namaqua Dove *Oena capensis*
Escapees recorded in metropolitan Perth in 1960s; have not established.

Peach-faced Lovebird *Agapornis roseicollis*
Small colonies established in metropolitan Perth in 1960s and on Eyre Peninsula, SA, in 1970s; western colonies have disappeared.

Wood Lark *Lullula arborea*
Imported into Victoria in 1857 and later; no records of liberation.

Red-vented Bulbul *Pycnonotus cafer*
Released and seen around Melbourne in early 1900s but none recorded for many years.

Hermit Thrush *Hylocichla guttata*
Introduced about Melbourne in 1860s–70s as Virginian Nightingales; unsuccessful.

European Robin *Erithacus rubecula*
Released in Victoria in 1860s–70s, possibly in 1857; failed to establish.

Nightingale *Luscinia megarhynchos*
Released at Melbourne in 1857 and 1858; survived for at least a year before disappearing.

Chaffinch *Fringilla coelebe*
Introduced repeatedly near Melbourne 1863–72 and at Adelaide 1879–80; all failed.

Bramblefinch *Fringilla montifringilla*
Nearly 80 released in South Australia 1879–80; failed.

Canary *Serinus canarius*
Several releases near Melbourne between 1861–72; all failed.

Siskin *Carduelis spinus*
Several releases in Victoria between 1864–72; failed to establish.

Linnet *Acanthis cannabina*
Released at Alfredton and near Melbourne late 1850s–60s, at Adelaide 1879–80, Sydney 1880; none established.

Bullfinch *Pyrrhula pyrrhula*
Possible release in Victoria in 1860s, definite release at Mt Lofty, SA, 1879–80; failed.

Hawfinch *Coccothraustes coccothraustes*
Chinese Hawfinches possibly introduced in Victoria in 1860s; failed.

Yellowhammer *Emberiza citrinella*
Released at Melbourne 1863–4, possibly several areas in New South Wales; all failed.

Ortolan Bunting *Emberiza hortulana*
Released near Melbourne in 1863; soon died out.

Common Cardinal *Cardinalis cardinalis*
'Virginian' Cardinals introduced in Victoria in 1860s or 70s; failed.

Black-headed Mannikin *Lonchura malacca*
Self-established aviary escapees in metropolitan Sydney from 1929 to at least 1960. Not recorded for about 20 years; probably extinct.

Java Sparrow *Padda oryzivora*
Over 200 released in Melbourne in 1863 and probably earlier; also Ballarat; all failed.

White-winged Wydah *Euplectes albonotatus*
Liberated around Sydney in 1931 and established colonies on Hawkesbury River near Windsor, NSW, up until late 1960s; no records since.

Red Bishop *Euplectes orix*
Established along Murray River (Woods Point), SA, in 1930s; still present in 1950s but no reports since. Other releases at Berri and Mt Lofty Ranges, SA, in 1930s and 40s failed. Liberations at Sydney in 1940s also failed.

House Crow *Corvus splendens*
A commensal of man carried in on ships. One at Geelong, Vic, in 1959; at least 15 at Perth 1926–50; turning up in ones and twos since. All destroyed, at least 30 between 1950–67.

619

THE FAMILIES OF BIRDS

Grey-crowned Babblers.

Classification by order and family

Closely related species are grouped into a genus, related genera into a family and related families into an order. In this way, the scientific naming of birds performs two functions. It puts a handle on every bird, and—by arranging birds in an hierarchic sequence of species-genus-family-order—it reflects their relations and evolution.

Altogether there are about 25 orders of living birds, grouped in the class Aves—birds. In Australia, there are representatives of about 81 naturally occurring families in about 19 orders, including seabirds in offshore waters. All of these groups are described below.

ORDER STRUTHIONIFORMES
Emus, cassowaries and allies
Two of the five families in this order occur naturally in Australia. Included in the order are emus, cassowaries, ostriches, rheas and the kiwis. All are bulky, flightless birds with powerful two- or three-toed feet, loosely webbed and often hair-like plumage, a flat and thickly boned palate, and a broadly rounded, raft-like breast bone. They all live in the Southern Hemisphere and are thought to have originated on the ancient southern super-continent, Gondwanaland.

Family Dromaiidae
Emus, pp44–45
Long-legged, three-toed ratites, with flattened bill, sparsely haired head, vestigial feathered wings, and plume-like grey feathering on the body. The feathers have narrow webbing and fully developed aftershafts, so that each feather appears 'doubled' in its sheath. Emus roam plains and open woodlands in small flocks, browsing mainly on vegetable matter and swallowing stones to help digest—triturate—hard food. Male—smaller—incubates and raises chicks. One species survives on mainland Australia; it is a national emblem.

Family Casuariidae
Cassowaries, pp46–47
Stout-legged, three-toed ratites, with narrow bill, casqued head, wattled neck, vestigial and spur-quilled wings, and plume-like black feathering on the body of the same structure as in the Emu. The inner toes have a spurred claw. Cassowaries inhabit tropical rainforests in New Guinea and Australia, feeding in ones and twos on fallen fruit. Male—smaller—incubates and raises chicks. Three species; one in Australia.

ORDER PROCELLARIIFORMES
Tube-nosed seabirds
Four familes of oceanic flying birds that come to land only to nest—usually in colonies on islands. They have a musky odour and long, plated bills with tubular nostrils. All are present in Australian waters.

Family Pelecanoididae
Diving-Petrels, p48
Chunky small pied petrels with paired, up-turned tubular nostrils on top of bill, stumpy wings and webbed feet far back on body for underwater steering. Feed by flying under water, catching fish and invertebrates and storing them in pouch under tongue; aerial flight low, whirring and direct, crashing through wave tops. Breed in colonies on islands, visiting at night, nesting in burrows and laying single white egg; both sexes share duties in shifts. Four species in southern oceans; one regularly in Australia.

Family Diomedeidae
Albatrosses, pp49–55
Great, rather solitary ocean wanderers—the largest of all seabirds—with pied or dusky plumage, stocky bodies, very long slender wings, short but strong webbed feet, and long hooked bills with short-tubed nostrils separated and sunk in horny plates on the bill. Long wings enable effortless gliding flight low over sea; strong webbed feet enable steering in air, swimming, and sedate walking on land; hooked bill grasps squid from surface of sea (mainly at night) and refuse from ships. Breeds in loose colonies, pairs courting with much bowing and bill-clapping and fencing, nesting on ground or on earth bowls, and sharing duties in shifts. About 13 species of which 10 are in southern oceans; nine in Australian seas, one breeding locally.

Family Procellariidae
Fulmars, petrels and allies, pp56–75
Rather small to rather large seabirds in pied, sooty or grey-white densely waterproofed plumage; paired tubular nostrils set on top of bill. Trans-oceanic migrants with long slender wings for both flapping and gliding flight; feet webbed and set far back on body for swimming, not walking; bill hooked, used for picking or filtering food from sea-surface. Breed in colonies, pairs courting in concerted flight and on ground, nesting in burrows, and sharing nest duties in shifts. About 60 species, some 40 of which visit Australian waters; only nine breed locally.

Family Oceanitidae
Storm-Petrels, pp76–78
Small often white-rumped petrels with nostrils in a single tube on top of the bill and long webbed feet and rather rounded wings adapted to feeding: either by pattering about over water with wings raised, or skimming or bouncing up and down on surface, or circling and swooping like terns. All pick plankton from surface. Usually solitary but flock on island breeding grounds, arriving at night, courting noisily in complex flight, nesting in burrows and laying a single usually spotted egg; both parents share nest duties in shifts, feeding young by regurgitation. About 21 species in all oceans; seven in Australian waters, five regularly, one breeding.

ORDER SPHENISCIFORMES
Penguins
One family, occurring in the colder waters of southern oceans.

Family Spheniscidae
Penguins, pp79–81
Flightless porpoise-shaped marine swimmers with flipper-like unfoldable wings for propulsion and thick, webbed feet placed back at the end of the body for steering and braking in water and for standing erect on land. Plumage slate-black above, white below and two-layered, with outer, oiled waterproof coat of overlapping shingle-like feathers and a dense underlying down (aftershafts) for insulation. Eat fish, crustaceans and squid captured in underwater chases with plated bill and held by tongue with recurved spines. Live in water, sleeping on surface, coming to land only to moult once a year and breed. Breed often in large colonies, both parents sharing duties in various shifts and nesting on mounds, feet or in holes. About 16 species; 11 recorded in Australian seas, one breeding onshore.

ORDER PODICIPEDIFORMES
Grebes and dabchicks
One family, occurring world-wide.

Family Podicipedidae
Grebes, pp82–83
Small to medium-sized fresh- and brackish-water diving birds, with slender bills, dense and furry waterproofed plumage, short wings, and broadly lobed toes set far back on the body to aid propulsion. Food of fish and invertebrates captured in underwater dives; flight fluttering, mainly at night. Both sexes share nesting duties, mating after elaborate courtship on water, and building floating nests of weed. Newly hatched young are striped and carried on parents' back, even under water. About 20 species; three in Australia, all with distinctive head plumage when breeding.

ORDER PELECANIFORMES
Cormorants, pelicans and allies
Fish-eating water birds with all four toes forward and webbed (totipalmate), sealed nostrils and rather coarse feathering that requires frequent waterproofing from a large preen gland, and which swim or fly-and-dive to catch food. Five or six families occurring throughout the warmer parts of the world; all in Australia.

Family Phaethontidae
Tropicbirds, pp84–85
White, tern-like seabirds, with rosy or golden flush to plumage; stout red tern-like bills with open nostrils and central tail feathers prolonged into two red or white streamer wires. Feed by high plunge-diving on flapping and circling aerial patrols, taking mainly fish and squid. Breed solitarily on ground in crevices and holes in banks and cliffs after spectacularly hovering and back-pedalling courtship flights. Both sexes incubate single buff egg and feed young bill to bill with regurgitated food. Three species in tropical oceans; two sporadic in Australian waters.

Family Fregatidae
Frigatebirds, pp86–87
Great-winged, black, aerial sea-hawks, with long hooked and plated cormorant-like bill and forked tails; chase other seabirds to pirate carried or disgorged fish and seafood. Completely aerial; hang-glide effortlessly on bent wings, swoop and turn at speed, come to land only to nest and almost never land on water where plumage quickly waterlogged. Breed in loose colonies, mating temporarily, the male attracting a mate by wing-spreading, bill-clappering and inflating a pouch of red skin under the bill into a balloon. Male brings material; built by female into a loose nest in trees and bushes; both sexes share incubation of chalky eggs and feed young by regurgitation. Five species in tropical seas; two regularly in Australian waters.

Family Phalacrocoracidae
Cormorants and shags, pp88–92
Black or pied sexually similar underwater coastal and continental fishers. Bill long and hooked for grasping fish underwater; facial skin often bare and coloured. Swim and fish by diving from surface, using wings to manoeuvre; spend much time perching with wings hung out, and fly and soar strongly. Breed colonially, in temporary pairs with little ceremony, building rough stick nests on ground or in low trees, and laying chalky blue-green eggs; both parents share all duties, feeding young by regurgitation down lower bill. About 29 species; five present and breeding in Australia.

Family Anhingidae
Darters, p93
Black or grey-and-white sexually dimorphic underwater fishers in fresh and brackish water; closely allied to and resembling cormorants—and perhaps of the same family—but have dagger-like bill with serrated edges for spearing fish under water. Soar much in air, perch on logs, swim on surface and submerge like submarine to stalk fish; rippled tail feathers aid swimming and slender neck S-shaped, hinged at eighth vertebra for darting lunges. Nest in small dispersed colonies, mating temporarily, displaying with wing-waving and snap-bows; nests and eggs as in cormorants. Both sexes share

nest duties, feeding young by regurgitation down upper bill. Two species; one in Australia and rest of Old World.

Family Sulidae
Gannets and boobies, pp94–96
Large, white or pied flying marine fishers that patrol surface waters on steadily beating pointed wings and plunge-dive spectacularly onto underwater prey from great height. Bill long, pointed, running on straight to top of skull to disperse forces of impact in dive, and finely serrated to hold fish. Breed in small to large colonies, in rather permanent pairs with elaborate mating and nest-building ceremonies. Nest duties shared by both sexes; young fed by regurgitation from throat. Nine species; four regularly in Australian waters.

Family Pelecanidae
Pelicans, p97
Great, white-and-grey swimming fishers which, ungainly on land, fly and soar buoyantly on broad wings and have long bills with a huge distendable pouch for catching fish and cooling by gular flutter. Swim on surface, in line or alone, dipping and sweeping bill to take prey; American Brown Pelican dives in flight. Breed in colonies on ground or trees, making meagre nest and mating temporarily. Both sexes share all nest duties; young plunge bill into parent's throat to be fed on semi-solids by regurgitation and are starved before fledging. Six species, on all continents; one endemic in Australia.

ORDER CICONIIFORMES
Herons, ibises, storks and allies
Large, long-necked and heavy-billed birds with loose plumage and long legs that wade and stalk in water to hunt aquatic vertebrates and invertebrates; vulture-like with hooked bill for carrion-feeding in American vultures. Their wings are moved by single laminated pectoral muscles and their feet, finely scaled, have three long unwebbed forward toes and a long hind toe. Chicks hatch successively, a day or more apart. Six families, some of disparate affinity, on all continents; three in Australia.

Family Ardeidae
Herons and bitterns, pp98–107
Medium-sized, long-necked, long-legged slim-bodied wading birds with dagger-like bill and an articulation at the sixth vertebra that enables them to dart the bill at prey. Flight slow and flapping, with head tucked in. They wait or stalk for food—fish, amphibians—in shallow, still water. Plumage, grey, white (in egrets) or brown, is groomed from powder downs on the breast, rump and, except in bitterns, inside of the thighs. Herons usually breed in colonies (except bitterns), growing elaborate nuptial plumes and mating temporarily with snap and stretch displays. Nests are platforms of twigs on trees or rushes in reeds (bitterns); eggs blue-green or white (bitterns). Both sexes share nest duties (bitterns excepted), feeding young by regurgitation by holding their bills crosswise in the nestling's. About 62 species, world-wide; 14 regular and breeding in Australia.

Family Ciconiidae
Storks, p108
Great, long-necked, heavy-billed, long-legged birds in bold black-and-white plumage and with part-webbed feet that nonetheless stalk prey—small vertebrates, large insects and carrion (Adjutant and Marabou Storks) as much in pasture as in swamp. Fly and soar on thermals with necks and legs stretched out. Breed alone or in colonies, mating permanently and courting by dancing and bill-rattling. Nests are bulky platforms of twigs on tree tops (or buildings); eggs plain white. Nest duties shared by both parents, feeding young by regurgitation.

Seventeen species, on all continents mainly in tropics; one breeding in Australia.

Family Plataleidae
Ibises and spoonbills, pp109–113
Large, long-legged, long-necked waders in prevailingly white plumage but glossy brown, partly black and red in some species; often crested and face or neck of bare skin. Bills long and down-curved (ibises) or spatula-shape (spoonbills), used to feed in shallow water, mud and pasture by probing or sweeping respectively. Fly with flapping interspersed with short glides; soar on thermals. Gregarious, pairing temporarily and nesting in colonies in low trees and reeds usually over water, building platform nests and laying white eggs. Nest duties shared by both sexes, one guarding, and young fed by regurgitation. About 29 species, on all continents; five breeding in Australia.

ORDER FALCONIFORMES
Day-active birds of prey
Strong-bodied short-necked carnivorous birds with sharply hooked bills for ripping and tearing; no caeca (blind pouch) in intestines; a waxy membrane or cere across base of upper bill through which nostrils open; sharp, taloned feet with three toes forward and one back for striking and grasping prey. Prey plucked, torn up and eaten in morsels; all parts digested by highly acid stomach. Female larger than male. Eggs white or marked with red-brown. Three families, of possibly disparate affinity; two in Australia.

Family Accipitridae
Kites, hawks and eagles, pp114–131
Small to very large raptors in brown, white and black mottled plumage; broad, rounded wings; crop for storing food; dense under-down from feather aftershafts (Osprey excepted). All hunt on the wing, gliding and soaring much, and stooping on to stationary prey or carrion. Powerful vision from enlarged eyes with additional image-receiving cone cells, picks out prey at great distances. Mostly solitary and territorial, but kites and vultures flock on food. Pairs often permanent, courting in aerial display, looping and presenting claws. Nest on stick platforms mostly in trees; male hunts and female incubates and feeds young. Young hatch successively, the younger often failing, and pass through two downs. About 218 species, world-wide; 18 in Australia, all breeding.

Family Falconidae
Falcons, pp132–135
Small to medium-sized raptors, most of which have notched upper mandibles, a black area or tear-mark through the eye and pointed wings, and eggs with buff inner surface. Talons lack spasmodic clutching mechanism of hawks and eagles. True falcons chase, strike and capture prey—other birds, bats, insects—on the wing, stooping at tremendous speed and killing by severing the neck with a bite. Others hover and drop on to terrestrial victims (kestrels) or take carrion and pirate prey from other raptors (American caracaras and milvagos). Solitary and territorial, mating temporarily or permanently, courting in aerial chases, bowing and courtship feeding. Nest a stick platform on rock ledge or in trees; male hunts, female incubates and feeds young on food brought. Young hatch simultaneously and pass through two downs. About 59 species, world-wide; six in Australia, all breeding.

ORDER ANSERIFORMES
Ducks, geese, screamers and allies
Duck- and fowl-like birds with solid palate, no crop and vestigial aftershafts to feathers; three toes forward and one reversed. Males have penis. Duck-billed and forward toes webbed in ducks;

fowl-billed and toes unwebbed on South American screamers. Chicks hatch together. Three families; two in Australia.

Family Anseranatidae
Magpie-Geese, pp136–137
Large, pied, long-legged goose-like birds with part-webbed toes and slender bill with slightly hooked nail intermediate between ducks and South American screamers. Male has coiled trachea. Graze on seeds and shoots on edge of swamps; rarely swim, and moult flight feathers sequentially without becoming flightless. Gregarious and breeding colonially in trios of one male, two female, all building unlined platform nests of weed over water and feeding young by placing food in mouth; eggs plain off-white. Chicks loosely downed plain grey with russet head. One species, endemic to northern Australia and southern New Guinea.

Family Anatidae
Geese, swans and ducks, pp138–157
Bulky, medium to large duck-billed birds with short, webbed feet and compact, waterproofed plumage. Feed by dabbling, diving and grazing on vegetable matter and invertebrates, the bill furnished with lamellae to sieve out food, and either swimming or walking—body horizontal—to do so. Often flocking but usually breed separately, displaying and copulating in water, and nesting in tree hollows or on platforms of water weed, all lined with feather down; eggs plain white to pale blue. Nest duties undertaken by both sexes or female alone in dabbling and diving ducks; young, densely downed in grey or patterns, leave nest in a day and feed themselves (Musk Duck excepted). Adults moult wing feathers together and become temporarily flightless after breeding. About 149 species, world-wide; 18 breeding in Australia, two introduced and established.

ORDER GALLIFORMES
Megapodes, quails, pheasants and allies
Fowl-like birds with cleft palate, crops for holding food, and aftershafts providing feather down. All feed on ground mainly on seeds and vegetable matter and scratch much with powerful feet of three forward toes and one behind. Wings short and round; flight laboured, or whirring in quail. Three families, mostly in warmer parts of Old World and Americas; two in Australia.

Family Megapodiidae
Mound-builders, pp158–161
Stocky, medium-sized fowls in grey or dusky unornamented plumage, with short sharp bills, short hairy crests or coloured wattles on head and neck, and stout feet with long, powerful toes and claws. Roost in trees. Pair permanent and territorial, both sexes of most species constructing and maintaining a nest mound of sand and decaying vegetable matter for much of year; some nest-burrow in warm volcanic sand. Eggs large, white or buff, incubated by nest mound; young hatch, climb out and run off alone, with advanced down and part-feathered wings, to fend without any parental care. About 15 species, restricted to southwestern Pacific between Philippines and Tonga; three breeding in Australia.

Family Phasianidae
Quails and allies, pp162–167
Small (quail) to large (turkeys) plump, ground-living 'game birds', many of which roost in trees; male often more brightly plumaged than female, often brilliantly so with ornamental tails in pheasants. Bill short and narrow; powerful feet run and scratch well and are often armed with spurs. Solitary or in coveys, adults mating temporarily and male courting with spectacular strutting and fanning of plumage, whirring of

wings and crowing. Female incubates and rears young mostly unaided, usually nesting in scrape on ground and laying large clutches of cream, sparsely spotted eggs; chicks heavily downed and precocial. About 210 species, on all continents; three native to Australia, all quail; three introduced and established.

ORDER GRUIFORMES

Button-quails, rails, cranes, bustards and allies
Small to very large thin-headed ground-feeding birds with cleft palates, and usually long necks, bills and legs for walking and wading. Most have enlarged caeca on the lower intestine and downy aftershafts to feathers. Twelve families, with representatives in all parts of the world; five in Australia, including the rail-like Jacanas that are usually placed with Charadriiformes.

Family Turnicidae

Button-quails, pp168–172
Small quail-like birds, differing from true quail in their cleft palates, feet with three forward toes alone, no crop, and sexual dimorphism in which female is larger and brighter, dominant to male, and has enlarged trachea. Secretive, living singly or in pairs, feeding on ground on seeds and insects, and pivotting on one foot while scraping with the other; flushes with quail-like low whirring flight. Voice a low booming, by female establishing territory; she mates with several males. Male incubates in pad on ground and rears precocial mottled-downy young which leave nest soon after hatching. Sixteen species, from Africa to Australia; seven in Australia, six endemic.

Family Rallidae

Rails and allies, pp173–182
Skulking, small to medium-sized thin-bodied marsh- and wetland-inhabiting birds, with slender to stout bills, and stout or long feet with very long toes—three in front and one behind—that aid walking on floating vegetation. Tail short and habitually flicked. Wings are rather rounded, and rails are poor fliers, yet they travel vast distances at night and have colonised isolated islands throughout the world; often become flightless after doing so. Roost and feed in rank vegetation of all kinds, eating range of plant and animal matter; all swim well, coots living mostly in water and diving for food, assisted by lobed toes. Most cryptically plumaged, and solitary, but larger swimmers—coots and waterhens—gregarious and dusky-purple plumaged with coloured frontal shields. Breed alone, mating temporarily after simple courtship, building cup-nests of weed in reeds or on ground, and laying large clutches of marked eggs. Both parents share nest duties; downy young plain dusky, often with coloured head marks, and precocial, leaving nest soon after hatching. About 141 species, world-wide, 10 extinct; 14 regular and breeding in Australia, two accidental.

Family Otididae

Bustards, p183
Medium- to large-bodied, long-necked and long-legged cursorial birds of open plains. Head broad with large eyes adapted to nocturnalism; bill short and narrow, taking seeds, invertebrates and small ground vertebrates; feet with only three forward toes; plumage of cryptically patterned greys and browns, affording camouflage on ground. Bustards fly heavily and prefer to hide by freezing on ground. Solitary or gregarious. Male, larger and brighter than female, is polyandrous, displaying before any females by strutting with extraordinarily puffed-out head and neck plumage, up-fanned tail of 18–20 tail feathers, and drooped wings. Female undertakes all nest duties, incubating marked eggs in scrape on ground, and rearing precocial chicks which

leave nest soon after hatching in sandy down peppered black. About 22 species, from Afro-Eurasia to Australia; one in Australia.

Family Gruidae

Cranes, pp184–185
Great, long-necked, long-legged, long-billed wading birds that resemble storks but differ in their cleft palates, enlarged intestinal caeca, elevated hind-toed feet, and habit of nesting and roosting in water on swamps or on ground. Wade sedately in water and swampy ground to take range of plant and animal food. Fly with neck and legs extended, often soaring to great height. Plumage white and grey, with bustle of plumes over rump from tail and inner flight feathers; plumed crests and red combs on the head. Solitary or gregarious, but pairs are permanent, cementing bonds by unison bugling each day; courtship involves spectacular, often communal dances. Both sexes build large platform nest of weed and rush, incubate clutch of off-white or plain light blue eggs, and rear precocial, tawny- or grey-downed young that leave nest within a few days. Fifteen species, on all continents except South America; two in Australia.

Family Jacanidae

Jacanas, p186
Small, rail-like birds of tropical ponds, with short and rounded wings allowing weak flight, and slender legs with very long toes spurred with enormous claws—three forward, one behind—enabling the birds to walk easily, short tail flicking, on floating pond leaves and vegetation. Sedentary and rather solitary, picking insects, snails and seeds from floating vegetation. Plumage patterned dark brown and white, often with red comb above bill; female larger and brighter. Polyandrous, female mating with more than one male and males undertaking all nesting duties and defending territory. Nest a raft of weeds on floating vegetation; eggs glossy tan scrawled black; precocial chestnut-and-white-downed chicks leave nest after several days. Eight species, on all continents; one regular and breeding in Australia.

ORDER CHARADRIIFORMES

Plovers, waders, gulls and auks
A heterogeneous assemblage of small- to medium-sized gregarious shore birds and waders with cleft palates and downy aftershafts, enlarged caeca on the intestine, usually 12 tail feathers and salt glands in skull over eyes. All feed on ground or water and roost and nest on ground; many undertake seasonal trans-hemispheric migrations. About 16 families, world-wide; nine in Australia.

Family Rostratulidae

Painted Snipe, p187
Small, snipe-like waders of stocky body, rather long four-toed feet, short rounded wings and tail, and rather long, slightly decurved bill with slightly broadened sensory tip for probing for invertebrates and seeds in mud on swamp edges. Nocturnal, hiding in squats by day where dappled brown, bronze and grey upper plumage aids camouflage. Flight weak and fluttering, interspersed with glides. Female larger and brighter than male, incubating and sharing rearing of young in South American species, but polyandrous and leaving incubation and care of young to male in Old World species. Two species; one in South America, the other from Africa through southern Asia to Australia.

Family Haematopodidae

Oystercatchers, pp188–189
Stocky pied or black waders of seashore, with stout red legs, only three forward toes, and long, straight red bill that is compressed at sides into a chisel to open shellfish. Feeds day or night at low tide, probing wet sand for items, mainly shellfish

which it opens by hammering, stabbing and scissor-like cutting of the hinging adductor muscle. Gregarious, but pairing permanently and nesting alone, holding territory with piping, trilling and strutting. Nest a scrape in sand; eggs marked, incubated by both sexes; precocial young fawn-downed above, hatch together and leave nest quickly, tended by both parents. About nine species, on all continents and New Zealand; two in Australia.

Family Pedionomidae

Plains-Wanderer, p190
Small, quail-like wader, previously thought to be related to button-quail but now shown to be most closely allied to South American seed-snipe, Thinocoridae. Plump body, short yellow bill and feet, and cryptic plumage pattern in which female brighter than male, all resemble button-quail; but feet have short hind toe, the skeleton is wader-like, flight is a slow fluttering, and eggs are plover-like. Nocturnal, feeding on insects and seeds on dry plains at night, sleeping in scrapes on ground by day. Loosely gregarious. Large bright female polyandrous, leaving males to incubate and rear precocial young which leave nest—a scrape in ground—quickly. One species, endemic to Australia.

Family Recurvirostridae

Stilts and avocets, pp191–193
Slim-bodied, slender-headed waders, with thin straight bills upturned in avocets, long spindly legs with only three forward, often part-webbed toes, and striking white-, black- and chestnut-patterned plumage that changes little with seasons. All wade or swim in water to pick food—planktonic organisms and tiny invertebrates—the narrow mouth passing only very small items. Gregarious, mating temporarily and nesting in loose to compact colonies, both sexes sharing all duties. Nest a platform of sticks or scrape by water; eggs plover-like; precocial chicks—downy spotted grey above, white below—leave nest quickly together, feeding themselves. About 13 species, on all continents; three in Australia.

Family Burhinidae

Stone-curlews, pp194–195
Medium-sized cursorial land waders with broad head and large pale eyes, usually short and plover-like bill, cryptically streaked grey-brown, black and white plumage, long wings, and very long legs with only three forward, part-webbed toes. Nocturnal, feeding on range of small vertebrates and invertebrates and calling with characteristic wailing. Fly well with fluttering beats but walk and run better, head held low and feet put down gingerly. Gregarious, but pairing permanently and breeding alone; courtship involves chasing and strutting by male, with wings drooped and short tail raised. Two cryptically marked eggs laid in scrape, incubated by both sexes with paired brood patches. Precocial young—sandy-downed lined black above—hatch together in advanced state and leave nest site at once, tended by both parents. Nine species, on all continents; two in Australia.

Family Glareolidae

Pratincoles, pp196–197
Rather small, plain sandy-brown waders with short, broad, down-pointed bills, wide gape, long pointed wings and large eyes, reflecting partly nocturnal habits. All live on dry, often hot sparsely vegetated plains and are largely insectivorous. Pratincoles are short-legged with an elevated hind toe and fork-tailed, and trawl aerially for most food; coursers are long-legged without a hind toe and square-tailed and chase all food on the ground. The Australian Pratincole blends traits of both pratincoles and coursers. All gregarious, pratincoles the most; all migratory or nomadic. Mating is temporary, following wing

displays in courtship; both sexes share nest duties. Nest a scrape, if that; eggs marked; precocial young downed in various tones and marks, staying at nest site for a day or so before moving off. About 16 species, throughout Old World to Australia; two species, one breeding, in Australia.

Family Charadriidae
Plovers and dotterels, pp198–206
Small to medium-sized waders with short necks and bills, broad black–patterned heads, rather plain grey-brown upper plumage, and slender legs with usually only three forward toes. Stance rather upright. Lapwings—the largest members— often have face wattles and sparred shoulders. Gregarious, feeding on range of invertebrates on usually fresh- and saltwater shorelines by walk-and-pick. Sexes alike and monogamous, breeding in isolated territories and sharing all nest duties; breeding plumage bright in migratory species. Nest a scrape or spare platform on ground; eggs pear-shaped and marked; downy young precocial, speckled fawn-and-black above, hatching together and leaving nest site quickly. About 64 species, world-wide, many migrants; 13 regularly in Australia and another four erratic or accidental visitors.

Family Scolopacidae
Sandpipers and allies, pp207–227
Small to medium-sized fresh- and saltwater shore waders, with slender legs and short hind toe, slim, straight or down-curved bills, and moltled grey-brown upper plumage aiding cryptic camouflage. Stance rather horizontal. Feed mainly by probing for small invertebrates in mud; phalaropes swim. Many gregarious and nearly all migratory, wintering in Southern Hemisphere in dull plumage and breeding close around Arctic Circle in bright nuptial plumage. Most territorial and solitary when breeding, courting in elaborate flights and displays; but mating systems variable, from monogamy in most to polyandry in Spotted Sandpipers and phararopes and polygynous leks in Ruffs. Nest usually a scrape or cup on ground; precocial chicks downed in cryptic tones and leave nest quickly together, feeding themselves tended by one or both parents. About 86 species, world-wide; about 32 fairly regular in Australia, but several are vagrants and more are accidental.

Family Laridae
Gulls, terns and skuas, pp228–247
Small to bulky aerial seabirds with short necks, long and rather pointed wings, rather plain white to grey plumage, and short feet with three forward webbed toes and a short elevated hind toe. They comprise three main groups: (1) skuas, which resemble gulls, but have mottled grey plumage, a horny cere over the upper mandible, and chase other seabirds to pirate food as well as scavenging; (2) gulls, prevailingly white carnivorous birds with stout round-tipped bills that scavenge for food; (3) terns, white or grey birds often with forked tails and black caps, that have pointed bills and which quarter surface water on the wing and dive for live food: fish and insects. All gregarious and most breed in colonies, nesting in scrapes or platforms on ground, both parents sharing nest duties; young in plain or patterned fawn down remain, fed by parents, at nest site till well advanced of fledging. About 96 species, world-wide; about 26 regularly in Australian waters, and several additional vagrants recorded.

ORDER COLUMBIFORMES
Pigeons, doves and allies
Squat, bulky, seed- and fruit-eating land birds with close, densely downed plumage in dispersed feather tracts but without aftershafts, a cered bill, and only vestigial caeca and preen gland. Crop present to hold food. Two families; the world-wide pigeons and the extinct, flightless dodos, Rhaphidae, of the Mascarene Islands. Sandgrouse, family Pteroclididae, of Afro-Asia are often included in this order but recent research suggests that they are land-adapted seed-eating waders, Charadriiformes.

Family Columbidae
Pigeons and doves, pp248–272
Small to large stocky thick-plumaged seed- and fruit-eaters; short, soft bills with wide gape and fleshy cere; short feet with three forward toes and one long toe behind. Range from large green arboreal fruit-doves to small, brown long-tailed ground doves and to giant grey crowned pigeons. Feed on ground (seeds) or trees (fruit) but nest and roost mainly off ground; seed-eaters drink regularly, by sucking. Sexes usually alike and mate temporarily; courtship by male bowing and sometimes display flights. Nest duties shared by both parents. Nest a skeletal platform of twigs; eggs plain white; young sparsely downed and stay in nest till fledging, fed by regurgitation on 'pigeon milk', a liquid from the lining of the crop. About 302 species; 22 regular and indigenous to Australia, three introduced and established.

ORDER PSITTACIFORMES
Parrots and cockatoos
Brilliantly coloured, coarsely plumaged fruit-, seed-, and nectar-feeding birds, with hooked, cered bill, fleshy tongue and finely scaled feet with two toes forward and two back (zygodactyl). Most have crop for storing food and all possess downy aftershafts, a solid palate and lack caeca on intestine. Colour, amusing mannerisms and ease with which fed on seed have made parrots popular in domestication for centuries. Sometimes split into 10 or more families, but all combined here in one, following convention. Occur on all southern continents, supporting theory that parrot-like birds arose on ancient southern super-continent, Gondwanaland. Most diverse in Australasia, where there are all but one or two of the 10–11 subfamilies.

Family Psittacidae
Parrots and cockatoos, pp273–318
Tiny to large stocky, hook-billed birds with thick heads, short necks and often long tails. Plumage bright, basically of greens conferred by structural hollows in feather barbs (Dyck-texture). Mostly tree-living—but also some groups feeding on ground—which zygodactyl feet adapted to climbing up and down branchlets, aided by hooked bill used as a third foot. Bill used to cut and pare seed coats from seed and to pluck fruit; plucked objects often held in one foot (the left) while being eaten. Drink by scooping, ladelling or sucking. Several subfamilies occur in Australia: (1) cockatoos in black or white plumage without Dyck-texture and with erectile coloured crests, powder downs, rounded tails and which feed on seed or larvae on ground or in trees; (2) lorikeets, green and with driving flight on pointed wings and tail, which have eversible brush-tipped tongues for sweeping nectar from flowers in trees and simple, thin-walled alimentary tracts to digest it; (3) fig-parrots, tiny, green, and with short wings and tails but heavy notched bills for chewing into ripening figs; (4) Psittaculine parrots, stocky and green with a red-and-blue female in one species, which have broadly rounded wings and tail, which cut seeds from fruit in the canopy of rainforests; (5) king parrots, with fast, graceful or erratically undulating flight, which feed on seeds on the ground or in trees and in which males are more brightly plumaged (with red) than females; (6) broad-tailed parrots comprising the rosellas and allies, with long tails and undulating flight and which, although resembling the king parrots in their feeding, have a white nape spot for submissive behaviour, a white bar on the wing of immatures, and buff-billed nestlings. Most are gregarious and flock, and all have harsh calls. Mating often permanent, forged by inelaborate display. Nest mostly in hollows in trees, laying plain white eggs incubated by female in Australian parrots or, in white cockatoos, by both sexes; the female is fed at or near the nest by the male. Both parents feed young by regurgitation, holding bill of chick in its own and pumping. About 340 species, on southern continents and southeastern Asia; 51 in Australia.

ORDER CUCULIFORMES
Cuckoos, turacos and hoatzins
Small to moderate-sized tree-living land birds with short parrot-like zygodactyl feet (two toes forward, two back or outer one reversible), and straight, sometimes heavy bills without cere over nostrils. Caeca present or absent, palate solid and feather tracts rather songbird-like; aftershafts present to feather-down. Three families; one in Africa, one in tropical South America, and the last, cuckoos, world-wide including Australia.

Family Cuculidae
Cuckoos, koels and coucals, pp319–327
Small to medium-sized mostly arboreal insectivores or fruit-eaters of slim build with narrow, often down-curved bills with circular nostrils and often long, tapered tails; some coucals and American Road-Runner terrestrial. Many call loudly and monotonously during breeding, into night. Plumage usually autumn-toned and barred, particularly on tail. Most groups (subfamilies) of cuckoos build their own nests, incubate and rear their young, sometimes colonially, both parents sharing nest duties (coucals). Cuculine cuckoos, however, are traditional nest parasites, laying single eggs in nest of host and leaving host to hatch and rear young. Plumage of parasitic cuckoos may mimic that of main hosts or a predator to frighten host; eggs of cuckoos also often mimic those of main hosts, individual birds laying different egg types to match. Hatching cuckoos eject host's own young from nest. About 130 species, world-wide; 12 in Australia, all parasitic but one.

ORDER STRIGIFORMES
Owls
Stocky, short-necked, broad-headed nocturnal birds of prey, with hooked, uncered bills for ripping and carrying prey, forward-facing enlarged tubular eyes with binocular vision and great light-gathering capacity, feathered feet and taloned toes with outer toe reversible, and soft plumage for silent flight. Ears enlarged and positioned asymetrically to pinpoint direction of sounds. Unlike diurnal hawks and eagles, owls have well-developed caeca on the lower intestine and swallow prey in large chunks or whole, voiding pellets; they lack a crop. One family, world-wide, often separated into two families—hawk-owls and masked-owls—both present in Australia.

Family Strigidae
Hawk- and masked-owls, pp328–334
Small to large nocturnal raptors that sleep by day in hollows and dark shelters, and hunt by night either by perching, looking and diving (hawk-owls) or by quartering habitat on wing and diving on prey (masked-owls). Plumage autumn-toned and dappled for camouflage, without aftershafts, and frayed-edged to silence flight, most in masked-owls; female usually larger than male. Two main groups, often treated as families: (1) hawk-owls with incomplete face discs, strong night sight but usually poorer hearing, pale eyes, slotted flight feathers, and which hoot territorially, carry prey only in talons, eat it in pieces, and lay rounded eggs; (2) masked-owls with complete facial discs, small dark eyes, huge

ear openings under the mask, rounded burred flight feathers, a comb on foremost claw and which merely hiss and screech, carry prey in bill and bolt it whole and lay oblong eggs. Mating temporary or permanent, the female undertaking all nest duties and fed inside or outside nest by male; or both sexes feed young. Nest a hollow, burrow or usurped nest of another bird; eggs plain white. Young, hatching successively, fed in nest by parent; through two downs before fledging. About 148 species, world-wide; nine species of both main groups in Australia.

ORDER CAPRIMULGIFORMES
Frogmouths and nightjars
Nocturnal insect-catchers with large, tubular eyes for night sight, wide gaping bills usually fringed by long bristles, and weak feet of three forward toes and one behind. Plumage soft, dappled in camouflaging browns and greys, with short aftershafts and burred edges for silent flight; 10 tail feathers. Intestinal caeca usually present and large; preen gland often missing or vestigial and replaced by powder downs.

Family Podargidae
Frogmouths, pp335–337
Large, sluggish bull-headed nocturnal birds with wide, heavy and hard frog-like bills with solid butter-coloured palates and slit side nostrils. Preen gland replaced by two large powder downs at base of back. Wings rounded, tail tapered and feet short-legged with long toes, the outer one with extra bone and part-reversible. Feed by perch-and-pounce in diving glides on large, often hard-shelled insects. Territorial in permanent pairs; perch, roost and nest in tree branches. Nest a small pad of sticks or, in Asian species, down mixed with moss and lichen; eggs plain white. Both sexes share duties, feeding white-downed young bill to bill on nest until fledging. About 13 species, from southeastern Asia to Melanesia; three in Australia.

Family Aegothelidae
Owlet-nightjars, p338
Small, long-tailed nocturnal birds with front-facing eyes, wide soft bills with split pink palates and slit nostrils at tip. Preen gland present and large, without powder downs; no intestinal caeca. Wings and tail rounded; rather long-legged and long-toed with outer forward toe irreversible. Feed variously, by perch-and-pounce, aerially. on wing, and by running on ground, taking small soft insects. Territorial in permanent pairs; perch in trees, roost and nest in clefts and hollows. Eggs plain white. Both sexes share nest duties, feeding white-downed young bill to bill in nest until fledging. Six to eight species, restricted to Australasian region; one in Australia.

Family Caprimulgidae
Nightjars, pp339–341
Medium-sized nocturnal birds with wide soft bills with split pink palates and round nostrils at tip. Preen gland vestigial, supplemented by powder downs; intestinal caeca present. Wings long, rather pointed tail square; both often marked white there and on throat; short-legged with long toes, the central one combed. Feed by trawling aerially on wing, open-billed, for flying insects, storing them in pouch in mouth. Territorial or migratory, pairing permanent or temporary, forged by weird territorial calls and displays on wing; roost, rest and nest on ground. Eggs marbled and marked. Both sexes share nest duties, feeding precocial coloured-downed young by regurgitation; young leave nest site at hatching. About 76 species, on all continents but mainly tropical Africa and South America; three in Australia.

ORDER APODIFORMES
Swifts and hummingbirds
Small to tiny aerial birds with pointed wings moved by short arm and long hand bones. Plumage often metallic, with 10 tail feathers. Feet tiny and weak, of three forward toes with or without hind toe. Naked preen gland and feather aftershafts present but no intestinal caeca. All lay small clutches of plain white eggs in small, smooth, hanging or perched cup nests. Three families, mostly in tropics; one reaching Australia.

Family Apodidae
Swifts, pp342–343
Small, long-winged, fast-flying, day-feeding aerial insect-eaters that almost live on the wing, some sleeping there, gliding in circles. Most sleep by clinging vertically to hard surfaces with weak feet; swifts can barely walk. Resemble swallows but for structure of their primitive voice box, feet with reversible hind toes, and split palate, revealing that similarities to swallows in porpoise-shaped bodies, sleeked plumage, pointed wings and short wide bills are convergent to manner of feeding. Generally flocking, many migratory and most nesting in colonies in sheltered caverns or hollows, some in dark assisted by echo-locating voice. Pair temporarily, both sexes sharing nest duties and building hanging cup nests of fibre often cemented with salivary secretions from glands in mouth; young fed by regurgitation at nest till fledging. About 82 species, world-wide; six in Australia, of which three or four regular and one or two breeding.

ORDER CORACIIFORMES
Kingfishers, rollers, hornbills and allies
Large-headed, stout-billed birds with much green and blue in plumage (except Hoopee and hornbills) and three forward toes fused to greater or lesser extent (syndactyl); hind toe present. Palate solid; feather aftershafts, intestinal caeca and preen glands all generally present. Nest in cavities or holes, laying plain white eggs; young naked at hatching. Nine or ten families, centred in tropics of New and Old World; three in Australia.

Family Alcedinidae
Kingfishers, pp344–355
Small to medium-sized thick-set perching birds with broad heads, long stout straight bills for grasping prey, and much blue in plumage; cartilaginous outgrowths from skull protect eyes. Forward toes joined for most of length, sometimes reduced to two, for clasping perches but making walking almost impossible. Wings rounded, allowing short dashing flights. Kingfishers are solitary stationary feeders, diving onto prey from set perch—into water for fish or on to ground for insects and small vertebrates— and returning to perch to eat, rest and sleep. Pairing temporary or permanent, and territorial at least when breeding. Nest unlined in tree hollow or burrow in bank. Duties shared by both sexes; helpless young fed bill to mouth in nest till fledging, their feathers long in sheath. About 90 species, on all continents; 10 in Australia, representing both tiny stumpy-tailed fishing kingfishers and longer-tailed land kingfishers.

Family Meropidae
Bee-eaters, p356
Small, slender green- and blue-plumaged birds with shortly syndactyl feet, pointed wings, tails often with attenuate tips to central feathers, and long, black, down-curved food-catching bills. Flight swift and graceful with arcing glides. Feed by sallying from set bare perch or by hawking to catch insects on wing, mostly venomous Hymenoptera; stings removed by rubbing stomach of bee or wasp on branch. Generally gregarious, flocking on migration and nesting in colonies; mating temporary. Nest holes burrowed in banks, unlined; young fed in nest until fledging, their feathers long in sheath. Both sexes share nest duties, the pair usually assisted by other colonial birds in feeding young. About 24 species, centred in Old World tropics; one in Australia.

Family Coraciidae
Rollers, p357
Medium-sized, thick-set, broad-headed and broad-billed birds with much blue in plumage; feet short but strong with second and third forward toes joined at base; tail square or outer feathers elongate; wings long and round-tipped. Feed on insects and small vertebrates by sallying from set high perches, either diving to ground (*Coracias*) or hawking on wing in swooping and floating loose-winged evolutions (*Eurystomus*). Solitary or in permanent or temporary pairs, holding exclusive territories; display in acrobatic flights with cackling. Nest a hole in tree of bank, unlined; both sexes share all nest duties; helpless young fed bill to mouth in nest till fledging, their feathers long in sheath. Eleven species, in Old World tropics; one in Australia.

ORDER PASSERIFORMES
Perching or songbirds
This most successful, diverse and widespread order comprises over half the world's birds. Its distinguishing features are a distinctively cleft palate, three free forward toes and strong irreversible hind toe flexed by free tendons, tiny feather aftershafts, vestigial intestinal caeca, and a complexly structured and muscled voice box (syrinx) which allows passerines to sing and defend territory by throwing the voice, so avoiding energy-expensive fighting. Nests complex, eggs variably marked, and young hatch naked and helpless. About 65 to 70 families, varying with opinion, in two main groups: true songbirds (oscines) with completely muscled syrinx fused into a drum, and subsongbirds (suboscines) with incompletely formed or muscled syrinx; about 33 in Australia, only one of which is suboscine (pittas).

Family Pittidae
Pittas, pp358–359
Thick-set, short-tailed, long-legged ground-feeders in rainforests, plumaged brilliantly in iridescent greens, reds, blues and black. Sexes alike. Voice box simple, without intrinsic muscles or pessulus, but pittas do sing simple territorial songs from trees; also roost there. Bill, black and heavy, used to rummage in litter and break open snails on stones or roots (anvils). Several migratory, flying at night. Solitary but pairing often permanent. Nest a rough globose dome on or near ground in thicket; eggs buff-white marked grey and red-brown. Nest duties shared by both sexes. About 26–27 species, in Old World tropics to Melanesia; three regularly in Australia, plus one vagrant.

Family Menuridae
Lyrebirds, pp360–361
Fowl-like ground-living passerines, largest of the order; rounded wings fitted only for gliding; long reticulately scaled feet with large toes and claws for ground scratching; prolonged tails of 14–16 feathers that are plumed and shimmered over head by males in display. Plumage brown with little sexual dimorphism except in tail. Voice box of unfused elements, with three pairs of intrinsic muscles; hypocleidium missing. Male polygynous, singing from display mounds or sites, with shimmering tails, in the most brilliant and prolonged songs of all songbirds, involving spectacular mimicry. Female builds nest, incubates and rears young along. Nest a coarse dome of sticks; single egg lavender-grey marked dusky; young densely black-, then grey-downed. Two species, endemic to Australia.

Family Atrichornithidae

Scrub-birds, pp362–363

Small, thicket-living insect-eaters, with strong reticulately scaled feet, rounded tails and brown plumage finely barred dusky on upper parts; throat white and breast black in males. Wings vestigial and rounded, with rudimentary clavicles and furcula, so virtually flightless. Forage on ground under deep cover; solitary and territorial. Voice box as in lyrebirds. Male sings powerfully from display points under cover, mating polygynously; female carries out all nest duties. Nest domed, on ground, lined with cardboard paste; eggs cream marked red-brown; young densely grey-downed. Two species, endemic to Australia.

Family Alaudidae

Larks, pp364–365

Small, ground-living insect- and seed-eaters of open field and grass in usually cryptic brown plumage; strong, running feet broadened and scaled down the back as well as the front; long-spurred hind claw; rather pointed wings with outermost tenth primary vestigial, and sometimes finch-like bills and short crests. Sexes alike. Male often has protracted song-flights over breeding territory; voice box lacks a pessulus. Build cup- or domed-nests on ground; eggs whitish or bluish marked grey or brown. About 75–77 species, in Old World, mainly drier parts of Afro-Asia; one native in Australia, one introduced and established.

Family Hirundinidae

Swallows and martins, pp366–369

Small aerial insectivores that feed on the wing, and resemble swifts but differ in their feet which, although very weak, are passerine in structure, and in their voice box with its usual passerine drum, allowing them to twitter in song on wing and from perch. Bill wide, body streamlined with thick, sleeked and often glossy plumage; wings long and pointed with only nine primary flight feathers; tail forked or square. Sexes alike. Often colonial. Pairing permanent or temporary, nesting in holes or building cup- or retort-shaped nests of mud pellets; eggs plain white or speckled red-brown. Both sexes share nest duties, female incubating most. About 80–81 species, on all continents; six in Australia, two erratic non-breeding summer visitors.

Family Motacillidae

Pipits and wagtails, pp370–371

Small, slender-tailed and -legged, ground-living insect-eaters that sometimes resemble larks but have booted hind feet and a pessulus in voice box, and which bob head and tail constantly up and down while standing. Bill thin and short. Sexes often alike. Walk and run on ground; fly with strong undulations, often in courtship song-flight over breeding grounds—wings have only nine primaries. Nest duties by female alone or shared; nest a substantial cup of fibre on ground; eggs off-white marked dusky. About 54 species, on all continents; five in Australia but four are erratic, non-breeding summer visitors in north.

Family Campephagidae

Cuckoo-shrikes, trillers and minivets, pp372–377

Small to medium-sized tree-living birds with rather stout, slightly hooked bills; stout but short feet better fitted for perching than walking (except Ground Cuckoo-shrike); dense soft grey, black and white plumage (plus red in minivets) that is groomed from powder downs on the flanks. Sexes alike or dissimilar in many species. Wings with tenth outermost primary well developed; flight of graceful, cuckoo-like undulations, refolding wings on landing. Feed on invertebrates and fruit, mainly in tree foliage by perch-and-sally or hopping. Solitary or in small flocks. Nest duties usually shared by both sexes (Australian species); nest a small neat saucer of cobweb-bound fibre on horizontal tree fork; eggs white to blue-green, marked red-brown to dusky. About 70–71 species, through Old World tropics to Melanesia; seven in Australia.

Family Pycnonotidae

Bulbuls, p378

Restless, small to medium, long-tailed round-winged fruit- or insect-eaters with well-developed tenth outer primary. Plumage dense, often tufted on back and patterned or crested on head; sexes usually alike. Bill short, slender, notched and bristled, and with operculate nostrils; feet usually short, weak and scaled. Mostly arboreal, sometimes terrestrial, feeding by gleaning, and hopping. Gregarious and often flocking but breeding in solitary territorial pairs; both sexes share all nest duties. Nest a cup of stems and fibre, supported or hanging low in foliage; eggs white to pink, marked heavily dark brown and grey. About 123 species, from Africa to eastern Asia and Moluccas; one introduced and established in Australia.

Family Muscicapidae

Old World flycatchers and allies, pp379–381

Small to medium-sized insect-catching perching birds with narrow to broad bills edged with straight rictal bristles, rather stout booted feet, wings with outermost primary well developed, and a 'turdine thumb' on the syrinx or voice box. Sexes alike or dissimilar. These are generalised invertebrate-eaters, and—including the Old World thrushes and robins—feed by gleaning among foliage, shuffling and hopping on the ground, or hawking out from perches on the wing. Solitary and nesting in exclusive pairs, the female builds and incubates while male defends territory; both sexes feed young. Nest bulky cup-shaped, in trees and shrubs; eggs white to blue-green marked brown and grey. About 438 species, throughout Old World and Africa and the New World (thrushes only); one indigenous to Australia, two introduced and established.

Family Pachycephalidae

Australian robins, whistlers and flycatchers, pp382–421

Small to medium-sized insect-eaters that resemble Old World flycatchers in form and behaviour but are indicated by recent molecular studies to be only convergently similar; all lack the 'turdine thumb' on the voice box. Range from flat-billed, hawking flycatchers to thick-headed and thick-billed perch-and-pounce shrub- and foliage-feeding robins and whistlers, to ground-hopping and -feeding thrushes. Flight often undulating; wings with tenth outermost primary well developed. Sexes alike or dissimilar; both sexes share nest duties or male only feeds young. Nests cup-shaped, variously textured, usually in trees; eggs white to buff, marked in greys and browns. About 225 species, centred in Australasia, to Africa and central Pacific; about 51–52 species in Australia. Still possibly heterogeneous and a mixture of several families.

Family Orthonychidae

Chowchillas, quail-thrushes and allies, pp422–428

Elusive medium-sized, often thick-bodied ground- and thicket-living insect-eaters with thin to stout bills, stout legs for running, and rather fibrous tails with white or spiny tips. Sexes alike or dissimilar. Wings rounded, with well-developed tenth outermost primary; flight weak and fluttering; bills without tomial notch and feet hop in whipbirds. All nest duties by female (except whipbirds); nest a cup or dome in thicket or on ground; eggs plain white, or marked dusky grey or pale blue spotted black (whipbirds). About 17 species, restricted to Australia–New Guinea; 10 in Australia.

Family Pomatostomatidae

Australian babblers, pp429–431

Bouncing, communal, ground- and branch-feeding insect-eaters of medium size in brown plumage; scimitar-shaped unnotched bills for probing and digging; rounded wings with long tenth outer primary; rather long fan-shaped tail. Move by rapid hopping in groups of up to a dozen or so; fly directly by flutter and glide. Female incubates and broods alone; male assists in nest building; all members of communal group feed young. Nests bulky domes, in shrubbery, built for cluster-roosting as well as nesting; eggs grey, scrawled dusky. Five species, in Australia and New Guinea; four in Australia. Formerly included with Old World babblers but molecular evidence indicates that they are closer to the Australo–Papuan logrunners.

Family Sylviidae

Old World Warblers, pp432–435

Small, generalised, cryptically brown- or green-toned insect-eaters with short slender often unnotched bills; weak rather rounded wings with well-developed tenth outer primary. Generally forage by gleaning in foliage, thicket and tussock. Most sing sweet territorial songs during breeding, from perch or in song-flight. Sexes alike or dissimilar. Usually in solitary pairs; female builds and incubates unaided, but male assists in feeding young. Nests mostly cup-shaped, in branches, low foliage on ground; eggs white, pink or blue, marked brown and grey. About 350 species, centred in Afro–Eurasia but reaching North America and the Pacific; nine species in Australia, one a summer migrant in north.

Family Maluridae

Fairy-wrens and allies, pp436–451

Small, wren-like insect- and seed-eaters with slender cocked tails of ten to six feathers, an interscapular gap on the dorsal feather tract, and auditory bullae on the skull. Sexes dissimilar; males often with much shining blue in plumage, females brown. Wings rounded with well-developed tenth outer primary; flight weak and fluttering with trailing tail. Bill thin, finch-like or flat and flycatcher-like, notched, with recurving rictal bristles. Feet rather long and usually slender, used for running and hopping. Feed by gleaning on the ground, in thicket, or leafy foliage. Communal in small territorial groups; female nest-builds and incubates unaided but male and other members of group help feed young. Nest a fibrous dome in low thicket; eggs white, freckled red-brown. Twenty-six species, in Australia–New Guinea; 20 in Australia.

Family Acanthizidae

Scrubwrens, thornbills and allies, pp452–481

Small wren- and warbler-like insect-eaters in dull brownish plumage with unbroken dorsal feather tract and often reddish or coloured rumps; broad tails of 12 feathers with frequent black subterminal band, often cocked in ground-living species. Bill thin or finch-like, notched, with fine or recurved rictal bristles. Sexes usually alike, often with white eye-ring or flecked forehead. Feet strong to weak, used for hopping only (except bristlebirds). Feed by gleaning on ground, in thicket or tree foliage. In solitary territorial pairs or local communal groups; female usually nest-builds and incubates alone, but male and other members of group help in feeding young. Nest a fibrous dome, from ground to high tree foliage; eggs white to dark buff, marked brown or grey, often laid at 48-hour intervals. About 62 species, restricted to Australia–New Guinea; about 40–41 in Australia.

Family Neosittidae

Sittellas, pp482–483

Small, pied, bark-foraging, arboreal insect-eaters; stumpy short-tailed body; rather long round wings with vestigial tenth outer primary; short, long-toed yellow feet for scrambling and hopping up, down and along branches. Bill unnotched, long, pointed and slightly upturned for probing; dusky with cream base. Sexes alike or dissimilar in head marks. Communal in small flocks. Female incubates unaided but male and other members of group assist in nest-building and feeding of young. Nest a bark-bound cup blending cryptically with dead supporting branches; eggs blue-white marked dusky. Two species, in Australia–New Guinea; one in Australia. Molecular evidence suggests that sittellas are modified Australian robins, Pachycephalidae.

Family Climacteridae
Australian treecreepers, pp484–489
Small, brown, bark-foraging, arboreal insectivores with buff bar in wings and black subterminal bar in rounded tail. Bill unnotched and unbristled, slender and downcurved for probing, mainly for ants; feet short, with long claws and forward toes partly fused (syndactyl) for hopping up, along and underneath but never down trunks and branches; some also hop-feed on ground. Sexes dissimilar in ear or breast marks. Solitary or communal in small groups in permanent territories; female incubates and sometimes nest-builds unaided but male and other members of group feed young. Nest a cup of fibre in tree hole; eggs pink-white marked red, laid at 48-hour intervals. Seven species, in Australia–New Guinea; six in Australia.

Family Meliphagidae
Honeyeaters, pp490–543
Aggressive, tiny to rather large tree-living insect-, nectar- and fruit-eaters in dull grey, brown, green and black plumage; tapered to square-cut tails and rounded to pointed wings with tenth outer primary usually well developed; flight swift and undulating. Bill usually long, slender and down-curved, unbristled, but notched and often toothed, with long protrusible tongue concavely channelled or grooved and split at tip into four, brush-tipped segments for sweeping up nectar and pollen; feet strong and sharp-clawed, used for hopping about branchlets, rarely the ground. Sexes usually alike, often with bare coloured face skin. Solitary and opportunistically gregarious but communal in small bands only in miners and melithreptine honeyeaters; female usually builds and incubates unaided but male assists in feeding young. Nest cup-shaped, perched or hanging in foliage; eggs pink-white or buff, marked red-brown or black. About 165 species, from Australasia to central Pacific; 65 in Australia.

Family Epthianuridae
Australian chats, pp544–547
Small, yellow-, red-, black-, and white-plumaged ground-feeding insectivores. Bill and tongue honeyeater-like but both short and slender with flanged nostrils; feet slender, for running on ground, not hopping. Wings round to pointed with short outermost tenth primary, promoting jerky, undulating flight. Sexes dissimilar, the male brightly coloured. Solitary to usually gregarious or communal, male courts and holds territory with display flights; female usually nest-builds under escort and male assists in incubation and rearing of young. Nest a cup in shrub or on ground; eggs pink-white spotted red, as in honeyeaters. Five species, endemic to Australia. Morphological and molecular evidence indicates that chats are closely allied to honeyeaters and perhaps best treated as a subfamily of them.

Family Nectariniidae
Sunbirds and allies, pp548–549
Tiny, jewel-like arboreal nectar- and insect-eaters that resemble hummingbirds superficially in form and some aspects of behaviour. Feet typically passerine, tail square or tapered, and wings round with well-developed tenth outer primary allowing swift undulating flight and hovering over flowers. Bill slender and down-curved, finely toothed, and unbristled, with protrusible tubular tongue split and rolled at tip to take nectar by capillarity. Sexes usually dissimilar, the male plumaged in glittering metallic blues, greens and reds. Solitary and pairing temporary; female builds purse-shaped or coarse hanging domed nest in foliage, assisted by male, incubates alone and is helped by male in feeding advanced young; eggs white to pale blue, spotted and scrawled grey, brown and black. About 115 species, in Old World tropics; one in Australia.

Family Dicaeidae
Flowerpeckers, p550
Small to tiny, bullet-shaped arboreal fruit-eaters, often vividly plumaged in iridescent red and black. Tail short and square and wings pointed, with only nine primaries; flight swift and direct. Bill short, unbristled and finely toothed and tongue shortly bifid and brush-tipped for feeding on nectar. Muscular stomach reduced to a blind sac, so fruit and nectar pass by while insects diverted to it for digestion, their hard parts later voided as pellets. Most feed on fruit of mistletoes. Generally solitary; mating temporary. Sexes often dissimilar, female duller and nest-building and incubating unaided; male assists in feeding young. Nest a smooth, felt-like purse hanging in foliage; eggs plain white (except *Melanocharis*). About 48 species, from India to Melanesia, in tropics; one in Australia.

Family Pardalotidae
Pardalotes, pp551–555
Tiny bull-headed insect-eaters of the outer foliage of eucalypts, with stumpy, scoop-shaped unbristled bills used for gleaning scale insects from leaves. Sexes similar. Plumage partly black marked white above, washed yellow below; tail short and square-cut; wings rather pointed, with only nine primaries. Flight swift and undulating. Solitary, in pairs or dispersed groups, nomadic or permanently territoral; both sexes share all nest duties, and male calls from vantage perches near nest. Nest a cup of fibre in burrow or tree hole; eggs plain white. Four species, endemic to Australia. Often considered related to flowerpeckers but recent molecular evidence indicates affinity with scrubwrens and thornbills (Acanthizidae).

Family Zosteropidae
White-eyes, pp556–557
Small, green, arboreal fruit- and insect-gleaners with small, thin, unbristled, unnotched bill and white feather ring around eye; tongue finely brush-tipped. Sexes alike. Tail square cut; wings with well-developed tenth outer primary. Gregarious in feeding flocks flying from tree to tree and hopping through foliage; mewing calls in contact. Breed in solitary pairs, mating temporarily; all nest duties shared by both sexes. Nest a hanging cup of fibre in foliage; eggs plain light blue. About 83 species, from Africa to Japan and southwestern Pacific; three species in Australia.

Family Fringillidae
Finches, pp558–559
Small, stout, seed-eaters with strong, conical unbristled bills for husking and crushing seed, strongly muscled stomachs, squared tails of 12 broad feathers, and rounded wings with only nine outer primaries; feet short but strong. Plumage often brightly coloured; sexes usually similar. Flight undulating; feeding on trees or on ground. Gregarious, breeding in pairs in or out of loose colonies; courtship by male involves song, special posturing and display flight; female builds nest and incubates alone, fed on nest by male; both sexes feed advanced young, mainly on insects bill to mouth or by regurgitation. Nest a cup of fibre in foliage; eggs white with brown marks. About 122 species, throughout America, Africa and Eurasia; two introduced and established in Australia.

Family Ploceidae
Weavers and allies, pp560–580
Small, thick-set, seed-eating birds with stout, pointed unbristled bills, short and square to long streaming tails, and rounded wings with short tenth outer primary. Plumage often brightly coloured and patterned, the sexes alike (most waxbills) or female dull (many weavers). Feed mostly on grain, augmented with insects, all stored in a crop; grass finches drink regularly. All hop on ground. Gregarious and flocking; mating permanently, monogamous (most waxbills) to polygynous (many weavers); nest duties all shared by both sexes (most waxbills) or incubation by female alone (weavers). Nests domed balls of grass in foliage, often with funnel entrance and, in weavers, sometimes colonial masses; eggs plain white (waxbills) or coloured and marked (weavers); young, fed by regurgitation by both sexes, have guiding mouth marks in waxbills. About 270 species, from Africa and Europe to Melanesia; 18 native to Australia, all waxbills, three introduced and established.

Family Sturnidae
Starlings and mynahs, pp581–583
Robust, medium-sized arboreal birds that nonetheless feed both on ground and in trees on range of fruit, invertebrates and refuse, and usually have much glossy black in plumage. Crop present for holding food. Sexes similar. Bill usually straight, shortly bristled and notched; feet strong, long and clearly scaled; tail usually short; wings rounded to pointed with well-developed tenth outer primary. Flight swift and direct; walk or run on ground. Gregarious and often flocking; monogamous, mating permanent or temporary, male assisting with nest-building and feeding young bill to mouth, but only female incubating. Nest a cup of grass in hole in tree or building, or massed domes of grass in tree foliage; eggs usually plain blue-green. Juvenile plumage streaked except mynahs. About 111 species, from Afro–Eurasia to Polynesia; one indigenous in Australia, two introduced and established.

Family Oriolidae
Orioles and figbirds, pp584–586
Medium-sized wholly arboreal birds with strong, slightly down-curved, finely bristled and often reddish notched bills and much yellow and bright green in plumage; immatures streaked. All eat a range of insects and particularly fruit. Sexes usually dissimilar, the male brighter. Feet stout and scaled, used for hopping; wings long and rounded, with tenth outer primary well-developed, promoting swift, undulating flight from tree to tree. Rather solitary (except figbirds), pairing and territory-holding permanent or temporary, announced by soft, carrying yodels; male often assists in nest-building and feeding of young but leaves most incubation to female. Nest a neat cup of fibre and twigs hung in foliage; eggs white or buff-pink or greenish with black and brown speckling. About 25 species, from Afro–Eurasia to New Guinea; three in Australia.

Family Dicruridae
Drongos, p587
Elegant, arboreal insect-eaters in glossy black plumage; long, forked and often curled or streamered tails. Bills stout, wide, black and notched, and long-bristled; wings pointed with well-developed tenth outer primary; feet short and scaled. Sexes alike. Feed mostly by hawking and sallying on wing from set perch in graceful aerial evolutions. Solitary or in permanent or temporary pairs; both sexes apparently share all

nest duties. Nest a spare cup of tendrils in foliage or fork; eggs pale grey-pink, marked red-brown and purple-grey. About 20 species, throughout Old World tropics; one in Australia.

Family Ptilonorhynchidae

Bowerbirds, pp588–596
Stout, medium-sized arboreal birds with thick, unbristled bills taking mainly fruit; strong scaled legs for bounding about foliage; rounded wings with long tenth outer primary for swooping flap-and-glide flight. Sexes usually dissimilar: male in satin blacks, yellows and browns, often with orange, yellow or lilac mane or nape bar; female dull grey-brown or green, often chevroned ventrally. Usually solitary. Mating mostly polygynous; male constructs elaborately decorated maypoles, avenues or platform bowers of sticks and leaves on ground for display and copulation, and often sings brilliantly over or in them, with much mimicry. Female comes to mate and leaves to nest alone; nest a coarse cup of twigs and fibre in foliage or tree crotch; eggs plain cream or blotched or lined grey-black. Eighteen species, in Australia–New Guinea; nine in Australia. Often considered closely allied to birds-of-paradise, but recent molecular evidence suggests that they are related to lyrebirds and treecreepers instead.

Family Paradisaeidae

Birds-of-paradise, pp597–599
Small to large, wholly arboreal crow-like birds of rainforest, feeding on fruit and insects by hop-gleaning and probing on trunks and foliage. Bill short to long and curved, notched but unbristled; feet stout and scaled; wings rounded with long tenth outer primary, promoting swooping flap-glide flight; tails short or central pair of feathers prolonged in wires or plumes. Sexes usually dissimilar, the female brown and barred and male exquisitely plumaged in metallic blues, greens, reds and yellows, and often with plated gorgets and elaborate flank plumes. Solitary or gregarious. Mating mostly polygynous; male displays alone or in concert usually on high perches with bizarre posturing and raucous calling. Female comes to mate and leaves to nest alone. Nest a rough stick-and-fibre cup in foliage, or domed; eggs white to pink-buff, spotted red-brown or streaked purple and red. About 41–42 species, centred in New Guinea; four in Australia.

Family Corcoracidae

Australian mud-nesters, pp600–601
Medium to large, ground-feeding crow-like birds that nest and clump-roost in trees. Bill thin and down-curved or short and stubby, taking mostly insects or seeds respectively, notched and shortly bristled; feet strong, long and scaled, walking with teetering action; tail long and bushy; wings rounded with long tenth outer primary, flying slowly by flap-glide. Sexes alike; plumage soft and thick, black or grey, with arrowed green gloss on mantle in adults. Closely gregarious in permanent, territorial communes of up to 15 or so (accrued family groups), with a senior breeding pair; most or all members of group share in nest-building, incubation and feeding young. Nest a bowl of mud on tree branch; eggs cream blotched black-grey. Two species, endemic to Australia.

Family Grallinidae

Magpie-larks, p602
Small to medium-sized pied, long-legged, ground-feeding insect- and snail-eaters formerly thought allied to Australian mud-nesters but since shown to be ground-living monarch flycatchers (Pachycephalidae); they will probably be transferred to latter family. Bills short, straight and thin, pale, notched and finely bristled; feet long and scaled; tail medium and often flicked about on perch; wings broadly rounded, with long tenth outer primary, flying slowly with lapping beats. Sexes dissimilar in face pattern; young compromise. Solitary or gregarious, ultimately monogamous in permanent territory, courting in wing-raising duets; both sexes share all nest duties. Nest a cup of fibre caked with mud on tree branch; eggs pale pink, spotted red-brown. Two species, in Australia–New Guinea; one in Australia.

Family Artamidae

Woodswallows, pp603–607
Stout, small to medium-sized aerial insect-eaters with dense, soft plumage groomed from powder downs on flanks; broad pointed wings with vestigial tenth outer primary promoting effortless flutter-glide flight. Bill short, thick and pointed, pale blue-grey with black tip, notched, with short bristles. Feet short and thick, scaled, allowing only weak hopping; tail short, square and twirled on perch. Sexes mostly alike in sleek grey and white plumage. Feed on long hawking flights or short sallies from set perches. Communal, often in large flocks, and most cluster-roosting at night in tree holes or lined on branches; sedentary to migratory. Mating monogamous, permanent or temporary; both sexes share all nest duties and additional helpers may feed young. Nest a spare cup of fibre in tree crotch or fork; eggs buff marked grey and dusky. Ten species, from India to Melanesia; six in Australia.

Family Cracticidae

Butcherbirds and currawongs, pp608–613
Strong-bodied, medium-sized to large raptorial songbirds in black or pied plumage that feed arboreally by perch-and-pounce or by walking and hopping on ground for live or scavenged food. Bills long, straight and hook-notched, shortly bristled, and all black or with grey-white base; feet short to long, scaled to smooth; tails long, contrastingly tipped; wings rounded or pointed, with well-developed tenth outer primary, flying in deep undulations or in fast direct flap-and-glide. Solitary to gregarious and flocking; mostly monogamous and permanently paired, female usually nest-building and incubating unaided but male assisting with feeding young. Nest a coarse bowl of twigs in foliage; eggs pale blue-green, marked red-brown and grey. Ten species, in Australia–New Guinea; eight in Australia.

Family Corvidae

Crows, jays and allies, pp614–617
Robust, medium-sized to large 'song' birds with strong, scaled feet and strong, dark down-curving notched bills, the nostrils of which are shielded by dense bristles. Plumage all black, pied, or toned in blues and greens, often glossed and sometimes crested; tails rounded or tapered; wings long and rounded with well-developed tenth outer primary, promoting floating flight with evenly beating wings. Sexes alike. Many feed by scavenging on ground; some are specialised insectivores or nut-eaters; all roost and nest in trees. Solitary to gregarious, and monogamous in permanent pairs; incubation by female alone but male assists in nest-building and feeding of young, with additional helpers in some jays. Nest a bulky cup of twigs and fibre in tree, rarely a hole or burrow; eggs buff to pale blue spotted grey-brown. About 105 species, on all continents; five in Australia.

Index of English names

Further information

This book provides the most comprehensive, authorative, and up-to-date summary of all the birds of Australia and their general behaviour. For enthusiasts wanting more specialised information—on specific birds or localities—there are many such texts available today; of these, those listed below are recommended.

Handbooks

North, A.J. (1901-1914). Nests and Eggs of Birds found breeding in Australia and Tasmania, 4 vols. Sydney: Australian Museum. Vol. 1 in facsimile edition published by Oxford University Press, Melbourne (1984); vols. 2–4 to come.

Field Guides

Beruldsen, G. (1980). A Field Guide to Nests and Eggs of Australian Birds. Adelaide: Rigby.

Pizzey, G. (1980). A Field Guide to the Birds of Australia. Illustrated by Roy Doyle. Sydney: Collins.

Simpson, K. and Day, N. (1984). The Birds of Australia: a book of identification. South Yarra, Vic: Lloyd O'Neil.

Slater, P. (1970, 1974). A Field Guide to Australian Birds, 2 vols (non-passerines, passerines). Adelaide: Rigby.

General Distribution

Blakers, M, Davies, S.J.J.F and Reilly, P.N. (1984). The Atlas of Australian Birds, Royal Australasian Ornithologists Union. Melbourne: Melbourne University Press.

Monographs of Special Groups

Birds-of-Paradise and bowerbirds
Gilliard, E.T. (1969). Birds of Paradise and Bower Birds. London: Weidenfeld and Nicolson.

Fairy-wrens
Schodde, R. (1982). The Fairy-wrens A Monograph of the Maluridae. Illustrated by Richard Weatherly. Melbourne: Lansdowne Editions.

Finches
Immelmann, K. (1965). Australian Finches in Bush and Aviary. Paintings by Neville W. Cayley. Sydney: Angus and Robertson.

Malleefowl
Frith, H.J. (1962). The Mallee-Fowl; the bird that builds an incubator. Sydney: Angus and Robertson.

Nocturnal birds
Schodde, R. and Mason, I.J. (1980). Nocturnal Birds of Australia. Illustrated by Jeremy Boot. Melbourne: Lansdowne Editions.

Parrots and cockatoos
Forshaw, J.M. (1981). Australian Parrots, second (revised) edition. Illustrated by William T. Cooper. Melbourne: Lansdowne Editions.

Lendon, A.H. (1979). Australian Parrots in field and aviary, the comprehensive revised edition of Neville Cayley's standard work. Sydney: Angus and Robertson.

Pigeons and doves
Frith, H.J. (1982). Pigeons and Doves of Australia. Adelaide: Rigby.

Seabirds
Serventy, D.L., Serventy, Vincent and Warham, J. (1971). The Handbook of Australian Seabirds. Sydney: A.H. and A.W. Reed.

Waterfowl
Frith, H.J. (1982). Waterfowl in Australia, revised edition. Sydney: Angus and Robertson.

Techniques of Bird Study

Balmford, R. (1980). Learning about Australian Birds. Sydney: Collins.

Bird Behaviour and Biology

Parry, V.A. (1970). Kookaburras. Melbourne: Lansdowne Press.

Reilly, P. (1972). Fairy Penguins and Earthy People. Melbourne: Lothian.

Rowley, Ian (1975). Bird Life. Sydney: Collins.

Regional Lists and Handbooks

Australian high country
Frith, H.J. (editor) (1984). Birds in the Australian High Country, fully revised edition. Sydney: Angus and Robertson.

Kimberley Division, northwest Australia
Storr, G.M. (1980). Birds of the Kimberley Division, Western Australia. Perth: Western Australian Museum Special Publication no.11.

New South Wales
Morris, A.K., McGill, A.R. & Holmes, G. (1981). Handlist of Birds in New South Wales. Sydney: New South Wales Field Ornithologists' Club.

Northern Territory
Storr, G.M. (1977). Birds of the Northern Territory. Perth: Western Australian Museum Special Publication no.7.

Queensland
Storr, G.M. (1984). Revised List of Queensland Birds. Perth: Records of the Western Australian Museum, supplement 19.

South Australia
Condon, H.T. (1968). Handlist of the Birds of South Australia. Adelaide: South Australian Ornithological Association.

Tasmania
Green, R.H. (1977). Birds of Tasmania. Launceston: R.H. Green.

Victoria
Wheeler, W.R. (1967). The Birds of Victoria. Melbourne: Victorian Ornithological Research Group.

Western Australia (excluding Kimberley Division)
Serventy, D.L. and Whittell, H.M. (1976). Birds of Western Australia, ed. 5. Perth: University of Western Australia Press.

Literature and History of Australian Ornithology

Whittell, H.M. (1954). The Literature of Australian Birds: a History and Bibliography of Australian Ornithology. Perth: Paterson Brokensha.

Australian Ornithological Societies

Of the many such organisations in Australia, only the senior national and state bodies are listed here. All produce a newsletter and many a journal.

National

Royal Australasian Ornithologists Union, 21 Gladstone Steet, Moonee Ponds, Vic., 3039.

Australian Bird Study Association, PO Box A313, Sydney South, NSW, 2001.

Avicultural Society of Australia, c/- 52 Harris Rd, Elliminyt, Vic., 3249.

State

Australian Capital Territory
Canberra Ornithological Group, PO Box 301, Civic Square, ACT, 2608.

New South Wales
New South Wales Field Ornithologists Club, PO Box C436, Clarence St, Sydney, NSW, 2001.

Northern Territory
Northern Territory Field Naturalist Club, PO Box 39565, Winnellie, NT, 5789.

Queensland
Queensland Ornithological Society, PO Box 97, St Lucia, Qld, 4067.

South Australia
South Australian Ornithological Association, c/- South Australian Museum, North Tce, Adelaide, SA, 5000.

Tasmania
Bird Observers' Association of Tasmania, GPO Box 68A, Hobart, Tas., 7001.

Victoria
The Bird Observers Club, 183 Springvale Rd, PO Box 185, Nunawading, Vic., 3131.
Victorian Ornithological Research Group, c/- 10 Sevenoaks St, Balwyn, Vic., 3103.

Western Australia
Royal Australasian Ornithologists Union, Western Australian branch, c/- Lot 36, Rabone Way, Boya, WA, 6056.

Acknowledgments

Sources

PART 1 Photographers: pages **8–9** Graeme Chapman (National Photographic Index of Australian Birds); **11** Robin Smith; **12** top Laurence Le Guay, bottom Eleanor Williams; **13** David Milledge; **14** top David Milledge, bottom A. Fox; **15** Richard Schodde; **16** top Allan Fox, bottom Anthony Healy; **17** top G.E. Schmida, bottom Anthony Healy; **18** top Lawrence Collings, bottom Richard Schodde; **19** Frank Woerle.

PART 2 Photographers: pages **20–1** C. Lalas (NPI); **23** A.G. Wells; **26** Graeme Chapman (NPI); **28** Peter Slater; **29** Thomas Lowe (NPI); **32** Vincent and Carol Serventy; **34** Koonwarra feather, courtesy of National Museum of Victoria. Drawings: page **35** top, after restoration by Frank Knight and G.F. van Tets (courtesy of South Australian Museum); bottom, after restoration by Henry Galiano and Pat Vickers Rich (courtesy of South Australian Museum).

PART 3 An oblique stroke separates the name of the person who contributed information on the species in the first edition from the name of the photographer. An asterisk after the photographer's name indicates that the bird was a captive when it was photographed. Pages **40–1** /Graeme Chapman (NPI); **43** /D. and M. Clampett (NPI); **44–5 Emu** Frank Crome/left John Carnemolla (Bruce Coleman Ltd/NPI), right Harold Pollock. **46–7 Southern Cassowary** Frank Crome/left Len Robinson (NPI), right Harold Pollock. **48 Common Diving-Petrel** Peter Fullagar/Michael Soper (NPI). **49 Wandering Albatross** Kenneth Simpson/W.D.F. MacKenzie (NPI). **50 Royal Albatross** Kenneth Simpson/K.R. Kerry (NPI). **51 Black-browed Albatross** Kenneth Simpson/Clem Haagner (Ardea/NPI). **52 Grey-headed Albatross** Kenneth Simpson/Michael Soper (NPI). **53 Yellow-nosed Albatross** Kenneth Simpson/S. Vanags (NPI); **Shy Albatross** Kenneth Simpson/Hans and Judy Beste (NPI). **54 Sooty Albatross** Kenneth Simpson/R. Croome (NPI). **55 Light-mantled Sooty-Albatross** Kenneth Simpson/B. Allwright (NPI). **56 Southern Giant-Petrel** Peter Fullagar/top D.E. Rounsevell (NPI), bottom W.D.F. MacKenzie (NPI). **57 Northern Giant-Petrel** Peter Fullagar/G.W. Johnstone (NPI). **58 Southern Fulmar** Peter Fullagar/K.R. Kerry (NPI). **59 Cape Petrel** Peter Fullagar/K.R. Kerry (NPI); **Great-winged Petrel** Peter Fullagar. **60 Tahiti Petrel** /F. Hannecart; **White-headed Petrel** Peter Fullagar/John Warham (NPI). **61 Providence Petrel** Peter Fullagar/Ederic Slater (NPI). **62 Gould's Petrel** Peter Fullagar/E.L. Hyem (NPI). **63 Kermadec Petrel** Peter Fullagar/Michael Soper; **Herald Petrel** /John Warham (NPI). **64 Soft-plumaged Petrel** Peter Fullagar/John Warham (NPI); **Kerguelen Petrel** Peter Fullagar/J.G. Sinclair (NPI). **65 Blue Petrel** Peter Fullagar/P.M. Sagar; **Black-winged Petrel** Peter Fullagar/Peter Fullagar (NPI). **66 Broad-billed Prion** Peter Fullagar/top Michael Soper (NPI), bottom T. Pescott. **67 Fairy Prion** Peter Fullagar/John Warham (NPI); **White-chinned Petrel** Peter Fullagar/Jouve (Jacana). **68 Slender-billed Prion** Peter Fullagar/P.M. Sagar; **Antarctic Prion** Peter Fullagar/Graham Robertson (Auscape International). **69 Streaked Shearwater** /Alan McBride (NPI). **70 Short-tailed Shearwater** Peter Fullagar/J.R. Napier (NPI). **71 Sooty Shearwater** Peter Fullagar/John Warham (NPI). **72 Flesh-footed Shearwater** Peter Fullagar/Norman Chaffer (NPI); **Fluttering Shearwater** Peter Fullagar/Michael Soper (NPI). **73 Hutton's Shearwater** Peter Fullagar/Geoffrey Harrow. **74 Buller's Shearwater** Peter Fullagar/John Warham (NPI); **Little Shearwater** Peter Fullagar/H.J. de S. Disney and Peter Fullagar (NPI). **75 Wedge-tailed Shearwater** Peter Fullagar/Cyril Webster (NPI). **76 Wilson's Storm-Petrel** Peter Fullagar/Peter Johnson. **77 White-bellied Storm-Petrel** Peter Fullagar/H.J. de S. Disney and Peter Fullagar (NPI); **Black-bellied Storm-Petrel** Peter Fullagar/John Warham (NPI). **78 Grey-backed Storm-Petrel** Peter Fullagar/John Warham (NPI); **White-faced Storm-Petrel** Peter Fullagar/Michael Soper (NPI). **79 Rockhopper Penguin** Kenneth Simpson/G.W. Johnstone (NPI); **Erect-crested Penguin** /P.J. Moors. **80 Little Penguin** Pauline Reilly/Michael Seyfort (NPI). **81 Fiordland Penguin** Kenneth Simpson/John Warham (NPI). **82 Erect-crested Grebe** Robert Storer/Chris Spiker (NPI). **83 Australasian Grebe** Robert Storer/Cameron Photographics (NPI); **Hoary-headed Grebe** Robert Storer/F.G. Craven (NPI). **84 Red-tailed Tropicbird** G.F. van Tets/E.L. Hyem (NPI). **85 White-tailed Tropicbird** G.F. van Tets/Tony Beamish (Ardea/NPI). **86 Great Frigatebird** G.F. van Tets/Vincent Serventy (NPI). **87 Least Frigatebird** G.F. van Tets/Vincent Serventy (NPI). **88–9 Black-faced Shag** G.F. van Tets/left W.D.F. MacKenzie (NPI), right Ron and Valerie Taylor (NPI). **90 Pied Cormorant** G.F. van Tets/Gary Weber (NPI). **91 Great Cormorant** G.F. van Tets/L. Thorpe* (NPI); **Little Black Cormorant** G.F. van Tets/Graeme Chapman. **92 Little Pied Cormorant** G.F. van Tets/I.R. McCann (NPI). **93 Darter** W.J.M. Vestjens/Hans and Judy Beste (NPI). **94 Red-footed Booby** G.F. van Tets/Vincent Serventy (NPI); **Brown Booby** G.F. van Tets/B. Higgins (NPI). **95 Masked Booby** G.F. van Tets/Douglass Baglin (NPI). **96 Australasian Gannet** G.F. van Tets/I. Watson (NPI). **97 Australian Pelican** W.J.M. Vestjens/W.D.F. MacKenzie (NPI). **98 Pacific Heron** G.F. van Tets/W.J. Labbett (NPI); **Great-billed Heron** G.F. van Tets/Bill Green. **99 White-faced Heron** G.F. van Tets/Ray Garstone (NPI). **100 Pied Heron** G.F. van Tets/Hans and Judy Beste (NPI). **101 Cattle Egret** G.F. van Tets/Hans and Judy Beste (NPI); **Great Egret** G.F. van Tets/D. and M. Trounson (NPI). **102 Little Egret** G.F. van Tets/W.J. Labbett (NPI); **Intermediate Egret** G.F. van Tets/Stanley and Kay Breeden. **103 Eastern Reef Egret** J.T. Recher/top Cyril Webster, bottom Len Robinson (NPI). **104–5 Rufous Night Heron** G.F. van Tets/Peter Slater (NPI); **Striated Heron** G.F. van Tets/Hans and Judy Beste (NPI). **106 Little Bittern** G.F. van Tets/Thomas Lowe (NPI); **Black Bittern** G.F. van Tets/J. Purnell (NPI). **107 Australasian Bittern** G.F. van Tets/Hans and Judy Beste (NPI). **108 Black-necked Stork** John McKean/top Robin Smith (NPI), bottom Frank Woerle. **109 Glossy Ibis** W.J.M. Vestjens/D. and M. Trounson (NPI). **110 Sacred Ibis** W.J.M. Vestjens/Tim Newbery (NPI). **111 Straw-necked Ibis** W.J.M. Vestjens/Thomas Lowe (NPI). **112 Royal Spoonbill** W.J.M. Vestjens/Tim Newbery (NPI). **113 Yellow-billed Spoonbill** W.J.M. Vestjens/I.R. McCann (NPI). **114–5 Osprey** Ian James Mason/David Hollands (NPI). **116 Pacific Baza** Ian James Mason/Michael Morcombe (NPI). **117 Letter-winged Kite** Ian James Mason/top Ray Garstone (NPI), bottom Norman Chaffer (NPI). **118 Black-shouldered Kite** John Calaby/Lindsay Cupper (Auscape International); **Black Kite** John Calaby/J.M. Cupper (NPI). **119 Brahminy Kite** Ian James Mason/Hans and Judy Beste (NPI). **120 Whistling Kite** John Calaby/J. Estbergs. **121 Square-tailed Kite** John McKean/Chris Cameron (NPI). **122 Black-breasted Buzzard** Richard Schodde/L. Cupper (NPI). **123 Brown Goshawk** Ian James Mason/John Dart* (NPI). **124 Grey Goshawk** Ian James Mason/top Garth May (NPI), bottom E. McNamara. **125 Collared Sparrowhawk** Ian James Mason/Colin Gill (NPI). **126–7 Little Eagle** John Calaby/Peter Slater (NPI); **Red Goshawk** Ian James Mason/Lindsay Cupper (NPI). **128 Spotted Harrier** John Calaby/Hans and Judy Beste (NPI). **129 Swamp Harrier** John Calaby/D. Hadden (NPI). **130 White-bellied Sea-Eagle** John Calaby/A.G. Wells (NPI). **131 Wedge-tailed Eagle** Michael Brooker/J. Estbergs (NPI). **132 Grey Falcon** John Calaby/A. Eames (NPI); **Brown Falcon** John Calaby/Graeme Chapman. **133 Australian Kestrel** John Calaby/A.G. Wells (NPI). **134 Australian Hobby** John Calaby/Norman Chaffer (NPI); **Peregrine Falcon** John Calaby/D. and M. Trounson* (NPI). **135 Black Falcon** John Calaby/David Hollands (NPI). **136–7 Magpie Goose** H.J. Frith/left Kenneth Fink (Ardea/NPI), right Michael Morcombe. **138 Wandering Whistling-Duck** H.J. Frith/Stanley and Kay Breeden. **139 Plumed Whistling-Duck** H.J. Frith/Len Robinson* (NPI). **140 Black Swan** L.W. Braithwaite/E. and F. Smith (NPI). **141 Mute Swan** H.J. Frith/Kenneth Fink (Ardea/NPI). **142 Freckled Duck** H.J. Frith/Ray Garstone (NPI). **143 Cape Barren Goose** H.J. Frith/F.M. Dowling (NPI). **144 Australian Shelduck** H.J. Frith/Ray Garstone (NPI). **145 Radjah Shelduck** H.J. Frith/Graeme Chapman (NPI). **146 Green Pygmy-Goose** H.J. Frith/D. and M. Trounson* (NPI). **147 Cotton Pygmy-Goose** H.J. Frith and Hugh Lavery/D. and M. Trounson* (NPI). **148 Maned Duck** H.J. Frith/Norman Chaffer (NPI). **149 Pink-eared Duck** H.J. Frith/Thomas Lowe (NPI). **150 Grey Teal** H.J. Frith/Colin Gill* (NPI). **151 Chestnut Teal** H.J. Frith/Len Robinson* (NPI). **152 Pacific Black Duck** H.J. Frith/Douglass Baglin (NPI). **153 Mallard** H.J. Frith/Kenneth Fink (Ardea). **154 Australasian Shoveler** H.J. Frith/Graeme Chapman (NPI). **155 Hardhead** H.J. Frith/Colin Gill* (NPI). **156 Blue-billed Duck** H.J. Frith/Chris Spiker (NPI). **157 Musk Duck** H.J. Frith/F. Collet (Ardea/NPI). **158 Orange-footed Scrubfowl** H.J. Frith/Hans and Judy Beste (NPI). **159 Australian Brush-Turkey** H.J. Frith/Len Robinson (NPI). **160–1 Malleefowl** H.J. Frith/Len Robinson (NPI). **162 California Quail** H.J. Frith/Avon and Tillford (Ardea/NPI). **163 Stubble Quail** H.J. Frith/I.R. McCann. **164 Brown Quail** H.J. Frith/D. and M. Trounson* (NPI). **165 King Quail** H.J. Frith/J.D. Waterhouse (NPI). **166 Common Peafowl** H.J. Frith/Chris Cameron (NPI). **167 Common Pheasant** H.J. Frith/S. Roberts (Ardea/NPI). **168 Red-backed Button-quail** K.A. Muller/F. Lewitzka (NPI). **169 Painted Button-quail** K.A. Muller/Norman Chaffer (NPI). **170 Little Button-quail** K.A. Muller/J. Bell (NPI); **Chestnut-backed Button-quail** K.A. Muller. **171 Red-chested Button-quail** K.A. Muller/L. de Ross* (NPI). **172 Black-breasted Button-quail** K.A. Muller/Alan Foster (NPI). **173 Red-necked Crake** H.B. Gill/William Peckover* (NPI). **174 Chestnut Rail** H.B. Gill/Ian Morris (NPI); **Lewin's Rail** Graeme Chapman and Mark Clayton/F.M. Dowling (NPI). **175 Buff-banded Rail** Graeme Chapman and Mark Clayton/T.A. Waite (NPI). **176 Australian Crake** Fred Smith/M. Carter (NPI); **White-browed Crake** H.B. Gill/Roy Mackay* (NPI). **177 Spotless Crake** Fred Smith/D. Hadden (Ardea/NPI); **Baillon's Crake** Fred Smith/Leslie Chandler (NPI). **178 Bush-hen** H.B. Gill/Len Robinson (NPI). **179 Tasmanian Native-hen** Michael Ridpath/F.M. Dowling (NPI); **Black-tailed Native-hen** Michael Ridpath/A.G. Wells (NPI). **180 Dusky Moorhen** Graeme Chapman/Hans and Judy Beste (Ardea/NPI). **181 Purple Swamphen** Graeme Chapman/Hans and Judy Beste (NPI). **182 Eurasian Coot** John McKean/Graeme Chapman (NPI). **183 Kori Bustard** H.J. Frith/Graeme Chapman (NPI). **184 Brolga** Hugh Lavery/L.J. Millar (NPI). **185 Sarus Crane** Hugh Lavery/Keith Ireland (NPI). **186 Comb-crested Jacana** John McKean/Norman Chaffer (NPI). **187 Painted Snipe** K.A. Muller/Thomas Lowe (NPI). **188 Pied Oystercatcher** A.J. Baker/T.A. Waite (NPI). **189 Sooty Oystercatcher** A.J. Baker/J.R. Napier (NPI). **190 Plains-wanderer** David Rushton/R.F. Kenyon* (NPI). **191 Black-winged Stilt** Arnold McGill/R. and D. Keller (NPI). **192–3 Red-necked Avocet** Arnold McGill/Peter Slater (NPI); **Banded Stilt** Graeme Chapman and Arnold McGill/E.N. Paton (NPI). **194 Bush Thick-knee** Arnold McGill/Hans and Judy Beste (NPI). **195 Beach Thick-knee** John McKean/Graeme Chapman. **196 Oriental Pratincole** Fred Smith/T.S.U. de Zylva (Frank W. Lane/NPI). **197 Australian Pratincole** G. Maclean/Peter Disher (NPI). **198 Banded Lapwing** G.F. van Tets/Len Robinson (NPI). **199 Masked Lapwing** G.F. van Tets/top W.R. Taylor (NPI), bottom Len Robinson (NPI). **200 Lesser Golden Plover** Fred Smith/D. and M. Trounson (NPI). **201 Grey Plover** Fred Smith/Tom and Pam Gardner (NPI); **Red-kneed Dotterel** Arnold McGill/Graeme Chapman (NPI). **202 Black-fronted Dotterel** Arnold McGill/A.J. Gibson(NPI); **Inland Dotterel** G. Maclean/Thomas Lowe (NPI). **203 Double-banded Plover** Fred Smith/D. Hadden (NPI); **Large Sand Plover** Fred Smith/D. and M. Trounson (NPI). **204 Red-capped Plover** Arnold McGill/Edgar Whitbourn (NPI). **205 Oriental Plover** Fred Smith/E.E. Zillman (NPI); **Mongolian Plover** Fred Smith/D. and M. Trounson (NPI). **206 Hooded Plover** Arnold McGill/T.A. Waite (NPI). **207 Ruddy Turnstone** Fred Smith/Richard Vaughan (Ardea/NPI). **208 Bar-tailed Godwit** Fred Smith/D. and M. Trounson (NPI). **209 Black-tailed Godwit** Fred Smith/Chris Knights (Ardea/NPI). **210 Whimbrel** John McKean/D. and M. Trounson (NPI); **Little Curlew** John McKean/Tom and Pam Gardner (NPI). **211 Eastern Curlew** John McKean/D. and M. Trounson (NPI). **212 Asian Dowitcher** /John Dawson. **213 Wood Sandpiper** John McKean/Ralf Richter (Ardea/NPI). **214 Greenshank** John McKean/D. and M. Trounson (NPI). **215 Marsh Sandpiper** John McKean/M.D. England (Ardea/NPI); **Common Sandpiper** Fred Smith/Hans and Judy Beste (NPI). **216 Grey-tailed Tattler** John McKean/D. and M. Trounson (NPI). **217 Wandering Tattler** John McKean/Edgar Whitbourn (NPI). **218 Terek Sandpiper** John McKean/D. and M. Trounson (NPI). **219 Red-necked Phalarope** Fred Smith/top Trevor Marshall (Ardea/NPI), bottom J.A. Bailey (Ardea). **220 Red Knot** Arnold McGill/D. and M. Trounson (NPI). **221 Great Knot** Arnold McGill/Derek Roff (NPI); **Pectoral Sandpiper** Fred Smith/Edgar Jones (Ardea/NPI). **222 Sharp-tailed Sandpiper** Fred Smith/top H.A.B. West (NPI), bottom D. and M. Trounson (NPI). **223 Red-necked Stint** Fred Smith/Graeme Chapman; **Long-toed Stint** Fred Smith. **224 Curlew Sandpiper** Fred Smith/D. and M. Trounson. **225 Sanderling** Arnold McGill/A. Rogers (NPI); **Broad-billed Sandpiper** Fred Smith/Trevor Marshall (Ardea/NPI). **226 Ruff** Arnold McGill/R.J. Blewitt (Ardea/NPI). **227 Latham's Snipe** H.J. Frith/Hans and Judy Beste (NPI); **Swinhoe's Snipe** John McKean. **228 Southern Skua** Kenneth Simpson/G.W. Johnstone (NPI). **229 Pomarine Jaeger** Kenneth Simpson/William Burlace; **Arctic Jaeger** Kenneth Simpson/Trevor Marshall (Ardea/NPI). **230 Pacific Gull** G.F. van Tets/top Graeme Chapman (NPI), bottom R.H. Green (NPI). **231 Kelp Gull** Arnold McGill/Michael Soper (NPI). **232–3 Silver Gull** M.D. Murray/left Michael Soper (NPI), right Vincent Serventy (NPI). **234 Caspian Tern** Warren Hitchcock/G.J.H. Moon. **235 Gull-billed Tern** Warren Hitchcock/Thomas Lowe (NPI); **Whiskered Tern** Warren Hitchcock/Edgar Whitbourn (NPI). **236 White-winged Tern** Warren Hitchcock/Graeme Chapman (NPI); **Bridled Tern** Warren Hitchcock/Graeme Chapman (NPI). **237 White-fronted Tern** Warren Hitchcock/Michael Soper (NPI). **238 Common Tern** Warren Hitchcock/Graeme Chapman (NPI); **Arctic Tern** Warren Hitchcock/Kenneth Fink (Ardea/NPI). **239 Roseate Tern** Warren Hitchcock/Graeme Chapman (NPI); **Black-naped Tern** Warren Hitchcock/Graeme Chapman (Ardea/NPI). **240–1 Sooty Tern** John McKean/left Len Robinson (NPI), right John Carnemolla. **242–3 Crested Tern** Warren Hitchcock/left Len Robinson (NPI), right A. Eames (NPI). **244 Little Tern** Warren Hitchcock/Ake Lindau (Ardea/NPI); **Fairy Tern** Warren Hitchcock/Edgar Whitbourn (NPI). **245 Lesser Crested Tern** Warren Hitchcock/Graeme Chapman (NPI); **Lesser Noddy** Warren Hitchcock/Vincent Serventy (NPI). **246 Common Noddy** Warren Hitchcock/E.E. Zillman (NPI). **247 Black Noddy** Warren Hitchcock/Michael Soper (NPI). **248 White-headed Pigeon** H.J. Frith/E. McNamara (NPI). **249 Feral Pigeon** H.J. Frith/D. and M. Trounson (NPI). **250 Spotted Turtle-Dove** H.J. Frith/Bruce Coleman Ltd (NPI). **251 Laughing Turtle-Dove** H.J. Frith/Jane Burton (Bruce Coleman Ltd). **252 Brown Cuckoo-Dove** H.J. Frith/E. Smith (NPI). **253 Wonga Pigeon** H.J. Frith/Len Robinson. **254 Emerald Ground-Dove** H.J. Frith/J. Purnell (NPI). **255 Flock Bronzewing** H.J. Frith/Graeme Chapman (Ardea/NPI). **256 Common Bronzewing** H.J. Frith/Graeme Chapman. **257 Brush Bronzewing** H.J. Frith/Graeme Chapman. **258 Partridge Pigeon** H.J. Frith/Hans and Judy Beste (NPI). **259 Squatter Pigeon** H.J. Frith/top A. Lindsey (NPI), bottom Graeme Chapman. **260 Crested Pigeon** H.J. Frith/Denis Green (NPI). **261 Spinifex Pigeon** H.J. Frith/Graeme Chapman. **262 White-quilled Rock-Pigeon** H.J. Frith/A.L. Hertog (NPI). **263 Chestnut-quilled Rock-Pigeon** H.J. Frith/Hans and Judy Beste (NPI). **264 Bar-shouldered Dove** H.J. Frith/Cyril Webster (NPI). **265 Diamond Dove** H.J. Frith/Pauline Reilly (NPI). **266 Peaceful Dove** H.J. Frith/Hans and Judy Beste (NPI). **267 Topknot Pigeon** H.J. Frith/Cyril Webster (NPI). **268 Torres Strait Imperial Pigeon** H.J. Frith/William Peckover* (NPI). **269 Wompoo Fruit-Dove** H.J. Frith/Peter Slater (NPI). **270–1 Superb Fruit-Dove** H.J. Frith/Len Robinson (NPI); **Banded Fruit-Dove** H.J. Frith/E.E. Zillman (NPI). **272 Rose-crowned Fruit-Dove** H.J. Frith/Harold Pollock (NPI). **273 Palm Cockatoo** Joseph M. Forshaw/D. and M. Trounson* (NPI). **274 Red-tailed Black-Cockatoo** D. Saunders/D. and M. Trounson (NPI). **275 Glossy Black-Cockatoo** D. Saunders/L. Pedler. **276 Yellow-tailed Black-Cockatoo** D. Saunders/Len Robinson. **277 White-tailed Black-Cockatoo** D. Saunders/Graeme Chapman (NPI). **278 Long-billed Black-Cockatoo** /Faye Phythian* (courtesy Perth Zoo). **279 Cockatiel** Joseph M. Forshaw/Len Robinson (NPI). **280 Gang-gang Cockatoo** Joseph M. Forshaw/J. Christesen (NPI). **281 Pink Cockatoo** Joseph M. Forshaw/Len Robinson (NPI). **282 Sulphur-crested Cockatoo** Joseph M. Forshaw/Jean-Paul Ferrero (Auscape International). **283 Little Corella** Robert Beeton/Graeme Chapman; **Long-billed Corella** Joseph M. Forshaw/Graeme Chapman* (NPI). **284 Galah** Ian Rowley/T. Pescott. **285 Double-eyed Fig-Parrot** Joseph M. Forshaw/Hans and Judy Beste (NPI). **286 Rainbow Lorikeet** Joseph M. Forshaw/top Len Robinson (NPI), bottom Hans and Judy Beste (NPI). **287 Scaly-breasted Lorikeet** Joseph M. Forshaw/K. and B. Richards (NPI). **288 Varied Lorikeet** Joseph M. Forshaw/Len Robinson* (NPI); **Musk Lorikeet** Joseph M. Forshaw/D. and M. Trounson* (NPI). **289 Purple-crowned Lorikeet** Joseph M. Forshaw/Alwyn Pepper* (NPI). **290 Little Lorikeet** Joseph M. Forshaw/D. and M. Trounson* (NPI). **291 Eclectus Parrot** Joseph M. Forshaw/D. and M. Trounson* (NPI); **Red-cheeked Parrot** Joseph M. Forshaw/Roy Mackay* (NPI). **292–3 Australian King Parrot** Joseph M. Forshaw/Len Robinson (NPI); **Red-winged Parrot** Joseph M. Forshaw/D. and M. Trounson* (NPI). **294–5 Regent Parrot** Joseph M. Forshaw/Len Robinson (NPI); **Superb Parrot** Joseph M. Forshaw/D. and M. Trounson* (NPI). **296 Alexandra's Parrot** Joseph M. Forshaw/Alwyn Pepper (NPI). **297 Budgerigar** Joseph M. Forshaw/J. Purnell (NPI). **298 Ground Parrot** Joseph M. Forshaw/Graeme Chapman*; **Night Parrot** A.H. Chisholm. **299 Red-capped Parrot** Joseph M. Forshaw/K. and B. Richards (NPI). **300–1 Ringneck** Joseph M. Forshaw/left Graeme Chapman, right Len Robinson (NPI). **302–3 Crimson Rosella** Richard Schodde/left Hans and Judy Beste (NPI); top near right Len Robinson (NPI); top far right D. and M. Trounson* (NPI); **Green Rosella** Richard Schodde/Dave Watts (NPI). **304–5 White-cheeked Rosella** Joseph M. Forshaw/top left Len Robinson (NPI), bottom near right Graeme Chapman, bottom right Graeme Chapman. **306 Western Rosella** Joseph M. Forshaw/Ray Garstone (NPI). **307 Blue Bonnet** Richard Schodde/Len Robinson (NPI). **308–9 Golden-shouldered Parrot** Joseph M. Forshaw/Len Robinson (NPI); **Hooded Parrot** Joseph M. Forshaw/Graeme Chapman (NPI). **310 Paradise Parrot** A.H. Chisholm/top C.H. Jerrard, bottom D. and M. Trounson. **311 Mulga Parrot** Joseph M. Forshaw/J. Purnell (NPI). **312 Red-rumped Parrot** Joseph M. Forshaw/F.G. Craven (NPI). **313 Blue-winged Parrot** Joseph M. Forshaw/Len Robinson (NPI). **314 Elegant Parrot** Joseph M. Forshaw/John Dart (NPI); **Bourke's Parrot** Joseph M. Forshaw/Alwyn Pepper (NPI). **315 Orange-bellied Parrot** Joseph M. Forshaw/Len Robinson (NPI); **Rock Parrot** Joseph M. Forshaw/Graeme Chapman. **316 Turquoise Parrot** Joseph M. Forshaw/Edgar Whitbourn (NPI). **317 Scarlet-chested Parrot** Joseph M. Forshaw/Alwyn Pepper (NPI). **318 Swift Parrot** Joseph M. Forshaw/Graeme Chapman* (NPI). **319 Pallid Cuckoo** H.J. de S. Disney/Graeme Chapman (NPI). **320 Oriental Cuckoo** I.J. Mason/P. Grant. **321 Brush Cuckoo** H.J. de S. Disney/Graeme Chapman (NPI); **Chestnut-breasted Cuckoo** H.J. de S. Disney/D. and M. Trounson* (NPI). **322 Fan-tailed Cuckoo** H.J. de S. Disney/Alan Coe* (NPI). **323 Black-eared Cuckoo** H.J. de S. Disney/Graeme Chapman (NPI); **Horsfield's Bronze-Cuckoo** H.J. de S. Disney/Graeme Chapman (NPI). **324 Shining Bronze-Cuckoo** H.J. de S. Disney/Graeme Chapman (NPI). **325 Little Bronze-Cuckoo** H.J. de S. Disney/top B. and J. Morgan* (NPI), bottom D. and M. Trounson* (NPI). **326–7 Common Koel** Ian James Mason/R.E. Viljoen (NPI); **Channel-billed Cuckoo** H.J. de S. Disney/Hans and Judy Beste (NPI); **Pheasant Coucal** H.B. Gill/B. and J. Morgan (NPI). **328 Powerful Owl** John Calaby/A. Lindsey (NPI); **Rufous Owl** John Calaby/E.E. Zillman (NPI). **329 Southern Boobook** John Calaby/I. Watson (NPI). **330 Barking Owl** John Calaby/Graeme Chapman. **331 Lesser Sooty Owl** /Hans and Judy Beste (Auscape International); **Sooty Owl** John Calaby/Len Robinson. **332–3 Barn Owl** John Calaby/Keith Ireland (NPI); **Grass Owl** John Calaby/Norman Chaffer* (NPI). **334 Masked Owl** John Calaby/T.A. Waite* (NPI). **335 Papuan Frogmouth** Frank Crome/D. and M. Trounson (NPI). **336 Marbled Frogmouth** Graeme Chapman/D. and M. Trounson* (NPI). **337 Tawny Frogmouth** Graeme Chapman/Graeme Chapman. **338 Australian Owlet-nightjar** Graeme Chapman/A.G. Wells (NPI). **339 White-throated Nightjar** Graeme Chapman/Norman Chaffer (NPI). **340 Spotted Nightjar** Graeme Chapman/Robert Miller (NPI). **341 Large-tailed Nightjar** Graeme Chapman/Hans and Judy Beste (NPI). **342 White-throated Needletail** Kenneth Simpson/N.W. Vincent* (NPI). **343 White-rumped Swiftlet** Kenneth Simpson/Alistair V. Spain (NPI); **Fork-tailed Swift** Kenneth Simpson. **344–5 Laughing Kookaburra** Veronica Parry/left Ray Garstone (NPI), right Harold Pollock (NPI). **346 Blue-winged Kookaburra** Veronica Parry/Harold Pollock (NPI). **347 Yellow-billed Kingfisher** Ian James Mason and Richard Schodde/D. and M. Trounson* (NPI). **348 Sacred Kingfisher** Ian James Mason and Richard Schodde/A.G. Wells (NPI). **349 Red-backed Kingfisher** Ian James Mason and Richard Schodde/D. and M. Trounson* (NPI). **350 Collared Kingfisher** Ian James Mason and Richard Schodde/E. and F. Smith (NPI). **351 Forest Kingfisher** Ian James Mason and Richard Schodde/E. Smith (NPI). **352–3 Buff-breasted Paradise Kingfisher** H.B. Gill/Len Robinson (NPI). **354–5 Azure Kingfisher** Richard Schodde/Michael Morcombe (NPI); **Little Kingfisher** Richard Schodde/Eric Lindgren (Ardea/NPI). **356 Rainbow Bee-eater** K.A. Muller/Michael Morcombe (NPI). **357 Dollarbird** K.A. Muller/John Warham (NPI). **358 Noisy Pitta** Murray Bruce/E. Smith (NPI). **359 Red-bellied Pitta** Murray Bruce/Ederic Slater; **Rainbow Pitta** Murray Bruce/Stanley and Kay Breeden. **360–1 Superb Lyrebird** Norman Robinson/left John Warham (NPI), top right Harold Pollock (NPI); **Albert's Lyrebird** Norman Robinson/E.C.J. Smith (NPI). **362 Rufous Scrub-bird** G.T. Smith/Michael Morcombe (NPI). **363 Noisy Scrub-bird** G.T. Smith/Graeme Chapman (NPI). **364 Singing Bushlark** Stephen Wilson/J. Purnell (NPI). **365 Skylark** Stephen Wilson/T.A. Waite. **366 White-backed Swallow** John McKean/I.R. McCann (NPI); **Barn Swallow** John McKean/J.A. Bailey (Ardea/NPI). **367 Welcome Swallow** John McKean/T.A. Waite (NPI). **368 Tree Martin** Graeme Chapman/J. Purnell (NPI). **369 Fairy Martin** S.G. Lane/F.G.

Craven (NPI). **370 Richard's Pipit** John McKean/Graeme Chapman (NPI). **371 Yellow Wagtail** John McKean/R. Fleming (Ardea/NPI). **372 Black-faced Cuckoo-shrike** Graeme Chapman/T.A. Waite (NPI). **373 Yellow-eyed Cuckoo-shrike** Frank Crome/Edgar Whitbourn (NPI); **White-bellied Cuckoo-shrike** Graeme Chapman/J. Estbergs (NPI). **374 Cicadabird** H.B. Gill and Ian James Mason/E. McNamara (NPI). **375 Ground Cuckoo-shrike** Graeme Chapman/Michael Morcombe (NPI). **376 White-winged Triller** Graeme Chapman/D. and M. Trounson* (NPI). **377 Varied Triller** Frank Crome and Ian James Mason/Norman Chaffer (NPI). **378 Red-whiskered Bulbul** Arnold McGill/D. and M. Trounson* (NPI). **379 White's Thrush** Arnold McGill/F.M. Dowling (NPI). **380 Blackbird** Arnold McGill/top A.J. Deane (Bruce Coleman Ltd), bottom T.A. Waite (NPI). **381 Song Thrush** Arnold McGill/R.J. Blewitt (Ardea/NPI). **382 Rose Robin** Frank Stewart/Norman Chaffer (NPI). **383 Pink Robin** Frank Stewart/Graeme Chapman (NPI). **384 Flame Robin** Frank Stewart/T.A. Waite (NPI). **385 Scarlet Robin** Frank Stewart/Ray Garstone (NPI). **386 Red-capped Robin** Frank Stewart/J. Purnell (NPI). **387 Dusky Robin** Frank Stewart/J.R. Napier (NPI); **Hooded Robin** Frank Stewart/Norman Chaffer(NPI). **388 White-breasted Robin** Frank Stewart/Graeme Chapman (NPI). **389 Western Yellow Robin** Frank Stewart/Graeme Chapman (NPI). **390 Eastern Yellow Robin** Frank Stewart/D. and M. Trounson* (NPI). **391 White-faced Robin** Frank Crome/D. and M. Trounson* (NPI); **Mangrove Robin** H.B. Gill and Ian James Mason/Graeme Chapman (NPI). **392 Pale-yellow Robin** Frank Crome/Michael Morcombe (NPI). **393 Grey-headed Robin** Frank Crome/J. Purnell (NPI); **White-browed Robin** H.B. Gill and Ian James Mason/Tom and Pam Gardner (NPI). **394 Northern Scrub-robin** Arnold McGill/D. and M. Trounson* (NPI). **395 Southern Scrub-robin** Arnold McGill/Norman Chaffer (NPI). **396 Lemon-bellied Flycatcher** Ian James Mason/J. Purnell (NPI). **397 Jacky Winter** Frank Stewart/J. Purnell (NPI). **398 Yellow-legged Flycatcher** Frank Crome/E.E. Zillman (NPI); **Crested Shrike-tit** Julian Ford/W.J. Labbett (NPI). **399 Grey Whistler** Frank Crome/D. and M. Trounson* (NPI); **Rufous Whistler** Arnold McGill/Graeme Chapman (NPI). **400 Olive Whistler** Arnold McGill/Tom and Pam Gardner (NPI); **Gilbert's Whistler** Arnold McGill/W.J. Labbett (NPI). **401 Red-lored Whistler** Arnold McGill/Graeme Chapman. **402 Mangrove Golden Whistler** Arnold McGill/Graeme Chapman (NPI). **403 Golden Whistler** Arnold McGill/top Gary Weber (NPI), bottom Norman Chaffer (NPI). **404 White-breasted Whistler** H.B. Gill and Ian James Mason/Graeme Chapman (NPI). **405 Little Shrike-thrush** Frank Crome and Ian James Mason/Cyril Webster (NPI). **406 Bower's Shrike-thrush** Frank Crome/J. Purnell (NPI); **Sandstone Shrike-thrush** Arnold McGill/J. Estbergs (NPI). **407 Grey Shrike-thrush** Arnold McGill/W.R. Taylor (NPI). **408–9 Crested Bellbird** Julian Ford/Graeme Chapman (NPI); **Yellow-breasted Boatbill** Frank Crome/R. and D. Keller. **410 Black-faced Monarch** Frank Crome/Len Robinson (NPI). **411 Spectacled Monarch** Frank Crome/Hans and Judy Beste (NPI). **412 White-eared Monarch** Frank Crome/Rob Drummond (NPI); **Frilled Monarch** Frank Crome/D. and M. Trounson* (NPI). **413 Pied Monarch** Frank Crome/J. Purnell (NPI). **414 Restless Flycatcher** Frank Stewart/W.R. Taylor (NPI). **415 Broad-billed Flycatcher** Frank Stewart/Graeme Chapman (NPI); **Leaden Flycatcher** Frank Stewart/Graeme Chapman (NPI). **416 Satin Flycatcher** Frank Stewart/top Graeme Chapman (NPI), bottom J. Purnell (NPI). **417 Shining Flycatcher** Frank Stewart/Norman Chaffer (NPI). **418 Rufous Fantail** Stephen Wilson/Malcolm McNaughton (NPI). **419 Grey Fantail** Stephen Wilson/Norman Chaffer (NPI); **Mangrove Fantail** /Graeme Chapman. **420 Northern Fantail** H.B. Gill/Graeme Chapman. **421 Willie Wagtail** Stephen Wilson/Cyril Webster (NPI). **422 Logrunner** Graeme Chapman/Norman Chaffer (NPI). **423 Chowchilla** Hugh Lavery/Len Robinson (NPI); **Western Whipbird** Julian Ford/Harley Webster (NPI). **424 Eastern Whipbird** Julian Ford/Malcolm McNaughton (NPI). **425 Chirruping Wedgebill** Julian Ford/W.J. Labbett (NPI); **Chiming Wedgebill** Julian Ford/Ray Garstone. **426 Spotted Quail-thrush** Julian Ford/Norman Chaffer (NPI). **427 Chestnut Quail-thrush** Julian Ford/R.F. Kenyon (NPI). **428 Cinnamon Quail-thrush** Julian Ford/Chris Cameron; **Chestnut-breasted Quail-thrush** Julian Ford/Graeme Chapman. **429 Grey-crowned Babbler** J.J. Counsilman/E. and F. Smith (NPI). **430 White-browed Babbler** J.J. Counsilman/Tom and Pam Gardner (NPI). **431 Hall's Babbler** H.B. Gill/Graeme Chapman; **Chestnut-crowned Babbler** Erhard Boehm/Robert Miller (NPI). **432 Clamorous Reed-Warbler** Arnold McGill/W.J. Labbett (NPI); **Little Grassbird** Arnold McGill/A.G. Wells (NPI). **433 Tawny Grassbird** Arnold McGill/Cyril Webster (NPI); **Spinifexbird** Arnold McGill/Graeme Chapman (NPI). **434 Zitting Cisticola** Arnold McGill/Graeme Chapman; **Golden-headed Cisticola** Arnold McGill/Len Robinson (NPI). **435 Rufous Songlark** Arnold McGill/Norman Chaffer (NPI); **Brown Songlark** Arnold McGill/Graeme Chapman (NPI). **436–7 Superb Fairy-wren** Ian Rowley/Gary Weber (NPI). **438–9 Splendid Fairy-wren** Ian Rowley/left A.G. Wells (NPI), right W.J. Labbett (NPI). **440 Purple-crowned Fairy-wren** Ian Rowley/Graeme Chapman. **441 Lovely Fairy-wren** /Edgar Whitbourn (NPI); **Red-winged Fairy-wren** Ian Rowley/Michael Morcombe (NPI). **442–3 Variegated Fairy-wren** Ian Rowley/left A.G. Wells, right W.R. Taylor (NPI). **444 Blue-breasted Fairy-wren** Ian Rowley/Michael Morcombe (NPI); **Red-backed Fairy-wren** Ian Rowley/N. and E. Taylor. **445 White-winged Fairy-wren** Ian Rowley/A.G. Wells (NPI). **446 Southern Emu-wren** Shane Parker/F. Park (NPI). **447 Rufous-crowned Emu-wren** Shane Parker/Michael Morcombe (NPI); **Mallee Emu-wren** /W.J. Labbett (NPI). **448 Grey Grasswren** Shane Parker/Len Robinson (NPI); **Carpentarian Grasswren** Ian James Mason and Richard Schodde/Graeme Chapman. **449 Black Grasswren** H.B. Gill/Graeme Chapman; **White-throated Grasswren** Ian James Mason and Richard Schodde/Ian Morris. **450 Striated Grasswren** Shane Parker/J.D. Waterhouse; **Eyrean Grasswren** Shane Parker/A.D. Trounson (NPI). **451 Dusky Grasswren** Shane Parker/Hans and Judy Beste (NPI); **Thick-billed Grasswren** Shane Parker/Graeme Chapman (NPI). **452 Eastern Bristlebird** G.T. Smith/J. Purnell (NPI); **Western Bristlebird** G.T. Smith/Graeme Chapman. **453 Rufous Bristlebird** G.T. Smith/J. Purnell (NPI); **Pilotbird** Stephen Wilson/E. McNamara (NPI). **454 Origma** Arnold McGill/Norman Chaffer (NPI); **Australian Fernwren** Frank Crome/Hans and Judy Beste (NPI). **455 Scrubtit** Arnold McGill/J.R. Napier (NPI). **456 Atherton Scrubwren** Frank Crome/Tom and Pam Gardner (NPI); **Tropical Scrubwren** Arnold McGill/David Hollands (NPI). **457 Large-billed Scrubwren** Frank Crome/J. Purnell (NPI). **458 Yellow-throated Scrubwren** Frank Crome/Malcolm McNaughton (NPI). **459 White-browed Scrubwren** Arnold McGill/Norman Chaffer (NPI). **460 Chestnut-rumped Hylacola** Arnold McGill/I.R. McCann (NPI); **Shy Hylacola** Arnold McGill/J. Purnell (NPI). **461 Redthroat** Arnold McGill/W.J. Labbett (NPI); **Rufous Calamanthus** Arnold McGill/Graeme Chapman. **462 Speckled Warbler** Arnold McGill/Norman Chaffer (NPI); **Striated Calamanthus** /A.J. Salter (NPI). **463 Weebill** Richard Schodde/Norman Chaffer (NPI). **464 Green-backed Gerygone** Richard Schodde/Ian Morris (NPI). **465 Brown Gerygone** Richard Schodde/Malcolm McNaughton (NPI). **466 Mangrove Gerygone** Richard Schodde/J. Purnell (NPI). **467 Western Gerygone** Richard Schodde/J. Purnell (NPI). **468 Large-billed Gerygone** Richard Schodde/E.E. Zillman (NPI); **Dusky Gerygone** Richard Schodde/Graeme Chapman (NPI). **469 Fairy Gerygone** Richard Schodde/D. and M. Trounson* (NPI). **470 White-throated Gerygone** Richard Schodde/Norman Chaffer (NPI). **471 Brown Thornbill** Stephen Wilson/I.R. McCann (NPI). **472–3 Mountain Thornbill** Frank Crome/Hans and Judy Beste (NPI); **Slaty-backed Thornbill** Stephen Wilson/R. Garstone (NPI). **474 Tasmanian Thornbill** David Milledge/T.A. Waite (NPI). **475 Chestnut-rumped Thornbill** Stephen Wilson/Graeme Chapman (NPI). **476 Western Thornbill** Stephen Wilson/Harley Webster (NPI); **Slender-billed Thornbill** Stephen Wilson/Graeme Chapman. **477 Buff-rumped Thornbill** Stephen Wilson/Michael Seyfort (NPI). **478 Striated Thornbill** Stephen Wilson/R.B. Legge (NPI); **Yellow-rumped Thornbill** Stephen Wilson/I.R. McCann (NPI). **479 Yellow Thornbill** Stephen Wilson/Norman Chaffer (NPI). **480 Banded Whiteface** Arnold McGill/D. and M. Trounson (NPI); **Chestnut-breasted Whiteface** Arnold McGill/L. Pedler. **481 Southern Whiteface** Arnold McGill/D. and M. Trounson* (NPI). **482–3 Varied Sittella** Ronald I. Orenstein/left Ray Garstone (NPI), right E.E. Zillman (NPI). **484 White-throated Treecreeper** Ronald I. Orenstein/Len Robinson (NPI). **485 Red-browed Treecreeper** Ronald I. Orenstein/J. Purnell (NPI). **486 White-browed Treecreeper** Ronald I. Orenstein/A.G. Wells (NPI). **487 Black-tailed Treecreeper** Ronald I. Orenstein/Graeme Chapman. **488 Brown Treecreeper** Ronald I. Orenstein/Graeme Chapman (NPI). **489 Rufous Treecreeper** Ronald I. Orenstein/John Brownlie (Bruce Coleman Ltd). **490–1 Red Wattlebird** J.T. Recher/Len Robinson (NPI); **Yellow Wattlebird** David Milledge/F.M. Dowling (NPI). **492–3 Little Wattlebird** J.T. Recher/Michael Morcombe (NPI); **Brush Wattlebird** /Graeme Chapman. **494 Striped Honeyeater** Frank Stewart/W.R. Taylor (NPI). **495 Spiny-cheeked Honeyeater** Frank Stewart/Eric and David Hosking (NPI). **496 Silver-crowned Friarbird** Ian James Mason/Graeme Chapman. **497 Helmeted Friarbird** Ian James Mason/Len Robinson (NPI). **498–9 Noisy Friarbird** Ian James Mason/left Keith Ireland (NPI), right Tom and Pam Gardner (NPI). **500 Little Friarbird** Ian James Mason/W.J. Labbett (NPI). **501 Regent Honeyeater** Frank Stewart/E. McNamara (Ardea/NPI). **502 Blue-faced Honeyeater** Ian James Mason/W.R. Taylor (NPI). **503 Bell Miner** Douglas D. Dow/J.D. Waterhouse (NPI). **504 Yellow-throated Miner** Douglas D. Dow/D. and M. Trounson* (NPI). **505 Noisy Miner** Douglas D. Dow/Norman Chaffer (NPI). **506 Tawny-breasted Honeyeater** Frank Crome/D. and M. Trounson* (NPI). **507 Macleay's Honeyeater** Frank Crome/Len Robinson (NPI). **508 Lewin's Honeyeater** Frank Crome/D. and M. Trounson* (NPI); **Yellow-spotted Honeyeater** Frank Crome/Graeme Chapman (NPI). **509 Graceful Honeyeater** Frank Crome/Norman Chaffer (NPI). **510–1 White-lined Honeyeater** Ian James Mason/E. McNamara (NPI); **Yellow-faced Honeyeater** J.T. Recher/Michael Morcombe (NPI). **512 Bridled Honeyeater** Frank Crome/Norman Chaffer (NPI); **Eungella Honeyeater** /T. Lindsey (NPI). **513 Singing Honeyeater** Frank Stewart/Norman Chaffer (NPI). **514 Varied Honeyeater** Frank Crome/top J. Purnell (NPI), bottom D. and M. Trounson* (NPI). **515 White-gaped Honeyeater** Frank Crome/Len Robinson (NPI); **Yellow Honeyeater** Frank Crome and Ian James Mason/John Warham (NPI). **516–7 Yellow-tufted Honeyeater** Frank Crome/Gary Weber (NPI); **White-eared Honeyeater** J.T. Recher/Ken Stepnell (NPI). **518 Yellow-throated Honeyeater** David Milledge/R. Good (NPI). **519 Purple-gaped Honeyeater** Ian Abbott/Len Robinson (NPI); **Grey-headed Honeyeater** Ian Abbott/D. and M. Trounson* (NPI). **520 Yellow-plumed Honeyeater** Ian Abbott/J.D. Waterhouse (NPI); **Grey-fronted Honeyeater** Ian Abbott/Robert Miller (NPI). **521 Yellow-tinted Honeyeater** Frank Stewart/top Hans and Judy Beste (NPI), bottom Peter Slater (NPI). **522 White-plumed Honeyeater** Frank Stewart/D. and M. Trounson* (NPI). **523 Black-chinned Honeyeater** Ian Abbott/Peter Slater (NPI). **524 Strong-billed Honeyeater** David Milledge/F.M. Dowling (NPI). **525 Brown-headed Honeyeater** Ian Abbott/W.J. Labbett (NPI); **White-throated Honeyeater** Ian James Mason/G. Webb (NPI). **526 White-naped Honeyeater** Ian Abbott/Ken Stepnell (NPI). **527 Black-headed Honeyeater** David Milledge/T.A. Waite (NPI). **528 Green-backed Honeyeater** Frank Crome/D. and M. Trounson* (NPI); **Brown Honeyeater** Frank Crome/Norman Chaffer (NPI). **529 White-streaked Honeyeater** Frank Crome/D. and M. Trounson* (NPI); **Painted Honeyeater** Frank Stewart/W.J. Labbett (NPI). **530–1 New Holland Honeyeater** J.T. Recher/Michael Morcombe (NPI); **Crescent Honeyeater** J.T. Recher/W.J. Labbett (NPI). **532 White-cheeked Honeyeater** J.T. Recher/N. and E. Taylor (NPI). **533 White-fronted Honeyeater** Frank Stewart/Norman Chaffer (NPI). **534 Tawny-crowned Honeyeater** J.T. Recher/A.G. Wells (NPI). **535 Brown-backed Honeyeater** Frank Crome and H.B. Gill/Norman Chaffer (NPI). **536 Bar-breasted Honeyeater** Frank Crome and H.B. Gill/Graeme Chapman (NPI); **Rufous-banded Honeyeater** Ian James Mason/J. Estbergs (NPI). **537 Rufous-throated Honeyeater** Ian James Mason/Graeme Chapman (NPI). **538 Grey Honeyeater** Ian Abbott/A.G. Wells (NPI); **Banded Honeyeater** Frank Crome and H.B. Gill/Graeme Chapman. **539 Black Honeyeater** Ian Abbott/top J. Purnell* (NPI), bottom Graeme Chapman (NPI). **540 Pied Honeyeater** Ian Abbott/top E. McNamara (Ardea/NPI), bottom Ray Garstone (NPI). **541 Eastern Spinebill** J.T. Recher/Robert Edden (NPI); **Western Spinebill** Ian Abbott/A.G. Wells (NPI). **542 Dusky Honeyeater** Frank Crome/D. and M. Trounson* (NPI); **Red-headed Honeyeater** Ian James Mason/Graeme Chapman. **543 Scarlet Honeyeater** Frank Stewart/J. Purnell (NPI). **544 Crimson Chat** Shane Parker/Gary Weber (NPI). **545 Orange Chat** Shane Parker/F.G. Craven (NPI). **546 Yellow Chat** Shane Parker/Graeme Chapman; **White-fronted Chat** Shane Parker/Graeme Chapman. **547 Gibberbird** Shane Parker/Robert Miller (NPI). **548–9 Yellow-bellied Sunbird** Frank Crome and H.B. Gill/left Len Robinson (NPI), right Keith Ireland (NPI). **550 Mistletoebird** John McKean/top W.J. Labbett (NPI), bottom Malcolm McNaughton (NPI). **551 Red-browed Pardalote** H.B. Gill/D. and M. Trounson* (NPI). **552 Spotted Pardalote** John McKean/top Jim Ralston (NPI), bottom J. Purnell (NPI). **553 Forty-spotted Pardalote** David Milledge/J.R. Napier (NPI). **554–5 Striated Pardalote** John McKean/left Michael Seyfort (NPI), right Graeme Chapman (NPI). **556 Pale White-eye** S.G. Lane; **Yellow White-eye** S.G. Lane/Graeme Chapman. **557 Silvereye** S.G. Lane/W.R. Taylor (NPI). **558 European Goldfinch** Alex Middleton/F. Collet (Ardea/NPI). **559 European Greenfinch** Alex Middleton/Avon and Tillford (Ardea/NPI). **560 House Sparrow** Mark Clayton/D. and M. Trounson* (NPI). **561 Tree Sparrow** Mark Clayton/Brian Bevan (Ardea/NPI). **562 Diamond Finch** Richard Zann/F.G. Craven (NPI). **563 Beautiful Firetail** Richard Zann/F.M. Dowling (NPI). **564 Red-eared Firetail** Richard Zann/Graeme Chapman. **565 Painted Firetail** Richard Zann/D. and M. Trounson* (NPI). **566 Star Finch** Richard Zann/D. and M. Trounson* (NPI). **567 Crimson Finch** Richard Zann/D. and M. Trounson* (NPI). **568 Red-browed Finch** Richard Zann/Norman Chaffer (NPI). **569 Plum-headed Finch** Richard Zann/H.L. de Ross (NPI). **570 Zebra Finch** Richard Zann/D. and M. Trounson* (NPI). **571 Double-barred Finch** Richard Zann/Graeme Chapman. **572 Masked Finch** Richard Zann/D. and M. Trounson* (NPI). **573 Long-tailed Finch** Richard Zann/D. and M. Trounson* (NPI). **574 Black-throated Finch** Richard Zann/D. and M. Trounson* (NPI). **575 Pictorella Mannikin** Richard Zann/Graeme Chapman. **576 Chestnut-breasted Mannikin** Richard Zann/Graeme Chapman. **577 Yellow-rumped Mannikin** Richard Zann/D. and M. Trounson* (NPI). **578 Nutmeg Mannikin** Richard Zann/D. and M. Trounson* (NPI). **579 Gouldian Finch** Richard Zann/D. and M. Trounson* (NPI). **580 Blue-faced Finch** Richard Zann/D. and M. Trounson* (NPI). **581 Metallic Starling** Frank Crome/Ray Garstone (NPI). **582 Common Starling** Mark Clayton/T.A. Waite (NPI). **583 Common Mynah** Mark Clayton/D. and M. Trounson (NPI). **584 Figbird** Graeme Chapman/top Cyril Webster (NPI), bottom Keith Ireland (NPI). **585 Yellow Oriole** Frank Crome/A.L. Hertog (NPI). **586 Olive-backed Oriole** Graeme Chapman/W.J. Labbett (NPI). **587 Spangled Drongo** Arnold McGill/John Handel. **588 Golden Bowerbird** Richard Schodde/Norman Chaffer (NPI). **589 Satin Bowerbird** Richard Schodde/top Len Robinson (NPI), bottom Tom and Pam Gardner (NPI). **590 Regent Bowerbird** Richard Schodde/Philip Green (NPI). **591 Fawn-breasted Bowerbird** Richard Schodde/E.E. Zillman (NPI). **592 Spotted Bowerbird** Richard Schodde/Gary Weber (NPI); **Western Bowerbird** /Graeme Chapman. **593 Great Bowerbird** Richard Schodde/R. and D. Keller (NPI). **594–5 Green Catbird** Richard Schodde/left Michael Morcombe (NPI), right Norman Chaffer (NPI). **596 Tooth-billed Catbird** Richard Schodde/Norman Chaffer (NPI). **597 Paradise Riflebird** Richard Schodde/Len Robinson. **598 Victoria's Riflebird** Richard Schodde/Len Robinson (NPI). **599 Magnificent Riflebird** Richard Schodde/D. and M. Trounson* (NPI); **Trumpet Manucode** Richard Schodde/William Peckover (NPI). **600 White-winged Chough** Ian Rowley/J. Purnell (NPI). **601 Apostlebird** Graeme Chapman/Graeme Chapman (NPI). **602 Australian Magpie-lark** Graeme Chapman/Cyril Webster (NPI). **603 Black-faced Woodswallow** Ian Rowley/D. and M. Trounson* (NPI). **604 Masked Woodswallow** Ian Rowley/Edgar Whitbourn (NPI); **Little Woodswallow** Ian Rowley/Graeme Chapman (NPI). **605 White-browed Woodswallow** Ian Rowley/A.L. Hertog (NPI). **606–7 White-breasted Woodswallow** Ian Rowley/Norman Chaffer (NPI); **Dusky Woodswallow** Ian Rowley/Robert Edden (NPI). **608 Black Butcherbird** Ian James Mason and H.B. Gill/Harold Pollock (NPI). **609 Grey Butcherbird** Graeme Chapman/D. and M. Trounson* (NPI); **Black-backed Butcherbird** H.B. Gill/Edgar Whitbourn (NPI). **610 Pied Butcherbird** Graeme Chapman/Norman Chaffer (NPI). **611 Australian Magpie** Ian Rowley/John Dart (NPI). **612 Pied Currawong** Ian Rowley/Harold Pollock (NPI). **613 Black Currawong** Ian Rowley/Tim Newbery (NPI); **Grey Currawong** Ian Rowley/Graeme Chapman. **614 Australian Raven** Ian Rowley/Graeme Chapman. **615 Forest Raven** Ian Rowley/T.A. Waite (NPI); **Little Raven** Ian Rowley/Graeme Chapman (NPI). **616 Little Crow** Ian Rowley/J. Purnell (NPI). **617 Torresian Crow** Ian Rowley/E.E. Zillman (NPI).

SECOND EDITION CONTRIBUTORS: Harry L. Bell — data on thornbills and Speckled Warbler; Richard and Molly Brown — data on White-breasted Robin and Clamorous Reedwarbler; Graeme Chapman — data on flycatchers, Western Yellow Robin and wedgebills; Leslie Christidis — genera of finches; Simon Ferrier — data on Rufous Scrub-bird; Jon Fjeldsa — data on grebes; Greg Jones — data on House Sparrow; Richard Jordan — data on Ground Parrot and Eastern Bristlebird; Richard Kingsford — data on Maned Duck; John Liddy — data on Mistlebird; Ian James Mason — data on cuckoos, Chowchilla and Australian Fernwren; Richard Noske — data on Crested Shrike-tit, Varied Sittella, treecreepers and Brown-headed Honeyeater; Brian O'Gorman — data on Diamond Finch and Beautiful Firetail; Gerry O'Neill — data on Rainbow Pitta; David Paton — data on small southern honeyeaters; Lester Short — taxonomy of White-cheeked Rosella; Graeme Smith — data on Noisy Scrub-bird and Western Bristlebird; Sonia Tidemann — data on Red-capped Robin and fairy-wrens; Richard Weatherly — data on falcons; Edward Wyndham — data on Budgerigar. All other text amendments and additions in this edition are the responsibility of the consultant editors.

PART 4 Photographer: pages **620–1** Graeme Chapman.

ENDPAPERS Brolgas, R. and D. Keller.

REFERENCE WORKS The publishers acknowledge their indebtedness to the following books and journals, which were consulted for reference: AUSTRALIAN FINCHES by Klaus Immelmann (Angus and Robertson); AUSTRALIAN GRASSLANDS Ed. by R. Milton Moore (Australian National University Press); AUSTRALIAN PARROTS by Joseph M. Forshaw (Lansdowne); BIRD FAMILIES OF THE WORLD Ed. by C.J.O. Harrison (Elsevier Phaidon); BIRD IN THE HAND by H.J. de S. Disney and others (Bird Banders' Assn of Australia); BIRD LIFE by Ian Rowley (Collins); BIRDS IN BASS STRAIT by Ken Simpson (BHP); BIRDS IN THE AUSTRALIAN HIGH COUNTRY Ed. by H.J. Frith (Angus and Robertson); BIRDS OF AUSTRALIA by J.D. Macdonald (Reed); THE BIRDS OF AUSTRALIA by K. Simpson and N. Day (Lloyd O'Neil); BIRDS OF SOUTH AFRICA by A. Roberts, revised by G.R. McLachlan and R. Liversidge (John Voelcker, South Africa); BIRDS OF WESTERN AUSTRALIA by D.L. Serventy and H.M. Whittell (Lamb Paterson); BOOK OF BRITISH BIRDS (Drive Publications Ltd, London); CHECKLIST OF THE BIRDS OF AUSTRALIA, Part 1 Non-Passerines by H.T. Condon (RAOU); COMMON AUSTRALIAN BIRDS OF TOWNS AND GARDENS by G. Chapman (Lansdowne); COMPLETE ATLAS OF AUSTRALIA (Reader's Digest); COM- PLETE BOOK OF NEW ZEALAND BIRDS (Reader's Digest); EAGLES, HAWKS AND FALCONS OF AUSTRALIA by David Hollands (Nelson); EUCALYPTS by Stan Kelly (Nelson); THE FAIRY-WRENS by Richard Schodde (Lansdowne); A FIELD GUIDE TO AUSTRALIAN BIRDS by P. Slater (Rigby); A FIELD GUIDE TO THE BIRDS OF AUSTRALIA by G. Pizzey (Collins); A FIELD GUIDE TO NESTS AND EGGS OF AUSTRALIAN BIRDS by G. Beruldsen (Rigby); FOREST TREES OF AUSTRALIA by Norman Hall, R.D. Johnston, G.M. Chippendale (Australian Government Publishing Service, Canberra); FUNDAMENTALS OF ORNITHOLOGY by Josselyn Van Tyne and Andrew J. Berger (Wiley, London); THE HANDBOOK OF AUSTRALIAN SEA-BIRDS by D.L. Serventy, Vincent Serventy, John Warham (Reed); HAWKS IN FOCUS: A study of Australian birds of prey by J. and L. Cupper (Jaclin Enterprises); INDEX TO CURRENT AUSTRALIAN ORNITHOLOGICAL RESEARCH by Douglas D. Dow (RAOU); INTERIM LIST OF AUSTRALIAN SONGBIRDS: Passerines by R. Schodde (RAOU); KOOKA- BURRAS by Veronica A. Parry (Taplinger); THE LITERATURE OF AUSTRALIAN BIRDS by H.M. Whittell (Paterson Brokensha); THE LYREBIRD by L.H. Smith (Lansdowne); NESTS AND EGGS OF BIRDS FOUND BREEDING IN AUSTRALIA AND TASMANIA by A.J. North (The Australian Museum, 1901-1914); NOCTURNAL BIRDS OF AUSTRALIA by R. Schodde and I.J. Mason (Lansdowne); OCEAN WANDERERS by R.M. Lockley (David and Charles, London); THE OFFICIAL CHECKLIST OF THE BIRDS OF AUSTRALIA, 1926 (RAOU); THE READER'S DIGEST GREAT WORLD ATLAS (Reader's Digest); REFERENCE LIST OF THE BIRDS OF THE WORLD by John J. Morony Jr, Walter, J. Bock and John Farrand Jr (American Museum of Natural History, New York); WATERFOWL IN AUSTRALIA by H.J. Frith (Angus and Robertson); WILDLIFE CONSERVATION by H.J. Frith (Angus and Robertson). Journals: AUSTRALIAN BIRDS (New South Wales Field Ornithologists Club); AUSTRALIAN BIRDWATCHER (The Bird Observers Club); AUSTRALIAN CORELLA (Australian Bird Study Assn); THE EMU (Royal Australasian Ornithologists Union); PALAEONTOLOGY; SCIENTIFIC AMERICAN; THE SOUTH AUSTRALIAN ORNITHOLOGIST (South Australian Ornithological Assn); THE SUNBIRD (Queensland Ornithological Society).

Typesetting by Dovatype, Melbourne.
Reproduction by Curman Lithographics Pty Ltd, Sydney.
Printing and Binding by Everbest Printing Co., Ltd.,
Hong Kong, in 1990 for Reader's Digest
(Australia) Pty Ltd, 26-32 Waterloo Street,
Surry Hills, NSW 2010.